MW00650373

Good luck!
Best,
Eric Hoffman

THE COMPLETE
ALPACA
BOOK

Second Edition · Revised

Second Edition • Revised

THE COMPLETE ALPACA BOOK

ERIC HOFFMAN
Primary Author and Editor

Contributing Authors

Karen Baum
DVM

Linda V. Carpenter
DVM

Nancy Carr
MD

Christopher K. Cebra
VMD, MA, MS, DACVIM

George Davis
MAgrSc, DSc

Robert P. Ellis
PhD

Juliet Gionfriddo
DVM, MS

Ty McConnell
DVM

Rufino Quilla
DVZ

Denis Ryan
MVB, MRCVS

D. Phillip Sponenberg
DVM, PhD

Ahmed Tibary
DMV, PhD, Dipl ACT

Robert J. Van Saun
DVM, MS, PhD, Dipl ACT/ACVN

Stuart White
PhD

Bonny Doon Press, Santa Cruz, California
2006

Editing
Pat Brewer, Sherry Edensmith, Robyn Brode Orsini

Proofreading
Robyn Brode Orsini

Cover and Book Design
Irene Imfeld

Typesetting and Production
Dickie Magidoff, Becky Chapman-Winter

Indexing
Thérèse Shere, Robyn Brode Orsini

The Complete Alpaca Book, second revised edition, offers a comprehensive compilation of information. No one author is knowledgeable in all the subject areas presented here. The authors chosen to contribute to *The Complete Alpaca Book*, second revised edition, are each recognized experts in their field, but knowledge and perception of knowledge are constantly changing. Peer review and fact-checking have been utilized to check accuracy; however, the authors and Bonny Doon Press shall have neither liability nor responsibility for errors, inaccuracies, or omissions.

Eric Hoffman and Bonny Doon Press suggest you consult appropriate professionals before instituting any change in your farm program that is suggested or implied by the information in this book. Recommendations are based on the experience of the authors and assume that a licensed veterinarian will supervise any diagnosis and treatment to guarantee the welfare of animals. The book's publisher and authors take no responsibility and assume no liability for damages alleged or otherwise attributed to any material appearing in *The Complete Alpaca Book*, second revised edition.

© 2006 by Eric Hoffman and Bonny Doon Press.

All rights reserved under international copyright: Berne Convention, Universal Copyright Convention, and Pan-American Copyright Convention. No part of this book may be translated, reproduced, or transmitted in any form of print or electronic media, both extant and as may be invented or come into use in the future, including but not limited to hard cover, paperback, digital editions, internet distribution, and CD ROM. Permission to reprint any material in this book must be granted by Eric Hoffman or Bonny Doon Press.

Library of Congress Control Number: 2006923093
ISBN 0-9721242-1-7; 978-0-9721242-1-8
First edition 2003
Second revised edition 2006
Printed in the United States of America on acid-free paper

Bonny Doon Press
121 McGivern Way
Santa Cruz, California 95060
phone (831) 426-8649; fax (831) 426-1426

www.bonnydoonalpacas.org
e-mail bonnydoonpress@bonnydoonalpacas.org

Contents Summary

Table of Contents

....

Section One

NATURAL HISTORY AND ECOLOGY

Alpacas in *ichu* grass, Mallkini, Peru.

A cria and a Quechua child.

14 Obstetrics and Neonatology 397
Ahmed Tibary

Alpacas await screening and export to Europe near Macusani, Peru.

Foreword

It is with great pleasure that I write the following lines as a foreword to the second revised edition of *The Complete Alpaca Book* written and compiled by my great friend Eric Hoffman. I have known Eric from the very first days in 1991 when he began researching his first book on alpacas in Peru.

Eric is one of the few people who is well known and respected by alpaca farmers in Peru, the alpaca fiber industry in Arequipa, and alpaca owners worldwide. In Peru he is noted for his activities involving screening alpacas exported from this country. His work in developing the Alpaca Registry in North America has influenced registries throughout the world, and not only that, it has influenced us Peruvians in the way we now look at alpacas.

The second revised edition of *The Complete Alpaca Book* celebrates the alpaca as an international animal. Through its well-researched pages, the importance of international cooperation in developing new alpaca populations and improving fleece is reiterated in many different ways. Like the first edition, this second edition should be on every alpaca owner's bookshelf. It covers everything from daily care, nutrition, and the practical needs of alpacas to identifying common and rare diseases and instituting breeding practices to achieve particular goals. The revisions broaden our understanding of diseases affecting herd health and offer the latest cures through the inclusion of new research and an expanded text from additional authors. The book walks the reader through the evolution and cultural significance of the alpaca, offers practical guidelines for the alpaca's health and husbandry, and pushes into areas that need to be addressed in the future if we as alpaca breeders are to move forward in the world marketplace.

This book will also be of interest to people who buy alpaca products and are involved in the alpaca business, because it will help them understand what it takes to create the fiber they process or the garments they like. As a manufacturer myself, reading this book opened my mind and helped me better understand the importance of good breeding and the effects it has on fiber and the products we offer. It shows us the direction in which we need to push our breeding programs in order to achieve the greatest potential of this precious animal and its fiber. In this edition we learn more about the special properties of alpaca fiber with the introduction of new scientific studies and data collected from many sources (including Michell & CIA) from around the world. The book's focus on understanding the fiber characteristics of alpaca and other camelid species, as well as its practical applications to specific processes, will help us in our ultimate goal of increasing the consistency of quality fiber and maximizing alpaca products in the marketplace.

The Complete Alpaca Book, second revised edition bridges the gap between alpaca breeders and manufacturers. The reader will be able to understand the entire context in which the alpaca is placed in the world today—all the way from birthing a good-quality alpaca to processing its fleece into a ready-made luxury garment.

I highly recommend the second revised edition of *The Complete Alpaca Book* as the bible for all alpaca owners and breeders, and as a fountain of knowledge for alpaca aficionados around the world.

Derek Michell
CEO, Michell & CIA
Arequipa, Peru
April 2006

A suri alpaca.

Preface

The alpaca and llama are the oldest form of livestock in South America, indeed in all of the Americas. Alpacas were created by indigenous people living in the high Andes in South America by applying selective breeding practices to wild camelids. As a breed, alpacas predate the coming of the Europeans by 6,000 years. Today, raising alpacas is a fledging enterprise in Australasia, Europe, and North America. The irony of being both a prehistoric type of livestock originating in the harsh Andean environment and a new form of livestock being celebrated in industrial countries as a recent discovery may be unique in the annals of livestock development.

When Murray Fowler, DVM, and I began research for what was to become *The Alpaca Book*, published in 1995, there was much to learn about alpaca husbandry. In part this was because most of the scientific studies and work with alpacas had been done in South America and were written in Spanish. And in part much of the literature available in English did not fit the needs of alpaca owners who found themselves trying to raise their animals in conditions where exposure to new diseases, diets, predators, and climate presented new medical and husbandry challenges. Just ten years ago, there was a fair amount of trial and error in alpaca management, and research was sporadic.

The Alpaca Book, the first comprehensive book solely about alpacas in the English language, was a sincere effort to share information on alpacas in a single volume. But we had no doubt that more, much more, information would become available. When I got around to completing the first edition of *The Complete Alpaca Book* in 2003, those words had become prophetic. The amount of knowledge about alpacas had increased exponentially, an increase partly due to tapping knowledge that has always been there. While gathering research for the first edition, I began to explore the great fund of knowledge about raising alpacas and fiber processing in South America. I became acquainted with fiber processors in Arequipa, key figures in government agencies charged with working with camelids, owners on the altiplano, researchers from around the world, managers of cooperatives, and the herders themselves.

As it came time to publish a second edition, I found myself looking at even more information about alpacas. I was besieged by researchers and veterinarians from many parts of the world wanting to be part of the second revised edition. At first this was flattering, but the formidable challenge became not so much to present new information as to identify that which is most likely to be useful to alpaca owners. My training as a science and natural history writer and university-level feature story instructor came in handy. I also relied heavily on established experts from universities and those employed in the large fiber-processing mills in Peru.

I found that not everything presented as new data could be supported by facts or credible research. For example, making conclusions about alpaca neonatology, fiber inheritance, or other characteristics based on studies of sheep interested peer reviewers and myself much less than verifiable studies based on alpacas or other camelid species. In reviewing new material, we wanted to know the writer's qualifications, the scientific method used to arrive at conclusions, and whether the material could stand the litmus test of a peer review. Footnotes and references to published materials were a requirement of submission. We also looked for conflicts of interest among the proselytizers of particular viewpoints. The review process identified and honed verifiable, up-to-date coverage in major topic areas.

I wanted to offer readers of the first edition of *The Complete Alpaca Book* the most accurate and comprehensive information available, and knowing that no one person could definitively cover all the essential topics, I originally sought writers from around the world. The 12 authors chosen include experts from Australia, Ecuador, New Zealand, Peru, and the United States. In the process of drawing from many sources, a distillation of information took place, causing the essentials to define themselves more clearly.

For this, our second revised edition of *The Complete Alpaca Book*, I have added two new authors and benefited from the contributions of a number of additional veterinarians, owners, and businesses from Bolivia, Canada, England, Germany, Italy, and Switzerland. These experts participated in the review process or shared new research with the authors of revised and new chapters.

Robert Van Saun, the author of Chapter 9: Diet, is an example of the excellent qualifications of the book's authors. Dr. Van Saun is one of two veterinary camelid researchers we could identify in the United States who is board certified in the field of ruminant nutrition. He is arguably the only veterinarian with advanced training in nutrition who, in more than a decade, has conducted studies on camelids with other researchers for publication in peer-reviewed scientific journals. Dr. Van Saun has attempted to meld South American literature on the dietary needs of camelids with studies done in North America.

Alpaca herding, Peru.

Other core experts include Ahmed Tibary, who discusses reproduction and neonatal care, and Phillip Sponenberg, who has been involved with genetic projects of many endangered breeds of livestock. I think Dr. Sponenberg's presentation offers an educated discussion of how genetics may work with alpacas.

Being an expert also comes from experience. Stuart White is of North American origin but is a longtime resident of Ecuador, where he raises alpacas in the remote Canar Province. Even though his doctorate is in geography, he has become a world authority on sarcocystosis, a widespread disease in the Andes that is often present in animals being moved to other parts of the world. The peer reviewers at Oregon State University said it was the most complete treatment of the subject that they had seen (all research cited was done in South America). Rufino Quilla, a well-known veterinarian, lives in Juliaca in the Peruvian highlands not far from Peru's largest alpaca herds, and knows the camelid-growing world throughout Peru. He offers a look at how these animals are raised in their native land—an essential viewpoint for anybody seriously attempting to understand their animals in the new alpaca countries.

Each of the other authors is as special as the ones mentioned; lack of space makes it impossible to give them all their due. I do want to mention two new authors for this edition: Chris Cebra and Nancy Carr. Chris Cebra is a mainstay at Oregon State University's Camelid Research Program in Corvallis, and is well known as a leading researcher and clinician with llamas and alpacas. He is noted for his knowledge and innovation in treating serious diseases. In this second edition he has written on digestive disorders and hepatic lipidosis.

Nancy Carr is a recently retired medical doctor who discovered bovine viral diarrhea virus in a camelid herd in Canada. Through sheer perseverance, which involved working with veterinary researchers in Canada and the United States, Dr. Carr helped bring to light the potential problems of a

disease previously thought to be unimportant and mostly associated with cattle. Understanding this disease and its ramifications will help owners make responsible decisions about quarantines on their ranches and will require scrutiny of existing procedures for alpaca transport and shows.

Many others have contributed to the second edition. Among them is Juan Pepper, an executive for 17 years with Michell & CIA in Peru. Pepper is a consummate professional whose willingness to share data about alpaca fiber has enriched the fiber chapters in this book. His input helps us understand the role of alpaca fiber in the world marketplace.

Chapter 10: Fiber Processing, Characteristics, and Nomenclature is also much improved with the contributions of many other new sources. Foremost among them is the first-of-its-kind comprehensive evaluation of huacaya alpaca fiber by Christopher Lupton, Robert Stobart, and Angus McColl. Their findings help establish parameters for many properties found in alpaca fiber.

Yocom–McColl Testing Laboratories has helped to demystify ambiguities about alpaca fiber with new technologies that encompass a broader range of objective measurement than that offered just a few years ago. Chapter 10 offers examples of the expanded Sirolan LaserScan histogram offered by Yocom–McColl, which can measure the percentage of medullation in light-colored fleeces and the amount of curvature in a sample, as well as the essentials of average fiber diameter, standard deviation, coefficient of variation, microns greater than 30, and spin fineness. The increasingly sophisticated and comprehensive measurements offered in the expanding capabilities of histograms ultimately empower alpaca breeders. Rather than rely on the opinions of others about fleece quality, breeders can now make objective evaluations of their fleece.

I'd like to mention two additional contributors: Jane Wheeler and Michelle Ing. Dr. Jane Wheeler's scientific work on prehistoric camelids has pushed our level of understanding about the origins of domestic camelids to new heights. We benefited by her review and comments on Chapter 1: Classification, Prehistory and History. Dr. Ing has a veterinary practice dedicated to camelids in central California and is an expert in camelid reproduction and care. I know new owners will find her advice on how to choose an agistor in Chapter 4: Husbandry to be invaluable if they must hire someone to provide housing and care for their alpacas.

I hope the second revised edition of *The Complete Alpaca Book* inspires and informs you, and results in the improved care of your alpacas.

Eric Hoffman
Santa Cruz, California
April 2006

About the Authors

PRIMARY AUTHOR AND EDITOR

Eric Hoffman is a California native, graduate of San Jose State University, former inner-city teacher, university journalism instructor, author or co-author of five books, science magazine writer, and past editor of numerous publications. He is proudest of his adventuring books published by Sierra Club Books. Eric's dual involvement in nature writing and the camelid business has resulted in more than 40 trips to South America, where he has traveled extensively to remote camelid-growing areas throughout Peru and Chile. He is the grandson of W. D. Hoffman, the prolific 1930s novelist of Westerns.

Eric has raised camelids for 30 years (llamas since 1976, alpacas since 1984). He is a llama packer and pack designer. He co-sponsored and participated in "llamathons," which were successful fundraisers for cancer and AIDs research. Llamath-

ons involved sponsored teams made up of highly conditioned llamas and human runners who competed against each other, sometimes on courses covering 20 miles at 12,000 feet. His *California Living* article "Sunny, the Pioneer" popularized llamas as pack animals in the United States, and the article shared in winning the prestigious Maggie and National Headliner Awards in 1980. Eric was awarded a Pushmi–Pullyu Award by the International Llama Association in 1992 for his articles about camelids published in national and international magazines.

Eric was one of the founders of the alpaca business in North America. In 1988, he authored the Alpaca Registry (ARI), the first camelid registry in the world requiring scientific verification (DNA) as proof of lineage. He served on the registry board during the formative years. He was also the founding two-term president of the Alpaca Owners and Breeders Association (AOBA).

Eric was editor and a primary author in developing the *Alpaca Registry Screening Manual*, which emphasizes easily understandable objective criteria for assessing alpacas. This system influences the quality of alpacas exported from South America to other parts of the world. From 1995 until the present Eric has screened more than 14,000 alpacas. He has been involved in the development of five camelid registries around the world.

In 1995 Eric co-authored *The Alpaca Book* with Murray Fowler, DVM. Eric was editor of the *Alpaca Registry Journal*, a peer-reviewed science publication in the alpaca community for many years. His articles on camelids have appeared in *Pacific Discovery* (California Academy of Sciences), *Wildlife Conservation* (New York Zoological Society), *Living Planet* (World Wildlife Fund), *Scanorama* (Sweden and the former Soviet Union), *Outside*, *Animals*, and *International Wildlife* magazines. His coverage of the *chaku* program and the resurgence of vicuñas in Peru was cited by the U.S. Department of Fish and Wildlife in policy decisions.

Eric has spoken at educational conferences in Australia, Chile, Canada, Germany, New Zealand, England, Peru, Sweden, Switzerland, and the United States. In 2005 he was the featured speaker at the British Veterinarian Camelid Society in London, where he addressed camelid behavior and stress, plus camelid evolution, conformation, and anatomy.

Eric enjoys life with his wife Sherry at their ranch in the Santa Cruz Mountains. He enjoys photography, birding, and hiking with his small dog, Dilly Dog.

CONTRIBUTING AUTHORS

Karen Baum, DVM, a native of Wisconsin, graduated from Iowa State University's College of Veterinary Medicine, and then completed an ambulatory internship at Ohio State University and a large animal medicine residency at Cornell University. She worked at a racetrack practice in Illinois before accepting a faculty position at the Virginia Tech College of Veterinary Medicine. After leaving the university, Dr. Baum managed

a llama herd. She is now president and owner of Little Doc's Veterinary Care in Huddleston, Virginia, a private large-animal practice emphasizing llamas and alpacas. Her special interests are newborns, problem breeders, intensive care, heat stress, nutrition, neurologic problems, and physical therapy. She is vice president and was president as well as secretary of the Alpaca Research Foundation, and is involved in ongoing research in the alpaca industry.

Dr. Baum reaches out to special-needs children and nursing home residents with her llamas and alpacas. Dr. Baum's farm is home to dogs, cats, potbellied pigs, ducks, turkeys, chickens, sheep, goats, cattle, horses, minihorses, and donkeys, in addition to her llamas and alpacas.

Linda V. Carpenter, DVM, graduated from Ohio State University in 1964. She has worked for the USDA for 31 years  in meat inspection, veterinary biologics, and general fieldwork. She has also contributed to two emergency disease task forces as well as task forces on brucellosis, tuberculosis, and foot-and-mouth disease, and has worked in Mexico and Bolivia on animal import projects. She is currently the area epidemiologist for Washington and Alaska, and is involved in a variety of projects, including national animal health monitoring, various E. coli research projects with Washington State University, and a marine mammal brucellosis project. She became familiar with alpacas and llamas during the 1990s as the supervising USDA veterinarian on many large exportations from South America.

Dr. Carpenter raises and shows Corriedale sheep. She spends most of her spare time on her 40-acre farm in western Washington with her Paso Fino horses, draft mule team, and a growing herd of alpacas.

Nancy Carr, MD, graduated in medicine in 1975 from Queen's University (Kingston, Ontario). She worked as a family doctor in various rural locations (Nova Scotia and New Zealand) before settling on a farm near Kingston in 1985 with her husband Paul. She started raising alpacas in 1998 and semi-retired from medicine in 1999. Events on their farm in 2003 and 2004, and her resultant detective work, led to the discovery that BVD virus was, in contrast to prevailing thought at that time, a serious health issue  for alpacas. She never would have guessed that her MD would be used to further knowledge about alpacas, and that her only claim to published scientific fame would be in a veterinary journal. She would like to acknowledge the help of Dr. Susy Carman, DVM, PhD, of the Animal Health Laboratory at Guelph University, in get-

ting the important information about BVD virus out to alpaca owners.

Christopher K. Cebra, VMD, MA, MS, DACVIM, is a graduate of the University of Pennsylvania College of Veterinary Medicine, interned at Cornell, and completed a residency and master's of science program at Colorado State University. He is certified as an internist and currently employed as  an associate professor of large animal internal medicine at the Oregon State University College of Veterinary Medicine. Camelids have provided a substantial chunk of his clinical caseload over the last 14 years, and Dr. Cebra has made many efforts to solve some of the mysteries of their physiology, diseases, and health care. Of particular interest have been gastrointestinal disorders and disorders of energy metabolism, several of which he described for the first time. He has written over two dozen peer-reviewed, PubMed-listed scientific articles and over 100 review-type articles on health topics of New World camelids, teaches courses that draw international audiences, and speaks worldwide to veterinary and owner audiences. When not working or traveling, Dr. Cebra enjoys taking his family to the beach, hiking through Oregon's greenery, and spending time with a good book.

George Davis, MAgrSc (Lincoln University), DSc (Otago University), is a senior scientist at the Invermay Agricultural Centre at Mosgiel, New Zealand. He has published 190 papers on sheep, cattle, and alpaca breeding and production  based on 32 years of experience in New Zealand and South Korea. Since 1989 he has led a program in alpaca production research, following a visit to Chile the previous year to acquire a research herd. He has authored 28 papers on alpacas and, as well as speaking at seminars in New Zealand, has been an invited speaker at several international alpaca seminars and conferences in the United States and Australia. He was a scientific and technical advisor to the *Alpaca Registry Journal* and is an advisor to the breed development subcommittee of the Alpaca Association of New Zealand.

He has identified previously unrecorded seasonal effects on gestation length and birth weight and a gene affecting the size of alpaca ears. His sheep research has resulted in the discovery of four major genes affecting prolificacy. In 1994 he was awarded the prestigious New Zealand Society of

Animal Production's McMeekan Memorial Award for his outstanding contribution to animal production. In 2003 he was elected a fellow of the Royal Society of New Zealand in recognition for research in advancement of science.

Robert P. Ellis, PhD, is currently a professor in the Department of Microbiology at Colorado State University, Fort Collins, Colorado. His primary research efforts have been

directed toward the better definition of diseases, such as colibacillosis and enterotoxemia, that affect livestock and improving their diagnosis and prevention. He has extensive experience in livestock production and management, and makes every effort for his research to be directly applicable to animal owners and producers. He is an internationally recognized expert on *Clostridium perfringens* enterotoxemia, perhaps the deadliest disease to camelids.

Dr. Ellis has collaborated with scientists in Peru and North America in attempting to fully understand and control this and other diseases common to camelids. He has contributed to a greater understanding of enterotoxemia by publishing in professional journals and trade publications such as *Llama Life* and the *Alpaca Registry Journal*.

Juliet Gionfriddo, DVM, MS, received her BS (1976) and DVM (1980) from Colorado State University and her MS in veterinary ophthalmology (1991) from Iowa State University. She is certified by the American College of Veterinary Ophthalmologists. She first became interested in camelids during her ophthalmology residency at Iowa State and did her master's degree research and thesis on the microbiology of camelid eyes. She

conducted research into camelid tears and cataracts while an assistant professor of comparative ophthalmology at Purdue University.

Dr. Gionfriddo is currently an assistant professor at the Veterinary Teaching Hospital at Colorado State University.

Ty McConnell, DVM, is a native of California, graduated with a Bachelor of Science degree from Cal Poly, San Luis Obispo, and received a Doctor of Veterinary Medicine degree in 1980 from the University of California, Davis. He has been in private veterinary practice in the Santa Cruz, California area since 1980, specializing in camelid medicine and surgery. Alpacas have been a special emphasis in his practice

since their first importation in 1984. Dr. McConnell cohosted the first veterinary conference on camelids for veterinarians in 1984 and has been an active participant in many other camelid conferences.

He has authored many articles published in *Llama Life* and the *Alpaca Registry Journal* about hypophosphatemia, first aid, obstetrics, neonatal care, and luxating patella. He has participated in ARI alpaca screenings of over 1,500 animals in South America and New Zealand. His hobbies and recreation include backpacking, sports, photography, and motorcycling.

Rufino Quilla, DVZ, lives in Juliaca, Peru with his wife and three children. He earned a veterinary degree (Medico Veterinario y Zootecnista) at the Universidad Nacional del Altiplano in Puno, near Lake Titicaca. He has run large quarantine stations in Tacna and elsewhere in Peru. He is a noted expert in housing and caring for alpacas undergoing the crowded conditions associated with quarantine. He was responsible for the care of many thousands of alpacas exported from Peru to North America. Dr. Quilla was often the principal selector of alpacas whose qualities would later be subjected to rigid screen-

ing requirements by alpaca registries around the world. His expertise in assessing fiber and conformation is highly respected throughout the alpaca export business.

In recent years he has overseen shipments to Europe and Australia. Dr. Quilla has a large herd of alpacas on his farm in the alpaca-rich Puno District.

Denis Ryan, MVB, MRCVS, graduated from University College of Dublin's Veterinarian School in 1984. After three years in practice in Ireland and the United Kingdom, he and his wife Darina emigrated to Australia. Dr. Ryan is a cross-species veterinary practitioner with 14 years of bias toward the South American camelid. He is the founder of Animal House Veterinary Hospital in Torquay, Victoria, the surfing capital of Australia. He worked with the first importation of alpacas from Peru to Australia. He has also contributed to the Alpaca Registry Inc. screening standards and is a trained ARI screener. His work as a screener for several registries has taken him to Australia, South and North America, and the United Kingdom.

Denis, Darina, and their three children live on a small farm just outside Torquay,

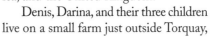

where they keep alpacas. He has almost no interest in surfing, but keeps a very keen eye on Australian viticulture!

D. Phillip Sponenberg, DVM, PhD, earned his doctorate in Veterinary Medicine at Texas A&M University in 1976 and his PhD in Reproductive Pathology and Genetics at Cornell University in 1979. He is currently a professor of pathology and genetics at the Virginia-Maryland Regional College of Veterinary Medicine, and is also the director of Student Affairs. Phillip has been interested in coat color genetics for many years, and has contributed to publications in peer-reviewed journals covering the genetics of sheep, goats, dogs, and horses, as well as the book *Equine Color Genetics*.

Dr. Sponenberg is the convener of the color group of the international Committee on Genetic Nomenclature of Sheep and Goats, which has recently expanded to cover all livestock species. He is active in rare-breed conservation and owns a Choctaw stallion and Tennessee myotonic goats. He has worked with the American Livestock Breeds Conservancy for many years. Serving as their unpaid technical coordinator, he works to assure the survival and good genetic health of breeds and strains of livestock and poultry with small populations.

He is also an avid spinner and knitter, and enjoys working with the wonderful array of alpaca colors—as long as the fiber quality is good!

Ahmed Tibary, DMV, PhD, Dipl ACT, earned his doctorate in Veterinary Medicine from the Veterinary School at the Institut Agronomique et Vétérinaire Hassan II (IAV) in Morocco in 1980, and a doctorate of science in Animal Production in 1989. He earned a master's degree in 1984 and a PhD in 1990 in theriogenology (animal reproductive physiology and pathology) at the University of Minnesota. He was board certified by the American College of Theriogenologists in 1991. He is currently on the faculty at the College of Veterinary Medicine at Washington State University.

From 1992 to 1998, Dr. Tibary served as scientific director at the Veterinary Research Center in Abu Dhabi, United Arab Emirates. He was instrumental in building a reference center for the study of infertility, artificial insemination, and embryo transfer in Arabian horses and racing camels. He has authored reference texts on equine reproduction and most recently a book on theriogenology in Camelidae, covering reproductive physiology, diseases, neonatology, and management of all species of camelids.

He has been involved with the alpaca breeding industry in North America for the past four years, conducting seminars and consulting on alpaca management and infertility.

Dr. Tibary enjoys interacting with alpaca breeders and, through this exchange of information, develops new ideas for research. He is also interested in computer technology applied to teaching, and his hobbies include sailing, equestrian events, photography, and digital video.

Robert J. Van Saun, DVM, MS, PhD, Dipl ACT/ACVN, received his DVM degree from Michigan State University in 1982. He practiced in northern New York in a predominately dairy practice prior to returning to Michigan State to complete an MS degree in nutrition and a residency in theriogenology. Dr. Van Saun completed a PhD program in ruminant nutrition from Cornell University. He is a board-certified diplomate of the American College of Theriogenologists and the American College of Veterinary Nutrition. For

eight years, Dr. Van Saun was on the faculty at the College of Veterinary Medicine, Oregon State University, and worked with the camelid industry in the Pacific Northwest. He has completed research projects dealing with vitamin D, hepatic lipidosis, and trace mineral nutrition in llamas and alpacas. Currently he is an extension veterinarian at Pennsylvania State University.

Most of his free time revolves around his two sons' various activities, including scouting, swim teams, and sports. He enjoys fishing, golf, and other outdoor recreation. Since moving to Pennsylvania, he and his oldest son have joined a Civil War reenacting group and enjoy reliving American history.

Stuart White, PhD, owns and operates an alpaca ranch in the Andes of Ecuador with his wife, Patricia Espadero, DVM. They manage 650 huacaya as well as 150 llamas. Stuart began

his herding life in 1985 with the import of 60 colored huacayas from Chile, in the hopes of reestablishing Ecuador's alpaca population, extinguished following the Spanish Conquest in the 16th century. He holds a PhD in geography and has taught at the University of New Mexico, Albuquerque. His research interests include high-altitude *paramo* grasslands, pre-Columbian land use and landscapes, and montane deforestation.

He is currently general coordinator of the Fundación Cordillera Tropical, dedicated to conserving wild habitat in the mountains of Ecuador.

ACKNOWLEDGMENTS

Many people contributed to the creation of this book by giving unselfishly of their time and expertise. Sherry Edensmith leads the list. She interrupted all other plans for over a year and served as counselor, editor, cheerleader, word processor, and organizer. This book would not be what it is without Sherry's involvement. Through it all, she remains my loving wife.

Peruvians Ignacio Garycochea, Derek Michell, Luis Chavez, Raul Rivera, and Juan Pepper made fiber processing comprehensible. Ignacio Garycochea spent countless hours verifying the factual content of Chapter 10: Fiber Processing, Characteristics, and Nomenclature, and helping with the pictorial story for this important chapter. Luis Chaves, general manager of Inca Tops, shared his vast knowledge of processing, and educated me about the sophisticated workings of the international alpaca fiber business. Derek Michell, the CEO of Michell & CIA, offered much inspiration through his encouragement and support. Gilberto Sarfaty, managing director of Prosur, added to the discussion of essential fiber characteristics for processing.

Drs. Rufino Quilla and Isabella Quiñaco of the Puno District were tireless sources of firsthand information, as was now retired CONACS minister Dr. Alfonso Martinez. Alvarado Cuba, general manager of Rural Alianza, was perhaps the single most enlightening source about alpaca breeding and husbandry practices for fiber quality. Don Julio Barreda, the creator of the Accoyo herd, and the suri breeders in the Santa Rosa region of Peru were also helpful.

Because Ramon Solis Hospital shared his 550-page book of abstracts and research, *Producción de Camélidos Sudamericanos*, with me, I became familiar with the impressive breadth and depth of scientific research in South America. Dr. Godofredo Mamani Choque at the Universidad de Altiplano was helpful because of his knowledge of camelid breeding and genetics. The dedication and brilliance of researcher Dr. Jane Wheeler, archaeozoologist, vice-president of CONOPA, and visiting professor at San Marcos University, has influenced the way in which alpacas are portrayed in this book.

Bolivians Tito and Billy Bohrt contributed knowledge of processing various species of camelid fibers. Argentinean researcher Adriana McGuire deserves mention for helping procure data on wild camelid fiber.

Lucrecia Bianchi-Salvadò, Monica Garcìa Gomero, Sandra Revilla Harker, Alejandra Revilla, and Dr. Renzo Morante helped with translations.

Canadians Lavona Fercho, Margaret Brewster, and Peter Rysko helped in a variety of ways. From Australia, Joann Rothique, Graeme Dickson, Ian Davison, and Carl Dowd always responded and shared their knowledge.

Joy and Ken Whitehead, from the United Kingdom, came through in the crunch with key photographs, and my thanks also extend to Nick Weber for his help on toxic plants and to Arnold Luginbühl of Switzerland for contributing to Chapter 3: Anatomy and Conformation.

In the United States, my appreciation starts with Paul and Sally Taylor, who sold me Sunny, the "pioneer llama," in 1976, followed by Tom Hunt, who conscripted me to sell the first large shipments of alpacas brought to the United States in 1984. It was their influence that led to my passion for camelids that developed into a lifetime pursuit.

More immediately in the creation of this book, help came from longtime breeders Susan Stackhouse and Lona Frank, who reviewed important chapters along with Dr. Karen Timm. Others who contributed their knowledge include Rick Evans, Jan Hensle, John Callen, Mary Reed, and Tilly Dorsey. Without the cooperation of Randy Snow, Bill Barnett, Phil Mizrahie, and Dar Wassink, the book would have been sorely lacking in statistics on large groups of animals. Angus and Margaret McColl retrieved data for the unique histograms and density studies found throughout the text. Thanks to Beverly Bell, who formatted figures and tables; UC Davis undergraduate Jonathan Martin, who produced the conformational aspects of alpacas in Chapter 3; graphic artist Zeke Smith for the drawings in Chapter 2; and anthropologist George Miller for sharing his historic maps and photographs.

I am deeply grateful to first-edition authors Karen Baum, Linda Carpenter, George Davis, Robert Ellis, Juliet Gionfriddo, Ty McConnell, Rufino Quilla, Denis Ryan, D. Phillip Sponenberg, Ahmed Tibary, Robert J. Van Saun, Stuart White, and Tumen Wuliji for sharing their expertise and knowledge. Without their contributions, this book would only be half the book it is.

The second revised edition of this book resulted in improvements because of the contributions, expertise, knowledge, and dedication of the following individuals not previously mentioned: authors Nancy Carr (expert in BVDV in camelids), Chris Cebra, (expert in all aspects of camelid health at Oregon State University), Michelle Ing (veterinarian specializing in camelid reproduction and health in central California), Iris Laudig (figures and tables, Chapter 10), Christopher Lupton (fiber scientist at Texas A&M), Lee Millon and F. J. Wortmann (microscopic images of fiber), Julie and Don Skinner (alpaca breeders), Bob Broadbent (president of the British Veterinary Society), Margaret and Angus McColl (review of material on fiber), and JoAnn McGrath (*Llama Life II*).

Dedication

The Complete Alpaca Book, 2nd edition, is dedicated to my fellow screeners, whose diligence, expertise, integrity, and hard work made a difference and improved the quality of emerging alpaca populations throughout the world.

Margaret Brewster
Robert Broadbent, DVM
Bill Calder, DVM
Craig Dorin, DVM
Lavona Fercho
Murray Fowler, DVM
Paul Jones, DVM
Jim Leech, DVM

Pat Long, DVM
Ty McConnell, DVM
Ewen McMillan, MVB, MRCVS
Nora Prehn, DVM
Denis Ryan, MVB, MRCVS
Brad Smith, DVM, PhD
Phil Switzer
Karen Timm, DVM, PhD

....

Photo Credits

All photographs in text are by Eric Hoffman except as noted below.
Front Matter   Francis Rainsford: xi.
Chapter 1   Linda Carpenter: 11 bottom left, 12 middle left & right bottom, 23 top right; Robert Ellis: 12 top; Michell & CIA: 15 top right; George Miller: 6 top left, 8 top left, 10 bottom right, 11 top right & bottom right, 12 bottom left, 13 top right, 14,16 bottom, 20, 23 bottom, 24 top left; Minden Pictures: 9 top right; Randy Snow: 9 bottom left; Ahmed Tibary: 17 bottom right; Joy Whitehead: 22 bottom left; Ken Whitehead: 10 top & bottom left.
Chapter 2   Beverly Bell: 40 bottom right; Hugh Bollinger: 55 bottom; Pepe Dion: 46 top right; George Miller: 45 top right; Susan Stackhouse: 34 bottom & top right, 54 top left.
Chapter 4   Leah Dewald: 93 top left; Tilly Dorsey: 86, 99 bottom right, 112 top right; Roger Haldane: 101; Michell & CIA: 85; Minden Pictures: 89; John Robbins: 97.
Chapter 5   Eileen Ausland: 131 top right; Sherry Edensmith: 124, 126 top left, 127 top, 129 top right, 134; Jon Robbins: 131 middle right.
Chapter 6   Susan Stackhouse: 139.
Chapter 7   Lavona Fercho: 150.
Chapter 8   Phil Mizrahie: 176; Zeke Smith: 175.
Chapter 9   Lona Frank: 222, 223; Arnold Lugenbühl: 187.
Chapter 10   Margaret Brewster: 291 top left, 292 bottom right; Inca Tops: 290 top right; Margaret McColl: 302, 303; Michell & CIA: 243 bottom left, 289 bottom left, 290 bottom right, 292 bottom left; George Miller: 280; Lee Millon: 251, 297 right column, 299; Phil Mizrahie: 259; K. H. Phan & F. J. Wortmann: 297 left column, 298; Susan Stackhouse: 271; Carol Weisner: 289 bottom right, 292 top left; Ken Whitehead: 289 center; Agnes & Richard Wildt: 289 top.
Chapter 11   Wayne Ausland: 321, 322; Sherry Edensmith: 323 top right; Russell Gent: 324 A & B, 330; George Miller: 319, Steve Murray: 328, 329; John Robbins: 325.

Chapter 12   Ahmed Tibary except for Eric Hoffman: 335, 336 bottom right, 338, 339, 340, 346 bottom right, 356.
Chapter 13   Ahmed Tibary except for Eric Hoffman: 361, 365, 369, 375 top right, 376, 377 top & bottom right, 378, 391; Dawnelise Regnery: 375 top left.
Chapter 14   Ahmed Tibary except for Beverly Bell: 407; Sherry Edensmith: 403, 406; Eric Hoffman: 397, 404, 405, 409, 410.
Chapter 15   Sherry Edensmith: 412 top left & right, bottom left & middle.
Chapter 16   Sherry Edensmith: 430; Lona Frank: 431.
Chapter 17   Lona Frank: 435; Taylor Phelps: 434.
Chapter 18   Stuart White & Instituto Pérez, Quito: 439; Stuart White: 437.
Chapter 19   Arnold Lugenbühl: 448; George Miller: 448 bottom, 449 top right, 450 middle & bottom, 452 top right; Minden Pictures: 450 top right.
Chapter 20   George Miller: 467.
Chapter 21   Juliet Gionfriddo: 485, 486, 487 top left, 488, 489; LaRue Johnson: 487 top right; Denis Ryan: 490, 491.
Chapter 23   Minden Pictures: 501.
Chapter 24   Don Julio Barreda: 528.
Chapter 25   Photos by D. Phillip Sponenberg except for Joe Fowler: 552 bottom right, 555 top left; Eric Hoffman: 549 top left, top right, & bottom left, 551 top left, 555 bottom right.
Chapter 26   Don Julio Barreda: 562 top.

Front Cover   Eric Hoffman: Male alpaca browsing, Mallkini, Peru.
Back Cover   Eric Hoffman: Suri alpacas in the morning sun, Juliaca, Peru.

Frontispiece caption   Domestic camelids at 12,000 feet (4,000 meters), Lauca National Park, Chile.

Section One

Natural History and Ecology

Overleaf A Quechua child watches over an alpaca herd in southern Peru.

Chapter 1

Classification, Prehistory, and History

Eric Hoffman

Guanaco standing among wild pastures and pinnacles.

Ausangate is a magnificent snow-covered peak south of Cuzco and the legendary source of llamas and alpacas. According to legend, Pachamama (mother earth) loans alpacas and llamas so that people of the puna can survive. Since the animals belong to Pachamama, they must be well fed and never be treated cruelly. If they aren't properly cared for, Pachamama will call them back to Ausangate and people will disappear.

—Ancient Quechua Legend[15]

ANDEAN PASTORALISM

Long before the nineteenth-century Austrian monk Gregor Mendel enlightened the Western world on theories of inheritance and genetics, long before the rise of the Roman Empire, and long before the ancient Egyptian pharoah Tutankhamen, a highland people of the Southern Hemisphere created two wonderful all-purpose animals through selective breeding practices—the alpaca and the llama. The world now knows the smaller of these two animals as the alpaca, producer of high-grade luxury fiber in an incredible assortment of colors. *Alpaca* is a Spanish word derived from the Aymara name *allpacu* or the Quechua names *pacos* or *pacochas*.[7,15,29] The Aymara and Quechua people are the traditional owners of alpacas. A brief conversation, recorded in the harsh physical environment of the Andes, captures the essence of this way of life.

One cold night in the Andean highlands, Felix Palacios and Nolberto Chambilla Mandamiento lay in their bedrolls looking at the stars. Around them knelt alpacas and llamas, their legs folded snugly under their woolly bodies. The animals' thick coats glistened with the frost that occurs 320 nights a year on the puna, the high, treeless plain. Felix, then a graduate student in anthropology at the Catholic University of Peru in Lima, asked Nolberto, an Aymara-speaking herder, "If all the alpacas and llamas died, what would happen?"

"We would die," Nolberto replied.

"Why?"

"Because we raise alpacas and llamas and they raise us."[15]

Felix Palacios has worked to record the beliefs of highland herders like Nolberto. Nolberto lives close to Lake Titicaca, which straddles Peru and Bolivia. He represents traditional Andean pastoralism. His livelihood depends on the exchange of native animal products from the inhospitable 14,000-foot (4,200-m) puna for agricultural goods grown at lower elevations. This is an ancient way of life based on the only pre-European livestock domestication in the New World, and it echoes back to the rise and fall of once-great civilizations. The highland herders share a kinship bond with their alpacas and llamas, a bond cemented by tradition, religious devotion, genuine affection, and harsh pragmatism.

3

Like their Inca forefathers, many of today's highland pastoralists collect their llamas, load them with highly prized raw alpaca fiber and woven cloth, dried llama and alpaca meat called *charqui* (a Quechua word from which we get the English *jerky*), and sacks of dried potatoes (*chuño*). The pastoralists and their animals trudge for days to villages in more temperate lower elevations, where they trade their goods for maize, wheat flour, squash, quinoa (grain similar to rice), amaranth grain, chili peppers, beans, and sometimes fruit. With agriculture marginal at best on the harsh puna, these bartering trips are necessary for survival.[7,15,17]

Movement of goods between highland herders, farmers of the temperate Andean valleys, and coastal fishermen was crucial to the development of Andean cultures, which culminated in the Inca Empire (1438–1532). Spanish conquistador Francisco Pizarro and 170 men put an end to the Inca Empire more than 470 years ago. Though the animals still figure prominently in Andean herders' culture and heritage, the pastoralists' way of life was forever altered by the Spanish Conquest. European beliefs and cultural disorientation broke down much of the social structure and belief system that once ruled the land, including the strict codes concerning animal husbandry practices.[12,15,20,26,27,34,36] Despite changes and constant pressures since the Conquest, Andean pastoralism has survived (some would say primarily as only a vestige of the past) because both the people and animals are well adapted to the harsh Andean environment.[15]

Of all the animals found in the Americas prior to European colonization, llamas and their diminutive woolly alpaca cousins had the most comprehensive influence. Like the buffalo in North America, llamas and alpacas were the source of meat, fuel (in the form of dried manure), and hides. But unlike the buffaloes, llamas and alpacas were fully domesticated animals, created centuries before the Incas by Andean people who bred wild forms of the South American camel family. The alpacas and llamas had the extra capabilities of providing fiber for weaving and transport for trading.[15,34,35,36]

Llamas and alpacas were let out each morning to graze on the puna, and they were returned to their rock corrals, known as *canchones*, each evening. These ancient corrals are spread throughout the *altiplano* (high plateau and drainage around Lake Titicaca, including southern Peru and northwestern Bolivia). For centuries they have been used to collect herds of alpacas each evening and provide resting places for llama caravans.[6,15,17]

The ancient pastoralists purposely created and maintained two kinds of domestic animals: the llama, a beast of burden (many of which were also fine fleeced) and the al-paca, a smaller form that was shorn for its high-quality fiber. Both animals were butchered. This level of domestication and differences between the two guaranteed a steady source of meat, high-quality textile fiber, and a means to move large amounts of goods through rugged mountain areas.[15,30,34]

ANCESTRAL BEGINNINGS

Llamas and alpacas are members of the camel family Camelidae, of which there are six living species. The ancestors of today's camelids evolved in North America between 11 and 9 million years ago. In its most distant forms the family dates back 35 million years.[3,4,30,31,34] The camelid story in South America began three million years ago when a wild form known as *Hemiauchenia* migrated across the Isthmus of Panama into South America (possibly with other forms of now extinct camelids). *Hemiauchenia*, looking somewhat like an over-sized, long-limbed, long-necked guanaco, became the direct ancestor of today's *Lama* and *Vicugna* genera, which first appeared in the eastern lowlands two million years ago. The *Lama* and *Vicugna* developed shorter limbs and other differences before moving into the high Andes approximately 12,000 years ago when the glaciers retreated at the end of the Pleistocene Age. *Paleolama*, a closely related, now extinct relative of *Hemiauchenia* that lived in South America, spread back up the Pacific Coast across the isthmus, through Mexico and to Texas, Louisiana, Mississippi, and Florida. Both *Hemi-*

The *Palaeolama* is one of the many early ancestors to today's vicuñas and alpacas.

Table 1.1 Classification of camelids and other Artiodactylids.

Class	**MAMMALIA**
Order	**ARTIODACTYLA**
Suborder	**TYLOPODA** Camelids
Family	**CAMELIDAE**
OLD WORLD	
Camelus dromedarius	Dromedary camel
Camelus bactrianus	Bactrian camel
NEW WORLD	
Lama guanicoe	Guanaco
Lama glama	Llama
Vicugna vicugna	Vicuña
Vicugna vicugna menalis	Peruvian, Chilean, and Bolivian vicuña
Vicugna vicugna vicugna	Argentinean and Chilean vicuña
Vicugna pacos	Alpaca
Suborder	**RUMINANTIA** Goats, sheep, cattle, water buffalo, giraffe, deer, antelope, bison

auchenia and *Palaeolama* and other ancestral forms living in North America became extinct about 12,000 years ago, leaving only *Lama* (the wild guanaco) and *Vicugna* (the wild vicuña) in South America. These two genera are the only two surviving wild forms in all of the Americas.

The camelid migration from North America to Asia also began about three million years ago via the land bridge connecting Alaska to Siberia. The eventual result was the one-humped dromedary camel (*Camelus dromedarius*) of Africa and the two-humped Bactrian camel (*Camelus bactrianus*) of Asia.[3,4,9,10,11,17,19,30,31,32]

The large-humped African and Asian camels (also known as Old World camels) look quite different from their much smaller South American brethren (also known as New World camels), but all six species have the same diploid chromosome number ($2n=74$) and can interbreed and produce live offspring. Although it was common knowledge that any combination of the four South American species could breed and produce fertile offspring, it was thought that crossing Old World with New World camels was a remote possiblity at best. However, on January 14, 1998, the birth of Rama, the product of a union between a 990-pound (450-kg) dromedary father and a guanaco mother, brought together Camelidae genes that had been separated for at least three million years. This feat was brought about at the Camel Reproduction Centre in Dubai, United Arab Republic, by British researcher Lulu Skidmore. It took more than 40 artificial inseminations and five ill-fated pregnancies before delivering a live birth.

The birth of the first ever cama demonstrates the genetic compatibility of all six species, even after millions of years of separation and many evolutionary changes in appearance and physiology. It's not clear if fertile offspring will ever occur from a union of genes between Old and New World camels, or if a successful mating would ever occur by natural means. The commercial value of producing a cama may be debatable, but Dr. Skidmore points out that Rama is adaptable to tough conditions and much stronger than a llama. According to Skidmore, the cama may be a prototype for a superior woolly pack animal that is more the size of a horse than a llama or camel—providing it can be produced consistently.[28]

ALPACA CLASSIFICATION: DENTITION AND DNA

When the Spanish arrived in South America, they recorded wild and domestic forms of camelids but made few distinctions between the "sheep of the land." Attempts in scientific circles to distinguish between the four species now recognized in South America didn't occur until 1758, more than 200 years after the Spanish arrived. During this time frame the Spanish eradicated millions of llamas and alpacas through the introduction of European livestock diseases and cruel policies toward the indigenous animals and the people who owned them. The Spanish influence severely impacted the llama and alpaca gene pool and may have eliminated entire races.

Confusion and debate have marked the classification of the four South American camel family species. The wild forms are the guanaco (*Lama guanicoe*) and vicuña (*Vicugna vicugna*). The domestic forms are the llama (*Lama glama*) and the alpaca (*Vicugna pacos*, known as *Lama pacos* for the last two centuries). Despite their ability to interbreed and produce fertile offspring, each remains classified as a separate species.

The debate on the genus classification of alpacas initially hinged on the similar dentition of vicuñas and alpacas, which is different from llamas and guanacos. For most of the 1990s archaeozoologist Jane Wheeler argued that alpacas are more closely linked to vicuñas than to guanacos or llamas. She pointed out that when the early nomenclature was adopted, only differences in guanaco and vicuña dentition were discussed, resulting in a separate genus for each, while the characteristics of llamas and alpacas were not considered. Thus, Wheeler contended that by default, the two domestic forms were assigned to the *Lama* genus, implying they both are direct descendants of guanacos. Even though Wheeler presented convincing evidence in the mid-1990s that alpacas belonged in the *Vicugna* genus, respected paleontologists and scientists specializing in camelid prehistory were resistant to her assertions.[8] Not

These 6,000-year-old pictographs chronicle the domestication of camelids.

Left Camelids are depicted as wild.

Below The camelid pictured here has a rope around its neck.

Table 1.2 Hybrid species of camelids obtained by natural means and artificial insemination.

Male Species	Female Species	Cross	Fertility of Cross
Vicugna pacos	*Lama glama*	Misti	Yes
V. pacos	*Vicugna vicugna*	Paco-vicuña	Yes
V. pacos	*L. guanicoe*	Paco-guanaco	?
Lama glama	*V. pacos*	Huarizo or pachocha	Yes
L. glama	*V. vicugna*	Llamo-vicuña	Yes
L. glama	*L. guanicoe*	Llamo-guanaco	Yes
L. guanaco	*V. vicugna*	Guanaco-vicuña	?
L. guanaco	*Camelus dromedarius* *		
C. dromedarius	*L. guanicoe*	Cama**	?
C. dromedarius	*C. bactrianus*		Low fertility
C. bactrianus	*C. dromedarius*		Low fertility

* Two pregnancies resulted from 50 inseminations of 30 females. One aborted at 260 days and one produced a stillborn female at 365 days.

**Six pregnancies occurred in nine females inseminated a total of 34 times. Two were reabsorbed at 25 and 40 days; two female fetuses aborted at 291 and 301 days; one female was stillborn at 365 days. One premature male (328 days) is still alive.

From Tibary A.: Semen Preservation and Artificial Insemination in Camelids. *Proceedings of the Annual Conference of the Society for Theriogenology*, Vancouver, Canada, pages 369–378, 2001.

until Wheeler and a team of international scientists developed DNA technology that precisely identified the origins of the domestic camelids did Wheeler put to rest the debate over the correct genus for alpacas. Because of Wheeler and her colleagues, we now know for certain that the wild progenitor of the alpaca is the vicuña, and the alpaca's name is *Vicugna pacos* and no longer *Lama pacos*, the name the alpaca had been assigned since 1758.[20,21,22,26,27,33,34,35,36]

The story of how DNA testing resolved this debate is one of perseverance and application of advances in the science of DNA. Working from the back of a small pickup truck, Wheeler, her husband Peruvian veterinarian Raul Rosadio, and British geneticist Helen Stanley collected blood from all four camelid species from remote populations in Peru, Bolivia, Chile, and Argentina until they had blood samples from 2,000 animals. The samples were sent to the Institute of Zoology in London, where geneticists Michael Bruford, Miranda Kadwell, and Matilde Fernandez analyzed the samples looking for recurring nuclear DNA patterns known as microsatellites. Work in microsatellites has helped geneticists determine the amount of hybridization that has occurred in other types of animals that can interbreed with related species. Bruford and Kadwell found two microsatellite groups that clearly separated guanacos from vicuñas—the two living wild camelid species in South America. They then looked for the same microsatellite arrangements in domestic llamas and alpacas, which emerged from both or one of the wild forms. "From our microsatellite work we are able to conclude that the vicuña is the wild ancestor of the alpaca and the guanaco is the wild ancestor of the llama," explained Bruford, who then took his work a step further and developed a DNA blood test to determine if hybridization has occurred in any given alpaca or llama. The results of the initial hybridization sampling were astonishing. Hybridization appears to be pervasive throughout the Andes. While 40 percent of llamas tested were hybrids with some alpaca or vicuña genes in their genetic makeup, 80 percent of the alpacas tested were hybrids with some guanaco or llama genes in their genetic makeup. "We discovered that it's not possible to tell whether an alpaca or a llama is a purebred by looking at it."[20,27,33,35,36]*

Without a doubt Wheeler, Rosadio, and Bruford took a giant step forward in understanding the origins of South American camelids and shedding light on the breadth of hybridization. Hybridization is thus the obvious influence on the decline of fiber quality in many South American al-

paca herds. By fine-tuning the microsatellite work to do more than prove the ancestry of the llama and alpaca, they created the first scientifically verifiable genotype test to determine the degree of hybridization in a particular llama or alpaca, whereas in the past assessing an animal's origins amounted to judging its phenotype (appearance). The ramifications of this scientific contribution may have widespread influence on future genetic practices among alpaca growers thoughout the world, especially if DNA-based registries make use of this knowledge. There are also unanswered questions about the correlation between hybridization and fiber quality or structural soundness in individual animals (regardless of their genotype). In general terms Wheeler's findings further document the problem of hybridization throughout the Andes.[13,20,26]

Wheeler and her team's work has permanently altered alpacas' scientific name. From 1758 until 2001, in scientific papers alpacas were usually listed in the *Lama* genus. Vicuñas were sometimes erroneously listed in the *Lama* genus as well, but there is now general acceptance of the vicuña's separate genus classification in the scientific community, which now includes a new member: *Vicugna pacos*.[14,20,22,33,35,36]

Some confusion also exists on the proper classification of alpacas because of their two coat types: *huacaya* and *suri*. These coat differences are not recognized as separate species: There is only one species of alpaca and the two coat types are often referred to as breeds. Origins for the two breeds are not known. The suri coat type has been identified on mummified animals (both alpacas and llamas) dating back 1,000 years,[26,33,35,36] and ancient pottery depicting suris may be 2,000 years old. The breeds probably existed much earlier than both the mummified remains and the pottery.

SPECIES COMPARISONS

The four South American humpless camels have much in common. They are genetically compatible with the same diploid chromosones ($2n=74$).[20,28,33] They are modified ruminants, i.e., cud chewers, but with a different stomach arrangement and digestive tract compared to cows, sheep, and other true ruminants (see Chapter 3: Anatomy and Conformation). They have long and supple necks, slender legs, two-toed padded feet, large round eyes, and wool-covered bodies. All are extraordinarily alert creatures and can survive in places where it freezes most nights and where forage is not plentiful. The wild forms, more than the domestic ones, are natural pacers, allowing efficient movement across wide-open spaces. The many-faceted methods of communication and herd behavior are also

---

*Dr. Jane Wheeler, vice president of CONOPA and visiting professor, Faculty of Veterinary Medicine, San Marcos University, Lima, Peru, April 2, 2001; and Dr. Michael Bruford, professor at University of Cardiff and head of Conservation Genetics, Institute of Zoology, London, personal communication, London, March 30, 2001.

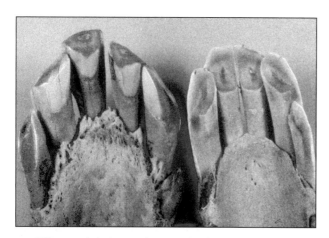

Differences in incisor teeth among South American camelids contribute to a greater understanding of their origins. On the left are enamel-encased incisors of guanaco or llama. On the right are alpaca incisors; there is no enamel on the tongue side of the teeth, a feature also found in vicuñas. Recently, Dr. Jane Wheeler and a team of scientists used DNA microsatellite testing to prove that alpacas originated from vicuñas, resulting in the name change from alpaca to *Vicugna pacos*.

distinctly similar across the four species, giving observable credence to their common ancestry.

Guanacos and Llamas

Even before Wheeler's recent work with DNA, paleontologists believed the llama was bred from the guanaco.[7,11,15] The dentition and skeleton of both animals are almost identical. Individuals in both species usually weigh between 200 and 380 pounds (90–160 kg), with the largest llamas being larger than the largest guanacos. Easily trained llamas make excellent beasts of burden. There are no wild llamas (or alpacas), but some wild hybrids reported in Argentina show pelage of llama influence. Subspecies of guanacos, which are wild, once roamed the Andes and adjoining plains, but today they are found chiefly in the southern Andes, Patagonia, and the continent's archipelago Tierra del Fuego. The overall guanaco population is thought to number more than 600,000 animals, mostly in Argentina. Ironically, in 1999 the number of guanacos in Peru (the country with the most alpacas and vicuñas) had dwindled to around 2,000 animals. In Bolivia, the most populous llama country, the guanacos are nearly extinct in the wild.

In contrast to llamas, whose coloration varies, guanacos are always distinguished by a brown coat, a black or grey head, and an evenly marked underside. Both guanacos' and llamas' woolly coats are two-coated—much coarse guard hair over the finer undercoat—which diminishes the com-

mercial value of the fibers. However, the guanaco is a much underutilized source of high-quality fiber. The undercoat on guanacos ranges consistently between 16 and 18 microns. Guanaco often has a standard deviation of 4.5, a coefficient of variation of 26.7, and only 1.6 percent of microns greater than 30 microns.[*] With recent technological advances in commercial dehairing machines, the guanaco's contribution to the natural fiber industry may become a reality.[**] Archeological evidence points to the fact that many (but not all) pre-Conquest llamas had fine fleeces of a single coat much like alpacas.[***] However, fine-fleeced, even-coated llamas are not common in today's llama populations.

Vicuñas and Alpacas

Prior to recent DNA studies linking alpacas and vicuñas, alpaca dentition suggested that the animal descended from the vicuña, but as explained earlier, not all paleontologists and camelid experts were convinced the vicuña was the sole ancestor. It was often suggested that other forms, such as the guanaco, llama, or now extinct breeds, may have played a part.[11] However, vicuñas and many alpacas have no, or very little, enamel on the tongue side of their incisors. These incisors differ from the llama incisors in that they grow continually. This growth allows the incisors to maintain function as they wear down from grazing grasses and lichens cropped close to the ground.[14,15,17,18,20,34,35,36]

Vicuñas and alpacas are smaller than llamas and guanacos. In skeletal structure, alpacas more closely resemble the northern vicuña (*Vicugna vicugna menalis*). In fact, DNA studies have shown the northern vicuña subspecies (*V. v. menalis*) to be the ancestor of the alpaca.[27,34,46] As the smallest of the four species, vicuñas weigh around 90 pounds (40 kg). They are the most delicate-looking members of the camel family, have large eyes, and are truly one of nature's most graceful creatures, both in a standing position and when gliding effortlessly over rough terrain at full speed with their necks held out over the ground. Usually found between 13,000 and 16,000 feet (4,000 and 5,000 m), they live in stark, uncompromising environments far above the tree line and adhere to fairly inflexible territorial lifestyles, which have contributed to their undoing at the hands of poachers.[7,8,16,17]

Like the guanaco, the vicuña has uniform markings. The coat is cinnamon with a white underbelly and a light-colored head. The *menalis* subspecies has a distinct white

---

[*]Yocom-McColl Testing Laboratory, personal communication, Denver, Colorado, April 1, 2000.

[**]Tito Bohrt, Bolivian camelid fiber processor, personal communication, Arequipa, October 12, 2000.

[***]Dr. Jane Wheeler, personal communication, April 6, 2001.

Meet the vicuña family. For decades scientists debated the origin of the alpaca. In the year 2000, DNA microsatellite samplings of wild and domestic camelids solved the question of origin: The vicuña is the wild progenitor of the alpaca.

Vicuña (*Vicugna vicugna*).

Alpaca, suri breed (*Vicugna pacos*).

Alpaca, huacaya breed (*Vicugna pacos*).

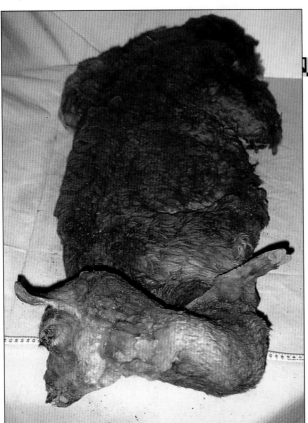

The El Yaral archeological site is located in a dry high-desert area of Peru, which allowed these mummies to remain intact for more than 1,000 years. The quality of the fiber on all of the mummies indicates that the ancient alpaca breeders had achieved an unsurpassed excellence in fiber quality.

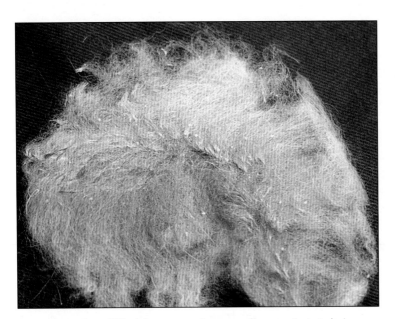

The pre-Incan El Yaral alpaca mummies possess fiber superior to today's alpacas. The fiber sample pictured here has an average fiber diameter of 17.9, with an incredible standard deviation of 1.

In the Museo Nacional de Arqueología in Lima, a mannequin representing the Incan period wears ancient high-quality alpaca clothing created by Incan weavers. This figure is holding a *quipu*. Under the Incas, shrine herds were managed by *llama camayoc* (also *llama michi*), the high-ranking herding class.

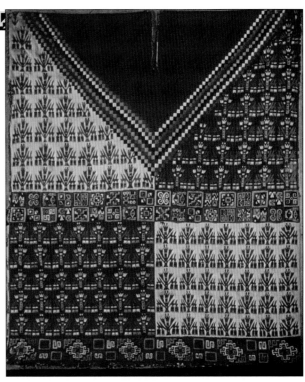

An intricately woven and dyed tunic worn by an Incan official (circa 1530). Among the Incas, clothing announced a person's position and social class.

A woman's hairpiece made from black alpaca (circa 400).

Incan pottery shows an ancient South American camelid.

Above Llama pack trains still connect highland villages to lower farming areas throughout the Andes.

Left Fertility doll replicas sold to tourists in Lima and the highlands are often partially made of ancient cloth found in gravesites.

A weaving from the pre-Incan period (circa 1400).

Samples of 2,000-year-old alpaca cloth.

The alpaca is the most color-diverse fiber-producing animal in the world. More than 22 common colors are marketed in Peru and more than 250 shades have been identified.

Aborted llama and alpaca fetuses are sold in downtown La Paz as good-luck charms to be put under the corner of a new house.

A tunic worn by a common soldier in the Incan army (circa 1530).

Incan gold pieces capture the essential ingredients of Andean pastoralism. These pieces survived the Spanish conquest.

A Quechua family poses near its alpaca herd.

Andean pastoralism is an ancient way of life involving people and alpacas and llamas.

A *llama michi* dances with a dead cria as part of a fertility ritual in Cuzco. In ancient times the *llama michi* were the respected social class responsible for the vast herds.

An alpaca hat fashioned by a Quechua herder in the highlands.

Quechua women and children at a cooperative breeding station in southern Peru release a large group of alpacas to graze on the treeless altiplano.

Vicuña.

Alpaca.

Guanaco.

Llama.

Bactrian camel.

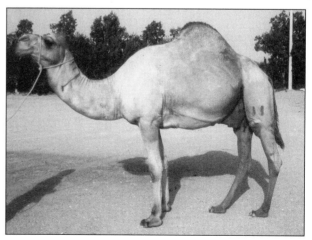

Dromedary camel.

Table 1.3 Differences between South American camelids and true ruminants.

	South American Camelid	Other Ruminants
Evolution	Family appears in North America 35 million years ago. Radiation to Asia and South America occurs 3 million years ago. Extinction of camelid ancestors in North America occurs 12,000 years ago.	Four compartment ruminants (bison, deer, etc.) take separate evolutionary path 40 million years ago.
Blood	Red blood cells are small (6.5 u) and suited to retain oxygen well. Predominate white blood cells are neutrophil; leukocytes.	Red blood cell larger (10 u); predominate white cell is up to 22,000 lympocytes; leukocytes up to 12,000.
Foot	Soft pad; two toenails; second and third foot bones are horizontal.	Hooves and soles; second and third foot bones are nearly vertical.
Digestive system	Foregut fermenter, with regurgitation, rechewing and reswallowing.	Foregut fermenter, with regurgitation, rechewing, and reswallowing, but no spitting.
Dentition	Dental formula: I1/3, C1/1, PM 1-2/1-2, M 3/3 $\times$ 2 = 28–32*	Dental formula: I0/3, C0/I, PM 3/3, M 3/3 $\times$ 2 = 32*
Reproduction	Induced ovulation; no estrus cycle; follicular wave cycle; copulation in kushed position, placenta diffuse; epidermal membrane surrounding fetus; cartilaginous projection on tip of penis; ejaculation prolonged (dribbler).	Spontaneous ovulation, estrous cycle, no follicular wave cycle, copulation in standing position; placenta cotyledonary; no epidermal membrane on fetus; no cartilaginous projection on the tip of penis; ejaculation short and intense.
Respiratory system	Soft palate elongated; primarily a nasal breather.	Soft palate short; nasal or mouth breather.
Urinary system	Kidney smooth and elliptical, suburethral diverticulum in female.	Kidney smoothed and lobed.
Parasites	Unique lice and coccidia, share gastrointestinal nematodes with cattle, sheep, and goats.	Unique lice and coccidia; share gastrointestinal nematodes.
Infectious diseases	Minimally susceptible to tuberculosis; no known natural bovine brucellosis; mild susceptibility to foot and mouth disease; no clinical disease with other bovine viral diseases.	Highly susceptible to tuberculosis, bovine brucellosis, and foot and mouth disease.

*I = incisors, C = canine, PM = premolar, M = molar

bib hanging from its chest. With the exception of the bib and some guard hairs, the vicuña's fiber is often referred to as the finest animal fiber in the world, between 11 and 16 microns thick (a micron is one-thousandth of a millimeter). (Actually, the illegally collected fiber from the rare and relentlessly poached chiru antelope of Central Asia is finer.)[15] However, vicuña remains in a class of its own as a legally obtainable fiber, compared to 14 to 40 microns in most alpacas and 16 to 70 in llamas, with average standard deviations of 5 for huacaya alpaca, 5.5 for suri alpaca, 7.0 for llama, and 3.5 for vicuña.* Human hair by comparison often exceeds 100 microns.[15]

Because of their valuable fleeces, vicuñas were in danger of extinction from heavy poaching for most of this century. Whole family units were often mowed down with automatic weapons. In the 1960s, the Peruvian government (with international support) successfully moved to protect them, and today there are more than 120,000 vicuñas, most of them in the Peruvian highlands, but also growing populations in Argentina (30,000), northern Chile (16,000), Bolivia (25,000), and a small transplanted herd in Ecuador. For most of the last 40 years vicuñas have been listed by the International Union for the Conservation of Nature and Natural Resources (IUCN) as an en-

dangered species with worldwide protection that forbids international trade in vicuñas or their by-products. In 1994 vicuña protection was downgraded, allowing them continued protection but permitting regulated capture (known as *chakkus* from the Incan period) and shearing of their fiber for international markets. Conservationists and responsible advocates of vicuña fiber use are hopeful that irresponsible and shortsighted hunting (which is easier than capturing and shearing) will not repeat itself.[5,8,15,16,17,19]

Alpacas (100–185 lb or 45–84 kg) are usually larger than vicuñas, about half the size of guanacos or llamas. Alpacas come in the widest assortment of colors of any fiber-bearing animal and their fleece is longer than vicuña's fleece and regenerates more rapidly. At Inca Tops and Michell & CIA, the two largest Peruvian wool-processing companies, fleeces are commonly separated into 22 shades in hues of black, brown, grey, caramel, red, fawn, and white. Alpaca fleeces are categorized as huacaya (wavy and spongy look) and suri (lustrous, straight fiber with no crimp). About 93 percent of alpacas have huacaya fleeces and 7 percent are suri. Known for its softness and lightness, alpaca fiber is second only to vicuña in the camel family.[15]

Alpaca fiber processing and production is a multi-million dollar industry in Peru, where about 80 percent of alpacas live. There are an estimated 2.1 to 2.5 million

---

*Yocom-McColl Testing Laboratory, personal communication, April 4, 2000.

alpacas, with 75 percent of them owned by traditional Quechua- or Aymara-speaking pastoralists in the highlands of southern Peru, Bolivia, northern Chile, and northwestern Argentina.[5,15,31,34,36] The rest are owned by large private breeders (8–10%) and agricultural co-ops (5–10%).* (Note: Censusing has been difficult due to meager funding and the unsafe conditions caused by terrorists operating throughout much of the alpaca-growing regions of southern Peru until the 1990s.)[16,34,36]

DOMESTICATION PROCESS

From camelid remains at sites once occupied by prehistoric people, archeologists have been able to date the first domestication of camelids. Their estimates are based on subtle differences between alpaca and vicuña teeth as well as corroborative evidence. In archaeozoologist Jane Wheeler's own words:

> The faunal remains from Telarmachay Rockshelter in the central Peruvian highlands produced three lines of evidence for alpaca domestication. First, *tarua* hunting decreased through time while camelid (90% vicuña, 10% guanaco) utilization increased. Second, the frequency of fetal/neonatal camelid (predominantly vicuña) remains increased abruptly from 35 to 55 percent around 6,000 years ago and continued to rise, reaching approximately 75 percent of the total over the next 3,000 years. Such a massive mortality exceeds natural causes and is best explained as a result of increased mortality due to human intervention (corralling). The third line of evidence shows us that the vicuña was the object of domestication, and the alpaca the result. In the adult vicuña, permanent incisors are hypsodont or rootless and grown continuously, in contrast with the root-forming juvenile milk teeth, and both forms lack enamel on the inner or lingual surface. At Telarmachay we find the appearance of adult animals with permanent incisors shaped liked vicuña milk teeth, suggesting the retention of a juvenile characteristic (neotony) in the domestic form. This characteristic is often ill defined in today's alpaca population due to extensive hybridization with llamas (between 80 and 90% of all alpacas are crosses), which had produced incisors intermediate in form between enamel-crowned, spatulate llama incisors and those of deciduous vicuña conformation.**

---

*Dr. Isabel Quicaño, personal communication, Juliaca, Peru, January 24, 2001.

**Dr. Jane Wheeler, personal communication, Lima, Peru, September 21, 2005.

Incan husbandry practices were intertwined with religious beliefs. The Spanish condemned these beliefs, inadvertently adding to the demise of the practices that had maintained alpacas and llamas. Felipe Guaman Poma de Ayala's sketch of a notice condemning the Incan method of slaughter known as *ch'illa* captures the clash in beliefs that still exists today. The notice's translation speaks for itself: "The butchers during the time of idolatry plunged their hands into the right of the heart. You should not slaughter camelids in this manner during these Christian times. You should slit the animal's throat. It is witchcraft and idolatry to kill camelids in this old way, and those that do should be castigated."

In the 6,000 years since domestication of alpacas and llamas, a series of "high" cultures rooted in Andean pastoralism flourished and perished. Most of these cultures are known by their archeological site names. The earliest was centered around the ancient ruin called Chavin de Huantar in central Peru. The Chavin culture, which peaked around 300 BC, left its mark throughout the Andes and coastal Peru in the form of immense stone figures depicting anthropomorphized eagles, condors, jaguars, monkeys, and caymans—mostly exotic creatures to a highlands people.[15,24]

Alpacas and llamas were conspicuously absent from Chavin art, but very much a part of their culture, according to George Miller, an anthropologist specializing in ancient Andean cultures at California State University, Hayward. "We know the Chavins ate a lot of alpaca and llama meat," says Miller, "but apparently they took their spiritual inspiration from animals more exotic than llamas and alpacas. To the Chavin, llamas and alpacas were no big deal, equivalent to a fabric store and a pickup truck."[15]

Indeed, the appearance of tropical creatures in highland art clearly indicates that the highland culture had contacts with tropical Amazonia and the faraway coast. In 1985 at an archeological dig near the coastal town of Arica in northern Chile, a piranha jaw was found, evidence that trade routes actually connected the Amazon to the coast 5,000 years ago. The fine fiber of the alpaca is thought to have been a primary barter item from the highlands.

The Chavin culture was followed by Moche, Nazca, and later Huari cultures, each dependent on Andean pastoralism and leaving behind characteristic textile products. The Pucara culture, which flourished near Lake Titicaca about 2,500 years ago, is thought to have bred the alpaca intensely for high-quality wool production, which was maintained by ensuing cultures. The Pucara textiles that have survived are among the most attractive hand-woven garments produced in the region. From a digging at a site of the Chiribaya culture, which existed in southern Peru 1,000 years ago, it was learned that the fiber of both alpacas and llamas of that period had lower micron counts and standard deviations than animals living today. Andean cultures didn't leave written records of the size of their herds or the volume in trade, but anthropologists speculate that the trade surpassed all other prehistoric cultures in both South and North America. Early Spanish accounts mention loyal Inca vassals of the Lupaka culture near Lake Titicaca owning 50,000 alpacas and llamas apiece.[15,17,24,25,33,35,36]

PRE-EUROPEAN HERDING AND HUSBANDRY PRACTICES

What is known about Inca husbandry (and their predecessors) is fragmentary, because pre-Hispanic Andean cultures had no written language and their Spanish conquerers so quickly destroyed them that many of the nuances of alpaca husbandry were forever lost. The Spanish rarely distinguished between llamas and alpacas, other than describing pack animals suitable for carrying booty and ore from mines. For example, when conquistador Francisco Pizarro kidnapped the Incan leader Atahualpa for ransom, 26,000 pounds (12,000 kg) of silver and 13,000 pounds (6,000 kg) of gold arrived by llama in a period of a few months. On a single day chroniclers recorded the arrival of 225 llamas loaded with gold. This sorry episode, which resulted in the

Despite Spanish colonial laws seeking to end Incan practices, the *ch'illa* lives on as a preferred method of slaughter in remote parts of the Andes.

garroting of Atahualpa after payment of the ransom, provides one of the few recorded glimpses into the early historic use of llamas as pack animals. Absent from the chroniclers' records is mention of the fiber-producing capability of the alpaca. However, by piecing together comments of the Spanish chroniclers and archeological and anthropological evidence, an impressive system of raising llamas and alpacas emerges.[2,12,15,36]

The production and use of fiber involved status, religious beliefs, and strict regulations with stiff penalties. The Incas were a regimented and organized society with a deep appreciation for perfection, which is reflected in their world-famous stonework and less well-known textiles on display in museums in Lima. The Incas held all species of South American camels in the highest regard and regulated both the use of wild camelids and the husbandry practices of llamas and alpacas. It appears that in the forever frigid Andean highlands an entire civilization obsessively pursued the acquisition and development of camelid fiber. Their civilization defined itself by the "silklike cloth" described first by the conquistadors. The entire civilization with its ingenious eye for detail and organization, put its best efforts into fine fiber and beautiful textiles.[12,15] Central to this effort was the development of the alpaca. In such an inhospitable, windy, and cold setting as the puna, one can imagine the desire to wear soft, prickle-free garments.

In their blind quest to acquire precious metals, the Spanish measured the wealth of the Inca Empire by its gold and silver. To the Incas status and wealth were in cloth, most of it coming from the alpaca. The Inca court counted its wealth in cloth. Armies were paid in cloth. Retreating armies burned warehouses full of cloth rather than allow a victorious army the spoils. Powerful vassals were placated by gifts of expertly woven cloth. During the period in which Atahualpa was held hostage by the Spanish, he told a story in which the finest cloth in the land had been sent as a gift to his brother Huascar, whom Atahualpa was warring against. His brother burned the gift—a supreme insult.[2,12,15,26]

A highly regimented state-controlled textile industry aimed at ensuring fiber quality for consumption and trade. Records of flock sizes, including their color, sex, and size, were kept on *quipus,* knotted recording devices (made of alpaca fiber) used by the Incas. Maintaining order for such a system was done without compromise.[12,15,24,36] A standing death penalty existed for Inca subjects caught with vicuña fiber or found molesting royal herds. *Chakkus,* or vicuña drives, were conducted with thousands of participants encircling wild vicuñas and driving them into massive stone corrals, where most animals were captured, shorn, and released. The luxurious fiber collected was reserved exclusively for the Inca nobility.[15] Apparently different kinds of fiber were distributed either partially or entirely according to one's social class. The Incan term *aluascay* refers to cloth woven from guanaco or llama and worn by commoners. *Gami* refers to alpaca cloth used by high-ranking officials and nobility, and *cumbi* (probably meaning exclusive or special) referred to vicuña cloth.[4] Armies wore uniforms of intricately dyed cloth with the tunic identifying rank. Records and historical accounts were also recorded on elaborately embroidered tapestries known as *quellcas.* Unfortunately, the *quellcas* were shipped off to Spain, where they disappeared before they could be understood and deciphered. In all of human history there may have been nothing like the Incan obsession with fine cloth. Fabric, often made of alpaca, was the medium in which Inca society defined its essence.[2,12,15,34]

Llamas and alpacas were central to Incan religious and ritualistic practices. In Cuzco, the Incan capital, a llama or alpaca was sacrificed every morning, afternoon, and evening to honor certain gods and to mark annual events such as harvest time and birthing seasons for the herds.[15,24,34] Shrine herds were managed by *llama camayoc* (also *llama michi*), a high-ranking social class whose members inherited their positions and were seen as herding experts.[2,15,34] There was an emphasis on breeding pure colors, with herds existing of all one color and with a special emphasis on breeding brown, black, and white animals for sacrificial purposes. Though the Incas used dyes, breeding for various natural colors was vigorously pursued. The Spanish described storerooms each filled with fiber of a single color.

The available evidence points to a commitment by the Incas to improve and keep separate the fiber qualities of the alpaca and the carrying capacity of the llama.[14,15,30,34,35]

An orphaned vicuña raised with alpacas and bred to alpacas.

The scarcity of skeletons of llama-alpaca hybrids from the Inca period suggests that llamas and alpacas were kept from interbreeding. Hybrid crosses are known as *huarizos* or *waris* (male llama and female alpaca), or *mistis* (male alpaca and female llama). The reason for avoiding the waris or mistis is that intermediate-sized animals without the carrying capacity of a llama or the fleece quality of an alpaca are not as useful as either pure form.[15,17,20,21,33,34,35,36]

The separation of llamas and alpacas during the Inca period may also have been due to each animal's dietary preferences. Alpacas tend to prefer wet areas, known as *bofadales,* that have soft-grass plant types such as *rama pasto* (*Calamagrostis* sp.) and *champa pasto* (*Muhlenbergia legularis*). Llamas prefer drier, coarser, strawlike plants that include *chilliwa* (*Bromus* sp.) and *ichu* (*Festuca dolicophyla*) (see Chapter 9: Feeding the Alpaca).* To this day dietary preference contributes to the natural separation of alpaca and llama herds, allowing herders, who typically have no fences, to rely partially on each species' natural inclination to separate. In a larger context the vast altiplano is drier and better suited for llamas in the southern part, which is now northern Bolivia, where most of South America's llamas are found today. The northern altiplano, in southern Peru, is wetter and better suited for alpacas.[7,24]

The sheer size of the area in which domestic camelids were found is astounding. In the 1400s the Inca Empire, also known as Tahuantinsuyu, meaning "four quarters of the world," began what would be the final pre-Hispanic

*Dr. Isabel Quicaño, personal communication, Juliaca, Peru, January 24, 2001.

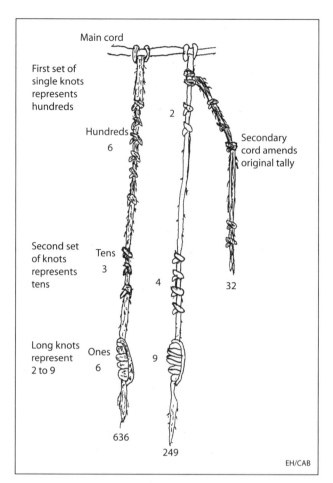

The pre-Hispanic cultures of the Andes assigned different qualities of fiber to different social classes, traded cloth like money, and kept track of accounts with the sophisticated knotted string known as the *quipu*. *Quipus* were used to count herds and were often made of alpaca fiber.

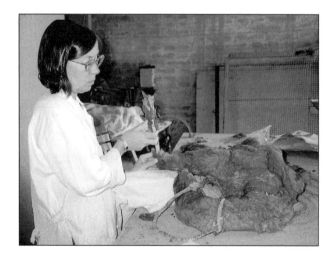

Scientist Jane Wheeler examines one of the El Yaral mummies.

Two *quipus* on display in Lima, Peru.

Above Nobody knows the origins of the suri breed of alpaca. This figurine depicting a suri is thought to be 1,500 years old. The replica and others like it were found near the coast, prompting speculation that the breed was a lowland animal prior to the Spanish Conquest.

Left The Spanish conquest: Spanish conquistador Francisco Pizarro captured and executed the Inca Atahualpa in 1532. The destruction of the Inca Empire that followed reversed the expansion of Andean pastoralism and marked the rapid decline of the strictly controlled husbandry practices that had developed and maintained alpacas and llamas.

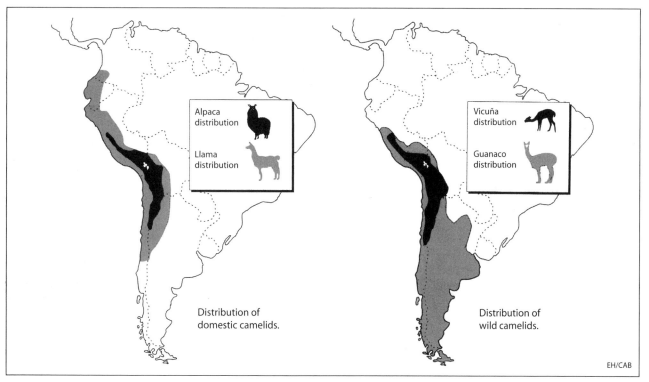

Distribution of domestic camelids.

Distribution of wild camelids.

EH/CAB

There are six recognized species in the camel family alive today. By most definitions the species are distinguished from one another by not being able to breed and produce fertile offspring. Not so when it comes to today's species of camels. Incredible as it may sound, unions between the large camels of Asia and northern Africa and the South American camelids can produce live offspring. Twice the union (by artificial means) between a guanaco and a dromedary camel have produced a "cama," demonstrating that while three million years of separation have drastically changed the appearance of camel family species, they remain reproductively compatible.

From left to right: a llama, an alpaca, a paco-vicuña, and a vicuña.

A *huarizo* is the product of a llama and alpaca breeding. Typically huarizos possess neither the fiber quality of an alpaca nor the packing powers of a llama.

Although there is ongoing debate about the existence of identifiable breeds of llamas among scientists studying llama morphology in South America, scientific literature recognizes two and possibly three varieties of llamas. Pictured above are two of them. On the left is the *ch'aku* (Quechua) or *t'awrani* (Aymara). This animal is woolly and stout in appearance. On the right is the *c'ara*, (Quechua and Aymara), which is lanky with short body fiber and very little fiber on its head and lower legs. This is the most common type in Peru, Bolivia, and northern Chile. Recent work in Argentina identified a possible third variety with unique fiber characteristics and body type from that region.

Rama the cama is a true anomaly, coming from a dromedary camel father and a guanaco mother. All six living species of the camel family have 2n=74 chromosomes.

True suri llamas are very rare. Many animals represented in South America as suri llamas are really huarizos from suri alpaca and llama parents. These animals are typically smaller than most llamas and possess some characteristics common to alpacas. However, some suri llamas have all the phenotypic characteristics of a llama (height, weight, banana-shaped ears, and so on).

Chili is a term used to describe an alpaca whose coat characteristics include both aspects of huacayas and suris.

Andean unification. The Incas eventually controlled what is now Peru, Bolivia, southern Ecuador, southern Chile to the Maule River, and northwestern Argentina.[2,12,15] Their empire took in 3,200 miles (5,000 km) along the spine of the Andes stretching from the Pacific to the Amazon.[15,17,34,35] Llamas were found in all of these areas, while alpacas appeared to be restricted more to the highlands, though their remains have been found in lowland sites as well. Ironically, on the fringes of the Inca Empire, remains of intermediate-sized animals, possibly huarizo culls, have been found. Quite possibly Incan trading partners, lacking knowledge of the finer differences between llamas and alpacas, ended up with the least desirable animals.[23]

Evidence supports the contention that fiber quality in domestic camelids prior to the coming of the Spanish was superior to today's animals. In 1991 a group of archeologists working at El Yaral in the pre-Incan Chiribaya culture found alpacas and llamas that had been sacrificed and buried. The Chiribayas flourished more than 1,000 years ago. Due to the extreme dryness of the region the animals had mummified and were perfectly preserved. Jane Wheeler was invited to examine the camelid remains. She later wrote:

Preconquest alpaca breeds have been found among the 1,000 year old El Yaral mummies. Fine fiber and extra fine fiber alpacas were distinguished based on physical appearance and average fiber diameter (1,600 fibers measured per animal). The former have fleeces averaging 23.6 (s.d. ± 1.9 micron), while the latter fleece's average 17.9 (s.d. ± 1.0 micron). Both groups had lustrous fiber ranging from wavy (crinkled) to crimped and dense to very dense. Hairs were visible in 3 of the 4 animals, but were not significantly coarser than the undercoat fibers. Indeed, fiber diameter variation both within and across the fleece was remarkably low, suggesting that rigorous breeding selection for fine quality fiber was being practiced.[26] (Note: Today's finest alpaca, classified by the fiber mills in Peru as *baby*, is 19 to 22 microns, and other fineness classifications often exceed 30 microns. Also, variability is much higher than in the El Yaral mummies.)

Wheeler and the team she worked with also found a distinctly fine-fleeced llama as well as a coarse-haired llama, possibly representing two different breeds. Among the mummified animals was one suri. Comparative studies of the level of follicle development on the fine-fleeced alpaca mummies and today's alpacas point to the likelihood of coarsening since the Conquest as well as a general hybridization of both llamas and alpacas. Wheeler concluded that the alpacas and llamas of ancient Peru possessed extraordinary follicle development resulting in

substantially finer, uniform fleeces than animals living today. One could argue that since 1532, alpaca and llama husbandry has declined steadily, with only a few exceptions.[15,34,35,36]

DECIMATION AFTER THE SPANISH CONQUEST

The Spanish conquest of the Incas severely disrupted native pastoralism, and with it, thousands of years of selective breeding. Chronicler Cieza de Leon wrote:

When the natives hid their flocks, the Spaniards tortured them with cords until they gave [the animals] up. They carried off great droves [of alpacas and llamas] and took them for sale in Lima for next to nothing. The soldiers and citizens took all the Indians' cloth and were selling it in the square at such low prices that it was sold at half weight. They were killing all the [llamas and alpacas] of the land they wanted for no greater need than to make tallow candles. The Indians are left with nothing to plant, and since they have no cattle and can never obtain any, they cannot fail to die from hunger.[15]

Estimates of the pre-Conquest population of alpacas and llamas run from tens of millions to 50 million animals.[6,7,8,28] Within 100 years of the Conquest, 90 percent of the llamas and alpacas disappeared from the taxation rolls of the Spanish, along with 80 percent of the indigenous human population.[12,31] The native pastoralists succumbed to European brutality, disease, and enforced starvation. "The Inca people weren't the only victims of the Conquest," says anthropologist Miller.

The Spanish brought a kind of zoological imperialism, which altered forever the complexion of the wild and domestic camelid populations throughout the Andes. Spanish horses, mules, sheep, swine, and dogs spread across the Andean landscape carrying foreign diseases and competing with the camelids for prime grazing areas. The only survivors were those in the marginal habitats where their evolutionary advantage allowed them to survive where European stock could not.[15]

The surviving pastoralists found themselves in a hostile world that condemned their religious beliefs, which were intertwined with their animal husbandry practices. In the eyes of many of the Spanish colonists who came after the conquistadors, the Quechua and Aymara pastoralists and their animals were inferior, not because of any empirical findings, but because of European ethnocentrism. Colonists condemned the natives' non-Christian religious beliefs

Dr. Enrique Franco (left) was a researcher at the La Raya Experimentation Station in the Andean highlands. Dr. Franco's efforts were hampered by terrorists, who twice damaged the facility and destroyed research during the 1980s. With terrorism eradicated, the future of the station looks somewhat brighter, but funding has been very meager. Here, assisted by Oregonian George Elser, Dr. Franco shows a group of North American alpaca and llama owners the differences between the ears of a huarizo and an alpaca.

In South America, alpacas are purchased for their meat as well as their fiber-producing qualities. Sides of alpaca are sold in villages throughout alpaca-growing regions. Dried alpaca and llama meat are traditional foods. When asked why this alpaca was selected for slaughter, the villagers smiled and said, "This one came close to our house when we were hungry."

(even after most pastoralists had converted to Catholicism) and viewed llamas and alpacas as undesirable *carne del tierra*, or non-European and therefore unfit for use. For the next 300 years Andean pastoralism survived on the fringes of colonial society at or below subsistence levels. The traditional pastoralists found themselves occupying the bottom rung of colonial society, separated culturally and racially and only marginally connected to the colonial economy.[15,17,23,25]

It wasn't until the mid-1860s that English wool importer Sir Titas Salt noticed sheep's fleece from Peru arriving at the docks in sacks made of a superb material with an impressive sheen and touch. There was even a bag full of this "odd" fiber, which Salt processed.[29] Actually some alpaca fleece had been processed in England as early as 1830, but it was Salt's "discovery" of alpaca that marked the beginning of European involvement in alpaca fiber.[29] This discovery eventually led to English investment and founding such well-known mills as Michell & CIA in Arequipa, Peru.[25] English ownership of the mills in Arequipa lasted until the 1990s when Peruvian and multinational groups bought them out. Most significantly, English involvement

brought international acclaim and helped establish alpaca as a luxury fiber.

TURMOIL IN THE TWENTIETH CENTURY

Despite English involvement and a resurgence of interest in Peru, the vast majority of alpacas remained in the hands of the Aymara and Quechua pastoralists through the nineteenth century. But in the first half of the twentieth century wealthy property owners and cooperative agricultural ventures had acquired large holdings of prime alpaca grazing land.[7,15,17,29,34] By the 1960s many of the largest alpaca herds, whose owners worked directly with the industrial mills in Arequipa, were large property owners.

However, in 1969 a military coup brought a period of radical land reform that continued into the early 1970s. These reforms and subsequent events had a dramatic effect on camelid raising, long after the military government gave way to a democratic one. During the reforms large holdings were confiscated by the government and redistributed to poor *campesinos* living on these estates or in nearby villages. Though the sentiment behind the reforms was to achieve equity for the rural poor and to rid the land of absentee landlords, the consequences were disastrous for the alpaca industry.[29*]

The new owners often lacked the management and husbandry skills to manage large herds of alpacas. This lack of knowledge resulted in cooperatives and large operations becoming financially stressed.[29] In some cases landlords, knowing land confiscation was coming, sold their entire herds to slaughter to retrieve some cash while forever divesting themselves of alpaca ownership. The size of the national herd and fiber output dropped precipitously. In 1967 the Peruvian alpaca population was estimated in excess of 4 million; in 1972 it was approximately 3.8 million; and by 1992 the population had dropped to between 2.1 and 2.5 million—a decline of nearly 50 percent.[15,23,25,34,36] By 2001 the low estimate of alpacas in the primary growing region was about 1.7 million animals.[**] This huge reduction is a result of shifting economic forces, mismanagement, drought, and a stretch of 15 years of terrorism throughout the prime alpaca-growing region that didn't subside until the 1990s. (Note: Most statistical census information reported in the literature between 1980 and 1995 is educated guesswork due to terrorist activities that discouraged census activities throughout the altiplano.)[29]

To head off the downward spiral of the alpaca business, the government encouraged the new owners to employ managers, economists, and experienced breeders named by the government. These "experts" were often political appointees frequently lacking skills in animal husbandry or financial management. Too often the result was further deterioration and exploitation for short-term gain.[27] For instance, prime alpacas, best suited for reproduction, were often sold for fresh (*chicharron*) or dried (*charqui*) meat.[7,15,23,25] The meat market in Peru and Bolivia is important and always an option when fiber prices drop or when the next shearing is too far away to solve immediate cash-flow problems. Ironically, even though alpaca meat is lean and fat-free, the price for a kilogram of alpaca meat usually runs about 30 percent lower than sheep and 50 percent lower than beef.[25,29]

After the land reforms ceased, alpaca growers attempting to adopt twentieth-century husbandry practices were met with even more difficulties. The civilian governments that followed the military one allocated meager amounts of money for agricultural development and droughts took their toll. The Shining Path terrorists directed their murderous tactics at educated Peruvians living on the puna and government employees working with traditional people, further setting back any advancement in the alpaca industry. There is no better example than what happened to La Raya Experimentation Station, a government- and university-funded high-altitude facility maintained for improving alpaca husbandry practices. On two occasions all records, equipment, and ongoing studies were destroyed or severely damaged. Among the materials lost were the data collected for the first comprehensive color coat inheritance study. In another government-run alpaca program the alpacas were killed by terrorists as a symbolic gesture to the Peruvian government. As a result of these terrorist acts, communication between agricultural educators and researchers at La Raya and traditional alpaca owners practically ceased. Researchers from abroad, who came to La Raya to help add to the knowledge base about alpacas, quit coming.[***] Well-educated alpaca owners rarely visited their herds on the altiplano for fear of being murdered. Those who survived were often forced to pay bribes to terrorists to keep their herds and estates intact. Few breeders were able to maintain herds with controlled or long-term breeding programs. These conditions persisted into the early 1990s. By 1994 many of the terrorist leaders were jailed, terrorism decreased considerably, and optimism about improving the alpaca industry increased. However, the social conditions that allowed the terrorists to gain a foothold still exist.[†]

Even the "model" herds in Peru that maintained a semblance of order during the peak period of terrorism did not use scientific verification (blood typing, a form of genetic fingerprinting) in recording bloodlines. In general, in Peru, Bolivia, and Chile record keeping for individual animals is usually nonexistent, though there were attempts to organize DNA-based alpaca registries in Chile and Peru when this book was going to press.[‡] Rural Alianza, the last large cooperative (possessing 40,000 alpacas), regularly records fleece weights for each alpaca when it is shorn and makes culling decisions primarily based on fleece weight and color. Animals yielding less than 4 pounds (1.8 kg) at their first shearing are culled, as are animals with specific conformational defects. However, generally, approaches to breeding are thought of in terms of herd development and not so much in terms of bloodlines and individual animals.[§]

---

[*]Dr. Renzo Morante, veterinarian and son of a herd manager of a large alpaca cooperative, Arequipa, Peru, January 10, 2001. Juan Avila, former large landowner and official of the International Alpaca Association, personal communication, Arequipa, Peru, May 25, 1994. [**]Dr. Isabel Quicaño, government veterinarian for Puno District, personal communication, Juliaca, Peru, January 24, 2001.

[***]Dr. Enrique Franco, former research veterinarian at La Raya, personal communication, Santa Rosa, Peru, May 20, 1994.

[†]Juan Avila, personal communication, May 25, 1994.

[‡]Peter Hill, industrialist and alpaca exporter, personal communication, Santiago, Chile, May 5, 2001, and Ignacio Garaycochea, Arequipa, Peru, May 5, 2001.

[§]Julio Alvarado, president of Rural Allianza, personal communication, company office on altiplano, Puno District, January 24, 2001.

TWENTY-FIRST CENTURY PROBLEMS

Hybridization and Weak Incentives

In the 1980s and '90s, because of the premium (double price) put on white and light fawn fiber by the mills, many of the most highly touted breeding programs primarily concentrated on breeding for white animals above all other considerations. Frequently, even fleece quality came second to color because the mills did not adjust their purchasing policies to pay more for top grades of fiber. Many observers of the economic conditions facing alpaca growers blame the hybridization (huarizos) of llamas and alpacas as a direct result of fiber-buying policies of the large fiber mills in Arequipa. Dr. Isabel Quicaño, who represents the national government agency CONACS in alpaca husbandry matters in the alpaca-rich Puno District, believes the hybridization problem will continue unabated until the problem is addressed with the proper financial incentives:

> The problem of increased hybridization and poorer quality fiber is not helped by the buying policies of many of the large mills. The emphasis is on fleece weight not fleece quality. There is very little financial incentive not to mix huacayas with suris or llamas with alpacas. The result is more and more huarizos and poorer quality fleeces. For example, in 1994 through 1996 the textile industry created a questionable disincentive for breeders because the fiber mills purchased fleeces based solely on weight with no regard to quality. This meant shearing a coarse llama was economically more beneficial to the grower than shearing a fine alpaca because the fleece weight is what matters. At this same time the Peruvian government understood the need to offer incentives and attempted to lead the way in paying more for quality. In 1997 the government bought fleeces directly from alpaca growers and paid more for fine, superfine and other higher grade fleeces. It is important for the fiber-processing industry to take a leading role in improving the quality of Peruvian fiber.*

On the other hand, the decision makers in the large fiber mills often state they have been buying based on quality and would like to do more, but cite middlemen who stockpile fiber and negotiate deals with the mills, making it difficult to reward the breeder producing the best fleeces.**

The president of Rural Alianza, Julio Alvarado, sees the overall problem of widespread hybridization slightly differently: "The government doesn't do enough in providing loans for alpaca farmers to help them get the capital to put together a profitable program. We need more educational programs about the reasons hybridization is a destructive force in our business."*** The debate on how to best handle hybridization will intensify because the problem has no quick remedies yet stymies the long-term potential of the international alpaca fiber market.

Hybridization is felt most acutely by the fiber mills who need good-quality fleeces to create high-caliber end-products. Luis Chaves, the manager of Inca Tops, says, "This is a major challenge for our business. We need to offer incentives for improved fiber quality."† Chaves has led the way in paying more for quality fleeces, but the effort is not industrywide and is sporadic because of the way in which fiber is purchased en masse in short periods of time each year.

Alpaca herd genetics and breeding practices are thus influenced by the large fiber mills. When the mills began paying more for white fleeces, the impact was immediate. The common way to create white or light fawn herds was by vigorously breeding those colors and culling all other colors.

Questionable Breeding Practices

Inbreeding and line breeding are not avoided and indeed are commonly practiced. Studs are chosen based on phenotype, and typically the stud's lineage is not known. Once selected, studs are usually introduced in a ratio of 4 to 5 males to 200 females. After a week or more, a new batch of studs is introduced and the original group is removed. This process is repeated until it is believed that all the females are pregnant or the breeding season comes to an end. Often conception rates are only between 40 and 60 percent (see the chapters in Section Four: Reproduction and Chapter 2: Behavior and Communication).[5]‡

Since multiple males are used and there is no system to determine who sired a particular offspring, keeping track of bloodlines is improbable. The most obvious result of these large commercial breeding operations has been production of a single or narrow range of coat colors at the expense of genetic diversity. These breeding operations report 80 percent white or light fawn offspring. A small number of operations make claims of producing animals that typically have top-quality fleeces as well as predictable colors.[29] On a mass scale, often involving thousands of

---

*Dr. Isabel Quicaño, personal communication, January 24, 2001.

**Luis Chaves, general manager of Inca Tops, interview, Arequipa, Peru, January 26, 2001. Derek Michell, executive for Michell & CIA, personal communication, March 30, 2001.

***Julio Alvarado, personal communication, January 24, 2001.

†Luis Chaves, interview, January 26, 2001.

‡Dr. Enrique Franco, per sonal communication, May 20, 1994.

animals, defective animals (possible products of "narrowing" the gene pool) are sent to slaughter or sold to animal dealers and small herders.

The traditional pastoralists operate differently than the larger operations. Since the time of the Incas, there has been no state-run alpaca management system. In the nearly 500 years since the Incas dictated husbandry practices, much appears the same, but today's indigenous breeders often apply individualistic approaches that are mixtures of superstition, ancient beliefs, cash needs, and imitations of the practices of large commercially run herds. The small herder is part of the larger Peruvian economy and is influenced by the pricing structure of the mills, but also operates on the assumption that much of the fiber produced will be used in home consumption and barter with neighbors. There is ample evidence that ancient husbandry practices, which seemed to ensure fineness, uniformity, and solid colors, are no longer practiced by traditional owners, who otherwise embrace Andean pastoralism much like their predecessors.[22,26,33,34,35,36]

The small herds usually produce greater diversity of color than the large entities, but the breeding of like colors (as was supposedly done under the Incas) usually occurs only by chance, due to the casual management of these herds.* Often the small herder runs his alpacas and llamas together, resulting in hybridization.[27,33,34,35,36] Inbreeding is commonplace, sometimes resulting in proliferation of undesirable traits. Herds of both llamas and alpacas with "gopher ears" (abnormally short ears) are often seen, demonstrating inbreeding.[29]** Among traditional herders, alpacas with extra toes, a condition known as polydactylism, are thought to bring good luck.[7,29] Consequently, multitoed animals are kept and bred with the hope of producing more good luck.[7,29] Culling is often based on haphazard criteria, but is conveniently accommodated by the meat market or home consumption. Anthropologists have recorded herders culling animals based on poor teeth, kempy fiber, failure to produce an offspring, poor temperament, and for having an "unlucky" color.[15]

There is little doubt that terrorism, preceded by radical government agricultural reform, resulted in a drop in fiber quality and price, weakening what should be a strong specialty fiber market. With the disruption of fiber prices, many animals were killed for food and llamas were often purposely crossed with alpacas to create a larger animal for food production.[20,25,29,35,36] Still, in a national herd numbering in the millions, many classic examples of phenotypic alpacas exist and reproduce on an annual basis, producing high-quality fleeces.

IMPORTATIONS, SCREENINGS, AND NEW ALPACA COUNTRIES

Prior to 1983 very few alpacas had ever been exported to countries outside the Andes. During the 1970s and '80s the first large-scale exportations of llamas from South America occurred as llamas became popular in the United States. The first importers who brought llamas into North America often made great profits. In 1983 and 1984 the first large-scale importations of alpacas to North America took place. Irv Kesling, an American living in Indiana, brought in a couple dozen alpacas as part of a shipment of llamas. This was followed by 270 alpacas and llamas from Arica, Chile, by American importers Tom Hunt and Jurgen Schulz. At the same time Californians Phil Mizrahie, David Mohilef, and Alex Perrinelle imported the first all alpaca shipment of 131 animals from Chile. These ventures proved profitable, with individual animals selling from $12,000 to $18,000 apiece.*** These importations began a worldwide surge in the 1980s and '90s in alpaca exportations from South America to countries that had few alpacas outside of zoos. In Australia Geoff Halpin, Roger and Clyde Haldane, Alan Hamilton, and Pat Viceconte pioneered the establishment of alpacas by bringing them there. In England Joy Whitehead and in mainland Europe Josef and Gilberte Kounen, Bill Barnett, and Arnold and Uli Luginbühl of Switzerland were pioneers. More than 20,000 alpacas were shipped from Chile, Bolivia, and Peru, primarily to the countries of the United States, Australia, and Canada. New Zealand, the United Kingdom, Poland, the Netherlands, Switzerland, Germany, France, Italy, Israel, and South Africa received alpacas. At first, a handful of importers controlled the import market by cleverly using the strict quarantine protocols between countries to limit the supply and regulate the rate of importations to the new alpaca countries and thus ensure the market did not become saturated.[1,9]

In the United States, Australia, New Zealand, United Kingdom, Germany, Chile, and other countries, alpaca organizations were formed to address the needs of alpaca breeders. In the United States, Eric Hoffman wrote an alpaca registry that required DNA verification of all offspring. With the help of alpaca breeder Susan Stackhouse and Dr. Cecilia Penedo at the University of California at Davis, the Alpaca Registry Inc. was founded. This first-of-

---

*Peter Kothe, personal communication, May 20, 1994.

**Dr. Rufino Quilla, well-known llama and alpaca veterinarian living in Juliaca, personal communication, May 20, 2001.

***Phil Mizrahie, animal importer and co-owner of Pet Center Inc., personal communication, March 16, 2002.

its-kind camelid registry effectively identified and separated the North American alpaca population from the already large llama population in North America. Today the alpaca population is well in excess of 60,000 animals and growing. This population cannot be crossed with llamas or huarizos because of the registry's guiding axiom: For a cria to gain entrance into the registry, its DNA (through a blood test) must prove to be compatible with both registered parents. Virtually all the alpacas in North America belonged to this registry by 1990.[12]

The challenge to the new registry became finding a way to incorporate newly imported animals into the registry to enhance the emerging gene pool. In the mid-1990s there appeared to be a wide range in the quality of alpacas entering North America. Importers could select from thousands of animals living in South America. Not all importers possessed the same degree of knowledge about alpacas or the same standards of animal care or ethics. The idea of screening inbound alpacas to specific desirable criteria for acceptance or rejection by the Alpaca Registry Inc. was hotly debated among North American alpaca breeders.

For the prospective alpaca owner determined to buy a freshly imported alpaca, the challenge was how to identify animals that were not only phenotypically attractive and produced good fleeces but also carried healthy genetic material that was free of defects. There is also growing political pressure to slow the rate of importation into North America. Registry-directed screening evolved as a way to force importers to select the best animals based on general health, phenotypic and fiber characteristics, and the absence of conformational defects (genotype testing had not been developed). After a series of meetings held at the University of California at Davis and Oregon State University, screening standards were adopted and all animals had to be screened (as well as pass through quarantine regulations) in order to be accepted into the Alpaca Registry. Dr. Brad Smith, Dr. Murray Fowler, and Eric Hoffman designed much of this system with input from the international community.

Much of the original screening standard was eventually adopted, in part or in full, by the Australian Alpaca Association (both as a screening standard and stud certification), British Alpaca Society, British Llama and Alpaca Association, Canadian Llama and Alpaca Association, Asociación de Creadores de Camelidos del Sur (Chile), International Lama Registry, and official Peruvian government policy. Most of these entities formed their own DNA-based registries.

Even though some registries, who screened many inbound animals, closed themselves to importations for political reasons, the net effect of the original screening standards was to set a world standard for an acceptable alpaca, albeit a standard that will be altered from time to time. Screening has also had an impact on the quality of developing herds in "new alpaca countries." The percentage of screened founder stock from one country to the next varies greatly (see Chapter 27: Maintaining a DNA Registry for the Good of the Breed).[13]

For large groups of alpacas that are established and registered in well-run accurate registries (which rely on blood typing/DNA testing), where bloodlines can be tracked and pedigrees developed, a great deal more predictability and security can be established in a breeding program that eliminates huarizo hybrids, improves fiber quality, and generally alters the alpacas in ways to make their fiber competitive with other leading luxury fibers such as cashmere. The challenge in the countries with DNA-based registries is to establish acceptable breeding goals and their own fiber markets to make alpaca a truly economically viable animal in today's world.[13]

REFERENCES

1. Anonymous: NZ Quarantine Quandary, *Alpacas* (Australia). Melbourne: Australian Alpaca Association, pp. 5–6, Autumn 1992.
2. Barnard, Carmen: *The Incas: People of the Sun*, pp. 1–152. New York: Harry Abrams, 1994.
3. Cabera, A.: Sobre los camelidos fosiles y actuales de la America austral. *Revista del Museo de la Plata* 33: 89–117, 1932.
4. Cox, B., R. J. G. Savage, B, Gardiner, C. Harrsion, D. Palmer: *Dinosaurier & Prahistorische Tierre*, pp. 174–179. Koln: Konemann, 2000.
5. Escobar, C. Rigoberto: *Animal Breeding and Production of American Camelids.* Ron Henning. 3-R Ranch (USA), p. 22, 1984.
6. Fernandez-Baca, S.: Utilizacion Comparativa de los Forrajes por la Alpaca y el Ovino. *Anales V Congreso Panamericano de Medicina Veterinaria y Zootecnia* 1: 352–355, 1966.
7. Flores-Ochoa, Jorge A.: *Pastoralists of the Andes,* pp 15–108. Philadelphia: Institute for the Study of Human Issues, 1968.
8. Franklin, William L.: Biology, Ecology and Relationship to Man of South American Camelids. *In Mammalian Biology in South America* (M.A. Genoways and H.H. Genoways, eds.), pp. 457–489. Lineville, PA: Pymatuning Laboratory, University of Pennsylvania, Special Publication Series 6, 1982.
9. Gentry, A., J. Clutton-Brock, and C. P. Groves: The Naming of Wild Animal Species and Their Derivatives. *Journal of Archaeological Science* 31: 645–651, 2004.
10. Guerin, C., and M. Faure: Paleolama (Hemiauchenia) niedae nov. sp., Nouveau Camelidae du Nordeste bresilien, et sa place parmi le Lamini d'Amerique du Sud. *Geobios* 32: 629–659, 1999.
11. Harrison, J. A. Revision of Camelinae (Artiodactyl Tylopoda) and Description of New Genus *Alforjas*. University of Kansas: *Paleontological Contributions* 95: 1–20, 1979.

12. Hemmings, John: *The Conquest of the Incas*, pp. 45–67. London: Harcourt Brace Jovanovich, 1973.

13. Hoffman, Eric: Creating Registries That Can Operate Internationally. Arequipa, Peru: International Alpaca Association, *Alpaca Fiesta 2000*, October 27, 2000.

14. Hoffman, Eric: The Many Ways Guanacos Talk. *International Wildlife* 23(4): 5–11, 1993.

15. Hoffman, Eric: Ships of the Andes. *Pacific Discovery* 43(2): 7–15. California Academy of Sciences, San Francisco, Summer 1989.

16. Hoffman, Eric: Protecting the Golden Fleece. *Wildlife Conservation*, pp. 36–41, October 1999.

17. Hoffman, Eric: South America's Camels. *Animals Magazine* 125(4): 10–14, July/August 1992.

18. Hoffman Eric, and Jane C. Wheeler: Vicuña, Alpaca, Guanaco Teeth. *Llama Life* 12: 29, Winter 1989-1990.

19. Hoffstetter, R.: High Andean Mammalian Faunas During the Plio-Pleistocene, pp. 218–245. In *High Altitude Tropical Biography* (F. Vulleumier and M. Monasterio, eds.). Oxford: Oxford University Press, 1981.

20. Kaldwell, M., M. Fernandez, H. F. Stanley, R. Baldi, J. C. Wheeler, R. Rosadio, and M. Bruford: Genetic Analysis Reveals the Wild Ancestors of the Llama and the Alpaca, pp. 2,575–2,584. London: *Proceedings of the Royal Society*, June 11, 2001.

21. Lavallae, D., M. Julien, J. C. Wheeler, and C. Karlin: Telarmachay chasseurs et apateurs prehistoriques des Andes I. *Editions Recherches sur les Civilisations.* Paris: ADPF, 1986.

22. Lozada, M. C., J. E. Buikstra, G. Rakita, and J. C. Wheeler: Camelid Herders: The Forgotten Specialists in the Coastal Senorio of Chiribaya, Southern Peru. In *The Foundations of Andean Civilization* (J. Marcus, C. Stanish, and P. R. Williams, eds.). Papers in Honor of Michael E. Moseley, Cotsen Institute of Archaeology, UCLA. In press, 2005.

23. Miller, George R., and A. L. Gill: Zoo Archaeology at Pirincay, a Formative Period Site in Highland Ecuador. *Journal of Field Archeology* 17: 49–68, 1990.

24. Moseley, Michael E.: *The Incas and Their Ancestors* (rev. ed.), p. 246. London: Thames and Hudson, 2001.

25. Orlove, Benjamin O.: *Alpacas, Sheep and Men: The Wool Export Economy and Regional Society of Southern Peru*, pp. 1–270. New York: Academic Press, 1977.

26. Pringle, Heather: Secrets of the Ancient Alpaca Mummies. *Discover*, pp. 57–66, April 2001.

27. Stanley, H. F., M. Kadwell, and J. C. Wheeler: Molecular evolution of the family Camelidae: A mitochondrial study. *Proceedings of the Royal Society* 256: 1–6, 1999.

28. Taylor, Paul: Camel/Llama Cross. *Alpaca Registry Journal*, pp. 29–31, Spring 2000.

29. Tuckwell, Chris: A Brief Look at the Peruvian Alpaca Industry. Australian Alpaca Association, *International Alpaca Industry Seminar, 1994 Proceedings*, pp. 5–23, July 1994.

30. Webb, S. David: The Osteology of Camelops. *Bulletin of the Los Angeles County Science Museum* 1: 1–50, June 28, 1965.

31. Webb, S. David: *Pleistocene Mammals of Florida*, pp. 171–260. Gainesville: The University Presses of Florida, 1974.

32. Webb, S. D.: Locomotor Evolution of Camels. *Forma et Functio* 5: 99–112, 1972.

33. Wheeler J. C., L. Chikhi, and W. M. Bruford: Case Study in Genetics of Animal Domestication: South American Camelids. In *Documenting Domestication: New Genetic and Archaeological Paradigms* (M. A. Zeder, ed.). Berkeley: University of California Press, 2005.

34. Wheeler, Jane C.: Evolution and Present Situation of South American Camelidae. *Biological Journal of the Linnean Society* 54: 271–295, 1995.

35. Wheeler, J. C., A.J.F. Russell, and H. Redden: Pre-conquest Breeds and Post-conquest Hybrids. *Journal of Archaeological Science* 22: 833–840, 1995.

36. Wheeler, Jane C.: *The Domestic South American Camelidae: Past, Present and Future*, In *European Symposium on South American Camelids* (M. Gerken and C. Renieri, eds.), pp. 13–28. Universita' degli di Camerino, Matelica, 1994.

Chapter 2

Behavior and Communication

Eric Hoffman

Young males play-fighting.

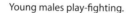

Alpacas are constantly interacting through a wide range of vocalizations, scent, and body movements. Understanding how alpacas communicate is both entertaining and an extremely valuable management tool.

After 6,000 years of domestication, alpaca behavior has been modified by human management and breeding, but communication among alpacas is still rooted in their ancestral past. A brief look at the behavioral research on vicuñas and guanacos gives us insight into the amazingly broad repertoire of communication alpacas have inherited.

For the most part wild camelids live in family groups that occupy specific territories that are controlled by a single male. This male, known as a territorial male, is aggressively vigilant and highly communicative. His activities are integrally linked to reproduction, the regulation of the number of animals living in his territory, the exclusion of all other sexually mature males from his territory, and providing a sense of order and stability for the raising of young. The modes of communication that occur in family groups and other settings are sometimes referred to as a language because messages are sent, received, and responded to, and communication of this kind influences and directs behavior within a herd.

For managers of domestic camelids, the kinds and frequency of behavior act as a barometer for assessing stress, gaining insights into the herd's hierarchical structure, and monitoring sexual activities and general health in a herd. By understanding their language, a manager gains valuable insights into the general compatibility of individual alpacas, the relative rank each alpaca holds in the herd's hierarchy, the levels of stress operating in a herd or with individuals, the reproductive readiness of females and males, the level of aggression in males, and the probable reproductive status in females (receptive, ovulated, or pregnant).

Scientific behavioral studies involve thousands of hours of research and strict adherence to methodology. Although vicuña and guanaco behavior has been studied thoroughly over many years, there are few studies of domestic alpacas and llamas, but plenty of anecdotal observations.

COMMUNICATION

Most alpaca communication falls into six categories: body posturing; ear, tail, head, and neck signals; vocalizations; scent and smell; locomotion displays; and herd response. Usually communication of one kind occurs in concert with other forms of communication.[2,3,4,5,7,8,9,10,11,13]

Body Postures

Whole-body posture is especially important to mature male guanacos and vicuñas, who spend much of their time advertising the boundaries of their territory. They stand and move in ways other camelids recognize as threatening. To a lesser extent females may strike poses similar to male body posturing, but as a display of dominance or aggression

Above A male guanaco stands high on a promontory to see inbound challengers, but also to signal approaching males that the territory is occupied.

Above If there is no high ground to enhance a broadside display, some males will improvise by standing on their hind legs and snorting to intimidate nearby males.

Left A male alpaca expressing territoriality in the confines of his pen. He stands on the highest ground he can find, just like his wild kin.

rather than a territorial display. Body postures can also communicate subordination, joy, and displeasure.[4,5,8,9,10,11]

Alpacas also use a number of body postures to communicate with one another, but because they are domesticated animals, their behavior is managed to some extent by people. We can only guess at how closely alpacas, if left on their own, would emulate their undomesticated cousins in uses of body posturing. Despite some differences, strong similarities do exist between the behaviors of alpacas and their wild relatives.

Broadside Displays Posturing by male vicuñas and guanacos is designed to signal aggression from far off. When a strange male approaches, the territorial male stands rigidly, his tail held high, ears pinned back, and nose tilted skyward. This posture is called a *broadside display* because the camelid often stands broadside to the animal he's trying to intimidate. In this way the territorial male can give

notice from a mile away that a territory is occupied. The posture also carries a warning that violence awaits the intruder. If a male intruder dares enter the turf held by a territorial male, the territorial male will attack. If the intruder doesn't immediately retreat, he can expect to be bitten on the neck, genitals, and legs and subjected to an exhausting neck wrestling contest, which may result in the loser being pinned to the ground or being chased from the area.[3,4,5,8,11]

Male alpacas will sometimes use a broadside display to intimidate a male in the next pen or a new arrival that is within eyesight of a resident male. A male in the company of females in an area the male considers his territory is more prone to strike this pose. Often a male alpaca's broadside display is somewhat modified from the pure form seen in vicuñas and guanacos. Instead of head tilted up and ears pressed snugly back, a male alpaca may strut sideways and stand sideways to the other animal, but in-

Left Female llama strikes a classic broadside display to intimidate two alpacas crowding into her eating space.

Right As a dog approaches, the entire herd strikes an alert stance. Tension builds as the herd tightens ranks and begins emitting alarm calls.

stead of tilting his head skyward he often keeps it in a normal position and opens his mouth slightly, pulling his lips back, sometimes while making a soft clucking sound. A male often displays in this way from the highest, most prominent place in his pen so he is clearly seen. A female may also strike a broadside display when she is intimidating another alpaca at a feeding station or elsewhere in a paddock. When a female sees a male approaching who intends to breed her, she may strike a broadside display, which tells an approaching male that he should take his amorous activities elsewhere or else!

Alert Stance The *alert stance* is a pose that is identical in the four South American camelid species.[3,4,7,9,11] If you've watched alpacas stare at a cat or dog walking along their fence, you've seen the alert stance. The alpaca stands with his body rigidly erect and rotates its ears forward in the direction it is staring. The tail is often slightly elevated.

Often an entire herd will strike this position, all of them directing their sight to the same object.

An alert stance signals curiosity about a change occurring in the immediate environment.[5,8,11] A person walking in the next field, a cat on a fence, or even a field mouse scurrying for cover can trigger an alert stance. This stance may be a precursor to an alarm call, or rapid flight, if the herd interprets the change as dangerous. Or the stance may result in members of the herd moving forward in unison to investigate or chase off an intruding animal, perhaps a cat or small dog that has entered their field. Alpacas have keen eyesight and often see creatures that are well hidden long before people are aware of a foreign presence near a herd.

Standoff The *standoff*, which is sometimes called a stare-off even though direct eye contact need not be made, is a common communication between two or more alpacas. Both alpacas and llamas demonstrate this body posture

The focus is intense when an alpaca adopts an alert stance.

Alert stance

Relaxed

Broadside display

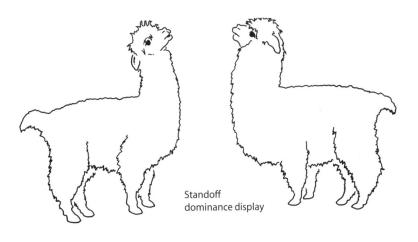

Standoff
dominance display

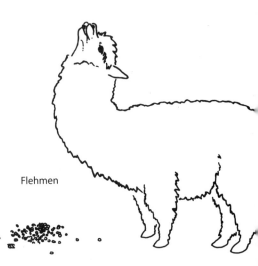

Flehmen

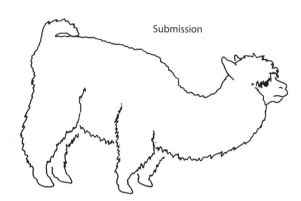

Submission

A young male alpaca signals submission to the adult male in the next pen.

Escalating aggression 1

Escalating aggression 2

Escalating aggression 3

Spitting

A feeding dispute. The cria on the right threatens its neighbor to make it go elsewhere.

Two llamas both stand their ground in a standoff, which may erupt into spitting if one animal doesn't back down.

fairly regularly. Two animals will stand rigidly within inches or a few feet of each other with their ears pressed back, neck fully extended, head tilted upward, and tail elevated. The standoff is a middle-grade show of aggression, often between alpacas of similar rank. Neither alpaca immediately yields to the other's show of dominance, thus the standoff. If one of the animals doesn't eventually walk away or turn its head, spitting, pushing, and aggressive noises may erupt. Females often resort to this behavior near sources of food or in defense of a cria. If two animals continually stand off and escalate to violent fighting, you may want to separate them into different pens to avoid continual stress (see Fighting in this chapter).[4,8,10]

Submissive Crouch A common behavior in both wild and domestic camelids, the *submissive crouch* is perhaps the most curious-looking full-body posture. While slouching slightly, the animal lowers its head, curving the neck toward the ground, and flips its tail onto its back while slouching slightly. This body posture, which is most readily seen in adolescent and young adult animals, signals to a dominant animal that its higher status is recognized and no challenge will be forthcoming. When a young male alpaca passes close to a stud in an adjoining pasture, he will strike a submissive crouch, indicating his inferior rank.

Adults also show submission to one another. Often, when two unfamiliar alpacas meet for the first time, one may strike this pose. When an alpaca on a halter and lead rope is led near an animal he considers dominant, he may demonstrate his lower rank with a submissive crouch. Often the youngest animal in a group will demonstrate submission, but not always. Some animals are submissive to others throughout their lives. In the wild, the territorial male guanaco has been observed striking a submissive crouch toward a female he hopes to entice into his territory. Similarly, some experienced stud alpacas will momentarily flip their tail forward and crouch slightly when a female is being led into their pen for breeding. However, as soon as the female is released, orgling and aggressive pursuit associated with breeding commences.[3,4,5,8,10,11]

The tail curved forward onto the back is perhaps the first behavioral signal seen in a newborn alpaca. Wobbling to its feet for the first time, either attempting to nurse or nursing, the cria usually flips its tail forward in the same manner older animals do when they are signaling submission. In a cria this behavior is usually associated only with nursing, but it probably signals the cria's low rank to herd members and the mother as well.

If an adolescent alpaca strikes a submissive crouch and slouches up to a person, the alpaca is communicating to the person as if he or she is a camelid.[4,5] In a male alpaca this behavior should be viewed with concern because it may be the first sign of serious behavioral problems ahead when the male matures and applies its aggressive territorial behavior toward people as well as camelids. However, an alpaca that confuses people with other alpacas is a rarity, usually a result of misdirected human management in which the herd's normal process of imprinting is interrupted. If a young alpaca begins submissive crouching whenever it comes in contact with people, the frequency of its interaction with humans will need to be severely curtailed and its social development carefully monitored.

Ear, Tail, and Head Signals

The position of the ear, tail, and head in concert with body posture is a chief form of visual communication to help maintain order in a herd.[4,5,8,11] Such body language is more subtle, with more nuances, than dramatic territorial displays or submissive crouches. In all species of South American camelids changes in ear positions by only a few degrees can signal alertness, contentment, or displeasure.

A relaxed alpaca holds its ears up or slightly back. An aroused alpaca showing an *alert stance* rotates its ears forward, cupped toward whatever has piqued its curiosity. "Ear talk" is prevalent around a crowded feeding station where animals are jostling for access. An alpaca uses a continuum of ear positions to express degrees of displeasure and aggression. The more the ears are laid back and the nose tilted upward, the greater the displeasure. If the intensity of an encounter builds, it can escalate into fighting. Commonly, when the ear messages and a sequence of other warnings are ignored, the transgressor is spit upon. Fighting may follow. Usually when an animal receiving warnings turns away, gives ground, or signals submission, tension subsides.

A variety of tail positions occur in concert with ear positions. Generally the higher the tail is held to vertical, the greater the warning that an expression of some sort of overt aggression is close at hand .

Movement along this continuum of warning behavior —with ears tilting back, nose held high, and tail lifting— often escalates rapidly. It is commonly seen when an animal eating near other members of the herd asserts its rank. It is also the common response of a bred female when a male draws near. She is signaling that she isn't interested in breeding and the male should desist or be spit upon or kicked. Often subtle visual cues accompany these signals, such as tightening of the lower lip (exposing the base of teeth and gum line) or dropping of the lower lip. Also, uptight alpacas may draw back their eyelids, exposing the white areas of the eye and giving the alpaca a somewhat bug-eyed look.

Vocalizations

Humming Alpacas are quiet but vocal animals. This apparent contradiction is resolved when you hear their soft humming, the most common sound emitted by alpacas. Apparently humming is a bonding sound and serves to maintain contact between two animals who rely on one another for nourishment or security. Humming is common between mother and cria, during separation from a herd, at times of mild and severe stress, and for no readily discernible reason. Researchers working with guanacos speculate that animals tailor inflections in humming to different situations: establishing contact, demanding milk, etc.[4,5,6]

Humming is not an aggressive sound. When it is continual, it usually signals discomfort or loneliness; when it becomes a markedly more frequent expression from a usually quiet alpaca that is showing other characteristics of a sick animal, it is signaling stress. The most earnest nonstop humming often occurs when crias are weaned and taken away from their mothers. They often hum continually for two or three days or longer, especially if their mothers are in an adjoining pen in full view. A youngster who is particularly upset about being weaned may pace and hum pathetically. In such instances humming becomes an indicator of stress. Some alpacas hum more than others for no apparent reason. However, if a previously quiet animal begins humming a great deal, there is usually a reason, and even if no other symptoms are apparent, owners should try to ascertain the cause.

Alarm Call The *alarm call*, which Charles Darwin described as a "peculiar shrill neighing," is a unique noise all alpaca owners will come to know.[2,5,8,9] All South American camelids employ the alarm call. Some llama breeders have dubbed the sound quacking (or chirping), because sometimes it sounds like a duck. The alarm call is emitted when a predator or other animal seen as threatening approaches. Alpacas aren't bashful about emitting it, though with alpacas it is often higher pitched than a llama's and may sound like a squeaky wheel bearing. Differences in pitch from one animal to the next often vary a great deal. The alarm call of a vicuña is often described as a "shrill whistling."[11]

An alpaca new to the farm is often more prone to emit an alarm call in response to house cats and other family pets or even a paper bag blowing through a pen. However, with nonthreatening pets that become known to a group of alpacas, the alarm call is not used. Alpacas are sometimes amazingly discriminatory in this regard, emitting the call when a stray cat is seen for the first time, but ignoring the family cat as it wanders along a fence. Males occasionally

Mother and cria hum to reassure one another that they are nearby.

This female llama snorts and clucks a warning.

sound off when females are moved from them or when nearby females are rearranged into different pens.

The responsible manager responds to an alpaca's alarm call, especially if the fencing scheme isn't absolutely dog-proof. If it is not clear why an alpaca is alarmed, look in the area the alpaca is staring. Alpacas always fixate on the source of their concern. It's obvious enough if a dog is standing on the other side of the fence barking, but in wooded areas a predator (or deer, raccoon, squirrel, or other unfamiliar creature) may be nearly impossible to detect in dense foliage without the aid provided by the alpaca's unflinching stare. Alpacas have keen vision and are very good at detecting intruders that conceal themselves. This should come as no surprise considering the stealth of mountain lions and human hunters, which are the deadliest natural predators of the alpaca's wild progenitor, the vicuña.

A group of alpacas often has a principal alarm caller, usually a dominant animal. Some alarm callers are much more discerning than others. Susan Stackhouse, an Oregon alpaca breeder, reports that after her dog has had its summer clip, one of her studs no longer recognizes the dog and treats it like a predator, alarm calling often for a week until the dog is accepted again. Other studs in the same paddock seem to recognize the dog with or without its image-transforming haircut.* Why some alpacas make such distinctions and other don't may have to do with smell, intelligence, or other factors.

---

*Susan Stackhouse, pioneer alpaca breeder, personal communication, Terrebonne, Oregon, May 12, 2002.

Snorting, Grumbling, and Clucking Wild South American camelids signal mild and moderate aggression with snorting, grumbling, and clucking noises.[5] In alpacas both males and females snort, but males seem to snort more often to announce their presence and aggressive intentions, often in combination with a broadside display. Dominant females will occasionally resort to snorting with body posturing.

Clucking, which sounds vaguely like a hen's cluck, is emitted occasionally from an animal intimidating its neighbor, but also when a mother becomes concerned

Two young alpacas reassure one another by humming. This exchange is known as a contact hum. Youngsters born at the same time often develop strong bonds.

This one-week-old cria signals to intruder that it is time to back off.

about her cria.[5] Some mothers seem to resort to clucking with neonates as a contact/bonding noise.

Grumbling seems to communicate a mild warning. The noise comes from deep in the animal's upper throat and sometimes has a slight gurgling quality. It often occurs between animals who have crossed the threshold of tolerance into one another's feeding space in a pasture setting. Rather than stop grazing and lift their heads, they grumble, letting the other animal know it's too close for comfort.

Screaming Screaming is probably the most dramatic demonstration of fear expressed by an alpaca. Alpacas seem more prone to resort to screaming than llamas. A few alpacas (in my experience, usually imported animals) resort to an ear-piercing scream when handled or cornered. As fear abates, through positive interactions with people, so will screaming. With some alpacas screaming becomes an ingrained response to being touched by a person, despite the efforts of an owner to overcome it through positive forms of desensitization. Alpacas will also scream when being attacked by a predator or aggressive alpaca.[5]

Screeching Screeching, which is equal in its deafening intensity to screaming, is associated with severe aggression and fighting.[5,8,11] A screeching alpaca is an angry animal, usually actively engaged in a fight. The sound is most often heard between males in a dominance or territorial dispute. Often the pursuing animal screeches while the pursued merely runs. Females occasionally screech, but more likely they will vocalize a deeper toned "croaking/growl" noise when they are angry.

Screeching should be a rare occurrence. Alpacas that continually screech at one another are inadvertently telling their owners that there is excessive stress between individuals or throughout a herd and the management policies need to be reviewed. Availability of food, incompatibility between individual animals, and stocking levels are worthy areas of initial focus. Possibly other factors need to be examined. Occasionally two animals will continually screech (and fight) because they are incompatible. If a group of alpacas is out of sight from your house but within earshot, screeching may be the only telltale sign you'll receive that serious stressful confrontation is an ongoing problem.

Spitting Spitting is a mild to severe form of aggression.[3,5,8] It is both a vocalization and an action—a moist and smelly tactile experience. The spit is regurgitated stomach contents (chewed grass or hay). This unusual, but universal, South American camelid form of communication has received more than its share of news coverage because it is a relatively novel way for an animal to communicate with its brethren and because people occasionally are spit upon.

Spitting is a response that appears early in an alpaca's life. Small crias spit (usually only air) to show displeasure if they are pestered by another cria. Adult alpacas commonly spit on precocious young alpacas who transgress the herd's hierarchical structure by bumping and possibly mounting adults during playfulness or attempting to nurse from the wrong mother. This form of discipline sets parameters of acceptable behavior for young animals without doing any physical harm to the youngster.

In most circumstances an alpaca warns that it intends to spit by pressing its ears back and tilting its nose up, often holding this pose before, during, and after it spits. Two animals may spit when one or the other has signaled that the distance between them is too close but neither has yielded. Some animals will strike the spitting posture and expirate only air, while others will spit as much regurgitated green matter as they can muster. Disputes are farcical when animals of equal stature square off. Using regurgitated food for ammunition, one animal fires past or directly into the face of its adversary, who may walk off or respond in kind. In a matter of seconds one animal usually yields. Often when an alpaca has been spitting, its lower lip droops, loosely exposing the animal's incisors for a few minutes following a vigorous exchange. If you hear a spitting squabble and enter a paddock after it has ended, the loose lip is a telltale sign that identifies combatants.

Spitting can occur any time one alpaca is fed up with another's presence. But most spitting occurs when alpacas crowd a feeding area or when males show too much interest in pregnant females. In fact, many breeders take a female's

Spitting usually occurs when signals are ineffective. Most spit exchanges last less than 10 seconds. Some alpacas are more prone to spit than others. Most alpacas won't deliberately spit on people.

Orgling: A male in the act of breeding (or attempting to breed) puffs his cheeks out as he emits the distinctly camelid sounds of orgling.

spitting rejection of a male as an indication she has ovulated or is bred. In herds in which the level of aggression is low, spitting is less frequent.

Alpacas usually don't spit on people, but occasionally they learn that people keep their distance if they are spit upon. If an alpaca warns you that it may spit, break off eye contact by looking at the ground, and back away. Eye contact seems to encourage the behavior. Another spit-avoidance tactic is to quickly raise your hand higher than the alpaca's head and firmly repeat the word "no" while looking down.

Many owners, although they interact with their animals daily, avoid being spit on. In part, this is because they can read the body postures and ear, tail, and head signals that precede spitting. Remembering which animals are prone to spit and which ones rarely spit makes a difference in how a manager interacts with a group. Regardless of a particular animal's temperament, when two animals are in a standoff, walking between them isn't smart, unless you want your ear or eye socket full of green spittle.

When the occasional voluminous spitter must be handled, wearing a raincoat or shielding yourself with a garbage can lid may be in order. Once the alpaca has been

haltered, tucking a cloth around the halter and over a spitter's nose spares the handler from becoming drenched. With the cloth in place the alpaca appears to wearing a veil. Alternatively, simply directing the spitter's head away from handlers will avoid a direct hit. Llama tack suppliers in North America sometimes carry spitting bags for llamas (and alpacas) that loosely envelope the whole muzzle.

Being spat upon is not the end of the world. Granted, the smell accompanying spit lingers 20 minutes or so, but alpaca spit is harmless. Many alpaca owners are quick to point out that spitting is a preferable method of communicating displeasure compared to other species that resort to tooth, hoof, and claw to express themselves.

Whistling Whistling is a relatively rare sound emitted by male alpacas when sexually aroused or anxious. The whistling sound is unmistakably single-pitched, shrill, and sharp, like a bird call. Among vicuñas the whistle is considered a form of the alarm call.[11]

Orgling *Orgling* is the melodious expiratory sound made by males during breeding and during the "sexual chase." The term is not found in an English or Spanish dictionary, but the word was invented by camelid breeder Andy

Tillman and has become accepted throughout North America. Orgling occurs throughout the act of copulation. Orgling helps owners to assess the pregnancy status of females in a herd not involved in the act of breeding. The sound of a male orgling during the act of mating attracts unbred females, who sit near the copulating pair to wait their turns. At least one prominent South American researcher thinks orgling, without actual contact, can stimulate some females to ovulate. If a female kept in a pen near a male's breeding pen behaves as bred and you know she was never exposed to a male, she may have ovulated from auditory stimulation.*

Above Unbred females are attracted to orgling sounds and declare their open breeding status.

Below Orgling stimulates this male cria, who emulates the stud by climbing on the stud's back.

Communication by Scent

Scent communication is not fully understood. Scent communication is important to all species of South American camelids. Both male vicuñas and guanacos mark their territorial boundaries with dung, as do domestic camelids within their enclosures. The universal importance of marking with dung was made clear to a researcher who witnessed a dung pile being frequented by alpacas and llamas from a nearby village and wild vicuñas at different times of the day.[11] The dung piles at the outer edge of a territory act as signposts, declaring occupation to animals passing through an area.[5,8,13] A dung pile also has significance to the family group that takes turns contributing to it. Wild vicuña family groups use dung piles as a means of labeling a specific area for use and orientation.[3,5,11] Some researchers speculate that the scents wafting out of dung piles may carry a number of messages and functions, some of them not yet understood.

In all settings where alpacas are kept, human intervention interrupts the kinds of natural territorial behaviors exhibited by guanacos and vicuñas. For alpacas living outside their native lands, human managers create their territory with fences. In South America, where fencing is minimal or nonexistent, herd composition (numbers of females and males) and territory are often controlled by herders; they move their alpacas throughout the day, and at night traditional herders move their herds into small stone-walled corrals. Still, regardless of the setting, alpacas persist in making dung piles, though they sometimes relieve themselves fairly indiscriminately.

Dung piles are also convenient collecting places for a herd's pregnancy status report. In a behavior known as *flehmen*, the male alpaca sniffs a dung pile (or the urine of females in his pen), tilts his head to a vertical position, and inhales loudly, often curling his upper lip. What he is doing is decoding the scent and the reproductive status of his females.[6,7,10,16] He may follow up by sniffing the rears of females to locate an unbred animal, or he may merely begin orgling and chasing the female he believes is unbred. An experienced male alpaca will often identify a female who has absorbed or aborted her fetus before the most diligent alpaca manager realizes an animal's pregnancy has terminated. (If the male is slow to notice a female who has absorbed or aborted, she might seek him out!)

Scent appears to be an important factor in a mother alpaca's ability to identify her cria and distinguish it from other crias. Many dams sniff and lick both ends of their

---

*Walter Bravo, PhD, expert on alpaca and llama reproduction, personal communication, Davis, California, January 14, 1994.

Top left Mothers accept or reject identical-looking crias based on scent.

Above A male demonstrates flehmen behavior as he sniffs a dung pile to check female reproductive status.

Left A territorial male vicuña marks a dung pile. Alpacas have inherited their behavior from vicuñas.

newborns. Alpacas will often sniff a person's face who has bent over to greet them. What this greeting signifies is not known.

Locomotion Displays

All South American camelids have a number of gaits such as "stotting," which seems to convey joy and possibly breeding readiness. Running motions also relay aggression or fear.

Stotting Also known as pronking, *stotting* is probably the most entertaining form of movement to watch. It is usually associated with play and involves graceful antelope-like leaps in which all four legs leave the ground simultaneously. The stotting animal holds its head high as it bounds proudly through the herd. This behavior is most often seen in crias and adolescent animals, but adults will join in too. Often all crias in an area will unite in stotting, sometimes in follow-the-leader fashion. If an entire herd of youngsters begins stotting, watch to see if an animal doesn't participate. Stotting requires a strong body and a feeling of good health. A young animal who is a chronic nonparticipant may be suffering from something other than a stodgy personality. Occasionally adult females enjoy a stot as much as the crias, even when they are pregnant or no males are present.

Some behavioralists studying wild camelids believe stotting in young females is a kind of flirtation behavior used by females attracting males for the first time.[4,8] Stotting has also been observed in adult male alpacas when they see a female being led to their pen for breeding. Whatever its purpose, stotting is an activity that embodies both the joy and beauty of South American camelids.

Aggressive Approach A dominant male alpaca enforcing his territory often runs in the direction (or along a fence line) of a challenger with his head held near the ground, his neck outstretched, and his tail held in a vertical or elevated position, all of which add up to a signal of hostile intent. The intended victim will often recognize this running style and flee the area. Females may also display an aggressive approach when chasing an unwanted animal from their pasture or away from their young. Identical lowered-head, raised-tail behavior has been observed in guanacos[3,6,7] and vicuñas.[11] Alpaca males operating in a university experimental sheep-guarding project in Utah display this aggressive approach behavior when chasing off a coyote or fox.[1] The idea seems to be to unnerve and chase away the intruder. Usually the pursuit stops within 100 yards (91 m) from where it began. If the pursuing alpaca overtakes a smallish animal, it may stomp on it with its front feet, veer off and stop, make another high-speed threatening approach, or merely stop and investigate by sniffing.

Alpaca owners should not rely on alpacas to combat predators. On the other hand, they should be aware that more than one small dog has been stomped after entering an alpaca pen with its owner. Some female alpacas will jump on a medium to large dog unexpectedly, even a dog standing next to a person showing no signs of aggression.

Fighting Fighting is the climax of aggressive communication in which signals failed to get the desired results. Fighting involves violent encounters that include high-speed chasing, spitting, screeching, biting, chest ramming, neck wrestling, and pinning. Fighting among female alpacas is generally less violent and much less frequent than with males, especially when compared to a herd sire dedicated to guarding his females and territory.[5,8] Fighting is the final means to achieving breeding rights, dominance, and rank.

Some fighting is inevitable, especially in male groups. Young males will spar (practice-fight) with one another at an early age, and chasing and fighting strengthen an animal's cardiovascular system and muscular development. However, fighting also exposes combatants to injury, especially if fighting teeth are not removed from mature males.

Ancient Moche pottery, dating to before Christ, captures the spectacle of camelids fighting. Fighting is an integral part of male behavior.

If just two of its members fight, an entire herd's level of aggression can become elevated.

Besides injuries incurred during the chase and the heat of battle, trauma has resulted from animals running into sharp objects, tripping in rodent burrows, being pushed off promontories, colliding with fences and gates, and being exhausted. The usual good alpaca judgment about how to safely interact with its environment is forgotten when a fight is on. Lacerated eyes, torn ears, and broken legs and necks are some of the possible consequences.*

An alpaca manager should consider the layout and obstacles in an enclosure that could cause injury when two animals are running at breakneck speed, intent solely on attacking or avoiding one another. Eliminating hazards (gopher holes, sprinkler heads, tree stumps, etc.) from male enclosures greatly reduces the likelihood of injury but does not eliminate it. To eliminate injury, a manager needs to eliminate the fighting itself, by incorporating management techniques that take into account the possessive territorial

---

*Ty McConnell, veterinarian specializing in llama and alpaca medicine, personal communication, Scotts Valley, California, May 5, 2002.

Biting, forcing one's opponent to the ground, and much screaming typifies fighting.

The herd of alpacas senses the dog will run if chased. Alpacas will attempt to chase off potential small predators, but are no match for a determined large dog.

tendencies of males and their proximity to females. A manager should also have every male's fighting teeth removed as the animal matures.

Managing active studs and bachelor herds requires different approaches than for females. For more on managing this aspect of male behavior and strategies in housing males, see Chapter 4: Husbandry.

Female fights generally occur in crowded feeding situations and take the form of standoff, spitting, and possibly pushing and ramming. On rare occasions two females that can't get along fight continually and become as violent in their resolve as males. These interactions should be discouraged. Pregnant females that fight violently may abort within a day or two. When two females can't work out their relationship, separating them into different pens is the best solution.

Herd Response

In some ways an alpaca herd is similar to a single organism—it is made up of individuals who respond to stimuli as a group and rely on one another for safety. Belonging to a herd has many advantages. Instead of one set of eyes and ears, dozens of sets detect danger. If a small predatory animal such as a fox appears near a newborn, the mother of the newborn usually relies on other members of the herd to chase off the predator. The herd offers greater safety to an alpaca than going it alone.

Banding Instinct The sounding of the alarm call from one alpaca results in a demonstration of the strong *banding instinct,* which seems to exist in alpacas more so than the other South American camelids. Typically, the herd unites in one mass and moves pressed closely together as a single

unit. Some alpacas running in this fashion exhibit a partial or full submissive crouch.

Anybody who moves a group of alpacas regularly will come to appreciate the banding instinct. When alpacas are herded they band tightly together, which makes moving an entire group relatively easy. Once the lead animal(s) commits itself to a particular direction or through a gate, the rest follow. The banding instinct demonstrates how dependent alpacas are on one another for a sense of security. However, older alpacas, who have become accustomed to their handler's herding and catching techniques, occasionally forgo the security of the herd and break from it in order to avoid capture. This sort of independence can become contagious and make the herder's job more difficult. The banding instinct must be taken into consideration and taken advantage of when training alpacas (see Chapter 6: Taming and Training).

Aggressive Herd Response Not all herd responses are defensive in nature. Alpacas can go on the offensive. If a group of alpacas senses a predator is unsure of itself, alpacas sometimes advance together and chase it from their

Trust can develop between a dog and a group of alpacas, but a small dog who becomes complacent can be surprised and injured when a new alpaca is introduced to the herd who isn't aware of the dog's acceptance.

Displaying their strong banding instincts, alpacas rely on the safety of the herd when they are frightened and moving away from danger.

paddock. When a cat or other foreign animal walks near a group of alpacas, one female may start in the intruder's direction using the aggressive approach. Once one alpaca commits, others usually join in chasing the animal out of the enclosure. This aggressive approach is typified by the head being held out and low to the ground and the tail being in a vertical position. Identical lowered head, raised tail behavior has been observed in guanacos and vicuñas chasing small predators.[11*]

Female alpacas will often protect a cria belonging to another female. An alpaca owner handling a cria will occasionally be surprised when females unrelated to the cria suddenly rush in to protect it. The females are treating people handling crias as predators, which makes sense considering an alpaca doesn't know a person's intentions. A protective response can take the form of spitting, screaming, bumping, and even jumping on people. Milder defensive responses are threatening body posture or just increased concern expressed with high-pitched contact hums and staying close to the cria. Threatening and anxious behavior, rather than physical contact, is the common response. Although a protective female can be a nuisance, it is somewhat reassuring for the alpaca owner to know aggression may await a predator that menaces a cria. A female that protects young aggressively should not be judged as an attacker of people—her response is likely a maternal instinct. Usually, turning your back to an aggressive female is enough to thwart her advances until you've finished han-

dling the cria. If not, gently push the female away. Striking or kicking an aggressive female is wrong and may cause her to escalate her aggression or result in an injury to her. If the situation becomes untenable, let go of the baby.

Keeping Sentinel Friends in the Herd To socialize alpacas to become more trusting toward people, a manager must be cognizant of a herd's potential response. Experienced alpaca owners like to keep a few *sentinel friends* in a herd—animals that let people approach and touch them in an open field. This lack of fear affects other members of the herd, whose curiosity often gets the better of them. Even skittish animals will approach and stand close to an animal that is interacting with people. The sentinel friends help define the personality of a herd in a way that is palpable to first-time visitors to an alpaca operation. Eventually the entire herd develops a greater acceptance of people, as long as these interactions are nonthreatening and aren't the precursor to inoculations, shearing, or other unpleasant, fear-evoking encounters.

ORIGINS AND EVOLUTION OF ALPACA LANGUAGE AND BEHAVIOR

Behavior is an integral part of evolution in all species—as important for survival or extinction of a species as any physical adaptations, though often more difficult to identify and understand. Many examples of physical adaptations that enhance a species' chances for survival are obvious. For example, a giraffe's long neck allows it to reach food resources in trees that are out of reach of other hoofed animals on the plains of Africa.

---

*Ken J. Raedeke, expert in guanaco behavior and herd dynamics, personal communication, Seattle, Washington, September 11, 1994.

The South American camelid family's behavioral and physical adaptations may be a little less obvious than the giraffe's, but they are no less remarkable. The vicuña, the ancestor of the alpaca, practices uninhibited language that began evolving 40 million years ago, when the hare-sized ancestors to today's members of the camel family first appeared in North America.[3,4,5,8,11,17,18]

Why alpacas behave the way they do is often poorly understood by alpaca owners, largely because alpaca behavior is not seen in the context of its evolution from the alpaca's wild relatives.

The environment in which a species lives influences the evolutionary path of its behavior and how it communicates. The high, barren *puna* of the Andes is sometimes referred to as a tundra zone. This open, treeless country is typified by freezing nights, warm days, thin air, and poor-quality forage. Visual acuity, mobility, protection against cold and heat, efficient utilization of food sources, protecting young, and frugal energy expenditures are important attributes for survival. Similarly, the *pampas* of Argentina, the historic stronghold of the guanaco, is generally open country where creatures can usually see other creatures a mile or more away. Vicuñas and guanacos developed efficient ways to communicate with one another through signals, scents, and sounds that are well suited for their open environment of vast vistas and little cover.

For example, they devised efficient ways to communicate the presence of predators, the most deadly being man, mountain lion, and fox (preying on young). Behaviors evolved that regulated population dispersal into small family groups that were spread in low densities over sparse, nutritionally poor landscape. This dispersal strategy increased chances for survival in times of drought. The Darwinian axiom, "survival of the fittest," rewarded the family groups of the strongest, most aggressive males. Generally the strongest territorial males claimed the best pastures, ensuring the females and crias living in their territories the benefit of best-quality forage. Family groups operated in a strict hierarchy with the male at the top, the females with their own pecking order, and crias at the bottom.[11]* This hierarchy is maintained through signals and vocalizations of submission and dominance with individuals occupying different social ranks. The hierarchy provides social order for a predictable, stable atmosphere conducive to the successful raising of offspring.

No species survives for long without reproductive success. In this area the wild camelids of South America became efficient, evolving unique communications to en-

hance reproduction. For example, the female's visual, auditory, and olfactory signals and internal hormonal changes communicate her willingness to breed. Other changes in behavior indicate that ovulation or pregnancy has occurred. And if fetal absorption or abortion occurs, the female signals that she is once again receptive to breeding, allowing rebreeding to occur quickly and efficiently (see Chapter 13: Female Reproduction).[14,15,18,19]

Tracing alpaca language and behavior to a specific ancestral species was debated for many years because experts disagree on the origins of the alpaca. But discoveries by Jane Wheeler, PhD, using DNA analysis, have proved that alpacas descended directly from vicuñas. It's important to remember that, as entertaining and nonsensical as some modes of alpaca communication may seem, all communication and behavior of the wild vicuña evolved to increase survivability of the species.[12]

At the same time, keep in mind that the alpaca was never a wild animal and to this day no known wild herds exist in South America or elsewhere. The alpaca was created as a domestic animal through selective breeding of wild vicuñas that began about 6,000 years ago.[7,17,19] As a result of domestication, alpaca behavior was slowly modified by selective breeding to exhibit behavioral characteristics most compatible with people. Thus, the resultant alpaca is easier to handle and manage than its wild cousins. How much a particular alpaca's behavior is similar to the wild vicuña varies between individuals. The intensity, frequency, and degree of certain behaviors and types of communication may vary a great deal depending on the individual's sex, age, and rank within the herd, and on how the herd is managed. Alpaca behavior can be best controlled, directed, and modified by human managers who are cognizant of an alpaca's behavioral characteristics and heritage.

IMPORTANT CONTEXTS OF ALPACA LANGUAGE

Interpreting alpaca communication has more meaning when the context in which communication takes place is considered and understood. Most alpaca language involves one or more of the following underlying components: territoriality, family group interaction, aggression, and the herd's hierarchical structure.

Territoriality

Like vicuñas and guanacos, male alpacas are polygamous and are protective of their females by nature. However, mature alpaca males exhibit varying intensities of territoriality. When properly managed—and often when left to themselves—alpaca males operate at the more genteel end

---

*Ken Raedeke, personal communication, September 11, 1994.

Overfamiliarization with young males can interrupt correct imprinting and result, later on, in an animal that is aggressive toward people.

its genetic material. So although alpaca studs commonly exhibit behavior seen in their wild brethren, their behaviors are usually less extreme as a result of selective breeding and management techniques. Stud alpacas, sharing a common fence, will often use it as a territorial boundary. It's not uncommon for two active studs that share a common fence to signal one another of aggressive intentions. They may flip their ears back, snort loudly, open their mouths slightly, pull their lips back, and jump crazily sideways. Occasionally they may rush the fence and spit on one another or charge up and down the fence line screeching. These actions are territorial in nature, meant to intimidate and discourage a would-be interloper. If the fence was taken away, the animals would most likely move from posturing to fighting in a matter of moments. Generally, housing the two males farther apart will reduce their aggressive tendencies. A corridor of 10 to 30 yards (9 to 27 m) between them is often a good policy.

Although their wild tendencies are often very much in evidence when male alpacas have been allowed to establish a breeding territory, alpacas are usually more flexible in their behavior than their wild kin. For example, a mature male alpaca, asserting himself with the nearest male, may go only so far as to position himself between females and the other male. Alpaca males assigned to share a herd of females sometimes get along with only minimal fighting, unlike vicuñas and guanacos that become solitary guardians repelling all intruders. In one large U.S. alpaca herd, 6 to 8 studs live year-round in a 10-acre paddock with over 200 females. Male fighting is rare.* Males are commonly mixed with females in many herds owned by traditional Quechua herders in southern Peru. Fighting is infrequent. However, in some large South American cooperatives a half dozen males introduced to 200 females are often removed after only a few days when they become obsessed with fighting one another in territorial disputes rather than breeding.

Why are some males prone to fight while others are more accommodating? Inheritance and age (older animals are often less tolerant) play a part, but an animal's location is also important, and human managers can manipulate this variable. Not allowing males to establish a sense of territoriality and possessiveness for a particular group of females will often result in a low level of aggressive behavior. Some U.S. alpaca operations house their studs in a single (or adjoining) corral at a distance of 50 yards (45 m) or more from their females. Studs are removed for a short duration for the act of mating. The mating takes place at a

of the spectrum of male camelid behavior, usually practicing subtle forms of dominance and threat communication. When management schemes fail to take into account a male alpaca's behavioral heritage, broadside displays followed by physically aggressive behavior can occur.

The wild territorial male assumes high risks because his role demands it. He must be in the prime of his life and in excellent condition because he must constantly patrol, chase, and fight to maintain his family group. Because of his constant patrolling, a territorial male is often the first animal to discover a predator, which may result in his early demise. Thus, the territorial male, while pivotal to the existence of a family group, is a transitional figure easily replaced should he falter. When he is injured or becomes unfit, plenty of other males are ready to assume his place. Males who are maturing, but have not reached the prowess of a territorial male, form male "bachelor herds." These herds occupy areas outside of the family groups. The bachelor herds are genetic reservoirs containing the next generation of territorial males. The replacement for a fallen territorial male is as close as the nearest bachelor herd or the neighboring territorial male who may collect the unescorted females into his family group.[3,5,8,11]

Unlike the wild camelids who are ruled by nature's laws, alpacas are subjected to human intervention. Managers select the male alpaca that will influence a herd with

*William Coburn, director of Africa Widlife Park, where many alpacas are housed, personal communication, Port Clinton, Ohio, September 5, 1995.

neutral site away from other males. The female never sets foot on the male's territory. With these techniques territorial possessiveness is never allowed to take root. This model of housing male alpacas is similar to the natural banding together of wild guanaco and vicuña bachelor herds. Typically, wild bachelor groups don't have a territory they defend, are out of sight of females, and are compatible with one another.

Regardless of how males are housed, the level of aggression is a factor breeders should consider in selecting a stud. A top alpaca stud should possess a single-minded, relentless, gentle (no biting or attacking) approach to breeding, and be generally calm and tolerant toward other males. Unlike the wild camelids, alpaca studs can have both a strong sex drive and a low level of aggression.

Occasionally two mature males in the same (or adjoining) pen develop a pattern of prolonged fighting and spend an inordinate amount of time screeching at one another or frantically pacing a common fence line. This may happen even when females are not present. If allowed to go on for too long, this behavior may result in a negative change in an animal's temperament. Risk of injury to combatants or to bystander alpacas sharing their pen is also increased.

Aggressive males that continually menace one another are also off-putting to visitors to an alpaca operation. Visitors go away remembering the fights rather than the gentle disposition that typifies most alpacas. If hostile fencemates become disruptive and dangerous to themselves, moving one of them out of sight usually calms both of them down. However, remember that an alpaca is a social animal and should never be housed out of sight of other alpacas—just out of sight of the steadfast adversary.

Family Group Interaction

The family group of vicuñas and guanacos is made up of a territorial male and a group of between 5 and 15 females and their offspring females.[11,13] The family group is the basic social setting in which all young vicuñas and guanacos are raised. Compared to the wild form, alpacas are raised in a somewhat modified family group setting. Nonetheless, wild or domestic, the family group is extremely important to the healthy behavioral development of a young camelid. People who intervene with a training or taming agenda in the initial six months of life, before a young animal is fully imprinted to the ways of the herd, may create a maladjusted animal that is difficult to manage and unpleasant to own.

The family group provides the social setting wherein young animals develop communication skills and patterns of behavior that benefit the herd. Youngsters learn the

Crias exuberantly play most vigorously at dawn and dusk.

parameters of acceptable herd behavior and are sharply rebuked if they don't abide by the herd's hierarchical structure.

In a wild camelid family group the territorial male acts as the gatekeeper. He signals and chases off other males who would disrupt the family group. Constantly on patrol, he establishes and protects the foraging area in his territory and is often the first to spot predators, though females are also constantly on the alert . The male also expels yearlings from the group, alleviating pressures on food resources and allowing his females to devote all their bodily resources to helping their newborns survive.

With alpacas much of the male gatekeeping role has been usurped by the alpaca manager, but raising and socializing the young to the ways of the herd is still done by the females. The females birth and raise their young with impressive vigilance, constantly communicating with their offspring about dangers and proper herd behavior. For example, a young animal that pesters a newborn is often spit on by its mother. Likewise, an adolescent male that makes sexual advances on a bred female may be chastised. Alpacas have both physical and mental health needs, and from time immemorial the herd has been making socially healthy animals. Thus, many longtime North American alpaca breeders don't begin training their young animals until a few weeks after weaning, which appears to give them a sufficient amount of time in a herd setting to allow them to learn the ways of the herd. As one longtime breeder puts it, "First I let my alpacas learn from alpacas about being an alpaca. Then I train them to interact with people."

Aggression

Although alpaca behavior tends to be more subdued than the unbridled belligerence that often erupts in wild camelids, much of alpaca language is nonetheless an expression of intimidation, ranging from the subtle positioning of ears and tail to spitting and outright fighting. Aggressive communication is a major part of the alpaca repertoire. Through constant signals of aggression alpacas make it clear which alpaca will dominate an eating area, which alpaca is subordinate, which alpaca gets the benefit of being cooled by a sprinkler, which female is not receptive to breeding, which male is dominant among a group of males, and much more. Depending on a particular alpaca's sex, age, and temperament, each animal will have a slightly different agenda to communicate to its neighbors. For the conscientious alpaca manager, the interplay is fascinating and useful. Aware of levels of aggression in the herd, the manager can make decisions to minimize extreme forms.

Hierarchy and Stress

Herd hierarchy has developed in many forms of wild hoofed animals as a way to bring order to a herd. In a hierarchy each animal has a rank, the older, calmer, wiser animals often directing the herd's behavior through warnings or threats of aggression. In a healthy environment, the hierarchy tends to create a predictable, protective setting for all members of a herd. In an imperfect environment, the hierarchy increases the amount of stress on members of the herd at the bottom of the pecking order. In wild herds, for example, during times of food shortage, overpopulation, disruptions from competing males, or attacks from predators, the hierarchy becomes a cruel social vehicle allowing the dominant, strongest animals the greatest likelihood of survival, at the expense of the subordinate members. Particularly vulnerable in hard times are the young and old. But nature isn't entirely heartless. Dispersal mechanisms allow animals to leave incompatible groups to seek out more hospitable surroundings.

Unlike a wild herd, an alpaca herd maintains its hierarchy within the boundaries and conditions defined for it by human beings. Managers control stocking levels; availability and placement of food, water, and shelter; protection of the young; and a herd's overall makeup in sex ratio and age. All of these factors contribute to the health of a particular herd's social structure.

In recent years neurobiologists at Stanford University and other institutions have been expanding their knowledge about kinds and degrees of stress in humans and other animals living in various forms of social hierarchies. Among the areas of their inquiry are what determines social rank, levels of stress that are beneficial or harmful,

Grouping weanlings together allows for a less stressful transition to living without mother's milk. Weanlings placed in adult groups can be pushed off feed and experience stress associated with being at the bottom of the pecking order.

deleterious effects of prolonged stress and instability on subordinate members of a group, and the rewards for achieving dominance.[14] Even though no members of the camelid family have been studied in this way, alpacas and their wild kin fit the criteria of highly social animals for which a great deal of generalized information has been accumulated.

In studies at Stanford University, social rank was found to influence functions of vital organs of baboons living in a wild troop. Generally, animals living at the lower end of the pecking order in harsh environmental conditions experienced impaired fertility, muscle wastage, depressed immunity to disease, and slow growth in youngsters (even when food was plentiful). Other conditions more likely to be found in animals at the bottom of any pecking order are permanent damage to vital organs, stemming from hormonal imbalances directly attributable to chronic stress, and a greater likelihood of injury. The baboon study and other studies concluded that stress caused by social conditions is not in itself necessarily harmful; indeed it may invigorate an animal. But prolonged or constant stress wrought with uncertainty and threats of violence from dominant members of the group can release an overabundance of hormones that alters an individual's biological processes.[14] Understanding, how stress-related diseases develop is complicated and entails interdisciplinary studies involving biology, physiology, neurology, endocrinology, and other disciplines—an approach not yet common just 15 years ago. A great deal of research, particularly in endocrinology (the study of hormonal communication

Bachelor herd members, such as this group of guanacos, are generally not aggressive toward one another when they are not near a female group. Housing alpaca males away from females tends to result in calmer and less aggressive male behavior, just like their wild vicuña cousins.

within the body), is currently pouring forth from a number of institutions.

Alpacas are born into a social hierarchy, generally dominated by older animals, in which displays of dominance, warnings, and threats are part of the daily routine. The rank of a particular individual affects the amount of stress he or she will experience. For example, subordinate adults become stressed when they find themselves in a crowded paddock where dispersal is impossible and food sources and cooling off places are dominated by the strongest, most aggressive alpacas. If the physical layout of an alpaca operation allows dominant individuals to intimidate their subordinates into not eating, or if there isn't enough food to go around, animals at the bottom of the pecking order may not receive adequate nutrition. Undesirable behavioral patterns, such as greater unpredictability, aggressiveness, pronounced submissiveness, skittishness, and general incompatibility are also possible by-products of the stress of life in the lower ranks.

Recently weaned alpacas suddenly placed in a herd of adults are particularly vulnerable to the stresses associated with being at the bottom of the pecking order. The author knows of herds that experience high levels of sickness and death among their recently weaned alpacas. Though the maladies have been of multiple types, stress appears to be the underlying cause. In these "problem herds" weanlings are typically placed with adults in tight quarters, with only one feeding station. For weanlings in this kind of an environment, eating becomes a gauntlet of threats, outright aggression, and getting the leftovers or nothing at all.

Alpacas living in an optimal environment, with a minimum of stressors, are usually compatible, tranquil creatures. In this kind of setting the hierarchy is basically stable, which enhances life for all members of the herd.

To a large degree it is up to the manager to create such an environment. He or she controls many factors that can amplify or reduce stress and, consequently, aggression. Examples of stress amplifiers are crowded conditions (too many animals in too small an enclosure); not enough feeding stations in *dry lot* conditions, causing alpacas to congregate and literally fight to get food; too many interactions with people or other nonalpaca species; and allowing intact incompatible males to behave violently. Examples of stress reducers include adequate space; compatible paddock groupings that take into account age, sex, and disposition; adequate and somewhat dispersed food sources; a minimum of male aggression; and adequate housing and safeguards to avoid overcrowding in extreme weather. Adhering to a feeding schedule and calm, quiet human interactions during feeding, visiting, catching, and veterinary work also serve to reduce stress. Even in an ideal setting, however, the manager needs to be alert to stresses derived in the herd's social dynamics, introduction of new animals, and unresolved hierarchical struggles.

People who have visited half a dozen alpaca breeding operations are often struck by marked differences in herd personalities, in terms of the animals' flightiness, irritability, and levels of aggression. Managing alpacas in ways that reduce stress is good for alpacas and good for business. A tranquil herd is the impression visitors should take home.

OTHER COMMON BEHAVIORS

Breeding Behavior

Understanding breeding behavior is essential to all alpaca managers. In fact, learning to accurately assess communication between male and female alpacas is perhaps the most important interpretation skill a manager can learn. (For details on breeding behavior and reproductive biology, see Chapter 12: Male Reproduction and Chapter 13: Female Reproduction.)

Cud Chewing

Alpacas generally chew cud (a ball of feed brought up from the stomach) when they are sitting in a sternal position (sitting upright on their sternum), often during the early morning hours. Cud chewing is an essential part of the digestive process, although their cud stomach anatomy differs from that of the more common ruminants such as deer and cows, and their way of chewing is also different. Alpacas

Cud chewing helps facilitate digestion and is a necessary part of each alpaca's daily routine. Morning is a good time to observe cud chewing.

Top Alpacas roll in dusty areas as a method of natural grooming.

Above Sunning or sprawling is common behavior in warm weather. It is sometimes practiced by an entire herd.

(and other South American camelids) use two-sided jaw motion—that is, the jaw moves laterally past the midline of the muzzle to both sides at equal distances. This is in contrast to the one-sided jaw motion of a ruminating cow in which the jaw protrudes out to one side and back to center. An alpaca fully absorbed in cud chewing swallows after between 20 and 50 chews.[11] Another cud is brought up from the stomach and is chewed and re-swallowed in a similar manner. You can watch the cud descend and ascend rapidly up and down an alpaca's neck. If an alpaca is disturbed or startled it will quit cud chewing. The absence of cud chewing in a 24-hour period may indicate that an alpaca is ill. Other clinical signs should be checked, and a veterinarian's assessment of the overall health of the alpaca with special focus on motility of the stomach may be warranted (see Chapter 15: On-Farm Assessment and Diagnosis).

Defecation and Urination

These necessary bodily functions play an important role in identifying territory and assessing the reproductive status of females. They are also key indicators of health. If an alpaca appears ill, one of the first things a manager should do is attempt to identify or witness urination or defecation. The frequency and consistency of the pellets are indicators of dietary processing that will help the manager or veterinarian assess the animal's condition. An animal that strains but produces neither urine or fecal matter indicates particular possible problems, while an animal that produces a watery stool indicates a different type of ailment (see Chapter 15: On-Farm Assessment and Diagnosis).

Grooming

Most North American alpaca owners probably think of grooming as something a person does to an alpaca with a brush before entering a show ring. However, alpacas actually groom themselves. They do this by rolling energetically on the ground, commonly in a dusty indentation. Usually the alpaca noses the ground and paws the surface before dropping to its knees, rolling to one side, and thrashing its legs back and forth rapidly for a few seconds. Then the alpaca rolls to the other side and repeats the maneuver. Even day-old newborns will dust themselves in this manner. Often when one animal chooses to roll, others will follow, frequently using the same bowl-shaped depression. Alpacas will roll on pasture, too, but rarely on a moist surface. Given a choice they greatly prefer a dusty area for rolling.

Alpacas will readily take advantage of standing water to cool off.

Crias chew on things indiscriminately and can eat something harmful to them. Housing for crias should take this behavior into account.

The exact purpose of rolling is not known, but alpacas share this behavior with their wild cousins. Guanacos and vicuñas make rolling a daily part of their routine. Afterward, they stand and quickly rotate their head back and forth rapidly, while shaking their ears to rid them of debris. Possibly rolling offers relief from external parasites, decreases matting, and may be a way to release tension under certain situations. Male vicuñas that have just chased off a rival male will often roll, as will females who have chased a fox.[11] A group of alpacas released from a vehicle into a new paddock often roll shortly after their feet touch the ground.

Scratching and Shaking

When an alpaca finishes a dust bath, it often shakes in a manner similar to a dog that has just emerged from a swim and shakes to dry off. Alpacas also scratch themselves intermittently throughout the day. This is normal behavior under most circumstances. Alpacas can reach most of their body with the toes of their hind feet. They stand on three legs using one rear foot to scratch their neck, chin, ribs, forelegs, and other parts of the body. A sick, weak, or very young alpaca sometimes loses its balance when it shifts its weight to three legs and attempts to scratch itself. Alpacas also scratch with their incisor teeth, using their long, supple necks to reach belly, rump, back legs, and flanks. They move their teeth in a rapid nibbling motion, usually for a few seconds, before resuming other activities. If an alpaca repeatedly scratches the same area, or scratching becomes so pronounced that you see hair loss or irritated skin, exter-

nal parasites are probably to blame and consulting a veterinarian is warranted.

Alpacas make use of bushes or fences to scratch. They will often seek out a particularly stiff-limbed bush, for example, and walk back and forth through it. Because alpacas seek out fences, bushes, and other large objects for scratching, managers need to make sure there are no hidden dangers, such as loose ends of wire, protruding nails, large splinters, or sharp branches, that could cause injuries.

Sunning or Sprawling

"Oh no," moaned the new alpaca owner on the phone to her veterinarian. "My alpacas have died. From my window I can see half the herd sprawled on their sides lying motionless. What should I do?" The answer is usually, nothing at all. On warm days alpacas will lie on their sides and arch their necks, exposing their undersides to the sun. Alpacas sunning themselves in this fashion typically lie very still and at first glance do appear dead. Often they can be approached and touched before they realize a person is near them. Occasionally some alpacas will strike a pose with all four limbs in the air, in the classic "belly-up" dead pose. Weather permitting, sunning is often done at the same time each day. More than one alpaca owner has panicked upon seeing this behavior for the first time.

Kushing

Kushing is the name given to the way that alpacas seat themselves in a sternal (upright on their sternum) position

Alpacas express themselves. This one has adopted an ear position and head tilt that says "Back off." It is always worthwhile to know what your alpaca is saying.

Wading, Cooling Off, and Swimming

Because alpacas are members of the camel family, it often surprises new owners to learn that alpacas seek out opportunities to stand, sit, and even swim in water. In fact, they are able swimmers, and they seek water to cool off. This is true of wild camelids also. Vicuñas will wade in streams and submerge their bodies,[11] and guanacos have been observed swimming between islands and across large rivers.[2] Some alpaca owners have discovered that on a warm day they can collect their entire herd by merely turning on a garden hose in a catch pen. A herd that has become accustomed to having its legs and undersides squirted will come running, often jostling one another for the best position in front of the hose. Initially most young crias are afraid of hoses and sprinklers, but they learn from the example of the other animals.

For the alpaca owner, having a pond where alpacas are kept poses some interesting problems. On hot days alpacas will stand in the pond. If they do this often enough, most of their hair will fall out to the water line, leaving no fiber on their legs, which may detract from their marketability. Alpacas tend to relieve themselves in water, fouling the pond as a source of safe drinking water. Ponds also pose hazards: A newborn cria may roll into a pond and drown; if alpacas cannot easily get in and out of a pond they may drown. It is fine to let animals cool off in water, but only under the watchful eye of the manager. (See Chapter 4: Husbandry for details on cooling alpacas with water.)

with all four legs folded up underneath their body. This is the normal resting position for all camelids. It allows them to keep their torso and abdomen warm, with their legs folded up around them, and puts them in a ready position to jump up and flee a predator. Camels are often loaded while kushed, and then asked to stand.

This alpaca serves as a guard animal in a herd of goats.

REFERENCES

1. Bollinger, H.: Alpacas as Guard Dogs. *Llama Life* 26: 24, Summer 1993.
2. Darwin, Charles, *Voyage of the HMS Beagle*. p. 492, Ward, London: Ward, Lock and Co., 1845.
3. Franklin, W. L.: Territorial Marking Behavior by the South American Vicuña. In *Chemical Signals: Vertebrates and Aquatic Invertebrates* (Muller-Schwarze and R. M. Silverstein, eds.), p. 455. New York: Plenum Press, 1980.
4. Franklin, W. L.: Biology, Ecology, and the Relationship to Man of South American Camelids. In *Mammalian Biology in South America* (M. A. Genoways and H. H. Genoways, eds.) Lineville, PA: Pymatuning Laboratory, University of Pennsylvania, Special Publication Series 6, 1982.
5. Franklin, W. L.: Llama Language, Modes of Communication in the South American Camelids. *Llama World* 1(2): 10–15, Summer 1982.
6. Gade, D. W.: The Llama, Alpaca and Vicuña: Fact and Fiction. *The Journal of Geography,* 8: 339–343, 1969.
7. Hoffman, E.: Ships of the Andes. *Pacific Discovery* 42(3): 15, 1989.
8. Hoffman, E.: The Many Ways Guanacos Talk. *International Wildlife* 23(4): 4–11, 1993.
9. Hoffman, E.: Charles Darwin on Camelid Behavior. *Llama Life* 26: 2, 1993.
10. Hoffman, E.: All About Alpacas: Understanding Alpaca Language and Behavior for Better Management. *Llamas* 8(3): 39–41, 1994.
11. Koford, C. B.: The Vicuña and the Puna. *Ecological Monographs Museum of Vertebrae Zoology,* University of California, Berkeley 27: 153–218, 1957.
12. Pringle, H.: Secrets of Ancient Alpaca Mummies. *Discover,* pp. 55–66, April 2001.
13. Raedeke, K. J.: Population Dynamics and Socioecology of Guanaco (*Lama guanicoe*) of Magellenes, Chile. Ph.D. thesis, University of Washington, Seattle, 1979.
14. Sapolsky, R. M.: *Why Zebras Don't Get Ulcers, a Guide to Stress, Stress-related Diseases, and Coping.* p. 366, New York: W. H. Freeman, 1994.
15. Thompson, S.: History of Llamas, Part I. *Llama Life* 17: 8, 1991.
16. Thompson, Stosh: History of Llamas, Part II. *Llama Life* 20: 12, 13, 1991–1992.
17. Webb, S. D.: Pleistescene Llamas of Florida (with a Brief Review of Lamini). In *Pleistocene Mammals of Florida* (S. D. Webb, ed.), pp. 170–213. Gainesville: University Presses of Florida, 1974.
18. Wheeler, J.: Camelid Domestication at Telarmachay. Paper presented at the Ethnobiology Conference IV, Columbia, Missouri, 1981.
19. Wheeler, J.: *On the Origin and Early Development of Camelid Pastoralism in the Andes.* Gainesville: Department of Natural Sciences, Florida State Museum, 1984.

Chapter 3

Anatomy and Conformation

Eric Hoffman

A sun-bleached skeleton on the altiplano.

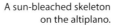

As an alpaca breeder, knowing why alpacas are put together the way they are and how their parts work are essential to a breeding program that values the many benefits of good conformation.

In one way or another I have dealt with camelid conformation for three decades. My initial involvement came while llama packing in the Sierra Nevada in California.[13] Later it was through competitive llamathons, races in which a series of human runners ran relay fashion alongside highly conditioned llamas for up to 20 miles, sometimes at 12,000-foot (3,871-m) elevations. The best llamas could carry 50 pounds (27.4 kg) and sustain 6-minute miles for longer distances than top human athletes. In Australia I participated in a grueling 10-day camel trek with huge dromedary camels carrying 400-pound (182-kg) loads through the rugged Flinders Ranges.[12]

There were many business trips to South America. Some trips included the treat of seeing family groups of vicuñas racing down *ichu* grass slopes effortlessly and as quietly as a breeze. During a stint in Patagonia, where guanacos live or die by their alertness and fleet-footedness to flee mountain lions and human hunters, I saw guanacos outrun a belligerent territorial male guanaco hell-bent on driving every trespassing camelid from his territory.[11] Other trips were nothing but hard work examining thousands of alpacas for various alpaca registries around the world. One of my primary tasks was to carefully assess the conformation and fiber of each alpaca submitted to determine acceptance; animals with significant defects were disqualified (see Chapter 27: Maintaining a DNA Registry for the Good of the Breed).[7,8,9,10]

An alpaca show judge in Peru once said, "I don't know why Americans are so interested in conformation. If the animal can get up and walk to eat, what else could matter?" This view doesn't acknowledge that the camel carrying 400 pounds couldn't have carried the immense load if he was conformationally unsound. The llamas winning llamathons always had superb conformation. These animals fell into narrow height, weight, and body score ranges. The vicuñas and guanacos running at breakneck speeds across rough terrain were living examples of perfect conformation in motion. Their design features were created and continually tested by hazards in their environments. In both domestic and wild camelids anatomy and conformation matter a great deal for well-being and long life, regardless of the species.

What is the difference between anatomy and conformation? For this discussion *anatomy* is the names and arrangement of body parts that make up an alpaca (see Figure 3.1), and *conformation* is the optimal arrangement and alignment of the structural anatomy for the most efficient movement and quality of life.

VICUÑAS—THE DESIGN OF A NATURAL PACER

The anatomy of an alpaca has been 35 million years in the making. The basic anatomical design of the alpaca was present millions of years ago in such long-extinct North American camelid ancestors as *Oxydactylus, Camelops, Stenomylus,* and *Hemiauchenia*.[1,10,15,19] *Hemiauchenia* is believed to be the first member of the camel family to cross from North America to South America via the isthmus at Panama, some three million years ago. This animal was large, bigger than today's South American camelids—it looked something like a gangly guanaco. Eventually there were just two wild forms: guanacos and vicuñas. Vicuñas (*Vicugna vicugna*) are the wild progenitor of alpacas (*Vicugna pacos*).[15] We can study vicuña anatomy and conformation to get a look at the essential aspects of alpaca anatomy and conformation. After all, the vicuña is the original form before humankind began the selective breeding practices that resulted in the alpaca.

Vicuñas are four-legged runners, designed to flee to escape danger. For all of their existence they have been a prey species that has been honed in evolutionary design to move across huge expanses of treeless country, relying on their ability to outdistance predators rather than take cover. Over thousands of years this same basic design has been tested with a changing cast of predators, some now extinct and others very much on the prowl among today's camelid populations.[1,6,10,11,15,19]

Not surprisingly mountain lions, bears, wolves, and foxes are also four-legged runners, relying on efficient movement to catch a prey species. This contest between prey and predator has created many kinds of animals that must rely on their innate ability to move as fast as their body design will allow them to go. Those who are slightly less efficient (slower) than their herd mates don't last long and are less likely to contribute to the gene pool. Over time the members of a prey species, such as a vicuña, become virtual carbon copies of one another—because usually only the most efficient movers get to propagate and live full lives. Anyone who has seen vicuñas glide across the landscape knows what it means to be designed so well by nature that efficient movement and grace become one.[6]

Vicuña (alpaca ancestor) anatomy is uniquely designed to travel efficiently and rapidly over flat or rolling country for sustained periods of time. Like all camelids vicuñas and alpacas have two-toed, padded feet that serve them well to maintain footing and balance on rough terrain. A vicuña's legs are two-thirds as long as its back, which means legs are longer proportionally to body size compared to most prey species. This design allows for less expenditure of energy

Vicuñas flee danger and demonstrate the reason conformation is important.

than a shorter-legged animal of the same general size and strength attempting to move at the same speed. The neck of the vicuña (and most alpacas) is proportionally long for the size of the animal, roughly the same length as the legs. The long neck allows the vicuña to graze in a fully upright position. If the vicuña's neck were shorter, the vicuña would have to stoop or drop to its knees to graze, which is hardly an advantageous position for reacting to a predator. The long neck also serves to help balance the animal when it is underway. The combination of the long neck, long legs, and relatively short body create the silhouette that is unmistakably South American camelid, regardless of the particular camelid species.[5,11,15,19]

The camelid family are natural pacers, i.e., they can travel using less energy by moving the limbs on one side of their body in unison and then doing the same with the other side in rapid succession. Pacing, as a means of locomotion, is energy efficient but not particularly stable. Because both limbs on one side move together and camelids have such a narrow base, the pacing vicuña is challenged not to lose its balance if it must make an abrupt turn. However, if traveling on relatively flat country in a direct line, pacing is a very efficient method of moving. With horses pacing has to be taught, but with camelids it comes inbred. Interestingly, of the four South American camelids, alpacas are the least prone to resort to pacing as a means of moving rapidly for a period of time. Vicuñas and guanacos readily pace. There is some evidence that conformational modifications in alpacas account for their reluctance and inability to break into a pacing movement like their wild kin.[3,4,5,6,9,11,18]

Undoubedly, pacing became an adaptation for outdistancing predators in the vast open areas where wild South American camelids evolved. Camelids have relatively narrow chests and hips for their height. Their front limbs are close together, allowing maximal extension and greater distance with each step compared to an animal with a broader chest and the same length legs. A person schooled in horse conformation would think camelids are incredibly *base narrow* (a walking and standing stance narrower than like animals). But this is a unique aspect of camelid design—each leg is only a few inches from the animal's midline (an imaginary line running lengthwise between the legs). In the rear this form of locomotion is further enhanced by narrow hips, no wider than the chest. The abdomen is also narrow and high, tapering toward the spine. This allows the hind legs to swing forward as part of the pacing gait, unencumbered by a large abdomen found on other hoofed animals such as horses and cattle.[2,3,4,9,10,14,17]

Vicuñas (and alpacas) are equipped with very keen eyesight, which usually allows them to detect a predator long before it has drawn to within striking distance. This combination of early detection of dangers and the ablity to efficiently and rapidly leave an area is key to their survival. A predator's best chance to get close is at night; during the day a predator's chance of getting close enough to use characteristically shorter more muscular limbs to rush and overtake a vicuña is remote. If a predator does get close, the vicuña may break into an initial gallop, which covers ground quickly but consumes a great deal of energy compared to pacing. The pacing gait follows, which might not stop until the predator is out of sight.

WHY DOES CONFORMATION MATTER IN ALPACAS?

The alpaca conformation story deviates somewhat from the vicuña.[15,19] Alpacas were bred from vicuñas, but they have been bred for more than 6,000 years and have lived in a semiprotected state. Alpacas don't occur in the wild. Domestication has resulted in plenty of efficient, correctly conformed alpacas that move like vicuñas, but it has also resulted in a sizable number of alpacas that possess conformational dissimilarities to their wild kin. Some alpacas have locomotion-inhibiting structural defects that would allow a predator to eliminate them from the gene pool if they were living in the wild. Pointing this out still doesn't fully answer the question asked by the Peruvian alpaca judge who wanted to know what the big deal is about conformation. If they're protected from predators because of their association with humans, why should conformation matter?

The answer has to do with quality of life and longevity. Alpacas with correct alignment of the limbs, correct dentition, and no anatomical defects will not only be more able to get away from predators, but also will live fuller and

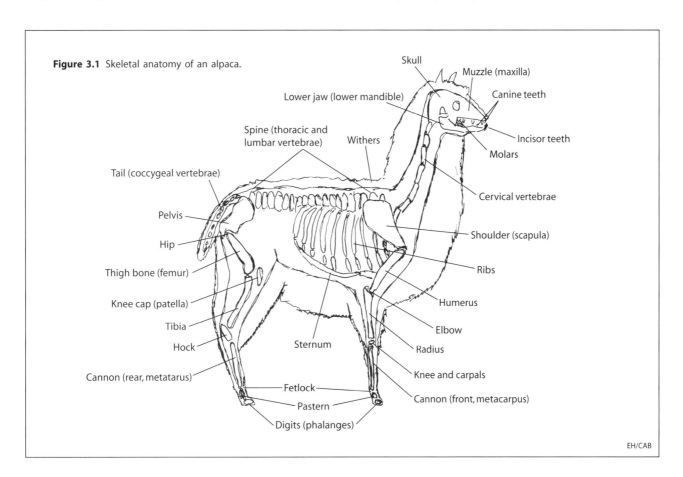

Figure 3.1 Skeletal anatomy of an alpaca.

Skull
Muzzle (maxilla)
Canine teeth
Lower jaw (lower mandible)
Incisor teeth
Molars
Spine (thoracic and lumbar vertebrae)
Withers
Cervical vertebrae
Tail (coccygeal vertebrae)
Shoulder (scapula)
Pelvis
Hip
Ribs
Thigh bone (femur)
Humerus
Knee cap (patella)
Elbow
Tibia
Radius
Hock
Sternum
Knee and carpals
Cannon (rear, metatarus)
Fetlock
Cannon (front, metacarpus)
Pastern
Digits (phalanges)

EH/CAB

longer lives and enjoy the many gaits their wild ancestors practice daily. When body parts are not aligned properly, the pressure points in joints cause uneven wear, causing the joints to succumb to pressures they weren't designed to take. In some cases ligaments, tendons, and muscles help compensate for poor alignment, but in the end if the parts are a poor fit, time and movement will develop into a situation likely to cause pain and eventually shorten an alpaca's life expectancy.[3,4,5,18]

Even if the specter of pain and a shorter life are discounted, the alpaca breeder who has had the privilege of appreciating the fluid, gliding motion of vicuñas or similarly athletic alpacas will most likely realize that breeding alpacas with correct conformation allows them to enjoy a full range of movements, some of them very graceful and exhilarating. The alpaca with conformational problems may never experience pacing or stotting because conformational flaws make these movements impossible.[4,18]

Vicuñas and alpacas are capable of other gaits. They can gallop somewhat like a horse and, of course, they can walk. Galloping is employed for maximum speed but does not last long due to acute energy drain. It is a more stable rapid locomotion for making sharp turns than pacing. Stotting or pronking (see Chapter 2: Behavior and Communication) is the most entertaining and graceful gait. The vicuña or alpaca springs forward and upward and seems to float through the air. The motion is repeated over and over each time all four limbs leave the ground, and the animal bounds forward like a deer, covering several meters in each leap. The gait is often described as a form of exultation or play. Stotting is most common in crias and weanlings around dusk.[3,4,5,6,9,11,18]

CORRECT CONFORMATION FOR ALPACAS

Conformation is fairly well documented in the work of anatomist Karen Timm, DVM, PhD,[17,18] and Murray Fowler, DVM.[2,3,4,5,6,8,10] For anyone who has worked as a screener for a registry, evaluating conformation becomes second nature. However, if the most accomplished screener were suddenly asked to judge a horse, cow, or sheep's conformation, he or she might grimace at the thought. Each

species is designed in a certain way for optimum conformation for that species. Perfect conformation for an alpaca isn't optimum for a zebra.

From the Front, Side, and Rear

The simple rule of thumb for conformational correctness for an alpaca approaching or going away is that the legs should appear straight. If you were to take a string with a weight on the end and hold it against the front of the alpaca's shoulder directly above its front leg, the string should pass over the middle of the knee and split the toes in a straight line. From the rear using the same technique, the weighted string should pass over the middle of the fetlock and end in the midpoint of the back of the foot.

Size

The four South American camelids differ from one another in average height and weight (see Table 3.1). In withers height and weight, alpacas fall between vicuñas and guanacos and are only larger than vicuñas. Size, as a consideration, can have some bearing on species determination if other nonalpaca features are present in an animal being considered to be an alpaca.

Size also needs to be considered in adults that are excessively small (less than 105 pounds). Such animals may pose a health or reproductive risk. The veterinarians and experienced breeders who contributed to the Alpaca Registry Inc. screening standards in 1996 designated the cutoff minimal size for adults at 105 pounds (47.5 kg). The British Alpaca Society put the minimum adult weight at 103 pounds for an adult size on screening forms used in 1998 through 2001.[2] The weight range in alpacas should be between 105 and 185 pounds (47.5 and 82 kg), and the withers height should range between 32 and 39 inches (81 and 99 cm).[7,8,9]

Proportion and Balance

Proportion and balance should also be considered when evaluating conformation. All animals may have legs, a torso, and a neck, but they are often not proportionally the same from one animal to the next. In a herd of alpacas some will appear to be long-legged and some short-legged,

Table 3.1 Size of four species of South American camelids.

	Adult Withers Height	Birth Weight	Adult Weight
Vicuña (*Vicugna vicugna*)	33–38 inches (84–97 cm)	8–20 pounds (3.6–9 kg)	78–140 pounds (35–64 kg)
Alpaca (*Vicugna pacos,* formerly *Lama pacos*)	32–39 inches (81–99 cm)	8–23 pounds (3.6–10.5 kg)	105–185 pounds (48–84 kg)
Guanaco (*Lama guanicoe*)	43–47 inches (109–119 cm)	18–33 pounds (8–15 kg)	215–260 pounds (98–118 kg)
Llama (*Lama glama*)	43–48 inches (109–122 cm)	17–45 pounds (7.7–20 kg)	220–500 pounds (100–227 kg)

while others may be long-legged but short-necked, and others may have long necks and long backs but proportionally short legs. If the neck and legs are in correct proportion to one another and with the torso, the animal is "balanced."

Murray Fowler may have been the first to point out the relative length of the neck and legs to the torso. In his widely shared work on this subject, he designates a correctly balanced alpaca to have a neck and legs that are two-thirds the length of the animal's back.[3,4,5,9] This basic rule was applied to all alpacas screened (more than 12,000 animals) into the Alpaca Registry Inc. (ARI), Canadian Llama and Alpaca Association (CLAA), Australian Alpaca Association (AAA), British Alpaca Society (BAS), British Llama and Alpaca Association (BLAA), Chilean registries, and emerging populations in Germany, Switzerland, and South Africa between the years 1996 and 2002.*

HOW TO EVALUATE CONFORMATION

To enable accurate evaluation, follow these two basic rules: (1) the alpaca must be relaxed and walking in a straight line and (2) if there are prodigious amounts of leg fiber, the legs may need to be wrapped with vet wrap to compress the fiber so the legs' true conformation can be seen.

A standing animal may assume poses and leg placements that do not accurately reflect its conformation. Always watch an animal walk before passing judgment on it. A walking animal is best evaluated in a narrow aisleway where it must walk in a straight line and where you can view the animal from the front, rear, and side, always while it is moving. The alpaca should walk at least 65 feet (20 m) in one direction and then reverse itself and walk in the other direction.

If the animal is excited or frightened, it will likely assume an inaccurate walking motion. Often, a frightened alpaca will squat down and broaden its base. If this happens, give the animal some space and allow it to relax into a normal body posture and walking motion.

Start by scrutinizing the feet and work up the animal's legs, one at a time. Watch where it places its feet as it comes toward you. Are the toenails pointed straight ahead? Do they point slightly in or out? Move your eyes up the animal's leg and look at the fetlock and pastern and the knee (front view) or hock (back view). If a line was drawn from the shoulder or hip, ideally it would pass down the leg over the middle of the joint and split the foot. Or does the leg deviate from straight at the joint, and if so, what is the

angle of the deviation? From the side view, the animal's motion and the angles in its limbs will also reveal defects.[2,3,4,7,8,18]

Using a Transparency as a Template

Veterinarians Brad Smith and Karen Timm screened alpacas and llamas for various registries for six years. They devised a simple template that allows a fairly precise assessment of leg faults. For example, on the ARI screening forms (adopted by other registries), if an animal is knock-kneed (*Carpus valgus*) with an angle of <5° from vertical it is considered to be a slight deviation, whereas an angle of <10° is considerd moderate, and >15° is considered severe and reason to disqualify an animal from a registry.[6,7,8,18] So if a fault is being evaluated and its severity must be measured accurately, using a template is a quick way to make a fairly accurate assessment.

A template is easy to create. Use a protractor to draw the various angles of limb deformities with an indelible marker onto an 8½ × 11-inch (20.3 × 28-cm) clear plastic transparency. The person making the evaluation kneels (within a few meters of the animal) to the level of the animal's legs, looks through the transparency and matches the angle on it that most closely coincides with the angle in the part of the leg being evaluated.

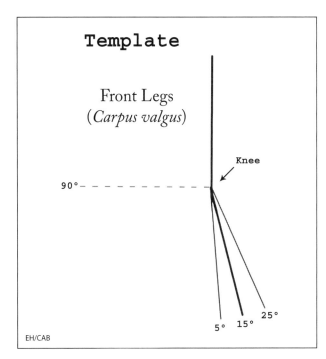

Figure 3.2 Front-leg angles. The template illustrates the leg's deviation from vertical. The angles expressed here are the same ones found on the screening forms in Chapter 27: Maintaining a DNA Registry for the Good of the Breed.

*Eric Hoffman, personal experience working as a screener for these organizations, Santa Cruz, California, 2002.

CONFORMATIONAL CHARACTERISTICS

Correct Front-leg Alignment and Common Alignment Problems

Correct front-leg conformation.

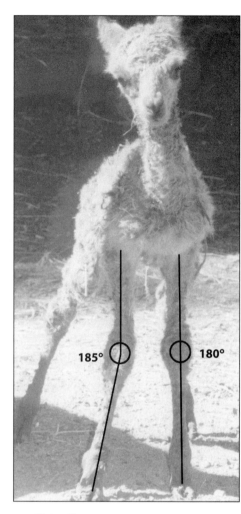

Slight <5°.

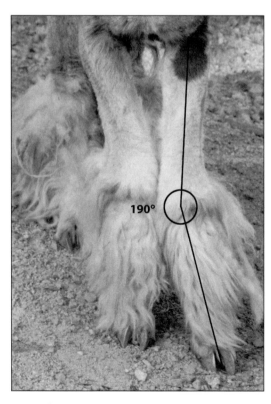

Moderate <10°.

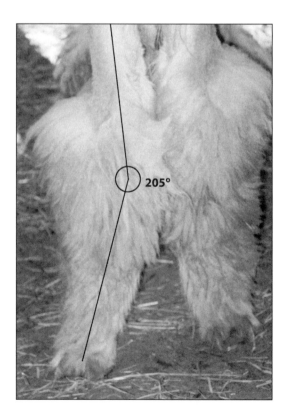

Severe >15°.

Most severe, crippling condition.

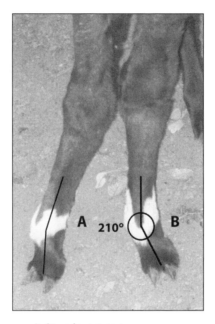

A Bowed out at carpus.
B Bowed in at carpus.

Windswept.

Correct front side.

Calf-knee moderate.

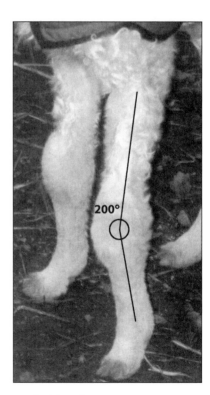

Buck-kneed.

Correct conformation, common to vicuñas.

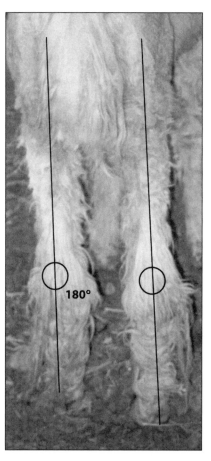

Correct alignment of rear legs for an alpaca.

Slight cow-hock, <5°.

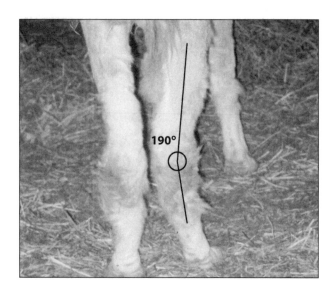

Moderate cow-hock, <10°.

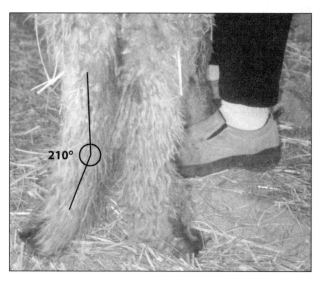

Severe cow-hock, >10°.

Side View

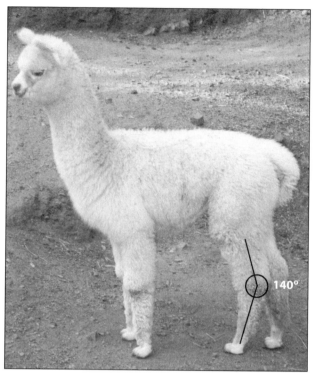

Correct rear sideview, about 140°.

Slight sickle-hock, <135°.

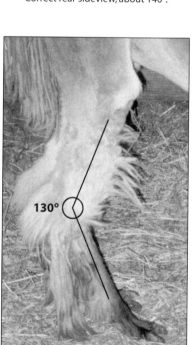

Moderate sickle-hock, <130°.

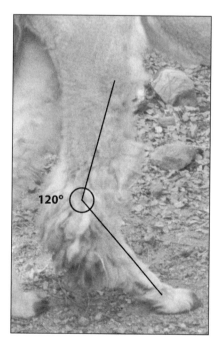

Severe sickle-hock, <125°.

Post-legged in the rear.

Fetlock and Pastern Alignment

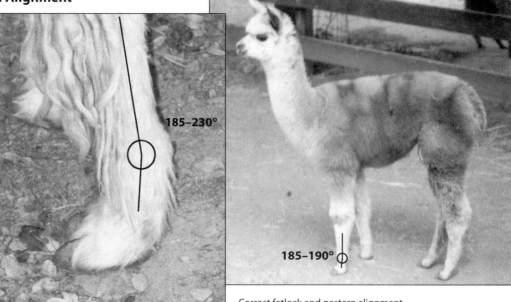

185–230°

185–190°

Correct fetlock and pastern alignment.

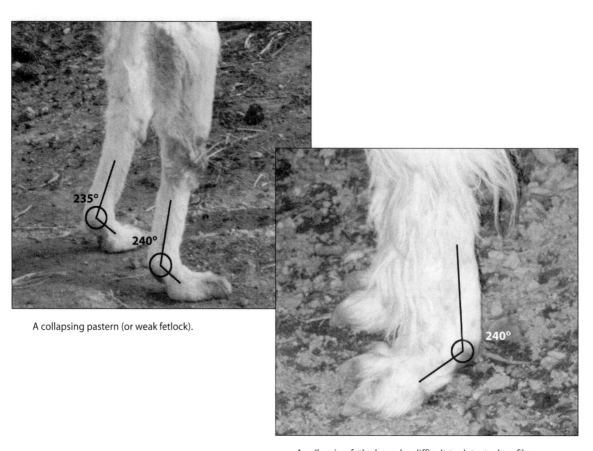

235°

240°

A collapsing pastern (or weak fetlock).

240°

A collapsing fetlock can be difficult to detect when fiber coverage is extensive.

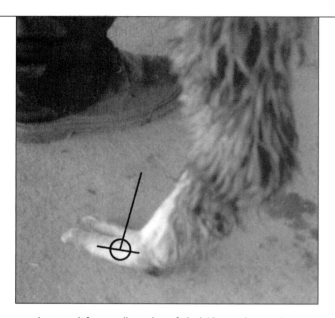

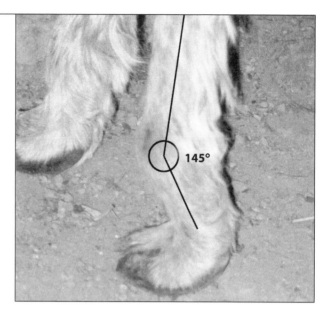

A severe defect: a collapsed rear fetlock (dropped pastern). The vertical line indicates correct leg alignment.

A cocked fetlock (ankle), 145°.

Table 3.2 Alpaca conformational traits.

Desirable traits

straight leg profile from the front and rear
correct leg structure from the side
fetlock (or pastern) with a slight backward tilt (80–85°)
straight topline
rounded rump
adult weight of 105–185 pounds (47.7–84 kg)
adult withers height of 32–39 inches (81.3–99 cm)
short triangular muzzle
spear-shaped ears
balance of leg and neck length 2/3 the length of the back
incisor alignment to the bottom of the front of the palate

Serious congenital defects

partial choanal atresia
one testicle (cryptorchid)
undersized or different-sized testicles
undersized vulva or tilted vulva
fused toes
choanal ani
severe overbite or underbite that misses the dental pad
wry face
gopher ears
twisted tail
pronounced swayback (lordosis)
pronounced humpback (kyphosis)
curvature in spine or neck (scoliosis)
extra toes or feet (polydactylism)
cocked ankle
calf-kneed
buck-kneed in adult
cow-hock: greater than 10 degrees
knock-kneed: greater than 15 degrees
post-legged in rear
sickle-hocked: approximately 125 degrees

Serious congenital defects, continued

luxating patella (knee cap loose enough to manually dislodge)
scrotal or umbilical hernia greater than 2/5 inch (1 cm)
hermaphroditism
hydrocephalic
banana ears (serious phenotype consideration)
llama muzzle (serious phenotype consideration)

Less severe negative traits

base wide
base narrow
slight cow-hock (less than 5°)
slight knock-knee (less than 5°)
slight sickle-hock (close to 135°)
pigeon-toed
weak pastern (or fetlock)
slight lordosis
slight kyphosis
tailset
llamalike muzzle

Negative locomotions

crossing the midline
winging
lameness of any kind

Aesthetic valuation (taste/art appeal)

length of ear
fiber coverage
length of tail
color of toenails
eye color (without deafness present)
eye or ear set
slight roman nose
nonessential fiber characteristics

Notes from Seven Years of Screening

The examples in this chapter show nomenclature plus both correct and defective conformation. In addition to these images, the following alphabetized list of defects and anecdotal impressions are offered, with the hope that they will help accurately identify conformational strengths and weaknesses. Some defects are found frequently, while others are rare or very rare (see Table 3.2). Following each defect and comment is a notation about the frequency of the defect in more than 12,000 alpacas screened in Chile, Bolivia, Peru, Australia, New Zealand, and Europe between 1996 and 2002.

Physical Defects

Base Narrow *Base narrow* refers to the natural leg stance of an animal being narrower (closer to the midline) than the norm. Compared to most other forms of livestock, alpacas (and the entire camelid family) are base narrow. Since narrow is normal in alpacas, to be considered base narrow an alpaca must be narrower than its herd mates. There is a gradient with mild and extreme forms. Base narrow is easier to evaluate on a shorn animal, because the body and legs are no longer hidden beneath its fleece.

There are several presentations of base narrow. It may be excessively narrow across the chest and hips, and its legs may be very straight but extremely close together from the animal's body to the ground. When walking, the foot placement will be very close to the midline. Base narrow may also be found in an alpaca with a normal girth, but with a leg conformation that is set narrowly in the chest (or hips) and track (foot placement when moving) on a narrow base. Other base narrow alpacas may have a normal chest girth and the legs are suitably attached to the body, but the legs angle toward the midline resulting in a stance that is base narrow. Such an alpaca may track with just a few inches separating legs and foot placement along the midline. Common.

Base Wide Often the *base-wide* alpaca will appear unduly round and squat. Leg set and tracking are wider than the norm. Base-wide animals are not as efficient travelers as normal animals. Fairly common.

Bowlegged Found most commonly on the rear legs, bowleggedness is an easy defect to identify in alpacas walking directly away. It is much more difficult to identify in animals walking in an arc or circle. Fairly common.

Buck-kneed This is hard to assess in a scared alpaca because a fearful alpaca will often crouch, giving the impression it is buck-kneed when it isn't. Rare.

Compression on joints can be severe during flight.

Calf-kneed This condition is fairly easy to assess from the side. Sometimes fiber on a leg will distort the leg's profile, making the leg look calf-kneed when it's not. When in doubt wrap the leg. Rare.

Camped Backward Also known as camped under, this defect is when the standing position of the front leg is behind perpendicular. It is more serious than camped forward, because balance is affected and joints and tendons are under greater stress. Rare.

Camped Forward Normal standing position of the front leg is ahead of vertical. Mildly restricts stride. Rare.

Choanal Atresia (Partial) Choanal atresia is not usually classified as a conformational defect, even though it is a gene-linked bone growth that blocks the normal airways from the nostrils to the nasopharynx.[17] A complete choanal atresia makes breathing and nursing at the same time impossible, and the prognosis for survival is poor. Crias born with a complete choanal atresia usually do not live long. However, animals born with a partial choanal atresia may have an impaired airway but still be able to live a fairly normal life.

Partial choanal atresia animals carry the gene(s) that create the defect and may help spread the condition in a population. Identifying animals with partial choanal atresia is challenging. Usually partial choanal atresias are first detected in field situations when an animal appears to be breathing through just one nostril or through a nostril and its mouth simultaneously as a continual means of breathing when it isn't experiencing stress or exertion. An additional telltale sign of the defect is one nostril flared and working overtime while the other nostril appears inactive and is not flared. If a partial choanal atresia is suspected, the examiner should hold the back of his or her hand close to each nostril to ascertain if air is moving through one or both. There may be reasons other than a partial choanal atresia for a blocked nostril, but if only one is working, a veterinarian should be called to fully assess the animal's condition. More common in some populations, rare in most.[17]

Cocked Ankle At first glance the fetlock appears to have been broken and to have healed incorrectly. The fetlock joint is forward over the front of the toes (approximately 95°) instead of being slightly to the back of the toes. A cocked ankle looks markedly different than a normal one. Still, this defect is often missed by experienced alpaca exporters and some show judges. Very rare.

Cow-hocked This rear-leg fault is one of the three most common conformational faults found in alpacas—very common in mild forms, less common in severe forms of 10 degrees or greater. In extreme forms the hocks may actually touch as an animal walks. Hair may be missing from hocks, and in extreme cases the hocks may be rubbed raw from normal walking. In severe forms an alpaca has difficulty running and keeping up with the herd. An alpaca with this defect may learn to swing its leg out and forward as a way to avoid rubbing. On heavily fibered animals watch the foot placement as the animal walks away from you. If the toes point outward instead of straight ahead, there is a good chance the alpaca is cow-hocked. Very common.

Down in the Pastern (or Weak or Collapsed Fetlock) First, let's clarify the terms. The fetlock is the ankle joint, located a short distance above the foot. The pastern is the short leg bone that extends from the fetlock to the foot.

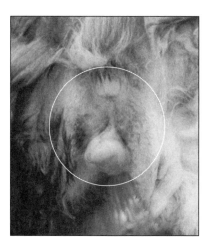

Intersex (underdeveloped male genitalia and vulva).

When talking defects, "weak fetlock" and "down in the pastern" usually mean the same thing.

The conformation of a pastern can't be evaluated properly unless the animal is standing on a hard surface where compression onto the joint (as the animal walks) can be fully seen. An animal standing in grass or a soft surface may have a structurally unsound fetlock that goes unnoticed. A weak fetlock usually worsens with age and eventually will collapse entirely, resulting in the alpaca walking on the bottom of its pastern as well as its foot. The condition is often detectable when the animal attempts to run because it may be the slowest member of the herd and appear clumsy, as if running in sand. Newborns often exhibit weak fetlocks that strengthen (as tendons tighten) in a few days and assume a correct profile. With older animals the defect usually worsens with time. It's not uncommon for animals reaching old age to develop weak or collapsed fetlocks. Common.

Extra Toes (Polydactyl) This defect is fairly common in South America, less so in North America, Australia, and Europe. Many South American breeders believe extra toes bring good luck, hence alpacas possessing them are bred to bring more good luck. In its extreme form there are extra feet, not just an extra toe(s). Extra toes are harder to detect than one might think, especially on dark animals with copious amounts of leg fiber. Often an extra toe (which is usually a single toenail with flesh behind it) is discovered only when the evaluator runs a hand down the leg and feels it. Usually an extra toe is found below the knee, sometimes on the back side of the cannon (*metacarpus*). It is most commonly found on the front legs. Rare in some regions, more common in others.

Fused Ear This defect is often overlooked in purchase agreements and examinations. It occurs on a gradient from very slight to pronounced. Look for fleshy material at the top and inside of an otherwise normal-looking spear-shaped ear. In the more extreme form the ear will look pinched on the top third. Rare.

Fused Foot This defect can be easily missed but is easier to detect with the alpaca standing on a hard surface. The first sign is that the toenails appear to be too close together and sometimes slightly elevated above the ground. When palpated, the foot is one hard mass with two toenails, not the normal two separate digits, each with its own toenail. Often more than one foot on the same animal is fused. Mobility is usually not markedly impaired. Rare.

Gopher Ears Gopher ears are easy to spot. This defect is the absence of a normal external ear, or a very short ear, rather than the normal spear-shaped ear. The defect is found in both llamas and alpacas. Gopher ears are thought to be inherited. The author has seen highland herds in South America in which gopher-eared animals were very common and other herds where not one was to be found. Rare to common.

Knock-kneed (*Carpus valgus*) A very common defect in mild forms of less than 5 degrees and moderate forms of 10 degrees, less common in severe forms of 15 degrees or greater. In moderate and severe forms the defect can be debilitating later in life. Easy to identify in moderate and severe forms, but can be deceptive in mild forms.[6,7,8,9]

Often huacayas with excessive leg fiber appear mildly knock-kneed when they are not. When in doubt, wrap the leg above and below the knee to eliminate fiber distortion. Watch foot direction and placement as the animal walks toward you. The first indicator may be toes that are turned out, but it is possible for an animal that "toes out" not to be knock-kneed. Young animals who are knock-kneed may grow out of the condition as they mature. Nutrition-deficient feeding programs can result in the development of knock-knees. Older animals with the defect rarely change. Very common.

Luxating Patella The patella is the kneecap found on the front of the convergence of the femur and tibia of the back legs. A *luxating patella* is one that can be dislodged from its normal position. The defect is identified by palpating the patella. A patella that can be easily rotated from its correct position indicates the leg is unsound.[16] Rare.

Pigeon-toed As with all foot defects, this one is best evaluated on a hard surface when the animal is walking slowly to and from you. Often just one foot is pigeon-toed. Rare.

Post-legged in Rear or Straight-legged in Front These defects are often missed because most people look for the more dramatic faults in rear legs that have to do with severe angulation; they are most readily detectable from the side. They may occur more frequently in alpacas that are taller than average. Where defects involving severe angles may damage a joint by uneven wear, the negative structural impact is one of too much compression on joints. Rare in the rear legs; very rare in front legs.

Sickle-hocked This is another of the three most common leg faults. It is easy to identify in severe cases (<125°),[2,7,8,9,10] but prodigious amounts of fiber on huacayas can disguise the defect, especially in its milder forms. Look carefully at the angle of the cannon bone from the hock to the fetlock and foot. Watch the rear foot placement as the animal walks past you. Does the foot touch the ground slightly in front of the hip or does it touch midway along the torso

Wry face.

under the stomach? This defect is harder to evaluate in a circular pen when the animal does not track in a straight line. An alpaca crouching and turning abruptly in a tight area may appear sickle-hocked when it is not. Very common.

Spinal Abnormalities *Lordosis* (swayback), *kyphosis* (humpback), and *scoliosis* (abnormal curvature in the spine) are the three most common spinal column defects. Scoliosis is viewed as the most serious and is a cause of automatic disqualification by registries around the world who screen alpacas for inclusion.[2,7,8,10] All three defects appear along a gradient from mild to severe. Scoliosis is difficult to detect in a fully fleeced animal unless the neck and spine are palpated thoroughly. Kyphosis is relatively common in mild forms. A huacaya carrying full fleece may appear to have kyphosis when the "hump" is only fiber. Lordosis is sometimes associated with older females who have had numerous pregnancies.

Wry Face Wry face can be missed in subtle forms, but gross forms are grotesque disfigurements. Examine the alpaca's face while standing directly in front of it. Look for a slight twist or drift in the ridge of the muzzle or incisors that appear to be off center to the upper palate.[14] Rare.

Locomotion Defects

Lameness There are many reasons for lameness. Veterinarian Murray Fowler, who pioneered early work in quantifying conformation in camelids, defined lameness as a "disabling alteration of gait, caused by mechanical interference or pain. Mechanical interference: Structural change

TOES

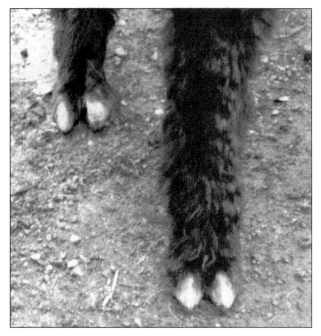

Correct conformation of toes.

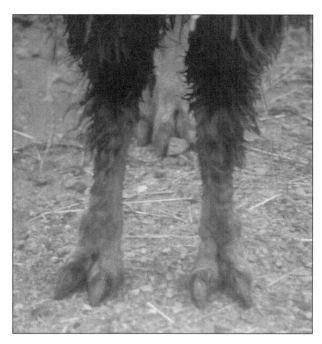

Splayed toes.

A syndactyl (a fused foot).

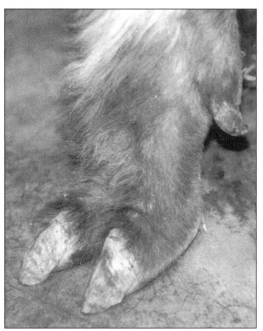

A polydactyl (an extra toe).

Polydactyl in extreme form (extra feet)

BASES

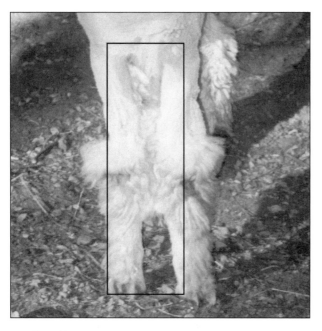

Correct base.

Base narrow, front, knock-kneed. Unshorn, this animal's narrow base would probably not be noticed because foot placement gives the illusion of a broader base.

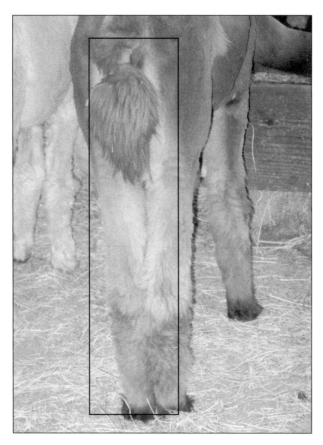

Base narrow, rear.

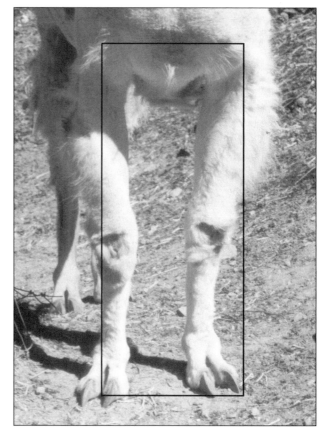

Base wide.

that results in a shortened stride or peculiar way of swinging a limb."[10]

Rope Walking and Crossing the Midline These two atypical walking motions are similar, with "crossing the midline" being the more extreme form. They are both considered undesirable. An alpaca is rope walking when its foot placement is directly on the midline, instead of on both sides of it. It is as if the animal is walking on a tightrope, i.e., rope walking. Crossing the midline is more extreme in that the animal actually crosses over the midline in the placement of its feet as it walks. In extreme cases the animal may appear drunk as it walks along with each step crossing in front of the last step.[2,8,17] Rope walking is fairly common; crossing the midline is rare.

Winging (also Paddling) This defect can occur with either front or back legs. The alpaca swings its leg(s) out as it walks rather than lifting each leg and placing it forward in a straight line. Sometimes the winging motion is associated with being pigeon-toed. Winging can also mean swinging a leg inward before finishing a step. Winging occurs on a gradient from very slight to exaggerated. If only one limb is put forward in this manner, it may indicate a past injury.[3,8,9,18] Rare.

DENTITION

Teeth are essential to the survival of an alpaca. Alpacas have large molars at the rear of the top and lower jaws for masticating food. If the teeth are poorly aligned, procuring forage and chewing may be difficult and food will not be consumed and digested efficiently. Alpaca incisors occur only on the bottom jaw. This feature, which is shared with other ungulates, often surprises new alpacas owners. "How can an animal eat with its top teeth missing?" you might ask. The answer is, it is easy. If the alpaca is grazing on pasture, it takes a mouthful of grass, holds it firmly by pressing the incisors against the dental pad, and then twists its head slightly and pulls, tearing the mouthful free to chew and swallow it. This efficient motion is repeated hundreds of times a day.

What Is a Good or Bad Bite?

When alpaca breeders talk of an animal's "bite," they are talking about the alignment of the incisors on the bottom jaw to the front of the palate on the top jaw. Alpacas shed their first incisors, but their adult incisors continue to grow well into midlife. Usually the angle and bite of the deciduous teeth (baby teeth) will be the same with the permanent teeth. In an optimum bite the incisors touch the palate very close to the front and are not seen when the alpaca's mouth is closed.

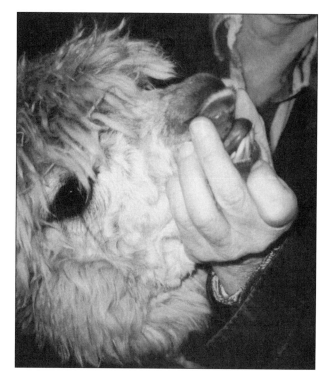
Correct incisor alignment.

The most common defect in alpaca teeth is readily apparent when the incisors protrude past the front of the palate and poke out between the top lips. Because the teeth continually grow, they will protrude an inch (2.5 cm) or more unless they are trimmed on a regular basis. Besides the loss of aesthetic appeal due to protruding teeth, incisors that are too long is a health risk for two reasons: It is harder for an animal to eat with teeth protruding past its mouth, and excessively long teeth will eventually break off, resulting in the loss of a tooth or a situation requiring veterinary intervention.

Overbite

Often an alpaca with protruding teeth is said to have an *overbite*. In actuality, one of two defects accounts for this condition. Either the lower jaw is too long (*inferior prognathia*) or the upper jaw is too short (*superior brachygnathia*). Usually, it is very difficult to determine which jaw is the culprit, but the protruding teeth indicate the alignment is incorrect. If teeth barely miss the underside of the front of the palate and push past the palate, they will need to be trimmed periodically. Though the incisors that are only a few millimeters out of alignment and the incisors that may be a full centimeter or more from the front of the palate represent the same defect, the bites that are grossly out of sync deserve further investigation. Sometimes a set of incisors that doesn't come close to the palate may indicate that the molars do not match well either, causing the alpaca to have a permanent problem in chewing food properly.

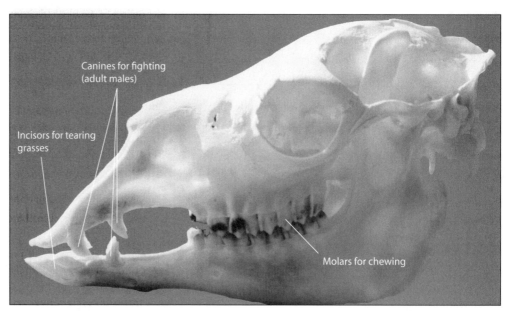

Canines for fighting
(adult males)

Incisors for tearing
grasses

Three types of teeth found
in alpacas and their uses.

Molars for chewing

An overbite is a common defect, and experts have debated its importance to the functional integrity of an alpaca's dentition. Alpacas with overbites have survived quite well in South America with minimal care. The screening rules created by the Alpaca Registry Inc. in 1996 were designed to make importers select animals with no overbites or very slight ones. The standards accepted animals with .5 centimeter overbite.[5,6,7] This was later changed to .3 centimeter.[9]

Overbite is a defect that should be considered on a gradient. Not all overbites are the same in terms of severity, but all overbites will require regular attention, i.e., trimming annually or semiannually, depending on the growth rate of the teeth. A trimmed tooth means the aesthetic appeal of the alpaca has been improved as well as its ability to eat, but it does not mean the jaw is any better aligned. Trimming teeth is a widespread practice (see Chapter 16: Routine

Herd Health). Anyone assessing an alpaca for purchase or show should attempt to determine if teeth have been filed or cut. Sometimes this can be difficult to determine.

Underbite

At the other extreme is the *underbite*, which is sometimes called "parrot mouth," or technically speaking, *inferior brachygnathia*. This defect is rarer than overbite and often poses more of a health problem. At the front of the top palate on all alpacas is a leathery dental pad designed to absorb the pressure of the bottom incisors when they close against it. This coming together of the incisor and palate is the process by which forage is consumed. The dental pad starts at the front of the palate and extends backward about $\frac{1}{2}$ inch (1.26 cm). In a severe underbite, the teeth will fall short of the dental pad and protrude into the roof of the mouth, which isn't designed to absorb sharp incisor teeth.

An overbite and neglected teeth.

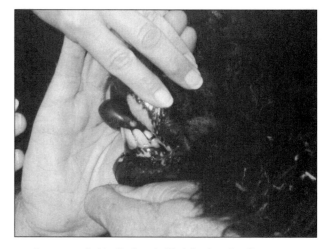

A severe underbite (incisors behind the dental pad).

THE TERMINOLOGY OF IMPERFECTION

To the new alpaca owner the terms desirable traits, faults, inherited defects, negative traits, defects, genetic defects, congenital defects, undesirable faults, unacceptable faults, unsound, phenotypic faults, injury, blemish, aesthetic values, and eye appeal are often bantered about in ways that cause confusion. What do these terms mean and when are they applicable?

We should always remember there are desirable traits —the traits that everyone agrees are desirable in an animal. Such characteristics as correct length of neck to back (balance), shape of head and spear-shaped ears (phenotype of alpacas), straight topline, and structurally correct legs are some desirable traits. We need to also always remember that there is no perfect animal. Try as we might, nature, in honing the vicuña, did a more consistent and purposeful job than we can ever hope to do with the alpaca.

"Blemishes" and "injuries" have to do with visible alterations in an animal that were caused by outside influences, such as broken bones, frostbitten ears, puncture wounds, or a torn ear due to fighting. Beware of the less-than-perfect leg structure that is characterized as an injury. Most leg faults are not from injuries.

We should remember that simplistic condemnations of animals with loosely applied terms often do more harm than good. For example, if an alpaca is labeled cow-hocked, does this mean it shouldn't be bred or it has no value? Or does it mean it can be bred, but only to an animal without a similar fault? In part the answer to such a question has to do with the severity of the defect. A barely detectable cow-hock of a few degrees is not the same as a cow-hock of 10 degrees that compromises an animal's ability to walk, pace, and run in a normal manner. Knowing when a defect is slight, moderate, or severe is important because purchasing and breeding decisions should be made from such determinations.

When we start looking for undesirable traits, the words genetic and inherited need to be used carefully, if at all. Very few genetic studies exist on South American camelids, so labeling a negative trait, defect, or fault as genetic may be very difficult to prove, and actually could be a reason for a legitimate grievance against a person defaming a particular animal or bloodline because of its alleged genetic content. *Congenital defect* is usually the most suitable term used to describe universally accepted faults. This means the defect may have resulted through inheritance or due to environmental and diet-related conditions that affected the unborn fetus. In other words, what caused the defect is unknown. As far as the author is concerned, there are four basic categories of imperfection: (1) unacceptable defects (congenital defects), (2) negative traits (or undesirable traits), (3) phenotype considerations, and (4) aesthetic valuations and fads.

Unacceptable (or Congenital) Defects

This categorization of congenital defects includes severe representations of common faults as well as faults of a serious nature such as cataracts, only one testicle, collapsed pastern, parrot mouth, wry face, cocked ankle, partial choanal atresia, gopher ears, gross balance inequities, pronounced lordosis or kyphosis, luxating patella, permanent crouching, severe cow-hock, sickle-hock or knock-knee, and other severe leg and conformational defects. An unacceptable defect is serious and will impair the quality of life and use of an animal. Many of these defects are suspected of being genetically transmitted.

Negative (or Undesirable) Traits

This catagory includes the mild end of the gradient on common leg faults (slight knock-knee, slight cow-hock), ear length, slight proportion and balance issues, mild lordosis or kyphosis, and coat color inconsistencies.

Some other traits that could be included in this less serious category are animals that are either base wide or base narrow, pigeon-toed, bowlegged, camped out in the rear, and camped forward. These defects are usually less serious, because the animal's general health is not impaired and the negative trait can be bred out in the next generation.

Phenotype Considerations

Phenotype refers to an animal's appearance, whereas *genotype* refers to the genes possessed by an animal that are partially revealed with each offspring it produces. In the world of South American camelids all four species can interbreed and produce fertile offspring. So identifying a particular camelid as having a full complement of the correct phenotype characteristics is an important goal for all alpaca breeders. When conformation and anatomy are discussed, phenotype characteristics are often not mentioned because technically they do not qualify as either anatomical or conformational considerations, yet these characteristics are part of an animal's anatomy and conformation.

Make no mistake—knowing the correct phenotype characteristics of any of the four species of North American camelids is important. It is an especially important skill for anyone sourcing animals in South America where hybridization between llamas and alpacas is commonplace. In the Alpaca Registry Inc. 1996 screening forms that were

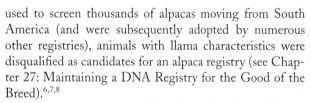

Rounded rear and low tailset is a phenotype characteristic of alpacas.

This alpaca's square rear and high tailset is a phenotype characteristic of llamas.

used to screen thousands of alpacas moving from South America (and were subsequently adopted by numerous other registries), animals with llama characteristics were disqualified as candidates for an alpaca registry (see Chapter 27: Maintaining a DNA Registry for the Good of the Breed).[6,7,8]

In some instances making determinations of llama characteristics is fairly easy because of some glaring llama characteristic in a would-be alpaca. The most common cross-species matings occur between llamas and alpacas. The offspring is a *wari* or more commonly *huarizo*. The most common llamalike characteristics found in alpaca populations are: banana-shaped ears (instead of spear-shaped), long muzzle common to llamas, size (more than 39 inches (99 cm) at the withers, high tailset (instead of alpaca-rounded rump with a low tailset), and coat characteristics (medullation present). Some longtime camelid vets also feel that the angle of the pastern and neck posture are different on llamas and alpacas. Vicuña/alpaca crosses (paco vicuñas) exhibit characteristics of both animals. Paco vicuñas are often characterized by short coats, medullation in the blanket, and extreme wariness. An alpaca with vicuñalike color marking is not necessarily vicuña in the bloodline.

Aesthetic Valuations and Fads

This category needs to be considered carefully because it has to do with the art, taste, or fad aspect of liking or disliking a particular alpaca, but may have no true bearing on the animal's quality or productivity. Often an aesthetic valuation is assigned great importance because it is supported by a group of people who have decided it is important, when in fact not a shred of scientific data supports the significance of the valuation. This can occur when a group or influential individual sees a marketing advantage in emphasizing a particular nonessential characteristic. Such attributes as the direction in the curl of a suri's locks, ear set, slight roman nose, light skin, color of toenails, length of wool cap (area between the ears), amount of fiber below the knee, and fiber characteristics that are irrelevant to fiber processing need to be dealt with cautiously.

Many dog breeds are excellent (and pathetic) examples of artificial criteria being given more importance than basic conformational traits. With some dog breeds the end result is a nice-looking dog who will be euthanized far short of normal life expectancy because of crippling conformational defects pervasive in the breed. In many show formats, aesthetic valuations have a habit of working their way into the show ring. Beware!

CORRECT PROFILE AND COMMON SPINAL DEFECTS

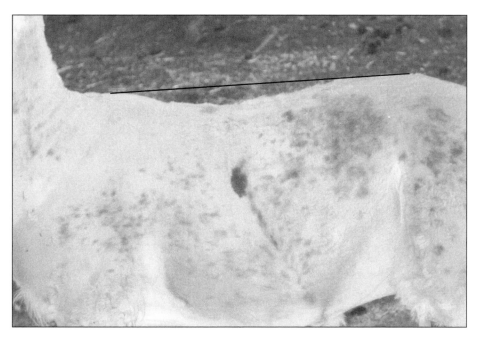

Swayback (lordosis).

Correct profile, slight angle toward shoulder or level with rounded rump.

Humpback (kyphosis).

PROPORTION AND BALANCE

Commonly accepted proportion for an alpaca.

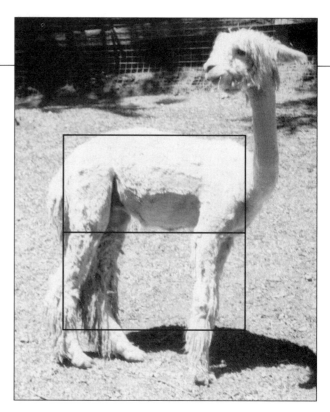

A long-legged alpaca.

A short-legged alpaca.

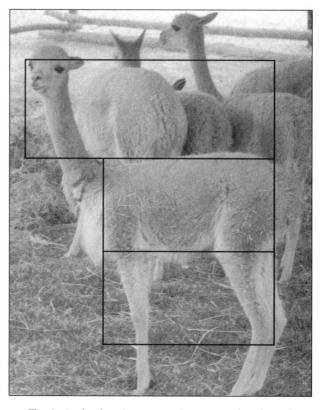

The vicuña, the alpaca's parent species, possesses long-legged conformation compared to many alpacas.

Proportion and balance differences between two alpacas.

Dwarfism.

Difference in size is significant in these two year olds.

HEAD SHAPE

An alpaca muzzle.

A llama muzzle.

An alpaca with an intermediate muzzle.

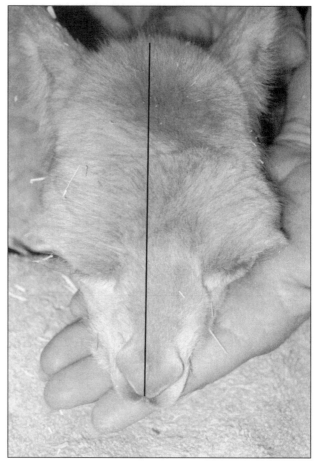

An asymmetric skull in a newborn alpaca.

EARS

A spear-shaped alpaca ear.

An intermediate ear.

Above A banana-shaped or rounded llama ear.

Left A bent ear in a cria is not a defect; it usually self-corrects with age.

A gopher ear, common to some herds in South America.

REFERENCES

1. Cox, B., R. J. G. Savage, B. Gardiner, C. Harrison, and D. Palmer. *Dionsaurier und Prahistorische Tiere,* pp. 274–277. Koln: Konemann, 2000.

2. Fowler, M., E. Hoffman, and B. Smith: Phenotype Characteristics Evaluation, Physical Examination Screening Checklist. British Alpaca Society, London, 1999.

3. Fowler, M.: The Gaits of Llamas and Alpacas. *Llamas* 5(4): 55–58, 1991.

4. Fowler, M.: Conformation. *Medicine and Surgery of South Amercian Camelids* (M. E. Fowler, ed.), pp. 357–361. Ames: Iowa State University Press, 1989.

5. Fowler, M.: Form, Function, Conformation and Soundness. *Llamas* 35: 45–53, 1986.

6. Hoffman, E.: Chaku, Capturing the Golden Fleece. *Living Planet* 6: 28–35, Winter 2001.

7. Hoffman, E.: ARI Amends Screening Criteria, Adopts Stricter Standards, *The Alpaca Registry Journal* 3(1): 72–74, Winter-Spring 1998.

8. Hoffman, E.: ARI Publishes Alpaca Screening Manual. *The Alpaca Registry Journal* 1(2): 13–34, Summer-Fall 1996.

9. Hoffman, E.: The Screening Process Critiqued and Praised at UC Davis Conference. *The Alpaca Registry Journal,* 1(2): 11–13, Summer-Fall 1996.

10. Hoffman, E., and M. Fowler: *The Alpaca Book,* pp. 85–93. Herald, CA: Clay Press, 1995.

11. Hoffman, E.: The Many Ways Guanacos Talk. *International Wildlife* 23(4): 4–12, July-August 1993.

12. Hoffman, E.: Camel Trek South Australia. *Llamas,* pp. 10–22, 1987.

13. Hoffman, E.: Sunny, the Pioneer Llama. *California Living,* September 1979.

14. Johnson, L.: Sleuthing Wry Face in Camelids. *The Alpaca Registry Journal* 2(2): 20–24, Summer-Fall 1997.

15. Kaldwell, M., M. Fernandez, H. F. Stanley, R. Baldi, J. C. Wheeler, R. Rosadio, and M. Bruford: Genetic Analysis Reveals the Wild Ancestors of the Llama and Alpaca. *Proceedings of the Royal Society,* pp. 2,575–2,584. London, 2000.

16. McConnell, T.: Patella Luxation. *The Alpaca Registry Journal* 3(1): 14–15, Winter-Spring 1998.

17. Smith, B., and K. Timm: Choanal Atresia Study Results: Sleuthing Genetic Problems. *The Alpaca Registry Journal* 1(2): 64–70, Summer-Fall 1996.

18. Timm, K.: The Whys and "What-fors" of Leg Conformation. *The Alpaca Registry Journal* 3(1): 8–14, Winter-Spring 1998.

19. Wheeler, J.: Origen, Evolucion y Status Actual. *Avances Perspectivas del Conocimiento de los Camelidos,* pp. 11–49. Santiago, 1991.

Section Two

Management

Overleaf Understanding alpacas' banding instinct helps in training and herding management.

Chapter 4

Husbandry

Eric Hoffman

Alpacas await release from *canchones,* the ancient and traditional rock corrals of the Andes.

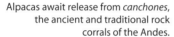

Good husbandry means efficiently providing the daily care for alpacas in ways that ensure good health, successful breeding and birthing, protection, successful fleece production, and the efficient use of the caregiver's time. The breadth of husbandry practices includes farm layout, fences, shelters, waterers, feeders, cooling and heating devices, shelters, veterinary care and medical supplies, restraining systems, hay purchasing and storage, mineral supplements, shearing activities, labor practices, manure removal, and record keeping. Good husbandry takes into consideration the special behavioral and biological needs of alpacas and is tailored to fit specific environmental conditions.

FOUNDATION OF A BUSINESS MANAGEMENT PLAN

Good husbandry practices are both the foundation and number-one priority of an alpaca operation's business management plan. A ranch management plan also includes budgeting for the purchase of alpacas, marketing and advertising, travel expenses, purchase of farm equipment, plus daily and spot labor costs and possibly show activities.

It is important to keep the nonhusbandry expenses and priorities in perspective within the business plan. Creating and paying for expensive advertisements, traveling to and from conferences and sales, deciding on embellishments for barns and fences, choosing a truck and trailer, and de-

signing a public display booth are time-consuming and often expensive. At times these nonhusbandry pressures will be important. You may feel compelled to sacrifice budget and time allocations that support good husbandry practices in order to free up funds to compete with the promotional efforts of competitors. Any alpaca business worth its salt always puts the care and management of alpacas first and relegates the "glitz" part of the business to secondary status. In the final analysis alpaca breeders are judged by the alpacas they produce and the care their animals receive. Perfecting all aspects of alpaca husbandry is the priority that results in long-term success.

FARM LAYOUT

A farm's layout deals with the relationships of buildings and enclosures essential to the daily running of a farm: pastures, aisles, hay storage, birthing area, catch pens, feeding stations, waterers, etc. A farm's layout is often in place when an alpaca operation is started because of the farm's previous history. Modifying a layout to suit alpacas can amount to major or minor renovations. If you are creating a new layout, thinking it through in terms of suitability for other livestock makes good sense should you ever sell the farm or raise animals other than alpacas.

Most importantly, create a layout that allows for efficient daily care. Layouts depend on terrain, size of acreage, numbers of females, numbers of males, climatic conditions,

A centralized farm layout places the barn at the hub of all corrals. This makes feeding animals, catching them, and moving them to another corral relatively easy.

and numerous other variables. Layouts fall into two general categories: *centralized* (focused around a central barn) or *dispersed* (spread among a number of outbuildings).

Generally, five alpacas per quarter acre is ample room, providing feeders are correctly placed. Regardless of the plan, most layouts should be able to accommodate alpacas in one or two general pastures or paddocks for the main herd and young. You should have separate pens for breeding, birthing, weanlings, individual males or bachelor groups, and quarantine facilities. It often seems that you can never have too many pens. Ideally, pens are interconnected, with catch pens appropriately placed for easy capture and transfer of animals from one pen to the next. In an ideal farm layout one person should be able to move any alpaca on the property from one paddock to another by merely opening gates and herding (possibly with a 20-foot length of plastic pipe) or baiting (with a bucket partially filled with grain). A carefully considered layout will take into account the daily activities of the caregiver and ways to maximize efficiency.

IMPORTANCE OF FENCING

Before the Fence Goes Up

The integrity of a fencing system can make the difference between the success or failure of an alpaca enterprise. Fencing is the most important passive protection alpacas receive from their owners.

The primary objectives of any fencing scheme are twofold: (1) to incorporate design features that keep the alpacas in and yet are safe and will not cause injury or death and (2) to protect alpacas from predators and disease-carrying animals. Secondary objectives include segregating alpacas into pens for weaning, breeding, maintaining desired stocking levels, pasture rotation, herd compatibility, easy capture, and segregating from other species.

Since many alpaca operations are on farms previously set up for other forms of livestock, modifying existing fences to suit alpacas is often necessary. To some alpaca owners, the need to modify existing fencing is not readily apparent. They assume an aesthetically attractive fence that contained horses and cattle will be adequate for alpacas. This can be a wrong assumption with tragic results. Alterations are often necessary to make a fence predator-proof, escape-proof, or trapping-proof.

Keeping Alpacas Safely Enclosed

Alpacas are easy animals to contain because they rarely challenge a fence and are reluctant jumpers. If an alpaca escapes from an enclosure, it usually stays as close as possible to the main herd behind the fence rather than wandering off. Alpacas usually exercise good judgment in negotiating hazards in a fence. However, alpacas have been injured and killed from fence design features that do not take an alpaca's habits and physical characteristics into account.

Since alpacas do not challenge fences, barbed wire is unwarranted for containing them. Never use barbed wire in part of a fence that an alpaca can touch. Barbed wire can cause serious eye injuries or lacerations, and it can ensnare an alpaca if its fiber becomes wrapped around a barb. However, barbed wire installed prudently on the *outside* of the fence works well as protection. Some alpaca breeders employ barbed wire at ground level outside the perimeter defense to deter dogs from digging under a fence or as a deterrent to deer by placing several strands above the 6-foot (1.8-m) level. If you incorporate barbed wire into a fence as a predator defensive measure, you should always be aware of the danger it poses to alpacas.

Hazards also exist in some types of field fencing in which distances between the stay wires are far enough apart for an alpaca to push its head and neck through. This type of fencing is usually referred to as field fencing and is in common use throughout North America, Australia, Europe, and parts of South America. Alpacas reaching through field fencing usually do so without incident, but if an alpaca (of any age) can put its head and neck through a wire mesh fence (usually in pursuit of greenery on the other side), there is increased risk to the alpaca's safety. Alpacas have entangled their neck fiber and necks in the wire joints in several brands of field fencing. In part this is due

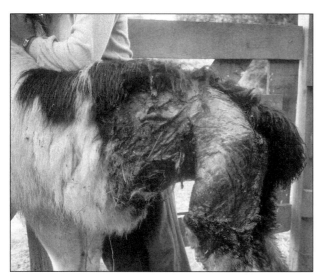

For most people it is a surprise to learn that in the United States the family dog (particularly German shepherds, huskies, and other northern breeds) is probably responsible for more stock kills than wild predators. This German shepherd awaits its fate in a California animal shelter. Its victim, a llama, barely survived. The dog was a family pet that was allowed to roam when the owner went to work. The dog tore away most of the skin on one side of the llama within minutes. Medical care was both lengthy and costly. Many alpacas have been killed by their owner's dog or a dog from a neighboring property. A dog-proof fence is essential to any alpaca operation.

to alpacas' long supple necks, a physical characteristic they don't share with sheep for whom field fencing is more appropriate (see "Field Fencing" for more details).

Fence-related injuries can be caused by sharp-ended strands of wire. Loose wire ends sticking out from a fence create sharp skewers that are rigid and especially dangerous in the heavier gauge wires used in better-quality fencing materials. It is important to snip wire ends flush with a fence and bend whatever remains in a direction away from the alpacas. Surplus fencing material and baling wire pose a very real threat as well. Strangulations and leg injuries have been reported from baling wire or discarded fencing that become wound around an animal's neck or legs. A fence must be clean of loose ends and free of neck- and leg-injuring hazards.

Gates are often the weak link in an otherwise sound fencing scheme. Gates should be tight-fitting to within 2 inches (5 cm) of the ground and posts, and the latching system must be foolproof and snug. Gates require regular maintenance. From time to time hinges loosen, latches become difficult to work, gateposts lean or break, and metal gates often rust. In areas of heavy snow and ice you may find it necessary to set the hinges a little higher in the winter so the gate won't freeze to the ground. Having a gate

maintenance kit is a good idea and the more standardized your gates are, the easier it is to maintain them, because parts are often interchangeable. To extend the life of a metal gate, use rust-preventive paint.

The height and other physical features of gates in a perimeter fence should be equal to the fence. Occasionally an alpaca putting its head through a gap between a loosely latched gate and fence post will become ensnared. When the alpaca attempts to pull its head back, the gate (possibly caught on neck fiber) draws back and tightens around its neck. Also, if precautions aren't taken, dogs are apt to gain access to a group of alpacas by digging or squeezing under a gate or pushing through a gap between a gate and post. Installation of a tight-fitting, dog-proof gate often requires a little extra thought. Buying a gate and installing it usually aren't enough. The gate may need to be modified to match the height of the fence and mesh may need to be attached to the gate to create a dog-proof threshold under it.

Knowing Your Local Predators

Any fencing scheme should take into account the habits and capabilities of local predators. The optimal fencing scheme should be able to eliminate all predators with the exception of avian and the large feline varieties.

The mountain lion (*Felis concolor*) is a secretive animal that is a traditional predator of wild and domestic camelids in South America. Its population is increasing throughout western North America, where it has occasionally taken llamas and alpacas in a wide range of habitats. The threat to a particular herd of camelids is "cat specific." Some mountain lions live in close proximity to alpaca and llama herds and elect not to attack them; others eat whatever is available.

Dogs On small to moderate-sized farms, the pet dog is probably the most destructive predator. It may surprise some readers to learn that dogs, often ones owned by neighbors, kill countless numbers of livestock throughout the world annually. Usually the marauding dog isn't a stray or wild, but someone's pet. It is not unusual for dogs that make wonderful pets to revert to their ancestral chase-and-kill instinctual patterns if allowed to intermingle with any kind of livestock without human supervision. In a survey taken in seven of California's most populous counties, 70 percent of the canine culprits were the northern breeds, which include German shepherds, huskies, malamutes, and mongrels possessing their genes. In many regions dogs cause more livestock deaths (horses, cattle, goats, sheep, etc.) than the sum total of all wild predators operating in the same area.[25] If a menacing dog is sighted and chased off, assume it will return. It is prudent to locate the roaming dog's owner and persuasively explain the reasons for responsible containment (needless injury and death to livestock, the destruction of the offending dog, and substantial financial liability) in order to avoid an attack at some later date. In many areas the law allows full indemnity (or

double indemnity) for animals lost to dog attack. Know your local laws regarding your rights and claims before there is an incident. If you know the law ahead of time, you can respond authoritatively with the law on your side.

If an attack occurs, make every effort to contain the marauding dog (alive or dead) and call the proper authorities to report what has occurred. Have the authorities remove the offending animal rather than return it to its owner. Photograph the dog, particularly if it has fiber hanging from its mouth, and the carcasses and injuries to victimized alpacas. Do not bury dead alpacas until the authorities tell you to do so. Often injuries are not readily apparent because alpacas are covered in fiber. If you suspect an animal was attacked but it appears uninjured, examine it carefully, especially its hindquarters, abdomen, legs, and areas where the fleece looks disturbed. Force the alpaca to run and watch its movement for evidence of injury.

A dog that kills or maims and escapes commonly returns a few hours or days later. Collecting money for damages from the dog's owner is much more problematic once the dog has left your property—even if you witnessed the attack and you lost an alpaca or the injuries were serious enough to require a veterinarian. Proving a dog was the actual culprit in a court of law can be time-consuming and very difficult. The best evidence for establishing responsibility is capturing the guilty canine.

Wild Predators In North America the smorgasbord of wild predators includes coyote, mountain lion (cougar), bear, wolf, fox, bobcat, lynx, and possibly badger and wolverine. Always the opportunist, the wily coyote is the most widely distributed of the wild predators. Bears of all kinds are also opportunistic, especially with crias—there are several reports of bears procuring a young llama for a meal. While I was on a llama pack trip, I saw three tethered llamas put an adult black bear to flight by surprising it with alarm calls, snorting, and broadside displays. This element of bluff common to llamas and alpacas will deter the curious predator but have no effect on a determined or experienced one. Make no mistake—llamas and smaller alpacas are no match for a determined large predator. When the chips are down, the only sure defense is running away.[20]

Wolves and wolverines are limited to Canada and remote northern places in the United States, including Alaska. The small felines (bobcats and lynx) are primarily rodent, bird, and hare eaters, but may attack cria-sized animals if opportunity knocks. Badgers are more widespread in the United States than most people realize. There have been no reported deaths due to badgers, but they are capable of taking a cria and are known to have dens in alpaca pastures. They seem content eating roots, small rodents, and carrion. Their burrow systems create a hazard that could result in a broken leg.

The fox in South America and Australia is deadly to newborns, particularly when a mother alpaca is alone and does not have the benefit of the herd's aggressive response to chase off a fox. The South American fox is a coyote-sized animal and more capable than the smaller foxes found in North America, Europe, and Australia.* Australia also possesses a feral wild cat that looks like a domestic cat but is often much larger. These cats are opportunistic and cunning.**

Because of their strength, size, and leaping and climbing abilities, the presence of mountain lions should prompt thoughts about additional strategies beyond fencing. Generally speaking, mountains lions are likely to live anywhere in the western United States and Canada where deer are common. The big cats are an increasingly common threat because they have received decades of protection and their social structure requires each generation to establish new territory. In areas in which open country is hemmed in by cities and farms, young lions often find themselves forced

The coyote (*Canis latrans*) is one of the few large predators that has increased its range since the onslaught of urbanization and agricultural development. Once a western grasslands loner that hunted mostly rodents, coyotes can now be found west of the Mississippi River in the United States, coast to coast in Canada, and as far north as Alaska. They range in size from barely larger than a fox to the height of a German shepherd. The coyote has increased in size and hunting proficiency in some regions. Where it hunts in packs, it takes down deer and like-sized livestock. An alpaca ranch in coyote habitat needs to have a coyote-proof perimeter fence.

into areas near people and livestock. Numerous incidents have been reported of mountain lions taking llamas.

Mountain lions are wary of human voices. Playing radios (programs in which human conversation are the staple, not music) in a pasture during the night and additional lighting are thought to deter mountain lions. However, dogs and coyotes seem to figure out the difference between a radio and a person fairly quickly. In the United States, agencies such as the Department of Fish and Game will often assist in removing a mountain lion that kills or begins to prey on domestic livestock.***

Large predatory cats the world over that opt to take domestic stock seem to have no problem making a meal of

*Rufino Quilla, Peruvian veterinarian, personal communication, Arequipa, Peru, October 15, 2001.

**Roger Haldane, pioneer Australian alpaca breeder and water buffalo dairyman, personal communication, Camperdown, Victoria, Australia, February 12, 1998.

***Bruce Elliot, wildlife biologist for the California Department of Fish and Game, personal communication, Monterey, California, August 15, 1994.

The dingo (*Canis familiaris*) of Australia fills a similar niche to the coyote of North America. The dingo proliferates despite persecution and is an opportunistic predator that sometimes hunts in packs. Fortunately, most dingoes live on the western side of the "dingo fence" (allegedly the world's longest fence), which protects the most populous alpaca-growing regions of Victoria and New South Wales. Western Australia and areas not as well protected are a different story. The fox (*Vulpes vulpes*) is probably a greater threat to crias because it is widespread throughout mainland Australia.

llamas and alpacas. An alpaca herd imported into Israel and kept in the Negev Desert was victimized by a leopard. Mountain lions regularly prey on wild guanacos in Patagonia.[24]

Shooting or poisoning predators on sight is usually an unwise strategy. Poisons are often ingested by harmless wild creatures as well as pet cats and dogs. Shooting works and is necessary in certain situations, but shooting a predator on sight may be counterproductive. For example, both coyotes and mountain lions are territorial in nature, and both often live in close proximity to livestock but steadfastly never hunt livestock. If these animals are known to be in your area but have never killed domestic stock, there's a good chance they would rather dine on wild creatures. Studies of wild predators around the world have often turned up surprising behavioral differences within the same population of predators when it comes to hunting habits and dietary preferences. For example, mountain lions in one region may continually attack cattle, while in another area the big cats will stroll past a pasture full of cattle at night for years while hunting deer. Removing a nonthreatening mountain lion or coyote usually means there will be a replacement, and it may be more aggressive toward domestic stock and have a different set of dietary preferences.

In Australia the plethora of poisonous snakes (the Elapid family is especially well represented) probably poses the most serious wild threat to alpacas. Snakes the world over are attracted to rodents and other food sources. Keeping rodent populations under control by tidying barns and making sure paddocks are free of hiding places is an important strategy. The dingo fence that runs from South Australia to Queensland effectively eliminates dingoes from most areas where alpacas live. Dingoes seen inside the fence are hunted aggressively. However, on the island state of Tasmania, Tasmanian devils are a logical threat, especially to newborns. Wedge-tailed eagles, which are a protected bird, are also a threat to newborns throughout Australia.* On rare occasions individual birds have been known to prey on newborn kids and lambs. If an eagle begins studying crias or is attracted to placentas left in a paddock, it is wise to keep newborns under cover until they are fully mobile.

In North America bald and golden eagles have been known to make a meal of dead or dying lambs and deer fawns on occasion. These protected birds are hard-pressed to lift from the ground anything greater than 7 pounds (3.2 kg), and a healthy alpaca cria is considerably larger than an eagle's carrying capacity under most circumstances. However, on very rare occasions deer fawns weighing around 10 pounds have been found in eagle nests; the fawns were probably captured on or near a mountaintop where the eagle could glide downward to its nest. Under unusual circumstances an extremely hungry eagle, raven, (skua and kea in New Zealand) and possibly other large predatory birds will attack a weak newborn lamb or fawn and overpower it if it's unprotected by its mother and too weak to get up and walk away. Presumably conditions such as this could exist for a newborn alpaca.

Guard Dogs One of the more successful defensive measures to protect your herd, beyond fencing, is to make one of several breeds of livestock guard dogs a fixture in your pastures. A number of large, powerful dogs (including great Pyrenees, Anatolian shepherd, Komondors, Akbash, and other breeds) have been selectively bred to identify and live with the herd they are introduced to guard. They repel predators, which in some cases may increase risks to human visitors and liability to the dog's owner, if the dog can't distinguish between a coyote sneaking up on some alpacas and a human customer who has come to wander through a herd. Often a guard dog appears to be doing nothing at all because no predators are ever sighted and the dog lazes away the days sleeping and taking it easy. The dog's marking behavior and presence are often enough to

---

*Roger & Clyde Haldane, personal communication, July 4, 1994.

keep a predator at bay, and its interaction with predators may occur in surprisingly subtle ways at night.

One caveat: Don't make the mistake of assigning a nonguard-dog breed (husky, German shepherd, etc.) to guard your herd because the dog seems loyal to you. These breeds are bred to herd or chase, and instead of protecting they will revert to chasing and eventually attacking. I know of many incidences in which the "trusted" family dog was assigned guard duty over a group of alpacas while the owners were away, but because of the dog's inbred nature it attacked the alpacas. A sad story makes this point vividly. An alpaca owner once fenced two German shepherds into a long, narrow chute that shared a common fence with a herd of alpacas. The alpaca owner reasoned that any predator coming near his alpacas would encounter the large dogs, which were aggressive with intruders of any kind. Instead of repelling predators (which they may have done with their barking), one dog dug under the fence separating it from the alpacas. Once in the enclosure it killed three alpacas.

Fencing Out Disease-carrying Animals

Fencing schemes should be aimed at keeping out disease-carrying wild and domestic animals. Possible carriers of diseases transferable to alpacas include deer, elk, pigs, kangaroos, and common forms of livestock such as sheep, goats, cattle, and horses. Other possible disease carriers, which are more challenging to fence out, include skunks, rats, cats, raccoons, and rabbits. Burrowing rodents and poisonous snakes pose risks that usually cannot be addressed by fencing schemes. The importance of fencing out particular animals varies from region to region. For example, white-tailed deer (*Odocoileus virginianus*) carry the deadly meningeal worm, which is sometimes transferred to alpacas. White-tailed deer live primarily in the midwestern and eastern parts of the United States and throughout southern Canada.[18] In areas where meningeal worm is especially prevalent and alpacas are kept on pastures that would attract deer, perimeter fencing needs to be 8 feet (2.4 m) high to keep out deer.

The carriers and transmitters of diseases are a forever-changing cast of characters involving a wide range of species. In some areas risks are very low; in other areas they are high. Sometimes a species that is populous in one region poses no threat, while in another region the same species carries high disease risks. For example, in one region skunks and raccoons are plentiful and known carriers of rabies, while a few hundred miles away raccoons and skunks are not as common and no cases of rabies have been reported for decades. Populations of foxes and bats may also be carriers in one area and not in another area.[6] Obviously, safeguarding alpacas against rabies transmission is

Some alpaca owners incorporate a guard dog with their herd. The Anatolian pictured here is one of several time-tested breeds specifically bred to live with and guard livestock from predators. All of the guard dog breeds are large and some are aggressive toward people in general. They are not applicable to all situations, but can be especially effective in large rural operations. However, don't make the mistake of assigning a nonguard breed dog to the task of herd protection. Large dogs given this task have been known to kill the alpacas when owners were away.

more appropriate where raccoons or skunks are populous and known rabies carriers, and less important in areas where these creatures rarely occur or are not carriers.

Familiarizing yourself with which wild creatures live near your alpacas, which ones are populous, and which ones are apt to carry diseases is important when deciding fencing schemes. Usually a phone call to a local veterinarian or county, state, or federal agency responsible for management of wildlife can help you—often several agencies have overlapping responsibilities. By communicating with a number of sources you will usually get a pretty clear picture about which wild animals carry diseases transferable to livestock. It pays to research this question and not rely on generalizations and hearsay.

Fencing out deer requires an 8-foot (2.4-m) fence, which will add appreciably to fencing costs. It will also affect the appearance of your farm. There's no reason to invoke costly strategies because someone halfway across the country did it—do it only if the wild creatures in your area pose a threat serious enough to endanger your animals. With some disease threats, fencing schemes will not be effective. A "hot wire" and a solid fence design will deter animals like raccoons from entering a paddock, but raccoons climb too well to be fenced out forever. Instead, in a rabies-endemic area a rabies vaccine is probably a better safeguard than a fence.

Disease transmission by domestic livestock, camelid and noncamelid, needs to be considered. For disease prevention, appropriate vaccinations and the quarantine of animals entering your property should be farm policy. Consult your veterinarian about the disease potential of any inbound livestock and fence accordingly.

Segregating Species

People new to alpacas sometimes plan on releasing their alpacas into a single large pasture with several other kinds of livestock. The plan is to let all the animals live together. However, the mixing of alpacas with other species is a somewhat questionable practice, especially in small enclosures. In South America alpacas are kept with donkeys, horses, cattle, and sheep. In South America where alpacas are kept with llamas, huarizo (undesirable crossbreed) offspring are common.

With entirely unrelated species, there are other concerns. A confrontation between a bull and an alpaca that I witnessed in Peru illustrates the possible consequences of the inability of two species to communicate effectively. A large bull approached a tethered alpaca, who warned the bull with a broadside display not to come any closer. Instead of retreating, the bull approached and rubbed its head on the alpaca, who promptly spit and repositioned

itself directly in front of the bull with an even more pronounced broadside display. The bull, now aroused and annoyed, lowered its head and appeared about ready to gore the alpaca when the child herding the bull hit it sharply with a stick to distract it. In this case alpaca language provided both a stimulus and a target for a much larger and stronger animal.

With goats, donkeys, horses, and exotic hoof stock, the same kinds of muddled communications occur when animals of different species have chance meetings in feeding and watering areas where animals congregate. In crowded areas or overstocked pastures, mixing different species of herbivores often results in added stress and danger to the smaller species.* In vast areas with no congestion around food or water sources, different species usually segregate themselves and cohabit an area peacefully. However, when in doubt, segregate.

Perimeter and Internal Fencing

Many alpaca breeders make a distinction between perimeter and internal fencing (also called cross fencing). The perimeter fence must be entirely predator-proof, which makes it more expensive to build and maintain than internal fencing (which must only contain alpacas). Ideally, the perimeter fence encircles the entire alpaca operation. The adage "a chain is as strong as its weakest link" is applicable here. Perimeter fencing must have the same degree of integrity throughout its entirety, regardless of number of gates, terrain, vegetation, watercourses, rock outcrops, and other environmental factors.[6] To protect a fence located in timber and brush, all precariously leaning and dead trees should be removed.

Internal fencing is designed to contain alpacas, which means the fence doesn't have to be as tall or contain features to deter predators or pest species. Internal fences can be flexible in design, possibly made of movable panels constructed and torn down as needs dictate. Pre-existing fences, originally designed for other kinds of livestock, are often entirely adequate. Some farms incorporate a strand or two of electric fence in conjunction with a pre-existing fence.

Minimal Requirements for a Perimeter Fence A predator-proof fence encompassing the perimeter of an alpaca operation should be thought of as mandatory. Many North American breeders are content with a perimeter fence 5 feet (1.5 m) in height, though others think 6 feet (1.8 m) is a safer height.[4] A few breeders, wanting to keep deer out

---

*Bill Coburn, director of African Safari Wildlife Park, personal communication, Port Clinton, Ohio, September 4, 1994.

PERIMETER FENCING

This 6-foot-high (1.7-m) game fence with a strand of barbed wire at the top (which is substantially higher than an alpaca's eye) is a deterrent against meningeal worm-carrying white-tail deer found in eastern North America.

No-climb fencing that is 5 feet (1.5 meters) tall is dog-proof. This alpaca owner smartly elected to guard the base with a "hot wire" to dissuade digging under the fence.

Inset Close-up of wire knot of 12.5 gauge no-climb fencing. No-climb held together by wire knots lasts longer and is more flexible than the same gauge no-climb held together by welded joints.

Gates are the weak link in many fencing schemes. This owner dog-proofed her gate with a concrete apron underneath it, so that predators cannot squeeze or dig their way into the alpaca enclosure.

This owner uses no-climb in a heavily wooded region. Instead of a hot wire at the base to deter digging predators, he ran taut barbed wire along the ground a short distance out from the fence.

of their paddocks, install 8-foot (2.4-m) fences. Leading Australian breeders are content with 4-foot (1.2-m) fences with a hot wire at the base on the outside to discourage foxes, dogs, and dingoes. The discrepancy between recommended heights for perimeter fence can be attributed in part to the greater variety of capable predators in North America and to the greater tolerance toward wandering dogs in hobby farm settings near housing tracts where alpacas are often kept. In contrast, in stock-raising areas in Australia, unescorted dogs seen in the vicinity of stock are often destroyed on sight. Dingoes, the most capable predator in Australia, are not much of a threat because most alpacas are farmed south of the "dingo fence" that protects the primary stock-growing areas in the states of New South Wales, Victoria, and South Australia. Dogs or foxes preying on young are the primary threats.[*]

Dog-proofing the Perimeter Fence First, a fence must be high enough and strong enough to prevent dogs from going through or over it—this is relatively easy to accomplish. Stopping animals from going under a fence is a little more challenging, but there are many ways to combat digging. Some of the time-tested digging deterrents are trenching and burying the bottom 12 inches (30 cm) of the fence; installing an electric wire along the bottom; or fixing a taut strand of barbed wire to the ground 8 inches (20 cm) outside the fence. The barbed-wire and hot-wire options are inexpensive and effective. Unfortunately, any child or adult walking barefoot is vulnerable to barbed wire. Electric wire and pets don't mix well either.

Burying a wire-mesh "apron" that is attached to the bottom of the fence is probably the most labor-intensive and expensive method to dog-proof a fence—but it is also the most foolproof. Zoos and animal parks sometimes incorporate aprons. The dirt around the exterior of a mesh fence is scraped away to a depth of 6 to 12 inches (15–30 cm) for a width of 24 to 36 inches (60–90 cm). Rust-resistant, heavy-gauge mesh the width of the trench is unrolled the length of the excavated area along the fence. Before the trench is backfilled, the apron is fastened to the bottom of the fence at 3-foot (90-cm) intervals. The advantages of an apron are that it is neither visible nor hazardous but it stymies the most persistent digging canine. Aprons are also often effective in keeping out badgers, skunks, and other burrowing animals. Sometimes burrowing animals that do not pose a predatory threat will dig a hole under a fence that is used later by a dog or coyote. It is a wise policy to inspect fence lines regularly.[**]

---

[*]Roger Haldane, personal communication, July 4, 1994.

[**]Lutz Ruhe, third-generation exotic animal dealer and former director of Happy Hollow Zoo, personal communication, San Jose, California, May 1994.

Catch pens are an important feature in an alpaca operation. Alpacas fed in a catch pen are easy to catch.

Minimum Requirements for an Internal Fence The primary objective for internal fencing (cross fencing) is to separate groups of alpacas from one another in a safe and effective manner. Fencing that is inadequate for perimeter fencing may be adequate for internal fencing. For such fences, 44 inches (1.1 m) is usually high enough. Materials used to construct internal fencing can be different from those used in perimeter fences.

Capture pens (called catch pens), quarantine areas, and birthing areas have extra fencing requirements. Pens for males may require reinforced fencing. Neonates may roll or squirm under a bottom rail into the next pen, so fences must be modified by adding mesh. A cria separated from its mother due to a poorly thought-out fence can result in tragedy. In its initial hours a neonate needs all the nourishment its mother provides. A baby that is separated and misses initial feedings is shortchanged in colostrum (first milk), which contains critical disease-fighting antibodies. A baby separated by a barrier is vulnerable to predators, stress, illness, and starvation.

Catch Pens Most alpacas avoid human contact and are difficult to capture in large pens. A *catch pen* is a small enclosure where animals are lured by food or herded so they can be caught and handled. Catch pens are an essential feature to all alpaca operations, and their size, shape, and materials often make the difference between safe and unsafe capture situations. Capture-type containment where animals are handled must be behind an escape-proof and injury-free fence. With rail fencing, in which the horizontal boards are far enough apart for an alpaca to squeeze through, alpacas will attempt to escape by writhing between the rails. An alpaca escaping in this manner stands a good chance of landing squarely on its neck on the other side of the fence. In such situations risk of injury is high, especially for juvenile animals, who are more willing than most adults to endanger themselves recklessly.

Therefore, a catch pen made solely of corral boards spaced in the usual manner needs to be augmented with mesh, such as 2 × 4-inch (4.1 × 10.2-cm) no-climb or comparable type mesh. Catch pens should be 5 feet (1.5 m) high. Though alpacas rarely jump, the catch pen is where they are most likely to try. A popular catch pen construction consists of a single horizontal board connected to each post running at the top of a 5-foot (1.5-m) no-climb fence.

Field fencing is not the appropriate material for catch pens. In the tight quarters of a catch pen an alpaca may elect to push its head and neck through holes in the field fence, while other animals careen around the pen smashing into the sides of the stationary animal whose neck is held snugly on all sides by wire mesh. If a fast-moving group of alpacas smashes into an animal whose neck is literally sandwiched between two wires, the consequences could be fatal.

The shape and size of a catch pen are somewhat contingent on the number of animals destined to use it at one time. Long (30-ft; 9-m), narrow (10-ft; 3-m), rectangular-shaped catch pens accommodate different-sized groups of alpacas nicely. For a small group, a pen 10 × 10 feet (3 × 3 m) does nicely. Also, a long, narrow pen partitioned with a gate or portable corral at the midway point allows the pen to be used as a sorting pen as well as a catch pen. The length can be variable but the 10-foot (3-m) width is important to maintain. Some breeders even prefer 8 feet (2.4 m) because this distance is narrow enough for one person to catch and sort through a group of alpacas without difficulty. Guiding an animal into a corner with outstretched hands and slow movements works best. Catch pens that are too wide or circular in shape defeat the purpose of a catch pen, which is the easy capture of alpacas.

Of course, alpacas that are familiar with people will not normally careen around a catch pen. Stress is reduced and reaction to handling is relaxed for both alpaca and handler if the time has been taken to tame the alpacas.

Alpacas fed in catch pens on a fairly regular basis are easy to capture. Simply put the food in the catch pen, wait for them to enter it, shut the gate behind them, and they're

Oregon alpaca breeder Susan Stackhouse demonstrates the ease of moving an animal from one pen to another via corridors.

yours to handle. Catch pens with one or more walls facing the direction of incoming weather and either partially or entirely covered with a roof can double as a stall and protect alpacas in inclement weather.

Quarantine Pens Quarantine is an important husbandry concept and a term well known to animal importers and government agencies entrusted with safeguarding a nation's livestock businesses. In large regions throughout the world, including North America, animal businesses have been wiped out because of the failure to properly quarantine disease-carrying animals. International borders are often strictly controlled in attempts to block the movement of diseases that could affect multimillion-dollar animal industries. The outbreak in 2001 of foot-and-mouth disease in the United Kingdom, and the ensuing government-ordered destruction of all ruminants (including more than 150 alpacas) in the affected regions, poignantly illustrates the importance of quarantine and the consequences when a deadly disease is not contained.*

Alpacas are part of the international livestock business. There is much rhetoric in various alpaca/llama journals

---

*Anonymous USDA veterinarian, personal communication, Hyattsville, Massachusetts, May 15, 2001.

about the dangers of diseases being brought to North America, Australia, and European countries from South America. Ironically, while governments are pressured to maintain high standards for importing alpacas and llamas, precautions directed at the safe movement of alpacas inside the borders of these alpaca-importing countries are often alarmingly casual. Many farms have no quarantine procedures whatsoever for inbound animals from other farms or even overseas locations. Yet moving alpacas (or any form of livestock) from one farm to the next is a primary means of disease transmission, despite stringent adherence to government disease-testing requirements. Each farm's policy should include a quarantine for a minimum of 15 days with any inbound animals. The quarantined animals should be set aside in a pen that does not share a common fence with alpacas already in residence. Ideally, quarantine pens should also be located downhill or far apart from resident animals so that the urine and fecal matter from newly arrived animals do not find their way into paddocks of resident alpacas. Farms offering stud service to alpacas from other farms need to carefully consider how their stud service can best be managed without increasing disease risk to the resident herd.

Birthing Pens Birthing is the magic moment when husbandry practices literally bear the fruit of the year's efforts. To minimize risks if a problem birth should occur, many breeders set aside a pen for late-term females. Usually this pen is in view of the house or another place people frequent, so the onset of labor and birth can be carefully monitored. Often, problem births that might have resulted in a dead baby are successful solely because of the vigilance of owners and managers who intercede and assist. Birthing areas should be especially secure, with fencing designed so a baby can't squeeze under a fence rail and become separated from its mother. No-climb wire is the fencing of choice for birthing areas. A special effort should be made to keep birthing pens clean and preferably unpopulated or only lightly populated most of the year. This will decrease the likelihood of a buildup of deadly bacteria such as *Clostridium perfringens* type A and other diseases related to high densities. Avoid the use of alpaca manure fertilizer in this pen.[26,34]

Susan Stackhouse, a pioneer alpaca breeder in North America, sets aside a small pen with pasture adjacent to the paddock housing late-term females. When a birth occurs, she moves the mother and neonate to the empty pen (with close physical visual contact to the birthing herd):

> I find the use of a separate pen helps a mother and cria in the cria's first two or three days of life. The separation from the herd, but with herd near and

entirely visible, allows the mother to feel secure and bond to her cria without hassles with other females and interruptions to the cria's attempts to nurse. Separation from the herd allows the mother to eat without competition from other females, which is important to the mother's health when she is young and not well established in the herd's pecking order.*

Other breeders don't isolate a female and her newborn in this manner, but move them into an enclosure with just a few animals, so the mother and cria can establish nursing and bond successfully. If there are too many animals, they may continually interfere out of curiosity, or older crias may attempt to nurse from the newborn's mother, getting in the way of the baby's critical first efforts to nurse. Both Stackhouse's approach and reducing the numbers in a birthing pen address the need to allow the bonding and initial nursing to take place in optimum conditions. Neither of these approaches should be confused with taking a mother and newborn from the herd to an entirely new environment where the mother is deprived visual contact of the herd. Isolation of this type may be detrimental to both the mother and newborn. Some mothers react badly to being moved and isolated, and begin pacing and obsessing so much that they neglect their cria's needs. Taking the time to assess a mother's reaction to your post-parturition housing arrangement is warranted. You'll find differences from one mother to the next.

The ideal birthing pen is relatively level pasture, free of hazards, with plenty of shade during the warm months and sunlight during the winter. The pen's environment should offer a buffer against extremes in weather, with access to housing suitable for a mother and baby during inclement weather. Earlier comments about maternal stress due to total isolation after giving birth also apply to late-term mothers. If they are moved to a birthing pen they should not be isolated from visual contact with the herd. Visual (and on rare occasions physical) isolation will often cause unwanted stress in a mother whose pregnancy is already causing enough stress. It is preferable that expectant mothers share the pen with at least one other alpaca or have visual contact and a common fence with other members of the herd.

Movable Panels and Portable Fences Every alpaca farm should have a stash of movable, lightweight, easy-to-interconnect fence panels, which allow a manager to construct temporary catch pens, quarantine areas, holding pens for shearing, showing pens, and aisles between pens, without going to the trouble and expense of building additional

---

*Susan Stackhouse, personal communcation, Terrebonne, Oregon, June, 2002.

Portable fencing panels are indispensable. They can be used to construct a catch pen or exhibit pen, and come in handy when traveling. Jon Robbins of Esparto, California, made the lightweight panels shown here. Several manufacturers in North America have designed lightweight panels specifically for alpacas.

pens. Many kinds of movable panels are sold. The heavy-duty panels necessary for cattle and horses are often unnecessarily strong, weighty, cumbersome, and expensive for alpacas. For alpacas, a tubular construction of lightweight steel or aluminum with 9-inch (23-cm) spaces between horizontal bars is adequate.

Stevens Llama Tique in Minnesota makes a 4-foot, 6-inch × 9-foot (1.4 × 2.6-m) custom panel that fulfills the requirements for safe alpaca containment: lightweight with horizontal bars spaced relatively close together. The panels interlock easily and require no bolts, rope, or wire. These panels are often fashioned into semipermanent enclosures. A person working alone can construct a catch pen suitable for 20 alpacas in a matter of minutes. The panels are easy to transport on car roofrack or in a small pickup truck.

Hog panels are another popular panel used for pen building. The most commonly sold hog panel measures 16 feet, 5 inches (5 m) in length and about 4 feet (1.4 m) in height. These panels are made of solid ¼-inch thick (.6 cm) rebar-type metal rods that are welded in a vertical and horizontal field fence-type grid configuration. The panels bend enough to fasten together in a circle as well as a square or rectangle. They are practically indestructible. The primary drawbacks are weight and difficulty of transport (because of the length and flexibility of each panel). Also, alpacas can stick their heads through the upper part of the panels, inviting some risk should an animal get its neck or head stuck.

TYPES OF FENCES

In a survey of alpaca operations in North America and Australia, the following fence types were in use: stone masonry, wooden rail and picket type, multistrand wire (barbless), New Zealand high-tensile fencing (electric and nonelectric), and a wide assortment of wire mesh material. Of these fences, some are predator-proof and others can be modified to be predator-proof.

Fence Posts and Installation

Fencing should be carefully selected and installed properly. This seems obvious enough, but I have seen numerous examples of expensive fencing material installed improperly and utilized carelessly. Each fence design and the materials for its construction must be used according to the manufacturer's recommendations.

Wooden posts must be made of rot-resistant wood, such as redwood, or treated with preservatives that resist dry rot and wood-devouring insects. There are great differences in quality and longevity between posts in the same general price range. It pays to ask questions about the comparative differences in types of posts. You may find yourself pondering using standard 4 × 4-inch (10.2 × 10.2-cm) square-ended posts or 4-inch (10.2-cm) or 6-inch (15.4-cm) round posts, possibly treated with different kinds of preservatives. Generally, the thicker the wooden post and the deeper the preservative penetration, the longer the post will last. A correctly prepared post will last 20 years, a poorly prepared post may not last a year. Or you can use metal or composite material posts.

Unfortunately, quality control in manufacturing wooden fence posts is generally lax. Therefore, there may be subtle but important differences between two posts that appear the same. For example, dry wood absorbs a preservative more readily, allowing it to penetrate deeper and better protect a post. A post must cure before it is subjected to preservatives. Freshly milled posts (made of "green" wood, still full of water from being part of a tree) will not absorb preservatives as well. Consequently, when a green post dries, wood-devouring bugs and dry rot will appear in the cracks, and the post will deteriorate rapidly. When shopping for posts, ask how the posts were processed, and lift and inspect a few posts lying in the yard. If they seem lightweight and straight, they are probably a good bet. If they are unusually heavy, cracked, or warped, shop elsewhere—these signs tell you that the posts are full of water and were probably processed too soon after milling.

Treated fence posts are sometimes soaked in fairly potent solutions, possibly containing toxins (such as arsenic) that act as pesticides. You may want to compare this aspect of selecting posts as well. Always wear gloves when handling and installing treated posts. The likelihood of an alpaca (a species with no incisors on the top mandible) chewing off enough of a treated post to poison itself is fairly low.* If chewing preservative-soaked posts becomes a concern, painting the posts with a unleaded-based paint will create a protective barrier.

The distance between posts depends on the fencing material (tensile wire, corral boards, mesh, etc.) selected. For example, standard corral board comes in 16-foot (4.8-m) lengths, and a post is placed every 8 feet (2.4 m). The postholes should be a minimum of 18 inches (46 cm) deep, deeper in soft soils. Corral board should be fixed to posts with #16 galvanized nails or 1.5-inch (3.8-cm) *dacrotized* wood screws designed for decking. (Dacrotized screws are a relatively new product with greater gripping power than nails and are easy to install with a cordless drill.) If a nail or screw is too short, the fence will fall apart as the wood dries and as the natural elements and activities of alpacas conspire to reveal the fence's structural inadequacies.

Wire mesh fences installed to T-posts must be connected to each post in at least three places by wire fasteners designed for mesh fencing. Generally with T-post and wire mesh fence systems, posts are spaced at 8- to 10-foot (2.4–3-m) intervals. Corner construction in wire and metal post fences requires extra reinforcing. Corners are typically made of reinforced wood posts, sufficiently strengthened to withstand the tension of a continually taut fence. Tautness throughout a fence is a key ingredient to a properly constructed wire fence of any kind. The tops of T-posts that are at or near the eye level of alpacas are sometimes sharp and jagged and can cause injury. To avoid this risk, attach smooth-finish "plastic caps" that are designed to snap to the tops of T-posts and protect animals from accidents.

Any bona fide fence installer knows how to construct an attractive, long-lasting fence, but installers not familiar with livestock may need a little coaching on dog-proofing the outermost fences and on which side of the post the fencing material belongs. As a general rule, the posts should be to the outside of the fence and the fencing material nailed, crimped, or otherwise fastened from the inside. This way alpacas pushing against a fence over a period of time can't force the fencing material away from the posts and destroy the fence's effectiveness. This installation is especially important in a catch pen and in corridors where animals congregate and push against a fence. With live-

stock on *both* sides of a fence, build the greatest strength to the side of tight confinement (such as aisleways) or to the side of the largest and strongest animals (aggressive males or cattle and other large species).

Wood and Plastic Rail Fencing

In North America rail fencing is probably the consensus favorite for historic and aesthetic reasons. In Kentucky horse farms, status is partially derived from the color of rail fences, white carrying more prestige than brown. Even without paint, rail fences date from before Abe Lincoln and are the storybook fences we learn to associate with a beautiful ranch or agricultural property. Aesthetics, history, and status aside, rail fencing without augmentation of wire mesh is not dog-proof. In most situations a determined dog can go under, through, and over (the rails act as rungs in a ladder). Rail fences, particularly when constructed from green wood that will dry rapidly in the sun, sometimes split and splinter along the edges, creating dangerous skewerlike splinters that may puncture and break off in an alpaca rubbing on a fence or sliding its neck through an opening to eat grass on the other side of the fence. Wooden rail fences require more maintenance than most kinds of mesh and strand wire fences because of dry rot, termite infestations, weathering, and the need for a protective coating. Some alpaca breeders use rail fences throughout their property to fulfill their aesthetic needs, but augment the perimeter fence by fixing dog-proof mesh to it and raising the height to at least 5 feet (1.5 m).

Standard corral fencing boards come in a uniform dimension of 1 × 6 inches wide and 16 feet long (2.5 × 15.2 cm × 4.8 m). With these dimensions, placing the top board at 44 inches (1.1 m) leaves equal spaces roughly 9 inches (22.8 cm) high between each of three of the boards. A 9-inch (23-cm) space between rails is usually narrow enough to stop young animals from squeezing between boards, though a neonate may still find a way. At 48 inches (1.2 m) or higher, the height distance between boards is about 10 inches (25.4 cm), which is too wide to contain young animals without adding mesh. Wooden rail fencing should be installed with the posts on the outside and the rails on the inside.

Plastic rail fences that look like wood are popular at some high-rent horse operations. This relatively new material is a successful attempt to create the appearance of a traditional wooden fence while eliminating the need for maintenance. Plastic fences, made of PVC pipe material in the shape of boards and posts, don't need painting, won't rot, and won't splinter. However, for predator control they are no more effective than wooden fences and although maintenance free, they are expensive. For alpacas, plastic

---

*Lud McCrary, owner of Big Creek Lumber Company, personal communication, Davenport, California, August 15, 1994.

A gate latch needs to be loose enough to allow for subtle changes in the gate's alignment, but designed well enough not to unlatch on its own.

New Zealand fencing is easily tightened and can be electrified.

Vinyl fencing is expensive, popular, and good-looking. As a perimeter fence the configuration shown above is *entirely inadequate*. Predators can easily enter and alpacas cannot escape. This kind of fence is adequate for cross fencing or internal fencing in both vinyl or corral board. If mesh is laid on the fence it is then dog-proofed.

Corral board fencing is attractive and adequate for internal fencing.

fence is an adequate internal fencing if designed in the three- and four-rail configurations used in horse operations. Even so, there is usually enough space under the bottom rail for a cria or small adult to wiggle under. Some plastic fencing is designed to allow flexibility in rail placement so the needs of different kinds of livestock can be more adequately addressed. For young alpacas, rails placed no farther apart than every 9 inches (23 cm) is best. As perimeter fencing, both 4-foot-high (1.2-m-high) wooden and plastic rail fences must be modified by adding both height and mesh or strand wire to adequately protect against predators.

Wire Mesh Fencing

When it comes to alpacas, the fences that offer the most protection are various kinds of wire mesh fences. In this discussion, we define mesh as wire woven in patterns too small for an alpaca to push its head or limbs through. This excludes field fencing (see next section).

Mesh wire is a popular fencing material among alpaca owners in North America. The gauge of the wire and the narrow spaces between the strands assure a high degree of safety without need for alterations. Generally, the heavier the gauge and the tighter the mesh, the greater the safety.

No-climb fencing (sold under copyrighted names such as *Stablemesh* and *Non-climb*) is perhaps the most popular perimeter fencing material in U.S. alpaca operations.[2] No-climb usually comes in 100-foot (30-m) rolls of 12.5 gauge with spaces between wires in a 2 × 4-inch (5.1 × 10.2-cm) mesh configuration. This gauge and design offer optimum safety, strength, and height for alpacas. The joints of the best no-climb material are held together with tied wire knots (or stiff stays) of heavy gauge wire, rather than being welded. It is often marketed as "stable-mesh stiff-stay horse fence" and is advertised in a 2 × 4-inch (5.1 × 10.2-cm) V or rectangular pattern that will not allow a horse's hoof to get caught. These designations do not necessarily mean the product is bound together by knotted wire or is 12.5 gauge. If you are ordering material by phone or from a catalogue, keep in mind that the 2 × 4-inch (5.1 × 10.2-cm) woven wire is what you want. Canine predators have great difficulty climbing 2 × 4-inch (5.1 × 10.2-cm) wire, and the 12.5 gauge strength means gnawing or pawing will have no effect.

No-climb held together by knotted wire joints is flexible enough to conform to gradual irregularities in the terrain without losing form and, under most circumstances, will last 20 years or longer. No-climb comes in 4-foot (1.2-m), 5-foot (1.5-m), and 6-foot (1.8-m) heights. Naturally, the taller a mesh fence, the more expensive it is. Most other kinds of field fencing come in a maximum 4-foot

(1.2-m) height, which necessitates adding two or more strands of barbless wire to the top of the fence in order to reach the minimum safe perimeter height of 5 feet (1.5 m).

No-climb 2 × 4-inch (5.1 × 10.2-cm) fencing comes in a less expensive welded wire form, where the joints are welded rather than held together by knotted wire. Welded wire is less flexible than woven knotted wire, and welded wire (even 12.5 gauge) tends to rust at the joints, causing the fence to need replacing more often than woven knotted wire. Given a choice of 12.5 gauge no-climb 2 × 4-inch (5.1 × 10.2-cm) mesh, select the knotted wire joints, not the welded. Light-gauge welded wire meshes are also advertised for stock use, but these are usually short-lived and deteriorate rapidly.[4]*

Field Fencing

Field fencing, which is sometimes called hog wire or sheep fence, is a popular and economical mesh fence that usually comes in a 4-foot (1.2-m) height but can be bought at 5 feet (1.5 m). The fencing material of choice throughout much of the sheep business, it is usually lighter gauge than no-climb and the distance between stays is considerably greater. One of the more popular field fencing configurations is 5 × 11 inches (12.7 × 27.9 cm) at the bottom of the fence and 19 × 11 inches (22.8 × 27.9 cm) at the top. Some field fences have uniform 6 × 6-inch (15.2 × 15.2-cm) squares.

Field fencing works best when it is kept in a taut state and its topmost wire is stapled to a wooden top rail that is nailed from one post to the next at the most common 4-foot (1.2-m) height. To achieve the necessary 5 to 6 feet (1.5–1.8 m) for a perimeter fence, string two or three strands of barbless wire above the top rail. By stapling the fencing to posts and the top rail, it will keep its tight shape and not sag.

Field fencing is more economical to purchase and easier to install than no-climb. It also conforms to terrain more readily. Its most significant drawback is that alpacas can put their heads and necks through its spacious holes, which can lead to serious accidents. A second drawback is that small animals such as raccoons, skunks, possums, and wood rats can easily move through a field fence.

Most manufacturers adhere to high standards of quality control to make the wire joints binding the field fencing consistently safe and snareproof. However, improper installation, defective joints, and wear and tear on a fence that animals continually press against sometimes cause wire joints to loosen and pull apart. This increases the

---

*Renee D'Onoforio, employee of Davis Wire Corporation, personal communication, Hayward, Califorinia, July 6, 1994.

potential for accidents. Any joint that becomes loose can entrap alpacas in field fencing. If an alpaca can't or won't pull itself free, panic, illness, injury, and death can result.

In these unfortunate occurrences, the victim is found oddly contorted with its neck bent back through the fence. Why would an alpaca inexplicably bend its neck through the same fence twice? A likely scenario is as follows: The alpaca sees greener grass on the other side and pushes through the fence until its neck is fully extended. Suddenly the alpaca gets an impulse to scratch its hindquarters, which it does by bending its long supple neck toward its rear, where it employs its incisors to scratch itself. Scratching in this manner is a reflex reaction in alpacas. Instead of backing away and pulling its head back through the fence before scratching itself, the alpaca makes the fatal mistake of attempting to reach back through the fence. With its head and neck bent through the fence a second time, it suddenly finds it can't draw its neck forward again because it is wedged and held fast between the fence's wire stays. With its head twisted back and neck bent in a severe lateral arch, the alpaca struggles to free itself and loses its balance. The weight of its own body in the ensuing struggle breaks its neck or strangles it. This type of accident is probably more likely to happen on a steep hill with loose footing than on a flat area. Recounting this sequence of events shouldn't be interpreted as a total condemnation of field fencing. Many alpaca operations have used field fencing for years without an incident. However, field fencing must be viewed cautiously when used with alpacas—safer kinds of fencing are available.

Electric Fencing

Electrifying one or more strands of wire as a deterrent to predators is an option that can be exercised with any fencing scheme. With high-tensile New Zealand-style systems, electrifying is accomplished easily by merely adding insulators to designated strands while the fence is being installed. The insulator encompasses the bare wire wherever it touches a post. With other types of fences, hot wires can be added after the fence is constructed. Manufacturers have created dozens of styles of insulators that can be nailed or attached to wooden and wire fences. Typically, insulators and a wire are attached to the outside of a fence near the bottom and another one near or at the top.

Numerous types of electric systems are on the market and can energize from 3 to 100 miles (5–160 km) of wire. Systems vary in voltage, safety features, and cost. Some systems rely on a 120-volt power source; others rely on a combination of 120-volt direct current and battery; and others are solely battery powered or a combination of battery and solar powered. Premier of Washington, Iowa,

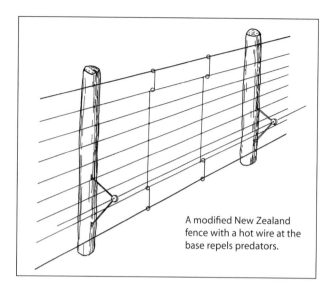

A modified New Zealand fence with a hot wire at the base repels predators.

Fi-Shock Inc. of Knoxville, Tennessee, and North Central Plastics Inc. (Red Snap'r) of Ellendale, Minnesota, are three leading companies in this field. Their catalogues describe a broad range of electric fence systems and accessories. Of this group of companies, Premier is well established in New Zealand and Australia.[6,7,14]

Plenty of livestock people are strong supporters of electric fences. With cattle, horses, hogs, and many exotic animals, electric fencing helps contain them. Electric fencing isn't needed to contain alpacas, but it does offer them added protection. A dog putting his wet snout on a pulsating 60 to 5,000 volts will never forget it. A dog coming into contact with a relatively high-voltage fence will writhe on the ground and whine loudly in obvious pain.

Electricity is a successful deterrent, but it is wise to carefully assess its potential advantages and drawbacks. In wooded areas fallen twigs and branches can interrupt the electrical current, shorting it and rendering the fence ineffective until the problem is fixed. Grass growing into a wire will short-circuit some systems, as will snowfall that buries a wire. With many electric fence systems, hot wires must be policed, especially during and after storms. Power outages, especially ones that occur when you're away from your farm, can leave your herd unguarded for long periods of time, if a battery component is not fully charged and functioning. Electric fences have also been known to start grass fires, though this is relatively rare.

Lastly, there have been a few reports of alpacas reacting badly when coming in contact with electrified fences. Generally, alpacas learn to stay away, but in one case a pregnant female attempting to nibble grasses on the other side of the fence pushed apart two high-tensile wires, one of which was electrified. The animal appeared paralyzed by her predicament and lay down screaming as the electric shock pulsed through her. The owner turned the power off and had to physically pull the animal from the fence. The same owner claims to have seen a female urinating on a fence while standing in water knocked off her feet when her stream of urine hit a hot wire. Neither animal exhibited long-lasting effects.* However, incidents such as these explain why many experienced stock people put the electric wire outside the fence, not inside. Always keep in mind that a hot wire anywhere on your property will make quite an impression on the family dog, cat, customer, or child.

High-tensile Fencing

High-tensile fencing, which is known as New Zealand fencing because the concept originated in sheep operations there, is a popular and economical form of fencing. Alpaca owners in North America, Australia, and New Zealand will usually eagerly point out that properly installed New Zealand fencing fulfills all the requirements of both perimeter and internal fencing at a relatively low cost.

Maintaining high tension is the key to the fence's integrity and requires periodic tightening of strands, which can be done with a simple wrenchlike mechanical device. Individual lines can be electrified to discourage predators, but this can be hard on family pets, small children, and the forgetful owner.

Spacing of the wire and the height of the fence are decided by the installer after consulting with the client, allowing the client a great deal of flexibility to tailor a fence to specific needs. If you are a do-it-yourselfer, proper installation is mandatory for the fence to work as it should. Strands should be spaced 4 to 6 inches (10.2 to 15.5 cm) apart at the bottom and farther apart higher up on the fence. Fence posts (especially at the corners) must be properly secured so that they can withstand the tension of a half dozen or more wires kept forever taut. Loose strands or strands placed too far apart defeat the fence's predator-deterring qualities. Insulators must be used for the wires that will later be electrified.[5,6,7,12,14]

Modified High-tensile Fencing

Roger and Clyde Haldane, the pioneering forces in alpacas in Australia, prefer a modified high-tensile fence in which the bottom and top wire are single strands of high-tensile wire. The 4-foot (1.2-m) space in between is filled with 7-line ring-lock fence, which is fastened to the high-tensile wires with clips. To deter dogs and foxes, an electrified high-tensile wire is added to the outside of the fence at a distance of 12 inches (30 cm) and about 12 inches (30 cm) above the ground. The wire is out of reach of alpacas but at the ready for predators who may try to push or dig under the fence. The 12 inches (30 cm) of clearance from the ground minimizes contact with vegetation, which may divert the electrical current. This fence is easily assembled and disassembled.**

Chain-link Fencing

Chain-link fencing will last indefinitely and repel the most fearsome predator, but it is expensive, highly visible, and not as easily combined with rail fencing as no-climb. No-climb is just as effective as chain-link but less visible and less expensive. Zoos commonly use chain-link for their biggest and strongest animals. In large veldtlike settings, the fence is often set several feet deep into the soil to prevent tunneling. Chain-link is now made in several colors besides the commonly seen steel gray. In settings with bountiful green foliage, black is the least obtrusive to the eye.

WATERERS

Alpacas need a constant source of water. Unlike their dromedary and bactrian camel relatives, alpacas have no special adaptations to survive long periods without water. Clean water should be available at all times.

The location of the water source should be easily accessible for alpacas and for the person charged with daily management. Water sources should be visually inspected daily, even if the source is fully automatic. The placement of a water source is important: It should be protected from excessive sunlight so the water doesn't overheat, and it must be protected against freezing conditions or snow levels that isolate it from alpacas. Water sources for alpacas generally fall into three categories: automatic, manual, and natural.

Automatic Waterers

Automatic waterers come in many shapes and sizes. Not all automatic waterers are appropriate for alpacas. For instance, automatic waterers in which an animal must push, nudge, suck, or paw to produce water will not work with alpacas, even though they work well with hogs, dogs, and other animals with different habits and predispositions than alpacas. With alpacas the automatic waterer must have a float valve or weight balance mechanism that regulates and replenishes the water level after drinking or evaporation.

---

*Arnie Feldsher, retired alpaca farmer, personal communication, Healdsburg, California, February 10, 1992.

**Roger Haldane, personal communication, July 4, 1994.

The generic, smallish, wall-mounted float-waterer is probably the most popular automatic waterer used by alpaca breeders in North America. This form of waterer is also popular with horse, cattle, and sheep operations. Though dimensions and names are slightly different from one manufacturer to the next, this waterer measures roughly 10 × 10 × 4 inches (25 × 25 × 10 cm) and holds about one-half gallon (1.9 l) of water. The Farnam Companies of Phoenix, Arizona, one of the largest manufacturers in the United States, makes the Floater Automatic, which is simply constructed and reliable. Designed to be hooked up to either common plumbing fixtures or a garden hose, it can be attached to a vertical surface (fence post, wall, etc.) at any height. Little Giant, another well-known farm supply manufacturer, makes the Dura-Mate, which has a larger holding tank (approximately 2 gallons (7.6 l) than Farnam's Floater Automatic. Like the Floater Automatic, Dura-Mate is designed to hang on a fence or wall. The Dura-Mate is less apt to freeze solid in mild winter areas and stores more water, but it is more time-consuming to clean than the Floater Automatic. Also, the Dura-Mate is relatively heavy to be supported by a fence board or unsecured post not set in concrete. Regardless of the brand name and varying dimensions, a small waterer should be placed approximately 20 inches (50 cm) above the ground. This height is low enough to allow crias access and is high enough to keep adults from obliviously contaminating their water by putting their feet in it to cool off.[2,3,5,9,10,11,12]

The small size of these waterers makes them easy to clean. Such waterers are well suited for crowded holding areas and a small amount of space. Under most circumstances properly installed float-waterers require little, if any, maintenance besides cleaning. Cleaning usually takes two forms: removing hay dropped in the water by alpacas and sponging the sides of the bowl to remove algae and bacteria. In cold months sticking your hand in the water to remove submerged hay isn't a pleasant experience—using a small aquarium fish net works well. In warmer months algae and bacteria can build up quickly. The shallow (4 inches; 10 cm), small-bowled waterers often double as birdbaths and in some instances result in a significant amount of bird droppings in the the drinking bowl! Birds or no birds, regular cleaning of waterers is warranted. Some breeders wash and scrub their waterers weekly with a coarse sponge. Others take things a step further and clean each waterer with bleach once weekly to get rid of bacteria. However, in most settings the buildup of harmful bacteria in a regularly cleaned waterer should not be a problem.

A few watering idiosyncrasies are worth mentioning. The smaller the bowl, the more apt the waterer is to freeze on cold nights. In regions where freezing temperatures

A steady supply of clean water is a necessity. This type of waterer is designed so that the flow is uninterrupted even in freezing weather.

may last through the day, small waterers need to be protected with water-warming devices. The small waterer's meager volume necessitates a backup source should the primary source of water fail, especially in situations in which a large number of animals are dependent on the waterer. Should the water source suddenly stop as a result of a power outage (in many rural areas electricity is vital because it drives submersible well pumps and heaters to prevent freezing) or broken pipe, the alpacas are without water until the problem is fixed. A lengthy power outage or difficult pipe repair can become a serious matter unless you have an auxiliary water source and enough buckets or containers to go around. Think through a backup plan for such events.

Clogged waterers are another potential problem. The valve that allows water into an automatic float-waterer may clog, stopping water from reaching the drinking bowl. Clogs are rare and usually occur after a pipe (that has waterers attached to it) is cut and repaired. The small plastic or metal flecks left in a pipe migrate to the pin-sized valve's opening and clog it. Clogs may also occur when water contains sediments. It is common to find a clogged waterer a couple of times a year in a system with a dozen or so waterers. Early detection of clogged waterers by daily checking prevents undue stress and hardship to the alpacas. To unclog a waterer, just remove the float guard and push a wire into the entry hole.

Float-waterers can also cease to function or malfunction after freezing, which can damage or reset the float. The float's adjustment regulates the inflow of water and the level of water in the bowl. An improperly set float can result in a waterer that constantly overflows or one that lets in an insufficient amount of water or none at all. Once the float is adjusted, the nut holding the float in place must be tightened sufficiently to prevent it from resetting itself. Sometimes the problem is the fence post to which the waterer is attached—it begins leaning or an alpaca's repeated pawing causes the waterer to pull away from the post and tilt. The waterer will then run continually regardless of attempts to adjust the float. The larger capacity wall- or fence-mounted automatic waterers (such as the 2-gallon (7.6-l) Dura-Mate, tend to pull over a light fence because of the weight of the water in the bowl. An automatic float-type waterer must be attached to an absolutely vertical surface to function optimally. Each waterer should have its own turn-off valve (preferably a ball valve, not a gate valve), so that if a waterer is out of use, needs cleaning, or needs repairs, it can be turned off independently of the rest of the watering system.

Automatic float-type waterers are made of either heavy plastic or galvanized steel. In areas where the pH of water is acidic, the steel waterers tend to rust and need replacing. Plastic waterers don't rust but may become brittle after years of constant sun. Some brands are made of black plastic, and the water in them readily absorbs sunlight and can become too hot to drink if the waterer is placed in direct sunlight. Under most circumstances waterers of all kinds serve animals better if they are situated in a shady area.

Other popular float-waterers are created by buying a float valve that can be attached to a container of your choice. Typically these valves are fastened to stock tanks, which sit on the ground and usually come in rectangular shapes. Most stock tanks stand 24 inches (61 cm) in height. Stock tanks have been used in cattle and horse businesses for decades and are usually made with 20- or 22-gauge, zinc-coated, galvanized bottoms. In recent years fiberglass and plastic stock tanks have been available in sizes and shapes similar to the time-tested galvanized tanks. Acidic water (with a pH of 6 or less) eats away at the galvanized tanks, but not plastic or rubber. Most stock tanks have a drain plug. All true stock tanks should have a rounded lip with no sharp edges. The dimensions of the rectangular tanks are 2 feet (61 cm) wide and 2 feet (61 cm) deep, and up to 10 feet (3 m) long. Capacity ranges between 70 and 700 gallons (265–2,650 l). A number of manufacturers make a sheep tank, which is only 1 foot (30 cm) deep, but this is not recommended for alpacas.[2,3,5,9,10,11,12]

The obvious advantage of stock tanks is their capacity to sustain a group of animals for several days, should water flow be interrupted. The greater volume also means water will heat up and cool off more gradually, reducing the chances of water being too hot to drink or freezing. The disadvantage is that tanks at ground level are inviting to alpacas who want to cool themselves during hot weather, especially sheep tanks only 1 foot (30 cm) deep. It would be the rare alpaca who would pass up the opportunity to step into such a tank on a hot day. (Alpacas are less apt to step into a 2-foot (.6-m) tank.) Alpacas standing in drinking water will often relieve themselves moments after their feet hit the water. Though it may look endearing to watch an alpaca climb into its water tank and sit down, it should be discouraged. There are other ways to give alpacas access to water for cooling themselves.

For cold-climate areas where deep freezes are common, several types of automatic waterers with built-in heaters are available. Many of the largest and longest-established farm suppliers carry a wide selection of these waterers with different bowl sizes, amounts of insulation, heights, installation requirements, and heaters. Some of these waterers are designed for hogs and calves and require the animal to either push with its snout or suck, which is not appropriate for alpacas. Brower, NASCO, Farnam, and Nelson are some of the better-known distributors and manufacturers of electricheated insulated waterers.[12] Floating and submersible electric heaters can also be placed in standard stock tanks.

Manual Waterers

From buckets to discarded bathtubs, a manual waterer is anything that holds water and must be filled by hand. If a discarded bathtub strikes your fancy, try to get a freestanding claw-footed tub. These old tubs have a rounded lip with no sharp edges, whereas more modern tubs often have sharp metal flanges that can cause injury.

Every herd has alpacas that will paw at a bucket to cool their feet. Sooner or later an unsecured bucket will be knocked over, putting an end to drinking water until it is righted and refilled. If a bucket is being used as a source of drinking water, it should be attached to a post or fence so it can't be up-ended. Some buckets are better suited for drinking water than others. A 20-quart (18.9-l) bucket with a flat back and a handle designed to hang from a wall bracket affords the greatest stability and versatility. The flat back is designed to fit snugly to a vertical flat surface or fence post and will not rotate if an alpaca rubs against it. Place an inexpensive wall bracket on the post so the lip of the bucket is at a height of 20 inches (50 cm), high enough to prevent an alpaca from putting its feet in the drinking water to cool off. A bucket should be big enough to supply a day's worth of water for every alpaca in a paddock. Many situations call for more than one bucket in order to disperse drinking activities and provide a sufficient amount of water. With more than a couple of alpacas, some breeders use 20-gallon plastic garbage cans, which are safe and the right height for drinking but not wading.

In freezing weather, water in buckets often freezes solid. Jim and Jan Faiks in Alaska reported that at −20°F (−29°C) a bucket of warm water freezes solid in about 2 hours. Water intake is important even in cold weather, and a strategy should be devised when freezing is a problem.

Natural Sources of Water

Vicuñas, guanacos, and many South American llamas and alpacas get their water from wet grasses, streams, and lakes. Wild camelids usually occur in fairly low densities and live in areas not heavily inundated by human activities. Water-fouling levels of bacteria and pollutants from crowded herd conditions and human activity are usually not a concern.

Alpacas, on the other hand, often live in tight quarters and high densities, and although they can generally use natural water sources with little risk of disease and drowning, there are some concerns. When alpacas have access to a pond or standing water, they will often congregate and stand in the water to cool off. While some animals are drinking, others are defecating and urinating, often directly next to each other. In such situations the chances of disease transmission are increased, especially if the pond is stagnant. Alpacas allowed to stand in water daily develop pronounced hair loss in areas that are submerged, giving the animals an odd shape and making their legs look abnormally thin and bony.

In ponds or lakes where alpacas have access to water deep enough to swim, access into and out of the water must be carefully assessed, particularly the angle and slipperiness of the slope under the surface. The slope should be gradual with no sudden drop-offs and no barriers to leaving the water. If a pond has dangerous entry and departure points, alpacas should be fenced out.

Alpacas readily drink from streams, and they will also wade and take to swimming on their own. Therefore, assuming a stream or river will act as a restraining barrier is erroneous. If the current is strong, access to a stream should be blocked. Streams and moving water carry waste away, but alpaca owners should consider the downstream effects of allowing their animals access.

FEEDERS

When I asked alpaca breeders in Peru about alpaca feeders, there was a short discussion followed by puzzled looks. Then there was another short discussion. Finally one grower pointed to miles of *ichu* grass, the mainstay of the alpaca diet on much of the *puna*. The translated answer conveyed the absurdity of the question in the South American context: "The alpacas eat grass. They don't need devices. They've always eaten this way." Probably none of these Peruvian breeders had seen alpacas outside their native puna. It's no wonder they thought the question sounded silly. But in North America, Australia, New Zealand, and Europe, alpacas are kept in a variety of environments. Some have unlimited pasture. Others rely on pasture part of the year and hay feed other parts of the year. Others are entirely kept in "dry lot" conditions (all feed is given to alpacas daily). Alpacas have been raised successfully in all of these settings. And in most of them, alpacas come in contact with feeders on a regular basis, either as the sole source of their daily food or as a source of supplemental pellet feed.

Since the South American setting for alpacas is not usually replicated elsewhere, the first important step toward a good feeder solution is the realization and commitment that there should be feeders. Generally, alpacas in North America, Australia, and Europe are kept in smaller areas than the herds of South America. Feeding alpacas on the ground, especially on small acreages, is not good husbandry. Rationalizing that it's okay to feed on the ground if the hay is placed far from manure piles is not valid. Alpacas walk on their food with the same feet that walk

Multiple feeders in a catch area allow the herd to disperse while eating.

FEEDERS

There are many feeder designs. The good ones do not allow an alpaca to ensnare its head or neck hair, minimize the loss of food, and can be utilized regardless of the weather.

The smooth plastic pipes used here safeguard animals from having their fiber caught on rough surfaces.

A catch pen, shed, and creep feeder all in one. A creep feeder (narrow openings) allows young animals to enter to eat, and keeps out pushy adults.

The large, roofed feeder can be approached from two sides. The horizontal bar makes it impossible for an alpaca to lift its head while feeding. This feature minimizes squabbles, which usually become full-fledged when alpacas lift their heads and square off.

Portable hay storage and feeder (12 × 18 ft) has the storage capacity for 5 tons of hay. Richard Guadian of Santa Cruz, California, makes this unit for both stationary and moveable use (by placing on skids). The feeders on both sides can accommodate 25 animals.

through the manure pile. In dry lot situations, bare soil may harbor bacteria populations that should not have direct contact with food. Feeding on the ground where alpacas and other livestock are housed also invites unnecessary exposure to a range of parasitic diseases. Manure, dirt, and feed don't mix, unless you're making compost outside the paddock.

According to the dictionary, a feeder is "a trough or vessel to supply stock and poultry in proper quantities without waste." There is no shortage of feeder designs and proponents for them. Regardless of design, all good feeders must meet certain conditions in order to serve alpacas well.

• The feeder should comfortably accommodate the number of alpacas dependent on it. Feeders should be in sufficient numbers and arranged to minimize jostling and hierarchical disputes. Occasional spats should be expected, but full-blown fights or the crowding out of young animals should not occur. One of the central objectives for managers should be to minimize stress by reducing crowded situations, and there's no more important place to pay attention to this axiom than the feeder, where animals must go for their nourishment.

• Feeders should be designed to reduce squabbles over food and diminish the likelihood of dominant alpacas monopolizing the feeder. Smallish round or square feeders, like the 4 × 4-foot (1.2 × 1.2-m) wooden feeders popular in the North American llama business, are acceptable if there are enough of them to allow the animals to spread themselves out. If the feeder's design forces alpacas to congregate around a focal point and eat while facing one another, squabbles are guaranteed. Drawing animals together in this manner is an unnatural feeding pattern—alpacas don't graze facing one another in a tight circle resembling a football huddle. If this pattern occurred in a pasture situation, threats would be exchanged, and alpacas would disperse or avoid the situation entirely. A small feeder that draws the animals together in this unnatural way reveals an owner's lack of understanding of alpaca behavior. Comments about alpacas' cantankerous nature at a hay rack should be interpreted by the manager as poor feeder design. In South America alpacas grazing in a large *bofadales* with seemingly limitless pasture seek a comfortable distance from the next nearest alpaca, often 10 feet (3 m) or more. Alpacas can adjust to close feeding situations, but their inclination to hierarchical struggles needs to be blunted. Lack of compatibility at the hay rack stresses the animals.

The best shape for feeders is long and narrow, allowing animals of lower rank to find a place some distance from the dominant alpacas. In a two-feeder situation, in which half the herd are yearlings, it's not surprising that the older animals congregate around the first feeder to receive hay while the younger animals rush to the second feeder. Maintaining two or more feeders in a paddock allows alpacas to sort themselves into compatible groupings.

Large feeders with vertical bars work well for 20 to 40 animals standing side by side. Attaching a horizontal bar across the vertical bars at about the height of an alpaca's withers forces alpacas to put their heads down to reach under the bar to get food. This subtle manipulation is thought to diminish aggressive behavior and allow more animals to fit at a crowded feeder,[21] since alpacas threaten one another most aggressively with their ear positioning and their heads held high. Spitting usually erupts from a head-held-high position. If alpacas can't pull their heads up to begin posturing, aggression usually doesn't escalate. Instead, warnings are reduced to mild grumblings and squeals. I have observed that alpacas eating from a hay feeder with a horizontal head bar sometimes bluff and threaten just prior to dropping their heads under the bar, but the presence of the bar seems to force even the most ornery alpaca to choose between confrontation and eating, and most opt for eating. The horizontal bar is usually nothing more than a 2 × 2-inch (5.1 by 5.1-cm) wooden board running the length of the feeder.

• Feeders must protect the food to maximize its utilization. Stationary feeders, planned for year-around use, must have a roof to fend off rain and snow. Portable feeders must be placed under cover if rain or snow is forecast. They should be lightweight enough for one person to move them or be designed to be pulled by a vehicle.

To prevent waste and extra cleanup chores, a feeder should be constructed so that all the food in it is entirely accessible. At the same time its construction should minimize an alpaca's tendency to pull hay from the feeder and spread it on the ground. The feeder should also hold pellets and grain as well as hay, in such a way that these supplements do not get spilled on the ground.[2,3,5,12]

Protection of food also means eliminating ways it can spoil. Feeders placed directly on the ground can absorb moisture after rains and allow bacteria and fungi to flourish. Air circulating around a feeder is a healthier approach.

• A feeder's design must put safety first. The feeder needs to be free of loose wire ends as well as nooks and crannies where an alpaca can get its head stuck. Construction materials must be used within recommended specifications. If grains or pellets are stored near or in a feeder, they must be out of reach of alpacas. Alpacas will overeat on grains and possibly become gravely ill.

The distance a feeder is placed above the ground has subtle safety ramifications. In the Andes alpacas graze and eat with their heads close to the ground, an eating position that has evolved over the centuries. An alpaca's body, most particularly its eyes and ears, is always above the eating surface—therefore, a feeder should be fairly near the ground. Somewhere between 8 and 20 inches (20 and 50 cm) allows all sizes of alpacas access to the feeder and also allows air under the feeder to keep it dry and free from ground moisture. Putting the feeder close to, but not on, the ground also discourages alpacas from standing or walking in their feed.

A feeder that is too high poses other problems. The most obvious problem is that the feeder may be out of reach of young animals, who begin eating within a day or two after birth. There is also increased risk of eye and ear injuries whenever a food source is above an alpaca's head. An alpaca eating from a hay feeder tends to burrow into the hay with its muzzle (often to find seeds that have fallen to the bottom of the feeder) until most of its head is submerged. The animal's large eyes are exposed to loose chaff and seeds, and its ears become potential receptacles for foxtails and debris. Debris-related eye and ear problems can also occur in grazing and with hay feeders that are close to the ground, but the likelihood increases when the food source is above the alpaca's head.[33] Designing a feeder along the lines suggested can be a creative and fun experience. Lastly, a feeder should be easily accessible to people, so it can be cleaned regularly with a minimum of hassle.

FOOD STORAGE

Food storage is a sometimes neglected aspect of alpaca husbandry. Feed should be stored in a dry, ventilated area protected from the alpacas and from other animals as much as possible. Alpacas will eat the bottom out of a large stack of hay, causing it to topple. They can also catch their necks in the baling wire or twine and strangle once they've eaten their way into a bound bale. Alpacas that get into "sweet feed" (crushed oats or barley) and other grain supplements will eat until they become very sick or even die.

Hay must be stored in a dry area, ideally with air circulating under, around, and over it. If hay is to be stored on the ground, placing it on pallets allows ventilation under it

Hay storage needs to be both well ventilated and entirely dry. Daily dispersal of hay requires time and effort that can be minimized by an efficient farm layout.

and protects it from ground moisture. Hay is best stored under a roof. If it is stored outside, it should be covered by a tarp when rain, snow, or fog is possible. However, covering hay with a tarp for prolonged periods can cause mold, so wooden 4 × 4-inch (10 × 10-cm) spacers should be placed on the hay at 4-foot intervals to allow air circulation, and the tarp should be secured in a way that allows air to move along the sides of the stack.

Easy access to the hay storage area is essential. The hay barn or storage area should be accessible to the large trucks that typically off-load hay. They use a "squeeze," which carries a "block" or 54 large bales (48 × 24 × 18 inches; 1.2 m × 61 cm × 45.7 cm) at a time. A barn or hay storage area should be easily accessible for a squeeze and contain no obstructions to driving a block to its storage place. Most squeezes carry a load 10 feet (3 m) high and 8 feet (2.4 m) wide, and need 11 feet (3.1 m) of vertical clearance to place a block in a barn. With different-sized bales, vertical clearance for a block may vary somewhat. If a barn is too difficult for a squeeze to reach or impossible to enter, the hay may have to be unloaded and stacked by hand, which is both labor-intensive and time-consuming. Squeezes are not stable on steep inclines, and many hay haulers will refuse to use one to deliver to a barn at the top or bottom of a steep hill. If you have a choice, hay storage should be designed for an entirely mechanized delivery. Loft areas are generally loaded with portable conveyer chutes or a block-and-tackle platform lowered and raised from the loft.

The ideal size of a storage area depends on the number of alpacas under your care and the seasonal availability of hay. Typically, hay is available for the best prices at harvest time each year, but climatic conditions can influence availability and prices. Ideally, purchasing all the hay you need for a year is best. This way you can analyze the single batch of hay, supplement if necessary, and provide a consistent year-round diet for your alpacas. If your storage area is inadequate, you will be forced to continually restock, and may have to turn to numerous sources of hay throughout the year. Multiple sources can result in an inconsistent nutritional program for your animals and greater expense for hay and analysis of hay.

Safeguarding supplemental foods against moisture and rodents is important, and can be easily done by using covered bins or plastic garbage cans for storage. Safeguarding this food against alpacas and other animals is equally as important. Supplemental feeds should be kept out of reach of animals, and the top of each container must be firmly latched or secured in a way that prevents alpacas and other animals, including rodents, from gaining entry. More than one alpaca has perished from gorging in a grain storage bin that was left open in an area to which alpacas had access.

COPING WITH HEAT

When and how to cool off an alpaca is a two-part question every alpaca owner should be able to answer. The correct answer and its practical application literally mean the difference between life and death to alpacas living in hot and humid regions of North America or to animals exposed to hot and humid spells in an otherwise moderate climate. Alpacas in apparent good health react differently to hot conditions—some animals are heat sensitive while others appear to be more tolerant. Crias and immature alpacas, with their small body mass, are more apt to be affected by severe conditions, be it hot or cold. Alpacas in their native Andes live in an environment of low humidity and temperatures that usually range between 29 and 70°F (−2 and 21°C), where it freezes most nights. By comparing these parameters to the annual averages and seasonal fluctuations in your area, you can determine how important combating high temperatures will be. In general, shearing, providing shade, and exposure to air currents is enough for most animals to withstand warm temperatures and relatively high humidity.

Heat Stress in Humid Conditions

In 1987, 59 llamas died from heat stress while undergoing a 90-day quarantine in the U.S. government's Harry S. Truman Animal Import Center in Key West, Florida.[1] A year later, the same importers scheduled a group of more than 200 alpacas for the same facility in the heat of sum-

An inexpensive toddler's wading pool works well to cool alpacas. Three alpacas can fit in a single pool at one time. Many animals will climb in and out of the pool in the course of the day.

Fans help cool animals.

mer when temperatures soar to over 90°F (32°C) with 95 percent humidity. David Pugh, DVM, and I were sent by the importers to Key West to meet with officials and to develop a protocol for coping with heat stress. Any time the combined temperature (Fahrenheit) and humidity (percent) exceeded 160, water would be turned on to cool the animals. This became known as the "80–80" rule: 80°F

A thermometer is essential to knowing when it is too hot or too cold. Know the acceptable tolerance and have a plan for when excessive high or low temperatures occur.

(27°C) and 80 percent humidity were designated the threshold levels to actively combat overheating in hot and humid climates. Because of differences from one animal to the next in heat tolerances, water was made available for animals to cool themselves if they chose.[22,30,31]*

Unlike the llamas that arrived with full coats under the same conditions in Key West a year earlier, the alpacas arrived shorn. They were also somewhat acclimated, having first moved from the altiplano to the coast of Brazil before entering the torrid conditions in Key West. Even though the combined temperature and humidity often exceeded 190, the use of water in conjunction with shearing and dietary adjustments worked well. Because of births, more alpacas left the quarantine station than had entered it. This seat-of-the-pants, high-stakes, heat-stress prevention experiment provided the first successful large-scale test on how to combat heat stress in a hot and humid climate.

In subsequent years, Pugh refined the 80–80 rule slightly. He now says, "If the total is 120 or less, there should be no problem. If the number is 150 or more, as many precautions as are available should be taken. As the number approaches or exceeds 180, extreme caution should be exercised, as alpacas are at great risk."** Some

evidence indicates that alpacas can adjust, over a period of time, to higher combinations of temperature and humidity than Pugh's recommendations, but until an owner is certain about his or her alpacas' reaction to heat and humidity, the 80–80 rule should be honored.[30,31]

Heat with Low Humidity

For periods of time each year, the 80–80 rule is applicable to the humid Southeast, Northeast, and Midwest in the United States, and Queensland and the Northern Territory in Australia. But the 80–80 rule has little relevance and can be misleading in hot, dry climates such as California, Arizona, Utah, or New South Wales, southern Australia, inland Victoria, and western Australia. A temperature of 100°F (38°C) with 20 percent humidity adds up to 120, and this may be lethal to alpacas without shade or other protection. In hot, dry climates, the 80–80 rule is best forgotten—a common fallacy is that humidity is the killer and that high temperatures are less important. Not so. High temperatures alone can cause severe heat stress. (See Chapter 21: Noninfectious Multisystemic Diseases for prevention and clinical signs of heat stress.)

Emergency Responses to Heat Stress

Running cool water from a hose on the areas of exposed skin underneath the animal is the most effective means to cool an animal (more effective than dousing or fanning). The idea is to keep a constant flow of cool liquid moving across as large a skin surface as possible until the body temperature moves downward into the upper end of the normal range. A cool-water enema, especially on young animals, is effective.[19,29] (See Chapter 21 for details.)

Natural Methods of Coping with Heat

The most problem-free and low-maintenance ways to cope with high temperatures is by working with nature. Taking advantage of prevailing breezes and creating shade are important and easy to do. If you're in a position to consider breezes before you construct fences and build shelter, make every effort to maximize regularly occurring air currents in paddock and shelter plans. Consider using overhangs on the sides of barns and ample shade trees in your paddock and shelter plans.

In California on a hot, sunny day the temperature in a redwood grove is often cool and comfortable, while in sunlight a short distance away the sun is so intense that stand-

*David G. Pugh, veterinarian instrumental in establishing protocol to help llamas and alpacas cope with heat stress at Harry S. Truman Animal Importer Center, personal communication, Key West, Florida, July 5, 1988.

**David Pugh, personal communication, May 12, 2000.

ing in it requires protection. Trees can create their own microclimate and buffer high temperatures. If planting trees is in order, deciduous (as opposed to evergreen) trees offer the greatest advantage. Deciduous trees provide summer shade but allow more exposure to the warming rays of the sun in the winter when they are needed most. When choosing trees consider the following: climate adaptability, growth rate, maintenance, longevity, pest and disease problems, leaf or fruit toxicity, seed and fleece compatibility, and structural integrity. Trees that produce seeds that cling to an alpaca's coat should be avoided. The limbs of some trees are prone to breaking in heavy winds or when heavy with water in the spring, and limbs have fallen on camelids taking refuge under trees in a storm. Maples, sycamores, willows, and poplars are usually fast-growing and adaptable to many soil and climatic conditions.[21]

Because alpacas will strip bark from a young tree and kill it, trees should be protected with a wire mesh wrap (with ample room to allow for trunk growth) to at least 5 feet (1.5 m). Building a fence around a tree will protect it from alpacas eating it, but if the fence excludes the alpacas from the shade, it defeats the purpose of planting the tree. To avoid eye injuries, tree trunks should be trimmed of branches lower than an adult alpaca's head.

Fans Electric fans are used by alpaca breeders to cool animals in humid and hot climates. Fans come in various sizes and have different capacities to move air. Wall or side fans are usually more effective than ceiling fans. Large industrial portable fans that stand on 3- to 4-foot (91–122-cm) metal pipe stanchions are popular in some large operations but expensive to buy and run. Freestanding portable 21 × 21-inch (53 × 53-cm) fans are much less expensive to purchase and usually less expensive to run. Large retail chains regularly stock inexpensive portable fans that fit the needs of alpacas. In the dimensions described above, look for a multiple speed, 120-volt model that draws about 2.2 amps. Some longtime alpaca breeders mount fans of this kind a foot (30 cm) above the ground in the wall of a shelter or barn. When the structure heats up in the afternoon and the outside air cools, the fans are switched on to pull cool air through the structure.

In extreme temperature and humidity situations, water-cooled fans and air-conditioners may be appropriate. Louisianans Dr. Jim and Laura Hudson house alpacas year-round in a humid and hot environment. They use Port-a-Cool evaporator fans, which spray a fine mist through a honeycomb radiator that is part of the fan.*

A soaker hose can accommodate as many as 20 alpacas on a hot day.

Consult a local veterinarian and other breeders before installing sophisticated water-cooled fans and air-conditioning. Creating great extremes in an alpaca's environment—an air conditioned shelter, for example, with very hot outside ambient temperatures—may create additional health concerns. Also, if not thought out thoroughly, misters can just add to the humidity and do more harm than good.[19] Usually the need for elaborate cooling systems can be greatly reduced if there is ample shade and the housing area is sufficiently insulated to withstand high daytime temperatures.[30]

Sprinklers, Hoses, and Ponds Water is, of course, nature's coolant, and many alpaca breeders use water to cool their animals. Cooling from underneath—putting water in contact with skin on the stomach, chest, and legs—works most effectively. Attempts to cool a group of alpacas should take into account the number of animals in a paddock and the ways they respond to water. For example, alpacas will often sit on top of a water source. Soaker hoses 25 to 30 feet (7 to 9 m) in length that allow several animals to kush (sit sternally with legs folded under the body) on water at once works well. This cooling method is inexpensive and can be expanded by adding more hoses. Some breeders report that

*Jim Hudson, physician raising alpacas in Louisiana, personal communication, Minden, Louisiana, September 4, 1994.

Shelters come in many forms, but all of them should keep animals dry and minimize stress from heat, humidity, and cold. This shelter is in a valley out of the wind, and is located in California, where it rarely freezes. Shown during wet weather, the roof keeps the animals and food dry, and the raised floor protects them from run-off.

This fully insulated barn in Maryland has stalls that can be heated or cooled depending on the weather. Such a substantial, thermoregulated structure makes sense when there are extremes in humidity and heat and cold.

a combination of soaker hoses and wet sand works well to keep the underside of an alpaca in contact with a cool surface.

Single-source sprinklers, such as stationary sprinkler heads, are not well suited as cooling devices. Alpacas will attempt to kush on the sprinkler, excluding other alpacas from a source of water, and possibly damaging the sprinkler or cutting themselves.

Alpacas become accustomed to being cooled by a garden hose. Often an entire herd will run toward a person with a hose and jostle for position. Standing in one place, a person can spray the underside of 20 or more alpacas in 5 to 10 minutes. Alpacas like their legs and underside sprayed. A herd attuned to this treatment can be enticed into a catch pen by merely turning on a hose.

Alpacas will also take advantage of ponds and standing water to cool off. This is an effective method, but there can be hazards. See "Waterers" for more details.

COPING WITH COLD

In their native land alpacas are accustomed to temperatures of 29°F (−1.5°C) at night, but generally alpacas can withstand temperatures above 14°F (−10°C). In areas that get colder than this, cold may be a problem, and in subfreezing temperatures, blizzards, or freezing rain with severe wind chills, alpacas should definitely be herded into cover. Animals left out on particularly cold nights have lost ears and parts of ears to frostbite and have died from exposure. Young animals are more apt to be affected by cold. For huacaya adults with a coat 2 inches (5 cm) or longer, temperatures dropping below −10°F (−23°C) should be considered dangerous. For a recently shorn huacaya adult or a suri in full coat, temperatures below 20°F (−6°C) should be considered potentially dangerous. The wind chill should be factored into temperature readings. A coat's length should be about 3 inches (7 cm) by the time winter arrives. Wet, cold weather is particularly dangerous to young and adult suris and young huacayas. Water that penetrates the coat and freezes near the skin can lead to death in a matter of hours.*

Icy conditions can cause a paddock to become as slick as a skating rink and dangerous to animals that attempt to move across it rapidly. Humans around alpacas on icy surfaces should take care not to startle them.

Preventing Hypothermia

Hypothermia occurs when the alpaca's body does not convert enough energy to maintain the temperature level for life's basic biological processes. Converting energy to thermoregulate body temperature is directly related to ingestion and digestion of food. Therefore, the availability of adequate amounts and quality of food is very important. Alpacas' dietary demands increase substantially in cold weather. Allocations, especially in dry lot situations, should be increased. Supplemental feeds should be considered.[17,19]

*Jim Vickers, veterinarian who housed large numbers of both suri and huacaya alpacas in subfreezing weather in northern Michigan, personal communication, Charlevoix, Michigan, September 10, 1994.

The length, density, and type of coat (huacaya or suri) influence an alpaca's ability to retain body heat. Prolonged rains, snows, sudden freezing rain, and any type of cold moisture that soaks the animal's coat to the skin can pose mild to substantial health risks. A three-sided shelter with its back facing incoming weather is usually necessary to protect alpacas. Taking measures to conserve heat for alpacas is sometimes necessary.[17,19] Adding bedding, such as manure covered by straw, will warm a stall, though there are hygiene risks with this method.* Stacking hay bales to make a temporary wall or draping burlap to create a lower ceiling creates a smaller space and sometimes helps contain heat.[12]

Dry space need not be heated, unless extreme conditions are at hand or unless newborns are at risk.[19] Electric radiant heaters that heat the air and bodies of the animals seem to work best. Under most circumstances heating a stall to between 33 and 38°F (1° and 4°C) is adequate for dry animals not exhibiting a chill by excessive shivering.[17] Conventional heat sources placed in stalls with choked-down ventilation may consume oxygen, give off fumes, or pose a fire danger. Electric heat lamps are dangerous and have caused barn fires. Space heaters that run on kerosene and produce noxious fumes have also been responsible for deaths when used in a closed area.

Alpaca breeders in cold climates also report that during shearing they opt to leave leg wool on older animals to help them cope with the cold. With animals near the end of their lives it is advisable not to shear them if they are incapable of producing a substantial fleece by the onset of the cold season. Remember that older alpacas regenerate their fleeces much more slowly.

Specially designed blankets and polar-lined fleece jackets are a great aide to crias, recently shorn adults, and adults at risk for other reasons. Blankets are very effective in minimizing wind chill in cold climates. Several manufacturers offer blankets tailored to fit alpacas of all sizes. The blankets (also known as jackets) are attached to the alpaca by Velcro straps that fit around the alpaca's midsection and at the base of the alpaca's neck. For the animal's safety, it is important only to use a blanket that will tear off easily if the alpaca becomes entangled. Many alpaca operations have incorporated the use of blankets into their cold or wet weather planning. In most situations, the use of blankets allows animals greater mobility and reduces risks related to overcrowding that can occur when too many animals are forced into a stall or barn. However, leaving blankets on animals for prolonged periods of time, especially if

Cold weather requires strategies to prolong life. This 18-year-old alpaca wears a windbreaker and is spared the wind chill on a subfreezing day.

the weather should suddenly become warm, carries the risk of overheating. Using blankets to combat cold and wet requires constant monitoring.[3]

See Chapter 21: Noninfectious Multisystemic Diseases for details on the clinical signs of hypothermia, its prevention, and emergency measures to combat cold-related health problems.

Extreme Cold

In extremely cold weather below −20°F (−29°C), longtime Alaskan alpaca breeders Jim and Jan Faiks move their alpacas into closed areas where they are outfitted with alpaca parkas and blankets.[17] According to the Faiks, coat length is an important variable in how well alpacas cope with severe cold. For huacaya adults with coats 2 inches (5 cm) or longer, temperatures dropping below 10°F (−23°C) should be considered potentially dangerous. Shearing should occur in the spring to assure the coat regenerates sufficiently. With animals that are slow to regenerate their fiber or animals that are overly sensitive to the cold, not shearing too closely is applicable. Too long a coat in snowy, wet conditions can cause problems even for huacayas. A long coat that collects snow becomes heavy, pulls downward, and parts along the spine, which exposes the alpaca's spine to icy air and frozen water, much in the same manner that suris are naturally exposed along the spine. Unless precautions are taken, an animal can become hypothermic.[29]

The Faiks combat this problem by "sewing" the fiber together along the backbone with a darning needle and

---

*Brad Sprouse, alpaca breeder, personal communication, Maple City, Michigan, August 10, 1994.

Effective housing comes in many forms. This mid-sized alpaca barn has three permanent stalls, plus an aisleway that can be made into two more stalls or a catch pen.

yarn. They prefer bright yarn because it is easier to remove in the spring. As a telltale sign that heat isn't being lost along the spine, the Faiks look for a totally frosted coat after a cold night. If there is frost on the coat except along the topline, they assume the insulating ability of the animal's coat is compromised along the back and valuable body heat is being unnecessarily lost.[17]

SHELTER

In South America alpacas live without the benefit of shelter in a temperature range from 29 to 70°F (−1.5 to −21°C), with annual precipitation of rain and snow averaging 24 inches (61 cm). Except for the three-month wet season between December and March, the weather is dry with low humidity. It freezes about 300 nights a year on the puna. Alpacas also cope with intense ultraviolet rays from the sun due to the thin atmosphere at the high elevation of the puna (12,500 feet plus; 3,810 m) and long days due to the region's proximity to the equator.[26] Alpacas have flourished in these climatic conditions for thousands of years.

In North America, Australia, New Zealand, and Europe, alpacas often live in considerably different. environments, and some of these new environments are extreme compared to the puna. Whenever a creature is expected to live in a place in which the ranges in temperature, humidity, and precipation are different than where the animal evolved, higher levels of stress can be expected. Alpacas living in temperature and precipitation ranges similar to those found in their ancestral land need minimal shelter—most of the time. Those living in excessively hot, humid, cold, or wet areas compared to their homeland need shelter to help them cope.

In South America heavy rains and snows or hot spells during the birthing season often result in high cria mortalities.[23] In North America, where even one cria death is often viewed as a significant financial and emotional loss, the availability of shelter becomes an important factor in decreasing mortality rates, especially of young animals. So, both as a hedge against surprise weather occurrences and as a means to create a more hospitable environment for alpacas, shelter of some kind makes sense.

Appropiate Shelter

Good intentions aside, "appropriate shelter" is a crucial yet somewhat elusive concept. Not all shelters improve the comfort and survivability of alpacas. The wrong kind of shelter may increase risks and stress, and sometimes it is inappropriate to use a shelter at all.

Just because a structure has a roof and walls does not mean it offers the kind of protection an alpaca needs. In fact, it is best for alpacas to live outdoors, not in a stall. The stall is the place of last resort to protect a sick animal or protect healthy ones from unusually harsh weather conditions. A structure must be designed or modified to combat the hostile climatic conditions in your region. In Calgary, Canada, winters are harsh and cold but summers are generally mild with low humidity. Coastal northern California is generally temperate year round. Arizona has dry summers but temperatures soar, much like most of inland Australia. In Georgia, summer heat reaches 100°F (38°C) with 90 percent humidity, a climatic condition far exceeding situations on the puna.

There is no perfect shelter for North America, Australia, Switzerland, or England, but there is a perfect shelter for alpacas in every region. Alpacas can be raised successfully in all of these diverse environments—if shelters are suitably designed to mitigate temperature extremes, humidity, wind, rain, and snow. Alpacas being raised in areas of high precipitation must have ample space under a roof to get out of the elements, but the structure can be lightweight if the cold is not excessive. In areas of severe cold, structures for mothers, crias, and sick animals must be insulated and occasionally heated. In places where alpacas are subject to heat stress, open areas facing prevailing breezes, cross-ventilation, fans, wetted sandy areas, and possibly soaker hoses may be part of a shelter's design.[21]

A myriad of shelter types are suitable for alpacas. Common shelters include barns originally designed for other livestock, three-sided sheds, movable sheds, and lightweight fabric-covered sun and rain screens constructed with lightweight pipes. Shelters are central to farm layout. Large multistalled barns with haylofts lend themselves to a centralized layout with paddocks radiating from a single structure. Multiple outbuildings and three-sided sheds usually create a more dispersed layout. Regional weather patterns, topography, size of the operation, pre-existing structures, budgetary concerns, and other variables influence the kinds of shelter provided for alpacas.[15,16,17] A shelter should be built according to building codes and make efficient use of space.

Essentials for a Safe Alpaca Stall

A stall is a compartment in a shelter where an animal is kept and fed. Most of us are familiar with horse stalls in rows inside a stable, where a horse receives its daily ration; many horses spend much of their lives standing in stalls. With alpacas, stalls are needed only in special situations and are not normally used for daily housing. Stalls should be clean places, rarely occupied but kept ready for special needs, such as a sick alpaca needing constant medication, a weak cria needing an environment in which temperature and humidity can be regulated, a clean environment where a veterinarian can perform minor surgical procedures, and a place to put an animal who must be observed on a continual basis.

Under most circumstances a stall measuring 10 × 10 feet (3 × 3 m) is adequate for a mother and baby or two adults. The stall must be enclosed with escape-proof material such as no-climb fencing. Four feet (1.2 m) is usually adequate, but 5 feet (1.5 m) is safer. Captive alpacas should not have head and neck access to the next stall or corridor, but a stall design that allows the captive animal to see other alpacas is good for the alpaca's social and physical well-being. Adequate air circulation is very important. Beware of using solid-wall and solid-door horse stalls or stalls that are solid to 4 feet (1.2 m). These can become heat traps and have contributed to the death of more than one alpaca when ventilation and air circulation were inadequate. A thermometer and humidity gauge should be hanging in any stall housing alpacas, at the level of an alpaca's withers. The combination of high humidity and high temperature can be deadly.

A number of materials make appropriate flooring, allowing for good footing and easy cleaning. Slick surfaces invite injury. Surfaces from which manure is difficult to remove become reservoirs for bacteria. Placing ½-inch (1.3-cm) rubber matting over either hard dirt or concrete provides a safe, comfortable surface for alpacas that is easy to clean and has good traction, especially when used in conjunction with bedding straw.

A water source should be off the ground (see "Waterers") so animals that have walked in manure don't foul it. Food should also be above the ground level (see "Feeders").

Building/Converting Considerations

If you are converting or building a barn, keep this in mind: Alpacas may taste your construction materials, so choose them accordingly, since some building materials are dangerous if ingested or touched. Although alpacas don't have a horse's destructive chewing capacity, they can chew into types of glued particleboard. Externally mounted electrical wire running through a pen or aisle should be placed in conduit. Alpacas will sometimes nibble at rubber insulation until the bare wire is exposed. They may also eat fiber glass and foam insulation.

If you are modifying a large barn for alpacas, try to fit it with doors big enough to allow delivery vehicles to enter (see "Food Storage"). This access allows efficient and uninhibited manure removal, feed deliveries, ventilation, herding, and emergency exiting.

If you have concrete floors, cover them with rubber mats. Straw on smooth concrete gives the illusion of an alpaca-friendly surface, but it is really a slick, potentially dangerous surface. Mats work well on raised and tamped dirt floors as well. Regardless of the type of flooring, its surface must offer good traction when wet or dry.

Even the most minimal facility should have a weather-proof stall set aside for emergencies and veterinary care. The weighing scale, tack, a restraining chute, and medical supplies should be kept near this area.[34]

An alpaca enjoys spring pasture.

ESSENTIAL EQUIPMENT AND MEDICAL SUPPLIES

What kinds of equipment are necessary for the daily running of an alpaca operation? This, of course, depends on the size of your operation, the terrain, farm layout, and budget. Essential equipment includes hay delivery equipment, manure removal tools, restraining devices, cooling and heating devices (see "Coping with Heat" and "Coping with Cold"), a scale, medical supplies, shearing supplies and equipment (see Chapter 11: Fleece Preparation and Shearing). For weighing alpacas, see "Scales for Weighing Alpacas" in this chapter.

Carts, Wheelbarrows, Shovels, Rakes, and Tractors

All farms need a hay delivery system and most need a manure removal system. For a small to medium-sized operation, the appropriate kinds of carts, wheelbarrows, rakes, and shovels are usually enough. For a larger operation, a tractor or like vehicle with various attachments may be necessary.

For delivering hay from storage to feeders, a two-wheeled lightweight cart is the preferred tool. Carts come in many sizes, designs, and materials. Before purchasing one, ask yourself these questions: Will the cart fit through the gates? Is the cart the correct size for the user to steer easily? Is the cart's carrying capacity suited to the amount of hay to be distributed? There is no need to walk the same route twice to deliver hay if a slightly larger cart will do the job in one delivery. Is the cart user-friendly? Can you lift hay in and out of it without straining your back? When moving, is the cart well balanced and easy to push? And is it built to last? Some carts are structurally marginal and built of lightweight tubing that will not last. Others are built of compressed wood products with a plastic veneer that warps and eventually disintegrates if left out in the rain. In recent years many manufacturers have come out with all-plastic carts, with inflatable tires and a carrying area that is designed to tilt for loading and unloading. Beware of catalogue purchasing unless you've already handled the cart you are buying. Lastly, a hay delivery cart should be used for that purpose only, and not alternately used for hauling manure. Feed and manure should never come into contact.

A wheelbarrow, preferably one with a lightweight fiberglass or plastic shell and an inflatable tire, is suitable for manure removal. If you're working on uneven surfaces and inclines, look for a two-wheeled-barrow, because it doesn't require strength and finesse to balance. A lightweight leaf rake and a wide, flat-nosed aluminum or plastic

Manure removal is a daily task in many operations.

snow shovel can be used in the same manner as a broom and dustpan for efficient pickup. For one or two animals, daily pickup can be done with a poop pan and rake commonly used on dog show circuits.

Restraining Devices

Alpacas are domesticated animals but often less than cooperative when it comes to toenail trimming, teeth cutting, injections, and other forms of routine handling. An experienced alpaca handler can usually restrain and "handle" an animal by rolling it on its side and holding it firmly to the ground, applying the correct amount of pressure on the neck and shoulder. The simplest form of restraint is to simply hold an animal around its neck, most effectively done by pulling the alpaca close to your body, possibly grasping (without twisting) an ear. With larger, stronger, uncooperative animals, a halter and lead rope wrapped halfway (for quick release should the animal begin to twist its neck violently) around a post makes controlling an uncooperative, untrained adult relatively easy. (Never secure the lead rope with a knot or multiple wraps around a post. If the animal suddenly flips or twists, being able to simultaneously release the tension on the rope is mandatory.) These techniques of restraint are inexpensive and effective but require strength, finesse, and willingness to "wrestle" a little with an alpaca in order to control it. Halters and lead ropes should be kept in an easily accessible area. In small operations many breeders assign a specific halter (with a name tag) to each animal and make sure it is adjusted to fit. See Chapter 6: Taming and Training for details on halters and training aids.

A number of restraining chutes and shearing tables (which double as general-purpose restraining devices) have been developed to better control alpacas. The key to assessing any kind of restraining device is the safety of the alpaca and your ability to work the device in a manner safe for both alpacas and people. More than a few animals have been killed in restraining chutes over the years, either from broken necks (due to twisting violently before the attendant could release the head/halter restraint rope/chain) or from ruptured organs (bladder) as a result of tightening a belly cinch too much. Don't buy chutes that do not incorporate "quick-release" devices that will save an animal's life should it struggle violently and become tangled or twisted in restraining ropes. Have the chute demonstrated to you using a fairly incorrigible animal to see if the chute performs as advertised. Also beware of belly cinches that restrict the abdomen (and the organs inside).

In 1995, New Zealander Russell Gent introduced a shearing (and restraining) table to the alpaca community. Gent's "table" and numerous modified versions of it by other manufacturers initiated a new approach to restraint that is both easy and trouble-free for animals and handlers. The table usually measures about 4 × 6 feet (1.2 m × 1.8 m) and comes with a squeeze arrangement. The table is tilted to a vertical position and the squeeze is opened to allow an alpaca to be positioned between the squeeze and the table. When the alpaca stands alongside the table, the squeeze is closed, pinning the alpaca to the table. The animal's feet are usually restrained with straps and the table is tilted into a horizontal position with the alpaca (now off its feet and powerless) fully restrained for shearing, toenail trimming, or inoculations. The best tables are contoured to the shape of an alpaca and are easy to work for two people. Usually one person is assigned to hold the head and neck while the other person works on the animal.

Scales for Weighing Alpacas

Weighing alpacas is a primary means of assessing their general health. Weighing a baby at birth and then tracking its weight allows a breeder to assess its rate of growth and general vitality. Loss of weight (or failure to gain weight) in a neonate or cria is often the first sign that all is not well. Weight losses in adults may also be the first sign an alpaca

Weighing a newborn with a fish scale and sling.

is experiencing stress from lactation, dietary deficiency, disease, or negative social activities.

Many kinds of scales are on the market and only some of them are appropriate for alpacas. For efficient use and accurate measurement, a scale must be easy to use and accurate to within one-quarter of a pound (113 g) for small animals, crias, and weanlings. For adults it should be accurate to 1 pound (2.2 kg) and have the capacity to weigh 250 pounds (136 kg). For neonates and crias, an assortment of fish scales (also known as milk scales) are available. These small scales are handheld, and the cria is put in a sling attached to the scale. Another method breeders use to weigh crias is to stand on a bathroom scale with and without the cria, then subtract to get the cria's weight. This method can be inaccurate if the scale is moved to different surfaces and inclines during subsequent weighings over a period of days. For adult alpacas numerous kinds of livestock scales work well. For ease in handling a scale is usually placed in a narrow passageway, so the alpaca must place all four feet on the scale when it walks down.

Alpaca owners often buy scales that are entirely too large and at the same time not accurate enough. The surface area of the scale need not be larger than 22 × 42

Weighing alpacas can be as easy as walking an animal down a narrow chute. This quickly constructed chute has the essential feature of fitting tightly to the sides of the scale, so that an alpaca will put its weight entirely on the scale.

inches (56 × 106 cm). Scale technology is changing rapidly: Traditional mechanical balance-and-spring scales are giving way to electronic strain-gauge technology with digital readouts that can measure the weight of a constantly moving animal, weigh the animal a half dozen times, average those measurements, and supply a readout accurate to one-tenth of a pound (45.4 g). These electronic scales have no moving parts, can typically be placed on any solid surface, are only about 2 inches (5 cm) thick, and weigh less than 50 pounds (23 kg). They are popular among veterinarians. There are many manufacturers; Technidyne Corporation of Howell, New Jersey, is among the largest.

Medical Supplies

Daily and intermittently scheduled care includes toenail and tooth trimming, routine inoculations, vaccinations, deworming, birthing, and medical treatment of minor problems. If you have not received training from a veterinarian or other qualified person, it is safer for the animals to work with your veterinarian on these matters. Regardless of your level of experience, however, you should have a medical supply kit and a birthing kit.

Consult with your veterinarian about which medical supplies you should stock regularly on your farm. In some instances buying supplies through mail-order catalogues cuts costs considerably. Commonly stocked items include toenail clippers (commonly sold as hoof shears), OB wire for cutting incisors, gauze, vet wrap, rectal thermometers, enema syringes (or baby enemas), stethoscope, syringes and needles (20 gauge for most situations) for vaccinations and medications, #18 puppy feeding tubes and 35 cc syringes for tubing newborns, insulated cria coats to warm newborns on cold nights, heating pads for newborns that must be warmed to help them regulate their body temperature, and bottles and nipples for newborns that must be fed from the bottle. If you are in a heavy rain area, lightweight rainproof coats for crias, subadults, aging adults, and suris of all ages (or animals that are freshly shorn) minimizes the risk of hypothermia for the young, old, and vulnerable, and still allows them the freedom of their entire paddock, instead of being locked in stalls during inclement weather.

Medicines Many types of medicines have expiration dates and require refrigeration, so inquire about the shelf life before making purchases. Don't buy more than you will use. Keep in mind that administering medicines and intervening in other ways is risky unless the person doing it fully understands the risks and procedures, and is generally best done after consultation with your veterinarian.

Common medicines that may be stored at the ranch include injectible antibiotics, vaccines, painkillers, lactation inducers, antivenin in areas with poisonous snakes, lubricants, electrolytes, sterile saline solution for cleaning wounds and dislodging material from eyes, topical antibiotics for both eye injuries and flesh wounds, parasite medicines, pro-biotics (to stimulate digestion in young animals), and treatments for intestinal tract disorders.[13]

Birthing Kit Every ranch should have a birthing kit, or more than one depending on the size and layout of your operation. A birthing kit should contain only items needed for assisting in a birth. The kit should be placed strategically near birthing pens or places alpacas are likely to give birth, and it should be rodent-proof and insect-proof. The items in the kit must be kept as sterile as possible. Soft plastic containers measuring 1 × 2 × 3 feet (30 × 61 × 91 cm) with pop-off lids make excellent all-weather containers. The kit should have a 7 percent iodine solution or chlorhexidine diacetate for drenching the newborn's umbilicus, a 35-mm plastic film canister, plenty of clean towels for drying the newborn, sterile lubricant (like K-Y), OB sleeves and exam gloves, a thermometer, and a plastic bag to carry away the placenta. (See Chapter

ALPACA'S NAME	Josie			BIRTH DATE 8/5/93 SEX F REG.NO. 99999
SIRE	Joseph	NO. xx DAM	Marion	NO. xx

DATE	OBSERVATIONS/TREATMENT	DATE	OBSERVATIONS/TREATMENT
1993		1995	
8/5	Born in Santa Cruz, California. Found at 7am dry, walking around. Gold, 17½# Nursed well all day	1/7	Rejected McGregor
		1/12	Progesterone = 4.1
		2/6	Progesterone = 3.1
		4/7	Progesterone = 2.7
		5/25	Ivomec Pour-on
8/6	IgG = 2600		
8/12	23#		
9/5	34#		
9/29	CD-T #1		
10/18	Blood for typing		
10/22	CD-T #2		
11/15	Ivomec Pour-on		
1994			
5/15	Panacur		
7/11	Ears crusty - KRS spray for ear mites		
7/18	Ears look much better		
7/25	Ears fine - CD-T		
12/22	Bred by BD McGregor		
12/23	Bred by McG		

Record keeping is essential to any conscientious husbandry program. These field notes may later be transferred to computer.

14: Obstetrics and Neonatology for details on the birthing process.)

RECORD KEEPING

Record keeping is a measure of a farm's professional commitment to raising alpacas. Every animal that is born on or visits a ranch should have a permanent record. Records fall into three basic types: health, reproduction, and fiber. A health record summarizes all inoculations, deworming, ailments, routine tooth and nail trimming, body weights, and behavior associated with health. A reproduction record should include breeding dates, behavioral responses of both the male and female during "field testing," progesterone levels, ultrasound results, length of gestation, difficulties in birth or passage of placenta, birth weight of the baby, scoring of the baby's general health, time elapsed from birth until commencement of nursing activity, the baby's IgG level, and other pertinent information having to do with the birth process.

Recording information about fiber is an often neglected aspect of alpaca record keeping. Ideally, permanent fiber samples should be kept in the form of a histogram on each alpaca (see Chapter 10: Fiber Processing Characteristics and Nomenclature), along with shearing dates and weights of each clip.

Computer programs are available to help breeders track all farm records. One very comprehensive program, LamaLogic™, allows alpaca owners to record all the information catagories mentioned, as well as to create and track boarding/guest records, breeder/owner contracts, registration forms, and invoices and show records—and you can add photos. The program will soon be available in languages other than English. For more information, contact simon@lamalogic.com or visit the website at http://www.lama logic.com.

CLEANING UP

Manure Removal

All livestock operations must deal with manure removal. The size of an area, type of surface (pasture, dirt, etc.), and the number of animals living on it affect the urgency and frequency of manure removal. On small acreages with high stocking levels, manure is often removed daily. Of the numerous reasons to remove manure on a regular basis, disease prevention, fly control, elimination of odor, and maintaining sanitary, attractive living conditions are among the more important. A wheelbarrow, leaf rake, and broad-nosed, lightweight snow shovel are the most economical removal tools. For those with the economic means and a zest for being fully motorized, there are manure removers with vacuums that are worked from a power mower or tractor.

Composted manure can be returned to pastures as a fertilizer, *with the exception of birthing pastures.* Properly composted manure is a useful soil amendment for gardens, ornamental shrubs, and pastures. Manure that is removed and piled on the farm should drain away from alpaca pens.[32]

Clostridium perfringens Type A, the bacterium that causes the deadliest disease affecting young alpacas in South America, is found in manure. The disease rears its ugly head in weather conditions that happen to coincide with the birthing season, often following a light rain that appears to stimulate proliferation of the deadly bacteria. It must be ingested and it strikes only the young, usually less than 60 days old, so keeping areas containing young crias clean is critical. If enough space is available on a farm, birthing and raising crias in pens kept clean and not used by livestock for a year may reduce risk of this disease.[23,28]

When introducing alpacas to a new pen, always place some fecal matter where you want the communal toilet to be, although this doesn't guarantee they will agree with your choice of site. Alpacas new to a paddock may ignore your efforts and start their own toilet at a spot they prefer.

Fly Reduction Strategies

A single fly is able to lay up to 1,000 eggs, which take 6 days to become egg-laying adults. Removing manure greatly reduces pest flies because it eliminates moist areas where fly eggs and maggots thrive, and since many kinds of flies need at least 72 hours for their breeding, egg, and maggot stages, daily manure removal interrupts the cycle.

Several strategies can be instituted in conjunction with manure removal. Fly traps and papers and pesticides are

Manure should be kept away from alpacas and preferably dumped on the down-hill side of the property.

well-known controls. Biological controls are another method that deserves mention. Scientists have identified and developed insects who prey on fly larvae. By purchasing and releasing these insects (usually species of tiny wasps, harmless to humans), flies are greatly reduced. Biological controls often take 30 to 60 days to establish, but once they are in place they become self-sustaining. Spalding Laboratories of Arroyo Grande, California, is a leading company in this field—they sell Fly Predators, which lay eggs inside a developing pupa in species of common pest flies.[9] When the predator wasp hatches, it kills the pupa by devouring it. This type of predatory wasp is not a nuisance to people or alpacas, is about the size of a pinhead, and lives its entire life cycle on manure piles. If the right number (300 per alpaca) of Fly Predators is established, they provide a long-term method of fly control by interrupting the reproductive cycle of the pest flies. Another advantage of biological controls is that they do not expose alpacas to pesticide sprays.[27,32]

Disposing of an Alpaca Carcass

Alpacas can be expected to live to between 14 and 22 years of age. When death occurs, especially on a warm day, the need to dispose of the carcass is readily apparent as the body begins the process of bloating and decomposition. In most countries local jurisdictions (counties, shires, etc.) have rules on how to properly dispose of a carcass. Check with the health department for specific instructions.

BOARDING ALPACAS (SHOPPING FOR AN AGISTOR)

People purchasing new alpacas will often board them from a few months to several years. Some alpaca owners never take possession of their animals at all, and rely on a boarding arrangement for their care and health. Commonly those who agree to board alpacas have alpacas of their own; they refer to this service as either boarding or *agisting*. *Agistors* usually accept a monthly fee to care for animals other than their own.

Agistors are not required to pass a test or go through a certification process before advertising their services, and can demonstrate significantly different levels of skill, knowledge, and commitment. Nor are boarding costs a guarantee of experience or the breadth and quality of services.

Michelle Ing, a well-known camelid veterinarian in Northern California, has a far-reaching practice that puts her in contact with a wide range of alpaca owners. She says:

> In choosing someone to care for your animals, I cannot emphasize enough the importance of visiting the potential agistor's farm with an experienced alpaca owner and breeder who knows how to care for alpacas. In addition to the appearance of a well laid-out farm, observe the animals in the enclosures. Pay particular attention to the females with their crias. It is such a welcome sight to see contented and ruminating females with energetic crias by their sides. If you watch alpacas during times of increased stress, such as birthing, lactation, and weaning, a well-managed farm will have animals that reflect such care.*

A board-and-care facility should be chosen according to certain important criteria. To that end, Dr. Ing developed a list of questions for people seeking agistment for their alpacas. Answers to these questions may be found throughout this book; refer to the index and to the following chapters: Chapter 2, Behavior and Communication; Chapter 4, Husbandry; Chapter 9, Feeding the Alpaca; and Chapter 20, Infectious Multisystemic Diseases.

1. *Physical Layout and Management*
   - Are perimeter fences predator proof? Are the fences strong and safe?
   - Are stocking levels and enclosure sizes conducive to a stress-free environment?
   - Are males housed away from females?
   - Are there enough enclosures and adequate space to house animals based on dietary, social, or birthing demands?
   - Are there several food distribution points? Are the animals fed from feeders? Does someone feed or check the feed at least twice a day?
   - Is the water source reliable and the water clean? Is the water accessible to both adults and crias?
   - Does shelter provide enough shade and proper ventilation?
   - Is shelter suitable for prevailing weather patterns? Are animals living in extreme weather conditions given clean and dry housing? When it is wet and cold outside, is the shelter warm? When it is hot outside, it the shelter cool? Are animals moved inside every evening?
   - How often is manure removed from enclosures?
   - Are dogs or other potential predators housed on the premises or nearby? How are alpacas protected from them? What is the breed of dog (some breeds are notorious for chasing and attacking livestock)?
   - Are cattle, sheep, or goats mixed in with the alpacas?

2. *Health and diet*
   - What forages and hays are fed to the alpacas?
   - Are all animals fed the same, regardless of age, pregnancy status, or sex?
   - Are the forages/hays analyzed? Is additional dietary supplementation provided, if considered beneficial? What are the known deficiencies in the area (for example, selenium in the Pacific Northwest and parts of California)?
   - Is there a pellet supplement? What is it supposed to do? How is it fed?
   - Does the agistor have a working knowledge of toxic plants? Are any toxic plants known to be on the farm or near the alpaca enclosures?
   - How is general health monitored (such as body scoring)?
   - Are records kept of illnesses, injuries, diarrhea, etc.?
   - What is the protocol for sick or injured animals? If an animal is sick, is the owner contacted?
   - If an animal is sick, when is the veterinarian contacted? Is an experienced veterinarian readily available for regular procedures as well as emergencies?

3. *Alpaca Behavior*
   - Does the agistor have knowledge of alpaca behavior? Can he or she distinguish the difference between

*Michelle Ing, DVM, Granite Bay, California, personal communication, October 12, 2005.

aggressiveness and dominance, submissiveness and sickness?

• If the agistor is responsible for reproduction, what is the breeding protocol and how is pregnancy confirmed?

4. *Services and Contract*

• Does the agistor provide for alpaca care as a full-time job or as a side job?
• Does the contract make clear what agistment services are to be provided?
• Does agistment include maintenance care, such as worming, vaccinations, and trimming toenails and fighting teeth, or are there additional charges for these procedures?
• Is shearing conducted annually?
• How is the contract renewed or terminated?

REFERENCES

1. Anonymous: 164 Bolivians Released, 59 Perish, *Llama Life* 3: 1, Autumn 1987.
2. Catalogue: Agri & Pet Products, Miller Manufacturing Company, P.O. Box 545/494 Villaume Avenue, So. St. Paul, MN 55075, USA (no date). Telephone (612) 451-1761, fax (612) 451-7951.
3. Catalogue: Chlarson, Ed and Nancy: Quality Llama Products and Alternative Livestock Supply, 33217 Bellinger Scale Road, Lebanon, OR 97355 (annual reprinting), 2002. Telephone (800) 638-4689, website www.llamaproducts.com.
4. Catalogue: Davis Wire Corporation, 31775 Hayman Street, Hayward, CA, 94544-6030, USA. Telephone (510) 471-6030, fax (510) 471-6818.
5. Catalogue: Equipment for Poultry, Livestock, Pets, Brower Highway 16 West, P.O. Box 2000, Houghton, IA 52631, or 4831 Esmar Road, Ceres, CA 95307, USA. Telephone (800) 553-1791.
6. Catalogue: Fencing That Works, Premier 1,: Washington, IA 52353, USA. Fax (800) 346-7992, e-mail infor@premier1supplies.com
7. Catalogue: Fi-Shock, Inc., 5360 National Drive, Knoxville, TN 37914, USA. Telephone in USA and Canada (800) 251-9288, fax (615) 673-4770.
8. Catalogue: Floater, Farnam Companies, Inc., P.O. Box 12068, Omaha, NE 68112, USA. Telephone (402) 453-9100.
9. Catalogue: Fly Predators Biological Fly Control, Spalding Laboratories, 760 Printz Road, Arroyo Grande, CA, USA. Telephone (888) 562-8160, e-mail: www.spalding-labs.com.
10. Catalogue: KV Vet Supply Co., P.O. Box 245, Route 1, South Highway 15 & 92, David City, NE 68632, USA, p. 199, Summer 1994. Telephone (800) 423 8211, fax (800) 269-0093.
11. Catalogue: Model 700 Livestock Waterers, Nelson Manufacturing Company, P.O. Box 636, Cedar Rapids, IA 52406, USA. Telephone (313) 363-2607.
12. Catalogue: NASCO Agricultural Science, NASCO West, Modesto, CA, USA (annual catalogue), p. 342, 1995. Telephone (209) 529-6957, fax (209) 529-2239.
13. Catalogue: Omaha Vaccine Company Master, P.O. Box 7228, Omaha, NE, USA (annual catalogue), p. 262, 1993. Telephone (800)-367-4444, fax (402) 731-9829.
14. Catalogue: Red Snap'r Fence Controller, North Central Plastics, Inc., Interstate 35W & Highway 30, P.O. Box 248, Ellendale, MN 56026, USA, April 1991. Telephone (800) 533-2091, fax (507) 684-3722.
15. Dewald, Leah: Fencing for Your Alpacas. *Alpacas*, pp. 15–17, Winter 1994.
16. Dewald, Leah: Ruminations on the Barn, *Llama Life* 26: 26, Summer 1993.
17. Faiks, Janet and Jim: Raising Alpacas in Cold Climates. *Alpacas*, pp. 22–24, Fall 1993.
18. Farrand, John, Jr.: The Audobon Society Pocket Guides—Familiar Mammals, New York: Alfred A. Knopf, p. 162, 1991.
19. Fowler, Murray: Thermal Stress in Llamas. *Llamas* 29: 17–20, May/June 1985.
20. Franklin, William, L., and Kelly J. Powell: *Guard Llamas*. Iowa State University Extension, Ames, IA, USA, pp. 1–12, June 1993.
21. Freeman, Pamela: Coping with Heat Stress at Oak Hill, *Llama Life* 14: 11, Summer 1990.
22. Hoffman, Eric: Facility at Key West Adapts to Receive Imports. *Llama Life* 7: 1, 26, Autumn 1990.
23. Hoffman, Eric: Robert P. Ellis., Ph.D, Discusses C. perfringens Type A. *Llama Life* 21: 6, Spring 1992.
24. Hoffman, Eric: Ships of the Andes, *Pacific Discovery*, California Academy of Sciences: 42(3): 7–15, Summer 1989.
25. Hoffman, Eric: When Dogs Go Bad, CalToday, *San Jose Mercury News*, pp. 16–27, June 27, 1982.
26. Koford, Carl: The Vicuña and the Puna, University of California, Berkeley, Museum of Vertebrae Zoology, Ecological Monographs, p. 15, 1954.
27. Mayerle, Joan, A.: How to Control Flies Without Dangerous Chemicals, *Llamas* 3(3): 26, May/June 1989.
28. Phillips, Leslie: Mystery Disease Impacts Camelid Herd, *Llama Life* 14: 6, Summer 1990.
29. Price, Terry: The Faiks Like Challenges: Raising Camelids in Arctic Weather and Exporting Alpacas to Australia, *Llama Life* 9: 2, Spring 1989.
30. Pugh, David G.: Heat Stress in Alpacas, *Alpacas*, pp. 20–22, Spring 1992.
31. Pugh, David G.: Heat Stress in South American Camelids, *Proceedings of the North American Veterinarian Conference*, Orlando, Florida, 1995.
32. Rubin, Amy: Manure Management. *Llama Life* 21: 8, 9, Spring 1992.
33. Schoenthal, Dan: Designing Feeders. *Llama Life* 7: 23, Autumn 1988.
34. Seikel, Jana Tinsley: Housing Your Llama. *Llama Life* 25: 16, 17, Spring 1993.

Author's Note: For Spanish-language readers interested in alpaca husbandry, try to get a copy of *Como Mejorar su Producción, Alpaguera* (Lima: JF Ediciones, 2005). This 200-page book covers most basic husbandry and disease issues in the South American setting. It was produced by the nonprofit research group CONOPA, which operates out of the University of San Marcos, Lima, Peru.

Chapter 5

Restraint

Eric Hoffman

The lasso is the common method of capture on the altiplano, but it must be done correctly to avoid injury.

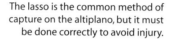

Restraint refers to capture and *restraining* an alpaca for routine procedures such as trimming toenails, collecting blood, cutting protruding incisors or fighting teeth, prepurchase examinations, applying medicines, and shearing. Generally an alpaca that has been trained to accept a halter and follow a person holding a lead rope is easier to restrain than an animal that has not. Untrained alpacas are more difficult to handle and more prone to injuring themselves or those handling them. Training an alpaca to be handled is an investment in a better life for that animal.

KNOWING ALPACA BEHAVIOR

Restraint amounts to much more than subduing an alpaca and rendering it incapable of running away. Totally effective restraint is a combination of knowing what techniques are appropriate for the situation and reading the response and level of defensiveness in the alpaca being restrained (see Chapter 2: Behavior and Communication).

Understanding Herd Behavior

Alpacas are the most herd oriented of all the camelid species. They have a strong banding instinct—the more they are confronted with danger, the more apt they are to press together in a single mass and move away from what frightens them. Thus, separating animals from a herd and attempting to drive them to a catch area is usually counter-productive. The harder you try, the more determined the animals being singled out for separation become to rejoin the herd.

The best strategy is always to catch a herd or group and sort inside a small enclosure. The idea is to capture animals without creating panic and fear. Harassed alpacas, especially adolescent animals, can cause accidents, such as trampling a cria, attempting to jump a fence, attempting to squeeze between rails in a fence, or greatly increasing irritability and stress throughout the herd. You can use herd behavior to your advantage and bait a herd into a catch pen by shaking a grain bucket or seeding the area with a favorite feed. Then the herd will usually enter the catch pen in a fairly relaxed state, with some signs of aggression between individuals (head tilted upward, ears pinned back, tail elevated) as the herd coalesces. A herd that is chased into a catch area by a group of people may be agitated and flighty. Allowing a herd collected in this manner to settle down before singling out individuals for restraint will reduce stress. Enticing an alpaca and its paddock mates into a catch pen is the best method (see Chapter 4: Husbandry).

Assessing Individual Alpacas

After a herd is captured, assess the group's general demeanor. Do the animals seem overly fearful, pushing together in a tight mass and careening around the enclosure, or are they relaxed but observant?

Now look at the individual alpaca. Approaching an alpaca to restrain it requires some knowledge of what to expect. Most alpacas will move away from people. They are accepting enough to allow people to be close, but they'd rather be just out of reach and prefer not to be handled.

An alpaca often gives an approaching person a fairly accurate read on how it may react to human contact. As you make contact, some animals will appear relaxed and will allow themselves to be handled with minimal restraint. Others may immediately flip their tail forward in a submissive gesture and lie on the ground screaming. Others may attempt to escape by sliding under a fence rail or spin out of your grasp just when you reach for them. Some may spit indiscriminately (or specifically aim at you) to express their displeasure. Usually the most fearful animals push to the back of the capture area and are the last and most difficult to be restrained when their turn comes to experience whatever procedure is being conducted.

Typically, as you approach an alpaca in a confined space, you'll notice that it will do its best to hide behind other alpacas or move away from you, possibly bolting to the other end of the pen. Alpacas rarely try to run "through" a person or be physically challenging. Occasionally, an alpaca will stand its ground and attempt to keep you away by spitting at you.

Approaching and Restraining

To force an alpaca into a corner where you can actually restrain it may require holding your arms out from your body and keeping your hands at the alpaca's eye level as you approach. By assuming an arms-out-at-the-shoulder-height posture, the alpaca sees a much wider figure approaching and a narrower escape route, which dissuades it from trying to run past you to freedom. Subtle movement, such as a flick of the hand at alpaca eye level, on the side the animal is eyeballing as an escape, usually results in the alpaca hesitating as you close in slowly and grasp it around the side of the neck.

Once an alpaca is cornered and you are within a couple of meters, it will usually turn its rear toward you. It still has a few options as you move slowly in to pull the animal's neck against your chest and thus restrain it. The most common response is to do nothing but freeze, and remain tense and ready to flee should the opportunity arise. Just before you put your arm around an alpaca, it may elect to kick with its hind legs, which is a common response to people, dogs, or even another alpaca. Your final approach should be along the side and slightly out from the alpaca's body, if the animal is unfamiliar with you. This way you will avoid the surprise kick.

Most alpacas are restrained without kicking. However, kicking can occur. Usually an alpaca's kicking motion is a

Holding an animal in position to conduct a uterine exam can be challenging. Animals react differently. The pressure along this alpaca's back convinced it to stay in place. Another alpaca might require another form of restraint. Successful restraint often requires employing a variety of techniques.

cow kick—the leg comes up and out slightly in a very quick motion. Alpacas will occasionally kick out straight to the rear. Kicking itself is not dangerous to an adult person unless your head is for some reason knee high or lower to the ground. The alpaca's foot is padded, which softens the blow, compared to hard-hoofed animals that are also much stronger. An alpaca kick is usually not higher than an adult human's thigh. A well-placed kick from a healthy adult may cause some bruising. It will definitely get your attention. A small child wandering up to an alpaca and startling it from the rear stands a chance of being kicked in the head, which should be an incentive to make sure small children don't run into the hindquarters of an alpaca. Children approaching from the front are generally treated with curiosity or casually avoided by alpacas.

Compared to llamas, alpacas tend to be more vocal and more apt to jump and buck, but because of their smaller size most people can safely restrain most alpacas once they learn various techniques. Alpacas that have become accustomed to being handled (taught to accept a halter and lead rope) rarely exhibit the extremes described here and are generally not challenging to restrain.

Avoiding Injury

Compared to most animals their size, alpacas are not prone to hurting people, even when they panic. However, one recurring type of injury needs to be mentioned. A handler who startles an alpaca by grabbing hold of it when its head is down is sometimes surprised when the alpaca suddenly jerks its head upward and inadvertently smacks the would-be handler in the face with the back of its head. The usual result is a bloody lip or nose. In one instance a llama did this so rapidly and with such force that the handler was knocked unconscious and sustained a severely broken nose, requiring surgery. The force of the head-to-head collision killed the llama. Head-to-head injuries are rare and can be entirely avoided if handlers are cognizant of this hazard in approaching a standing alpaca with its head at ground level.

Identifying and Restraining Dangerous Males

Aberrant males (sometimes referred to as suffering from "berserk male syndrome") are rare, but they need to be mentioned when discussing restraint.

Adult male alpacas have razor-sharp fighting teeth (if they haven't been removed) that can lacerate another alpaca in one bite. The teeth are designed to tear and maim opponents in territorial and hierarchical disputes involving breeding rights. In the wild both territorial male guanacos and vicuñas occasionally inflict crippling injuries on males that challenge them. The canine teeth, which erupt as the male alpaca matures, are inherited from their wild progenitor, the vicuña.

A male alpaca will not bite people unless he is aberrant—usually a consequence of receiving too much human attention before he was weaned. New alpaca owners often unknowingly create aggressive males by being overly friendly to a developing male cria whose normal imprinting process becomes confused. The aggressive behavior doesn't start until the cria reaches sexual maturity (around 22 months) and begins to assert itself. A normal breeding male will never bite or act aggressive toward a person and can be handled and led by children.

All the rules change with a male who is aggressive toward people. I once trained a berserk male llama to lead, carry a pack, and climb into a trailer. The animal was readily trainable, but in the end the training masked the dangerous behavior and didn't eliminate it—when someone stood with his or her back to the llama, he would still attack. Attack consists of rearing and crashing into people with the knees, attempting to knock people off their feet, and biting. The point of this sad anecdotal tale is that males that are aggressive toward people should be considered very dangerous.

Only an experienced animal handler should attempt to restrain an aggressive male. Keep in mind that if an animal attacks once, chances are it will do it again. To my knowledge, it is extremely rare for a male who behaves this way to be changed through training. Such animals are often euthanized.

HANDS ON!

The approach to restraining an alpaca will vary greatly depending on the alpaca and the procedure that is planned for it. An alpaca that is going to receive a simple injection will likely be restrained differently than an alpaca scheduled to have his fighting teeth removed. The person who is to work on an alpaca (shearer, veterinarian, shipper, trainer, new owner, etc.) should be told about the kind of training the animal has had. A halter-trained animal used to going to public events will usually need minimal restraint, whereas an animal that has never been handled will need to be approached with a different mind-set. Central to correctly applied restraint is that the amount of control should be no more than is necessary. Most forms of restraint include one other axiom: Control the head without endangering the fragile neck.

Too much and too little restraint can be a bad thing. Too little restraint can prolong a procedure (creating unnecessary struggle and stress) and result in injury to the alpaca or handler. Too much restraint can cause unnecessary stress and result in injury or death. Finesse and reading each animal are the keys to optimum restraint, not overwhelming strength. The experienced handler has a number of restraint methods in his or her repertoire and learns to apply the techniques that are appropriate. A well-trained animal may merely need to be held around the neck gently while the task being performed is completed. A never-handled animal may need to be taken off its feet and laid on the ground, where it is carefully held in a position that totally immobilizes it, so that procedures can be performed in a controlled way. On the ensuing pages, numerous types of restraint are illustrated and explained.

Cornering an Alpaca for Capture

Once a group of animals has been collected in a catch pen, individuals are likely to be restrained for procedures such as inoculations, drawing blood for progesterone testing, teeth trimming, and various kinds of examinations. The next step is to choose an animal to capture, and force it into a corner where you can physically restrain it. This requires anticipating the alpaca's possible escape routes and cutting them off as you approach slowly but deliberately. Often the animal being pursued will be in a group forced into a corner. Since captured animals will often turn their rumps toward you when you draw near, use this to your advantage. As you approach along the animal's flank, sweep the arm closest to the animal above its back and to the neck. This is the "capture arm." The arm to the outside serves as a distraction and is the "decoy arm." Hold your decoy arm out from your body and at eye level to the alpaca. It is important that the alpaca clearly see the hand so it is alert to its presence. If the animal appears likely to bolt, wiggle the finger in your decoy hand slightly so the alpaca is transfixed on it while the capture hand draws around the neck. In a steady, fluid motion, put your capture arm around the

To corner an alpaca in a catch pen, walk slowly with arms extended.

A halter and lead-rope restraint.

side of the alpaca's neck, draw the alpaca gently into your chest, and presto, the alpaca is restrained!

Halter and Lead-rope Restraint

In an ideal world all alpacas would be restrained using a lead-rope restraint method. Unfortunately, to create animals tractable enough to stand quietly on a lead rope while they undergo various routine procedures requires not only that they have been socialized to accept a halter and lead rope, but also that they will cooperate in the handling of various body parts, such as inspecting teeth, eyes, ears, genitalia, and feet. It's important that the halter fit correctly, so that air flow through the nostrils is not impaired or that an alpaca is not able to pull its head free because of the halter's loose fit, should it decide to resist by pulling on the halter.

Lead-trained animals whose legs are desensitized (see Chapter 6: Taming and Training) will stand while their toenails are trimmed. It is a joy to work with animals such as these. The best of the animals restrained in this fashion can be entirely shorn with the handler needing only to hold them on a short lead with their head positioned close to the handler's body. Alpacas in this elite behavioral grouping are the product of owners taking the time to properly train their animals to interact with people in a positive manner.

Training helps immeasurably, but it also needs to be stated that a genetic component contributes to temperament. There are identifiable bloodlines whose natural demeanor is calm and accepting, and there are bloodlines

whose demeanor is agitated and explosive, trained or untrained.

Lead-rope to Fence-post Restraint

Often an alpaca that is fairly well trained will behave well on a lead rope until unfamiliar interactions begin (injections, attempts to secure a leg to trim a toenail, etc.). The animal may react by bucking and attempting to pull free and flee, and restraining the animal can become a wrestling match. For some people an alpaca's strength may be more than they can handle. For the semi-trained, halter-broken animal that becomes somewhat incorrigible, wrapping the lead rope one-half turn around a fence post eliminates the contest of who is the stronger. The animal's pulling strength is absorbed by the post, not the handler. The handler controls the situation because he or she still holds the end of the rope.

With a fence-post restraint, the handler also has a free hand to help a veterinarian or to perform other tasks. This restraint is safest and most effective if the alpaca's head is given at least 6 inches (15 cm) of rope from the fence post. The animal should be sandwiched between a fence on one side and the handler on the other side, taking away attempts to spin, buck, and pull free. If the animal continues to buck wildly, the handler may need to stabilize the alpaca's head and make sure the animal does not smash its head (teeth) into the post. Most animals will simply pull backward, making the rope taut, and stop moving. Some may opt to sit down.

A lead-rope to fence-post restraint (rope with a half turn around the post).

While holding the rope, lift the rear leg for toenail trimming.

It is paramount that the lead rope is wrapped only one-half turn around the post and no more. This way, if an animal suddenly jumps wildly, twists, loses its footing, and is suspended from its neck (a rare occurrence that can result in a broken neck), the handler can let go of the rope and the animal will fall free. A half turn around a post will not allow the animal to be suspended. On the other hand, if the rope is wound a full turn or more around a post, the outcome will likely be entirely different and not an event you'll want to remember. If a full wrap has been employed, weight pulling down on the rope may make it impossible to free the animal. (Though it's macabre to contemplate, this would be like lifting a person hanging from a gallows to get the rope from around the victim's neck—a difficult feat for even a very strong person.) If an animal is suddenly off its feet and suspended by its neck, it must be freed instantaneously or the consequences can be fatal. Though most restraint goes smoothly enough, safeguarding the animal requires knowing what can go wrong and how to prevent it.

This technique is often effective for toenail trimming, applying ear and eye procedures and medications, teeth trimming, examinations of various kinds, and shearing.

Neck and Shoulder Hold

This is probably the most useful form of restraint. The handler pulls the alpaca's head near his or her body and stabilizes the alpaca with the other hand at the base of the neck over the withers. Most animals accept this type of restraint for simple procedures (injections, toenail trims,

A neck and shoulder hold.

A one-person neck and tail hold.

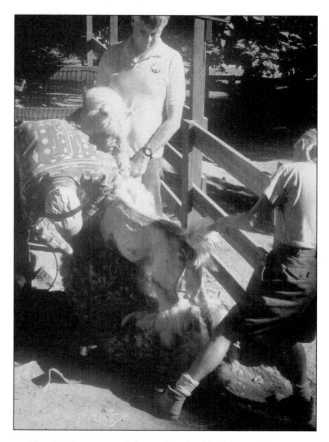

Two handlers accomplish a neck and tail hold during shearing.

application of medications, etc.). Some alpacas can be shorn from this position. The key is to hold the animal against your chest. If it moves or bucks, the downward pressure on the shoulders and the tight control of the head minimizes breaking free and becoming uncontrollable. It also minimizes the chance of being whacked in the face by the animal's head. The most common human error in applying the neck and shoulder hold is holding the animal away from one's body, which means that if the alpaca attempts to break free, the handler finds that using his or her hands is not sufficient to restrain a determined animal. If the animal's attempts to break free occurs when it is held against the chest, the handler is in a much stronger position to hold on. The key to this technique is sensing the comfort zone in the alpaca being held. Some animals are more easily restrained with a light touch, while others will react better when held more firmly. Knowing how much pressure to apply is one of the many joyful aspects of alpaca raising!

Neck and Tail Hold

This technique is useful with animals that spin, kush, or rear up. The tail is a convenient handle. For this hold to be successful, the handler and alpaca need to be physically compatible in size. Some handlers will find they don't have

sufficient reach to both hold the neck and the tail. In such situations a second handler holding the tail achieves the goal. Some animals (particularly stud males) often protest tail holding (proximity to genitals is too much for them) and will become more agitated and difficult to control. If the reaction is more agitation, don't use this type of restraint. The tail hold works on some animals, but not all. It is particularly helpful for alpacas being shorn and for toenail trimming sessions. There is some danger in using this technique. The tail should not be twisted and the animal should not be lifted off the ground by its tail. This may result in permanent injury.

Ear and Neck Hold

Commonly known as "earing," this hold is more effective on llamas than alpacas. Some alpacas respond poorly to earing; others stop resisting. The way in which the ear is held is important. The ear should be firmly held but not twisted or pulled. Some owners think earing is bad and makes animals head shy. This has not been my experience in training many llamas and alpacas to accept a halter. Instead, I've found that alpacas either accept earing or don't. Earing doesn't work on all animals, but it will work on many. It is a good technique (when it works) on animals being restrained for dental work, eye exams or medication,

An ear and neck hold.

Holding a neonate under its sternum while standing on a bathroom scale to weigh it. (Deduct the handler's weight from the combined weight.)

and any procedure that requires the head to be immobile. Obviously, if the animal's reaction is counterproductive, it should be discontinued.

Neonates

Neonates are generally easy to restrain. A neonate in kushed position can be straddled by someone kneeling. The person doing the straddling should not sit on the animal, just straddle it to restrain it. By holding the head, a cria can be "tubed" with milk and examined. In other situations a cria merely needs to be lifted up off the ground and held chest high while a veterinarian or caregiver administers medicines, takes a temperature, or examines it. The person's weight is not needed to hold the animal in place. More thought often needs to be given to what to do about a protective mother who doesn't want her baby molested by people. Moving the neonate to a catch pen and locking the mother out will allow you to work without her interference.

Straddling a Weanling

Weanlings and young adults are the most challenging to restrain. Like teenage people, weanling and young adult alpacas are athletic and strong, but are often reckless and prone to make poor judgments. Weanlings will attempt to jump fence, twist, and buck wildly when restrained, and they are apt to hurt themselves if caution is not exercised in working with them. I recommend not tying these animals unless they are clearly trained. Neck and shoulder restraint is often effective. Depending on the size of the handler and the size of the alpaca, straddling the animal while in a standing position is often effective. If you opt for straddling, both your feet should be planted firmly on the ground. Otherwise, if the animal attempts to flee, you may find yourself taking an unexpected ride.

Grasping a Leg for Toenail Trimming

Toenail trimming is a constant chore for anyone managing alpacas. Some animals require no trimming, while others require trimming several times a year. The person doing the trimming should understand how to safely secure a foot and how to trim the toenails correctly without injury.

Through training (see Chapter 6: Taming and Training) it is possible for an alpaca to become desensitized in its legs (willing to have its feet handled without resistance). Encountering such an alpaca is all too rare. Most alpacas will barely tolerate their front feet being held and will often resist by kicking when someone attempts to grasp their back feet.

Straddling a weanling to administer oral medication.

Grasping a leg for toenail trimming.

Regardless of a particular animal's training and acceptance, the first step is to restrain the animal so its feet can be handled. In flexing the legs to get a foot into the position where the toenails can be trimmed, care needs to be taken in not stressing joints or forcing legs to bend in ways for which they are not designed. When an alpaca lies down to avoid toenail trimming, its nails can still be trimmed by rolling the animal slightly to one side and trimming the toenails while the animal remains in a kushed position.

Note that when grasping the back leg, the grasp in the pastern area must be firm and fast. The leg must be moved to the trimming position quickly, or the animal will resist and kick free, possibly kicking the handler. The handler's head should be out of kicking range at all times when attempting to grasp a back leg.

With the foot secure the actual nail trimming should be done methodically, with care taken to make sure the angle of the cut is correct and does not involve the pad of the foot. Alpacas have sustained serious foot injuries when a trimmer cuts a toenail and unwittingly slices through the foot pad because the trimming device is held facing the

foot. Such injuries are painful for the animal, time consuming to medicate, and can heal slowly.

Injury is entirely avoidable when a toenail is cut in the correct direction, with the tips of the trimmer pointed away and to the front of the nail, never turned facing the foot. The other rule is that the nail cut should be parallel with the bottom of the foot and not at an upward angle that will cut into the quick, producing copious amounts of blood and unnecessary pain. Your initial nail-trimming experiences are best done under the guidance of an experienced person who understands what needs to take place for both your welfare and the alpaca's.

Restraining Chutes

Restraining chutes designed for South American camelids were invented in North America to control llamas, which are larger and stronger than alpacas. Many chutes designed for llamas aren't appropriate for alpacas. Many alpaca owners do not use restraining chutes and others see them as indispensable. In part the desire to use a chute defines the manner in which an owner is willing to interact with an alpaca when it is reacting to injections, tooth trimming, and other unpleasant procedures.

With a chute the handler has no risk and the alpaca is sometimes restrained so effectively that it is endangered. Generally alpacas emerge from a "chute experience" unscathed, but I know of animals killed and injured in restraining chutes. Beware of chutes that cross-tie the head in a manner that is difficult to release. An animal that jumps and twists and is suspended from its head or neck may be a dead animal. Beware of cinches that lift or restrict an animal by means of straps or cinches. I once attended a llama conference in which a demonstration of such a chute killed

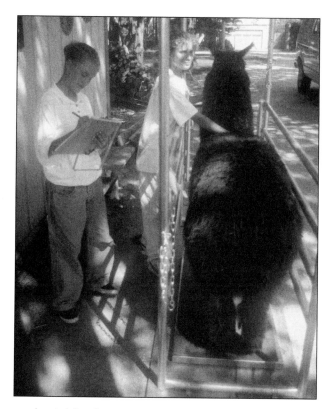

A restraining chute.

Californian Wayne Ausland uses a restraining table for shearing.

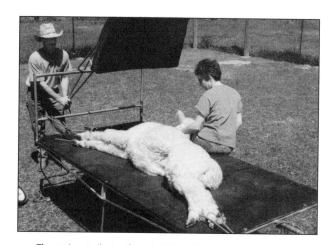

The major attribute of a restraining table is that even the most incorrigible alpaca can be restrained. This table, designed by Jon Robbins, is padded, making it more comfortable than the wood surface of many tables.

the llama (ruptured bladder) in front of an audience of several hundred people. Beware of mesh-walled chutes that may ensnare an alpaca's leg. Lastly, beware of chutes made of metal bars, especially ones with a back gate. Such chutes can contribute to broken legs when a defensive alpaca kicks out violently against a solid metal bar!

A safe chute should restrict the alpaca's movement with a minimum of constraining cinches, cross-ties, etc. A simple and effective restraining chute can be constructed with a post placed in the ground 9 inches (23 cm) from a wall. A piece of plywood attached to the post with hinges serves as the other wall to the chute. The alpaca is outfitted with a halter and lead rope. It is put against the wall and its head and neck are finessed past the post until the animal's shoulder is up against it. The hinged side is pushed gently against the animal's side, thus sandwiching it between two flat surfaces. When an alpaca is forced into this kind of chute, it will extend its head and neck through the gap between the post and wall. The rope is run through an eye bolt fixed at eye level. The end of the lead rope is always hand held, never tied. If an animal twists into a life-threatening position, the ability to release the head from restraint (lead rope) is critical.

A chute of this general configuration works well for most procedures. However, toenail trimming is better done outside of the chute. An animal placed in a chute should never be kept there any longer than the procedure takes to complete. An alpaca in a chute is experiencing stress, and the handler needs to work quickly and efficiently to return the alpaca to its more tranquil surroundings.

Restraining (Shearing) Tables

Those of you who feel uncomfortable holding your animals in any of the restraining holds described, and who desire more control and certainty in the outcome of your restraining experiences, can thank Russell Gent. He's the New Zealander who invented the "alpaca shearing table."

Carrying an adult alpaca (grasp your partner's forearm under the alpaca's abdomen).

keep your legs clear of the animal's back legs should it flail to free itself. If need be, put the animal gently onto the ground and take a breather, and repeat the lift until the alpaca is where you want it.

Lifting an alpaca in this manner is also appropriate when loading an alpaca into a vehicle that is too high off the ground or when an alpaca refuses to load. The method is simple and works well. If the animal panics while facing a vehicle, turn it away from the vehicle, lift it, and slide it into the vehicle, rear end first. Often an animal is calmer entering a vehicle in this way.

Chukkering

Chukkering is an Australian term that has been adopted by exporters and importers throughout the world. It is a method of forcing an animal into a kushed position by tying its back legs to its body. Chukkering assures that an animal will not move because it can't stand.

Chukkering of one sort or another has long been a method of restraining alpacas for truck transport on the altiplano. Entire shipments of alpacas, numbering hundreds of animals, are chukkered on the floors of DC-8 jet freighters hauling alpacas between continents. In balancing an airplane load with a large live cargo, keeping animals stationary is a concern. Chukkering has also been used to transport animals in small airplanes and trucks without adequate sideboards. (A more common method of international transport is to place alpacas in open-air pallets measuring as large as 12 × 12 feet (4 × 4 m) without tying. Alpacas are free to move around in the pallets but restricted from moving about the plane and causing load concerns.) Chukkering is also employed in situations such as rendering a male incapable of mating while in transport, should he be housed with a group of females.

Chukkering an alpaca requires careful tying and a knowledge of knots. First, select a soft, fairly thick rope, and fashion two loops in the rope about 12 inches (30 cm) apart. Then tie the rope around the animal slightly in front of the pelvic area, with the loops positioned where the hind legs would rest if the animal were in a natural kushed position. Knots that do not unravel or slip are necessary to successfully chukker an animal. Slide the back legs into each loop. When this is done, the alpaca can no longer stand.

It is extremely important that neither of the loops holding the back legs nor the rope around the body restrict the flow of blood or any other aspect of natural functions. An animal chukkered too tightly can be badly injured. With proper chukkering, large numbers of animals have been restrained and have arrived at a faraway destination unscathed. However, injuries to males' scrotums have been reported.

Designed to shear alpacas by securing them to a tilt-up table, this device has caught on throughout the alpaca-raising world because it works well. This shearing table not only serves as a sound shearing device, but also works well for numerous medical procedures and routine maintenance such as toe trimming, blood collection, collection for pregnancy tests, and teeth cutting (see Chapter 11: Fleece Preparation and Shearing).

Carrying an Adult Alpaca

How do you move an alpaca a short distance when it refuses to walk and sits down? This stubbornness can be especially frustrating in rough terrain where a wheeled cart or vehicle can't be used. The answer: Carry the alpaca with a friend. Adult alpacas weigh between 100 and 200 pounds (45–90 kg). The animal's weight is cut in half when two people share equally in lifting it.

Standing on opposite sides of the alpaca, grasp your hands underneath the animal's abdomen, up against the back legs. With your other hands hold the animal across the chest in front of its front legs. When you stand to walk,

Chukkering.

When selecting an animal for chukkering, give it a chance to void its bowels before being forced into a kushed position. It is more difficult and unsanitary for alpacas to relieve themselves in a kushed position.

The Take-down

The *take-down* is the term sometimes used by screeners when an animal is moved from a standing position to lying on its side. Between 1995 and 2002 screeners working in South America and on other continents examined more than 12,000 alpacas for many different alpaca registries around the world. All of these alpacas were manually lifted from a standing position and laid on the ground on their side (lateral recumbency) so their underside could be visually examined for extra teats, umbilical hernias, and other defects. There were no reported injuries, though the actual take-down manuever requires a combination of sensitivity, strength, and finesse on the part of the person assigned this chore (most often low-wage, hard-working quarantine workers).

The take-down can be done relatively easily to a juvenile alpaca, but it is more challenging with an adult. The animal's size and strength are factors to be considered in attempting a take-down. With a juvenile or short adult the usual method for the take-down is to stand facing the side of the alpaca. Bend over the animal's back to reach and grasp the inside of the two legs (one for each hand) that are on the side where you are standing. Lift the alpaca up and

out, and lay it on its side, as gently as possible. Move quickly to hold the alpaca to the ground by putting the correct (not too much) weight across the base of the neck and shoulder. Often the animal will struggle and kick out with its back legs, but it cannot get up if the person applying the pressure to the neck and shoulder does the job properly. Usually the kicking stops after a short while. If one of the reasons for a take-down is to trim the back toenails, have a second person grab the back legs and pull them firmly (but not too hard) until they are extended away and back at about 45 degrees from the animal.

The take-down with a heavy or large alpaca is a little more challenging and may not always be possible. However, I have seen Quechua men, who are often short in stature, perform take-downs on full-sized llamas on the altiplano. The technique for a large animal is different than the preferred method described above. If one person is attempting to do this, reaching the inside legs from over the alpaca's back may not be possible. The animal's sternum can serve as a handhold to lift the animal and begin the rotation of its body. As the animal is lifted, the handler pushes his thigh into the side of the animal, while pulling the animal toward him. If all works correctly, the animal finds itself on its side. Lifting an animal that is 200 pounds (90 kg) is a tall order for many people. Keep in mind that the lift alone won't result in a take-down. The lift must be accompanied with a simultaneous rotation of the animal's torso.

The take-down sequence and toenail trim.

The take-down is not advisable for everyone. There is danger of injury to the handler, primarily due to the heavy lifting and brief but strenuous struggle. Alpacas don't like to be put on their side and will resist as much as possible. The alpaca can be injured if it is not laid on the ground as gently as possible. The idea isn't to slam the alpaca to the ground, but rather to lift and rotate the animal to the ground. Make sure the chosen surface is smooth and freed of rocks and other debris.

Moving Sick and Incapacitated Alpacas

What if you are confronted with a medical emergency? If you find a sick or disabled alpaca that cannot walk on its own and the animal's only hope is to move it to a veterinary hospital as fast as possible, you have several options. Many livestock feed outlets sell "calf sleds," made of heavy gauge plastic, with a rope tied to one end. Load the sick animal into the sled and drag it to your vehicle. Other methods include placing the animal on a piece of plywood and dragging it, or having four people lift the animal. Still another method is to fashion a tarp into a stretcher and carry the animal to a conveyance.

Once the animal is inside the conveyance, attempt to keep it in a sternal position with its neck slightly elevated. Do not allow it to roll onto its back.[1,2]

REFERENCES

1. Fowler, M. E.: *Medicine and Surgery of South American Camelids.* Ames: Iowa State University Press, pp. 24–34, 1989.
2. Hoffman, E., and M. E. Fowler: *The Alpaca Book.* Healdsburg, CA: Clay Press, 1995.

Chapter 6

Taming and Training

Eric Hoffman

A mother and her small child meet an alpaca for the first time.

Centuries of selectively breeding alpacas have created predictable, easy-to-manage animals: herd oriented, intelligent, and with a stoic aloofness similar to the outward behavior of the Andean people who bred them.

If 500 vicuñas were released from a corral and allowed to disperse over a vast, fenceless plain, it would be ludicrous to send a child to round them up and herd them back into the corral. The vicuña, the wild progenitor of the alpaca, can be counted on not to cooperate. Yet, Aymara and Quechua women and children release their alpacas from rock corrals (*canchones*) each morning and herd them back each night. This comparison of wild vicuñas and domestic alpacas illustrates how effectively generations of Andean pastoralists have modified wild camelid behavior to suit human needs. Today alpacas are generally born with easily managed and predictable dispositions, and there are no wild or feral alpacas anywhere in the world. They are exceptionally well suited for herding, and they quickly accept the patterns of movement to and from pastures that are chosen by their handlers.[7,12]

In North America, Australasia, and Europe, the three regions with the greatest interest in alpacas outside South America, people are often attracted to alpacas because of their endearing looks. These owners may view their animals as fiber producers and investments, but often they also desire to interact with alpacas as pets.

A well-adjusted alpaca is curious and accepting of people, but a bit standoffish, not fawning like a dog. In fact, most alpacas don't like to be touched and are comfortable interacting with people as long as they stay just out of reach. Training techniques that are successful with dogs, horses, and other domestic animals don't always work with alpacas, leading some people to interpret an alpaca's behavior as fearful, stubborn, and uncooperative. These interpretations may have some truth, depending on the individual animal, but an alpaca's initial skittishness is usually easily overcome. It makes good sense to understand as fully as possible the ancestral roots of alpaca behavior (see Chapter 2: Behavior and Communication). The most successful, efficient, and minimally stressful taming takes place within the structure of that behavior.[7,11,12,13,20]

REASONS FOR TAMING AND TRAINING

In a strict sense alpacas come tame. That is, they are manageable domestic animals. But for this discussion, *taming* refers to making alpacas more accepting of people, while *training* refers to teaching animals to perform particular acts.

An alpaca that can be easily caught, handled, and habituated to human routines will enjoy a safer and less stressful life. This is readily apparent in all phases of alpaca husbandry: routine maintenance, such as toenail trimming and annual injections; medical emergencies that require rapid loading and travel to a veterinarian; shearing; and changes of location, such as walking an alpaca on a lead rope to a paddock at the other end of the property or transporting

Californian Sherry Edensmith demonstrates how to approach and catch an alpaca in a small pen. Alpacas rarely attempt to push by a person.

one to a local elementary school where children can touch its soft coat. A trained alpaca moves through these events with a minimum of stress, whereas an animal that has not had the benefit of training may experience a great deal of stress and possibly injure itself when it is handled. It is worth the time to train alpacas. Also, of two animals that are otherwise equal, the trained alpaca is more marketable than the untrained one.[1,19,21]

Setting Reasonable Expectations and Goals

What are reasonable expectations and goals for the training process? This depends on the size of the herd and the attitude of the owner. Minimal requirements for individual alpacas are as follows.

1. *Be easy to catch.* Capturing alpacas easily is largely a function of good farm layout and habituating alpacas to entering catch pens by baiting, driving, or other means.[8,24] (See Chapter 4: Husbandry for tips on construction of catch pens and methods of enticing alpacas to enter.)

2. *Be halter and lead trained.* Alpacas should learn to accept wearing a halter without a struggle and to be directed by a human handler by means of a lead rope attached to a halter.

3. *Be desensitized.* This key ingredient to taming refers to overcoming an alpaca's fear of being handled. When desensitization is complete, an alpaca should allow its neck, back, and legs to be handled without a struggle.

4. *Be trained to load in a trailer.* An alpaca will most likely need to be transported at some point in its lifetime. Transportation is stressful to an alpaca and potentially more so to an untrained one. An alpaca should be trained to step in and out of a trailer or van in a cooperative, safe manner. This ability can become crucially important if a small person, who cannot lift or control an alpaca, is suddenly faced with an emergency, such as a trip to a veterinarian or rapid evacuation (forest fire, flood, etc.; see Chapter 8: Transportation).

Exceptional Training Goals

Most alpacas can be trained to handle the minimal goals listed above, but an alpaca with a suitable temperament can be trained to do more.

1. *Come when called.* Once alpacas become habituated to grain or pellets (always in small amounts; see Chapter 9: Diet), they will come running when it is about to be distributed. Alpacas will learn to associate a call such as "paca, pacas" with feeding and in time will respond to the call, even if they do not get a treat each time.

2. *Respond to "stand" command and other verbal cues.* Alpacas and llamas can be taught to sit down (kush) and stand on verbal command. The "stand" command is useful in catching or showing an alpaca. Verbal commands can extend to a narrow range of other behaviors.[3,4]

3. *Carry a light pack.* The llama is the true South American pack animal, but alpacas can also carry light loads.

A well-trained alpaca will accept a halter without struggling. It should fit high on the muzzle and be loose enough for the lower mandible to move freely for eating and chewing cud.

Historically alpacas have not been used to carry loads. The pack's weight should not exceed one-quarter of the animal's weight or 25 pounds (11.4 kg), whichever is greater. I have packed with llamas for nearly 30 years and learned that there are significant personality differences in animals when it comes to trail performance. The animal's willingness to walk, amount of fleece, structural integrity, and conditioning must be considered. The best llamas are remarkable pack animals, capable of 20 miles a day with 3,000-foot (1,000-m) vertical climbs in a single day. Highly conditioned llamas are capable of sustaining a 7-minute per mile pace for 7 miles, while carrying 50 pounds (22.2 kg). Not as much is known about alpaca stamina. Owners contemplating packing with alpacas should read articles on various aspects of training (tethering, for example), first aid, and the requirements of a sound, safe pack.[1,16]*

4. *Pull a cart.* In the 1980s llama owners were somewhat astounded when Jim Faiks (Alaska), Bobra Goldsmith (Colorado), Paul and Betty Barkman (California), and Stubb Johnson (Iowa) demonstrated that a llama is capable of pulling a cart in the same predictable manner as a horse or mule (though with considerably less towing power). These pioneer trainers took llama training down a new path. There is no reason to assume alpacas aren't as capable of learning to pull a cart, though their small stature limits their pulling capacity to lightweight undertakings.

5. *Show and perform.* A percentage of people who own most kinds of domestic animals like to interact with their animals in competitive formats. Most of these contests with alpacas showcase the animals and often provide the general public with its first contact with alpacas. Most competitions fall into one of two categories: showing or performing. A show animal is judged on criteria such as soundness and fleece, and must be responsive, stand correctly, and allow judges to pick through its fleece without losing composure. A performance animal is judged almost entirely on its training.[6,16] An alpaca negotiating an obstacle course must overcome its natural fears and demonstrate willingness to follow its handler through water, over jumps, into trailers, past barking dogs, etc. Animals that are not prepared properly may cause the owner embarrassment and create an unfavorable impression.[22,26]

METHODS, EQUIPMENT, AND REFERENCE BOOKS

In the short time that llamas and alpacas have become popular in North America (since the mid-1970s for llamas, the mid-1980s for alpacas), great strides have been made in training methodology. For example, in South America haltering and lead training animals are rare. There, alpacas are herded in large groups, and attention to individuals is uncommon.

*For example, see the the information located at www.llamapacks.com.

In the United States llamas have been trained to run in endurance races, pull surrey carts, sit and stand on command, and negotiate complicated obstacle courses (in a few instances without the security of a lead rope). In general, most of the techniques used on llamas apply to alpacas; however, alpacas have a stronger banding instinct (see Chapter 2: Behavior and Communication) than many llamas. For the person experienced with llamas, the pronounced banding characteristic of alpacas requires an adjustment in training philosophy.

To date, several books on llama training and a couple of books dedicated to training both alpacas and llamas are available. You will find numerous approaches to training in these publications. It's important to identify the techniques that make the most sense to you. The trainer's confidence in what he or she is doing is essential to a successful outcome. Each book has its strengths and unique focus, and the authors have a great deal of interest and experience in camelid training. Regardless of the approach you adopt, here are several important prerequisites to consider in successfully training alpacas.

1. *Be patient, move slowly, and talk softly.* Training any kind of animal requires understanding and patience. Although events usually unfold as planned, assume there will be surprises that will put you to the test. Also, assume all alpacas are trainable to the "reasonable expectations and goals" listed previously. Though there are common responses to training, each animal is different. The simplest expectation (for example, that an alpaca will take a step in response to your tug on the lead rope) may take an inordinate amount of time to accomplish with one animal, but only seconds with another.

Your own body movements should be slow and deliberate. Grabbing, running, and other quick movements escalate the alpaca's desire to escape. When approaching an untrained animal in a catch pen, move slowly behind it. Holding your arms out from your sides makes it more difficult for an alpaca to race past you. Watch the alpaca's eyes and body language and anticipate its desire to flee. If the animal appears to be eyeballing an escape route, move to cut it off. If you move slowly, a flick of the hand closest to the anticipated exit often deters the alpaca or freezes it momentarily. You'll notice that alpacas respond and reposition themselves in a catch pen based on fairly subtle movements of the catcher.

Usually an animal about to be handled will position its hindquarters toward the trainer. When it strikes this position, slowly move to grasp the animal around the neck. If this can be done in a slow motion, it works better for both alpaca and handler. Talking softly seems to help allay fear.[9,13,15]

Lead training is easier to accomplish by letting an alpaca that is already lead trained walk directly ahead of the animal being trained. In this photo, the second alpaca is on a lead for the first time. It is nervous but follows readily. All alpacas have a strong banding instinct. In this case, the instinct to stay close to another alpaca made it possible to train the second animal without a struggle. In a few short sessions, the student alpaca learned to walk on a lead rope independent of other alpacas.

2. *Use equipment and tack correctly.* The essential equipment consists of a catch pen (see Chapter 4: Husbandry), a properly fitting halter, a lead rope, and a 4-foot (1.3-m) lightweight buggy whip (or piece of plastic pipe). The whip (or pipe) is never used to strike the alpaca, but serves as an extension of the trainer's hands and arms. The length and lightness of a whip gives the trainer better control of an animal about to be caught and, while leading an alpaca, the ability to reach to the animal's rump and "tickle" it from the rear to encourage forward movement. This whip (or like object) is also used in desensitizing an alpaca's legs.

The halter must fit correctly and be well made so that it doesn't suddenly release when an alpaca tugs or jerks its head. Do not attempt training unless the halter fits correctly. Too loose or too tight can result in a failed training session, injury to the alpaca, and a negative learning experience for both alpaca and trainer.[5,15,18,25]

3. *Use finesse, not overpowering strength.* Training alpacas requires more finesse than strength. Towing, dragging, or jerking an alpaca is counterproductive and may injure the animal. The successful trainer reads each animal's response and adjusts his or her approach accordingly, which requires outthinking the alpaca-student. For example, if an alpaca refuses to budge, a tug-of-war will accomplish little, even if you have the strength to skid the animal forward by tugging on the lead rope. Instead, by moving about 45 degrees off the alpaca's nose and pulling on the lead, you force the animal to make a crossover step to maintain its balance—and lo and behold, the alpaca has begun walking. You might find you have to move back and forth across the

nose several times to convince the animal to take steps before it begins tracking in a straight line. The animal may suddenly explode by leaping and bucking (a common response during the first 15 feet of lead training). Don't panic—merely stand your ground and keep the rope taut and low with the animal's head toward you (this way the alpaca can't twist its neck and hurt itself). You'll find an alpaca that explodes will usually exhaust itself in a minute or two and stand or sit in a matter of moments. After the animal regains its calm, training can proceed.[9,15,18,27]

4. *Use a trained companion alpaca to lead train a beginner.* This point can't be stressed enough. An alpaca cooperates much more readily in the company of a trained alpaca acting as a companion lead animal. Lead-rope training is the most challenging exercise alpaca owners are likely to encounter when training their animals. Using and making use of their banding instinct is a great help in easing an inexperienced alpaca into accepting a lead rope and behaving in a responsive fashion (see Chapter 2: Behavior and Communication).

Lead training is accomplished most efficiently with two or three people and two or three alpacas. A halter and lead rope are secured to a trained alpaca, preferably the beginner's mother (providing she is not overly protective) or a familiar paddock mate. The beginner is also haltered and attached to a lead rope. For best results, separate the pair from the herd so the learner's entire focus (and yearning to be close to another alpaca) will be on the one remaining animal. With the animals positioned side by side, the trained animal is slowly led away. Its handler should always be aware of what the untrained animal is doing and respond accordingly. For example, if the beginner starts to balk and slows down or stops, the trained animal should also slow down or stop—always staying about half a body length ahead. Usually the student will follow with very little coaxing. As the two move along, the follower learns about the confines of the lead rope. A third person's presence to the rear often helps keep an animal moving, although some animals tend to spin sideways. In that case, positioning the third person on the side to which the animal spins usually stops this behavior.

Usually, a beginner will understand the lead rope in about 15 to 20 minutes. As the alpaca's understanding increases and its fear subsides, it can be guided to walk parallel to its companion animal. When this seems to work well, the learner can be coaxed ahead of its companion and take its turn as lead animal. Ultimately, the alpaca is considered trained to lead when it walks with a slack lead and follows in the direction human handlers take it, regardless of what other alpacas in the

Of the South American camelids, llamas are true pack animals, but some alpacas are good lightweight packers as well.

vicinity are doing, You'll find that some animals enjoy leading and take readily to walking alone, while others are content only if they follow another alpaca. Many animals are lead trained in two or three sessions; others take longer.[13]

Trying to lead train an alpaca alone often results in pathetic humming, various forms of uncooperative behavior (sitting, bucking, balking, etc.), and an expressed desire to rejoin the herd. It is not impossible to train an alpaca solo, but it usually involves a great deal more stress and strain to both the trainer and the student.

5. *Adjust training techniques to fit the animal.* Animals do not respond to training identically. Some animals can be trained to halter, lead, and load into trailers in a matter of minutes; others may take much longer. Some will perform favorably only in the company of other alpacas. The training books discuss the many different responses animals may present to a trainer. Two common responses are the "explosion" and the "sit-down." The explosion and a brief description of how to respond were described in point 3. The main objective in this situation is to avoid injury to you or the alpaca. The sit-down, often accompanied by screaming (see Chapter 2: Behavior and Communication), is sometimes difficult to overcome. Dragging an animal to its feet isn't the best solution. Some animals will refuse to get up, no matter how hard you pull. In fact, you can lift some animals entirely off the ground and they will refuse to lower their legs to stand. Better approaches are to lift the animal to its feet by grasping it under the sternum, or to have one or more trained alpacas slowly begin to walk away from the animal, which will often persuade it to follow.

6. *Eliminate distractions.* A common distraction that causes havoc during training is the family dog. A dog may be a family pet, but an alpaca usually views it as a predator. Other distractions include motor vehicles, unfamiliar kinds of livestock, loud and curious people (children who run and gyrate can be especially disruptive to training efforts), and windy conditions that cause familiar forms (trees, tarps, etc.) to move.

7. *Consider safety.* Though injuries during training are rare, they can occur, especially with young animals, who tend to be more flighty than adults. Despite its apparent thickness, the alpaca's long neck is thin. Avoid allowing an alpaca to position itself in a way that allows its neck to twist backward. This often occurs when an inexperienced animal is given too much lead rope and suddenly bolts ahead of its handler. The alpaca's head should be controlled and pointed in the vicinity of the handler, and the animal should walk behind or to the side of the trainer. An alpaca walking ahead of the handler is not under control.

The chances of human injury are slight but can occur. Avoid bending over an alpaca's lowered head. Be aware that a panicky alpaca may bring its head from ground level to an alert position suddenly and with enough force to smack a person. This is not a hostile reaction, but if you're the recipient of a head-to-head blow, you'll think you've been slugged by a prize fighter. Some alpacas will occasionally kick with their hind legs during training. Their kick is lightning fast, but because of the alpaca's small size and padded feet, the full-force kick usually results in no injury or only a slight bruising or scratch from the animal's toenail. A child or adult who bends down near an alpaca's hindquarters may be at risk to be kicked in the face, which can result in a serious eye injury. Always respect the hindquarters.

8. *Avoid creating maladjusted, improperly imprinted male alpacas.* Alpacas are herd animals whose inbred behaviors are reinforced by interactions with other members of the herd. The most crucial period for an alpaca's psychological development appears to be the first months of life. Alpaca crias that are given too much human attention during this period may become maladjusted and possibly aggressive toward people when they mature. There have been cases of llamas, alpacas, and tamed vicuñas and guanacos who have had this developmental phase interrupted by too much of the wrong kind of human intervention. The price for meddling in the imprinting process, particularly with males, can be tragic. In some cases the male must be destroyed be-

Iowan Stubb Johnson was a feature at many llama auctions in the Midwest during the 1980s with his precision pulling team of perfectly matched llamas. So far, no such team exists with alpacas, but alpacas are as able to learn as these llamas.

cause of the danger it poses to people after it matures. Llamas and alpacas who have spent their early months in petting zoos must often be destroyed. Females can develop pushy personalities and be quick to spit on people.[2,23]

Owners can head off a tragedy or milder forms of unwanted behavior by being alert to certain signs. A young alpaca who has become imprinted by people will act submissively toward a person by crouching and flipping its tail up onto its back, signaling that person as it would another alpaca. It is having difficulty distinguishing between people and alpacas. If a young male begins signaling submission to people who enter his paddock, every attempt should be made to minimize human interaction and to keep the male in a herd situation that will absorb his interests. When a confused male matures and becomes territorial, he may attack (ram, bite, etc.) or attempt to mount people. Generally, males who are raised in the confines of the herd with minimal human interaction during the first six months don't become maladjusted.

It is not uncommon for bottle-fed babies (due to lactation problems or death of the mother) to have behavior problems later in life. However, bottle-fed crias can become normal adults if human interaction during feeding is minimal. For example, some owners leave a baby with other alpacas so it will bond with the herd, and they bottle-feed the baby by pushing the bottle's nipple through a board with a hole in it, so the cria doesn't associate the milk with people.

Even though some training processes strive to successfully desensitize and train very young animals, the safe course for males is to hold off until after weaning. Though the incidence of male imprinting problems is rare, such problems do occur, and new owners with no knowledge of alpacas' inbred behavioral tendencies are apt to lavish too much attention on an adorable youngster, causing it to develop incorrectly.[24]

ESTABLISHING PATTERNS OF GROUP BEHAVIOR

Alpaca herd behavior has some subtle nuances to consider in management decisions. Like a cat, an alpaca is consumed by a natural curiosity to investigate new things in its environment. I once watched two crias walk with their noses pressed to the ground, just inches above a tiny bug as it crawled across the paddock. The insect's movement was of great interest to the alpacas, who stayed glued to its progress until it left their pen.

Alpacas constantly watch and investigate their environment. When a gate is left open, an entire herd will often move through the opening without hesitation, as if the herd had already discussed that "the grass is greener on the other side of the fence." To a novice owner, animals escaping in this manner might appear to be a challenge to capture and return to their pen. However, the alpaca has an inborn conservative side to it as well that can be an asset to the alpaca manager. Alpacas love to investigate, but at day's end (or in a short amount of time) or if frightened, they also have a strong tendency to want to return to their primary living area.

Throughout South America this pattern of dispersing during the day and returning at night is relied upon daily. Whole herds of alpacas are let out of their *canchones* and allowed to graze for most of the day. In the afternoon a herd of 2,000 or 3,000 animals can be prodded by a small child and en masse the whole herd will regroup, turn around, and return to the corral for the night. This type of foraging-walking-returning pattern becomes so imprinted that entire herds will actually disperse and return on their own.

Herds and small groups will learn a dispersal and return pattern that can become fairly complicated. For example, in small farm situations animals will often learn to congregate at a gate at an expected time, as if they have an appointment to be there. When the gate is opened they will pass through it until they reach another gate, where they will wait until it is opened. I have known herds that will pass through three and four gates in this manner to reach a grazing area, and at day's end repeat the performance with no human involvement other than opening successive gates.

The point of explaining alpacas' ability to disperse and regroup on home turf is to give alpaca owners more foraging options. By and large, alpacas are capable of learning and sticking to patterns in a very predictable manner. Knowing this allows managers to make greater use of available pasture and rotation of pastures. Of course, if alpacas are being dispersed into less secure surroundings for foraging, predators and other hazards need to be considered.

This alpaca characteristic of going somewhere and returning has other applications as well. I have known several studs who can be released into successive pens until the animal reaches a female selected for breeding. When the breeding is completed, these males (with only minimal ushering) will return through successive gates and pens to their original holding area. Not all males are capable of doing this, but many are.[11,12,13]

PLANNING TO MINIMIZE MALE AGGRESSION

Like their wild progenitor, the vicuña, the male alpaca has strong territorial instincts. When allowed to live with a group of females, some males become belligerent toward other males (even ones housed in nearby pens) and develop into agitated, nervous animals that spend much of their time pacing fences and threatening any visible male. This behavior can become unsettling and annoying if the male screeches and stands on fences to intimidate nearby males. Often a male behaving like this elicits similar responses from nearby males until aggression displays are a constant spectacle, hardly a harmonious and desirable situation. When a male who has become obsessive about his territory is returned to an all-male setting, he may be overly aggressive and eventually need to be housed in a separate paddock to control his aggression. The aim of the alpaca manager should be to minimize this type of behavior and attempt to create an environment in which males do not become management problems.

Nature gives an example worth emulating. Territorial male vicuñas are intolerant animals, driving all challengers away and consuming all their time guarding their territory and the females living in it. Yet, large bachelor herds of young males and older males without a territory often live together harmoniously. Why? The bachelor herds operating away from the territorial males and without the close proximity of females aren't experiencing the behavioral mechanisms that bring on aggression and uncompromising territoriality (see Chapter 2: Behavior and Communication).

The alpaca manager can create a similar situation by housing the males as far away from his females as possible. When breeding occurs, a stud can be moved to a breeding pen (a neutral place) for that breeding and returned to his bachelor group. In this manner he never establishes a territory and is never put into a position that triggers his

Some public relations assignments are harder than others. Find the alpaca.

San Franciscan Dr. Greg Moon jogs with an alpaca named Dustin.

highly territorial instincts. He is a breeding male, but one who lives in a bachelor herd. Often large numbers of breeding male alpacas can be housed in a single paddock, provided the group is made up of individuals who haven't developed hostile and intolerant patterns that are more apt to be brought on by prolonged time with female groups. This strategy to put a lid on male aggression allows the manager to house more males in a single paddock, and the males can live a harmonious life not filled with fighting.[11,12,13]

REFERENCES

1. Barkman, P., and B. Barkman: Teaching a Llama to Tether. *Llamas* 1(4): 59, 1987.
2. Barkman, P., and B. Barkman: Llama Male Management. *Llamas* 2(3): 67, 1988.
3. Barkman, P., and B. Barkman: Teaching a Llama to Work Leadless. *Llamas* 3(6): 43, 1989.
4. Barkman, P., and B. Barkman: Training to Kush. *Llamas* 5(8): 35, 1991.
5. Daugherty, S.: Halters. *Llamas* 4(3): 67–68, 1990.
6. Fercho, L.: Loose Lead Training. *Llamas* 5(4): 131, 1991.
7. Franklin, W. L.: Biology, Ecology, and the Relationship to Man of the South American Camelids. In *Mammalian Biology in South America* (M. A. Genoway and H. H. Genoway, eds.). Lineville, PA: Pymatuning Laboratory, University of Pennsylvania, Special Publications Series 6, 1982.
8. Goldsmith, B.: How to Catch the Uncatchable Llama. *Llamas* 2(3): 57, 1988.
9. Hoffman, E.: Training the Small Fry. *Llamas* 1(2): 43–44, 1987.
10. Hoffman, E.: Sunny, the Pioneer Llama. *California Living, San Francisco Chronicle*, 1979. Reprinted in *Llamas* 6(8): 64–69, 1992.
11. Hoffman, E.: The Many Ways Guanacos Talk. *International Wildlife* 23(4): 4–11, 1993.
12. Hoffman, E.: Ships of the Andes. *Pacific Discovery* 42(3): 7–15, 1993.
13. Hoffman, E.: Understanding Alpaca Language and Behavior for Better Management. *Llamas* 8(3): 39–40, 1994.
14. Hyder, L., and J. Mayerle: Showmanship and Obstacle Courses. *Llamas* 4(3): 98–111, 1990.
15. Mallon, J.: How to Train a Llama in Ten Minutes. *Llamas* 5(4): 109, 1991.
16. Mallon, J.: Performance Training, Part 2. *Llamas* 2(2): 49, 1991.
17. McGee, M.: TTEAM Approach to Llama Training. *Llamas* 1(4): 64–68, 1987.
18. McGee, M.: TTEAM Approach to Halter Training. *Llamas* 6(3): 59, 1992.
19. McGee, M.: TTEAM Approach to Toenail Trimming. *Llamas* 6(6): 69, 1992.
20. McGee, M.: Llama Watching. *Llamas* 7(4): 101–104, 1993.
21. McGee, M.: The TTEAM Approach to Training and Handling. *Alpacas*, pp. 20–22, December 1994.
22. Rais, J.: Obstacle Courses. *Llamas* 5(5): 38, 1991.
23. Rolfing, S.: Berserk Male Syndrome. *Llamas* 1(5): 70–73, 1987.
24. Taylor, P.: Herding Llamas. *Llama Life* 10: 24–27, 1989.
25. Taylor, S.: Halters. *Llamas*, pp. 18–19, 1985.
26. Vaughan, D., and D. Vaughan: Making Sense of Show Classes. *Llamas* 4(3): 83–84, 1990.
27. Vreeland, E.: Training People for Llamas. *Llamas* 5(6): 95, 1991.

TRAINING BOOKS

1. Barkman, P., and B. Barkman: *A Well Trained Llama: A Trainer's Guide* (expanded and revised), 101 pages, 1989.
2. Bennett-McGee, M.: *Camelid Companion*. Raccoon Press, 386 pages, May 2001.
3. Goldsmith B.: *Training Llamas: What Every Llama Should Know* (1-hour, 54-minute video). Hart Productions, Juniper Ridge Press, 1986.
4. Goldsmith, B.: *Training Llamas to Drive* (video). Hart Productions, Juniper Ridge Press, 1989.

These books may be ordered from Quality Llama Products, telephone (800) 638-4689, e-mail sales@llamaproducts.com.

Chapter 7

Shows

Eric Hoffman

A show stopper in Arequipa, Peru.

A show can be a wonderful event. Shows can offer a forum to evaluate, improve, and promote qualities in the alpaca as a fiber-producing animal. Shows provide many people their first contact with alpacas. Show results can influence the industry and a breeder's income. Shows are a gathering place for members of the alpaca community. They are a forum in which all that is right and all that is wrong with the industry are expressed. This chapter explores the opportunities and challenges that shows present to alpaca owners.

HISTORICAL BEGINNINGS

In North America the Llama Show Association, established in 1988, changed its name to the Alpaca and Llama Show Association (ALSA) to acknowledge the increasing alpaca numbers in the existing llama show format. The first training session for judges specifically dedicated to alpacas took place in Bonny Doon, California in 1989, and the first alpaca show was held in Grass Valley, California in 1990. Murray Fowler, DVM, who is well known for his knowledge of camelid anatomy, helped steer the initial discussions establishing criteria for alpaca conformation.

Fiber as a topic received sporadic input from a variety of sources during the initial years. ALSA and AOBA (Alpaca Owners and Breeders Association) held the first Alpaca Fiber Judging Clinic in 1998. Peter Kothe, a renowned expert from the fiber industry in Peru, and Dr.

George Davis, an animal research scientist in New Zealand, addressed would-be judges.[1]

In 2001, AOBA developed the AOBA Show Division, creating a second show entity in North America. At this writing the two show organizations (ALSA and AOBA) have very similar show rules and employ most of the same judges. ALSA was the first organization to amass and publish a comprehensive judging manual. Now both ALSA and AOBA publish judging manuals. The 139-page *The Llama and Alpaca Judging Manual* (ALSA) and the 98-page *Alpaca Show Division Handbook* (AOBA) explain their show rules and terminology. These publications are updated periodically.[1,2]

Alpaca shows have been held in Australia since 1990. The Australian Alpaca Association (AAA) now oversees both regional and national shows across the breadth of Australia. The AAA publishes the *Australian Alpaca Association Showing Rules Manual,* a 56-page explanation of all phases of showing.[4]

Alpaca shows have also been conducted in Peru, Chile, England, New Zealand, and Germany.

WHY DO PEOPLE SHOW ALPACAS?

Animal shows have ancient origins dating back many hundreds of years. People show alpacas for a number of reasons. Some breeders enjoy the social networking that shows offer within the alpaca community. They attend to look for animal types and pedigrees that may enhance their breeding program, to monitor industry trends, and to show the outcome of their own breeding programs. Some breeders live and breathe show results, which are featured prominently in their marketing and promotional efforts. Many breeders rarely or never attend shows.

Why Are Shows Important?

Even though the majority of alpaca owners do not participate in shows on a regular basis, they should be knowledgeable about the decisions made in the show ring. The criteria used to pick winners set trends in motion that may substantially increase or decrease the value of their animals. Shows represent the alpaca business to the public and create the public perception of breed excellence. Being a show winner can be beneficial for a farm's advertising and sales.

Can You Market Animals Without Participating in Shows?

Although shows are seen as a way to gain a marketing advantage, the knowledgeable buyer often finds the best animal for the best price by shopping outside of the show circuit. Because an animal is not shown does not mean it is defective or not a potential show winner. Some longtime breeders who produce sound, fine-fleeced alpacas don't enter shows. Some of these breeders have philosophical and ethical objections to various aspects of how shows are conducted and view dependence on shows as an exercise in political maneuvering and an unwanted vexation in their quest of acquiring good-quality alpacas. Some breeders are concerned about the stress and risk of exposure to disease that accompany shows. Marketing alpacas without participating in shows has worked well for many breeders.

HALTER SHOWS, OBSTACLE (OR HANDLER) SHOWS, AND FLEECE SHOWS

There are three basic categories for showing alpacas: halter (live animal showing), performance (an obstacle course where an animal demonstrates its training for use as a public relations animal), and fleece shows (fleeces separated from the alpaca). These three categories have subdivisions for public relations, youth, and other areas of interest.

Fleeces are judged anonymously so that judges do not know who owns a particular fleece.

At the time of this writing, both the halter and performance classes involve the owner or handler presenting an animal before a judge. In these live alpaca competitions, the animals are judged against one another. The "best" animal in a particular class is awarded top honors based on how it stacks up against the other contestants. In the larger

A proud Peruvian with his ribbon-winning alpaca.

shows champions are chosen from a final competition made up of the winners of each class.[2]

Classes and Levels

Alpacas are grouped by breed type (suri or huacaya), age, sex, and color in all the show systems. There are minimum and maximum class-size requirements. For example, in the AOBA system, four animals of the same color make up a minimum class size. When a minimum of four can't be achieved, groups of like animals (three or less) are combined with another class (in the same general color group) to make a class large enough to judge. There are also maximum sizes for classes. The definition of what constitutes a color class may change somewhat from time to time.

Separating animals into a wide range of color classes allows more people to participate and have a positive experience showing. It also works well to promote the amazing color diversity found in alpacas. Generally 3 to 4 age groups and about 20 colors are recognized, depending on the system.

In the AOBA judging system, shows are identified by levels. Levels are determined by estimating the total number of entries based on the previous year's show. There are four levels: Level I is 24 to 74 entries, Level II is 75 to 174, Level III is 175 to 349, and Level IV is more than 350 alpacas.[2] Only certain judges are authorized to judge the larger shows where class winners are shown against one another to produce a champion.

Criteria for Judging

Halter shows are usually judged on criteria thought to best exemplify the breed or species. Except in performance or showmanship classes, the two basic types of criteria for alpacas are conformation and fiber. A show result is a comparison and opinion, not a comprehensive exam. So far in the development of show judging, alpacas are not judged against an ideal or standard with specific requirements. Thus, there is ongoing debate about judging criteria.

In nature, with wild animals such as the vicuña (parent species of the alpaca), the criteria for breed excellence are entirely governed by natural selection, i.e., survival of the fittest. The animal's appearance and design have been honed by millions of years of evolution. The result is an animal superbly designed for its environment. The vicuña is an agile, alert creature with extremely fine and dense fleece characteristics. It is superbly adapted to detect and flee danger and to keep warm in the harsh highlands.

With domestic animals such as the alpaca, nature's role of selection and emphasis is usurped by people whose knowledge about animals varies and whose motivations for emphasizing various characteristics may or may not enhance the breed or species. When an animal is perceived to have market value, owners often disagree about which qualities make their animal more valuable than someone else's. With many breeds of animal (including alpacas), agreeing on what constitutes excellence, what criteria to apply, what traits or characteristics to emphasize, and how to judge them are all in constant debate. If there is no agreement about what criteria to emphasize in determining excellence, people of like perspectives may band together and attempt to influence the standard in a number of ways: by presenting solid scientific evidence, by influencing the training and selection of judges, or by changing the rules. The stability and credibility of shows are directly linked to the quality of participation.

Show Committees

In practice most breed associations have a standing committee (or committees) that oversee show rules and how judges are chosen and trained. They monitor judge and exhibitor evaluations of individual shows to ensure that problems are addressed. Show committees are usually appointed positions and can become political in nature, especially if there are aggressive special interest groups or if there is polarization on show issues in the ranks of the owners. The way in which a special interest operates is difficult for novices to detect. This is particularly possible with fiber, which is a multifaceted topic with many contending views (see Chapter 10: Fiber).

Bonny Doon, California, 1989: Murray Fowler, DVM, discusses alpaca anatomy at the first alpaca show judging clinic ever held in North America.

A well-functioning show committee avoids fads and draws on solid scientific information as well as differing viewpoints that are well researched. The committee's deliberations attempt to improve the animal while being as inclusive to the needs of owners as is possible. If there is more than one valid view on a subject, they are shared with judges and the exhibitors. A well-run show committee assimilates and educates rather than alienates.

Training Judges

Show committees are usually responsible for overseeing the training of judges. With the systems operating today, this involves written tests, field tests, an apprenticeship, judging small shows first, and then moving up to the larger shows. Those interested in becoming a judge should contact these organizations. The steps to become a judge are explained in each organization's handbook. Many people have successfully completed the preliminary work to become a judge, but quit due to politics, the finances involved, or the time commitment necessary for training. Some judges successfully complete training but are never called to judge a show.[1,2,4,7] Training is only a small part of the job. The more experience the judge has in livestock and fleece evaluation, the more able he or she will be to withstand the rigors of judging classes of 20 and shows of a thousand.

I co-chaired the ALSA/AOBA Show Committee for two show seasons in the 1990s, created the written test for judges, and co-created the fiber tests. As with any group of people, the test scores varied. Some of those who had the most difficulty with the tests went on to become judges, and some of those who demonstrated the most aptitude didn't.

Usually judges have not done original research on alpacas, are not veterinarians, and do not hold degrees in animal science. Many judges have never been involved in fiber processing. Their knowledge comes from information gathered from their own experience or information they have learned from instructors selected by show committees. The training manuals that have been compiled by AOBA, ALSA, and AAA contain a great deal of information on various aspects of alpacas. Judges are taught how to identify certain characteristics.

Certification and recertification are terms used in judging circles. *Certification* means that the person has successfully qualified to be a judge. Judges are *recertified* from time to time to monitor competency. Recertification is usually done using judges' feedback, testing, and training over a three- or four-day weekend.

AN OVERVIEW OF DIFFERENT SHOW CRITERIA

When considering what criteria are appropriate to include in an alpaca show manual, we can look at criteria used for other livestock and we can look at criteria used for pet species to decide what makes sense. Distinguishing between artificial criteria and essential criteria is another way to look at this process of arriving at meaningful standards. Finally, we can look at the evolution of the species standard in place now and compare it to the breed standard for alpacas.

Livestock Show Criteria

In general, show criteria for livestock (which includes alpacas) emphasize aspects of the animal that highlight its fitness, good health and, most importantly, productivity (fiber and offspring).

For example, a Black Angus cow is judged on the squareness of its conformation and its weight at a particular age. Like most livestock breeds, the criteria emphasized for the Black Angus underscore its breed characteristics (what distinguishes it from all other cattle), which are strongly linked to the animal's purpose.

Its weight at a specific age is important, because this compares its productivity to animals of the same age and declares how much value (weight) it produces. The animal's frame (structure) is important, because without a sturdy, square frame, the proposition of lugging around an overbuilt, meat-laden body becomes problematic. Other aspects of a Black Angus are less important but nonetheless part of its breed standard. These secondary characteristics, like the shape of the head and color, mostly have to do with distinguishing the breed from other types of cattle.

Grass Valley, California: The Alpaca and Llama Show Association (ALSA) conducts the first alpaca show ever held in North America. From left to right: Carol Blaha, Charlene Worrell, Bill Barnett (background), and Diane Longo.

Pet Show Criteria

Show criteria for pet species (dogs, cats, parakeets, etc.) are often predicated on a different set of assumptions and goals than those of livestock. In the pet show arena, the end use or product is often no longer important, but the characteristics of the breed are of tantamount importance. Many pet breed standards have strong foundations in practical use (hunting, rescuing, and swimming in dog breeds, for example), but as the breed's purpose becomes obsolete or more generalized, its practical considerations often wane.

Some of the outcomes are downright horrifying from genetic and quality-of-life perspectives. English bulldogs, which are bred to have massive heads with pushed-in faces, are a good example. Often puppies can be born only by Cesarean section because their heads are too large to fit through the birth canal. The bulldog is also a hopeless mouth breather that will drool endlessly because its pushed-in face restricts the use of the nostrils and breathing. Cat breeds have often been tampered with in strange ways, too. The Sphinx breed spends its life naked, without the protection of fur, as an outcome of selective breeding. Such a cat depends on warmth and human care to survive.

Dozens of other breeds of cats and dogs have gone down paths that jeopardize the breed's general health and ability to survive. Often the breed's problem has to do with emphasizing distinguishing characteristics while ignoring essential characteristics that are the underpinning of a long and pain-free life. However, many pet breeds, adhering to breed standard criteria, are characterized by good health and temperament and have few breed-specific congenital problems. The variable here is the quality of human input.

By and large all these pet breeds belong to tightly controlled registries that fuss and scratch over the slightest rule change. These animals are shown and given ribbons for achieving excellence in their breed standard, no matter how nonsensical it becomes. Often the motivation for developing odd and rare breeds is profit. The drive for profit operates on a simple axiom: The more unique and rare the breed, the more likely it is to fetch a high price. A second common motivator to developing a unique or distinguishing characteristic has to do with internal competition among breeders. Breeders vying for top honors push the limits of the breed and hope to announce the unique (or exaggerated) outcome as "the best of breed" and collect top honors if they can convince a show committee to endorse what they've done.

Recognizing this process of attempting to separate one's self slightly from the whole for self-benefit is essential to understanding the underpinning of showing animals. Showing is competitive, and competitors approach

Show judge Jim Carpenter assesses fiber quality from the midside of a young alpaca in the first alpaca show held in North America.

getting ribbons in as many different ways as people find to succeed in society at large.

Artificial Criteria

Artificial criteria are those with no scientific basis and no connection to the animal's purpose. Remember the pet show standards, which identify and preserve breed traits, sometimes to the individual animal's detriment and with no rhyme or reason as to why particular characteristics are emphasized. Artificial criteria also make their way into the alpaca show ring (either *de jure* or *de facto*) when application of a criterion in the ring has no, or only a remote, bearing on the animal's conformation or end product (fiber quality). Artificial criteria sometimes hide under the more familiar but vaguely applied terms of "style," "character," and "presence." Artificial criteria assert themselves at shows during tough calls.

In the linear show world, where ranking is mandatory, there are the inevitable difficult calls when two or more animals are basically equal. In Australia (AAA) the size of testicles is the deciding factor in choosing a winner in very similar male alpacas. Often the deciding characteristic is something subtle (some might say contrived), such as the amount of fiber coverage on the lower leg or head, or other "refinements" that distinguish one animal from another. There might be other identifiable features or characteristics, such as ear set or skin coloration, that have no known benefit to the species yet loom into importance when competition is keen. In suri the tightness of the curl compared

White suri adult male, show class, in Arequipa, Peru.

to another suri with a slightly less tight lock structure might make a difference. In these instances, the unknown importance of subtle characteristics with little or no bearing on fiber quality becomes a deciding factor. Thus, characteristics can become important, whether they are officially part of the show rules or not. Artificial criteria confuse breeders about what to emphasize in selecting animals, and they directly benefit the breeders who possess animals with the artificial criteria thought to be essential (see Chapter 10: Fiber Processing, Characteristics, and Nomenclature and Chapter 26: Breeding to Improve Fleece Quality).

Essential Criteria

Essential criteria are facts that can be scientifically proven and are universally agreed upon as important judging criteria. Often these criteria emanate from veterinarians or scientific researchers in both animal care and fiber production. Many types of livestock have been improved using this scientific method and review in the past 200 years.

For example, there are lists of mutually agreed upon defects common to alpacas. When one of these defects (see Chapter 3: Anatomy and Conformation) is identified on an alpaca, there is no doubt it is a defect. Compiling a list of defects is essential to establishing desirable conformational traits. Coupled with general soundness are the alpaca's essential phenotypic physical characteristics and fiber criteria like those found on the screening forms in Chapter 27: Maintaining a DNA Registry for the Good of the Breed. These essential criteria define what could be considered a species standard.

Fleece Judging Criteria

Fleece judging generally occurs in two formats: on the animal in halter classes, which includes the animal's conformation in the judging evaluation, and as shorn fleeces, where the judging criteria focus solely on the fleece. Various alpaca associations around the world have developed fleece judging scorecards.

Show committees and breed associations place importance on particular fleece characteristics through the point values they assign to characteristics named on the fleece judging scorecards. The importance given to certain characteristics has changed over the years and may vary from one association to another.

In the 2003 Alpaca Owners and Breeders Association (AOBA) huacaya scorecard (see Figure 7.1), luster and crimp are both awarded a possible 10 points, while density, a primary component of fleece weight, is only awarded 5. This emphasis may reflect the belief of some alpaca breeders in the "new" alpaca countries that crimp is a marker for other desirable fleece qualities. The actual importance of crimp, or the degree of crimp as a marker, is a subject of debate. According to the large fiber processors in Peru, three of the most essential characteristics for alpaca fiber processing are: fineness, fleece weight (density, staple length), and the lack of medullation (see Chapter 10: Fiber Processing, Characteristics, and Nomenclature).*

The same essential areas of weight, fineness, and lack of medullation apply when evaluating suri. Suri fiber is

*Gilberto Sarfaty, managing director, Prosur, personal communication, April 2003; Luis Chavez, personal communication, April 2003.

unique in its smooth handle, luster, and angoralike lock appearance. In the AOBA 2003 scorecard shown in Figure 7.2, the essential areas of handle and fineness (20 points), lack of medullation (5 points), density (5 points), length (7 points), and weight (15 points) make up 52 points of the 100 points possible.

Luster is awarded a possible 20 points. Emphasizing luster in this fashion makes sense in that it highlights a desirable suri characteristic, but luster is a quality that can be manipulated by applying artificial additives to a fleece. Lock style receives a possible 10 points. Among many fleece judges lock style has come to mean tightly twisted locks known as pencil locks. There is presently very little scientific data correlating lock structure to fineness, luster, or lack of medullation. Some breeders favor a particular kind of lock structure because they like its appearance on the animal. Emphasizing characteristics that are nonessential to what is desirable for processing amounts to embracing artificial criteria. From the South American processor's perspective the lock structure is irrelevant. In commercial processing, very fine suri fleeces without pencil locks are commonly sorted into the top-grade class of fiber (see Chapter 10: Fiber Processing, Characteristics, and Nomenclature).

Species Standard and Breed Standard

There is a lot of talk about breed standards in the alpaca business outside of South America. *Breed standard* is a term used in livestock and pet animal businesses that means the description of a breed. Usually, once a standard is codified, animals that don't meet the breed standard are either included as lower-value animals or not allowed into the registry.

A Breed Is Not a Species A breed is a certain type of animal within a species. Members of the breed share characteristics that have been selectively maintained by human intervention. In dogs and cats there are literally hundreds of breeds, all of them from one or two species. With cattle, which can interbreed with one another, there are many breeds. A breed standard is often fairly precise. For example, Korat cat breeders who want show champions must have cats with the following characteristics:

- Tail: medium length and tapering but not too whippy
- Legs and feet: back legs slightly longer than the front ones with strong muscles
- Body: medium sized, semicobby, compact, fit, and muscular
- Coat: silver-blue, short, fine, and glossy, and lying close to the body
- Ears: large and high set but not too upright
- Head: heart shaped with a large but flat forehead
- Eyes: large and prominent but not bulging, bright, clear, and green.[10]

Some breeds require measurements of body parts. In cats, a breed standard is thought to be necessary because there are many breeds of cat and each needs a description (standard) to distinguish it from other breeds. There is often no practical application for criteria included in a breed standard.[10] For example, the heart-shaped head necessary in a Korat cat to meet its breed standard does not make it a better hunter, friendlier, or longer living.

Evolution of the Alpaca Species Standard There are two breeds of alpaca: huacaya and suri. Officially they are one species, *Vicugna pacos*. Alpacas are somewhat unique because they can breed with other camelid species and create fertile offspring (see Chapter 1: Classification, Prehistory, and History). At this time, the only description of an al-

Figure 7.1 Huacaya fleece judging criteria (AOBA 2003).

Characteristic (Huacaya)		Possible Score
Fineness and Handle: Fineness 15 Handle 5		20
Uniformity of:	Micron	8
	Length	7
	Color	5
Character & style:* Crimp		10
Lock type/Density*		5
Brightness (luster)*		10
Lack of medullation		10
Lack of impurities/ Stain/Fleece damage		5
Annualized clean fleece weight		20
Total		100

* Areas of controversy.

Figure 7.2 Suri fleece judging criteria (AOBA 2003).

Characteristic (Suri)		Possible Score
Handle and fineness: Handle 10 Fineness 10		20
Uniformity of:	Micron	8
	Length	7
	Color	8
Character & style:* Lock Style		10
	Density	5
Luster*		20
Lack of medullation		5
Lack of impurities/ Stain/Fleece damage		5
Annualized clean fleece weight		15
Total	100	

*Areas of controversy.

paca is a species description, which might most accurately be described as a *species standard*, because it was created to describe a species, not a breed. The alpaca species standard and the alpaca screening forms (known initially as the Alpaca Registry [ARI] screening forms) emanated out of meetings with industry leaders and knowledgeable veterinarians at the University of California at Davis and Oregon State University in the late 1990s. These forms have influenced judging organizations and show rules.

Information from alpaca experts around the world went into the creation of these forms. They describe the ranges in weight, height, ear and muzzle shape, general balance, and optimum fiber characteristics for an alpaca. Fiber is evaluated objectively by laser-scan histogram. Fiber characteristics of huacayas and suris are treated differently, but otherwise the alpaca is assessed as a species. Distinctions between countries of origin and slight differences in appearance are not attempted or deemed important.

The screening forms emphasize phenotypic characteristics common to all alpacas as a way to identify and eliminate huarizos (camelid offspring from alpaca and llama parents) from ever entering the gene pool of the DNA-based alpaca registry.

To pass screening, each animal needs to be free of a great number of defects described on the forms. The documents are designed to be highly objective in what they measure and strong enough to stand a legal challenge. They have been used to screen more than 15,000 alpacas worldwide, and have been adopted by registries and breed associations around the world. For example, the Australian Alpaca Association's Stud Certification form came directly from the original ARI screening forms (see Chapter 27: Maintaining a DNA Registry for the Good of the Breed).[8,9] The form's criteria have changed from time to time. While the criteria might not represent everyone's ideal alpaca, the criteria did attempt to identify universally acceptable characteristics and not go any further than to describe a healthy, conformationally solid animal with good-quality fiber.

For the show ring, associations and judges have basically incorporated the same criteria with recommendations from industry specialists. Animals are judged for conformation, soundness, balance, and movement. With a high dollar value assigned to many show-winning alpacas, and longevity more of an issue in North America than South America, ALSA mandated that judging an alpaca be based on 50 percent conformation and 50 percent fleece. At the time of this writing, AOBA membership also voted to endorse the 50 percent/50 percent judging rule. Where histogram analysis is not available in the show ring, judges must assess the fiber subjectively.

The author enjoys attaching ribbons to winners in Peru.

Lessons Learned from Screening One of the many lessons learned from applying these forms throughout the Andes is that many shapes and sizes of alpacas fall into the general species standard found on the screening forms. There are animals with excellent fleeces that are plump, thin, small, middle-sized, or large. Defects do not seem to be correlated to body type.

Another lesson is that there are a significant number of congenital defects in randomly selected alpacas in South America (the origin of all herds). For the foreseeable future, purging populations (by not breeding them) of the more serious defects and improving fiber quality while drawing on the widest gene pool seems like the safest course for herd improvement, rather than a tightly defined definition like the example of the Korat cat.

Impact of Standards When we talk of breed standards, we need to think of the genetic and financial impact. Who benefits? Will alpacas be improved as a result? How is improvement defined? Is the standard something that will benefit all breeders and fiber processors in the long haul, or a front for exclusivity in the marketplace? Does a proposed breed standard contain artificial criteria in its description designed to elevate part of the population while devaluing the rest? Is there enough statistical scientific data to justify narrowing the gene pool in a meaningful way?

It is important to keep in mind that the species standard, found in the screening forms, will be challenging enough for some time to come. The forms were styled for young adults and were never intended for established older populations. Most adult alpacas in the United States, Canada, and Australia would be hard pressed to qualify under the screening standard that has been applied to animals selected for export from the millions of alpacas in South America. The screening standard's purpose was simply to identify a healthy, defect-free alpaca with good fiber, and nothing more. The standard was lenient about the nonessential criteria. The screening forms have proved to be challenging enough for many exporters attempting to find several hundred animals capable of meeting the standard.

I think improving conformation and fiber are the first steps forward. As simple as this may sound, there is plenty of work to be done in these areas. Most plans for a "breed standard" that I have reviewed have been thinly veiled marketing schemes designed to establish exclusivity. So far, the AOBA membership has voted against an alpaca breed standard.

CONFLICTS OF INTEREST

When I surveyed U.S. and Canadian breeders who have more than ten years' experience in raising alpacas about the current show system, more than 75 percent were concerned about a conflict of interest between judges and exhibitors. A significant number of long-term breeders mentioned alpaca judges they respected a great deal for both their expertise and integrity. They also mentioned judges who they felt lacked credibility due to serious ethical lapses in business dealings and pervasive involvement in marketing alpacas severe enough to warrant permanent dismissal as a judge. In some conversations, separating fact from innuendo and rumor was difficult, but in other cases loss of faith seemed justified.

In researching what other types of breed shows do about conflict of interest, the responses were revealing. Basically, this problem plagues almost all animal shows because show judges, regardless of the kind of animal, are usually selected from the ranks of animal owners or handlers—people with a vested interest and often a conflict of interest. When a guinea pig judge was asked what rules had been adopted for conflict of interest, she answered, "We have a rule. You can't judge any guinea pig you sold until two weeks after you sold it." In the world of guinea pigs, two weeks is apparently sufficient time for a conflict of interest to dissipate to the objectivity necessary for judging.

When I attended a horse show in rural Oregon to interview a horse judge about conflict of interest, the meeting never occurred because of a conflict of interest! As the judge announced the winners of several halter classes, the crowd began to boo and stomp their feet. By the time the fourth winner was announced, most of the audience was booing and yelling insults. "Fix" dominated the catcalls. The judge never stopped smiling, walked away from the podium, climbed into his pickup truck, and left. Apparently the judge was well known, as were his recent brokering activities, which included selling all of the winners to new owners. Despite the crowd's disapproval, the show results became permanent records.

To my knowledge, the alpaca business has never had a protest like the one in the aforementioned horse show. However, in the alpaca business there has been confusion about what comprises a conflict of interest and interesting rules on what to do about it. It was a surprise to discover that the conflict-of-interest rules for judges in the Alpaca Owners and Breeders Association and the Australian Alpaca Association in 2002 are nearly identical in emphasis and wording, though there are significant differences in show formats and judging criteria (see Table 7.1).

The thrust of these rules is that judges shouldn't fraternize with show contestants during a show, sleep at their houses, or read any show catalogues. The judges are escorted on show day to make sure their objectivity is not compromised. This might be an effective strategy if the judge were from Mars with no previous contact with the people whose animals will be shown. However, judges are earthlings, not Martians. Judges often come from the ranks of alpaca owners, and some of their best friends are alpaca owners. In some instances, judges are competitors or have done business with the people whose animals they are judging.

Owners desiring an objective assessment of their animal in the show ring should consider whether their present conflict-of-interest rules provide adequate assurance of unbiased judging. In 2003, the AOBA Show Division adopted a code of ethics for show participants, superintendents, exhibitors, handlers, and judges that "is intended to prevent both explicitly unethical behaviors as well as situations that may foster or give the appearance of impropriety." A copy of the Ethics and Protests section of the *2003 AOBA Show Handbook* was mailed to all AOBA members. It can be hoped that having this defined code of ethics, a structured protest process, and penalties for infractions will help create a level playing field for breeders and animals competing in AOBA-sponsored alpaca shows.

Methods of Handling Conflicts of Interest

How is conflict of interest dealt with in society at large?

In most countries, "Statements of Economic Interests," "Disclosure Statements," and definitions of conflict of interest are codified laws applied to people occupying roles of trust requiring objectivity to ensure that they have no vested interest in the outcome of their official decisions. Safeguarding the majority by requiring people in decision-making roles to disclose income and abide by conflict-of-interest rules is practiced worldwide.

For example, a school board trustee in California who is elected to serve as an unpaid official must fill out the seven-page "Form 700: Statement of Economic Interests" annually and attest to all earnings and business relationships under penalty of perjury.[6] He or she does this solely

Table 7.1 Comparison of ethics and conflict-of-interest requirements of judges in Australia and North America.

NORTH AMERICA	AUSTRALIA

Section 3: Ethics Relating to Judges
(from AOBA Show Division Handbook, 2002)

A. A Judge shall avoid accepting an invitation to judge classes at more than one show in an area within a period of six months except in the case where no other Judge is available.

B. The Judge shall not be a house guest of any exhibitor prior to or during the course of the show. The Judge shall refrain from socializing with exhibitors until completion of the show.

C. The Judge shall not exhibit alpacas or alpaca fleece at any show at which he or she is judging.

D. Where a judge is officiating as a Halter Class Judge, members of his/her immediate family shall not exhibit alpacas in those halter classes. If the person is officiating as a Fleece Judge at a show, members of his/her immediate family shall not exhibit fleeces.

E. On arrival at a show the Judge shall proceed immediately to the show management office for orientation and directions. No person other than a show official or ring steward shall engage the Judge in conversation before judging commences.

F. Show officials shall take appropriate steps to ensure that the Judge does not see the alpaca show catalog until all judging is completed. The Judge shall refuse to examine any catalog that comes to his/her attention by any means until judging is completed. Prior to the show, the Judge shall not examine or have contact with any alpacas entered in the show.

G. No person shall accompany the Judge into the judging ring except persons appointed for that purpose by Show management.

H. The Judge may at his or her absolute discretion direct the removal of an alpaca or person from the competition on grounds of bad conduct, including any of the behavior described in Section 4(A.)

I. Removal of an exhibitor from the ring is at the absolute discretion of the Judge and such exhibitor shall be escorted out by the Ring Steward.

J. No rejudging of a class shall be permitted.

K. A Judge's final decision shall not be protested except on the grounds the judge has committed a breach in the AOBA Show Division Rules. Any protest must follow proper procedures as laid out under the Ethics and Show Rules Committee rules.

L. Any alpaca which the Judge deems to be unsound or unfit to compete shall be removed from the ring by the Ring Steward at the direction of the Judge.

Source: *AOBA Show Division Handbook,* 2002 Show Season (7/02 revision).

Judges (excerpts from **AAA Showing Rules Manual,** *2002)*

8. Judge's acceptance of invitation to Judge. Judge shall avoid accepting an invitation to judge alpaca classes at more than one Show in a Region, except in the case where no other Judge is available.

9. Judge not be a houseguest of exhibitor (similar to AOBA i.e., not to be house guest of an exhibitor the night before, or during show).

10. Judge/Apprentice Judge and immediate family/partner not to exhibit (people can't exhibit animals before a judge who is part of their family).

11. Actions of Judge before judging begins (must meet chaperone prior to proceeding to Show Office; no person other than show officials and the chaperone shall speak to judge prior to judging).

12. Judge not to refer to Show Catalogue (very similar to AOBA).

13. Persons who may accompany Judge into the judging arena (very similar to AOBA, i.e., only show officials).

14. Handler of animal not to address Judge (handler who addresses judge in ring can be removed immediately).

Source: *Australian Alpaca Association Showing Rules Manual,* 2002.

White suri male champion in Peru. Note alpaca's fleece length, which makes judging conformation difficult. In this show, fleeces were not supposed to be more than two years old, but when the handler was asked the age of this animal's fleece, he indicated it was three years old.

Author's Note: Stricter standards for ethical behavior, procedures for registering complaints and protests, and definitions of infractions with standardized penalties have been included in the *2003 AOBA Show Handbook.* These new standards address many of the conflict-of-interest issues raised in this chapter. I applaud AOBA's attempt to seriously address conflict-of-interest concerns. Organizations around the world that are creating show systems can benefit by carefully studying the *2003 AOBA Show Handbook.* These rules are as yet untested but are steps in the right direction. Notification was received too late to include the changes in this printing of *The Complete Alpaca Book.*

Table 7.2 Excerpts from the California Fair Political Practices Commission's Statement of Economic Interests.

These rules govern the conduct of public officials, such as court judges and school board members in the state of California.

The Political Reform Act (Gov. Code section 81000–91015) requires most state and local government officials and employees to publicly disclose their personal assets and income. They also must disqualify themselves from participating in decisions that may affect their personal financial interests. Statements of Economic Interests are public documents. The filing officer must permit any member of the public to inspect and copy any statement during normal business hours.

Gift prohibition Most state and local officials, employees, and candidates are prohibited from accepting gifts totaling more than $320....

Honorarium ban Most state and local officials ... are prohibited from accepting any honorarium for any speech, article published, or attendance at a conference, convention and meeting.

Loan prohibition State and local public officials may not receive any personal loan totaling more than $250 ... from anyone who contracts with their governmental agencies.

Disqualification Public officials are ... required to disqualify themselves from making, participating in, or attempting to influence governmental decisions that will affect their financial interests.

The following pertinent passages are from the "Terms and Definitions" section of this statute:

Commission income means gross payments received as a broker, agent, or salesperson.... You may be required to disclose the names of commission income...

The "source" of commission income generally includes all parties to a transaction, and each is attributed the full value of the commission.

Note: If your pro rata share of commission income from a single source is $500 or more, you may be required to disqualify yourself from decisions affecting that source of income, even though you are not required to report the income.

Source: Fair Political Practices Commission, State of California, 2002.

Table 7.3 Definition of conflict of interest in the state of California.

Conflict of interest A public official or employee has a conflict of interest under the Act when *all of the following occur*:

1. The official makes, participates in making, or uses his or her official position to influence governmental decisions,

2. It is reasonably foreseeable that the decision will affect the official's economic interest,

3. The effect of the decision on the official's economic interest will be material, and

4. The effect of the decision on the official's economic interest will be different than its effect on the public generally.

Source: Fair Political Practices Commission, State of Califonia, 2002.

A light fawn huacaya class being shown in Arequipa, Peru.

for the honor of serving his or her community. He or she is required to do this because board decisions include allocations of funds to all kinds of projects. The funds allocated are not supposed to benefit the trustee personally. A trustee can't be paid by someone who is awarded a contract that he or she voted to approve. In street parlance, this is known as a kickback. In effect, it is taking a payment (like a sales commission) for making a decision that favors the person paying the commission.

Table 7.2 gives excerpts from the "Statement of Economic Interest" required of public officials in California.

Conflicts of Interest for Alpaca Judges

Is the conflict-of-interest standard for the unpaid school board trustee appropriate for the judges of expensive livestock? In talking to show organizers, judges, and partici-

pants, it is clear that opinions vary widely on what constitutes a conflict of interest and what types of rules are appropriate. Table 7.3 defines conflict of interest in the state of California.

Do judges have influence over the value of animals? The answer is, yes. In fiscal year 2002, AOBA's projections claimed alpaca sales would top $80 million in the United States.[5] In 2002, the ARI board of directors explained the financial value of an alpaca to the U.S. Department of Agriculture by suggesting to the government that AOBA show judges were highly trained and capable of assigning financial worth to all alpacas.[*]

Is it possible for show judges to benefit personally from their decisions? Of course, if a judge was unethical and

*Rick Evans, former AOBA president, personal communication, October 2, 2002.

open to being bribed, he or she would benefit. Other activities can corrupt a judge's objectivity, for example, working as a sales agent. Here's a scenario that occurred at a large regional show in North America. Two judges performed ring duties. Though many farms were represented, several farms won most of the top honors. The farms that won most of the ribbons included the show organizers', who were instrumental in the selection of judges. Three weeks later, alpacas that had been purchased from one of the farms winning the ribbons at the show were examined for export at the home of one of the judges. The judge was also the sales agent who had located the animals for a foreign buyer.

This situation raises many questions and concerns. What actions are appropriate to ascertain the extent of the problem of judges working with exhibitors to sell animals, advertising themselves as experts, and using their judge status as their calling card? Is this behavior a violation of any existing rules of conduct for judges? If a judge is doubling as a sales agent, is he or she in effect an association-endorsed sales agent as well as a judge?

There are judges who use shows to procure clients. And there are judges who don't search for clients and believe they should not use their position for financial gain. The point here is that many decisions about what constitutes moral and ethical conduct have been left to the individual judges.

Tables 7.4 and 7.5 offer approaches to the identification of conflicts of interest and disclosure of economic interests. Table 7.4 illustrates what was required of alpacas screeners who, like judges, came from the ranks of alpaca owners. Alpaca screeners could not act as sales agents for

Figure 7.3 E-mail from Rick Evans, former AOBA president, on ethics and standards.

—Original Message—

From: KENAOBA@#aol.com
To: AlpacaOwners@ aol.com
Sent: Monday, March 18, 2002 6:24 PM
Subject RE: WE ARE SERIOUS ABOUT ETHICS

By now many of you may have heard that the AOBA Board of Directors, in concurrence with the AOBA Show Committee, declined to certify the halter show portion of the upcoming North American Alpaca Show to be held April 7, 2002 in Springfield, MA. This decision was based on Part X, Ethics and Protest Section 3, "Ethics Relating to Judges" in our Show Handbooks. Given the nature of the issues raised and their implications for the Industry, the Board of Directors feels strongly that the entire AOBA membership needs to be aware of what happened in this particular case.

On October 23, 2001, Ms. Polly Scofield, our Show Division Administrator, granted pending AOBA Show Certification to both halter and fleece shows of the North American Alpaca Show. Shortly after pending status was granted , it came to light the show organizers had scheduled the following seminars to be conducted by AOBA judges over the course of the 4-day event: [*a description of courses: Defining the Ideal Alpaca, Defining the Perfect Alpaca, and the names of the judges who taught them followed.*]

Note: [*name of judge*] is serving as an AOBA judge under the "grandfathering exception" allowed to her by the AOBA BOD. She has not completed the AOBA Judges Clinic, but is scheduled to [do] so this fall...

After reviewing the situation, the Board determined that the fleece show and presentation by [name omitted] on alpaca fiber does not violate ethics provisions of the AOBA Show Handbook, because fleeces in a fleece show are "anonymous" in the sense that the fleece judge never knows the fleece that he or she is judging.

However, in the case of halter judges, the proposed seminars clearly violate the ethics provisions of the Show Handbook that prevents halter judges from interacting with show exhibitors before or during any event in which they would be judging. This rule was in both our original show handbook and in the current 2002 show handbook that would govern this particular show.

The AOBA Board feels that the ethics section of the AOBA Show Handbook is the foundation of our show division and that exceptions to its provisions should not be allowed. It is on these grounds that the AOBA Board declined to certify the North American halter show. Clearly, the core question here evolves around the industry's definition of "ethical conduct of alpaca judges." But as you start to explore that question, other questions arise which are not addressed anywhere in the AOBA's Show Handbook or in the AOBA By-Laws. One of those questions is the propriety of an AOBA judge offering his or her personal opinion at an AOBA Certified Show on the definition of an "ideal or perfect alpaca," when no such definition has been established by the industry in the form of a specific standard. This is particularly sensitive in view of recent industry surveys on the breed standard question that indicated 79% of our voting farm members did not want a specific alpaca breed standard at this time, fearing that a specific breed standard would create a marketing platform that would favor one type of alpaca over another (Accoyo vs Peruvian vs Chilean vs Bolivian vs North American and so on).

So, the basic question here is.... WHOSE SHOW DIVISION IS IT ANYWAY?

The answer is that the AOBA Show Division belongs to the AOBA membership and it should be driven by the will of the majority of that membership. In other words, the Board of Directors feels very strongly that It is the AOBA membership who should be making determinations as to the definition of "an ideal or perfect alpaca," not the alpaca halter judges that serve the industry. We also feel strongly that if we are going to have rules that establish ethical conduct for judges, that those rules should be enforced without exceptions...

THIS NOT FUN!

I have to tell you dealing with Show Division issues has been one of the most challenging aspects of the Board's work over the past year or so.

The issues are tough, the politics are fierce ....

Rick Evans, President (of AOBA, 2001)

buyers, describe animals they'd screened, or buy animals from anyone they had done business with for two years.[3]

Disclosures of the type suggested in Table 7.5 would at least show certifying organizations the sources of a judge's income and provide the information necessary to make effective rules to deal with any conflicts of interest. Disclosure would also protect the reputations of highly ethical judges who would be able to declare their noninvolvement in conflict-of-interest issues.

Figure 7.3 presents excerpts from an internet posting to the AOBA membership by then-president Rick Evans (2001), which illustrates the need to clarify and resolve ethical concerns about the conduct and roles of judges.

Evans was faulted by some for publicly chastising a judge, but he was quick to point out that the issue was already being aired publicly and the names were well known.

For his willingness to take the bull by the horns and explain the board's position, Evans incurred the wrath of one of the judges he was asked to reprimand. The judge sent a mass e-mailing of his own in response to Evans' that was both threatening and unrepentant in tone. According to this communication, Evans had "better look out." This judge and the probationary judge who caused the show de-certification were later recertified as judges, which further entrenched them in the AOBA show system.

CHAOS: A LAWSUIT TO CHANGE SHOW RULES

America is the most litigious society in the world. It wasn't long until AOBA president Rick Evans found that the incident just described was a precursor to another even more

Table 7.4 Phenotype screener requirements (conflicts of interest).

a. A Screener will not screen alpacas of any Importer who has sold the Screener (or members of the Screener's immediate family) animals during the last two years.

b. A Screener or member of the Screener's immediate family cannot represent an Importer as a sales representative or be a paid consultant with an Importer.

c. Upon request of the ARI BOD, a Screener must disclose the sale prices of all imported alpacas purchased by the Screener during the time period a Screener is actively engaged in screening and within a year after quitting the screening program.

d. A Screener will not purchase any alpacas they have screened for a period of one year after the importation group is released from quarantine in North America.

e. A Screener will not act as an agent or consultant for prospective buyers of any animals the Screener has screened, nor will the Screener work as a consultant outside of North America for persons wanting to purchase alpacas for purpose of importing into North America.

f. Screeners may purchase imported alpacas, providing accurate and complete details of each transaction are submitted to the ARI BOD.

g. A screener will not own or invest in alpacas being imported into North America.

h. A Screener who quits the program after successfully completing it and who becomes employed or consults for financial gain for an Importer within two years of severance with ARI, will compensate ARI $3,000.00 for training and certification.

i. A Screener will not use the title of "Phenotypic Screener, Phenotype Screener, or Screener" in ranch advertising or promotional literature.

Source: Alpaca Registry Inc., Import Phenotypical Screeners' Requirement, 1996. Note: Rules terminated in 1998 at the cessation of screening activities.

Table 7.5 Hypothetical financial disclosure statements and background information for alpaca judges.

Financial disclosure statements

1. List all alpacas owned by you, members of your family, and your partners. Provide the animal's name and registration number.

2. List the names of persons and entities in the alpaca business from which you derived income in the past 2 years: direct sales of live animals, sale of live animals of business partners or co-owners, sale of fleeces, commissions, consulting fees, or lectures. Income is defined as cash payment, discounted prices, transportation costs, or any other benefit that can be assigned a monetary value.

3. List all stud services rendered by a stud you own solely or in partnership. List each female by name and registration number. Also, list any commissions received for procuring stud services.

4. List all stud services you paid during the last two years.

Background information

1. List all civil and criminal lawsuits in which you are (or were) named as a defendant or plaintiff.

2. List all convictions, fines, sentences or judgments against you as a result of a plea of guilty or decision by jury or judge for criminal or civil violations, other than misdemeanor traffic violations.

3. Please list positions you've held in the alpaca community: If you left any of these positions prior to completion of term; please explain.

Verification

I have used all reasonable diligence in preparing this statement. I certify under penalty of having my judging activities curtailed or revoked that the foregoing information is true and complete.

Date signed_____

Signature_____

extreme test. Evans chaired the AOBA meeting when a series of bylaws affecting shows was approved by the membership. Unfortunately for Evans and the board majority, the passage of these resolutions did not please a number of well-financed large breeders.

Through a vote of the membership, the following bylaws were passed (2002):

A. Breed standards—AOBA cannot adopt breed standards without approval of two-thirds of voting members.

B. 50/50 alpaca judging (conformation and fleece)—AOBA can't change the 50/50 rule without two-thirds vote of the voting membership.

C. Comparative alpaca judging—any change from the current comparative judging method will require two-thirds vote of the voting membership.

When these bylaws received majority support from all those participating in a general vote, most people assumed the issues had been decided. The membership had spoken and exercised self-determination. Based on 11 years of bylaw adoption in the same manner, there was no reason to believe they wouldn't be incorporated into the rules.

Not so. A small group of members who had opposed the bylaws began verbally assaulting the board, alleging that the board had acted improperly and that the vote had not been done correctly. The indignation and allegations expressed made it look as if the board had circumvented the rules and should resign.

Behind the insults and assertions of dishonesty and incompetence was a different story. The accusers were primarily large breeders wanting to invalidate the election results. They argued that the vote on the bylaws wasn't valid. At the root of the accusations about improper conduct was the claim that it took two-thirds vote of the entire membership to effectuate a bylaw change instead of two-thirds of those who voted. There was some ambiguity in the way the rules were written.

In the AOBA elections over the previous 11 years, the highest voter turnout was 52 percent, similar to the number of registered voters who vote in national elections in the United States. All matters in AOBA's history requiring a membership vote for approval were decided by the people who bothered to vote, not the entire membership. The position taken by the litigants (who became known as the intervenors in court documents) against AOBA in this case would have meant that most of the bylaws enacted by AOBA had been done improperly. Had this position prevailed, it would have severely damaged the organization's ability to function. In the end, the court endorsed the view that the AOBA board had done its best to institute the bylaws voted into existence by popular vote and that the bylaws would stand.[5]

Anyone wanting to understand the justification for such litigation should read copies of the court documents in which the intervenors explain their reasoning (contact the District Court, Larimer County, Colorado, phone (970) 498-6100). Interested parties should also read a well-reasoned and compelling counterview written by attorney and new alpaca owner Joy Elkins. Her letter condemning the intervenors' behavior, motives, and rationale was sent to most of the AOBA membership.[5]

Lastly, excerpts from the court judgment of this "frivolous lawsuit" are included here (Figure 7.3). Three of the litigants suing AOBA continue to be AOBA board members; one is a show judge and another chairs the Show Committee.

One of the biggest issues facing alpaca owners in North America is how to deal with this style of politics. It has been used repeatedly and most often successfully. It starts with personal attacks and accusations and escalates to threats of litigation, and in this case, actual litigation.

Disagreements expressed in this way are extremely disruptive and are a turnoff to people contemplating acquiring alpacas. What is at stake is the ability of the alpaca community either to function under a set of rules where differing points of view are respected and the outcome of a vote is honored or for the alpaca community to be run by those who can effectively intimidate others.

FOOD FOR THOUGHT ABOUT JUDGES AND SHOWS

A show judge's job is part art critic and part conformation and fiber evaluator. It's a tough job requiring skill, consistency, and integrity. Since show results directly or indirectly influence the value and breeding criteria of many alpacas, it is important that all breeders be involved in the dialogue about what criteria to emphasize in show judging and ensuring the integrity of the show system. I offer the following points for our ongoing discussion.

1. *Adopt comprehensive conflict of interest rules and background checks.* Shows are an important part of the alpaca business. Assuring their integrity is necessary and desirable for everyone involved with alpacas. If shows are to be taken seriously, meaningful conflict-of-interest rules need to be in place. Reporting sales fee commissions and requiring background checks for judges would be a big step in the right direction.

2. *Define the roles of judges and put an end to empire building.* There are judges who show up, do a good day's work for the industry, and go home with no other involvement. In contrast, there are judges who use their title to broker deals, seek out clients, and play kingmaker. They are quoted in

Figure 7.3 Frivolous lawsuit challenges show rules voted on by AOBA members and is dismissed.

District Court, Larimer County, State of Colorado
201 LaPorte Avenue, Suite 100
Fort Collins CO 80521-2761
(970) 498-6100

FILED COMBINED COURTS
L?R ???. COUNTY, CO

AUG ?? 2002

SHERLYN K. SAMPSON
CLERK OF COURT

THE BOARD OF DIRECTORS OF THE ALPACA OWNERS
AND BREEDERS ASSOCIATION, INC. a Colorado
Nonprofit Corporation:
Petitioner(s)

RODNEY CLANG (CO), JERRY AND LIBBY FORSTNER
(MAGICAL FARMS, OH), MICHAEL SAFLEY
(NORTHWEST ALPACAS, OR), KENNETH MADL
(AVIANA FARMS, CO), GREG MECKLUM (PACIFIC
CREST ALPACAS, OR), JIM MORTON (JCS ALPACAS,
OR), JAN DAVIS (DERWYDD ALPACAS, CA), ARLIN
McCROSKIE (A&A ALPACAS, CO), FLOYD ROMANIK
(INDIAN SUMMER ALPACAS, RI), AND ANA ROMANIK,
AMY McCROSKIE, AND STEVE HULL, CURRENT AOBA
BOARD MEMBERS:
Intervenor(s)

♦ COURT USE ONLY ♦

Case No. 02CV753

Courtroom: 5B

ORDER

This matter is before the Court with regard to various pending motions. The Court has reviewed these motions, the argument in support of and in opposition to same, and the various attachments and other submissions of the parties; being fully advised in the premises, the Court finds, concludes, and orders as follows.

<u>INTERVENORS' MOTION TO DISQUALIFY COUNSEL</u>

The Court has reviewed this motion and finds it to be entirely without merit. The motion contains a lot of overheated assertions ("a mergers and acquisitions lawyer", "unfair opportunity to interrogate if not intimidate", "hurriedly scheduled", "now privy to material possibly confidential or detrimental") but

does not contain any basis in Colorado law for the requested relief. The motion alleges no facts which would impose any legal or ethical requirement on counsel for the Petitioner to withdraw or be disqualified. The client is the entity, acting through its board of directors, and counsel for Petitioner has acted appropriately in representing this Petitioner. The motion is without merit, and should be denied. It also appears to the Court that, since it is entirely lacking in any legal basis, it is, as a matter of law, frivolous, supporting the requested award of attorneys fees.

IT IS THEREFORE ORDERED that the Motion to Disqualify Counsel is denied.

<u>MOTION TO CORRECT CAPTION, DISMISS, AND FOR SANCTIONS</u>

This motion is denied. The Board is the Petitioner; it is undisputed that a majority, either the seven who originally voted in favor of this action or the four who now seem to support it, favors the relief sought by the Board from this Court. The Court can perceive no need to change the caption. The argument given in support of dismissal is rambling, irrelevant, and silly. There is no legal basis for the relief sought. The assertion that the statute relied upon by the Petitioners is "an obscure and unused statute" would imply that statutes, like muscles, gain strength through use. Very simply, the motion makes no sense, it is frivolous, and it is denied.

<u>INTERVENORS' MOTION TO RECONSIDER</u>

The Court has reviewed the argument submitted and finds that this motion should be denied. The order previously entered, on July 19, 2002, appears to the

Court to be consistent with Colorado law and appropriate pursuant to the statute. Nothing has been presented that would be a valid basis for reconsideration. That there is a minority on the board of directors, or some members of this group, who disagree with the action taken by the majority, while interesting, does not support the relief sought.

IT IS THEREFORE ORDERED that the Motion for Reconsideration is denied. The stay previously ordered while these matters were being briefed is vacated. The order entered by this Court July 18, 2002 (the order is dated July 18, 2002 and file stamped July 19, 2002) remains in full force and effect. The Verified Motion to Set for Mediation or Hearing is denied as moot.

<u>ATTORNEYS FEES</u>

The various motions filed by Intervenors are found by the Court to be frivolous within the meaning of C.R.S. 13-17-102. They make assertions of fact which are irrelevant, and do not support the relief sought; they contain no legal support or justification. They have needlessly expanded the litigation. Based upon these determinations, and the request of Petitioner for an award of attorneys fees, the Court orders that Petitioner file an affidavit setting out the attorneys fees incurred, together with any brief in support of this request, within 20 days of this date. Intervenors, and counsel for Intervenors, may have 20 days thereafter to file a response brief, counter-affidavits, or other submissions as they deem appropriate on the issue of attorneys fees. Thereafter the Court will enter

an order addressing the request that attorneys fees be assessed against Intervenors and/or counsel for Intervenors.

Dated this **23** day of August, 2002.

BY THE COURT:

JAMES H. HIATT
District Court Judge

CERTIFICATE OF MAILING

This is to certify that on the **24** day of August, 2002, a true and correct copy of the above and foregoing Order was delivered to the attorney of record and parties appearing *pro se* in the following manner:

For counsel in Fort Collins who have agreed to such procedure, by placing said copy in the attorney pick up files located in the Larimer County Justice Center, 201 LaPorte Avenue, Suite 100, Fort Collins, Colorado.

For all other counsel and/or parties appearing *pro se*, by placing said copy in the United States Mail with the correct postage affixed thereon.

cc:

Frederick T. Winters, Esq.
LeBoeuf, Lamb, Greene & MacRae, LLP
633 Seventeenth St., Suite 2000
Denver, CO 80202

farm ads, and their endorsement as a judge undoubtedly attracts clients.[11] Should this behavior be prohibited?

3. *Adopt procedural safeguards.* Beware of a system that becomes entrenched and unwilling to amend itself. An amendment to safeguard show integrity might mean introducing subtle changes, such as selecting judges for shows by drawing names from a hat rather than allowing a group of exhibitors to choose the judges.

4. *Consider term limits for judges.* Should judges be retired entirely after several years of service or rotated onto an inactive list for periods of time? Should all judges be reviewed automatically after three to five years of service and retired if they have specified types of demerits?

5. *Consider higher pay.* The judges' pay scale should be reviewed. Presently judges earn from $70 to $400 for the largest shows of over 350 animals. This is an inadequate amount of money for the task they perform. The only financial incentive for judges should be appropriate compensation for their work. Pay should be commensurate with the value of the animals being judged and the skill necessary to judge professionally.

6. *Reexamine goals and face issues head on.* What do we want to accomplish with shows? Do we always want to embrace a linear system of judging in which there is one winner per class and one champion in the bigger shows? Does this serve the industry or individuals best? Shows are supposed to demonstrate breeding excellence. In Chapter 24, Dr. D. Phillip Sponenberg outlines a showing system in which animals are awarded different-colored cards based on how they score against preset criteria. In such a system many animals might be awarded the top classifications while others receive a lesser rank. This system would allow a more rapid improvement of the breed by identifying a larger number of animals worthy of making a genetic contribution (see Chapter 24: Basic Genetic Principles and Implications for Breeding).

Does it help the purity of the suri breed if phenotypic suris from known huacaya/suri crosses are allowed to be shown? Do crosses dilute a breed's gene pool or enrich it? Crosses are extremely hard to identify in the show ring. What is the job for the show committee or show superintendent in this regard?

What refinements and incentives can be added to fleece shows to enhance their importance in the community? The future of the alpaca industry is in fleece production.

It is important that we keep shows in perspective. A show is a celebration of the beauty of alpacas and their incredible color diversity and fineness. The best judges can display great competence and consistency ranking animals

Diane Longo with her blue-ribbon winner at the first alpaca show in the United States in 1990.

in order of judging results, but none of the great ones will claim their selections are a definitive evaluation. A show provides entertainment, a point of comparison, and bragging rights.

REFERENCES

1. Alpaca and Llama Show Association, Inc.: *The Llama and Alpaca Judging Manual.* 607 California Avenue, Pittsburg, PA 15202, 139 pp., 2000.
2. Alpaca Owners and Breeders Association, Show Division: *Alpaca Show Division Handbook* (abridged version reprinted July 2002). P.O. Box 184, Chewsville, MD 21721, (e-mail: aobacertshow@stargate.net), 98 pp., 2002.
3. Alpaca Registry Inc.: Import Phenotypical Screeners' Requirements. Kalispel, MT, 2 pp., 1996 (suspended in 1998).
4. Australian Alpaca Association Inc.: *Australian Alpaca Association Showing Rules Manual,* Unit 2, 613 Whitehorse Road, Mitcham, Victoria 3132, Australia (e-mail: alpaca@alpaca.asn.au), 56 pp., 2002.
5. Elkins, J.: The Actions of the Intervenors—an Outsider's Point of View. Joy Elkins, Tucson, AZ, 5 pp., September 10, 2002.
6. Fair Political Practices Commission: Form 700: Statement of Economic Interests. State of California, 428 J Street, Suite 620, Sacramento, CA 95814 (www.fppc.ca.gov), 2002.
7. Fercho, L.: Alpaca and Llama Judges. *Camelid Quarterly,* Alberta, Canada, September 2002.
8. Hoffman, E.: ARI Publishes a Screening Manual. *The Alpaca Registry Journal* 1(2): 13-34, Fall 1996.
9. Hoffman, E.: The Screening Process Critiqued and Praised at U.C. Davis Conference. *The Alpaca Registry Journal,* 1(2) 1–13, Fall 1996.
10. Perry, E.: Thailand's National Treasures. Your Cat. Scamford, UK. pp. 74–75, September 2002.
11. TenHulzen, David and Nancy: *Park View Alpacas.* West Linn, OR 97088, 58 pp., 2002.

Chapter 8

Transportation

Eric Hoffman

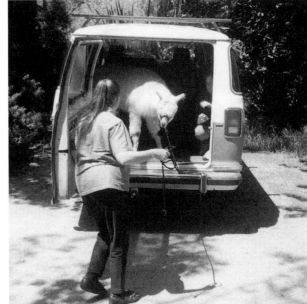

California Robyn Houts unloads her alpaca from a van.

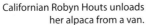

Regardless of the kind of transportation employed to move alpacas, traveling is stressful for most of them, whether or not they exhibit overt signs of stress. The owner has the responsibility of knowing which stressors are present and how to minimize them. Most alpacas are transported as a result of business transactions in which they are bought and sold. They also travel to schools, breeding services, veterinary care facilities, shows, and other public events.

In South America alpacas are often herded to markets or stacked like cord wood in large trucks with their legs bound to their bodies (not a recommended or humane practice).

Alpacas are generally cooperative travelers. They are also small enough and adaptable enough to be moved in different kinds of motorized vehicles, trailers, sea-going freighters, and small and large aircraft. However, not all vehicles large enough to transport them are appropriate for the job.

The alpaca's traveling environment should be comfortable, with enough space so each animal can relax and move freely. It should also have adjustable and ample ventilation or adequate air-conditioning, a way to dispose of waste, and available food and water.

PRETRIP REQUIREMENTS

Documentation and Government Requirements

Only healthy alpacas should be moved, unless they are being transported to a veterinary facility, and appropriate documentation should accompany them. Moving animals from one country to another often requires lengthy and expensive quarantines and working with federal authorities in two or more countries, plus a hefty bank account and the ability to deal with different cultures.

It is the owner's responsibility (in consultation with a veterinarian) to find out what special tests, permits, or other documentation are required at the point of destination. Owners frequently procrastinate until there is insufficient time to carry out the tests or obtain necessary permits. Seven to ten working days should be allowed to collect samples, send them to the laboratory for analysis, and have a report returned to your veterinarian.

The United States Within the United States alpacas must have health certificates to travel from one state to another. In addition to the health certificates, many states require tests to verify that alpacas are not carrying diseases such as

159

tuberculosis, brucellosis, or blue tongue. To find the requirements of a particular state, call the office or check the website of the state veterinarian. Contact information for all of the state veterinarians is listed at the USDA website: www.aphis.usda.gov/vs/sregs/official.html.

In the United States a few states require an approved import permit before an animal is allowed into the state. This requires that the health certificate be approved at the state veterinarian's office in the state of origin. This, in turn, is forwarded to the state of destination for an import permit to be issued. It may be weeks before such a permit is issued. Always inquire about the correct documentation requirements soon after an animal has been purchased.

I am well aware that even though a state may require health certificates, there may be no inspection at the border. Some owners may ask, "Why bother?" Even if there is no border inspection, you may be asked to produce the documents at any time (for example, if you are stopped by any law enforcement officer or become involved in a vehicular accident). You may be cited if you fail to produce the appropriate documentation or may be required to return the animals to the state of origin. Don't lose sight of the fact that these requirements exist for the protection of the livestock. The owner/transporter who cuts corners to avoid state-mandated requirements incurs financial and liability risks, should it be discovered after delivery that the new alpacas are disease carriers and the new owner's herd has been exposed to a deadly, contagious disease.

Canada To transport alpacas within Canada, check with Agriculture Canada for testing requirements. In Canada alpacas and other livestock are required to possess a transportation authorization permit prior to travel.*

Other Countries Australia, New Zealand, and European countries have regulatory agencies that should be contacted prior to moving alpacas from one region or country to the next. The requirements change from time to time, so it is wise to check with authorities before departure rather than be greeted by new requirements before your reach your destination.

Transportation Insurance

Travel insurance is an important consideration, especially with high-priced livestock investments. Many alpaca sellers in North America urge or write into their sale agreements that alpacas be insured for transportation. New buyers are often not aware of the risks associated with transporting alpacas, so it is important for the seller to explain. Both "named perils" and "full-mortality" types of

policies usually include transporting alpacas in their coverage. If there is the slightest doubt about the limitations in coverage of a particular policy, phone the insurance company to find out if transportation is covered, and ask if there are any conditions that will void the coverage.

If you don't normally insure your alpacas, most of the livestock insurers catering to llama and alpaca owners offer 15-day "named perils" and "full-mortality" insurance policies that cover transportation and the first few days at an alpaca's new farm. Procuring a full-mortality insurance policy usually requires an examination by a qualified veterinarian, which establishes the state of health of the animal. Sometimes this exam is the only record of an alpaca's general health at the time of sale. If a problem occurs during or directly after transport, or if an alpaca becomes gravely ill or dies within the first few weeks at its new home, this record may be the deciding factor in court proceedings.

The new owner may blame the seller regardless of the conditions surrounding an illness or death. Given a health exam that verifies the alpaca's condition within 30 days prior to transport and given insurance, the buyer's efforts to recover a financial loss will be directed toward the insurance company, not the seller. Having insurance as part of selling and buying alpacas is a wise business practice.

Vehicle and Trailer Maintenance

Before a trip, check the condition of vehicles and trailers and correct any health hazards peculiar to various types of transportation. For example, be sure that exhaust fumes do not flow into a trailer. Brakes, tires (including the spare), wheel bearings, batteries, lights, and licenses should be checked. Most wheel bearings on trailers need regular maintenance. A wheel-bearing failure can take a great deal of time to fix and possibly endanger the alpacas on board if the breakdown occurs in hot weather, in dangerous traffic, or in an area where it is unsafe to leave a vehicle to get help. A bearing that has failed and is ignored can wear through the axle, causing the wheel to break away from the trailer. If a trailer is rarely used, bearing grease should be replaced every six months. Every 12 months will usually suffice for a trailer used regularly.

Tires may become cracked and weak from the sun long before the tread wears thin. Always check that the spare is inflated, and make sure your tire-changing equipment will work on the trailer.

Depending on what they are made of, trailer floors tend to rot or rust. Often there is no sign the floor is unsafe because rubber matting hides the problem. More than one horse has fallen through a trailer's floor while speeding down the highway. It doesn't take much imagination to realize the excruciating pain and injury that result when an animal's leg is ground down from scraping the pavement.

---

*Corrine Houston, past president of the Alberta Alpaca Association, personal communication, Calgary, Canada, 1994.

Although an alpaca weighs much less than a horse, a trailer floor neglected long enough may give way even for an alpaca. Look under the mats and check the floor's structural integrity at least once a year.

TRAINING AND PREPARING ALPACAS TO TRAVEL

Travel is stressful for alpacas, but the stress can be greatly reduced if an alpaca has been familiarized with the surroundings in which it will travel and if it travels with another alpaca, preferably one to which it is bonded. The latter condition is not always possible, but remember that alpacas are herd animals with strong banding instincts. When an alpaca travels with another alpaca it relies on for security and companionship, it will naturally be less anxious. Also, an alpaca trained to a lead rope and halter and familiar with tight quarters probably experiences less stress and is more apt to load and unload into a vehicle without struggle or fear. A manageable alpaca can be unloaded en route to stretch its legs and relieve itself. In an emergency, a trained, vehicle-wise alpaca can be unloaded rapidly and tied out with little risk of injury to itself or the handler.

Pretrip preparation should ensure that eating and drinking will not be interrupted during the journey. Something as subtle as familiarizing the alpacas with the types of water containers used on a trip may be important. For a few days before the trip, water the alpacas in plastic or metal buckets like those to be used in transit. Alpacas are sometimes reluctant to drink water from new sources, and in hot weather this could be disastrous. The odor or taste of new water may be disguised by pretraining alpacas to drink water containing two drops of vanilla extract or oil of eucalyptus.[9]

Many alpacas kush when they are traveling, especially for the first three to five hours. Some alpacas may opt not to drink or eat for hours while a vehicle (or ship or airplane) is underway, while others will move about casually eating and sitting in different places. Although fairly uncommon, some alpacas will press against windows, hum constantly, walk over the tops of kushed alpacas, get up and down many times at the slightest bump in the road, and generally make nuisances of themselves to both fellow alpacas and the transporter. Most of this kind of agitated behavior subsides after the first 30 minutes, though occasionally an animal is a poor traveler and will remain agitated for an entire journey. A female that responds badly to traveling may be a poor candidate for travel while pregnant or outbreeding (traveling to and from a stud service). On occasion, stressful travel has been associated with the termination of pregnancies.

Alpacas that travel often usually become accustomed to it. Transporters should be aware of how the alpacas under their care handle the transition of eating, drinking, and relieving themselves in the new situation. Matching the rhythm of the farm as closely as possible is desirable.

The experienced transporter takes into account the tendency of alpacas to stay down while traveling and adjusts care strategies accordingly. Alpacas that are reluctant

Training an alpaca to load and unload will result in less stress for both alpaca and handler.

to stand will usually eat from a kushed position, providing food is placed near enough. Once an alpaca is relaxed enough to eat, it usually eats off and on throughout the journey, with most activity occurring near dawn and dusk.

The process of eating seems to relax alpacas. If a vehicle has one or more animals that are reluctant to eat or drink, it is a good idea to stop in a rest area and turn off the motor to eliminate noise and vibrations. If alpacas don't get up on their own after a few minutes, they should be gently encouraged to stand. This often stimulates curiosity that leads to drinking and eating. Stopping for 15 to 20 minutes every three hours is especially important if crias are on board, because some mothers refuse to stand when the vehicle is moving. Any reluctant alpaca is more apt to stand and investigate its surroundings in a stopped vehicle than a moving one. However, in cross-country trips most alpacas become accustomed to movement and will stand to nurse, eat, drink, and relieve themselves in patterns similar to those they've developed at home. The animal with a somewhat glazed look that stays down and appears to wall itself off from the others is the one deserving of concern.

RULES OF THE ROAD FOR TRANSPORTING ALPACAS

Whatever the conveyance, the distance of the journey, or climatic conditions, the following Rules of the Road address 12 essential concepts for successfully transporting alpacas:

1. *Alpacas come first.* The well-being of the alpacas must be the primary consideration. Animals' lives may be at stake. From the moment the alpacas are on board until they are safely unloaded, the number-one priority should always be their welfare.

2. *Be prepared to cope with extreme temperatures.* Always determine your route (including stopovers) prior to departure, and only go forward with a travel plan if you are certain that the temperatures ahead will not cause the temperature in your travel conveyance to exceed acceptable maximums and minimums. People often ride in a climate-controlled vehicle, while the alpacas they are transporting travel without benefit of cooling or heating systems.

Heat is usually more of a problem than cold. Transporting in spring and fall is usually safer because temperatures tend to be less extreme. Traveling at night may also offer refuge from high temperatures. Shearing the alpacas may be necessary.

Without a correctly designed transport vehicle, summer temperatures can create dangerous situations.

Before departure check that the vehicle is safe when the power is turned off. Many forms of transportation are safe only while moving, when the airflow passing through the vehicle protects animals against heat buildup or when air-conditioning is fully functional. As a general rule both ambient humidity (in percent) and temperature (in Fahrenheit or Celcius) should be monitored. Temperatures as low as 75°F (19°C) in humid conditions and 85°F (30°C) in dry conditions cause problems depending on associated variables (see Chapter 21: Noninfectious Multisystemic Diseases).[3,5,10,11,12]

The best way to learn how well a vehicle combats heat is to take it out for a spin during a hot day with a person in the cargo area. Monitoring the temperature and humidity during a two-hour drive and again after the vehicle sits for an hour in direct sunlight will indicate how safe the vehicle is. Remember that due to the collective body heat, the temperature will be higher with alpacas on board.

Cold is usually relatively easy to combat, but driving conditions in cold weather, especially when towing a trailer, can become dangerous, and unplanned delays can pose problems. In subfreezing temperatures airflow from the outside should be restricted. If the airflow is correctly adjusted, the body heat emanating from a group of animals contributes warmth to the travel

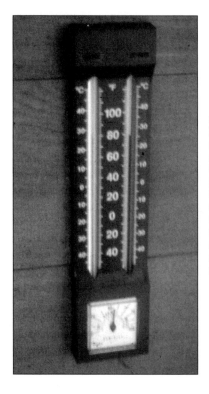

A thermometer with a humidity gauge is mandatory when transporting alpacas. In large vehicles, where temperatures may vary due to the proximity of venting and stagnant air pockets, several thermometers may be necessary to accurately monitor the ambient temperature throughout the vehicle.

space. The floor should be well insulated because alpacas sit most of the time they are traveling, which exposes their undersides (and vital organs) to the floor. A thick rubber mat covered with straw bedding usually provides sufficient insulation.

For cold-weather shipments involving suris and huacaya crias, the inside of the transport conveyance should not drop below 32°F (0°C). Adult huacayas usually can withstand as low as 10°F (−14°C) without a problem, providing no direct air current is on them and that they do not have wet coats, which will chill them.* Monitoring the ambient temperature is important but is only a crude measure. Each animal may have a slightly different threshold of tolerance to cold. Some may begin shivering at 32°F (0°C); others may show no signs of chill at −25°F (−34°C). A hypothermic alpaca may or may not shiver before becoming listless and dull, and its body temperature will be below the bottom range of normal: 98°F (34°C).[9,13] (See Chapter 21: Noninfectious Multisystemic Diseases for the clinical signs of hypothermia.)

As a backup in situations involving young animals or adults that chill easily (such as those recently shorn), some owners in northern regions have designed snug-fitting polar fleece jackets.[10] Keep in mind that animals sensitive to the cold don't have the option of warming themselves with exercise when confined to a traveling conveyance.[2,9,12]

3. *Reroute or cancel if necessary.* If the climatic conditions en route will push temperatures above or below acceptable levels, and cooling and heating devices in the vehicle can't adequately compensate, it's probably in the best interest of the alpacas to reassess the route. Consider traveling at night; cancel the trip until seasonal weather patterns are more favorable; or consider alternate forms of transportation.

4. *Carry two kinds of thermometers and a humidity gauge.* Always mount a weather thermometer and humidity gauge in the compartment holding alpacas. If the temperature exceeds 80°F (27°C) or when combined temperature (Fahrenheit) and humidity (percentage) exceed 150,[11,12] visually monitor the respiration rates and institute ways to cool the traveling compartment, if need be. Visual monitoring should also be done in warm to hot temperatures with low humidity. Observations may require increasing the airflow through the compartment, activating internally mounted fans,

turning on the air-conditioner, or dousing alpacas' undersides with water from a hose or buckets.

A clinical thermometer, which should be part of the onboard medical kit, is also an important tool. If an alpaca begins to show signs of heat stress, take its temperature to determine the level of intervention that is necessary. Signs of heat stress include rapid or open-mouthed breathing, dullness and loss of appetite, prostration, and an elevated rectal body temperature (over 106°F; 41°C).[3] If any of these signs appear, take action to cool the alpaca.[3,10,11,12] (See Chapter 21: Noninfectious Multisystemic Diseases for a detailed explanation.)

5. *Plan ahead, especially for long trips.* For trips longer than 10 to 14 hours, decide in advance where you will stop and sleep. In hot weather, traveling at night is often the smartest strategy, providing the trip doesn't extend into the next day when you are exhausted and should sleep. Many types of transport conveyances become heat traps when the vehicle stops and airflow ceases. If you are using a vehicle that poses heat risks because of its design or due to excessively hot weather, not stopping for anything but fuel and "fast food" may be mandatory. Two drivers may be necessary to keep the vehicle underway. My experience in moving a group of alpacas across the United States vividly illustrates this point. The trip had been planned months in advance and included expensive airline tickets and a transcontinental truck rental. On a muggy June night 12 alpacas were loaded into a step-van for a journey from Ohio to California. The vehicle had been

Vermonter and commercial animal hauler Conrad Grillo checks for excess heat in his rig's wheel bearings. Maintenance is doubly important when hauling livestock. An untimely breakdown in the wrong conditions can be disastrous.

*Jim Vickers, DVM, alpaca veterinarian formerly from northern Michigan, personal communication, 1994.

modified to ensure ample ventilation. The backdoor could be rolled open to the 4-foot (1.2-m) level because we had fastened 5-foot (1.5-m) hog fence across the opening. The plan was to drive through the night to take advantage of the cool air. Still, at night the temperature hovered around 80°F (23°C) and the humidity was high. The plan called for sleeping between 6:00 am and 9:00 am, then traveling on through the next day. Through the night the alpacas seemed relaxed, though two animals demonstrated flared nostrils and slightly elevated respiration rates. At dawn the heat and humidity worsened. By 8:00 am, the ambient temperature rose another 10 degrees. Even while driving about 60 miles (96 km) per hour with all windows in the cab open and the back door rolled open, the travel compartment temperature hovered at 95°F (35°C). The airflow passing through the windows and out the back of vehicle cooled the animals, but when the vehicle stopped in traffic, the temperature would climb rapidly to around 100°F (38°C) and the vehicle became a sauna. Stopping for a rest was now impossible because of the likelihood of heat stress. With no place to offload them, the only way to keep the temperature down inside the vehicle was to keep moving. Not falling asleep at the wheel became the overriding challenge. The afternoon temperatures soared. The drive became an exhausting exercise in sleep deprivation and worry about the animals that covered 1,400 miles (2,240 km) before it was safe to stop.

Five months earlier in 60°F (22°C) weather, the same route presented no significant challenges, except coping with boredom. There are lessons to be learned from this predicament: Travel with a light sleeping bag and bag lunch. You may find it necessary to take advantage of roadside shade or cool night temperatures on a lonely stretch of highway to get much-needed sleep. Traveling with sleeping gear and food also holds for winter driving when a road may be closed due to snow, flooding, or ice. Always keep in mind that meal stops and catching sleep can be entirely controlled by the weather.

6. *Have a disposal plan for feed, water, and waste.* Naturally an alpaca's bodily processes continue while traveling. Although the travel environment's temperature is always a top concern, on longer trips you must be vigilant about the routine of feeding, watering, and disposing of waste. How you manage this routine depends on the number of animals you are transporting and the kind of conveyance you are using.

Alpacas should have food and water throughout their journey. The food should be provided in a way

Double bucketing minimizes spilling water.

that is easily accessible to all alpacas on board and least prone to contamination from urine and fecal matter. Some alpaca shippers lay food along the inside walls of the vehicle, where alpacas can easily eat but are not apt to defecate and urinate on it. Other transporters use feed hay for bedding, so food is available wherever an alpaca chooses to sit. When the food is used as a toilet, the transporter stops, cleans out the soiled hay, replaces it with bedding straw, and redistributes feed hay along the sides. Another transporter uses feed bags suspended in the interior of the vehicle. Enough food should be on board for the trip and the transition period at the end of the journey when the alpacas are moved from one feed source to another.

Watering is a bit tricky. Water can spill, soaking the floor and stimulating alpacas into relieving themselves. If the journey begins in a remote area where roads are curvy and rough, no water should be offered until a smooth, even road surface is reached. Water should be poured from an onboard source into the water containers. You don't want to waste time looking for a hose from an unfamiliar water source when you have alpacas on board. All onboard water containers need to be secure, either fastened to the vehicle or designed in a way that will not allow them to tip over.

Another method I have successfully used is "double bucketing." A shallow, broad-based (18 in.; 45.5 cm) bucket is placed inside a larger (26 in.; 66 cm), broad-based bucket. The Dura Rubber Flex Bucket works well.* Put the water in the small bucket, and the larger

*Agra and Pet Products. Catalogue. Miller Manufacturing Company, P.O. Box 545, 494 Villaume Ave., So. St. Paul, MN, 55075.

one catches any overflow, which prevents the traveling compartment from becoming soaked. In a crowded compartment more than one water source is important, because dominant animals may intimidate subordinates into not drinking or an alpaca may block access to water by sitting in front of it.

Alpacas are more willing than llamas to defecate and urinate in a strange environment. Still, many alpacas will wait hours in a vehicle before relieving themselves. Make periodic stops so that they can stand, and trained alpacas can be off loaded, so they can relieve themselves. Carry a container of alpaca dung, spread a few pellets in an appropriate spot, and lead the alpacas to investigate them. Dropping a few pellets in the conveyance near the back door of a trailer or van often stimulates the creation of the "traveling toilet" well away from food and water and easily accessible for cleaning up.

Removing manure and urine-soaked bedding is part of the task of hauling alpacas over vast distances. Use a small rake and bucket. Waste material can be disposed of in a dumpster or placed in a plastic bag for later disposal. Some haulers place old carpet in the area of the vehicle the alpacas are expected (or encouraged by the sprinkling of a few pellets) to relieve themselves. They throw away the fabric when it becomes saturated and replace it with a new piece.

Many shows now have a communal dung pile near the back gate of the show ring to encourage defecation outside the ring. Owners taking an alpaca to a veterinarian for a reproductive examination are advised to give the alpaca an opportunity to empty its bladder before commencing the examination. Often defecation and urination can be stimulated by walking an alpaca through a moist area, or puddle, or running a hose on its feet.

7. *Be prepared for emergencies.* North Americans live on a continent in which thousands of automobile accidents maim and kill people each year. Most of us are able to put such dreadful statistics out of our minds and rely on good driving to avoid dangers. However, drivers traveling with alpacas have extra responsibilities. Not only must such drivers use ordinary good judgment and follow the traffic laws, but also they must remember they are the guardians of the alpacas under their charge.

Drivers of any kind of livestock should have contingency plans for the emergency that they hope never occurs. Tragedies have been reported in which high daytime temperatures killed alpacas in stop-and-go traffic when airflow ceased to cool them. In one instance, alpacas died because a driver left his animals unattended in an inadequately ventilated vehicle while he ate lunch. In another case, a flash trailer fire, probably from a discarded cigarette, raced through bedding straw and killed all the llamas on board. Obviously, having an evacuation plan should be at the top of any emergency contingency list.

Halters and lead ropes should be available for each animal. The halters should be prefitted, attached to a lead rope, labeled for each animal, and kept in an easily accessible place in the vehicle (not on the alpacas). Another necessary item is a picket line. By stringing a line along the ground (or between two trees or vehicles) and securing it at both ends, you can attach alpacas via their lead ropes, effectively tethering all alpacas in your vehicle, and be free to cope with any problems.

It is good policy to have a medical kit on board, especially for a long journey. A kit should includes a flashlight, a rectal thermometer, syringes, appropriately gauged needles for injectible medicine, sharp scissors with blunt tips, vet wrap bandages, and a stomach tube appropriate for the size of the alpacas on board. Medicines should include a sterile saline solution (4-ounce clear plastic bottles are a handy size) for flushing debris from an eye or wound, antibiotic eye ointment, a wound cleanser and first-aid cream, electrolytes to be added to water on long trips, an injectible antibiotic and painkiller, and bandages that can be secured against a wound with vet wrap to stop bleeding. All medicines should be approved by your veterinarian and applied only in the circumstances, amounts, and manner recommended. If an animal becomes ill or injured, the best strategy is to make sure it is as comfortable as possible and out of immediate danger. Then phone your veterinarian or the nearest qualified veterinarian for guidance. The measure of a good trip is one in which the medical kit is never opened.

8. *Carry plenty of water.* Carry extra water in a 5- to 10-gallon (19–38-1) closed container. The amount you carry is contingent on the number of animals on board, weather conditions, and length of journey. Extra water comes in handy for filling water containers when there is no available running water. More importantly, extra water is your emergency source for cooling an alpaca that overheats.

I once found myself pulling three alpacas in an enclosed but well-ventilated trailer in slow traffic for a prolonged period of time. Despite a trailer fan sucking air in from the outside, the slow traffic minimized airflow to the point of dire concern. Pulling to the shoulder and taking a quick read of the trailer's thermometer

Often individual alpacas are moved between farms in four-wheel-drive vehicles, which are so high off the ground that loading an alpaca into one can pose a challenge.

Here an alpaca aficionado demonstrates a sure-fire technique. She lifts the alpaca (notice the placement of her arms) and slides it into the vehicle rear end first.

Note the placement of the tarp, so the alpaca's legs do not slide between the car's chassis and the bumper. This needs to be remembered for both loading and unloading.

revealed a temperature near 100°F (38°C) and one alpaca breathing rapidly through its opened mouth. The animal was clearly heat stressed. I moved the vehicle to a shady area and all animals were off-loaded and tied out. The animal showing heat stress was cooled by pouring the contents of the onboard water container into a bucket and placing the alpaca's two front legs in the bucket. Slowly the animal's respiration rate decreased and its breathing returned to normal.

Standing the animal in water, rather than pouring it over him, conserved water so it could be used again for cooling purposes. If water is in short supply, pouring it over an animal may be shortsighted and offer only token relief. If you are ever transporting a group of alpacas showing heat stress and have neglected to devise an emergency cooling plan, try to locate a hose and run water on the animal's undersides and legs. Soaking the blanket area (back) may create a watery envelope that actually causes more acute heat stress. Of course, the best plan is to avoid such situations by traveling with sheared animals on mild days in vehicles that remain comfortable at a variety of speeds.

By employing the "two people alpaca lift," Sherry Edensmith and Rick Harker demonstrate how an untrained or unwilling alpaca can be loaded safely into a vehicle of any shape or size. This is an important technique when hoisting large alpacas. Two people sharing in the task reduce the weight by half for each person.

Top left Two alpaca aficionados demonstrate the alpaca lift wrist grasp.

Top right They grasp the alpaca under the abdomen and in front of its chest and lift the animal into the vehicle.

9. *Avoid overcrowding and incompatible mixes.* When is a vehicle crowded? It depends, in part, on the conditions in which alpacas are traveling. For example, more alpacas can generally be safely carried in cool weather. How much space an individual alpaca needs is also contingent on other variables such as group compatibility, age differences, and pregnancy status. There is no scientifically researched recommendation for a correct number of alpacas for a given amount of shipping space. My "guesstimate" for minimum floor space requirements, based on successful hauling for more than 25 years, is 14 square feet (1.3 sq m) per animal for a short haul and twice that space for a long haul. Adhering to space requirements should also include separating alpacas of different sizes and hierarchical status. Adult males usually travel together without problems, but they should always travel separately from females and young animals.

10. *Know how to safely load and unload alpacas from your vehicle.* Each vehicle has different strengths and weaknesses in hauling alpacas. Of primary consideration is how to safely load and unload alpacas into your vehicle. A trained alpaca is easy to load and unload, but not all alpacas are trained to travel and some vehicles have inherent physical hazards that pose threats to even the best-trained alpaca. Alpacas are often moved in four-wheel-drive sports utility vehicles, station wagons, and pickup trucks. The height of many of these vehicles makes them difficult for alpacas to get into. Gaps between tailgates or between side doors and the chassis are dangerous to alpacas and can result in a broken leg. These gaps should be covered during loading and unloading.

To protect the carpeting and upholstery, some breeders first lay a slick plastic tarp in the cargo area for collecting urine and fecal matter and then put straw onto the tarp. A plastic tarp that is slippery and noisy to walk on is not ideal, and putting a layer of straw on it doesn't eliminate the noise and slick surface. Instead, a canvas tarp offers both better footing and a quiet surface.

If an alpaca refuses to get into a vehicle, it may help to back the vehicle against an incline to reduce the height of the step in. Or the "alpaca lift" may be in order: Two people face one another on opposite sides of the alpaca. They stoop and reach under the alpaca with one arm and firmly grasp one another's wrists directly in front of the back legs. Simultaneously, they grasp wrists under the alpaca's chest in front of the front legs. Once both people have a firm hold, they stand erect and lift the alpaca off the ground and into the vehicle. The key to this technique is conscripting two people who can comfortably lift and control their half of the weight. Most adult alpacas weigh 100 to 175 pounds (45–80 kg). The animals tolerate the alpaca lift with only minimal resistance, providing the maneuver is completed in a matter of seconds. Under no circumstances should an alpaca be lifted by its fiber. Do not drag untrained animals in a headlock or pull them by their ears, tail, or fiber. This causes unnecessary stress, discomfort, and fear—and injury is possible. With untrained animals it works best to maneuver the conveyance as close to their pen as possible to minimize the stress of loading.[9]

Unload with all gaps between bumpers and tailgates covered and direct each animal to the ground in a controlled manner. A soft landing area is preferable. Don't assume that if a kushed alpaca is pulled from a vehicle it will automatically extend its legs to break its fall. Maybe the legs have "gone to sleep." Alpacas that have been traveling for quite awhile will often take some time to decide to use their legs for the purpose for which they are intended. Allow these animals a little extra time to make the transition on their own.

11. *Consider pregnancy risks.* Pregnant alpacas are shipped successfully all the time, but there are stress-related risks, especially for females in their last trimester. Females shipped in this late stage sometimes abort their fetuses en route or shortly after arriving. Of course, many factors can cause spontaneous abortion, and this phenomenon of posttravel aborting may have multiple causes, but the stress of travel has to be one of them. Such factors as overcrowding, excessive heat or cold, or rough handling may contribute. Many alpaca breeders wait until a late-term female gives birth and allow the baby to gain strength for a month or more before shipping them.

12. *Carry emergency phone numbers.* What do you do if a medical emergency occurs or your vehicle becomes inoperable due to mechanical failure? Everyone hopes this never happens, but rather than ignore the possibility, carrying a breeder's directory and the names and telephone numbers of qualified veterinarians nearest your travel route can make the difference between inconvenience and tragedy.

Commercial animal haulers usually know of animal exchange yards that can be relied on if their vehicle should fail them or dangerous weather conditions should overtake them. One commercial hauler has literally knocked on doors of farms when emergencies have occurred. He reports that in rural America people are generally more than happy to help, but help will not be forthcoming unless the driver takes the initiative to break the ice and explain what is needed. This may take the form of finding a veterinarian to stitch a laceration or give fluids to a dehydrated animal. It may require employing a garden hose to cool animals, or making use of a shady paddock where alpacas can be off-loaded while a trailer is repaired.

COMMERCIAL SHIPPERS

Numerous individuals, some with company names, advertise the transportation of animals. Some have experience and own appropriate vehicles. However, no license is required for animal transport, other than for the vehicle. Alpaca owners must rely on the shipper's reputation. How well a shipper is prepared to move alpacas can be partially ascertained by asking questions based on information in the previous section, "Rules of the Road for Transporting Alpacas." Half the battle in choosing a shipper is finding out if the shipper is knowledgeable about the needs of alpacas. The other half of the battle is assessing the shipper's commitment and dedication to his or her job.

Important questions to ask include:

• How does the shipper cope with extremes in temperature?

• What will be the route of travel?

• How will layovers and rests be handled?

• What is the vehicle or trailer size?

• Will the shipper stop to allow crias to nurse?

• How many animals will be placed in a single compartment?

• Will alpacas travel in the same compartment with llamas or other species?

• What other kinds of animals have occupied the shipping trailer in the last week?

• Is the trailer or vehicle disinfected after unloading each shipment of animals?

• Will the shipper pick up and deliver to your ranch, or will the owner be responsible for transporting alpacas to a rendezvous point?

A commercial alpaca-hauling vehicle. Numerous types of conveyances are appropriate for moving alpacas. The key is to be able to deal with hot and cold weather and have ways to establish varying amounts of airflow. This large commercial trailer is insulated.

• Does the shipper plan to off-load the alpacas at a stock transit point where they will await the arrival of another vehicle before continuing their journey?

• If alpacas are to be off-loaded in this manner, how long will they have to wait, and how safe is the transit point in terms of management, correct fencing, exposure to common livestock diseases, and the availability of food, water, and ample shade?

• What kind of flooring and bedding will be provided?

• What is the shipper's emergency plan if the vehicle must be unloaded in a hurry?

• Is there enough water on board if animals must be cooled in a breakdown emergency?

• Is the shipper fully insured and does the insurance extend to live cargo?

• Will the shipper enter into a written contract covering your areas of concern?[10]

As a general rule the owner should supply the shipper with ample hay and a prefitted halter and lead rope for each alpaca. Instruct the hauler to leave the halter off unless an alpaca is to be unloaded, and not to tie an alpaca inside a stall. The last point is especially important if the hauler is used to moving horses.[4]

TRAILERS AND TRAILERING

Trailers used for alpaca transport vary from home-constructed rigs for carrying one animal to luxurious air-conditioned multianimal types. Some have built-in living space for people. Horse trailers are often used because they are readily available and information about them is easily acquired. The height requirement for a horse is not necessary for an alpaca, and horse trailers are often excessively heavy and overbuilt for hauling alpacas, but designing and building a customized trailer under most circumstances is more expensive. However, it is possible to find builders who will meet your specifications for not much more than a standard trailer.

Conventional stock trailers, designed for cattle and sheep, are often closer to the ideal for alpacas because they tend to be shorter, lighter weight, compartmentalized with ample space, and well ventilated. However, some stock trailers are noisy and rattle loudly when underway. Noise is a stressor that should be eliminated if possible. Assess the noise level in a trailer prior to purchase. Usually rattling noises are caused by loosely fitting interior doors that can be secured and quieted.

Gathering information about the vehicle to pull the trailer is also important. Using an underpowered or inappropriate vehicle is dangerous. The trailer hitch should be

The trailer has ample airflow because of air scoops and fans.

The importance of locking doors can't be overemphasized. There have been several incidences of unlocked doors coming open on freeways and the alpacas tumbling out!

installed by a competent mechanic and be rated for a specific drawbar weight. The hitch should be solidly attached to the frame of the vehicle. Hitches that attach only to the bumper are not appropriate for animal trailers unless they are attached to heavy-duty steel bumpers as are used on pickups and large trucks. Safety regulations require that the trailer be chained to the vehicle. All running lights, turn signals, and brake lights must be functioning, even for daytime travel.

Trailers may be constructed of steel, aluminum, or combinations of either fiberglass or wood components. Four factors must be considered to assess a trailer's suitability for alpacas: comfort and safety for alpacas, structural integrity, weight (tongue and gross), and compatibility with a tow vehicle. The ideal trailer is strong, as lightweight as possible, aerodynamically sound, and capable of different kinds of hauling assignments (mixed males and females, females with crias, etc.). People may argue the relative merits of a single- versus a double-axle trailer, but a single-axle trailer in not as safe as a double-axle one. A blown tire on a single-axle trailer can be fatal; however, since alpacas are not heavy animals and kush while traveling, the danger is not as acute as with horses, which stand with the bulk of their weight far above their center of gravity.

A gooseneck or fifth-wheel trailer provides the most balanced ride for the animal, but necessitates a truck dedicated to that trailer. Some trailers have a small ramp leading up to the floor of the trailer for loading and unloading. Others require that the animal step up to load. Alpacas usually prefer to step up rather than use a ramp. It is unwise to pull or push an alpaca into a step-up trailer. If you are pulling the animal into the trailer, a leg may slip under the trailer and be fractured.

Appropriate training prior to loading would obviate problems of this nature, but often animals are not trained and the hauler, seller, and possibly buyer are faced with how to safely load a scared animal. If the alpaca is reasonably well halter trained, leading it to the back of the trailer and then patiently coaxing it with mild tension and release on the lead rope often works. Many alpacas will hesitate for up to a minute before jumping in. One person can keep tension on the lead rope while the other lifts the front legs (one at a time) into the trailer to help the alpaca through the transition period. With untamed or recalcitrant alpacas, hoisting them in the "alpaca lift" described earlier is the best solution.

Another consideration for alpaca safety and comfort is trailer flooring. Although alpacas are surefooted and can generally walk on smooth surfaces, it is not appropriate to leave either a metal or wood floor of a trailer bare. Rubber mats are the most desirable covering because they provide footing and insulation from both heat and cold. Most alpacas lie down as soon as a journey begins, and a rubber mat provides a more comfortable surface. Some owners use indoor-outdoor carpeting. Straw is often used—it provides insulating material in cold weather, but it does not provide footing. It absorbs urine and is easy to replace. Using straw for bedding on long journeys is unwise, especially if no feed is supplied. Hungry or bored alpacas may eat the straw, and if unaccustomed to it, may develop digestive upset. Straw bedding that is replaced daily plus copious amounts of feed hay is a better combination. Sand may be used, but wood shavings or sawdust become embedded in the fiber coat and are difficult to remove.

A few more cautions:

• Don't tie an alpaca when trailering. Animals have become entangled in a tied lead rope and strangled, unbeknownst to the driver.

• When using covered horse trailers, the area above the rear doors should be blocked with netting to preclude the unlikely event of an alpaca attempting to jump or climb out.

• Doors must be secured in the shut position with a safety latch or lock. There have been several reports of doors coming open during a journey and animals tumbling out.

• Trailers that are vented for horses may provide inadequate ventilation for alpacas. Ventilation is important not only to provide air for breathing but also to dissipate heat.

Drivers who are inexperienced in pulling trailers containing animals must practice slow acceleration and deceleration, particularly for standing animals. Avoid quick lane changes, and decrease speed on winding roads. Leave plenty of room behind the vehicle in front to allow time for slower braking.

RENTAL VEHICLES

The reality of shipping alpacas is that many people resort to using rental vehicles. I do not generally condone the use of rental vehicles. Some rental vehicles can be modified to transport alpacas in a safe fashion, but others should never be used under any circumstances. This discussion addresses the rental vehicle question by distinguishing between totally unsafe vehicles and marginally unsafe vehicles, with the hope that good judgment will be exercised. I take no responsibility for any problems that may occur.

I strongly condemn shipping alpacas in vehicles where the cab is separated from the cargo area (often called a "box van" or "mini-moving van"). These small vanlike trucks are designed for moving nonliving cargo—they have no windows or ventilation, making it impossible to view animals while driving or to create a healthy airflow. Attempts to put mesh across the back as a means of ventilation are dangerous. Even if the mesh is firmly secured, there is no airflow from the front compartment. This lack of air movement allows exhaust fumes to backdraft into the cargo area when the vehicle is underway. Modifying a cargo area of this type for front to back ventilation would require an act of vandalism. This condemnation also applies to rental trailers built in a similar fashion. Pickups without shells and open-stake-sided flat beds are also inappropriate because an alpaca may jump or climb out.

Only a few vehicles among those commonly offered for rent can be modified for safe use for alpacas. For middle-sized shipments the Ford Econoline 350 box van with a 14-foot (4.2-m) moving-van cargo bed allows fairly decent airflow through the cab's front windows and into the cargo area, which is connected to the cab with a walk-through space. This truck is common in the Budget, Hertz, and U-Haul rental fleets. However, the truck needs to be modified slightly before alpacas can be safely transported. A piece of 5-foot (1.2-m) hog panel spanning the back of the bed and attached to the two side walls needs to be fixed in place. Fashioning a door in this panel wide enough to load

Preparing a cargo van for a long-haul trip includes rerouting air conditioning from the passenger area (note pipe), a thermometer, and a container for watering alpacas on flat stretches when water won't slop out of the bucket.

and unload animals also may be necessary. With the hog panel in place, the vertical sliding door can be raised as high as 5 feet (1.2 m) and secured. With the cab windows open, air passes into the cargo area and out the back of the vehicle. The Econoline 350's 14-foot bed measures 8 feet (2.4 m) wider, which adds up to enough floor space for eight adult alpacas. You'll have to ask specifically for this vehicle (similarly constructed ones are made by other manufacturers) because booking computers in rental company offices don't distinguish between the Econoline 350 with a 14-foot bed and vehicles of similar size that have no cross-ventilation capability.

The most common rental vehicle utilized by alpaca owners for small shipments is probably the cargo van that has an open area from the driver's area to the cargo bay. Creating adequate ventilation in these vehicles can be difficult. If there are no windows in the cargo area, the van is unusable unless there is air-conditioning. If the van has air-conditioning, it must be modified because the air-conditioning is generally adequate only to cool the cab and the area immediately behind it. Solid panels behind each seat often inhibit the airflow into the back of the vehicle. Also, with no venting in the back of the van, hot, stagnant air builds up.

However, several modifications can be made to cargo vans to assure greater temperature control. A temporary air duct made of 4-inch (20-cm) plastic drain pipe can be duct-taped and wired to an air vent in a dashboard and extended into the cargo area. By shutting off the cab's other vents, all the air produced by the cooling unit travels through the duct into the cargo area. This method will do the job on all but the most unbearably hot days. A section of pipe can be purchased at any construction supply business. I used this technique while traveling through Arizona in 95°F (35°C) heat. The inside temperature remained at a steady 75°F (28°C).

If you find yourself in a van that will not cool off because of failed air-conditioning or other reasons, place a 2×4-inch (5×10-cm) block of wood between the side door and the van's chassis. With the block acting as a spacer holding the door ajar, tie the door in place with a strong piece of rope. With the door ajar in this manner, the 2-inch (5-cm) gap between the door and the chassis becomes a giant air scoop, inhaling air into the vehicle as it moves down the road. While not elegant, possibly illegal, and uncomfortable for the driver, this jury-rigged effort might save your alpacas.

AIR TRANSPORT

In recent years, shipping alpacas by air has been the preferred method of animal importers who have moved alpacas from South America to North America, Europe, Israel, South Africa, Japan, China, New Zealand, and Australia. Shipments of hundreds of animals are often placed on a single aircraft; occasionally shipments of a dozen travel internationally. International flights of alpacas must be arranged in conjunction with quarantine laws and are thus often directed to specific airfields near government-run quarantine centers. Probably the largest air shipment of alpacas ever undertaken was by Canadians Ken Schurek and Florette Schnelle. They moved nearly 600 alpacas from New Zealand to Australia in a rented Russian Antonov-124, one of the largest freight aircrafts ever to fly. The price tag for the three-hour flight was nearly $350,000.[1] Considering the vast distances involved, the great advantage of air travel is that the alpacas are safely on their new continent in a relatively short time, providing the people who ship the animals do so carefully and humanely.

Shipping alpacas by air need not be associated with large, expensive international shipments. Alpacas have also been shipped individually and in small groups in a wide range of aircraft, including regularly scheduled domestic flights on large commercial jetliners and privately owned light aircraft. Though traveling by air is usually more expensive than land, in certain situations alpacas can be air shipped for a comparable cost, while offering the benefit of being less stressful than a lengthy road trip. Therefore, don't discount the use of air travel, especially for young animals. Since the size and weight of the inhabited shipping container determine cost, shipping weanlings by air is often about the same cost as shipping a large dog.

Dealing with Commercial Airlines

There are a number of variables to consider when shopping for a commercial airliner to carry alpacas. First, of course, is to locate an airline that will do it. Many airlines will not ship live animals; others do it seasonally or only under certain weather conditions. Often airline agents will explain that if ground-level temperature at the departure or destination exceeds 85°F (29.4°C), the airline will refuse to load the animal, even if the space has been reserved and paid for. This rule—made for alpacas' safety—has been adopted by most airlines worldwide in accordance with international agreements.[8] If an alpaca is held off a flight due to weather, the airline usually allows the animal on a flight at some later date for no extra cost. However, to play it safe, find out the airline's policy for last-minute refusals prior to booking the flight.

Check the flight plan. Cargo agents may forget to check if the plane is scheduled to stop and unload part of its cargo en route, but this fact can be critical to an alpaca's welfare. The greatest danger on commercial flights occurs during loading periods when an animal may be left in the sun on the runway or when an airplane's air-conditioning is turned off. With jumbo jets, huge pallets of cargo, of which a "crated" alpaca is part, may sit on a runway for 30 minutes to an hour. This loading time may not be important if the weather is cool, but in hot weather the alpaca's survival is at issue, even if its crate is well ventilated. The astute airline cargo agent should work closely with the alpaca owner and allow an animal to be loaded into its crate in a hangar a short while before being loaded into the cargo bay. Airline personnel need to alert their counterparts at the receiving end to make sure the alpaca is off-loaded promptly into a cool area to await pickup. Shipping at night is often better to avoid heat.

Because the temperature in a shipping environment and the circulation of air in and around a crate are critical to an alpaca's survival, the crate should be placed on the outside edge of a pallet (defined here as a collection of merchandise on a loading elevator), not in the center where larger container crates on either side of the alpaca can choke off the airflow or greatly reduce it. The temperature and pressurization in the cargo area are controlled by the pilots. Some shipping agents will ask you what temperature you'd like for the alpaca during flight. If an agent doesn't ask, inquire and suggest 60°F (12°C); a pressurization of 12,000 feet (3,657 m) is safe. If other animals, such as parrots are on board, you may have to settle for a higher temperature—but do not accept anything above 80°F (23°C).

The person receiving the alpaca should arrive at the airport before the flight arrives in order to expedite locating and uncrating the alpaca. I once helped a cargo crew look for a crated alpaca among the unloaded pallets of a 747 cargo carrier. With three people searching immense pallets, it took 20 minutes to locate the crate (sandwiched between two large crates of furniture). If I had not been there, the alpaca could have gone unnoticed for hours, because the ground crew had not been alerted that a live animal was in one of its pallets. The alpaca was found in good shape, primarily because the crate was built properly, allowing airflow around it even in these circumstances. Always coordinate activities at both ends of a flight.

For peace of mind and to establish an alpaca's arrival condition, require in writing that the people delivering and picking up the alpaca contact one another to verify the animal's arrival and its apparent condition within minutes after it is unloaded from an airplane. A signed delivery receipt attesting to the animal's general appearance and apparent health is also a good idea for both seller and buyer. This documentation may be critical if claims are made about the alpaca's condition days after its arrival.

Containers for Commercial Air Travel

Alpacas traveling on a commercial jet are shipped either in a shipping crate designed specifically for an individual alpaca or in walled shipping pallets commonly large enough to carry up to ten adult alpacas, though sizes vary depending on the type of jetliner. In shipping pallets alpacas can move about freely, and the area over their heads is not covered, allowing the animals ample ventilation. The floor is usually lined with a layer of plastic, covered by carpet or blankets nailed to the floor, and topped off with bedding straw. Hay is usually put along the sides.[4]*

In the United States individual animals are often shipped in crates designed and constructed to the specific measurements for that animal. The crate is usually built with enough head room for the alpaca to stand with its

neck and head in a fully upright position and enough fore and aft space for an alpaca to stand and kush in a normal up-and-down motion. The crate should have enough space to allow air to circulate on both sides of the alpaca, and it should be entirely smooth and free of protruding nails, sharp edges of wire mesh, or other sharp objects. When the weight of the container plus the animal exceed 132 pounds (60 kg), forklift spacers must be provided. Metal bracing of the corners of the container is required.

Occasionally airlines will have requirements of their own, and at times well-intended airline regulations don't make good sense for alpacas. For example, I was once told by an airline to provide enough space in the crate for the alpaca to turn around. This requirement contradicted the recommendations of the International Airline Transport Association (IATA), which recommended in 1993 that "the dimensions of the container must sufficiently restrict movement to prevent the animal from turning around therefore trapping and injuring itself or from kicking and breaking the container."[8] If an airline's "above-and-beyond requirements" seem unreasonable and pose a danger to the alpaca, talk with the airline official responsible, and mention the IATA recommendations if they apply. Airline employees usually become flexible when they are given documentation that allows them to justify changing their guidelines. A good source for such documentation is the nearest large zoological garden. Zoos are experienced in shipping live animals.

Crates are usually built of ½- to ¾-inch (1.3–1.9-cm) plywood with an external frame made of 2 × 4-inch (5.1 × 10.2-cm) boards. The external frame is the key to the structural integrity of the crate and essential for ensuring life-sustaining ventilation. The external frame acts as a "spacer," so that nothing can be put directly against the walls of the crate and cut off the air supply. Usually one-third of the surface area of the crate's walls, ceiling, and doors is dedicated to ventilation, with special care given to the area nearest the alpaca's head when the animal is either kushed or standing. The challenge in providing ventilation is doing it in a way that does not allow an alpaca to extend a leg or its head into a crack and become snared .

A person with carpentry skills can build a crate in one day, provided the materials are at hand. First measure the alpaca's head height, length, and width. Add a few inches to height and width and a couple feet to the animal's length. After construction, paint "Live Animal" in a half-dozen places on the crate in the language of the receiving country as well as in English. From any angle a person should be able to understand that a living creature is inside. Paint vertical arrows pointing up and write "up," which in-

*Murray Bruce, New Zealand breeder who often ships alpacas overseas, personal communication, Caithness Farm, New Zealand, 1994.

dicates the crate's correct orientation to the forklift drivers. When the crate is complete, walk the alpaca into it to make sure the fit is comfortable. Check for sufficient headroom and enough fore and aft space for the alpaca to get up and down without a struggle.[9]

Hay is usually used for bedding material, at least in the front third of the crate. The water container should not be filled to capacity because it will spill. The container should be securely fastened to the side of the crate, as far forward as possible at the "head" end. An unsecured container can work its way underneath the alpaca and cause it to have a most uncomfortable flight. On relatively short flights consider omitting the water altogether. With all the movement involved (forklifts, elevators, takeoff, landing), the water tends to spill, leaving the entire floor wet for the trip's duration. Once the flight has leveled off, many airlines will follow watering and feeding instructions, if there is a small access door specifically for that purpose.

When you go to the airport, wait as long as possible to load the alpaca, and secure the crate's doors only when it is absolutely certain that the flight will not be delayed. Load the animal in a quiet area accessible to a forklift. If you don't, you may find that the crate and animal are too heavy for two people to lift. Sometimes handles are screwed to the crate's exterior so four people can share in lifting it. This makes handling easier and reduces the chances it will be accidentally dropped.

Small Aircraft

Small aircraft offer an efficient way to move alpacas, often at a cost comparable to ground travel. In North America single-engine Cessna 172s and 182s have successfully moved alpacas great distances. When the ground temperatures were too high to safely deliver alpacas from California to Texas, Patty Burrell was contracted to fly two weanlings over 1,000 miles from San Diego to Austin. Burrell removed the back seats of the airplane, placed plastic on the floor, and covered the plastic with an old blanket and hay for bedding. The two weanlings stayed kushed for most of the seven-hour flight, seemed relaxed, and ate hay as they droned along.[5]

Washingtonian Ralph Uber has piloted alpacas many times in his twin-engine Piper Seneca. Uber has moved as many as six young alpacas at one time. He says, "Alpacas

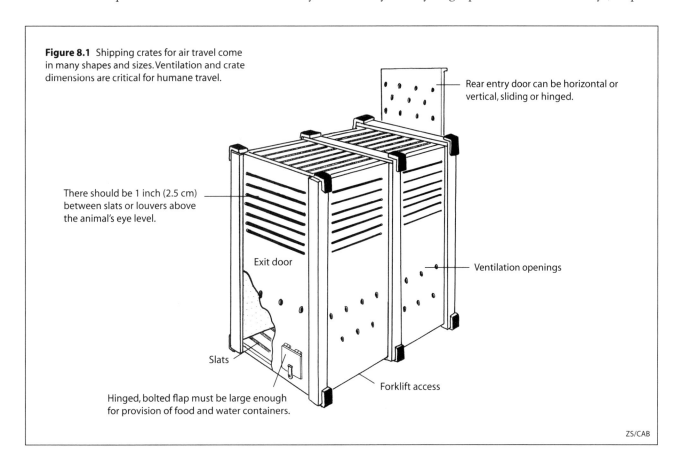

Figure 8.1 Shipping crates for air travel come in many shapes and sizes. Ventilation and crate dimensions are critical for humane travel.

Rear entry door can be horizontal or vertical, sliding or hinged.

There should be 1 inch (2.5 cm) between slats or louvers above the animal's eye level.

Exit door

Ventilation openings

Slats

Forklift access

Hinged, bolted flap must be large enough for provision of food and water containers.

ZS/CAB

The international movement of alpacas has become a sophisticated business with a half dozen exporters from different nations moving most of the animals to points around the globe. In the early days of exportation from South America, which commenced in late 1983, lack of understanding about the needs of camelids sometimes resulted in unacceptable losses. There are still significant differences between the knowledge, expertise, and ethical conduct of exporters. But some of the best exporters operating today can move as many as 400 animals at a time without losing a single animal. Some of the areas of improvement are: custom pallet construction, preparatory diet, shearing, flight routing, and restraining techniques.

make better flying companions than some people I know." Jim Faiks of Alaska, who has also transported alpacas via small plane, agrees but thinks untrained alpacas should be restrained by tying their back legs to their bodies for the flight.

All three of these pilots flew at an altitude of 12,000 feet (3,650 m) without pressurization. When surface temperatures are too high to attempt ground transport, remember that for every 1,000 feet (304 m) of altitude the temperature drops 3.6°F (2°C).

When using light aircraft , consider these issues. Select an airplane that has removable seats and a door suitable for loading alpacas. In calculating the number of alpacas you can carry, keep in mind that each seat in most light airplanes is designed to carry 175 pounds (67.5 kg).* Weanlings are the most efficient to move because of their small size.[2,6,10] There are no reports of an alpaca climbing into the lap of a pilot or hijacking a plane!

---

*Patty Burrell, pilot, personal communication, Butte, Oregon, 2001.

TRANSPORTING SICK AND INJURED ALPACAS

Dealing with Illness

An ill alpaca may refuse or be unable to remain in a kushed position. It may roll to its side. If possible, the alpaca should be encouraged to lie on its right side to minimize the possibility of passive regurgitation and subsequent inhalation of stomach contents. However, when riding in the back of a pickup or in a trailer, the jarring the alpaca experiences lying on its side may be quite stressful. The alpaca can be cushioned with an inflated air mattress or sacks filled with straw. Alternatively, you can partially deflate the vehicles tires.

Avoid giving a sick or injured animal water while traveling. Make certain that the alpaca is able to cope with ambient temperature and humidity conditions, keeping in mind that an ill animal may not be able to thermoregulate as well as a healthy alpaca.

Be cautious when unloading an ill alpaca. A healthy alpaca may be able to comfortably jump from a pickup bed, but an ailing animal may fall flat on its face or may be so weak that it is unable to move itself at all. A canvas tarp or piece of plywood can be used to lift the alpaca out.

If an ill alpaca is able to stand, get it to a grassy area so that it can urinate and defecate. This is particularly important if a rectal examination is to be performed.

Dealing with Fractures

A fractured bone requires a veterinarian. Because each fracture is unique, it is difficult to address all possible situations. Fractures of the long bones of the lower leg should

After a 1,500-mile journey, two alpacas are prepared for unloading. Halters and lead ropes are attached. Alpacas are often slow to rise after such a long journey. Allowing them to collect themselves will result in an orderly unloading. If pulled too quickly from the vehicle, animals may not extend their legs and fall and be injured. Note the all-weather carpeting that was removed and cleaned along the way. The feed was placed along the walls to minimize the mixing of forage and fecal matter.

be immobilized before attempting to transport the injured alpaca to a veterinary facility. Splint material can be polyvinyl plastic pipe cut lengthwise, strips of plywood, metal rods, branches from a tree, or rolled-up newspapers. Do not attempt to straighten misaligned bones—simply stabilize them in the position found. Cotton or newspaper can be used for padding. Bind the splints to the limb with vet wrap bandage, gauze bandage, or strips of cloth torn from an old bedsheet.

Alpacas can be forced into the kushed position by placing a rope loop around the body just in front of the hips (see Chapter 5: Restraint). Avoid this technique when dealing with hind-limb fractures. Fractures of the upper limbs are difficult to stabilize except by flexing the lower leg and binding the entire limb to the body.

Rigging a temporary sling inside a trailer or truck, using a large bath towel or piece of canvas, may be appropriate. Cut two holes near the center of one end approximately 6 to 8 inches (15–20 cm) apart and big enough for the alpaca's legs to go through. Gently lift a forelimb and insert the foot through one hole; then repeat with the other forelimb. Pull the end without the holes back under the abdomen to make a sling, then fasten a short section of rope to each corner by first folding the corner of the towel over a small rock (1 in; 2.4 cm), then putting a slipknot around the cloth and the rock and pulling it tight. Tie the ropes to the sides of the trailer or partition. The animal should be supported in such a way as to relieve the pressure on the injured leg, and the feet should still touch the floor of the trailer. A person should ride beside the animal.

MEDICAL PROBLEMS ASSOCIATED WITH TRANSPORT

Travel sometimes causes injuries. An alpaca may be bruised, lacerated, or suffer fractures when thrown against a wall by the vehicle's sudden swerve or braking, or when stepped on by another alpaca. Loading and unloading are also critical times.

Choking

Choking is the result of an alpaca's unsuccessful attempt to swallow a mouthful of feed. The animal will usually hold its head near the ground and attempt to dislodge the feed with a coughlike sound. A retching reflex may also occur. Avoid the use of pellets when transporting—they are notorious for causing this problem. Some cases of choking may be relieved spontaneously, but others require medical treatment.

Colic

Stress can cause either increased or decreased motility of the gastrointestinal (GI) tract. Coupled with the ingestion of unaccustomed feed (such as straw), this can cause blockage in the GI tract and a buildup of gas that painfully stretches the bowel. An alpaca with colic will incessantly get up and down, attempt to roll, and assume strange positions (see Chapter 15: On-Farm Assessment and Diagnosis and Chapter 21: Noninfectious Multisystemic Diseases). If the signs persist for more than a few hours, seek veterinary assistance.

Infection

An incubating infection may be hastened by the stress of transport. Depending on the origin or destination of the transport, the animal may have been exposed to infectious agents at shows, sales, outside breeding establishments, or en route through contaminated water and feed sources, insect vectors, and inhalation of dust (coccidiodomycosis).

Miscellaneous Conditions

Other potential medical problems include injury resulting from a vehicle or trailer accident, inhalation of carbon monoxide fumes (faulty mufflers, tailpipe positioning, and backdraft from some kinds of open-ended vans), strangulation, entanglement in a tied lead rope, and nerve paralysis of a forelimb from lying on the leg.[7]

REFERENCES

1. Alpacas Flown to Australia. *The Outlook,* February 4, 1992. Published in Auckland, New Zealand.
2. Faiks, Janet, and Jim Faiks: Flying Alpacas. *Alpacas,* pp. 18–21, Summer 1994.
3. Fowler, M. E:. Thermal Stress in Llamas. *Llamas* 27: 17–20, May-June 1985.
4. Greth-Peto, F.: A Comprehensive Look at the Transportation Industry. *Llamas* 4(3): 93–96, 1990.
5. Hoffman, E.: Alpacas Delivered by Light Aircraft. *Llama Life* 15: 26, Autumn 1990.
6. Hoffman, E.: Facility at Key West Adapts to Receive Imports. *Llama Life* 7: 1 & 26, Autumn 1988.
7. Hoffman, E., and M. Fowler: *The Alpaca Book,* p. 158. Herald, CA: Clay Press, 1995.
8. *Live Animal Regulations,* 20th ed., Resolution 620, Attachment A. International Air Transport Association, 2000 Peel Street, Montreal, Quebec, Canada H3A 2R4, 1993.
9. Mallon, J.: Headin' Down the Road. *Llamas* 5(7): 109–111, 1991.
10. Price, T.: The Faiks Like Challenges: Raising Camelids, Arctic Weather, and Exporting Alpacas to Australia. *Llama Life* 9: 2, Spring 1989.
11. Pugh, D. G.: Heat Stress in Alpacas. *Alpacas,* pp. 20–22, Spring 1992.
12. Pugh, D. G.: Heat Stress in South American Camelids. *Proceedings of North American Veterinarian Conference.* Orlando, FL: Auburn University, 1995.
13. Purdy, S. R.: Winter Care for Alpacas and Llamas. *Large Animal Health* 2: 1, Winter 2002.

Chapter 9

Feeding the Alpaca

**Robert J. Van Saun, DVM,
MS, PhD, Dipl ACT/ACVN**

Bofadales, the preferred plant
community on the altiplano.

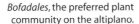

W e are all aware of the science of nutrition from a very fundamental perspective: a daily desire to consume foodstuffs in order to provide nutrients needed to support our body's functions. All humans consume foods to survive, but we do not all consume identical foods or follow the same diets. Recommended daily allowances (RDA guidelines) have been established for people of various ages; however, most people have no idea whether their diet meets these goals. Often a balanced diet is considered one incorporating a daily multimineral and vitamin supplement. Fortunately for us, the many different food items and sources that constitute our diet allow us to easily obtain these nutrients.

From a health-disease perspective, some foods and meal patterns are better than others. Tremendous differences of opinion exist as to optimum diet and approach to nutrition for people. Obviously many factors influence what and how we eat: inherent metabolic differences, cultural and social influences, taste preferences, food availability, ethical concerns, and many more. Research attempts to provide science-based evidence for determining appropriate healthy diets, irrespective of individual preferences. However, human nutrition is constrained by the type of studies one can perform. Most information is based on surveys and epidemiology studies of populations over time. As a result, recommendations often change; consider how

many times certain food items have been promoted as either good or bad, then the reverse. Good nutrition reflects an attitude of moderation; one must avoid pendulum swings too far to the right or left.

The study of animal nutrition is not fundamentally different from human nutrition and forms the foundation of understanding human nutrition. However, the availability of numerous controlled studies completed on many different animal species has allowed animal nutritionists to describe digestive capabilities and determine specific nutrient requirements for a given species under differing productive activities. These data then provide necessary information by which animal managers can formulate appropriate diets to feed their animals to maintain health and support productive functions.

In contrast to the human nutrition situation, feeding animals has greater challenges in meeting nutritional needs. Feed ingredients that constitute an animal's diet generally originate from a single geographic area and reflect any nutritional deficiencies or toxicities present. The body of scientific data on a given animal's nutrient requirements and feeding recommendations are reviewed and compiled by a scientific board appointed by the National Research Council (NRC) and published in a summary report. These NRC reports of animal nutrient requirements have been published and revised over the years for a wide range of laboratory, companion, and agricultural species. To date there is no NRC report detailing nutrient requirements for alpacas; however, a new report detailing small ruminant nutrient requirements, including llamas and alpacas, is in progress and should be available in 2006.

In spite of reams of scientific studies on animal nutrient requirements, the practice of feeding animals is still considered part science and part art. Even though we may know much about the nutritional needs of an animal, how we deliver those nutrients through various feed combinations and feeding methods has tremendous impact on the final outcome of animal health and performance. This is the "art" of nutrition. People become good animal feeders by having a background in animal sciences, extensive animal management experience, or some combination of the two. Unfortunately, this art of nutrition may often lead to biased feeding recommendations as to how to explicitly feed an animal. Many persons managing alpacas have limited background and experience in animal feeding and become entrapped by many of these feeding myths and biased opinions. In reality there are many ways, not just one right way, in which a person can adequately meet an alpaca's nutrient needs. Within any given geographic area, feed ingredient availability and nutrient analysis relative to animal requirements, coupled with practical feeding methods, will dictate the feeding program.

Unfortunately, when it comes to basic feeding practices for alpacas, we are short on science and long on art. Articles addressing some aspect of New World camelid nutrition represented less than 10 percent of total citations covering the years 1967 to 2001 in a web-based bibliography.[2] Most of the nutritional citations addressed digestive function, feed preference, comparative digestive efficiency, and nutritional disease, with only a couple specifically addressing nutrient requirements. Obviously this lack of information prevents good science-based nutritional recommendations from being presented.

With this paucity of information, alpaca owners are listening to any and all information that may help them to better feed and manage their animals, irrespective of source and documentation. This chapter provides some basic foundational science to help you better understand the why and how of feeding alpacas. Available information is reviewed based on how it would impact feeding practices of alpacas and llamas. Some latitude is taken in extrapolating data from other species to llamas and alpacas to fill in obvious gaps in our knowledge. In an effort to simplify the scope of nutritional science to be covered, topic areas are divided into three basic components: (1) animal factors, (2) feed/diet factors, and (3) feeding management factors. Each of these areas will be discussed to provide you with a fundamental understanding of how to best feed your animals. Finally some specific issues pertaining to an evaluation of your nutritional program and specific nutritional diseases are discussed.

ANIMAL FACTORS—UNDERSTANDING THE BEAST

To understand how to feed an animal correctly to maintain good health and optimize productive functions (e.g., growth, pregnancy, lactation, fleece growth), one needs to understand how the animal works. The following discussion addresses unique aspects of New World camelid digestive anatomy and physiology that impact our understanding of nutrient assimilation and utilization. Using available data and extrapolating from other species within the noted constraints of camelid physiology, specific recommendations for nutrient requirements are defined. Additional reviews of llama and alpaca digestive anatomy and physiology and its impact on feeding practices are available.[10,11,32,39,42,59,62,63,111,113,123]

Applied Digestive Anatomy

Ruminant herbivores, including cattle, sheep, goats, and deer, are unique animals in their ability to derive nutrients from low-quality forages. This ability has nothing to do with the animal's digestive enzymes, but totally depends upon the mutually beneficial (symbiotic) relationship between host animal and microbial populations residing in the anaerobic fermentation system (i.e., rumen) located just anterior to the true stomach. What separates ruminant herbivores from nonruminant herbivores is their ability to chew their cud. The ability to regurgitate swallowed feed material (cud chewing) for continued chewing (remastication) provides the rumen microbes greater surface area to feed materials, thus allowing greater extent of degradation. Ruminant animals are the most efficient fiber-digesting herbivores.

New and Old World camelids (suborder Tylopoda) are ruminant animals in that they have an expanded forestomach to facilitate microbial fermentation of ingested feedstuffs and they chew their cud. However, camelids are not considered "true ruminants" as a result of some very distinct anatomic and physiologic differences in their digestive tracts compared to the variety of ruminant species. Although both groups seemingly have evolved a similar system of nutrient assimilation, it was accomplished through a process of parallel evolution.[123] Table 9.1 provides a comparison between various domestic species relative to digestive anatomy and feeding preferences.

The most striking difference between camelid and ruminant digestive tracts is anatomic, camelids having only three distinct compartments associated with the foregut and stomach as compared to the four-compartment ruminant organ.[128] As a result of the anatomic differences, one should not attempt to use ruminant terminology to label the chambers of the camelid forestomach. The large anaerobic (i.e., oxygen limited) fermentation chamber is divided into two distinct compartments labeled C-1 and C-2 (see Figure 9.1). The fermentation chamber is connected to the third forestomach component (C-3) by a small tubular canal. Compartment 3 is an elongated tubular organ that

has fermentation activity in the proximal portion, with the lower one-fifth having gastric secretions containing proteolytic digestive enzymes and hydrochloric acid. This would be similar to the digestive activity of our stomach. Proportional volumes of the forestomach from the three compartments are 83 percent (C1), 6 percent (C2), and 11 percent (C-3).[113,128]

Another unique feature of the camelid forestomach is the presence of small saccules in both C-1 and C-2 (see Figure 9.1).[128] These saccules are lined with a glandular (i.e., secretory function) epithelium as compared to the stratified squamous (i.e., protective and absorptive func-

Table 9.1 Comparison of gastrointestinal tract characteristics and feeding behavior among various domesticated species.*

	Animal Species				
	Cattle	**Sheep/Goat**	**Alpaca**	**Horse**	**Pig**
GI Tract Type	*Ruminant Herbivore*	*Ruminant Herbivore*	*Pseudo-ruminant Herbivore*	*Colonic Fermenting Herbivore*	*Nonruminant Omnivore*
# Stomach compartments	4	4	3	1	1
GI compartment	*gal (% of total)*	*gal (% of total)*	*gal (% of total)*	*gal (% of total)*	*gal (% of total)*
Forestomach	60.4 (64.3%)	6.9 (59.0%)	6.54 (51.8%)	—	—
Abomasum/Stomach	6.1 (6.5%)	0.9 (7.7%)	0.8 (6.3%)	4.8 (8.6%)	2.1 (29.2%)
Subtotal	**66.5 (70.8%)**	**7.8 (66.7%)**	**7.34 (58.1%)**	**4.8 (8.6%)**	**2.1 (29.2%)**
Small intestine	17.4 (18.5%)	2.4 (20.5%)	2.7 (21.4%)	16.9 (30.2%)	2.4 (33.3%)
Cecum	2.6 (2.8%)	0.3 (2.6%)	0.3 (2.3%)	8.9 (15.8%)	0.4 (5.6%)
Large intestine	7.4 (7.9%)	1.2 (10.2%)	2.3 (18.2%)	25.4 (45.4%)	2.3 (31.9%)
Total tract	**93.9 (100%)**	**11.7 (100%)**	**12.6 (100%)**	**56.0 (100%)**	**7.2 (100%)**
Feeding behavior	Bulk roughage grazer	Intermediate browser	Intermediate browser	Bulk roughage grazer	Meal feeder

*GI compartment capacities modified from Ensminger et al., 1990 (reference 33).

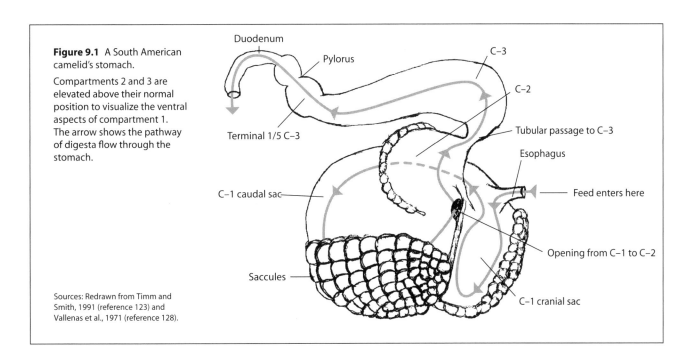

Figure 9.1 A South American camelid's stomach.

Compartments 2 and 3 are elevated above their normal position to visualize the ventral aspects of compartment 1. The arrow shows the pathway of digesta flow through the stomach.

Sources: Redrawn from Timm and Smith, 1991 (reference 123) and Vallenas et al., 1971 (reference 128).

Duodenum
Pylorus
C–3
C–2
Tubular passage to C–3
Terminal 1/5 C–3
Esophagus
Feed enters here
C–1 caudal sac
Opening from C–1 to C–2
Saccules
C–1 cranial sac

tion) epithelium of the remaining area.[107] Two functions have been attributed to the glandular epithelium of these saccules. A secretory function has been suggested where bicarbonate and phosphate ions are released, aiding fermentation buffering capacity.[30] Increased C-1 buffering capacity would maintain a more stable pH, complementing the buffering function of saliva and promoting greater microbial fermentation. Other investigators did not find significant secretory capacity, but suggested that these saccules aid in rapid absorption of fermentation end products (i.e., volatile fatty acids) and solutes.[107] Compared to other ruminants, llamas and alpacas had higher C-1 pH and greater volatile fatty acid (VFA) absorption following feeding, suggesting that both functions may be present in these saccules.[78,129,130]

Motility of the forestomach is a critical function with regard to continual fermentation activity. Forestomach motility ensures constant exposure of the ingested feedstuffs to microbial attachment and subsequent degradation. Similar to true ruminants, forestomach motility in camelids occurs in two distinct phases (A and B waves compared to α and β waves in true ruminants).[52] Beyond this, forestomach motility is dramatically different. In camelids, C-2 contracts strongly followed by contraction of the distal aspect of C-1 (A phase). Phase B initiates when the cranial portion of C-1 contracts followed by contraction of C-2 and the caudal portion of C-1. This B phase may repeat itself three to six times during a cycle the before a brief rest period and the beginning of a new cycle.

Eructation (i.e., burping of gases) may occur three to four times during each motility cycle. In comparison, camelids have greater forestomach activity compared to the single bi- or triphasic contraction per minute of true ruminants.[52] This increased motility pattern found in camelids may also have some bearing on the observation that these animals are fairly resistant to forestomach gas accumulation or bloat as opposed to true ruminants. Increased motility patterns also account for the more thoroughly mixed homogeneous nature of camelid forestomach contents compared to more stratified air, fibrous mat, and liquid layers found in true ruminants.

Beyond the forestomach system, camelid small intestinal digestion and absorptive processes seem to be identical to ruminant and nonruminant animals. The hindgut also has some fermentation capacity, but to a much lesser extent compared to the forestomach. The primary purpose of the hindgut is water absorption along with some absorption of VFAs, vitamins, and minerals. Very little data are available detailing the role of hindgut function in camelids. With this understanding of differences in anatomy and physiology of the camelid forestomach and a

basic knowledge of the dynamics of an anaerobic fermentation system, we can make some informed extrapolations as to the nutritional needs of the South American camelid, in spite of the lack of research information.

Microbial Fermentation

Studies of fermentation characteristics show that the anaerobic fermentation process and end-product VFA production for camelids are similar to true ruminants.[127,129,130] Microorganisms (bacteria, protozoa, fungi) found in the camelid forestomach are the same ones found in other anaerobic fermentation systems (e.g., ruminant forestomach and equine hindgut).[98] This observation is also supported by an ability to transfer rumen contents (transfaunate) from cattle, sheep, or goats into camelids. Population dynamics of the different bacteria species found in the forestomach will depend upon the prevailing source of ingested material. Camelids consuming predominately grasses will have a greater mass of cellulolytic (i.e., fiber-digesting) bacteria compared to lactating dairy cows or feedlot beef steers as a result of their greater grain (starch) consumption.

Bacteria and other microorganisms, which reside in the rumen and other similar digestive fermentation systems, are capable of partially degrading complex carbohydrate compounds (e.g., cellulose, hemicellulose, starch, pectins, fructosans) consumed by the host animal. Partial degradation of carbohydrates releases energy for use by the bacteria, with smaller carbohydrate compounds (VFAs) remaining to be absorbed and utilized by the host animal. There are a number of possible end-products generated by fermentation, but the most abundant VFAs are acetate (two-carbon chain), propionate (three-carbon chain), and butyrate (four-carbon chain). Acetate is the primary end-product of fiber (e.g., plant cell wall material) fermentation, whereas propionate and butyrate are end-products of sugar and starch fermentation. Llamas and alpacas, similar to other ruminants, utilize acetate and butyrate in their cells for energy or synthesis of fat. Propionate has a different fate in the animal. Nearly all absorbed propionate is converted in the liver to glucose. Glucose is known as the blood sugar molecule and is the primary energy source for the body. Implications of fermentation and blood glucose are further discussed in the next section "Physiologic Differences."

Rumen and camelid forestomach bacteria use energy released from dietary carbohydrate fermentation to support bacterial protein synthesis. Essentially this means the microbes are making more microbial cells (i.e., reproducing). Why is microbial reproduction so important to the host animal? Microbial cells contain over 62 percent protein, which is highly digestible to the host animal in its true stomach. Many forages consumed by ruminant and camelid animals are inherently low quality and low in protein. Thus greater amounts of bacterial protein generated in the fermentation vat provide larger amounts of available protein to support animal functions. It is to the host animal's advantage to promote microbial fermentation and resultant bacterial protein production (see "Physiologic Differences").

The rumen fermentation system described above is a marvelous system; however, one needs to recognize that ruminant animals (inclusive of camelids) are not born with a functioning rumen. From a nutritional perspective, the newborn calf and cria are nonruminant animals. The fermentation system requires anatomic and physiologic development before it is capable of accomplishing extensive fermentation of feeds to provide nutrients. Anatomic size and muscular motility as well as physiologic development depend upon the type of diet fed the young preruminant animal (i.e., calf, cria). Table 9.2 shows changes in relative size contribution to stomach compartments for a developing calf.[136] It can be inferred that a cria undergoes similar size changes over time. A need for proteolytic digestion of milk, which takes place in C-3 (cria) or abomasum (calf), accounts for its greater proportional size in the young milk-fed animal. Similar to the anatomy in ruminants, there exists a muscular groove in the camelid forestomach that shunts suckled milk from the esophagus to C-2/C-3, thus bypassing C-1 and preventing milk from being fermented. As the fermentation system develops and milk supply diminishes, microbial end-products provide an increasingly larger percentage of nutrients to the animal. Data from Samaniego (1977, cited by San Martin and Bryant) showed that relative size changes in alpacas occurred over 8 weeks and microbial activity reached adult levels by 12 weeks of age.[113]

Research with calves and lambs has shown fiber fermentation in the rumen not to be a major stimulator of rumen development. The VFA end-products butyrate and propionate seemingly stimulate rumen epithelial development and metabolic activity.[9,75] Acetate, the end-product of fiber (forage) fermentation, has a minimal effect on rumen development. Whether or not these findings hold for developing camelids is not known. If similar relationships do exist for camelids, then feeding strategies for weaning crias should be adjusted accordingly. In calves and lambs, feeding a creep feed containing some readily fermentable carbohydrates from grain sources augments rumen development. A similar practice could be applied to crias. If these assumptions are true, then one would wonder how crias not fed concentrates (grains), as in their native environment, make the transition. Grasses growing under rainy season conditions in South America will naturally contain significant amounts of sugars. These plant sugars can be fermented into propionate and butyrate in the rumen of the cria, thus initiating development. Poor-quality forages (i.e., mature hays, dormant pastures) take longer to ferment and may not stimulate compartmental development, thus delaying a cria's ability to transition easily to solid feed diet. This may also result in a poor growth rate and increased health problems associated with the weaning process.

Physiologic Differences

Rate of Passage and Digestive Efficiency Similar to ruminants, llamas were shown to have differential selectivity in retaining water and particles, based on size.[53] Water passed through C-1/C-2 more quickly than particles, and larger particles (2.5–4 cm) were retained slightly longer than smaller particles (0.2–1 cm). Comparative studies between camelids and true ruminants show that consumed feed material passes more slowly through C-1 than the rumen.[24,35,110] This slower rate of passage results in feed materials being retained within the fermentation chamber for a prolonged period of time. As a direct consequence of longer retention time, camelids have greater degradation of ingested feed material compared to true ruminants, especially for the cell wall fraction.[25,35,44,46,47,58,59,79,110-112] The digestive advantage for camelids over ruminants is most obvious when comparing the digestion of poor-quality, low- protein forages.[47,79,111,113,137] This digestive advantage is minimized when feeding higher-quality forages.

Studies looking at the liquid passage rate suggest a more rapid movement of liquid through the forestomach of camelids than true ruminants.[24,110,111] This observation may explain the greater buffering capacity of camelids resulting from more microbial VFA end-products being washed out of the fermentation system.[127,130] A more rapid liquid passage rate would result in greater microbial yield as a consequence of more cells being in a state of active growth.[135] The combination of greater degree of degrad-

Table 9.2 Relative changes in anatomic size of the stomach compartments associated with animal age.**

Stomach Compartment		Newborn	2–3 Months	Adult
Ruminant	*Camelid*			
Rumen	C–1	25%	65%	80% (83%)**
Reticulum	C–2	5%	5%	5% (6%)
Omasum		10%	10%	7–8%
Abomasum	C–3	60%	20%	7–8% (11%)

*Equivalent compartments for the camelid stomach are designated and similar relative changes in size are inferred.
**Final relative size comparisons for adult camelids.
Source: Modified from Walsh et al., 1983 (reference 134).

ability coupled with increased microbial yield provides camelids with a distinct advantage in dealing with lower-quality feeds compared to other ruminants.

Dry Matter Intake Although the observed slowed rate of passage in camelids has digestive advantages, it comes with a potentially negative consequence: reduced feed intake capacity. Feed intake is defined as the total quantity of feed consumed. All feeds vary in their water content from very low (<10% in dry feeds) to very high (>80% in fresh pasture). To standardize a measure of intake and be able to compare intake values across feeds, we usually measure dry matter intake. Dry matter intake is determined by subtracting a feed's water content from its wet weight. For example, if an animal consumed 10 pounds of feed that contains 20 percent water, then 8 pounds of dry matter (10 lb − 2 lb water = 8 lb dry matter) is consumed. Dry matter intake can then be presented as a percent of body weight for comparisons.

Beef cattle, sheep, and goats at maintenance (no productive functions) will have a predicted dry matter intake between 1.5 and 2.0 percent of body weight.[93,96,97] Granted there is much individual variation as well as feed ingredient-based issues that control feed intake. For ruminants, amount of dietary fiber measured as neutral detergent fiber (see "Fiber" under "Analytical Procedures") directly impacts intake capacity. As neutral detergent fiber content of feeds goes up, intake capacity is reduced.[84] Observations of feeding behavior in North America would suggest that camelids at maintenance have a dry matter intake between 1.0 and 1.5 percent of body weight, although higher intakes are feasible.[39,42,62,63] On average, this is about a 30 percent decline in intake capacity compared to other ruminants.

Measuring dry matter intake for an animal is a difficult procedure if it is not housed individually. Obtaining dry matter intakes for pastured animals is a real challenge. A number of studies have measured camelid dry matter intake under varying feeding and housing conditions in comparison to sheep.[25,78,105,110–113] There is not complete agreement among study findings, and some studies show similar intake levels (% body weight basis) as previously described, while others show slightly higher intake levels. Most studies confirmed that camelids had lower intake levels compared to sheep, but others showed no difference[44] or even higher intake by camelids.[137] Differences in dry matter intake results across studies may reflect wide differences in the forage quality used. Both neutral detergent fiber[79] and protein[111,113] content influence intake capacity, somewhat differentially for camelids and ruminants.

San Martin and Bryant summarized intake data from a large number of studies for alpacas and llamas compared to sheep in penned and pasture situations.[113] Average intake for llamas and alpacas was 2.0 and 1.8 percent of body weight, respectively. These are higher values than typically expected, but still were lower than what was observed for sheep fed the same diets. Alpacas ate on average 20 percent less than sheep across studies, whereas llamas ate more than 30 percent less than sheep. When intake for llamas and alpacas were adjusted for metabolic body weight (i.e., body surface area to mass ratio), there were no differences between llamas and alpacas, but intake was 26 percent lower for improved and 36 percent lower for unimproved pastures compared to sheep.[110]

Urea Metabolism Urea is a nonprotein nitrogen (NPN) compound synthesized by the liver and usually expelled from the body in urine. Breakdown of protein releases ammonia (NH_3), a potent cellular toxin. Being converted to urea in the liver rapidly detoxifies ammonia. Protein breakdown occurs naturally in the body as a part of cell turnover, but this can be accentuated during periods of dietary protein or energy deficiency as the body harvests protein to make glucose. In ruminant animals including camelids, microbes are primarily responsible for ammonia production as a result of their dietary protein degradation activity. Fermentation microbes utilize all forms of nitrogen compounds, including urea, to meet their nitrogen needs to support microbial protein synthesis.

As already alluded to, dietary protein potentially is limiting in low-quality forage diets. Ruminant animals can compensate somewhat for low dietary protein by recycling urea through saliva back into the rumen. This evolutionary adaptation in ruminant animals provides the rumen microbial population with needed nitrogen even when dietary protein is limited. In return the microbial population provides the ruminant animal with high-quality microbial protein, thus giving the rumen animal a distinct advantage over nonruminant herbivores in meeting the challenges of utilizing low-quality forages.

Blood urea nitrogen (BUN) concentration measures the amount of urea present and often is used as a measure of kidney function. Urea is readily filtered from blood by the kidneys, so when kidney function is compromised, BUN concentrations will rise. Blood urea concentrations can also be used to assess dietary protein status in ruminants.[50] A number of clinical pathology laboratories have determined and published reference ranges for a variety of clinical chemistry parameters, including BUN.[36,70,77,115] On the surface the reported BUN reference range looks similar for cattle and sheep compared to llamas and alpacas. Reference ranges reported for cattle and sheep usually represent a normal expected BUN concentration range relative to kidney function. From a nutritional perspective, a working range for BUN concentration would be 10 to 20 mg/dl, with values <10 and >20 suggesting low or excessive protein, respectively. Most dairy cattle will maintain a BUN concentration between 12 and 18 mg/dl. Reference ranges for llamas and alpacas reflect summary data of samples collected from healthy animals, suggesting no indication of kidney disease. None of these studies had any data as to the level of dietary protein supplementation. However, in comparing llama and alpaca to ruminant BUN data, it would seem camelids have higher (>20 mg/dl) BUN concentrations.[36,70,77,115]

Higher BUN concentrations in camelids suggest they are being overfed protein relative to requirements, metabolize urea differently from other ruminants, have an inherently high metabolic rate of protein turnover, or some combination. Results from a llama urea metabolism study would suggest llamas have a lower rate of urea turnover and kidney urea excretion rate compared to other ruminants.[57] These differences allow the llama to recycle more urea to the forestomach for use by bacteria to produce microbial protein. In addition to recycling more urea to bacteria, llamas have been shown to have greater urease activity, the enzyme needed to metabolize urea, than other ruminants.[57] Greater urea recycling and utilization coupled with the slower rate of passage in C-1 are critical physiologic adaptations of camelids, allowing them to survive in their native environment under harsh conditions consuming low-quality forages for a significant portion of the year.

Glucose Metabolism Glucose is a simple six-carbon sugar that plays a role of primary energy provider to the body. All body tissues can metabolize glucose; however, when in short supply, some tissues can metabolize fatty acids derived from fats for energy. Glucose is an important substrate for the mammary gland, as lactose (milk sugar) is synthesized from 2 molecules of glucose. Glucose availability to the mammary gland dictates the milk production level as defined by lactose synthesis capacity. Lactose content of llama milk is greater (6.5 versus 5.0%) compared to ruminant animals.[89] Remembering that all dietary sugars are fermented to VFAs, and only propionate can be converted to glucose, where does the camelid obtain the needed glucose?

Glucose metabolism in camelids is an enigma. Ruminant animals maintain low blood glucose concentration (45–75 mg/dl) compared to nonruminant animals (75–115 mg/dl, horse; 85–150 mg/dl, pig).[70] Preweaned milk-fed calves are not functional ruminants and will maintain a higher blood glucose concentration similar to nonruminant animals. As the rumen becomes functional, blood glucose will decline to adult concentrations. In contrast to

Ichu grass dominates the grazing habitat in much of Peru and Bolivia.

ruminants, llamas and alpacas maintain higher blood glucose concentrations (mean: 126 mg/dl; range: 103–160 mg/dl) more similar to that of nonruminant animals. Although there is some variation among laboratory ranges, all show higher concentrations for camelids compared to ruminants.[36,70,77,115] Llamas and alpacas also display an extreme hyperglycemic response (blood glucose concentrations >200–300 mg/dl) in response to even minimal stress situations.[19,20,36] Elevated blood glucose can be somewhat explained by recent research showing a sluggish insulin response and moderate insulin resistance, somewhat similar to a diabetes condition, in llamas and alpacas.[19,20]

How can llamas and alpacas maintain these high blood glucose concentrations and display such hyperglycemia in a dietary situation that seemingly is limited in available glucose or glucose precursors? The primary dietary glucose precursor is the VFA propionate originating from starch fermentation. Amino acids from protein can be readily converted to glucose in the liver by a process termed gluconeogenesis. Perhaps camelids utilize amino acids in support of blood glucose content, which would possibly explain the higher BUN concentrations previously described. Supportive evidence for this hypothesis comes from data generated in a feed restriction study of hepatic lipidosis.[126] In this study, feed restriction resulted in a significant decline in BUN concentration over time, consistent with observed responses in ruminants. When individual llama responses were evaluated, a differential response in BUN was noticed relative to lactation status. Nonlactating and late lactation (>10 weeks) llamas showed a gradual decline in BUN concentration in association with feed restriction. In contrast, lactating llamas showed marked increases in BUN with a decline occurring following refeeding.[126] One could speculate that the increase in BUN was a result of body protein mobilization in support of milk production, given that the nursing crias did not lose weight during the trial. Clearly, further research into glucose and protein metabolism in camelids is warranted.

Animal Requirements—Understanding Essential Nutrients

Llamas and alpacas as well as all other animals require five essential nutrients: water, energy, protein, minerals, and vitamins. A requirement for an essential nutrient is based on maintenance of normal body functions over time and is adjusted accordingly to accommodate other physiologic states (growth, pregnancy, lactation, and work). As previously stated, there is no published NRC report documenting nutrient requirements for llamas and alpacas. In most cases, camelid feeding recommendations have been extrapolated from those of sheep, goats, and cattle.[93,96,97] In spite of the aforementioned anatomic and physiologic differences, no available data suggest inherent metabolic differences between camelids and ruminants in essential nutrient requirements to support various physiologic functions. With a functional understanding of camelid digestive anatomy and physiology, one could make appropriate recommendations based on well-established databases for sheep, goats, and beef cattle. Each of these essential nutrients is described more completely in the following sections.

Daily requirements can be described on a nutrient density (percent [%], parts per million [ppm]) or totals (pounds [lb], grams [g], or milligrams [mg] per day) basis. *Animals require specific amounts of nutrients daily to meet needs. It must be remembered that animals only eat amounts of nutrients and not percentages!* This statement is a critical issue for the novice nutritionist to understand. Nutrient density values are relatively easy to understand. For example, if a growing cria and pregnant alpaca require 16 percent and 10 percent dietary protein, respectively, most people would understand that the cria has higher protein requirements. When requirements are defined on a density basis, an often overlooked critical flaw is the dependency of dietary adequacy on feed intake. Amount of a given nutrient consumed is equal to the dietary nutrient density times feed intake. Even though dietary nutrient density may be adequate, if the animal does not consume sufficient amounts, then nutrient intake will be deficient. Let's say our pregnant alpaca requires 0.3 pounds of protein daily.

For this example we stated that 10 percent crude protein was adequate for pregnant alpacas. This would suggest the alpaca is expected to consume 3 pounds of dry matter (3 lb intake × 0.1 lb protein/lb feed [10%] = 0.3 lb protein). Now let's imagine our pregnant alpaca is feeling heat stressed, socially inferior, or available feed is limited, and as a result consumes 2 pounds dry matter. This results in the alpaca consuming less (2 × 0.1 = 0.2) protein than required. Therefore, when describing dietary nutrient content on a density basis, one needs to consider dry matter intake and how it impacts daily nutrient intake. This issue is a concern when extrapolating nutrient requirements from cattle, sheep, or goats to camelids.

Water Water is the most essential nutrient; however, it is also the most neglected nutrient. Water plays important roles in body temperature regulation and provides an aqueous medium for all metabolic reactions. Young animals are approximately 85 to 90 percent water, whereas adults are between 60 and 70 percent depending upon fat content (more fat, less water).[106] Llama milk is 87 percent water; therefore water consumption is critical to lactating animals.[89] An animal's ability to consume dry matter is dependent upon water availability; however, llamas were shown to have less reduction in dry matter intake compared to goats when water was restricted.[106] This does not suggest one should ever attempt to restrict water to llamas and alpacas, especially under heat stress conditions. Animals can derive water from drinking, feed, and metabolic sources. Metabolic sources generally account for only 5 percent of total needs. Feeds vary tremendously in water content, from <10 percent in most dry feeds to >80 percent on lush pasture. Fresh, clean, high-quality water should be available for free choice at all times.

Water quality can be evaluated subjectively by its odor, taste, and smell. Objective water-quality evaluations include determinations of pH, total salinity and hardness, microbiologic culture, and contaminant content. Ideal water pH is near 7, but most animals will tolerate water with a pH range from 6 (slightly acidic) to 9 (slightly basic). Water pH can be easily measured with litmus paper or commercially available battery-operated pH meters. Other measures of water quality will need to be completed by a certified laboratory. Contact a chosen laboratory to determine appropriate methods for sample collection. Tables 9.3 and 9.4 present suggested guideline values for water quality relative to total dissolved solids and mineral contamination.[91]

Total water requirement is determined by body weight, physiologic state, level of activity, production level, dietary composition, and environmental conditions. The water requirement has been related to energy intake (1 ml per kcal

Table 9.3 Guidelines for interpretation of total dissolved solids content in waters.

Total Dissolved Solids (mg/l or ppm)	Interpretation
<1,000	Relatively low salinity; suitable for all classes of livestock
1,000–1,999	Satisfactory for all classes of livestock; may produce transient diarrhea in animals not accustomed to them, but should not affect health or performance
2,000–4,999	Temporary water refusal and diarrhea may be seen when animals are introduced to them; may reduce productivity in dairy cattle
5,000–6,999	Likely to reduce productivity in dairy cattle; may reduce growth rates; may result in water refusal and diarrhea. Avoid if possible
7,000–10,000	Unfit for poultry or swine; considerable risk in all other species. Animals may subsist on them. Avoid
>10,000	High saline water; not recommended for use under any conditions. Dangerous, avoid

Source: Modified from National Research Council, 1974 (reference 91).

Table 9.4 Recommended limits of concentration of some potentially toxic substances in water.

Mineral	Safe Upper Limit (ppm [mg/l])*
Arsenic (As)	0.2
Cadmium (Cd)	0.05
Chromium (Cr)	1.0
Cobalt (Co)	1.0
Copper (Cu)	0.5
Fluoride (F)	2.0
Lead (Pb)	0.1
Mercury (Hg)	0.01
Nickel (Ni)	1.0
Nitrate-N (NO_3-)	100.0
Nitrite-N (NO_2-)	10.0
Vanadium (V)	0.1
Zinc (Zn)	25.0

*Milligrams per liter = mg/l; ppm = parts per million; both are equivalent measures.
Source: Modified from National Research Council, 1974 (reference 91).

Optimum spacing for grazing.

of metabolizable energy intake) or metabolic body weight (122 ml/kg BW$^{.75}$).[42] Metabolic body weight is a method to relate body surface area to live body mass and is calculated by raising live body weight in kilograms to the 3/4 power (kg BW$^{.75}$). Metabolic research has found that energy requirements were more proportional to body surface area than mass.[92] A more general rule of thumb for water intake is 2 to 3 times dry matter intake or 3 percent (adult maintenance) to 8 percent (growth, lactation level) of body weight daily (see Table 9.5). Water intake should be increased in hot weather and humid conditions to approximately 10 to 15 percent of body weight daily.

Energy Quantitatively, energy is the most important nutrient, from an animal performance perspective, as it supports all body functions. Unlike other essential nutrients, energy is not described by a single physical entity such as protein, calcium, or selenium. Rather, energy is an abstrac-

tion, which can only be measured in its transformation from one form into another.[92] Energy is defined as the ability to perform work and is derived from oxidation of carbohydrates, fats, and proteins. In nutrition, chemical energy is measured by heat production as molecules are oxidized (burned or metabolized). Heat production, hence terminology in measuring energy, is quantified as calories or joules (1 calorie = 4.181 joules). One calorie is defined as the amount of heat required to raise 1 milliliter of water from 16.5 to 17.5°C. From a practical standpoint, a calorie is a very small unit of energy; therefore, larger units termed kilocalories (kcal; 1 kcal = 1,000 calories) and megacalories (Mcal; 1 Mcal = 1,000 kcal) are used in nutrition to describe animal energy requirements.

During the digestive process, energy stored within chemical bonds of carbohydrate, fat, and protein molecules is released and made available to the animal in varying degrees. The total amount of energy in a feed (termed

Table 9.5 Predicted water requirements and calculated water intakes at differing percentages of live body weight.

Body Weight		Water Requirement*		Water Intake Based on % of Body Weight							
		ME	MBW	3%		8%		10%		15%	
kg	lb	liters/d	liters/d	liters/d	gal/d	liters/d	gal/d	liters/d	gal/d	liters/d	gal/d
10	22	0.5	0.7	0.3	0.1	0.8	0.2	1.0	0.3	1.5	0.4
20	44	0.8	1.2	0.6	0.2	1.6	0.4	2.0	0.5	3.0	0.8
30	66	1.1	1.6	0.9	0.2	2.4	0.6	3.0	0.8	4.5	1.2
40	88	1.3	1.9	1.2	0.3	3.2	0.8	4.0	1.1	6.0	1.6
50	110	1.6	2.3	1.5	0.4	4.0	1.1	5.0	1.3	7.5	2.0
60	132	1.8	2.6	1.8	0.5	4.8	1.3	6.0	1.6	9.0	2.4
70	154	2.0	3.0	2.1	0.6	5.6	1.5	7.0	1.8	10.5	2.8
80	176	2.3	3.3	2.4	0.6	6.4	1.7	8.0	2.1	12.0	3.2
90	198	2.5	3.6	2.7	0.7	7.2	1.9	9.0	2.4	13.5	3.6
100	220	2.7	3.9	3.0	0.8	8.0	2.1	10.0	2.6	15.0	4.0
125	275	3.2	4.6	3.8	1.0	10.0	2.6	12.5	3.3	18.8	5.0
150	330	3.6	5.2	4.5	1.2	12.0	3.2	15.0	4.0	22.5	5.9
175	385	4.1	5.9	5.3	1.4	14.0	3.7	17.5	4.6	26.3	6.9
200	440	4.5	6.5	6.0	1.6	16.0	4.2	20.0	5.3	30.0	7.9
225	495	4.9	7.1	6.8	1.8	18.0	4.8	22.5	5.9	33.8	8.9
250	550	5.3	7.7	7.5	2.0	20.0	5.3	25.0	6.6	37.5	9.9
275	605	5.7	8.2	8.3	2.2	22.0	5.8	27.5	7.3	41.3	10.9
300	660	6.1	8.8	9.0	2.4	24.0	6.3	30.0	7.9	45.0	11.9

*Predicted water requirement under isothermic conditions. ME = 1 ml water per 1 kcal of metabolizable energy. MBW = 122 ml per kg of metabolic body weight.

gross energy [GE]) can be partitioned into definable components, namely digestible, metabolizable, and net energy, based on what proportion of the gross energy is potentially available to the animal at different phases of the digestive and utilization process (see Figure 9.2).[92] Digestible energy (DE) is that portion of gross energy not excreted in feces. As its name implies, it is feed energy that was digested and made potentially available to the animal. Metabolizable energy (ME) is a portion of digestible energy that is not lost in urine or as fermentation gases. This is energy available to the animal, which may used for various productive functions. Finally, net energy (NE) is the portion of metabolizable energy that is used to maintain body physiologic functions (maintenance) or some productive function (e.g., tissue growth, pregnancy, lactation, fleece growth). Another commonly used energy term is total digestible nutrients (TDN). Total digestible nutrients is defined as the sum of digestible protein, sugar and starch carbohydrates, fiber, and fats. Digestible fat is multiplied by 2.25 to account for its greater energy density compared to carbohydrates. Although TDN is often mistakenly equated with DE, it fits into the energy scale somewhere between DE and ME.

In attempting to define energy requirements for an animal, GE is of no value since it does not account for any differences in digestibility among feed sources. On a GE basis, corn cobs have the same energy value as corn grain.

At the other extreme, NE most precisely defines feed energy truly available to the animal. However, measurement of feed NE values is tedious and complicated, and requires highly specialized metabolic chamber equipment. Most commonly used across species and easily obtained through simple digestion trials is DE. In nonruminant animals, DE and ME are reasonably close in value; hence there is no need for additional measures to determine ME. However, for ruminant animals, including camelids, DE significantly overestimates feed energy, especially for forages and fiber by-product feeds as a result of energy lost in gases generated during fermentation (see Figure 9.2). Additional energy losses in urine from microbial degradation are also accounted for with ME determinations. Therefore a more accurate measure of the energy requirement for ruminant animals and camelids would be ME.

Fats are not a significant source of energy in the alpaca diet since they are not present in substantial amounts (<4% of dry matter) in a forage-based diet. Additionally dietary fatty acids, especially polyunsaturated fatty acids, are very inhibitory to fiber-fermenting microbes. Carbohydrates, including sugars, starches, hemicellulose, and cellulose, are the primary source of energy in camelids. Amounts of dietary sugars and starches need to be somewhat limited and balanced against hemicellulose and cellulose as part of dietary fiber to prevent abnormal acid conditions in the forestomach (see "Forestomach Acidosis"). As with other

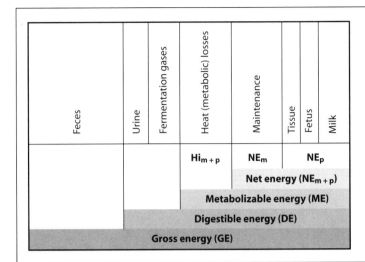

Figure 9.2 Dietary energy available to an alpaca.

Hi = heat increment
m = maintenance energy
p = energy used for productive purposes

forestomach fermenting animals, the primary source of energy for the host animal is VFAs, end-products of carbohydrate fermentation. The animal host will metabolize VFA compounds and transfer the energy into high-energy bonds within a specialized molecule, adenosine triphosphate (ATP).

In two different studies,[16,114] the maintenance ME requirement for llamas was determined to be 61 and 84.5 kcal/kg $BW^{.75}$ Again, energy requirements are defined relative to kilograms of metabolic weight (surface area) and not mass. Although the higher value is generally used and believed to reflect North American feeding conditions, an averaged value of 72.85 kcal ME/kg $BW^{.75}$ might be a reasonable compromise given problems of obesity in many camelids.[134] Also this value is similar but somewhat lower than maintenance ME values determined for sheep (99.9 kcal/kg $BW^{.75}$),[96] goats (101.4 kcal/kg $BW^{.75}$),[93] and cattle (133 kcal/kg $BW^{.75}$).[97] Given that most management systems for llamas and alpacas are pasture based, the maintenance energy requirement needs to be adjusted for activity level. Activity level accounts for muscular energy expended as the animal roams its environment in the daily search for food. In confinement feeding systems, where animals are housed comfortably and provided feed, activity expenditures are minimal and maintenance ME do not need to be adjusted. Depending upon the distance necessary to travel to find forage and the topography of the terrain covered, maintenance energy may need to be increased up to 75 percent to account for this activity expenditure (see Table 9.6).[94]

Table 9.6 Metabolizable energy (ME) prediction models for llamas and alpacas in various productive functions.*

Physiologic State	Prediction Model	Comment/Description
Maintenance	72.9 kcal/kg $BW^{.75}$	Needed to support all basic body functions without any environmental stresses
Activity/Work Level	Based on goat NRC	
Low	1.25 × maintenance	Light work or grazing on moderate to good-quality pasture
Moderate	1.50 × maintenance	Moderate work or grazing semiarid rangeland pasture, hilly conditions
High	1.75 × maintenance	Heavy work or grazing sparse grassland, mountainous conditions
Growth	7.25 kcal/g of gain	Based on goat data and does not account for changes in composition of gain. This amount is added to maintenance.
Pregnancy		
1 to 8 months	72.9 kcal/kg $BW^{.75}$	Maintenance energy only, no significant pregnancy requirement
8th to 9th month	65.3 × birth wt (kg) – 33.5	Add to maintenance energy
9th to 10th month	131.7 × birth wt (kg) – 39.7	Add to maintenance energy
10th to 11th month	203.5 × birth wt (kg) + 86.1	Add to maintenance energy
Lactation	946.2 kcal/kg milk	Multiply this value by estimated daily milk production (kg) for total lactation energy

*Total daily energy requirement (kcal/day) for a given animal is the sum of the appropriate physiologic states.

Metabolizable energy requirements in support of other physiologic states (i.e., growth, lactation, gestation, work) were extrapolated from sheep and goat requirement data, but not specifically confirmed for alpacas (see Table 9.6). The amount of ME required to support growth depends upon the rate of gain (grams/day) and the composition of gain (fat and protein %). Growth data and composition of gain data are lacking for alpacas and limited for llamas. Alpaca's growth rate has been observed to be between 0.25 and 0.5 lb/day (113–227 g/day) (see "Growth" under "Feeding Management Practices"). Until more definitive data on rate of gain and compositional changes are obtained, the energy requirement to support growth in alpacas can be estimated using the NRC goat model, 7.25 kcal ME/g gain, since goats have a similar range for growth rate (50–150 g/day).[93] This estimated value for gain is similar to that suggested by Fowler (8.92 kcal DE/g equivalent to 7.31 kcal ME/g) and overestimates energy for gain in younger, rapidly growing animals compared to older animals as a result of differences in the composition of gain.[42] Energy required for gain must be added to maintenance for total growing animal energy requirement.

The pregnancy ME requirement is a function of energy needs to support fetal, placental, uterine, and mammary gland growth. Llamas were found to gain between 10 and 15 percent of their live weight at conception over the gestation period with the majority of weight gain (>60%) occurring during the last two months.[118] This fetal growth pattern is similar to other species and would apply to alpacas. This pattern of growth suggests changing requirements as the pregnant alpaca progresses through the last three months of gestation. Two different methods were developed to predict the pregnancy requirement. A simple model using metabolic body weight to predict maintenance and pregnancy requirements was extrapolated from a sheep equation by proportionally decreasing the coefficient multiplier to account for the lower maintenance energy need of camelids compared to sheep.[96] The equation, 160.9 kcal/kg BW$^{.75}$ estimates total ME energy requirements for maintenance plus pregnancy, and should only be used for the last three months of pregnancy. This is identical to the recommendation made by Fowler in adding 93 kcal DE/kg BW$^{.75}$ (76.26 kcal ME/kg BW$^{.75}$) to maintenance.[42] A second method, based on sheep data adjusted for gestation day and birth weight, is more dynamic, accounting for differences in birth weight and month of gestation (see Table 9.6).[96,133] Expected birth weights for alpacas are between 6 and 9 kilograms (13.2 and 19.8 lb), but compiled records of birth weights on a farm should be used. A comparison between the two camelid models shows that the simpler model is reasonably close to predicting requirements for the tenth month of gestation (±7%), but overpredicts total ME for eighth (+40–60%) and ninth (+15–30%) months.[133]

Lactational energy requirements are a function of milk composition and total yield in addition to maintenance requirements. Llama milk composition was determined in 83 animals on 8 farms in 4 states (Colorado, Illinois, Kentucky, Michigan).[89] Reported mean milk composition was 13.1 percent total solids, 6.5 percent lactose, 3.4 percent protein, and 2.7 percent fat. Compared to other ruminants, llama milk is higher in lactose and slightly lower in fat. Of all domestic ruminants, sheep milk has the highest protein and fat content. Lactose content was slightly lower in first-lactation llamas, and milk protein content varied by farm, suggesting dietary influences. Based on these composition data, llama milk contains 700.2 kcal NE/kg. Using a 74 percent efficiency of converting ME to milk energy results in 946.2 kcal ME/kg of milk produced.[96] This value falls between the estimates of llama milk energy suggested by Fowler (1,257 kcal ME/kg)[42] and Johnson (822 kcal/kg),[63] most likely due to differences in the milk composition used, based on available data. Milk production during lactation has not been well quantified or modeled for camelids. Suggested production amounts range from 0.75 to 2.5 kg/day (1.65–5.5 lb/day), equivalent to 710 to 2,082 kcal ME needed per day to support lactation.

A final productive function requiring additional energy and protein above maintenance is growth of fiber or fleece. Energy deficiency or restriction has been shown to slow wool growth and reduce fiber diameter in sheep.[96] In severe cases of energy deficiency, wool growth will cease, creating a weak spot or "break" in the staple of wool.[96] Somewhat similar effects of nutrition on fleece characteristics were found in alpacas. Male alpacas fed a low-energy, low-protein, submaintenance diet had lower clean fleece weight, fiber length, and length to diameter ratio compared to alpacas fed a high-energy, high-protein diet.[109] Fiber diameter was slightly higher in alpacas fed the better diet, but the difference was not significant. In contrast to nutritional influences on wool growth characteristics in sheep, alpaca fiber has differential growth in length and diameter where fiber length is augmented better than fiber diameter. Recommendations for energy and protein requirements to support mohair production by Angora goats have been generated (see Table 9.7).[93] These recommendations can be used as general guidelines in accounting for fleece production in alpacas.

The previous discussion presents a complicated but science-based approach to estimating energy requirements for alpacas. If we are to move forward in better managing our animals for optimum health and productivity, this kind of approach is needed. However, a simpler approach may be accomplished by multiplying maintenance energy by

Table 9.7 Suggested metabolizable energy (ME) and crude protein (CP) amounts needed in addition to animal maintenance to support various levels of fleece yield.

Fleece Yield		Nutrients	
kg	*lb*	*ME (Mcal/d)*	*CP (g/d)*
2	4.4	0.06	9
4	8.8	0.12	17
6	13.2	0.18	26
8	17.6	0.24	34

Source: National Research Council, 1981 (reference 93).

some defined factor, as is done in other species where requirement data are lacking. (For example, suggested increases in gestational energy requirement for months 8, 9, and 10 would be $1.25\pm.05$, $1.5\pm.1$ and $1.9\pm.1\times$maintenance, respectively. Energy requirement for growth ranges from $2.5-3\times$maintenance for the first 3 months, $1.5-2\times$maintenance for months 4–6, $1.5\times$maintenance from 6–12 months, and $1.1-1.3\times$maintenance from 12–24 months of age. Lactation energy requirement ranges from $2-3\times$maintenance.) How well you are meeting your animal's energy needs can be easily evaluated by repeated monitoring of body weight changes and body condition score (see "Evaluating and Monitoring Nutritional Status").

Protein The alpaca protein requirement has been estimated by Huasasquiche (1974)[59,113] to be 2.38 grams (g) digestible protein/kg $BW^{.75}$, which is lower than that estimated for goats (2.82 g digestible protein/kg $BW^{.75}$ or 4.15 g crude protein/kg $BW^{.75}$).[93] Using factors to account for dietary protein digestibility and availability,[96,97] this camelid digestible protein value would be equivalent to 3.45 g crude protein/kg $BW^{.75}$. Another suggested estimate for the crude protein requirement is 31 g crude protein/Mcal digestible energy.[42] Using this model, predicted crude protein requirements would be just slightly less than those predicted using the above equation. For an adult 70-kilogram (154-lb) alpaca, this would be equivalent to 77.3 to 83.5 grams crude protein a day. However, if one calculates the crude protein to digestible energy ratio using original data, the protein to energy ratio is much higher, 47 grams crude protein per 1 Mcal digestible energy, consistent with the idea of a higher protein requirement in camelids.

Current methods to estimate protein requirements for sheep and cattle are based on a factorial approach. Using a ratio of 48 grams crude protein to 1 Mcal metabolizable energy, protein requirements for other physiologic functions were estimated.[134] General recommendations for dietary protein levels are as follows: 8 to 10 percent for maintenance, 10 to 12 percent for late gestation, 12 to 14 percent for lactation, and 12 to 16 percent for a young growing animal. The ranges in dietary crude protein shown represent calculated dietary densities assuming an intake level of 1.5 to 1.75 percent of body weight. If intake is less, then these values should be increased by 1 to 2 percent.

However, the protein requirement is much more complicated than digestible or crude protein in a forestomach fermenting animal. In ruminant animals, protein requirements are defined relative to microbial and animal needs. Dietary protein can be fractionated according to its solubility and degradability within the fermentation vat. Microbial populations can utilize highly soluble and degradable dietary protein, whereas daily amino acid requirements for the animal are derived from digestion of microbes and undegradable dietary protein. Unfortunately, there are no data with camelids relative to these protein fraction requirements. Clearly there is a tremendous need for more information on protein metabolism and dietary needs in alpacas.

Minerals Mineral requirements have not been established for camelids. Minerals are inorganic elements classified into two groups: macrominerals or microminerals (trace minerals) based on daily amounts required. Macrominerals are required in grams (g) or ounces (oz) per day and include calcium (Ca), phosphorus (P), magnesium (Mg), potassium (K), sodium (Na), chlorine (Cl), and sulfur (S). Microminerals are required in milligrams (mg) per day and include cobalt (Co), copper (Cu), iodine (I), iron (Fe), manganese (Mn), selenium (Se), and zinc (Zn). Macro- and micromineral functions, disease, and significant inter-

Alpacas are entirely dependent on people in dry lot feeding situations.

relationships are summarized in Tables 9.8 and 9.9. More detailed information on minerals and their metabolism can be found in any general animal nutrition reference text.[33,42,69,71]

Although there are no data defining mineral requirements, there are also no data suggesting that camelids are distinctly different with regard to any specific mineral to any of the other domesticated ruminant animals. Data presented in Tables 9.10 and 9.11 were extrapolated from data available for sheep and cattle. Table 9.10 presents NRC nutrient recommendations for beef cattle and sheep on both a nutrient density and totals basis. These nutrient recommendations were then calculated to an amount per kilogram of body weight. Surprisingly, these calculated values were very similar between beef cattle and sheep. Nutrient recommendations for camelids were then extrapolated from these data taking into account this difference in dry matter intake capacity. On a nutrient density basis (see Table 9.11), camelids have slightly higher requirements. Again, this is only a result of differences in dry matter intake.

These extrapolated nutrient recommendations can be used as a starting point for *minimum* suggested nutrient concentrations in formulating diets. One study evaluating Se status of llamas showed pregnant and lactating female llamas had improved Se status when fed >1 mg Se/day.[54]

However, llamas receiving lower Se intake were able to maintain reasonably normal blood Se concentrations. Assuming pregnant animals have slightly higher requirements, these observed data are consistent with the calculated maintenance Se requirements presented as well as other recommendations.[102] Further research is necessary to determine if camelids have trace mineral requirements higher or lower relative to other ruminants.

Of the ranges given for each mineral (see Table 9.11), lower values would be appropriate for maintenance animals and the higher values for growing and lactating animals. *One must remember that all of these minerals will cause disease in both a deficient and an excessive state.* Although there are limited published studies documenting classic micromineral deficiency diseases in camelids, it is assumed the disease process is similar. Published reports on clinical cases and experimentally induced iron deficiency disease resulting in anemia and poor growth support this contention.[87,88]

Another documented micromineral-related disease process associated with Cu is similar to what is seen in other species. Sheep are well known to be extremely sensitive to excess dietary Cu (>10 ppm);[96] however, camelids do not seem to be as keenly sensitive but are prone to toxicity. Three different studies have reported cases of copper toxic-

Table 9.8 Summary of macromineral functions, deficiency problems, and toxicities.

Mineral	Major Functions	Deficiency Problems or Symptoms	Interrelationships or Toxicities
Calcium (Ca)	Bone and teeth formation; blood coagulation; muscle contraction; milk production; nerve conduction; cell permeability	Rickets (young) or osteomalacia (adults); lactational eclampsia; muscle weakness; decreased bone cortex density	Highly regulated with parathormone, calcitonin, and Vitamin D; excess P, Mg, and fat decrease absorption
Phosphorus (P)	Bone and teeth formation; blood buffer; acid-base balance; high-energy bonds; cellular metabolism	Rickets (young) or osteomalacia (adults); muscle weakness, alert downer cow; postparturient hemoglobinuria; pica	Vitamin D required for renal reabsorption and bone deposition; excess dietary Ca, Mg, Al reduce availability; excess P may cause urinary calculi, nutritional secondary hyperparathyroidism
Magnesium (Mg)	Enzyme activator; nerve conduction; ATP activation; bone formation	Hyperexcitability; tetanic convulsions; grass tetany	Availability decreased by K, Ca, fat
Potassium (K)	Osmotic pressure; acid-base balance; major intracellular cation	Hypokalemia; muscle weakness; lethargic; diarrhea; pica	Excess reduces Mg absorption; cardiac toxicity at higher intakes
Sodium (Na)	Major extracellular cation; osmotic pressure; cell permeability; ion potentials; acid-base balance	Reduced growth; pica; polydipsia/polyuria	Salt toxicity >8%; water availability dependent; nervous condition with staggering gait, blindness, hypertension
Chlorine (Cl)	Major extracellular anion; osmotic pressure; acid-base balance; hydrochloric acid secretion	Reduced growth; pica	Metabolic acidosis
Sulfur (S)	Sulfur-containing amino acids; biotin; thiamine; hoof and fleece growth	Reduced growth rate; poor wool growth	Non-thiamine-responsive polioencephalomalacia; interferes with Cu availability

Source: Modified from Jurgens, *Animal Feeding and Nutrition,* 1988 (reference 69).

Table 9.9 Summary of micromineral functions, deficiency problems, and toxicities.

Microminerals	Major Functions	Deficiency Problems or Symptoms	Interrelationships or Toxicities
Cobalt (Co)	Component of vitamin B_{12} (ruminants and camelids only)	Megaloblastic anemia; enzootic marasmus (ketosis), reduced growth, body weight	Cobalt needs to be supplied to rumen microbes; toxicity unlikely
Copper (Cu)	Hemoglobin synthesis; bone formation; pigmentation; myelin formation; Ox-red Rx; immune function	Achromotrichia; neonatal ataxia (swayback); DOD; hypochromic-microcytic anemia; immune failure	High Fe, Zn, Se reduce availability; excess Mo and S inhibit utilization and storage in ruminants; toxicity a problem in camelids, results in hemolytic crisis
Iodine (I)	Thyroxine formation	Goiter, stillbirths, infertility; malformations, hairless neonates; immune failure	High intakes reduce uptake efficiency; toxic intake results in goiter, fetal malformations
Iron (Fe)	Cellular respiration; oxygen transport	Hypochromic-microcytic anemia; easily fatigued	High Ca may decrease absorption; Cu status influences metabolism; excessive amounts are pro-oxidants
Manganese (Mn)	Bone formation; activator of enzymes with CHO; lipid, protein metabolism	Impaired fertility; abnormal bone formation; poor growth; impaired immune function	Excess Ca and P decrease availability; toxicity unlikely
Selenium (Se)	Antioxidant, cellular; iodine function; immune function	White muscle disease; acute death; nutritional myodegeneration; retained placenta; impaired immune function	Sulfate, acid soil conditions interfere with Se availability; acute toxicity from parenteral products, respiratory collapse
Zinc (Zn)	Component of >90 enzymes influencing all aspects of metabolism; immune function	Anorexia; parakeratosis; poor skin and hair formation; male infertility; impaired immune function	High Ca, phytates, or oxalates bind Zn; high Zn interferes with Cu metabolism

Source: Modified from Jurgens, 1988 (reference 69).

Table 9.10 Maintenance requirements (density and totals basis) for copper, iron, manganese, selenium, and zinc for beef cattle, sheep, and camelids (extrapolated).

Nutrient	NRC Requirement (Maintenance) Beef Cattle (500 kg BW)	NRC Requirement (Maintenance) Sheep (80 kg BW)	Averaged Requirement (per kg BW basis)	Extrapolated NW Camelid Requirements* (80–165 lb BW)
Cobalt	0.1 ppm 0.88 mg/d	0.1 ppm 0.13 mg/d	1.76 µg/kg BW	0.12–0.14 ppm 0.06–0.14 mg/d
Copper	8–10 ppm 72–90 mg/d	7–10 ppm 9.1–13 mg/d	0.15 mg/kg BW	9–12 ppm 5.5–11 mg/d
Iodine	0.5 ppm 4.4 mg/d	0.1–0.15 ppm 0.13–0.2 mg/d	9.5 µg/kg BW	0.6–0.76 ppm 0.34–0.71 mg/d
Iron	50 ppm 450 mg/d	30–50 ppm 39–65 mg/d	0.7 mg/kg BW	47–56 ppm 25–52 mg/d
Manganese	40 ppm 360 mg/d	20–40 ppm 26–52 mg/d	0.36 mg/kg BW	24–29 ppm 13–27 mg/d
Selenium	0.1–0.3 ppm 0.9–3 mg/d	0.1–0.3 ppm 0.15–0.7 mg/d	5.3 µg/kg BW	0.35–0.42 ppm 0.2–0.4 mg/d
Zinc	20–40 ppm 180–360 mg/d	20–33 ppm 26–45 mg/d	0.53 mg/kg BW	35–45 ppm 19–40 mg/d

*Camelid requirements shown are for dietary concentration (upper values) and total amount consumed (lower values). Calculated nutrient intake ranges are based on an assumed 1.5% dry matter intake for 80 lb (36.6 kg; smaller value) and 165 lb (75 kg; higher value) body weight animals.

ity in llamas and alpacas.[15,68,138] In all cases, llamas or alpacas were consuming a diet containing in excess of 30 ppm Cu and a high (>10:1) Cu to molybdenum (Mo) ratio. As with other ruminants, and maybe more so given the slower rate of passage in the forestomach, Cu status is interdependent with molybdenum and sulfur status. A suggested ratio of Cu:Mo in the diet is 6–10:1.[101] In contrast to Cu toxicity concerns, Cu deficiency was suggested as a cause of anemia in a llama,[4] thus underscoring the idea that we need a balance in providing dietary nutrients. Although

Table 9.11 Suggested dietary macro- and micromineral concentrations for camelids based on sheep and cattle data and adjusted for reduced dry matter intake.*

Macromineral	Requirement (% DM)	Micromineral	Requirement (ppm)
Calcium	0.2–0.75	Copper	9–12
Phosphorus	0.17–0.38	Cobalt	0.12–0.14
Magnesium	0.13–0.22**	Iron	47–72
Potassium	0.6–0.96	Iodine	0.6–1.3
Sodium	0.07–0.14	Manganese	24–64
Chloride	0.15–0.25	Selenium	0.35–0.48
Sulfur	0.19–0.23	Zinc	35–54

*Lower values are for maintenance of adult animals and higher values are for growing and lactating animals.
**May need to be increased (.25–.35%) if forages containing high amounts of potassium (>1.5%) are being fed.

Table 9.12 Potential sources for mineral supplements.

Supplement Name	Primary Mineral
Mono- or dicalcium phosphate	Calcium, phosphorus
Limestone (calcium carbonate)	Calcium
Dolomitic limestone	Calcium, magnesium
Monosodium phosphate	Phosphorus, sodium
Calcium sulfate (gypsum)	Calcium, sulfur
Salt	Sodium, chloride
Sodium bicarbonate	Sodium
Potassium chloride	Potassium, chloride
Magnesium oxide Magnesium sulfate (Epsom salt)	Magnesium
Cobalt carbonate Cobalt sulfate Co-glucoheptonate (Copro®)**	Cobalt*
Copper oxide Copper sulfate Cu-lysine (CuPlex®)**	Copper*
Ethylenediamine dihydroiodine (EDDI)** Iodized salt Potassium iodide	Iodine*
Iron carbonate Ferrous sulfate	Iron*
Manganous oxide Manganous sulfate Mn-methionine (Manpro®)**	Manganese*
Sodium selenite Sodium selenate	Selenium*
Zinc oxide Zinc sulfate Zinc methionine (ZinPro®)**	Zinc*

*Trace minerals are commonly combined with salt to form trace-mineralized salt, which can be fed free choice or incorporated into the diet at appropriate levels.
**Organic mineral forms.

Cu status can be influenced by dietary sulfur, it also plays another important role of some consequence with camelids. Sulfur is incorporated into sulfur-containing amino acids that are found in high abundance in wool fibers. Like sheep, camelids have an increased need for adequate sulfur in the diet to ensure proper wool production. There are numerous interactions between many minerals, which may lead to induced secondary disease problems, suggesting that indiscriminate supplementation of minerals is not appropriate.

As for mineral supplementation sources (see Table 9.12), inorganic sources from sulfate and carbonate forms are usually more bioavailable than the oxide forms. Many producers have also included some organic forms of minerals to overcome perceived deficiency syndromes. One good example here is zinc. Clinically there seems to be a zinc-responsive dermatosis problem with domesticated camelids. Improvements in the condition have been observed when zinc methionine (ZinPro®) has been supplemented.[62,63] Organic forms of minerals are protected from pregastric alteration and generally are considered highly available. However, there is more than one form of organic mineral and not all forms result in positive supplementation responses. Overall, organic forms of minerals are more expensive than their inorganic counterparts. Organic forms are best used in situations of stress or reduced intake capacity.

Vitamins Vitamin requirements are also not well understood for camelids. Vitamins are organic compounds that cannot be synthesized by the body to meet needs, and function as cofactors in nearly all metabolic processes (see Table 9.13). A more detailed discussion of vitamin functions can be found in many basic nutrition reference texts.[33,42,69] Vitamins are generally classified as either fat-soluble or water-soluble. Many different compounds may have similar biologic activity defined for a given vitamin. Therefore, vitamins are not measured by weight like other nutrients, but rather by comparative biologic activity. Vitamin activity or potency is measured in international units (IU) and quantified by some defined standard. For example, 1 IU of vitamin A activity is defined as the amount of vitamin A activity from 0.3 μg retinol (vitamin A alcohol).

As with other ruminants, it is hypothesized that all necessary B-vitamins (water-soluble) are synthesized by bacteria in the forestomach and therefore are not required in the diet. However, under certain stress conditions or fermentation disorders, B-vitamin supplementation may be beneficial. Many B-vitamins are found in and easily supplemented with feeding yeast extract or commercial probiotic products.

Fat-soluble vitamins, namely vitamins A, D, and E, are the most important for camelids and should be supplemented in the diet. Vitamins A and E will be adequately ingested if llamas and alpacas are grazing on fresh pasture.

However, when fed stored, sun-cured hay, vitamins A and E may be insufficient.[26,54,120] One published report has documented a vitamin E-related muscular disease in a llama, similar to what is seen in other species.[21] In contrast, vitamin D is very low in pasture but is higher in sun-cured forages, although possibly not high enough to meet needs without supplementation. Vitamin D deficiency has been implicated in a hypophosphatemic rickets syndrome of young growing crias (see "Rickets and Bone Development").[131]

Vitamins A, D, and E all play important roles in the growth and development of the cria (see functions in Table 9.13). Based on information from other ruminant species and preliminary data in llamas and alpacas, these fat-soluble vitamins do not cross the placenta but are transferred very efficiently into colostrum and to a lesser extent into milk. As a result, crias are born with very low concentrations of vitamins A, D, and E. Consumption of colostrum by the cria is the primary source of these essential vitamins, assuming the dam was adequately supplemented. If dietary vitamin levels are inadequate, parenteral (injectable) supplementation may be necessary to maintain the proper health and growth of the cria. Pregnant llamas and alpacas can be supplemented orally or parenterally in late gestation (<7 weeks prior to giving birth) to boost colostrum vitamin concentrations.

A similar mathematical extrapolation process was completed to generate suggested fat-soluble vitamin requirements for camelids (see Table 9.14). Similar to predicted mineral requirements, dietary vitamin concentrations are slightly higher for camelids to account for lower dry matter intake. One unique feature of llamas and alpacas seems to be present with vitamin D. Preliminary research on oral vitamin D supplementation has shown that minimal serum vitamin D concentrations can be maintained by suggested requirements based on other species, but dietary supplementation at higher levels may be necessary to minimize potential problems with vitamin D-responsive rickets.[119]

Fiber Fiber is not a specifically required nutrient relative to the llama or alpaca. Without the forestomach fermentation system, the animal is incapable of extracting any nutrients from dietary fiber. However, fiber is an essential nutrient substrate for the microbial populations inhabiting the forestomach. Dietary fiber is classically defined as any carbohydrate compound that cannot be broken down by animal digestive enzymes. However, all carbohydrates except sugars and starches are considered dietary fiber by this definition. In a more practical approach, only those complex carbohydrate compounds fairly resistant to fermentation are considered fiber and defined as neutral and acid detergent fiber (see "Fiber" in the "Analytical Procedures" section). Long-stem forage is necessary to stimulate rumination and provide sufficient habitat for fiber-fermenting bacteria. Current recommendations would suggest a minimum of 25

Table 9.13 Biologic functions of fat-soluble and water-soluble vitamins.

Vitamin Designation		
Letter	Chemical Compound	Biologic Functions
Fat-soluble Vitamins		
A	Retinol, retinoic acid	Vision, bone and cartilage formation, reproduction, immune function
D	Cholecalciferol (animals) Ergocalciferol (plants)	Bone formation, calcium-phosphorus regulation, immune function
E	Alpha-tocopherol	Cellular membrane antioxidant, immune function
K	Menadione	Blood clotting
Water-soluble Vitamins		
B_1	Thiamine	Coenzyme in energy metabolism, transketolation reactions
B_2	Riboflavin	Component of flavoproteins FMN and FAD, which function in cellular respiration
B_3	Pantothenic acid	Component of coenzyme A and acyl-carrier protein; important in the metabolism and energy release from protein, fat, and carbohydrates; nerve transmission as acetylcholine
B_6	Pyridoxine	Coenzyme in various aspects of protein, carbohydrate, and fat metabolism
Niacin	Nicotinic acid Nicotinamide	Constituent of NAD and NADP, having functions in cellular respiration and transfer of H+ equivalents
B_{12}	Cyanocobalamin	Coenzyme in protein, carbohydrate, and fat metabolism in the transfer of single carbon units; needed for conversion of propionate to glucose in ruminants
Biotin	Biotin	Coenzyme for CO_2 transfers in metabolism of fats, carbohydrates, and protein; needed for good hoof growth
C	Ascorbic acid	Wound healing, blood vessel integrity, antioxidant

Table 9.14 Maintenance requirements (density and totals basis) for vitamins A, D, and E in beef cattle, sheep, and camelids (extrapolated).

| Nutrient | NRC Requirement (Maintenance) | | Average Requirement (per kg BW basis) | Extrapolated NW Camelid Requirement* (80–165 lb BW) |
	Beef Cattle (500 kg BW)	Sheep (80 kg BW)		
Vitamin A	2,800 IU/kg 25,000 IU/d	2,900 IU/kg 3,760 IU/d	47–50 IU/kg BW	3,000–3,300 IU/kg 1,800–3,500 IU/d
Vitamin D	275 IU/kg 2,450 IU/d	350 IU/kg 450 IU/d	5.0–5.5 IU/kg BW**	333–366 IU/kg** 411–686 IU/d
			25–30 IU/kg BW***	1,500–2,000 IU/kg*** 1,050–1,650 IU/d
Vitamin E	15-60 IU/kg† 135-540 IU/d	15 IU/kg† 20 IU/d	0.25–0.5 IU/kg BW	17–33 IU/kg 25–33 IU/d

*Vitamin activity is measured in international units (IU). Camelid requirements shown are for dietary concentration (top values) and total amount consumed (lower values). Calculated nutrient intake ranges are based on an assumed 1.5% dry matter intake for 80 lb (36.4 kg; smaller value) and 165 lb (75 kg; higher value) body weight animals.

**These values may maintain minimal serum vitamin D concentrations and may not prevent vitamin D rickets.

***Adjusted vitamin D requirement, based on preliminary data suggesting a higher vitamin D requirement of 25–30 IU/kg BW. Extrapolated requirements reflect this higher requirement for camelids.

†Requirements for vitamin E based on IU per kg of dry matter intake.

percent crude fiber in the diet. Using the current terminology for fiber analysis, a dietary minimum of 21 to 25 percent acid detergent fiber (ADF) of dietary dry matter would be recommended. Using neutral detergent fiber, a minimum recommendation of 30 to 35 percent of dietary dry matter might be a reasonable starting point. This is much higher than minimum requirements for cattle, which is consistent with the greater forage fermentation capacity of camelids.

Modifiers of Nutrient Requirements

Similar to recommendations made by the NRC for nutrient requirements of various animal species, extrapolated requirements for camelids discussed thus far have assumed an isothermic environment. This means that environmental temperature is within a range in which the animal does not need to expend additional energy to either generate more heat to keep warm (i.e., cold stress) or reduce heat production to keep cool (i.e., heat stress). The upper and lower environmental temperatures where an animal does not need to expend additional energy to regulate body temperature is called the thermoneutral zone.[94] Ruminant animals generally have a lower thermoneutral zone compared to humans as a result of the heat generated by forestomach fermentation activity. This gives ruminant animals an advantage in surviving in cold environments, which is a great advantage to llamas and alpacas in their native environment. Alpacas exposed to cold temperatures over time will require additional dietary energy to maintain body temperature. This is even more important in crias, as they have greater surface area to body mass and lose more heat to the environment.

Besides environmental temperature, humidity and wind speed can impact animal energy requirements.[94] Animal insulation factors such as skin thickness, length of fleece, and coat condition (i.e., dry, wet, muddy) can lead to either increased or decreased conduction and convection heat losses to the environment.[94] Environmental temperature, wind speed, and animal insulation factors are all additive. Models predicting cattle energy requirements in varying environmental conditions show upward to a 75 percent increase in maintenance when animals are exposed to cold, windy conditions and their haircoat is wet or muddy.[94,97] This has tremendous implications for crias in winter months and emphasizes how important it is to keep them dry and out of prevailing winds.

FEED FACTORS—UNDERSTANDING FEEDS AND THEIR COMPOSITION

Feed costs account for the greatest portion of total production costs in any animal agricultural production system. Feed costs must be appropriately balanced with providing adequate nutrients to meet defined requirements. To provide an appropriate diet, the producer must have a basic understanding of feedstuff quality and influencing factors. Additionally, producers should have a functional knowledge of analytical procedures, which are used to evaluate quality.

Feed Definitions

All feed ingredients are classified by their nutritional composition characteristics and assigned to one of eight different feed categories by an International Feed Identification System.[33,71] The eight categories include three subcategories of roughages, energy concentrates, protein supplements, mineral supplements, vitamin supplements, and additives. These feed categories are not mutually exclusive, as some feeds have properties of more than one category, but ultimately they are placed into a single category accounting for their primary use in animal diets. Detailed information on feed ingredients and their composition can be found in any nutrition reference text.[33,71,95]

Roughages and Forages The terms roughages and forages can be equally interchanged. Forages are derived from bulky plant material, usually the entire plant or residual stems, leaves, or both from a plant. Nutritionally, forages are high in fiber content (>18%) and generally low in energy density (<70% TDN).[33,71] Forages are primarily composed of cell wall structural carbohydrates, cellulose, and hemicellulose, thus requiring microbial fermentation to be utilized by the animal. Protein and other nutrient content are variable and dependent upon the plant species. Forages can be harvested in a fresh, dried, or ensiled state, resulting in three subcategories: dry forages, pasture and range plants, and silages.

Dry forages (e.g., hay) are those feeds in which the plant is harvested and allowed to dry to less than 15 percent moisture content. It is critical that moisture content be reduced to facilitate storage of forage material over time. High-moisture hay (>15% moisture) has potential problems with heating and mold growth. Dried forages include such feed ingredients as hay, straw, fodder, stover, and forage by-products (i.e., corn cobs, cottonseed hulls, soybean hulls). During the drying process, whether natural or mechanical, nutrient losses may occur. This is particularly important in drying forages for hay production. Changing environmental conditions in many geographic areas make production of good hay quality quite a challenge. Hays derived from grass or legume plants (see "Forage Types") are one of the most common forages fed to camelids in North America.

Two alternatives to overcome dried forage production limitations are to harvest forage directly, as in pasture and rangeland grazing, or to partially dry (i.e., wilt) the cut plant and allow it to ferment (e.g., ensiling). Although a common method of forage harvesting and storage, ensiled feeds are not generally fed to camelids. This is not to say that ensiled feeds cannot or should not be fed, just that ensiled feeds may not be practical for many camelid feeding systems.

Pastures and rangeland are a third subcategory of forages and an important one in feeding camelids. Native grasses and legumes comprise most of the rangeland plant varieties. Most cultivated grass and legume species can be used either for pasture or hay production. Other plant species that may be grazed include a wide variety of broadleaf, nonwoody plants (forbs) and woody plants (browse).

Harvesting forages as pasture minimizes nutrient losses associated with the drying process, but other problems exist. Pasture and rangeland grazing requires intensive management to maintain quality forage. Forage quantity is high in the spring during rapid plant growth but greatly reduced during the dry summer months when plants enter dormancy. Irrigation can be used to maintain plant growth during summer weather, but is not feasible in many situations. Blending of plant species or varieties can promote more even plant growth over the changing weather conditions. The animal stocking rate needs to be matched to forage availability. Under- or overgrazing may result in more undesirable weeds and toxic plants infiltrating into a grazing area. Unconsumed forage will rapidly mature, becoming low-quality forage. Utilization of pasture and rangeland depends upon the interaction between feed availability, stocking density, and animal feeding behavior.

Energy Concentrates Feeds with high-energy density (>70% TDN) and low in fiber (<18%) are called energy concentrates.[33,71] Protein content is usually moderate to low and deficient in calcium. As their name implies, they are feeds concentrated with readily digestible energy in the form of carbohydrates (sugars and starches) or fats (animal or vegetable). Fat sources are highly concentrated forms of energy, 2.25 times more than carbohydrates, but not a significant part of the camelid diet. Cereal grains such as corn, barley, oats, wheat, millet, and milo are typical energy concentrates and can be fed individually or as some combination (corn-oats-barley). Often cereal grains are processed (ground, flaked, steamed, extruded) to increase their starch digestibility and energy availability. The amount of these cereal grains consumed must be tightly controlled, as their excessive intake may result in forestomach acidosis (see "Forestomach Acidosis"). Other feeds categorized as energy concentrates include milling by-products of cereal grains (wheat bran, wheat middlings, corn hominy), beet and citrus pulps, and root crops (beets, potatoes, turnips, carrots).[71] These products also contain moderate amounts of readily fermentable fiber. Liquid energy sources, such as molasses products, are high in sucrose and are used for improving palatability. Milling by-products and molasses are common ingredients used in many commercial supplements.

Protein Supplements Protein supplements are feeds of animal or plant origin containing more than 20 percent protein or protein equivalent.[33,71] Energy and fiber content may be high or low. Mineral content varies with source. Common plant protein sources include oilseed meals from soybean, cottonseed, peanut, sunflower, and canola. Milling and distiller by-products, such as corn gluten meal and distillers' and brewers' grains, are other plant-based protein sources. Animal protein feeds include blood meal, meat meal, and fish meal, as well as milk protein sources. Camelids, like ruminants, have the potential to utilize dietary nonprotein nitrogen products like urea and biuret; however, little data on feeding recommendations for camelids are available.

Mineral Supplements Mineral supplements are those feeds containing single or multiple sources of macrominerals, microminerals, or both (see Table 9.12). The amount of any given mineral depends upon its mineral source and bioavailability. Inorganic mineral forms vary from none or poorly available (many oxide forms) to highly available (sulfate, carbonate forms).[33,71] Organic mineral forms (chelates, proteinates) are generally more available, but this also varies by form. Organic minerals are much more expensive compared to inorganic forms. Commercial blends of various mineral supplements are available in loose or compressed block salt-based products. Llamas and alpacas do not lick; therefore, block-type minerals are not recommended for use.[42,113] These products vary tremendously in their specific mineral content, source (see Table 9.24), and expected feeding rate. Mineral products designed to be fed free choice are salt based to limit intake. Other mineral products need to be force fed with or within a palatable supplement carrier. Most supplement feeds commercially available for camelids are combinations of energy, protein, mineral, and vitamin supplements. Camelids, like other animals, do not have the capability to specifically select nutrients in which they are deficient. A self-feeding individual mineral source is not a recommended feeding system.

Vitamin Supplements Vitamin supplements are feed ingredients that contain single or multiple sources of fat-soluble or water-soluble vitamins or some combination. Water-soluble vitamins (B-complex vitamins) are generally not considered necessary in ruminant or camelid diets, as microbial populations of the forestomach synthesize them. Vitamins A, D, and E are most commonly supplemented in ruminant diets. Vitamins A and E are found naturally in pasture and green feeds in large amounts, so additional dietary supplementation is unnecessary. Vitamin D can be synthesized naturally with exposure to sunlight. However, when animals are not consuming pasture or not exposed to sunlight, additional dietary vitamin supplements might be necessary. Vitamins are readily oxidized upon exposure to light, heat, and pro-oxidants (minerals). Most commercial vitamin supplements contain specially stabilized synthetic forms of these vitamins in variable amounts, but their activity can be reduced over time.

Additives Feed additives are nonnutritive products added to the basic feed mix to enhance growth or other productive function, to increase efficiency of feed utilization, to preserve feeds, or to benefit animal health or metabolism.[71] Additives do not meet any nutritional requirement. Medications or additives that prevent or treat disease are considered drugs and are highly regulated. Examples of nondrug additives include yucca, aloe vera, kelp, yeast, probiotics, glycosaminoglycans, omega-3 fatty acids, oligomannosaccharides, mineral oil, bentonite, artificial flavors or colors, and ethoxyquin, to name a few. Some of these additives have specific purposes as binding or blending agents (mineral oil, bentonite), a preservative (ethoxyquin), and flavoring or coloring agents. Other additives have purported beneficial effects like improved digestion (yeast, yucca, probiotics) and joint health (glycosaminoglycans). Products maintaining status as a nutritional supplement but claiming some medicinal benefit are termed nutraceuticals. These products are not necessarily bad, but their inclusion adds to feed costs and may or may not bring any perceived benefit.

Feed Analysis

Any feeding program's goal is to achieve an appropriate balance among available feed ingredients, so that the total ration nutrient composition meets the daily nutritional needs of the animal. To accomplish such a feat on a day-to-day basis, one needs to have some information about the nutrient content of feed ingredients. Tremendous variation exists in nutrient composition between different feeds. Even within a feed ingredient, there is potential for significant variation in composition. This is especially true for forages. Forages harvested off the same field within the same year can have very different composition as influenced by environmental conditions and cutting time.

A variety of biologic, chemical, enzymatic, and other sophisticated analytical methods are used to evaluate nutrient content and availability of feeds.[33,71] Chemical methods can directly measure quantities of compounds associated with an essential nutrient; however, they tell us nothing about availability. Biologic, enzymatic, and other sophisticated methods provide a more nutritional perspective to feed analysis, thus helping us to better understand just how the animal will interact with its feed. More information is needed to routinely apply these analytical techniques to feeding camelids. The most practical approach to feed analysis is one of chemical composition—direct determinations of moisture, ether extract (fat), ash (mineral), nitrogen (crude protein), and fiber fractions (see "Analytical Procedures"). Proximate analysis was the name given to the traditional wet chemistry methodology. A comparison between required essential nutrients, feed chemical composition, and analytic methods used in feed analysis is summarized in Figure 9.3.

Although wet chemistry analysis is considered the "gold standard" for feed testing, simpler and less expensive methods with shorter turnover time were needed. Newer technological advances have brought a rapid, lower-cost analytical technique termed near infrared reflectance (NIR) spectroscopy.[1,33,64] In NIR, ground feed samples are exposed to infrared light, molecular bonds either absorb or reflect this light, and the reflectance pattern is measured and compared to a standard. Critical to the accuracy of NIR testing is laboratory quality control standardization for feed types. In general, NIR analysis has high accuracy in measuring crude protein and fiber fractions compared to wet chemistry, but is less accurate in measuring feed mineral content.[23,64] Many certified feed laboratories are capable of completing wet chemistry, NIR analyses, or both. Certified feed analysis laboratories around the world can be found through the National Forage Testing Association website (www.foragetesting.org). Proper feed sampling procedures must be used to submit appropriate samples for analysis (see "Forage Testing").

Analytical Procedures

Dry Matter (DM) Dry matter is defined as the non-moisture portion of a feed ingredient or diet. The sum of moisture and dry matter content of a feed on a percent of total will always equal 100. Dry matter contains the essential nutrients within a given feed ingredient. Feeds, and thereby diets, vary widely in their moisture content. Pas-tures and liquid feeds have a moisture content between 75 and 90 percent (10–25% DM). Dried feeds usually have less than 15 percent moisture (>85% DM). Moisture or dry matter content of a feed is determined by heating a weighed sample of feed in a convection drying oven until a constant weight is reached (24–48 hours). Dry weight is expressed as a ratio to the original sample weight (moisture + DM) or converted to a percentage. For example, a feed sample weighs 150 grams wet and 50 grams dry. The DM ratio would be 0.33 (50/150) and the percent DM, 33.3 percent (50/150 × 100). The moisture content of this feed would be 66.7 percent (100 − 33.3 or [150−50]/150 × 100).

Why is knowing moisture content important? One important aspect is our ability to compare the nutrient content of different feeds on an equal basis. The nutrient content of a feed can be determined on an "as-fed" (AF; moisture included) or dry matter (moisture excluded) basis. Intuitively, nutrient content will always be higher on a DM compared to AF basis for any feed, as the inclusion of water dilutes the nutrients within DM. From Table 9.15, it can be seen that pasture has much lower nutrient content on an AF basis; however, when corrected for water content, both pasture and hay have equal nutrient content. To appropriately compare these two feeds equally, nutrient content needs to be converted to a DM basis. Feed moisture determinations also facilitate calculations and monitoring of animal DM intake. Finally, DM determinations can be used to evaluate whether or not feed moisture content is within expected ranges. Excessively wet or dry feeds may lead to problems with molding (wet hay), abnormal fermentation (silages), or reduced animal intake.

Essential Nutrients	Chemical Components	Analytical Procedures		
Fatty acids, fat-soluble vitamins	Lipids, pigments, sterols	Ether extract		
Protein, amino acids	Nitrogen-containing compounds—protein, nonprotein nitrogen	Kjeldahl procedure (crude protein)		
Inorganic minerals	Ash	Ashing (complete combustion)		
Carbohydrates / Glucose	Sugars	Nonstructural carbohydrates**	Nonfiber carbohydrates***	
Carbohydrates / Glucose	Starches	Nonstructural carbohydrates**	Nonfiber carbohydrates***	
Carbohydrates / Dietary fiber	Soluble fiber			
Carbohydrates / Dietary fiber	Hemicellulose		Neutral detergent fiber	
Carbohydrates / Dietary fiber	Cellulose	Acid detergent fiber	Neutral detergent fiber	
Carbohydrates / Dietary fiber	Lignin*	Acid detergent fiber	Neutral detergent fiber	

Figure 9.3 Comparison of essential nutrients, feed chemical composition, and analytical testing procedures.

*Lignin is not truly a carbohydrate compound but is so intimately associated with cell wall carbohydrates that it is often included as such.

**Newer methods are being used to measure starch content.

***Determined by difference (100 − CP − EE − NDF − Ash).

Table 9.15 Comparison of nutrient content expressed on as-fed (AF) or dry matter (DM) basis for generic grass pasture and hay.

	Nutrient Density Basis*	% Nutrient Content				
		DM	Protein	NDF	ADF	Calcium
Grass Pasture	AF	20	2.2	11.0	8.0	0.12
	DM	100	11.0	55.0	40.0	0.60
Grass Hay	AF	90	9.9	49.5	36.0	0.54
	DM	100	11.0	55.0	40.0	0.60

*Conversion formula: AF nutrient content = DM nutrient content × DM ratio or DM nutrient content = AF nutrient content ÷ DM ratio. DM ratio is 0.2 for pasture and 0.9 for hay in this example.

Crude Protein (CP) Feed protein content is determined by using the Kjeldahl procedure (see Figure 9.3).[33,71] In actuality protein cannot be directly measured; it is estimated from feed sample nitrogen (N) content. The Kjeldahl procedure uses heated sulfuric acid to digest all organic material and convert all N to ammonia. Ammonia production is precisely measured and calculated back to total N and then to protein. On average all biological proteins contain 16 percent N; therefore protein content is estimated by multiplying N percent by 6.25 (6.25 = $1 \div 0.16$). Crude protein does not differentiate between N in feed samples coming from true protein or other nonprotein nitrogen (NPN) compounds, nor does it differentiate between available and unavailable protein. Additional methods of partitioning feed N fractions relative to animal (amino acids) and rumen (nitrogen) needs are being applied to ruminant animals. These methods most likely have application to camelids, but data are lacking. One measure certainly important to camelid nutrition is further discussed under "Acid Detergent Fiber."

Although issues have been raised concerning applying crude protein as a feed measure, it continues to be a commonly used measure of feed quality. Crude protein content is very different across feeds, but within a feed, higher protein is usually associated with higher quality. This certainly is true in forages. As forages mature, their crude protein is diluted with increasing fiber content. Forage fertilization practices can alter this relationship, suggesting that crude protein should not be solely used as a quality criterion without evaluating fiber content.

Ether Extract (EE) Ether extract is a chemical method by which all lipid (fat) soluble compounds are extracted by being dissolved in ether (see Figure 9.3). Following extraction, the ether is evaporated off, leaving the dissolved feed sample residue. This fraction accounts for nearly all lipid-soluble compounds, including triglycerides, fatty acids, pigments, sterols, oils, alcohols, and organic acids. Fatty acids and fat-soluble vitamins are the essential nutrients contained within this feed fraction. Additionally, triglycerides (esterified fats) can contribute to energy needs of the animal. This technique is of little value in evaluating feed quality, except in the cases of comparing feeds with high fat content.

Fiber Total fiber cell wall content, or structural carbohydrate content, both essentially the same concept, was traditionally measured by a procedure termed crude fiber. A sample of dried, fat-extracted feed is boiled in weak acid for 30 minutes and then in weak alkali for an equal time period. During this process, soluble carbohydrate is removed, leaving fiber and mineral portions. The loss occurring on combustion of this residue is the measured crude fiber content. Although still used as a standard measure of fiber on feed analysis tags, crude fiber does not define the total cell wall fraction (indigestible or slowly digestible material) of feedstuffs. In the digestion process, much of the hemicellulose and lignin is solubilized, thus underestimating the total cell wall.[135] This results in an overestimation of energy values for forages in comparison to concentrates. As a result, a new procedure to determine cell wall content was developed.

The detergent feed analysis system developed by Van Soest involves separating feed samples into soluble and insoluble fractions with neutral and acid detergents.[49] The neutral detergent-soluble fraction represents all of the highly digestible feed components. The insoluble fraction, termed *neutral detergent fiber (NDF)*, contains hemicellulose, cellulose, and lignin, which better represents the feed total cell wall portion. As cell wall production increases, as occurs in advancing plant maturity, NDF content increases. Neutral detergent fiber content of a feed impacts dry matter intake and rumination activity in ruminant animals. Rumination activity increases and dry matter decreases with increased feed NDF content. Within a given feed, NDF is a good measure of feed quality and plant maturity.

Feed samples boiled in acid detergent will solubilize hemicellulose in addition to the neutral detergent-soluble fraction. This leaves *acid detergent fiber (ADF)* containing cellulose, lignin, and other very resistant (indigestible) substances. Acid detergent fiber is a subfraction of NDF, containing all of the very slowly fermentable and indigestible feed components. Due to its nature, ADF is often used to predict the energy content of feeds. A fraction of feed N can also be found in ADF. This N component is comprised of heat-damaged, indigestible proteins. Completing a Kjeldahl procedure on the ADF fraction will determine the amount of bound N, which can then be converted to unavailable protein (acid detergent-insoluble protein or ADIP).[49] Unavailable protein can be subtracted from crude protein to estimate the amount of truly available dietary protein. Most hays will have <5 percent unavailable protein, but values exceeding 15 percent suggest extensive heating of the forage. Like NDF, ADF is a good indicator of feed quality; higher values within a feed suggest lower-quality feed.

Minerals Total feed mineral content can be measured by a procedure where the feed sample is completely combusted into ash. This does not separate out any individual minerals and does not separate macro- and microminerals of interest from silica and other less important minerals. Selected macrominerals (calcium, phosphorus, magnesium, potassium, sodium, and sulfur) and microminerals (iron, copper, zinc, manganese, and molybdenum) can be determined using sophisticated wet chemistry atomic absorption spectroscopy. Feed chloride content can be determined using a special ion probe. As previously stated, NIR analyses are not very accurate in determining feed mineral content. Mineral analysis is not always done since it is the most expensive test. Feed mineral content has no bearing on feed quality evaluation.

Other Feed Fractions Energy content is often used to compare feeds and evaluate quality. Feed energy content is not directly measured like other nutrients, but is derived through regression equations. Traditionally, ADF alone or with CP was used to predict the energy value of various feeds. Currently, feed energy is predicted using a summation equation that accounts for differences in feed component digestibility.[140] Most laboratories report feed energy values based on cattle equations, reporting TDN and NE values. The question is, how applicable are these predicted values to camelids? Cattle energy values are the best estimate we have and should reasonably reflect feed energy for llamas and alpacas given the similarity in digestive function. In comparison, predicted cattle feed energy availability would be inappropriate for use in swine or horse diets, given anatomic and physiologic differences in digestive capacity. However, in considering the differences in fiber degradability between ruminants and camelids, one would anticipate that cattle energy predictions may be too low for lower-quality forages.

In Figure 9.3, a large portion of feed carbohydrates, especially those associated with higher digestibility and glucose production, are not measured. The neutral detergent-soluble carbohydrate fraction of feed is termed *non-fiber carbohydrates (NFC)*. This fraction is not directly measured, but determined by difference. Inherently, all laboratory errors associated with other feed fractions will be compiled into the NFC fraction. Although susceptible to error, NFC represents a highly available portion of a feed, and as such positively reflects on the evaluation of feed

quality. More recently some laboratories have offered an enzymatic analysis for feed starch content, helping to further define the more digestible portion of NFC, termed *nonstructural carbohydrates* (NSC).

Forage Types

As previously defined, forages are bulky, high-fiber, and generally low-energy feeds derived from plants either entirely or in part. Forages can be harvested directly by the animal, as in pasture, or mechanically harvested, dried, and fed, as in hay. From the previous discussion of llama and alpaca digestive anatomy and physiology, it is obvious that forages must constitute a majority of their diet. Indeed, in their native environment forages comprise 100 percent of their diet, even when managed domestically. Observations of llama and alpaca feed selection in their native environment show a wide range of forages consumed that are dependent upon season.[13,46,47,59,60,104,110,111]

In contrast, supplement feeding is often part of llama and alpaca feeding management outside of South America. Is there a significant departure in forage quality accounting for this difference, or is it animal adaptations in feeding behavior and selectivity? Having a better understanding of alpaca anatomy and physiology, the next step is to understand differences between forage plants relative to composition and quality. Most forage plants used for animal feed can be separated into two large botanical families: grasses and legumes. An in-depth discussion of specific forages and associated agronomic practices is beyond the scope of this review; if interested, several books and articles are available.[6,7,40,41,51,59,74,76,85,86,116,117]

Grasses Without grasses, life on earth could not survive. Grasses (family Gramineae or Poaceae) are the third most abundant group of plants in the world, following daisies and orchids, with more than 10,000 species.[6,12,76,85] Grass plants account for the greatest amount of photosynthetic energy transfer into vegetative growth in support of animal and human food production. Grasses comprise 10 of the 15 most agriculturally important crops for food production.[12] This is not hard to envision when you consider that all cereal grain-producing plants, such as corn, wheat, rice, rye, barley, oats, sorghum, and millet, are grass species. In addition, most processed sugar is derived from sugar cane, a grass. Native and cultivated grasses account for a majority (60%) of all domesticated livestock feed, especially beef cattle, sheep, and camelids. Most wild herbivores subsist on grassland vegetation. Grasses cover more than one-third of the earth's land area, and all continents, excluding Antarctica, contain grasslands. Unfortunately, inappropriate management, overgrazing, industrialization, expanding world populations, and many other factors have greatly reduced or altered native grasslands on all continents. Many native North American grasses previously covering the middle two-thirds of the United States have been replaced with European or Asian grass species by settlers, either intentionally or inadvertently. Of the most agriculturally important grass forages in North America (see Table 9.16), all are introduced species.[6]

Detailed information on grass plant anatomy and biology can be found in a number of excellent forage texts.[6,12,40,76,85] This discussion briefly touches on important points as they relate to feeding llamas and alpacas. Grasses are distinguished by their narrow leaves with parallel veins, round hollow stems, and inconspicuous flowers (termed inflorescence). A leaf is attached to the stem by its base (sheath) wrapping around a thickened, solid portion of the stem (node). The leaf proper (blade) contains photosynthetic organelles and a fibrous midrib of structural carbohydrate and lignin to maintain some rigidity. Leaves are the most digestible portion of a grass for animals. The supporting midrib rapidly declines in digestibility with advancing plant maturity due to the increasing presence of structural carbohydrate.[86,135] This decline in leaf digestibility is not seen in legume plants (see "Legumes"). A majority of the grass plant mass occurs underground as a highly branched root system. This minimizes water loss through evaporation, allowing grasses to survive under arid conditions where trees and other vegetation cannot.

Grasses also tolerate predation (animal grazing) and competition better through their reproductive mechanisms. Unlike most other plants that grow from the tip of a leaf or shoot, grasses grow from the leaf base.[6] This allows leaf regrowth following grazing, clipping, or burning. Certain grasses generate new growth (tillers) from their base (crown), resulting in a clump of growth (see bunch grasses, Table 9.16).[6,85] Other grasses send out horizontal stems either above (stolons) or below (rhizomes) ground to generate new shoots and roots.[6,85] When the distance between new shoots is small, the grass forms a dense mat (sod) preventing other plants from encroaching.

Photosynthesis is the process by which plants use radiant energy to combine atmospheric carbon dioxide with other nutrients from the soil (water, nitrogen, miner-

Table 9.16 Some common temperate and tropical grass species typical of North and South America.

Temperate (C3) Grasses					Tropical/Subtropical (C4) Grasses			
Scientific Name	*Common Name*	Season	Growth	A/P*	*Scientific Name*	*Common Name*	Growth	A/P*
Paspalum notatum	Bahiagrass**	Warm	Bunch	P	*Andropogon gerardii*	Big bluestem	Bunch	P
Cynodon dactylon	Bermudagrass**	Warm	Sod	P	*Buchloe dactyloides*	Buffalograss	Bunch	P
Calamagrostis sp.***	Blue-joint grass, nappa pasto, sora pasto, tullo pasto	Cool	Bunch	P	*Cenchrus ciliaris*	Buffelgrass	Bunch	P
Pao sp.***	Bluegrass	Cool	Sod	P	*Zea mays*	Corn (maize)	Bunch	A
Agropyron desertorum	Crested wheatgrass	Cool	Sod/Bunch	P	*Pennisetum purpureum*	Elephantgrass (napiergrass)†	Bunch	P
Paspalum dilatatum	Dallisgrass	Warm	Bunch	P	*Andropogon gayanus*	Gambagrass	Bunch	P
Festuca sp.***	Fescue,** llama pasto, iruichu	Cool	Bunch	P	*Panicum maximun*	Guineagrass†	Bunch	P
Sorghum halepense	Johnsongrass††	Warm	Sod	P	*Hymenachne amplexicaulis*	Hymenachne	Sod	P
Muhlenbergia sp.***	Muhly	Cool	Bunch	P	*Pennisetum clandestinum*	Kikuyugrass	Sod	P
Stipa sp.***	Needlegrass, ichu	Cool	Bunch	P	*Melinis minutiflora*	Molassesgrass†	Bunch	P
Dactylis glomeratus	Orchardgrass**	Cool	Bunch	P	*Brachiaria brizantha*	Palisadegrass	Bunch	P
Phalaris arundinacea	Reed canarygrass**	Cool	Sod	P	*Digitaria eriantha*	Pangolagrass	Sod	P
*Bromus unioloides****	Rescuegrass	Warm	Bunch	P	*Brachiaria mutica*	Paragrass	Sod	P
Lolium sp.	Ryegrass**	Cool	Bunch	A/P	*Chloris gayana*	Rhodesgrass†	Sod/Bunch	P
Hordeum sp. (barley) *Avena sativa* (oats) *Triticum* sp. (wheat)	Small grains	Cool	Bunch	A	*Panicum virgatum*	Switchgrass	Sod	P
Bromus inermis	Smooth bromegrass**	Cool	Sod	P				
Sorghum sudanense	Sudangrass††	Warm	Bunch	A				
Phleum pratense	Timothy	Cool	Bunch	P				

Source: Barnes et al., 1995 (reference 6), and Mislevy, 1985 (reference 83).

*Annual (A) or perennial (P) grass.

**Primary seeded forages used in the United States; all are introduced species.

***Plant species belonging to these grass genera are commonly found in South America and consumed by llamas and alpacas.

†Warm-season tropical grasses that are cold tolerant.

††Can be toxic.

als) to synthesize carbohydrates and proteins in support of plant growth and ultimately animal production. Thereby, amount and intensity of solar radiation, soil nutrient content and characteristics, seasonal environmental temperature swings, and precipitation patterns influence a geographic region's potential for grass growth and nutrient content.[6,85] Grasses are one of the most highly adapted plants, having the ability to grow in geographic regions ranging from arctic to tropical conditions.

Grass species are classified into two groups, temperate and tropical grasses, based on their initial compounds synthesized during photosynthesis (C_3 versus C_4) and optimum growth temperature (see Table 9.16).[6,85] Temperate grasses generate three-carbon compounds from photosynthesis and grow best in cooler environments (0–20°C; 32–68°F). Tropical grasses produce four-carbon compounds during photosynthesis and start to grow between 10 and 15°C (50 and 59°F) and reach maximal growth at 30 to 35°C (86–95°F). Although not universally true, trop-

ical forages generate more structural carbohydrates (fiber) and have lower protein compared to temperature forages, and hence are of lower digestibility (see Table 9.17). On average, tropical forages are 15 units lower in digestibility compared to temperate forages.[135]

Grasses can have annual (require yearly reseeding) or perennial (yearly regrowth without seeding) growth patterns. Within the temperate grasses there are differences in adaptation to growing conditions. Some temperate grasses (see Table 9.16) grow at cooler temperatures (cool-season grasses), while others grow best with higher environmental temperatures (warm-season grasses). Cool-season grasses (see Figure 9.4) grow during spring and fall and are dormant during the hot summer months. Warm-season grasses grow best during the hot summer months. Warm-season grasses tend to be more drought resistant than cool-season grasses. Pasture mixtures of cool- and warm-season grasses maintain forage mass and quality more uniformly through the growing season in temperate regions.[34]

Table 9.17 Typical test value of temperate and subtropical alfalfa and grass hays harvested at various stages of plant maturity (all values on dry matter basis).

Hay Type and Maturity Stage	Crude Protein (CP)	Acid Detergent Fiber (ADF)	Neutral Detergent Fiber (NDF)	Metabolizable Energy (ME)	Total Digestible Nutrients (TDN)
Temperate Forages					
Alfalfa*					
Prebloom	>19	<31	<40	1.03–1.13	63–66
Early bloom	17–19	30–35	40–46	0.98–1.02	60–62
Midbloom	13–16	36–41	46–51	0.92–0.97	56–59
Late bloom	<13	>41	>51	<0.90	<55
Grass,*****					
Prehead	>18	<33	<55	0.98–1.07	60–65
Early head	13–18	34–38	55–60	0.85–0.91	52–56
Head	8–12	39–41	61–65	0.75–0.84	46–51
Posthead	<8	>41	>65	<0.75	<46
Subtropical Forages					
Alfalfa*					
Prebloom	25–30	30–32	33–41	1.03–1.13	63–65
Early bloom	19–27	34–37	40–47	0.95–1.02	58–62
Midbloom	18–23	35–39	46–51	0.90–0.93	55–57
Late bloom	17–18	>41	>51	<0.89	<54
Grass,†					
Prehead	18–19	32–33	64–69	0.84–0.98	51–60
Early head	8–18	34–40	64–79	0.74–0.82	45–50
Head	6–11	39–43	70–80	0.66–0.72	40–44
Posthead	4–9	39–47	71–81	<0.66	<40

Source: Adapted from Van Soest, 1994 (reference 135) and National Resource Council, 1982 (reference 95).

*Alfalfa growth stages: prebloom = bud to first flower; early bloom = up to 1/10 of plants in bloom; midbloom = 1/10 to 2/3 of plants in bloom; late bloom = >66% in bloom.

**Grass growth stages: prehead = late vegetative to early boot stage; early head = emergence of seed heads (inflorescence); head = further emergence of seed heads, seeds become well formed; posthead = seeds fully matured and released.

***Summary analysis from orchardgrass, reed canarygrass, smooth bromegrass, and tall fescue.

†Summary analysis from bahiagrass, pangola, and bermudagrass at 2–3 (prehead), 4–6 (early head), 6–8 (head), and 10 (posthead) weeks of growth.

Legumes In contrast to grasses, which are monocotyledon plants, legumes are dicotyledon plants belonging to the family Leguminosae (Fabaceae). Cotyledons store reserve food for the new seedling to grow from the seed. Legume seeds are packaged within a unique fruit (pod) with a characteristic shape for differing species.[6,76,85] Perennial, biennial, and annual growth patterns can be found among legume species. There are approximately 12,000 species of legumes with 4,000 being grown in North America.[6,76,85] Important agricultural temperate legume species include alfalfa (*Medicago sativa*), soybean (*Glycine max*), peanuts (*Arachis* sp.), clover (*Trifolium* sp.), sweetclover (*Melilotus* sp.), bird's foot trefoil (*Lotus* sp.), lespedeza (*Kummerowia* sp. or *Lespedeza* sp.), lupine (*Lupinus* sp.), vetch (*Vicia* sp.), and various pea species.[6,85] Clovers come in many species, including red, white, alsike, subterranean, arrowleaf, ball, berseem, and crimson. Tropical legumes are also plentiful and include jointvetch (*Aeschynomene* sp.), alyceclover (*Alysicarpus* sp.), rhizoma and pinto peanuts (*Arachis* sp.), *Centrosema* species, desmanthus (*Desmanthus* sp.), various *Desmodium* species, leucaena (*Leucaena* sp.), and many other species.[6,76] Alfalfa (lucerne) is the single most important agricultural forage grown, often called the "queen of forages." Over 55 percent of total hay grown in the United States is alfalfa or an alfalfa-grass mixture.[71] Legumes have a more narrow geographic adaptation range compared to grasses and require more input to persist and maintain productivity.[6,85]

Legumes, especially alfalfa, are structurally very different from grasses, resulting in important nutritive differences. Legumes have a tap root with lateral branches rather than the highly branched root system of grasses.[6,85] Depending upon species, the legume tap root can reach deep (2–4 ft) into the soil, providing the plant an opportunity to withstand drought conditions. Alfalfa is fairly heat tolerant and will maintain growth throughout the summer (see Figure 9.4). Through a symbiotic relationship between *Rhizobium* bacteria and root hairs forming specialized root nodules, legumes can take advantage of bacterially generated ammonia.[6,85] *Rhizobium* bacteria using plant carbohydrates convert atmospheric nitrogen into ammonia, which then can be used by the plant to make protein. As a result, legumes characteristically will have higher plant protein content compared to grasses (see Table 9.17). The ability to fix atmospheric nitrogen also increases soil nitrogen resources for other plants, thus making seeding combinations of legumes and grasses beneficial to grass growth, which otherwise would require more nitrogen fertilization.

Structurally, legumes have a more distinct separation of stem and leaves. The legume stem is highly fibrous and lignified to support the plant's weight. Legume species vary

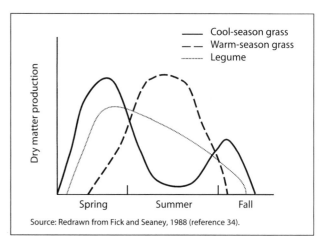

Figure 9.4 Relative seasonal growth patterns for cool- and warm-season grasses and legumes.

greatly in plant stem length, diameter, branching, and woodiness. Leaves are arranged alternately on the stem and are connected by finer branches (petioles). Leaf arrangements are species specific. Alfalfa and clover have a compound trifoliate (three leaflets) arrangement on a branch. Leaves contain all the photosynthetic organelles and, unlike grasses, have no structural rib. Like grasses, legume leaves are highly digestible, and their digestibility is not reduced with maturity. Legume stems, however, become highly lignified with maturity and their digestibility is greatly reduced. As a result of these structural differences, legumes have higher energy content, which is not reduced as significantly with maturity, compared to grasses (see Table 9.17). Observed or averaged nutrient content of common grass and legume forages fed to llamas and alpacas in South America (see Table 9.18) or used for hay (see Table 9.19) and pasture (see Table 9.20) production in North America are shown for comparisons.

Forbs and Browse All herbaceous (nonwoody) broadleaf vegetation that is not classified as grasses, grasslike, or legumes is collectively grouped as forbs.[33,71] In most people's minds, these plants would best be known as ornamental plants and weeds. Browse includes all woody plants, primarily trees, bushes, and shrubs.[33,71] When an animal consumes browse, it is usually eating selected structures such as buds, leaves, and twigs. The amount of forbs and browse consumed by an animal depends upon feeding behavior (see "Feeding Behavior") and prevailing conditions of available vegetation.

In most continents other than North America, forbs and browse are significant components of the feeding system for many animals, including llamas and alpacas. Given the abundance of high-quality, cultivated forages in North

Table 9.18 Nutrient composition of various forages consumed by llamas and alpacas in South America (all values on a dry matter basis).

Forage Common Name (Scientific Name)	Mature Stage	CP %	ME (Mcal/kg)	Fiber %	Ca %	P %
Crimson clover (*Trifolium* sp.)	Pasture	17.0	2.30	27.7	1.38	0.29
Fescue (*Festuca dolichophylla*)	Midbloom	8.3	1.74	41.3	0.09	
	Mature	2.5–4.8	0.99–1.82	35.4–44.3	0.2–0.5	0.04–0.06
Iruichu (*Festuca orthophylla*)	Vegetative	6.6		44.0		
	Mature	1.4	4	2.7		
Llama pasto (*Festuca rigida*)	Pasture	10.3		54.4 (ADF) 70.4 (NDF)		
Ladysmantle (*Alchemilla* sp.)	Mature	10.9	2.29	28.9	1.9	0.24
Muhlenbergia (*Muhlenbergia* sp.)	Early	6.8	2.13	31.2	0.37	0.13
	Midbloom	7.1	1.80	39.6	0.16	0.13
	Mature	5.8	2.35	27.5	0.41	0.13
Reed canarygrass (*Phalaris arundinacea*)	Midbloom	13.0	2.05	27.1	0.36	0.33
Grama ichu (*Stipa brachyphylla*)	Mature	1.9–2.7	1.68	36.3–37.9	0.12–0.17	0.06–0.07
Ichu (*Stipa* spp.)	Mature	3.1–5.1	1.63–1.83	35.4–37.6	0.16–0.20	0.05–0.09
Tisna (*Stipa obtusa*)	Mature	5.5	1.69	39.3	0.19	0.11
Plantain (*Plantago* sp.)	Pasture	14.7	2.50	35.4	0.16	0.26
Nappa pasto, sora pasto, tullo pasto	Early	6.2	2.12	33.8	0.38	0.11
(*Calamagrostis* sp.)	Midbloom	8.9	2.00	33.9		
	Mature	4.6	1.92	32.0	0.64	0.07
Rescuegrass (*Bromus unioloides*)	Early	12.5	2.15	24.9	0.57	0.30
	Midbloom	10.4	1.95	35.6	0.29	0.21
Spikesedge (*Eleocharis* sp.)	Pasture	15.5	2.24	34.1	0.32	0.19

Sources: Fowler, 1998 (reference 42); San Martin, 1987 (reference 110); Genin et al., 1994 (reference 46), and McDowell et al., 1974 (reference 80).

America, the consensus is that forbs and browse are of much lower quality and may even be deleterious. Perceptions of poisonous plants, noxious weeds, and eating tree bark all combine to reinforce this association of low-quality feed with forbs and browse. However, many animals around the world survive and flourish on these vegetative resources. Deer, moose, eland, giraffe, and goats are all animals that preferentially consume forbs and browse.[135] Llamas and alpacas will make use of forbs and browse during the dry season in South America and when the opportunity arises in North America.[13,46,59,60,104,110,111] Compared to cultivated forages, minimal data are available to confirm or refute the low-quality status of forbs and browse.

Llamas and alpacas have been observed to consume blackberry leaves, a common forb in North America, when present in a pasture. Seasonal compositional analysis of blackberry leaves shows them to be of high quality, approaching that of a legume plant (refer to Table 9.22).[100] Besides its protein and energy density, blackberry leaves have significant amounts of many minerals often deficient in grass forages. Data summarizing many reports also sug-

gest potentially high-quality vegetation from tree and shrub leaves. Digestible dry matter from tree and shrub leaves ranged from 17 to 67 percent, where most studies showed a range from 34 to 64 percent.[61] Crude protein content of these leaves was also wide ranging, from 6.9 to 33 percent.[61] Leaf material from a tree legume was found to have a crude protein content of 22.5 to 29.4 percent and 19.4 to 28.8 percent for wet- and dry-season growth, respectively.[61] In situations where the prevailing forage is mature with high fiber and low protein, it would seem that consumption of browse and forb material may be an appropriate resource for the animal in making up for dietary deficiencies from forage.

Sedges and Rushes These two plant groups are grasslike in appearance and are often confused with grasses. Both sedges (family Cyperaceae, approximately 4,000 species) and rushes (family Juncaceae, approximately 400 species) have linear leaves with parallel veins and inconspicuous flowers.[12] Sedges have solid, nonjointed, and often triangular stems compared to the hollow, round, jointed stems of grasses. Sedge flowers are structurally different

Table 9.19 Nutrient composition of various dried forages (grasses and legumes) available in the North America. All nutrient values, excluding dry matter, are on a dry matter basis.

	DM	NDF	Lignin	TDN	ME	CP	NFC	Fat	Ash	Ca	P	Mg	K	Na	S
Grasses	%	% DM	% NDF	% DM	Mcal/kgg					% DM					
Bahiagrass Hay	90	72	11.11	51.0	1.84	8.2	9.7	1.6	11	0.5	0.22	0.19	0	0	0
Bermudagrass Late Vegetative	91	76.6	8.57	49.0	1.77	7.8	7.6	2.7	8	0.26	0.18	0.13	1.3	0.08	0.21
Brome Hay Prebloom	88	55	7.69	60.0	2.17	16	21.4	2.6	10	0.32	0.37	0.09	2.32	0.02	0.2
Brome Hay Midbloom	88	57.7	6.06	56.0	2.02	14.4	19.3	2.2	10.9	0.29	0.28	0.1	1.99	0.01	0
Brome Hay Late bloom	91	68	11.11	55.0	1.99	10	13.8	2.3	9	0	0	0	0	0	0
Brome Hay Mature	92	70.5	11.27	53.0	1.92	6	16.2	2	7.2	0.26	0.22	0.12	1.85	0.01	0
Fescue Meadow Hay	88	65	10.77	56.0	2.02	9.1	18.3	2.4	8	0.37	0.29	0.5	1.84	0	0
Fescue Alta Hay	89	70	9.29	55.0	1.99	10.2	10.8	2.2	10	0.39	0.24	0.23	2.38	0	0
Fescue K31 Hay	91	62.2	6.35	61.0	2.21	15	13.4	5.5	9	0.51	0.37	0.27	2.3	0	0.18
Fescue K31 Hay Full bloom	91	67	7.46	58.0	2.10	12.9	11.2	5.3	8	0.43	0.32	0.17	2.3	0	0.26
Fescue K31 Mature	91	70	10.00	44.0	1.59	10.8	11.4	4.7	6.8	0.41	0.3	0.16	1.96	0.02	0
Meadowgrass Hay	90.7	65.9	9.80	62.0	2.24	6.6	18.0	2.8	7.5	0.22	0.13	0.15	1.71	0.389	0.15
Meadow Hay	90	67.6	5.00	60.0	2.17	13.4	5.3	3	11	0.26	0.15	0	0	0	0
Oat Hay	91.9	51	16.50	68.0	2.46	7.8	30.8	3.8	7.38	0.16	0.18	0.12	1.55	0.346	0.15
Oat Straw	92.2	74.4	20.00	45.0	1.63	4.4	14.5	2.2	7.8	0.23	0.06	0.17	2.53	0.42	0.22
Orchardgrass Hay Early bloom	89	59.6	7.70	65.0	2.35	12.8	20.2	2.9	8.5	0.27	0.34	0.11	2.91	0.01	0.26
Orchardgrass Hay Late bloom	90.6	65	11.40	54.0	1.95	8.4	15.7	3.4	10.1	0.26	0.3	0.11	2.67	0.01	0
Prairie Hay	91	72.7	6.00	48.0	1.74	5.3	11.1	3	8	0.35	0.14	0.26	1	0	0
Reed Canarygrass Hay	89	64	6.25	55.0	1.99	10.3	15.8	3.1	10	0.36	0.24	0.22	2.91	0.02	0
Ryegrass Hay	88	41	4.88	64.0	2.31	8.6	40.9	2.2	10	0	0	0	0	0	0
Ryegrass Hay Mature	92	68	16.20	58.0	2.10	7	14.7	2.5	8.5	0.28	0.17	0.08	1.7	0.005	0.12
Sorghum Sudan Hay	91	66	6.06	56.1	2.03	11.3	15.8	1.8	9.6	0.51	0.31	0.37	2.08	0.02	0.06
Timothy Hay Early bloom	89	61.4	6.56	59.0	2.13	10.8	22.6	2.8	5.7	0.51	0.29	0.13	2.41	0.01	0.13
Timothy Hay Full bloom	89	64.2	8.82	56.0	2.02	8.1	22.1	2.9	5.2	0.43	0.2	0.09	1.99	0.07	0.14
Timothy Hay Late Vegetative	89	55	5.45	62.0	2.24	14	24.3	3	8	0.45	0.4	0.11	3.05	0.07	0.13
Timothy Hay Midbloom	89	63.7	7.46	57.0	2.06	9.7	19.9	2.7	7	0.48	0.23	0.13	1.82	0.01	0.13
Timothy Hay Seed Stage	89	72	12.50	47.0	1.70	6	15.9	2	6	0	0	0	0	0	0
Wheat Straw	89	78.9	16.47	41.0	1.48	3.5	9.0	2	7.7	0.17	0.05	0.12	1.41	0.14	0.19
Wheatgrass Crest Hay	92	65	9.23	53.0	1.92	9	17.5	2.3	9	0.26	0.15	0	0	0	0
Legumes															
Alfalfa Hay Early Vegetative	91	36	14.72	67.0	2.42	23.4	30.9	3.2	10	1.5	0.33	0.21	2.51	0.12	0.54
Alfalfa Hay Late Vegetative	91	39	16.67	64.0	2.31	21.7	29.6	3	10	1.5	0.33	0.21	2.51	0.12	0.54
Alfalfa Hay Early Bloom	91	42	16.90	62.0	2.24	19.9	29.6	2.9	9.2	1.63	0.22	0.21	2.51	0.12	0.54
Alfalfa Hay Midbloom	91	49	18.91	60.0	2.17	17	27.3	2.39	8.57	1.39	0.24	0.35	1.56	0.12	0.28
Alfalfa Hay Full Bloom	91	51	20.39	56.0	2.02	13	29.0	1.8	9	1.19	0.24	0.27	1.56	0.07	0.3
Alfalfa Hay Late Bloom	91	55	22.18	53.0	1.92	12	27.4	1.6	8	1.19	0.24	0.27	1.56	0.07	0.3
Alfalfa Hay Mature	91	58	24.83	50.0	1.81	14	24.7	1.3	7	1.18	0.21	0.22	2.07	0.08	0.25
Alfalfa Hay Seeded	91	70	24.30	45.0	1.63	12	14.3	1	7	1.18	0.21	0.22	2.07	0.08	0.25
Alfalfa Hay Weathered	89	58	25.86	48.0	1.74	10	28.5	0	8	2.29	0.23	0.27	2.42	0.06	0
Alfalfa Meal Dehydrated 15% CP	90	55.4	26.00	59.0	2.13	17.3	19.3	2.4	9.9	1.38	0.25	0.29	2.46	0.08	0.21
Birdsfoot Trefoil Hay	91	47.5	19.15	59.0	2.13	15.9	31.1	2.1	7.4	1.7	0.23	0.51	1.92	0.07	0.25
Clover Ladino Hay	89	36	19.44	60.0	2.17	22.4	32.9	2.7	9.4	1.45	0.33	0.47	2.44	0.13	0.21
Clover Red Hay	88	46.9	17.86	55.0	1.99	15	33.1	2.8	7.5	1.38	0.24	0.38	1.81	0.18	0.16
Vetch Hay	89	48	16.67	57.0	2.06	20.8	26.4	3	7	1.36	0.34	0.27	2.12	0.52	0.15

Source: Modified from feed composition tables in National Research Council, 1996 (reference 97).

Table 9.20 Nutritional composition of pastures (grass, legume, mixed) in North America.
All nutrient values, excluding dry matter, are on a dry matter basis.

	DM	NDF	Lignin	TDN	ME	CP	NFC	Fat	Ash	Ca	P	Mg	K	Na	S
	%	% DM	% NDF	% DM	Mcal/kg					% DM					
Bahiagrass 30% DM	30	68	10.29	54.0	1.95	8.9	12.3	2.1	10	0.46	0.22	0.25	1.45	0	0
Grass Pasture Spring	23	47.9	6.00	74.0	2.68	21.3	19.5	4	10.4	0.55	0.45	0.32	3.16	0	0.2
Grass Pasture Summer	25	55	7.00	67.0	2.42	15	20.9	3.7	9	0	0	0	0	0	0
Grass Pasture Fall	24	67	6.50	53.0	1.92	22	0.9	3.7	10	0	0	0	0	0	0
Leg Pasture Spring	20	33	8.00	79.0	2.86	28	29.1	2.7	10	1.71	0.3	0.36	2.27	0.21	0.36
Leg Pasture Summer	23.2	38	8.50	66.0	2.39	22.2	29.4	2.9	10.2	1.71	0.3	0.36	2.27	0.21	0.36
Meadow Spring	15	53	8.00	44.8	1.62	20.3	14.1	3	10	0.26	0.15	0	0	0	0
Meadow Fall	20	52	8.00	51.9	1.88	13.4	21.9	3	10	0.26	0.15	0	0	0	0
Mix Pasture Spring	21	41.5	7.00	79.0	2.86	26	22.3	3.2	10.25	0	0	0	0	0	0
Mix Pasture Summer	22	46.5	7.80	67.0	2.42	19.5	23.8	3.2	9.4	0	0	0	0	0	0
Napiergrass Fresh 30d	20	70	14.29	55.0	1.99	8.7	10.2	3	9	0.6	0.41	0.26	1.31	0.01	0.1
Napiergrass Fresh 60d	23	75	18.67	53.0	1.92	7.8	11.0	1	6	0.6	0.41	0.26	1.31	0.01	0.1
Pangolagrass Fresh	21	70	11.40	55.0	1.99	9.1	13.2	2.3	7.6	0.38	0.22	0.18	1.43	0	0
Range June Diet	20	65.6	5.00	64.9	2.35	11	13.0	3	10	0.26	0.15	0	0	0	0
Range July Diet	20	67.7	5.50	62.3	2.25	10.5	11.3	3	10	0.26	0.15	0	0	0	0
Range August Diet	20	63.7	8.00	59.4	2.15	9.7	15.9	3	10	0.26	0.15	0	0	0	0
Range September Diet	20	66.6	9.00	57.3	2.07	6.9	15.2	3	10	0.26	0.15	0	0	0	0
Range Winter	80	66.1	11.00	50.5	1.83	4.7	17.3	3	10	0.26	0.15	0	0	0	0
Red Top Fresh	29	64	12.50	63.0	2.28	11.6	15.3	3.9	8	0.62	0.37	0.25	2.35	0.05	0.16
Sorghum-Sudan Pasture	18	55	5.45	65.0	2.35	16.8	20.3	3.9	9	0.49	0.44	0.35	2.14	0	0.11

Source: Modified from feed composition tables in National Research Council, 1996 (reference 97).

from grasses and arranged spirally on the stem. Compared to grasses, sedges and rushes grow in cooler, wetter regions. Rush stems can be either solid or hollow and their flower is distinctly different from grasses and sedges in having three petals and sepals. Although not an economically important forage crop in North America, a number of sedge (*Carex* spp.; *Eleocharis* spp.) and rush (*Juncus* spp.) species are selectively consumed by llamas and alpacas in South America.[13,46,59,60,104,110,111]

Forage Quality

Three processes define forage quality: an animal's ability to consume (intake), digest (digestibility), and assimilate (availability) essential nutrients contained within the feed. Simply put, forage quality means that an animal can obtain a greater portion of its daily nutrient needs from forage alone. The most important determinant of forage quality is the stage of plant maturity when harvested, irrespective of plant species.[22,86] Plants, like humans, grow and mature over time. A mature plant is one that has developed reproductive components to the point of generating seeds. The immature plant is one prior to reproductive parts (seeds, flowers) development. Immature plants have higher moisture content and less cell wall structure, making them more

digestible. Although there are differences among grass species in how quickly they mature and their physical characteristics relative to animal acceptance, stage of maturity at harvest is more important than selecting a particular species in producing quality forage.

Mature plants contain greater amounts of structural cell wall components, as measured by NDF, and lignin for cell wall reinforcement, as reflected in ADF amounts. This increase in lignin and fiber results in a dilution of energy, protein, and other nutrients, as well as a decline in nutrient availability. Both alfalfa and grasses show similar declines in crude protein and increases in NDF and ADF content with advancing maturity (see Table 9.17). Predicted forage energy content also declines with maturity, but more quickly in grasses as a result of described differences in plant anatomy and fiber distribution. Similar maturity effects can be found when comparing forage nutrient content data within a forage species (see Tables 9.19 and 9.20). These data also show a decline in forage mineral content with advancing maturity.

A second important factor influencing forage quality is plant species—legume versus grass forages. Due to inherent botanical differences, legumes are higher in protein and energy, and have less NDF compared to grass forages of similar maturity (see Table 9.17). Legumes also have higher calcium content compared to grasses (see Table 9.19). As a grass matures, its nutrient availability is more dramatically reduced compared to legumes. Thus mature grass hay has greater potential feeding problems as a result of its greatly reduced nutrient availability.

Environmental effects such as temperature, sunlight, fertilization, moisture, disease, and predation can have tremendous influences on how rapidly a plant matures and its nutrient content.[6,22,85] Increased temperature will increase yield, cell wall content, and lignification, all negative factors on nutrient availability. Increased light will also increase yields, but the plant will be more digestible as a result of the increased sugar content due to greater photosynthetic activity. Ultimately light and temperature, by their combined effects on plant growth and maturation, control forage quality differences between first-, second-, and third-cutting forages from the same field. If you think about this, springs are cool with increasing day length, summers hot with long days, and fall cool with short days. Fertilization generally increases protein content and have variable effects on cell wall content and digestibility.

Forage harvesting and storage techniques also influence quality.[22] Harvesting techniques resulting in leaf loss greatly reduce forage quality. Mechanical harvesting for hay production or improper climate when drying can result in significant nutrient and quality loss. Storing hay at improper moisture (>15%) will result in molding and heat production, thus seriously reducing forage quality. Heat production from mold growth can induce heat damage to protein, making it unavailable, or worse, be significant enough to induce spontaneous combustion of the hay and storage facility.

Forage quality can be assessed by sensory and chemical methods (see Table 9.21). The gold standard in assessing forage quality is to obtain quantitative measures (NDF, ADF, crude protein) of a representative forage sample. When there is concern about forage heating during storage, then measuring unavailable protein (ADIP) (see "Analytical Procedures") may also be used to assess forage quality. Other measures of NDF fermentability and dry matter digestibility are being used for other species, but application to alpaca feeding has not yet been explored. In the absence of chemical testing, one can obtain some rudimentary assessment of forage quality using your senses of sight, smell, and touch. Sensory evaluation can at least provide some idea of maturity stage, foreign material presence, and forage-handling practices. Sensory evaluation does not provide any good assessment of nutrient content and should not be solely relied upon for forage purchasing decisions.

Table 9.21 Sensory evaluation and chemical tests in assessing forage (pasture and hay) quality.

Testing Method	Description/Comments
Sensory Evaluation	
Visual	
Stage of maturity	Look for the presence of seed heads (grass forages) or flowers or seed pods (legumes), indicating more mature forages
Leaf to stem ratio	Look at forage and determine whether the stems or leaves are more obvious; good-quality legume forages will have a high proportion of leaves, and stems will be less obvious and fine
Color	Color is not a good indicator of nutrient content, but bright green color suggests minimal oxidation; yellow hay indicates oxidation and bleaching from sun, and hay will have lower vitamins A and E content
Foreign objects	Look for presence and amount of inanimate objects (twine, wire, cans, etc.), weeds, mold, or poisonous plants
Touch	Feel stiffness or coarseness of leaves and stems; see if alfalfa stems wrap around your finger without breaking; good-quality hay will feel soft and have fine, pliable stems
Smell	Good-quality hay will have a fresh-mowed grass odor; no musty or moldy odors
Chemical Testing	
Moisture/dry matter	Measures amount of moisture in forage; moisture content will determine how well the forage will store without molding; goal for any hay <15% moisture (>85% dry matter)
Neutral detergent fiber	Measures total cell wall content of plant and indicates maturity; the higher the value, the more mature and lower quality the forage; goal <45% alfalfa and <55% grasses
Acid detergent fiber	Measures the more indigestible portion of the cell wall and reflects degree of lignification; higher values indicate more mature, lower-quality forages; goal: <40% alfalfa and <40% grasses
Crude protein	Crude protein content reflects maturity of forage as well as fertilization amount; good-quality forages generally will have higher protein content; goal >9% grasses and >15% alfalfa

Forage Quality and the Need for Supplements

What is expected forage quality and is it of concern in feeding alpacas? In comparison to other feeds, forages have the most variability in nutrient composition as a result of various factors influencing composition (i.e., plant species, stage of growth, soil fertility, management practices). Mean and range nutrient composition data, representing forages harvested across the United States, were generated by plant groups (legumes versus grasses) from Tables 9.19 and 9.20. These data are consistent with forage analysis findings from a study of 709 samples obtained from 23 states.[90] Table 9.22 compares these summarized forage nutrient content data to suggested nutrient requirements for alpacas. In reviewing protein, energy, and fiber values for these forages, pasture and legume hay are generally of higher quality and less mature than typical grass hays. Comparing nutrient content of grass hay, to alpaca requirements, one can see that there is potential for energy and protein deficiency, especially for the highly productive animal. Of interest is the observed nutrient analysis of blackberry leaves, a typical forb consumed in the northwestern United States. Nutrient content of blackberry leaves is very complementary to grass hay, being higher in energy, protein, and calcium. This observation reinforces the idea that if provided an opportunity to selectively graze, llamas and alpacas can potentially meet their nutritional needs in the face of poor-quality forages.

From the data presented, forages are deficient in a number of minerals, most notably zinc, copper, and selenium. This is consistent with the summary study where 77 percent, 69.5 percent, and 66.7 percent of forages were either marginally deficient or deficient in zinc, selenium, and copper, respectively.[90] Most forages grown across the United States are deficient in zinc. If legume hays are being fed, then calcium excess is present, which may further exacerbate zinc deficiency. Iron content of all forages is high, which can interfere with copper availability. Another notable difference is the excessive amount of potassium in all forages relative to its requirement. High dietary potassium can interfere with magnesium availability in ruminant animals. Supplementation with vitamins A, D, and E will depend upon the forage type and quality. Pasture is sufficiently high in vitamins A and E, whereas stored hay is commonly low in all vitamins.[26] This suggests that some additional source of minerals and vitamins through a supplement is necessary to balance out a forage feeding program.

In recognizing nutrient variability in forages and addressing consumer demand, feed manufacturers in North America have produced a variety of supplements for llamas and alpacas. These supplements range from complete

Table 9.22 Comparison of nutrient content of legume and grass hays and pasture (grass and mixed) typical of North American forages to suggested nutrient requirements for camelids. Tabular values are mean and (range).

Nutrient	Estimated Requirement*	Average (Normal-Range) Nutrient Content			
		Legume Hay	Grass Hay	Pasture	Blackberry Leaves
% of Dry Matter					
Crude Protein	8–14	16.6 (10–23.4)	9.6 (3.5–16)	14.7 (4.7–28)	13.6 (12.5–15.2)
TDN**	50–65	56.9 (45–67)	55.5 (41–68)	61.1 (44.8–79)	64.3 (63–65)
ME, Mcal/lb	0.82–1.1	0.94 (0.74–1.1)	0.91 (0.67–1.1)	1.0 (0.74–1.3)	1.05 (1.03–1.07)
NDF**	>30	49.5 (36–70)	65.2 (41–78.9)	58.3 (33–75)	34.9 (31.1–39.2)
ADF**	>20	38.3 (27–59)	45.5 (23–55)	36.3 (18–52)	26.6 (24.4–30.6)
Calcium	0.2–0.85	1.43 (1.06–2.29)	0.34 (0.16–0.51)	0.56 (0.26–1.7)	1.2 (0.84–1.62)
Phosphorus	0.16–0.40	0.26 (0.21–0.34)	0.24 (0.05–0.4)	0.26 (0.15–0.45)	0.25 (0.16–0.36)
Potassium	0.5–0.8	2.06 (1.31–2.51)	2.1 (1.0–3.1)	1.96 (1.3–3.2)	0.87 (0.51–1.51)
Magnesium	0.12–0.20	0.29 (0.15–0.51)	0.17 (0.08–0.5)	0.29 (0.18–0.36)	0.48 (0.35–0.63)
ppm (mg/kg) of Dry Matter					
Copper	8–13 ppm	10.5 (6–22)	8 (4–16)	9 (4–16)	7.5 (4–12)
Iron	50–100 ppm	484 (42–900)	219 (0–515)	650 (0–1,–700)	178.5 (106–282)
Manganese	45–50 ppm	45 (8–81)	92.6 (26–166)	95 (30–270)	121 (88–178)
Selenium	0.4–0.6 ppm		0.01–0.3***		NA
Zinc	40–47 ppm	23 (14–43)	24 (11–38)	26 (17–42)	20 (12–27)

*Lower values represent nutrient requirements for maintenance, while higher values would support early growth or lactation.

**TDN = total digestible nutrients (a measure of energy content); NDF = neutral detergent fiber (a measure of total fiber); ADF = acid detergent fiber (a measure of indigestible fiber).

***Certain areas of central North America (Great Plains) have high soil selenium and forages with adequate to toxic selenium content.

Source: Average data determined from National Research Council, 1996 feed composition table (reference 97) and range data summarized from forage analyses representing northwestern and eastern United States.

supplements (see Table 9.23) containing protein, energy, fiber, minerals, and vitamins to free-choice mineral products (see Table 9.24). These data show that there is a tremendous range in nutrient content across these products. Part of this variation can be attributed to differences in expected intake of the pellet or mineral.

To better compare supplements, amounts of each nutrient were determined for a defined animal (see Table 9.25). Free-choice mineral intake calculations were based on the expected intake taken from the feed tag. In simply comparing nutrient amounts delivered to suggested nutrient requirements, mean nutrient amounts across products meet or exceed needs. However, there is still much range in nutrient delivery, in some cases more than 20-fold differences. As already addressed, specific nutrient requirements of camelids have not been defined. As a result, most commercial camelid supplements mimic current products for sheep, cattle, horses, or some variation on the theme. Nutrient content of many supplements does not account for variation in forage nutrient content, let alone whether grass or legume forages are being fed.

Another concern is the confounding effect of expected intake. Most products are based on other domestic species and inherent feeding practices have similar feeding directions. For the pellet products, most intake expectations are fairly reasonable at 136 to 227 grams per day (0.3–0.5 lb/day). However, others expect more than 0.45 kilograms per day (1 lb/day) intake, which would be nearly 40 percent of the diet as supplement. Many people would not feed that much and certainly not to overweight animals. If intake of these products is less than recommended, then overall nutrient intake will be lower, possibly insufficient to meet needs. This concern is a more critical issue for mineral products. The expected intake of most of these products is 14 grams per day (0.5 oz/day) up to 57 grams per day (2 oz/day). Practical feeding experience suggests, at best, free-choice salt-based mineral intake of 7.1 to 9.4 grams per day (0.25–0.33 oz/day). If this is what you observe with your animals, then the calculated nutrient amounts in Table 9.25 need to be reduced by one-quarter or one-third to account for the lower intake. This opens the door for even more potential problems with inadequate nutrient intake using these products.

Table 9.23 Comparison of guaranteed (as fed basis) analysis of 17 commercial pellet supplements fed to llamas and alpacas.

Nutrient	Units	Commercial Pellet Products												Lite Pellet Products			Custom Pellets	
		A	B	C	D	E	F	G	H	I	J	K	L	M	N	O	P	Q
Intake*	lb/day	0.45	1.0	0.3	0.375	0.5	1.5	0.35	0.45	1.0	1.1	1.0	0.45	0.45	0.525	0.45	1.0	0.25
Crude protein	%	14	16	18	15.2	14.1	14.1	15	15	15	14	14	13	8	10	8	15	11
Crude fat	%	3	2	1.2	2.4	1.9	3.5	2.9	2	2	2	2	2	1.5	1	1	2.75	
Crude fiber	%	8	11.5	8	10	22.8	14.3	10	17.5	18	15	15	18	20	19.5	25	16.9	13
Total ash	%		11.5	15	9.1	7.5	6	9.5	11.5			15	11	14.5			13.44	
Calcium	%	1.4	2.125	2	2	0.7	0.6	2.01	1.6	1.3	0.9	1.2	1.65	1.8	1.6	1.4	1.8	3
Phosphorus	%	1.1	0.9	1.4	1	0.45	0.45	1	0.8	1.2	1.2	0.8	0.8	1.1	1.2	1	0.8	1
Magnesium	%	0.9		0.38	0.34	0.3	0.3	0.3			0.5	0.5	0.4			0.9	0.5	
Potassium	%	1	1		1.07	1.23	0.82	0.95					1.2			1.1	1.14	
Sodium	%		0.76		0.41	0.28	0.28	0.42			0.45		0.19				0.465	0.38
Chloride	%			0.7	0.46	0.46	0.68						0.31				0.683	0.62
Salt	%		0.7	1							1	1.2	0.5	2.5			1	1
Sulfur	%			0.28	0.26	0.19	0.26										0.272	
Cobalt	ppm			22	2.9	0.64	0.6	5.3			5	0.5					2.5	
Copper	ppm	12		500	16	20	25	25	50		25	25	50	25	50	15	50.229	18
Iron	ppm			400	480	353	270	400			425	200					605	100
Iodine	ppm			400	3.9	1.9	1.9	0.21			2.5	1				4.87		
Manganese	ppm	85		2000	320	200	200	320			250	150	100			105	469.27	
Selenium	ppm	4	2	7.7	2.1	0.65	0.65	3.5	6	4	4.5	4.5	6	3.9	4	4.5	13	6.6
Zinc	ppm	125		2400	410	211	210	500			400	200	300			140	480	500
Vitamin A	IU/lb	9,000	8,000	45,000	17,727	5,909	8,636	10,909	11,000		13,636	13,500	9,000		11,000	8,000	12,344	25,000
Vitamin D	IU/lb	1,400	1,000	17,650	3,017	1,000	1,000	5,000	5,000		2,272	2,500	2,800		8,000	1,500	20,000	5,000
Vitamin E	IU/lb	250	20	275	304	20.5	50	309		400	182	275	360	400	400	350	400	800

* Based on calculated intake rate using feed-tag information for a 150-pound alpaca.

Table 9.24 Comparison of guaranteed (as-fed basis) analysis of commercially available mineral supplements for llamas and alpacas.

Nutrient	Units	Commercial Mineral Products										
		A	B	C	D	E	F	G	H	I	J	K
Feeding rate*	oz/day	1.0	1.75	1.0	1.0	2.0	0.5	0.5	0.5	0.5	0.75	2.0
Calcium	%	8.5	13	12.5	12.5	8.7	9.9	8.5	8.5	8	7	4
Phosphorus	%	4.5	16	3.1	7	4.4	4.5	4.5	4.5	6.5	5	3
Magnesium	%		0.5			1.7		0.6	0.5	0.6	0.375	0.5
Potassium	%		0.4			1.5		2.8	3	2.8	0.25	1.5
Sodium	%		5			4	8.55	8.55	8	7.6		
Chloride	%						13.95	13.95	13	13.4		
Salt	%	28	12	2.75	19		22.5	22.5	21	20		20.9
Sulfur	%		0.6							0.325		
Cobalt	ppm	20	30			8.8	20	20	20	20	12	
Copper	ppm		200			110	27	27	600	200		
Iron	ppm	1,050	4,000			5,280	1,050	5,000	5,000	5,000	1,500	
Iodine	ppm	31	120			8.8	30	30	30	30	35	
Manganese	ppm	6,300	2,000			3,520	630	1,500	1,500	1,500	300	
Selenium	ppm	20	30	90	90	8.8	20	70	70	70	0.15	6.2
Zinc	ppm	7,000	3,000			4,510	7,000	8,000	8,000	9,000		
Vitamin A	IU/lb	200,000	90,909			60,000	200,000	225,000	225,000	250,000	105,625	100,000
Vitamin D	IU/lb	20,000	22,727			20,000	20,000	25,000	30,000	30,000	12,500	25,000
Vitamin E	IU/lb	3,200	182	500	500	500	3,200	4,800	5,200	7,000	250	200

*Feeding rate based on product label directions.

Table 9.25 Comparison of calculated mean, minimum, and maximum daily nutrient intake for 17 pellet supplements and 11 free-choice vitamin-mineral salt products routinely fed to camelids.

Nutrient Content	Units	Requirement*	Pellet Products			Vitamin-Mineral Salt Products		
			Mean	Low	High	Mean	Low	High
Expected intake	lb/oz	2.25 lb	0.66 lb/d	0.25	1.5	1.46 oz/d	0.5	2
Crude protein	g	105.5	41.1	12.5	96.0			
Crude fat	g		6.9	1.6	23.8			
Crude fiber	g		46.4	10.9	97.4			
Calcium	g	4.1	4.2	1.6	9.7	2.7	1.1	6.5
Phosphorus	g	2.4	2.7	1.0	6.0	1.8	0.6	8.0
Magnesium	g	1.5	1.4	0.47	2.5	0.23	0	0.96
Potassium	g	10.2	3.1	1.5	5.6	0.4	0	0.85
Salt	g	5.6	3.3	1.0	5.4	6.4	0.8	11.9
Cobalt	mg	0.27	1.1	0.14	3.0	0.49	0.26	1.49
Copper	mg	11.5	12.5	2.0	68.1	4.7	0.4	9.9
Iodine	mg	1.0	7.6	0.03	54.5	1.2	0.4	6.0
Iron	mg	51	117	11.4	274.7	98.5	14.9	300
Manganese	mg	48	93.1	17.4	272.4	69.6	6.4	199.8
Selenium	mg	0.6–1.0	1.0	0.15	2.25	1.1	0.28	2.55
Zinc	mg	48	112	25.5	326.9	152	99.3	255.9
Vitamin A	IU	3,375	7,826	2,954	15,000	8,391	4,951	12,500
Vitamin D	IU	2,045	1,900	500	5,300	1,469	586	3,125
Vitamin E	U	33.75	172	10.5	400	92.1	11.7	219

*Based on extrapolated requirements (Tables 9.10, 9.11, and 9.14) for a pregnant female weighing 150 pounds (68.2 kg) consuming dry matter at 1.5 percent of body weight.

Evaluating Supplement Adequacy

The ideal supplement would be one that is readily consumed (palatable), has a nutrient content to complement the forage program, and is consumed at a rate sufficient to meet the desired intake of all nutrients. Most supplements are purchased on the basis of word of mouth from other producers, based on their experience, or whatever is available at the local feed store. Given that your animals' health and productivity and farm profitability depend upon the nutrition program, one needs to obtain as much information about a particular product as possible. The first place to start is reviewing the information provided on the feed tag. Most feed tags will provide limited analyses, usually crude protein, crude fiber, crude fat, calcium, phosphorus, and possibly salt and ash. Other product literature may be available with more details. Feed-tag information does not provide you with energy or trace mineral content.

Reviewing the ingredient list on the feed tag can provide some insight about potential energy sources. Ingredients like corn, oats, and barley will provide much carbohydrate for energy. Fiber sources, which can provide some energy, include wheat middlings, wheat bran, soybean hulls, cottonseed hulls, or forage products (generic by-product term). Protein sources include primarily soybean, canola, or corn gluten meals. The first three ingredients generally set the trend for the product. To really have a good understanding of what a particular supplement product contains, one needs to have a sample analyzed for nutrient content through a certified feed analysis laboratory. Ideally, forage should also be sampled for nutrient content for best evaluation, but averaged nutrient content from tables can be used as a guide. If forage testing is not completed, one should err on the higher side for desired nutrient delivery from supplements.

The second step in evaluating supplement adequacy is to determine how well the supplement nutrient profile complements the forage nutrient profile. For this you need to be able to interpret and use the information presented on the product feed tag. The difficult part here is interpreting and comparing nutrient concentrations of differing products based on label information. This can be a difficult task. You need to compare "apples with apples"; therefore, you must carefully read label information and convert information to an equivalent basis for comparison. For example, nutrient content of a product may be presented on a per pound basis, per ounce basis, or per dose basis. These are not necessarily the same for all products. Nutrient content may be presented as a percent (%) or part per million (ppm). Table 9.26 shows some basic conversion factors helpful in comparing and using label nutrient values.

Table 9.26 Common nutritional conversion factors.

Units Given	Units Wanted	Conversion
oz	g	multiply by 28.4
lb	g	multiply by 454
lb	oz	divide by 16
lb	kg	divide by 2.2
kg	lb	multiply by 2.2
g	kg	move decimal to left 3 places (multiply by .001)
g	mg	move decimal to right 3 places (multiply by 1,000)
mg	g	move decimal to left 3 places (multiply by .001)
mg	µg	move decimal to right 3 places (multiply by 1,000)
mg/kg	ppm	same value
µg/g	mg/kg	same value
mg/kg	µg/kg (ppb)	move decimal to right 3 places (multiply by 1,000)
µg/kg (ppb)	mg/kg	move decimal to left 3 places (multiply by .001)
mg/kg	mg/lb	multiply by 0.454
mg/kg (ppm)	%	move decimal to left 4 places (multiply by .0001)
%	mg/kg (ppm)	move decimal to right 4 places (multiply by 10,000)

Two methods can be used to assess the adequacy of a given supplement. First one could calculate the total amount of a given nutrient that would be consumed from the supplement and then compare this value to the extrapolated nutrient requirements presented in preceding tables. This can be easily accomplished for selenium using Table 9.27. Using this table, mineral products must have 90 to 120 ppm selenium to meet daily needs at an expected intake of 7.1 to 9.4 grams per day (0.25–0.33 oz/day). Or to consume 1 milligram selenium, a pellet must have between 4 and 8 ppm selenium in order to feed less than 0.45 kilogram (1 lb) of supplement. For other nutrients, multiply amount fed (as-fed or dry matter basis) times nutrient content (as-fed or dry matter basis, respectively). For example, from Table 9.23 product B, at 0.45 kilogram (1 lb) intake (as fed) the animal would consume 4.1 grams of phosphorus (1 lb × .09 × 454 g/lb). Feed-tag information is always on an as-fed basis, whereas feed analysis reports will have both as-fed and dry matter nutrient content values. If your supplement meets each of these nutrient requirements without accounting for the forage, then you can assume the supplement is adequate. If the supplement does not meet the suggested requirement, then determine if sufficient amounts of the nutrient in question are available

Table 9.27 Calculated amounts of either selenium intake (A) or selenium-fortified supplement (B) needed to achieve specified levels of selenium intake.

A. Free-Choice Mineral Supplements

Selenium (ppm)	Daily Salt Intake (oz)				
	0.25	0.33	0.5	1.0	1.25
30	0.21	0.28	0.4	0.85	1.1
50	0.35	0.47	0.7	1.4	1.8
90	0.64	0.84	1.3	2.6	3.2
120	0.85	1.12	1.7	3.4	4.25

B. Selenium-Containing Supplements

Desired Selenium Intake	Supplement Selenium Concentration (ppm)				
	0.3	1.0	2.0	4.0	8.0
mg/day	lb supplement needed to be consumed per day				
0.5	3.7	1.1	0.6	0.3	0.15
1.0	7.3	2.2	1.1	0.55	0.27
1.5	11.0	3.3	1.7	0.85	0.43
2.0	14.7	4.4	2.2	1.1	0.55
2.5	18.4	5.5	2.8	1.4	0.7

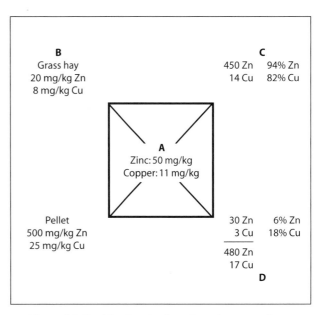

Figure 9.5 Nutritional evaluation of supplements using a Pearson square.

The box in the center (A) contains the desired nutrient content of an alpaca's diet. The left side of the graph (B) shows the nutrient content of two different feeds to be blended together to meet dietary requirements. The values shown on the right side of the graph (C) represent differences across diagonal lines (absolute values).

These values are summed (D) and the percent contribution for each feed is calculated. The diet would need to be 94 percent or 82 percent grass hay and 6 percent or 18 percent pellet, respectively, based on calculations to meet zinc and copper requirements (A).

from the forage. In general, forages provide very few additional trace minerals, except for iron and manganese. This method requires a fair number of calculations and this process could be greatly enhanced by using a computer spreadsheet.

A second method of assessing the nutritional adequacy of a given supplement is to use a Pearson square calculation method. The Pearson square is a method used to determine how to combine two feed products to achieve a desired nutrient content. For the example shown (Figure 9.5), you would need to feed 94 percent grass hay with 6 percent pellet to balance the diet for zinc. In contrast, you would need to feed 82 percent grass hay and 18 percent pellet to balance the diet for copper. To put this in better perspective, if the animal will consume 1.5 percent of body weight, then 6 percent of 1.5 percent (1.5 × 0.06 = 0.09%) requires the pellet to be fed at 0.09 percent of body weight or 0.09 kilograms (0.2 lb) per 100 kilograms (220 lb) of body weight. If the feeding directions suggest feeding at 0.3 kilogram (.66 lb) per 100 kilograms (220 lb) of body weight, then this product will be more than adequate in supplying zinc. The same calculation for copper would show that 0.27 kilograms (.59 lb) per 100 kilograms (220 lb) of body weight (1.5 × 0.18 = 0.27) must be fed. In comparing results, the pellet provides far more zinc at the suggested feeding rate and just enough copper. This calculation can be completed for any or all nutrients to assess the adequacy of a supplement.

FEEDING MANAGEMENT—MEETING NUTRITIONAL NEEDS

Feeding management is that part of nutritional science entering the realm of art. In many instances feeding animals the same diet on two different farms will result in divergent responses. Feeding management is the integration process of providing an adequately formulated diet to animals in a manner resulting in sufficient consumption to meet daily nutrient needs. Factors to consider in feeding management include feed availability, environment, housing and feeding facilities, animal grouping strategies, and all interactions.

In developing a feeding plan, one must first define the number and varying physiologic states of animals to be fed. Consider your current and future animal numbers. A feeding system must then be developed around the herd. Feeding facilities must account for size, number, and placement of feeders or pasture acreage and expected stocking density (see Chapter 4: Husbandry). With a breeding herd, what kind of animal segregation can be accomplished with the facilities to best meet individual nutritional needs? The environment in which the animals are housed should also be considered. How good is the ventilation when the animals are inside? Do the animals have to wade through knee-high mud to get to pasture or hay racks? What kinds of feed storage facilities are needed to support the number of animals? These are all important questions to consider in planning your herd's nutritional program; of course, one must make compromises in one or more areas to accomplish objectives within financial limitations.

Feeding Behaviors

One final piece to the feeding management puzzle is feeding behavior. If one is to have a successful feeding program, irrespective of facility planning, an understanding is needed of the animal's feeding behavior and how it may be impacted by social behaviors. Llamas and alpacas, like other domestic species, establish and reestablish a strong social hierarchy, which can derail a well-planned diet (see Chapter 2: Behavior and Communication). Feeding behavior defines what forages are preferred by llamas and alpacas and how selective they may be in consuming other available forages in an environment. The more selective the feeding behavior, the more adaptable the animal is to harsh conditions.

An animal's ability to select feeds depends upon two factors: anatomy and feed availability.[135] Both llamas and alpacas have a narrow mouth structure with prehensile lips, allowing them to be extremely discriminatory in selecting the feed to be consumed. Grazing with various degrees of selective feeding behavior is seen with llamas and alpacas. Llamas show a preference for grazing drier areas dominated by lower-quality, tall bunchgrasses (*Festuca, Stipa, Calamagrostis*) (see Tables 9.16 and 9.18).[29,46,59,110,113] Llamas consume more tall grasses and fewer leaves compared to sheep, and overall dietary quality is lowest compared to alpacas and sheep.[46,113] Alpacas are highly adaptable grazers with opportunistic selective feeding habits. Alpacas will graze tall grasses during the wet season, but short grasses, grasslike plants, forbs, browse, and grass seeds when tall grasses are limited during the dry season.[13,60,104,105,110-113] Compared to sheep, alpacas selected more tall grasses and grasslike plants during the rainy season and had a dietary composition intermediate between llamas and sheep.[111,113] These observations would classify llamas as a bulk- and roughage-consuming herbivore, compared to an intermediate browser classification for alpacas. This classification

is consistent with expected grazing strategies based on differences in body size between these species.[135]

Feeding Systems

Llamas and alpacas can be adequately maintained on a pasture, confinement, or combination feeding system. Pasture usage will be dictated by local climatic conditions, plant varieties and seasonal availability, and grazing methods. Variations in rotational grazing methods, agronomic practices, and irrigation can greatly improve pasture usage, carrying capacity (animal stocking density), and quality. Confinement or dry lot feeding systems primarily provide conserved forage (hay) and rely minimally on pasture. Confinement systems require decisions relative to forage type fed, forage harvesting or purchase practices, storing capacity, and feeding mechanisms. Successful feeding systems can vary from 100 percent pasture to 100 percent hay and all variations in between.[10] To meet any potential nutrient deficiencies, various types of supplements may be added to any of these feeding systems.

South America All llamas and more than 80 percent of alpacas are agriculturally managed in four countries: Peru, Bolivia, Argentina, and Chile.[113] An extensive pastoral feeding system based on native forages is the traditional management approach in South America.[13,104,113] No supplements and rarely conserved hay are fed due to associated costs, availability, or traditional practices.[42,113] Available Andean grassland ecosystems—altiplano, pajonales, and bofedales—are traditionally used for pasture. The Andean high plains (puna) are located at elevations exceeding 4,000 meters (>13,000 feet) and are characterized by cool temperatures, intense solar radiation, and seasonally intermittent rainfall.[13,104,113] Diurnal ambient temperatures range from 65°F (18°C) to 10°F (−12°C) with more than 300 days of frost.[42,113] Annual rainfall in this region varies between 10 and 100 centimeters (3.9 and 39.4 in.), 75 percent of which comes between December and March, establishing a defined wet and dry seasonal pattern.[42,46,104,113]

Seasonal growth and quality of forage is determined by this precipitation pattern. During the wet season, plant growth is rapid and of high quality but extremely limited in length (3 to 4 months). In contrast, growing conditions for a majority of the year are associated with minimal precipitation and minimal plant growth. Availability of forage is extremely limited during the dry season, and what is available is very mature and of low quality (see Table 9.18).[42,46,104,111,113] Altiplano and pajonales regions are characterized by a diversity of vegetation, but dominated by coarse bunchgrasses.[104,113] Bofedales ("perennial green") are high altitudinal, naturally occurring wet areas with a tremendous variety of plants, predominately sedges, reeds, forbs, and small grasses.[104,113] With these two diametrically opposed growing seasons, llamas and alpacas are exposed to an abundance of high-quality forages during the wet season, but then must endure and survive through the prolonged dry season of minimal low-quality forages. Their capacity for selective feeding and ability to utilize lower-quality forages more efficiently allow llamas and alpacas to survive and flourish under seemingly harsh conditions.

Alpacas will graze tall grasses, forbs, and leaves during the wet season. During the dry season, short grasses (68%), forbs (8–29%), and grass seeds (up to 20%) will be consumed.[13,60,104,105,110,111,113] In bofedale regions, grasslike plants, sedges, and reeds will dominate (78%) the diet.[104,105] Bunchgrasses account for 48 to 75 percent of llama diets throughout the year.[46] Other soft grasses account for an additional 10 to 30 percent and shrubs only greater than 10 percent of the diet during the wet season.[46] In deference to the low-quality forages dominating during the prolonged dry season, llamas and alpacas, through their selective feeding behavior, were able to maintain diets between 9 and 10 percent crude protein across seasons.[111,113] Alpacas in southern Peru consumed diets consisting mostly of bunchgrasses ranging from 5.7 to 20.8 percent crude protein and 64 to 67 percent digestibility during the dry season (May to November).[60] Dietary analysis of diets consumed at bofedale and altiplano sites showed lowest crude protein (7.5% and 6%, respectively) during the dry season (July and August) and highest (16% and 15.5%, respectively) during the wet season (January and February).[104]

Body weight and condition score changes mimic seasonal forage growth patterns. Llamas and alpacas gain significant body weight and condition and give birth during the wet season in concert with high-quality forage availability. During the dry season, animals lose considerable weight and condition and are in various stages of malnutrition.[79] Survivability and productivity depend upon body reserves from the previous wet season. As a consequence of this "feast-and-famine" seasonal cycle, reproductive rates are low (40–60%), suckling crias have high mortality rates (30%), and growing animals have low body weight gains.[79] As a consequence of this feeding situation, animal obesity is scarcely a problem, but animal productivity is severely compromised.

North America In comparison to South America, llamas and alpacas raised in North America are exposed to a greater diversity of environmental conditions, ranging from extreme hot and humid environments (southern United States) to extremely cold winter conditions (north-

Two types of forage: orchardgrass (left) and alfalfa (right). Knowing the strengths and weaknesses of available hays and their nutritional content is fundamental to providing the best possible diet.

ern United States, Canada, and Alaska). The average winter daily temperature in northern North America falls below −15°C (5°F) and may decline to −35°C (−31°F).[14] These are environmental extremes llamas and alpacas never experience in their native environment. Hot and humid environments bring challenges of preventing heat stress, a significant health risk for llamas and alpacas. Cold, wet conditions also have challenges associated with providing effective protective shelter and increased energy intake to compensate for additional maintenance requirements.

Unlike the situation in South America, feeding management schemes for North America span the entire spectrum of possibilities: intensive or extensive, pasture or confinement, and all combinations. Along with the diversity of environments and feeding management schemes, North American systems have forage challenges to address. At first instance, one might argue that North American forages are of higher quality compared to South America, but reviewing data in Tables 9.18 through 9.20, one sees much similarity in range of forage quality from low to high. The significant difference is availability of low- or high-quality forages year-round. South American camelids must contend with nine months of low forage availability combined with declining quality. In contrast, North American llamas and alpacas can potentially receive high- or low-quality forages throughout the year, with availability only constrained by sporadic regional drought conditions. As a result, feed-related problems range the full spectrum from potential malnutrition to obesity, with a tendency toward greater incidence of obesity.[42,63] A low-quality forage at the wrong time can result in some devastating animal health problems, even deaths. Obesity is also not a healthy condition for animals.

The issue here is not necessarily a direct comparison of nutrient content of forages between North and South America and resultant complacency about feeding programs, but adequately providing needed nutrients to maintain the high productivity and health of the animals. Most managers in North America would not accept the observed low reproductive and high mortality rates noted for South America. Availability of quality forages year-round and supplement use allow for improved reproduction, growth rate, and animal health performance.

The Advantage of Blending Forages

Often the question of forage type is asked relative to feeding llamas and alpacas. Is alfalfa better than grass or vice versa? There really is no simple answer. Alfalfa hay has received much negative press relative to feeding camelids, often associated with causing obesity or perceptions of detrimental effects from high calcium intake. For reasons previously described regarding anatomical differences between legume and grass plants coupled with the llama's and alpaca's keen ability to select high-quality plant components, one can understand the potential overeating concerns with alfalfa. However, unless grass is effectively managed to maintain a moderate to high-quality product, it too can be just as deleterious.

As we relate the forage to meeting the nutrient needs of the animal, moderate-quality grasses can easily meet energy (48–53% TDN) and protein (8–10%) needs of the maintenance animal, except in unusual cases. Most alfalfa hays will greatly exceed the protein, calcium, and energy needs of the animal. However, most nonmature pastures will maintain a protein level that meets or exceeds the protein content of alfalfa hay (see Table 9.20). Grasses, especially the mature ones, will have difficulty in being able to meet the energy or protein needs of the lactating or late pregnant animal without the addition of supplements. In most instances, a blend of alfalfa and grass hay may best match the nutrient requirements of the animal without supplementation. How can one decide on how much of each to feed?

The Pearson square can be used in this situation to help design forage mixtures to meet desired needs. In the example presented (Figure 9.6), mature grass hay is blended with alfalfa hay to achieve a diet with sufficient energy and protein to support a pregnant alpaca. Completing the calculations shows that a diet consisting of 80 percent grass hay and 20 percent alfalfa hay would meet these needs. An advantage of using forage blends is the tremendous flexibility it provides a feeding program. Lower-quality forages can be fed exclusively to maintenance and obese animals. One can then add appropriate amounts of alfalfa or other legume forage to modify dietary energy and

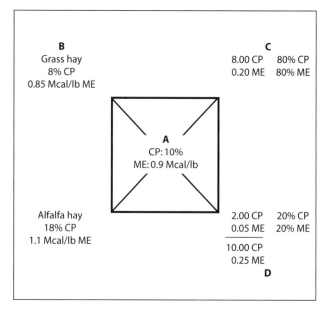

Figure 9.6 Use of a Pearson square to formulate diets for energy and protein.

See Figure 9.5 for a description of how to use a Pearson square. Here, feeding a diet of 80 percent grass hay and 20 percent alfalfa hay would meet the desired density of dietary energy and protein.

protein content for other higher-requirement feeding groups. Forage blends also allow for some individual animal selectivity, which may be good or bad. Another advantage to this system is the ability to transition animals from one diet to another without abrupt dietary changes. One can also substitute a pellet supplement in place of the alfalfa hay to determine the appropriate blend of grass hay and pellet to meet defined dietary nutrient content. The Pearson square can be a very useful tool in formulating or evaluating diets with various supplements.

Feeding Management Practices

Feeding animals to their specific nutritional needs is the primary objective of any feeding program. Individual hand feeding best accomplishes this objective, but is labor intensive and impractical in large herds. Given the alpaca's social behavioral hierarchy, individual animals would need to be tethered while eating to ensure that each animal ate its intended diet. Grouping animals with similar nutritional requirements is a reasonable compromise.[11] With animal grouping strategies, specific nutrient needs can be targeted and feed resources appropriately allocated. Group feeding programs need to account for social hierarchy and provide sufficient feeders to allow all animals equal feed access. A feeding program should have the capability to segregate different animal groups in order to meet their specific nutrient needs (see Table 9.28). Most operations would not

Table 9.28 Suggested feeding groups based on physiologic state and nutrient requirements.[1]

Group	Physiologic State	Feeding Plan	Dietary Guidelines[2]
Nursing dams with crias	Lactation	Highest nutrient requirements, feed best-quality forages, with energy/protein supplements	60–70% TDN, 12–14% crude protein, 0.45–0.62% Ca, 0.32–0.45% P[3]
Weanlings up to 1½ years	Growth	Highest nutrient requirements, feed best-quality forages, with energy/protein supplements	55–65% TDN, 14–16% crude protein, 0.53–0.73% Ca, 0.27–0.38% P[3]
Males over 1 year	Maintenance	Low requirements unless working, then adjust accordingly, low-to-moderate quality forage	55–60% TDN, 8–10% crude protein, 0.3–0.48% Ca, 0.21–0.28% P[3]
Pregnant females 1–8 months	Maintenance	Low requirements, but ensure no loss of body condition, adequate protein, minerals, and vitamins	50–55% TDN, 8–10% crude protein, 0.2–0.24% Ca, 0.12–0.2% P
Pregnant females 9–11 months	Pregnancy	Moderate to high forage quality with supplement for additional mineral and vitamin needs	55–70% TDN, 10–12% crude protein, 0.45–0.56% Ca, 0.28–0.33% P[3,4]
Breeding females	Maintenance	Low to moderate; ensure do not become fat or lose condition	50–55% TDN, 8–10% crude protein, 0.2–0.24% Ca, 0.12–0.2% P
Obese females	Submaintenance	Low; low-quality forages with mineral/vitamin supplement unless pregnant	40–50% TDN, 8–9% crude protein, 0.2–0.24% Ca, 0.12–0.2% P

[1]More precise dietary needs will be determined by level of production (milk, rate of growth), environmental conditions, and desired changes in body condition.
[2]Ensure adequate available water and free choice of salt. White salt should be used when trace minerals are included in a supplement. Otherwise trace mineral salt should be available.
[3]These feeding groups require higher amounts of trace minerals and vitamins, preferably delivered by a supplement (refer to text for details).
[4]Dietary energy and crude protein content may need to be increased further in later pregnancy if dry matter intake drops below 1.5 percent of body weight.

have the capability to separate out this many groups; however, a number of these groups could be combined as a result of similar requirements. When group feeding, especially if similar nutritional groups are combined, one needs to be aware of the possibility of overfeeding one or more individuals and make appropriate adjustments.

Maintenance and Activity (Working) As there is no lean time similar to the dry season in South America, feeding programs for North America need to focus more closely on maintaining an appropriate level of intake without obesity, yet minimizing great fluctuations in energy balance because of their negative impact on reproduction and fleece growth. There is much individual variation in just what diet is necessary to maintain optimum body condition. Many animals can do quite well on low-quality forages with only mineral and vitamin supplementation. Some forage quality may be such that a small amount of protein might be necessary. In a pasture system, one may need to have the animals consume some low-quality forage before heading out to pasture to minimize their intake of higher-quality feeds. This effect may be accomplished by managing grazing intensity manipulations: more animals, smaller paddocks, longer grazing periods. However, one must be careful and remember the selective feeding behavior of alpacas. They may be obtaining a much higher quality of feed than you think possible, based on pasture quality, and by browsing available forbs, diet quality may be greatly increased.

With animals that are performing some level of activity, energy requirements will be increased proportional to the duration and activity level. Increasing energy in the diet can be achieved by improving the forage quality of-

fered or by offering a supplement. Small amounts of cereal grains or commercial pellets can be used. Commercial pellets may be preferred to cereal grains, as they also include some minerals. Muscular activity associated with work requires not only additional energy but also minerals that are lost in sweat.

Pregnancy A most desirable outcome from a pregnancy is to have a healthy, vigorous cria, no health complications with the dam, and successful rebreeding within 30 days. Nothing can be more frustrating for an owner after the long wait than to have something go wrong with the newborn cria, especially if the pregnancy was difficult to conceive. Research with cattle and sheep has shown pregnancy nutrition influences colostrum quality and quantity, milk yield and composition, neonate viability, and future fertility of the dam. Dietary issues of concern in meeting pregnancy requirements are maintaining adequate energy and protein intake and appropriate supplementation of minerals and fat-soluble vitamins. From a management standpoint, issues such as level of intake, forage quality, body condition monitoring, and environmental stressors must be considered.

There are no significant changes from maintenance for energy and protein requirements during the first eight months of pregnancy. Maintenance energy and protein (9% crude protein) will be sufficient. Feeding a moderate-quality forage or lower quality with a complete supplement should meet these needs. The goal of the dietary program during early pregnancy is to have the female in moderate body condition (score of 3–3.5) and maintain this score. Body weight should remain fairly stable or slightly increase (<2–5% increase). One should not attempt to force an overweight pregnant female to lose significant weight during pregnancy, as it may adversely affect birth weight or induce hepatic lipidosis in the female. Minerals and vitamins should be adequately supplemented, preferably by feeding a supplement at a fixed amount. A free-choice mineral is generally not sufficient in meeting mineral needs.

As the female progresses through the last three months of pregnancy, energy and protein needs will increase. Intake will at best remain stable or possibly be slightly reduced. Increased needs for energy and protein (10–12% crude protein) can be met by either adding an additional supplement to the diet or increasing to a higher-quality forage program. You do not want to make abrupt changes in diet, so it is better to add alfalfa or high-quality grass forage than to switch completely over to a different forage. The late-pregnancy diet should be similar to and allow a smooth dietary transition into the lactation diet. During these last three months, females should maintain slightly more than moderate body condition (3.25–3.75) for body reserves to support lactation. Body weight should increase 10 to 15 percent above prepregnancy weight to account for fetal and uterine growth.[118]

Mineral and vitamin intake should continue, as it is needed by the female and being deposited into the fetus to support its growth after birth. The newborn cria relies on mineral storage in the liver to maintain normal body functions while on a predominately milk diet. Consumption of solid food, containing minerals and vitamins to augment liver stores, usually does not occur until two months of age or later. If liver mineral reserves are exhausted, immune function will be compromised, resulting in increased disease susceptibility as well as decreased growth rate. If the pregnant female is not on pasture, then supplementation of vitamins A, D, and E are necessary. Very little of these fat-soluble vitamins crosses the placenta, but they are concentrated in colostrum, which is the primary source for the newborn cria. Injections of vitamins A, D, and E can be helpful in augmenting colostrum concentrations of these nutrients as well as preventing associated deficiency disorders. If necessary to give injectable supplements, best responses are obtained when given within the last four weeks of pregnancy. One must be careful to minimize stress to the pregnant female when giving such injections late in pregnancy. Appropriate daily dietary supplementation is the preferred method.

Lactation Nutritional management of the lactating female is focused on supporting milk production. During early lactation not only is the female pouring nutrients into the mammary gland for milk production, she also needs to repair the uterus and prepare the reproductive system to initiate another pregnancy cycle. The purpose of the lactation process is to generate sufficient quantities of milk to support cria growth and development. Nutritional requirements for lactation are a function of milk production and composition. Llama milk composition has been defined,[63,89] but the shape of the milk production curve has not. In most domestic species, milk production increases rapidly over the first four to six weeks, and then slowly declines until the time of weaning. If llamas and alpacas follow a similar production curve, then animals in early lactation are under tremendous nutritional challenge.

As with other species, dry matter intake declines to its lowest level on the day of parturition, then slowly increases with lactation. However, milk production and the outflow of nutrients greatly exceed the intake of nutrients due to low feed intake. This results in the lactating animal needing to mobilize body fat and other reserves to support milk production. As a consequence, lactating females lose body weight and condition. Dietary composition, feed intake, and level of milk production together determine the severity and duration of body weight and condition loss in early lactation. The lactating female has the highest nutrient requirements and should be fed the highest-quality forage, and may still require additional energy and protein supplementation to minimize body weight and condition loss. If a female loses too much body weight or condition, then milk production and reproductive ability may be compromised. Early embryonic death is often associated with animals in severe negative energy balance. Adequate mineral and vitamin supplementation must be maintained throughout lactation to replace nutrients lost in milk. Insufficient dietary calcium or phosphorus will decrease milk production, whereas if other trace minerals or vitamins are deficient, then their concentrations in milk will be decreased and thereby unavailable to the growing cria.

If a lactating female is losing too much weight in early lactation, then supplementing the cria with a creep feed may be necessary (see "Growth"). Weaning the cria can occur between four and six months, depending upon the cria's ability to consume solid feed and milk production by the dam. The body condition score should be closely monitored throughout lactation to ensure the diet is adequately meeting nutritional needs. Depending upon an individual's milk production curve, body weight and condition gain to replace reserves may occur in mid- to late lactation or following weaning. It is important to make sure females regain lost weight but do not gain additional weight and become fat.

Lack of milk production (agalactia) by the dam may also be a problem. Systemic disease, mammary disease, nutritional deficiencies, and feed toxins are potential causes. If body condition loss is not excessive (>0.75 score loss) and cria growth rate is reduced, then the lactating female should be evaluated. Certain varieties of fescue grass are infected with a mold (endophyte). This imparts better resistance characteristics to the grass, but a toxin is released (ergovaline). When consumed in late pregnancy, ergovaline can induce physiologic changes that reduce milk production.

Growth Nutritional management for growth can be divided into three critical phases: (1) colostrum feeding at the time of birth, (2) milk feeding up to weaning, and (3) postweaning growth. The first phase focuses on ensuring adequate passive protection and improved survivability. The second feeding phase accounts for the period of rapid growth and the preparation of the forestomach to adapt to solid feed intake. The final phase is a period of slowing growth and body structure maturation. Growth curves have been published for llamas, but not alpacas.[118] A mean (±15% variation) cumulative body weight and daily gain growth curve was generated for alpacas using llama data and scaled proportionally to alpaca body weights (see Figure 9.7).

Of first concern in managing the growing cria is the adequate ingestion of good-quality colostrum.[121] Crias should ingest all the colostrum a dam produces.[63] Colostrum intake guidelines for other species suggest an intake amount equivalent to 10 to 15 percent of birth weight. If the dam produces insufficient colostrum, cow or goat colostrum is a sufficient substitute.[121] Talk with your veterinarian about biosecurity concerns relative to Johne's disease in using cow or goat colostrum. Adequacy of colostrum intake can be assessed by measuring total protein 48 hours or more after birth or using test kits specifically measuring antibody concentrations.[28,139] In addition to colostrum intake, other nutritional issues of concern are vitamins A, D, and E and selenium, depending upon geographic region. Newborn crias are born nearly devoid of fat-soluble vitamins and rely on their ingestion from colostrum. If maternal nutrition was somewhat limited in these nutrients, usually seen when fed stored hay, then additional supplementation may be necessary. Selenium can be efficiently transported across the placenta, but if the dam did not receive sufficient selenium, the cria may be born with minimal liver reserves.

The nursing phase is associated with a period of rapid growth. Maternal milk production will essentially dictate daily gain through the early nursing phases. If a cria is unable to maintain expected rates of gain, then both dam and cria should be evaluated. Insufficient milk production by the dam will require use of a milk replacer, possibly with creep feeding of the cria to maintain expected growth rates. Milk replacers formulated for calves or kids have been used successfully in crias.[121] Since the forestomach fermentation system is not yet developed to assimilate forage, highly digestible creep feed should be fed. Carbo-

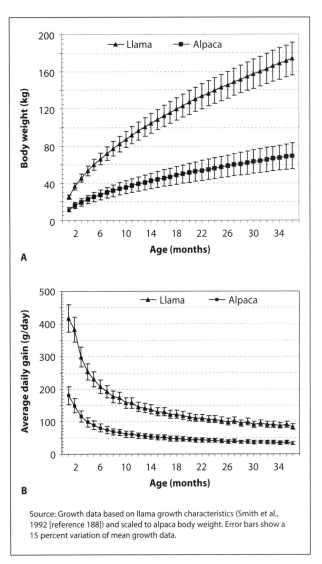

Source: Growth data based on llama growth characteristics (Smith et al., 1992 [reference 188]) and scaled to alpaca body weight. Error bars show a 15 percent variation of mean growth data.

Figure 9.7 Predicted cumulative body weight (A) and average daily gain (B) for alpacas from 1 to 36 months.

hydrate sources should be extruded, flaked, or similarly processed to increase starch digestibility. Protein sources should be highly digestible—either milk proteins, processed soybean, or alfalfa meal—and contain 18 to 20 percent crude protein. Most commercial creep feeds for calves, lambs, or kids would be appropriate. Crias will begin to nibble at dry forage within the first week of life. Weaning usually occurs between four and six months of age. Crias to be weaned should be consistently eating more than 2 pounds (1 kg) of feed per day.

Even though forestomach fermentation end-product concentrations are similar to adult values at 12 weeks of age, this does not mean the weanling can be placed on typically adult diets. High-quality forages are needed to support growth requirements and compensate for the lower efficiency of fiber fermentation. Nothing can set a recently weaned animal back more than a poor-quality diet. Dietary nutrient content and forage quality should be gradually decreased over the next 12 months to accommodate the lower rate of gains. Growth rate and body condition score should be regularly monitored throughout the postweaning growth phase to ensure dietary adequacy and prevent condition gain as the rate of gain slows.

Geriatric Alpacas A growing proportion of the alpaca population is becoming aged (12 or more years old). There is very little data on feeding aged ruminants, let alone any other domestic animal. Most information on managing aged animals has been derived from observation and personal experiences. A study of geriatric llamas and alpacas cited leg conformation, teeth, and low body weight as primary concerns.[124] For an animal to maintain durability, good leg conformation and absence of obesity are essential to minimize joint deterioration and subsequent arthritis problems.

In the geriatric study, 10 percent and 55 percent of animals were classified as emaciated (body score 1/5) and thin (body score 1.5–2.5/5), respectively.[124] The cause of low body condition in geriatric animals may be due to teeth problems, digestive or metabolic inefficiency, or some combination. Lactational drains in older animals may exacerbate these problems. A reduction in an older animal's social status may decrease her ability to consume sufficient feed. Excessive molar wear, wave patterns, or other occlusal surface abnormalities or tooth abscesses all lead to inefficient food mastication, limiting the digestive extraction of nutrients. Damage to the digestive tract lining as a result of chronic parasitism may also result in weight loss. An unknown factor is whether or not there are changes in the body's ability to effectively maintain normal tissue structure and function. The digestive tract is a metabolically active tissue with cells being lost and replaced on a daily basis. If an animal's ability to replace cells and other structural components diminishes with age, then one can expect a decline in digestive efficiency with resultant decline in body weight.

Few data have been reported on dietary support for the aged animal. A single report working with older horses suggests an increase in dietary protein and phosphorus content as well as utilization of more highly processed, digestible feeds.[103] The concept of increasing protein fits well with the hypothesized decline in body repair efficiency. For aged llamas and alpacas, increasing dietary protein 1 to 3 percentage units above what would be recommended for a given physiologic state might be appropriate. Additionally, one might increase the energy content of the diet and use more fermentable fiber sources, and minimize coarse, ma-

ture forage. Commercial pellets containing wheat bran, soyhulls, beet pulp, citrus pulp, distiller grains, or similar forage by-products would be appropriate. Although higher fiber seems contradictory, one must remember that forestomach microbes are not declining in efficiency and they will still make high-quality nutrients for the animal. However, for the microbes to digest forage, they must be reduced in particle size, which is normally done by chewing. Feeding ingredients with reduced particle size, yet readily fermentable, will help to maintain good nutrient outflow from the forestomach. These dietary changes must accompany a regimen of monitoring body condition, teeth wear, and parasite load. Aged animals may be less efficient in maintaining body temperature, therefore needing additional shelter or coat to protect from cold weather.

EVALUATING AND MONITORING NUTRITIONAL STATUS

Given the seemingly overwhelming details provided on nutritional requirements, feeds, and feeding management, how does one simply determine if a nutritional program is working? It must be remembered that we are working with biologic systems that do not always respond in a predictive manner. Also, as previously described, many outside factors, most importantly environmental, can influence an animal's response to diet. An obvious measure of nutritional adequacy is good animal health and performance. In general an animal with a bright and alert attitude and smooth, shiny appearance is considered healthy. However, alpacas are stoic and their fiber coat can hide many changes. The first rule to remember in nutritional management is: *Never fix anything that is not broken!* Unfortunately, fixing things after they become broken is not the best approach either. Owners working with their veterinarian should establish some routine monitoring process for their nutritional program.

Body Condition Scoring

By far the single best method of evaluating your nutritional program is body condition scoring. Body condition scoring is a method that subjectively grades animals by the amount of subcutaneous fat stores into defined "fatness" categories. A body condition scoring system for llamas and alpacas ranking from 1 (emaciated) to 10 (obese) has been described.[56,63] However, body condition scoring systems validated for other species rank from 1 (emaciated) to 5 (obese) with 0.5 scores, equivalent to a 1 (emaciated) to 9 (obese) scoring system.[14,31,108] A five-point system covering physical states of emaciated (1), thin (2), average (3), fat (4), and obese (5) is shown in Figure 9.8. Using a scaling system consistent with other species allows one to follow established body condition recommendations through

Score	Description of Animal	Frontal Profile	Rear Profile	Spinous to Transverse Process	Paralumbar Fossa
1.0 *Emaciated*	No visible or palpable fat or muscle between skin and bones. Ribs, dorsal spinous and transverse processes, and pelvic bones are individually prominent. Extreme loss of muscle mass.	Prominent "V" keel	Acutely inverted "V"	 Deep depression	Gaunt, tucked-in fossa
1.5 *Poor*		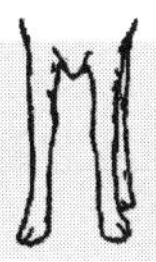	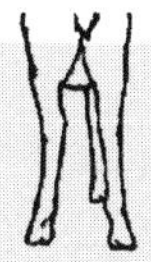		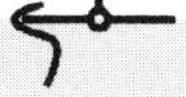
2.0 *Thin*	Slight cover over bony structure. Ribs, spinous processes still visible and easily palpated as sharp. Less muscle mass loss.	Gradual flattening of sternum	Gradual filling of "V"	Obvious depression	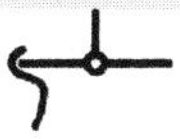 Prominent shelf
2.5 *Borderline*				 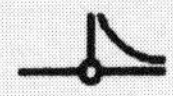	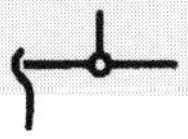
3.0 *Moderate*	Overall smooth appearance. Slight fat cover over ribs and other bony processes. Ribs and spinous processes can be palpated with slight pressure. No muscle mass loss present.	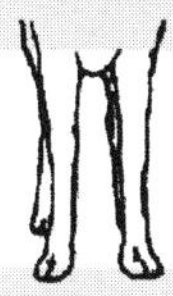 Moderate fat	 Moderate fat	Smooth, concave curve	Slight shelf
3.5 *High moderate*				 Smooth slope	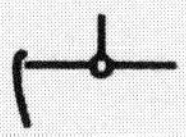
4.0 *Excess*	Fleshy appearance with visible coverage of fat. Moderate to firm pressure necessary to palpate bony structures under skin.				No shelf 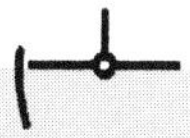
4.5 *Fat*		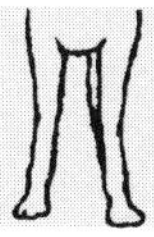		Nearly flat	Edge barely discernible
5.0 *Grossly obese*	Excessive fat cover over entire body with smooth, rounded appearance. Bony prominences cannot be palpated, even with firm pressure. Bulging fat pads visible around tailhead.	Sternum bulging in fat	Inguinal area bulging in fat	 Rounded	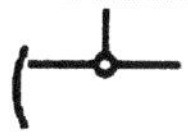 Buried in fat

Sources: Adapted from Edmonson et al., 1989 (reference 31); Hilton et al., 1998 (reference 56); and Russel, 1991 (reference 108.)

Figure 9.8 Body condition scoring sheet for alpacas.

the life cycle. An underlying hypothesis, which needs to be validated, is that fat deposition and mobilization from internal and subcutaneous storage occurs in a similar fashion in llamas and alpacas as in all other species. At present there are no data to suggest any such differences.

As with sheep, to properly score the body condition of a llama or alpaca, one needs to palpate through the fiber coat to feel the ribs, shoulder, loin, and pelvis for thickness of fat cover. Additionally, one should visualize the degree of fatness in the brisket (chest) and inguinal areas. As animals lose fat, these areas become more pronounced and angular, whereas with fat deposition, they become smooth and rounded. The ideal body condition is 3.0, having a

moderate amount of body fat. Although some individuals will maintain lower or higher body condition scores and remain healthy, this is just inherent individual differences in metabolism. Body condition scores 2.0 and below or 4.0 and above are considered abnormal and represent extremely thin or fat animals. Most animals other than those in late pregnancy or lactation should maintain a body condition score between 2.5 and 3.25. Late-pregnant animals should have a slightly higher body condition (3.25–3.5) to have reserves to support impending lactation. Lactating animals will lose body condition rapidly as they produce milk. Lactating animals should not lose more than 0.5 to 0.75 condition scores. A loss in body condition implies that consumed intake of feed is deficient in energy, protein, or both. Important times to assess a body condition score are during early to mid-pregnancy, early to mid-lactation, and periodically (4 to 6 times per year) comparing with other animals of the herd to assess energy status.[56] As a diagnostic tool, body condition scoring is the least expensive and yields excellent information relative to animal energy balance. However, body condition scoring is often overlooked as a herd management tool because it is viewed as being too time-consuming.

Forage Testing

The importance of forage quality to a nutrition program cannot be overemphasized. Visual and chemical measures of forage quality were described (see "Feed Analysis," "Analytical Procedures," and "Forage Quality") and summarized (see Table 9.22). Briefly, forage quality is best tested with chemical measures of moisture, crude protein, and neutral and acid detergent fiber. Visual assessment is based on identifying properties of maturity (i.e., stem thickness, flowers, seed heads), leaf-to-stem ratio, and foreign object presence. In addition to the chemical measures for quality, one should have macro- and micromineral content determined. This would allow one to best determine the need for additional supplements and evaluate which supplements best match their forage. A similar testing battery can be completed on supplements to determine specific nutrient content and critically evaluate their appropriateness (see "Evaluating Supplement Adequacy").

To obtain usable information from feed testing reports, one must submit a representative sample of feed to an accredited feed testing laboratory. Feed laboratories in your area can be found through the National Forage Testing Association (www.foragetesting.org). To best sample hay, one should use some form of coring device (Penn State Forage Sampler, Nasco catalog, www.enasco.com/prod/home). This instrument is a long, hollow, metal tube with a sharpened edge and attaches to a hand or electric drill. Extensions are available to drill to the center of large round or square bales. You should obtain a core sample from 10 to 20 percent of the bales. Combine all core samples into a clean, dry pail and mix thoroughly. This sample can then be packaged into an airtight plastic bag and submitted to the laboratory. Be sure to properly identify the sample. Separate samples should be taken from each field and cutting for best information. If you purchase hay, you should test each purchased lot.

Obtaining representative pasture or browse samples is much more difficult. The goal is to mimic the selective feeding behavior of the animals in obtaining a sample. For pastures a ring is tossed randomly around the pasture and clippings are obtained. Be sure not to clip too far down the

An alpaca consumes pellets designed to supplement hay that is deficient in key minerals. The contents of pellet supplements vary greatly from one manufacturer to the next. Knowing the nutritional nature of both hay and supplement is necessary to formulate an optimum diet. Alpacas in South America are not fed supplements.

plant. Animals generally do not eat down to the dirt, and if you contaminate the sample with dirt, this will affect your mineral content values. For browse you will have to watch what animals eat and selectively harvest similar feeds. Once you have collected sufficient material to submit, place in an airtight plastic bag and freeze the sample. High-moisture samples like those from pasture and browse should be sent to the laboratory frozen.

Feed testing results will be in the form of a report listing nutrient content for the given sample. Generally laboratories will report nutrient content on an as-fed (wet weight) basis and a dry matter (water excluded) basis. Dry matter nutrient content will always be the larger number, as it represents the amount of nutrient in the sample without the water weight. In comparing nutrient content across feeds, one should use only dry matter values, as feeds vary tremendously in their moisture content. One can compare the nutrient content of commercial supplements on an as-fed basis since most products contain between 8 and 12 percent moisture. Interpretation of results for a specific feed will depend upon that type of feed. For forages, Table 9.17 can be used to assess quality and Tables 9.19 and 9.20 to assess overall nutrient content in comparison to average values (dry matter values). To assess your supplement or mineral product, Tables 9.23

and 9.24 can used for comparison (as-fed values). Additional information about forage testing can be obtained from agronomy specialists with agricultural universities or extension personnel.

Blood Metabolite Analysis

Besides evaluating an animal's physical attributes relative to health and disease, analysis of blood is often used to determine presence of disease. Many studies have established normal blood chemistry parameters for llamas and alpacas.[36,77] The intent of these parameters is to determine normality or abnormality relative to specific physiologic functions. It is well known that nutrition can influence many physiologic and metabolic body functions. As such, a number of blood parameters can be used within a defined framework for evaluating nutritional status. Blood metabolite analysis in unhealthy animals is best used to help in disease diagnosis. To best assess nutritional status using blood metabolites, one should sample only healthy animals so as not to have confounding effects of disease on blood parameters. It should be stated that blood analysis without appropriate body condition scoring, animal examinations, and feed evaluations is not an appropriate way to assess nutritional status.

Energy Besides the body condition score, blood concentrations of nonesterified fatty acids (NEFA) and β-hydroxybutyrate (BOHB) reflect energy balance. Mobilization of body fat, a consequence of deficient energy intake, is directly measured by blood NEFA concentration. If the energy balance is severely deficient, excessive amounts of fat are mobilized, greatly increasing NEFA concentration. Elevated NEFA concentration can be related to the disease hepatic lipidosis (see "Special Nutritional Problems"), a severe and often fatal metabolic disease. Blood NEFA concentrations are similar to those of other species.

Since NEFA (fatty acid) molecules can vary in length from 6 to over 26 carbons, the unit of measure for NEFA concentration in blood must be related to the presence of a NEFA molecule and not total molecular weight. The NEFA unit of measure is termed an "equivalent" (Eq), which accounts for the single acidic component of the molecule and is independent of molecule size. Blood NEFA concentration is then reported as mEq per liter (mEq/l). Another unit of measure used is molar concentration or moles of fatty acids per liter (M). Blood NEFA concentrations may also be reported as micromolar (μM), which is 1,000 times the mEq/l value. Values <0.3 mEq/l (300 μM) are considered at or near energy balance. Latepregnant and early lactation animals should have NEFA concentrations <0.4 mEq/l (<400 μM) and <0.6 mEq/l (<600 μM), respectively. Values in

Loose granular salt is offered in feed and water areas.

excess of 0.8 mEq/l (800 μM) would be considered a serious health threat.[126]

Another measure of energy balance is BOHB. Blood BOHB is elevated when blood glucose is low and fat mobilization is taking place. The liver is responsible for generating BOHB as a partial breakdown product (termed a ketone body) of fat. Elevation of BOHB is often associated with elevated NEFA. In contrast to other ruminants, camelids are not as prone to produce ketone bodies, but when elevated, they are significant indicators of nutritional problems. Values greater than 6 mg/dl would be of concern for negative energy balance, and BOHB concentrations exceeding 12 mg/dl are possibly indicative of hepatic lipidosis (see "Hepatic Lipidosis").[126]

Protein Similar to other ruminants, blood urea nitrogen along with total protein and albumin can be used to assess protein status. All values will be lower than normal in the face of dietary protein deficiency. Total protein and albumin will decline only after a prolonged (>1 month) dietary protein deficiency. Blood urea nitrogen will respond fairly quickly to dietary protein changes. Values consistently below 12 mg/dl are suggestive of dietary protein deficiency. Excess dietary protein would be suggestive, without other evidence of kidney disease, when blood urea nitrogen concentrations exceed 35 mg/dl. More data are needed to better refine these criteria based on a better understanding of camelid protein metabolism.

Minerals and Vitamins A number of studies have measured various blood mineral and vitamin concentrations in normal llamas and alpacas in an effort to establish some diagnostic criteria.[8,26,36,54,120] Macrominerals that are homoeostatically regulated, i.e., calcium, sodium, and to some extent phosphorus and potassium, will not show dramatic changes in their blood concentrations over a wide range of dietary situations. This then makes them poor indicators of metabolic status, unless the homeostatic mechanism is deranged. Blood magnesium concentration is fairly representative of dietary intake, although urinary magnesium may be a better indicator.

For trace minerals, whole blood or serum concentrations are buffered from acute changes as a result of dietary problems through the mobilization of storage minerals, usually from the liver. This suggests that liver trace mineral status may be a better indicator of dietary adequacy. Limited studies have addressed camelid liver mineral status.[66,82] Many trace mineral concentrations in blood are influenced by disease. Bacterial infections induce sequestering of iron and zinc and elevation of copper. This could certainly confound interpretation of blood mineral status. Fat-soluble vitamins can be easily assessed via serum or liver concentrations. Again, liver concentrations would reflect a storage pool. Besides diet and disease, blood mineral and vitamin concentrations are influenced by age and physiologic state.[120] Blood mineral and vitamin concentrations can yield some very useful information relative to nutritional status, but the information must be carefully interpreted relative to dietary information and other influencing factors.

SPECIAL NUTRITIONAL PROBLEMS

Llamas and alpacas seemingly respond to nutrient deficiencies and toxicities in a similar manner as other species. Nutritional and metabolic diseases of llamas and alpacas have been reviewed.[39,42,134]

Starvation

Starvation is defined as a prolonged complete deprivation of feed intake. Fortunately, true starvation cases are the exception rather than the rule. More typically encountered is a situation of protein-energy malnutrition (PEM) in which energy, protein, or both are deficient in the diet over a period of time. Body weight loss and a decline in body condition score are the most common clinical signs of the disease.[14,99] Growing animals will also show a slowing or nearly complete cessation in gain. Pregnant and lactating females experiencing PEM may be prone to hepatic lipidosis.[125] Time frame and severity of body weight and condition loss will depend upon the degree of dietary energy and protein deficiency. Animals found early in the disease process can be recovered with appropriate feeding therapy and supportive care; however, those becoming weak and recumbent have a very poor prognosis even with aggressive therapy.[99]

Due to their higher requirements, young growing animals, late-pregnant females, and lactating females are the first ones to show signs.[99] Beyond physiologic state and its impact on increasing requirements, environmental conditions, especially extreme cold, will tremendously increase energy needs. Animals raised in the northern regions of North America are exposed to environmental temperatures much lower than their native habitat. In these cold conditions, animals will need to expend additional energy to maintain body temperature. Based on data for other species, maintenance energy is increased 1 percent for every 1°C (1.8°F) below an animal's lower critical temperature.[94] Based on data from sheep and assuming a full fleece, the lower critical temperature for llamas and alpacas would be approximately 0 to 10°C (32–50°F).[94] If animals are wet, mud covered, or exposed to wind chill, then maintenance energy may be increased as much as 75 percent. Clearly, PEM is a potential risk for llamas and alpacas raised in extreme northern climates.[14]

Routine body condition scoring or body weight estimates can be used to diagnose potential problems. A thick fleece can readily hide body weight and condition changes from view, thus requiring a hands-on condition score or body weight measure. Once unexplained body weight or condition score loss has been identified, one needs to determine a cause. Chronic infectious, parasitic, and dental diseases can induce body weight and condition losses similar to PEM.[14,99] However, most animals afflicted with an infectious or parasitic disease have reduced appetites, in spite of their energy deficit. In contrast, PEM animals maintain a healthy appetite until near the terminal stages. Protein-energy malnutrition is often a secondary after-effect to chronic (long-standing) disease conditions. Work with your veterinarian in having the animal undergo a thorough physical examination and laboratory testing to determine a possible diagnosis.

The most common reason for PEM is poor-quality forages coupled with the animal's inability to consume enough to meet needs.[14,99] As previously described, the neutral detergent fiber of forage is the limiting factor to intake. Llamas and alpacas experience varying degrees of PEM in South America during the dry season where both forage quality and availability are limiting. Animals giving birth during the dry season are much more prone to PEM and secondary infectious and parasitic disease problems, often leading to their demise. Prevention of PEM is based on appropriate feeding regimes where forage quality is matched to the nutrient needs of the animal. Where forage quality is insufficient, providing supplemental feeds is necessary. To achieve such feeding programs, forage quality needs to be evaluated by chemical analysis. Routine assessment of energy status by body weight or condition scoring is a recommended practice, especially for those animals with higher energy requirements and prior to and during the cold weather season.

Obesity

In contrast to the nutritional situation of PEM, obesity is the complete opposite. Like any other domesticated animal or human, intake of dietary energy (carbohydrate, fat, or protein) in excess of requirement will result in fat deposition. If excess energy intake occurs over time, obesity will result. With the seasonal fluctuations in available forages in South America, obesity is not a problem. Obesity is considered one of the more prevalent nutritional problems in North American llamas and alpacas.[42,63] Feeding too high a quality forage relative to requirements, as well as overfeeding additional supplements, are the primary causes of obesity. Many supplements are touted as low-energy feeds ("lite" products), but fiber can be readily fermented to available energy sources. Deleterious effects of obesity include greater susceptibility to heat stress, metabolic derangements, infertility, and associated locomotive problems.

To prevent obesity one has two options: Either increase energy expenditure or reduce energy intake. An animal's energy requirement is primarily a function of lean body weight (3.0 condition score weight) and physiologic state (maintenance, growth, pregnancy, lactation). Packing and other activities will increase energy expenditure, but this is not always a viable option. Reducing energy intake is the obvious approach. Energy-dense supplements should be limited. Forage intake, quality, or both need to be reduced for obese animals. Feed lower-quality forages exclusively or prior to grazing to minimize pasture intake. Segregate obese animals so they cannot "steal" food from others. Increase stocking density or grazing intensity to reduce intake. Graze obese animals only on mature pastures. There is much individual animal variation in the propensity for obesity. Therefore, owners must routinely assess body weight or condition score in a process of achieving the appropriate nutritional balance to maintain an optimum condition for a given animal.

Forestomach Acidosis

Ruminal acidosis can be seen in any ruminant animal inadvertently exposed to excessive amounts of fermentable carbohydrates (sugars and starches) in a single large meal. Dietary sugars and starches can be readily fermented to

another VFA, lactic acid. Normally lactic acid is consumed by specific bacterial populations that convert it to propionate (glucose precursor). However, if excessive amounts of lactic acid are rapidly generated, forestomach pH will drop, inhibiting many bacterial populations. If the pH drop is sufficiently severe (<5.0), a potentially life-threatening condition of acidosis can occur similar to that of ruminants.[18] Affected animals will be dehydrated, lethargic, and depressed. Forestomach motility will be reduced and diarrhea may be present. This condition is an emergency situation requiring proper diagnosis and treatment by a veterinarian. Camelids are not generally prone to this problem as a result of their feeding behavior and forestomach buffering capacity.

Since this problem is sporadic and often associated with accidental exposure to grain storage bins, prevention mainly revolves around maintaining animal-safe storage facilities. Inappropriate feeding programs (excessive grain feeding) and aggressive feeding behaviors may increase potential risk. If group feeding, be sure all animals have equal opportunity to consume the offered grain. Oftentimes one or two dominant animals may preferentially consume a substantial portion. Gradually change grain products, as differences in ingredient composition and grain processing can greatly affect the forestomach fermentation rate. Products containing mostly processed barley and corn grain have the highest potential risk of inducing acidosis in an inappropriate feeding situation.

Hepatic Lipidosis (Fatty Liver Disease)

Hepatic lipidosis is a well-known syndrome in periparturient dairy cattle and sheep, and in anorexic cats, and a sporadic problem with fat horses and ponies. There are limited reports of hepatic lipidosis in llamas and alpacas in the literature;[3,17,65,125] however, producer groups and practicing veterinarians have an increased interest in the pathogenesis of this disease process. Camelids of a variety of ages, gender, body condition, and reproductive status are susceptible to the development of hepatic lipidosis. Conditions that place increased energy demands, such as pregnancy and lactation, contribute to hepatic lipidosis. Social and environmental stresses or other illness appear to also predispose camelids to loss of appetite, weight loss, and accumulation of fat in the liver (see Chapter 21: Noninfectious Multisystemic Diseases).[125]

A retrospective study of 31 histologically confirmed cases of hepatic lipidosis in llamas and alpacas revealed a predominately middle-aged, pregnant,or lactating female population to be affected.[125] However 22.6 percent of the cases were male and ages ranged from 5 months to 18 years. These demographics of affected animals are very different compared to hepatic lipidosis in other ruminants. In these cases there was no significant association with any infectious, parasitic, or toxic causative agent. The most common factor documented in histories from these camelids was recent severe loss of appetite or weight loss. This period of not eating or weight loss varied from a couple of days to several weeks. Overweight, normal body condition, and thin animals were all represented in the affected group. Biochemical measures associated with negative energy balance (NEFA), liver dysfunction (bile acids), and muscle damage were consistently elevated. Lipemia (high blood fat content) and ketonemia (high blood ketone body content) were not consistently associated with hepatic lipidosis in this retrospective study population compared to other literature reports.[3,17,65] These data suggest similarities in the pathogenesis of hepatic lipidosis in camelids to other species and not just ruminants. A common theme in most cases of hepatic lipidosis in camelids is a period of low feed intake (anorexia) prior to clinical signs.

In a study where lactating and nonlactating llamas were feed restricted, in an effort to model the disease process, approximately 50 percent developed hepatic lipidosis.[126] All llamas lost large amounts of body weight; however, no animals became depressed or recumbent. Blood tests showed the expected increases in liver enzymes—bile acids, gamma-glutamyl transferase (GGT), aspartate transaminase (AST), and sorbitol dehydrogenase (SDH)—in those that developed hepatic lipidosis, but not in those that simply lost weight. Affected animals also had higher BOHB and had NEFA concentrations above 1.0 mEq/l (1,000 µM). When affected llamas were returned to normal feed, weight increased, blood values gradually changed toward normal, and liver fatty infiltration, based on biopsies, disappeared. This is a significant finding showing that the condition is reversible when normal levels of nutrients and calories are consumed. This study has shown that it is difficult, but possible, to induce hepatic lipidosis in llamas by feed restriction, which suggests that loss of appetite alone may not be enough to cause this problem.

The key to preventing and treating this disease is increased understanding of the unique metabolic processes of camelids. Prevention is based on ensuring adequate energy and protein intake, especially in pregnant and lactating females, with good-quality forage and appropriate supplementation. Intensive supportive care and dietary management, including parenteral nutrition, must be used to treat severely affected animals.[132] Close monitoring of feed intake in sick animals is absolutely critical to prevent potential deaths.

Rickets and Bone Development

Abnormal bone growth is a common problem in young growing animals of all domestic species. Rickets is one such nutritionally related metabolic bone disease characterized by a failure of mineralization of the bone osteoid and cartilage matrix, resulting in visibly swollen joints and lameness.[131] If left untreated, long bones become deformed, leading to angular limb defects and proneness to fractures. Absolute or induced deficiencies of calcium, phosphorus, vitamin D, or some combination have been identified as causes of rickets. Absolute minimal daily amounts of all three nutrients are required; additionally, amounts of the three nutrients must be maintained within appropriate relative ratios to allow for normal mineral deposition in growing bone.

A rickets syndrome in three- to six-month-old llamas and alpacas has been described.[37,38,55,131] Affected crias show a slowed rate of growth, reluctance to move, a humped-back stance, and shifting leg lameness. On physical exam joints were enlarged, most obviously the carpus (knee). Hypophosphatemia (low blood phosphorus; <3 mg/dl) is the most consistent diagnostic finding besides radiographic bone changes.[37,38,131] A seasonal incidence has been recognized with this syndrome, most cases occurring during the winter months of December to March in northern latitudes of North America.[122,131]

Survey and supplementation trials suggest that this hypophosphatemic rickets syndrome of llamas and alpacas is a result of vitamin D deficiency.[131] Vitamin D is required not only to support bone mineralization, but also to facilitate intestinal absorption of phosphorus. Serum vitamin D and phosphorus concentrations show a seasonal pattern where lowest values occur during December to March and highest values during June to September in the Northern Hemisphere.[122] Vitamin D is naturally synthesized in nonpigmented areas of the skin upon exposure to sunlight. More darkly colored and heavily fleeced llamas and alpacas have lower vitamin D concentrations, but shearing increases skin exposure, and subsequently, vitamin D concentration.[122] Intensity and angle of the sun at the most distant latitudes within the Northern or Southern Hemisphere may be insufficient during their respective winter months to maintain adequate vitamin D status without dietary supplementation. Seasonal variation in blood vitamin D concentrations has also been implicated with susceptibility of long bone fractures.[100]

Susceptibility of crias to this syndrome also seemingly has a seasonal component. Crias born in the fall and winter months have greater risk than those born at other times of the year. In the Northern Hemisphere, crias born between

A large alpaca herd bands together as it is moved from one pasture to the next.

March and August had significantly greater serum vitamin D concentrations through the first seven months of life compared to crias born between September and March.[122] Intuitively, fall-born crias never obtain vitamin D reserves from summer sunshine, compared to spring-born crias. Fall-born crias will have lowest concentrations of vitamin D and phosphorus during the period of rapid growth compared to spring-born crias. To ensure adequate vitamin D reserves to meet the challenge of rapid growth, crias born during periods of reduced day length should receive appropriate vitamin D supplementation.

Treatment and prevention of this syndrome can be accomplished with therapeutic or preventive vitamin D supplementation.[119,131] Vitamin D can be effectively supplemented by injection, oral dosing, or increasing dietary levels. Injections of vitamin D3 between 1,000 and 1,500 IU/kg body weight (455–680 IU/lb body weight) have been shown to maintain adequate serum vitamin D concentrations for up to three months.[67,119] Oral gels delivering vitamin D3 at 33,000 IU every two weeks or 100,000 IU once monthly have also been used successfully.[131] Both of these methods can be used to effectively treat an affected cria or used as a preventive measure. Recommendations for daily vitamin D intake year-round are presented in Table 9.14 (see "Vitamins" under "Animal Require-

ments"). Vitamin D is one of the more potentially toxic nutrients, and therefore, care must be taken in not exceeding recommendations with indiscriminate supplementation.

Urolithiasis

As a consequence of differences in genito-urinary anatomy, male llamas and alpacas are prone to blockage of the urethra, a tube emptying urine from the bladder to the outside.[48] Crystallized minerals (uroliths) are primarily responsible for urinary tract blockage, termed urolithiasis. Urolithiasis is a common problem encountered in male sheep, goats, and cattle. In most cases from these species, struvite (magnesium-ammonia-phosphate) crystals secondary to high grain feeding and low dietary calcium-to-phosphorus ratio are causing the blockage. Various calcium salts, phosphatic complexes, silica, and oxalates are all potential mineral sources causing uroliths.[48] Although not a common disorder in llamas and alpacas, silicate and struvite crystals have been reported.[72,73]

Clinical signs associated with urolithiasis depend upon the degree of blockage and severity of surrounding tissue reactions. If blockage is complete, retrograde pressure will build in the bladder to the point of rupture and subsequent death of the animal. Two reports of bladder rupture secondary to urethral blockage have been reported in a llama[81]

Vicuñas band together after being captured.

and alpaca,[27] although mineralized stones were not specifically identified in either animal. Incomplete blockage results in variable stages of difficult urination (stranguria), exaggerated and prolonged urination posture, urine dribbling, and blood-tinged urine.[48] Affected animals may be depressed and lethargic, grinding their teeth (bruxism) and showing signs of abdominal distention and pain. This disorder should be considered an emergency and a veterinarian contacted to complete a thorough evaluation to determine potential prognosis. The therapeutic approach will depend on the severity of the blockage, duration, and secondary complications.

Little is known about how urolithiasis occurs in llamas and alpacas and it is assumed that the disease process is similar to other ruminants.[48] Nutritional alterations are the primary concern and focus of prevention. Goals of a dietary prevention program are to increase water consumption with the addition of salt to the diet and to maintain appropriate amounts of calcium and phosphorus in the diet with a calcium-to-phosphorus ratio between 2:1 and 4:1.[48] Certain plants and mature western grasses may contain large amounts of oxalates and silicates, respectively, which can potentially contribute to urolith formation. Struvite crystals can be prevented by dietary modification to induce urine acidification. Traditionally, dietary supplementation (0.5–1% of dry matter) of ammonium chloride has been used. More palatable commercial products capable of acidification are available, as they are commonly used in dairy cattle rations prior to calving to prevent milk fever. However, little data are available, to validate the efficacy and safety of prolonged feeding of such products to llamas and alpacas.

Toxic Plants

Most common among toxic plants is the accidental exposure of llamas and alpacas to ornamental flowers and shrubs. Most grazing animals learn to avoid poisonous plants indigenous to their environment. Potential risk for consumption of poisonous plants occurs when little forage is available. Avoid placing animals, especially those being used for packing or other work, in a situation where their desire to eat compromises their plant discriminatory abilities. Specific plants toxic to llamas and alpacas are covered in detail in Chapter 23: Poisons.

SUMMARY

Nutrition of llamas and alpacas is not necessarily complicated, in spite of an overwhelming plethora of data, details, and calculations. The intent here was to provide readers with a strong foundation on which to make sound decisions, based on functional knowledge, relative to their feeding management approaches. The current state of knowledge on alpaca nutrition is limited, but many essential components are available. An attempt was made to consolidate available information, show application, and then challenge readers to think at a higher level. Although extrapolation from other species is of limited value, it does provide a sound starting point. Clearly more scientific information specific to these animals is needed. Given that the majority of the money needed to maintain an alpaca herd goes to nutrition, owners also need to be informed about various aspects of agronomy. Understanding the fundamentals of forage growth and its impact on composition is absolutely essential to making your nutrition program work. Distributing available forages to match quality with animal requirements will provide you the greatest return on investment through improved animal health and performance. The final phase is knowledge application—integrating issues of animal numbers, forage resources, and handling and feeding facilities into an economically sound nutrition program designed to maintain good animal health and meet your desired level of productivity. Again, alpaca nutrition does not have to be complicated, only as much as you need to meet your defined herd production goals.

REFERENCES

1. Abrams, S. M., J. S. Shenk, M. O. Westerhaus, and F. E. Barton: Determination of forage quality by near infrared reflectance spectroscopy: Efficiency of broad-based calibration equations. *Journal of Dairy Science* 70: 806–813, 1987.
2. Anonymous: The South American Camelids: Llamas, Alpacas, Guanacos, and Vicuñas 1967–2001. Bibliographic index, USDA National Agricultural Library, 2001 (Updated May 2002), www.nal.usda.gov/awic/pubs/llama.htm (Accessed August 2002).
3. Anderson, D. E., P. D. Constable, K. E. Yvorchuk, N. V. Anderson, G. St-Jean, and L. Rock: Hyperlipemia and ketonuria in an alpaca and a llama. *Journal of Veterinary Internal Medicine* 8: 207–211, 1994.
4. Andrews, A. H., and A. Cox: Suspected nutritional deficiency causing anemia in llamas (*Lama glama*). *Veterinary Record* 140: 153–154, 1997.
5. Bakker, M. L., I. J. Gordon, and J. A. Milne: Effects of sward structure on the diet selected by guanacos (*Lama guanicoe*) and sheep (*Ovis aries*) grazing a perennial ryegrass-dominated sward. *Grass and Forage Sci* 53: 19–30, 1998.
6. Barnes, R. F., D. A. Miller, and C. J. Nelson: *Forages, Volume 1: An Introduction to Grassland Agriculture,* 5th ed. Ames, Iowa: Iowa State University Press, 1995.
7. Barnes, R. F., D. A. Miller, and C. J. Nelson: *Forages, Volume 2: The Science of Grassland Agriculture,* 5th ed. Ames, Iowa: Iowa State University Press, 1995.
8. Bechert, U. S., and B. B. Smith: Serum macro and micro element concentrations in the llama. *Vet Clin Nutr* 3(4): 119–127, 1996.
9. Beharka, A. A., T. G. Nagaraja, J. L. Morril et al.: Effects of form of the diet on anatomical, microbial, and fermentative development of the rumen of neonatal calves. *Journal of Dairy Science* 81: 1,946–1,955, 1998.
10. Blalock, C.: Feeding & Nutrition. *Llamas* 7(4): 116, 1993.
11. Blalock, C.: Feeding & Nutrition (Part 2). *Llamas* 7(5): 43, 1993.
12. Brown, L.: *Grasses: An Identification Guide.* Boston: Houghton Mifflin Co., p. 240, 1979.
13. Bryant, F. C., and R. D. Farfan: Dry season forage selection by alpaca (*Lama pacos*) in southern Peru. *Journal of Range Management* 37(4): 330–333, 1984.
14. Carmalt, J. L.: Protein-energy malnutrition in alpacas. *Compendium for Continuing Education* 22(12): 1,118–1,124, 2000.
15. Carmalt, J. L., K. E. Baptiste, and B. Blakley: Suspect copper toxicity in an alpaca. *Canadian Veterinary Journal* 42: 554–556, 2001.
16. Carmean, B. R., K. A. Johnson, D. E. Johnson, and L. W. Johnson: Maintenance energy requirement of llamas. *American Journal of Veterinary Research* 53: 1,696, 1992.
17. Cebra C. K., F. B. Garry, and M. L. Cebra: Tick paralysis in eight New World camelids. *Veterinary Medicine* 91(7): 673–676, 1996.
18. Cebra, C. K., M. L. Cebra, F. B. Garry, and E. B. Belknap: Forestomach acidosis in six New World camelids. *Journal of the American Veterinary Medical Association* 208(6): 901–904, 1996.
19. Cebra, C. K., S. J. Tornquist, R. J. Van Saun, and B. B. Smith: Glucose tolerance testing in llamas and alpacas. *American Journal of Veterinary Research* 62(5): 682–686, 2001.
20. Cebra, C. K., S. A. McKane, and S. J. Tornquist: Effects of exogenous insulin on glucose tolerance in alpacas. *American Journal of Veterinary Research* 62(10): 1,544–1,547, 2001.
21. Chauvet, A. E., G. D. Shelton, and B. J. Darien: Vitamin E deficiency associated with myopathy in a llama. *Progress in Veterinary Neurology* 7(4): 149–152, 1996.
22. Cherney, J. H., and M. H. Hall: *Forage quality in perspective.* Agronomy Facts No. 30, Penn State University, 1998 (www.psu.edu/agronomy/facts).
23. Clark, D. H., E. E. Cary, and H. F. Mayland: Analysis of trace elements in forages by near infrared reflectance spectroscopy. *Agronomy Journal* 81(1): 91–95, 1989.
24. Clemens, E. T., and C. E. Stevens: A comparison of gastrointestinal transit time in ten species of mammal. *Journal of Agricultural Science, Cambridge* 94: 735–737, 1980.
25. Cordesse, R., M. Inesta, and J. Gaubert: Intake and digestibility of four forages by llamas and sheep. *Annales de Zootechnie* 41: 70, 1992.
26. Dart, A. J., H. Kinde, D. R. Hodgson, J. R. Peauroi, A. W. Selby, J. Maas, and M.E. Fowler: Serum α-tocopherol, vitamin A, and blood selenium concentrations, and glutathione peroxidase activity in llamas fed alfalfa hay. *American Journal of Veterinary Research* 57(5): 689–692, 1996.
27. Dart, A. J., C. M. Dart, and D. R. Hodgson: Surgical management of a ruptured bladder secondary to a urethral obstruction in an alpaca. *Australian Veterinary Journal* 75(11): 793–795, 1997.
28. Drew, M. L., and M. E. Fowler: Comparison of methods for measuring serum immunoglobulin concentrations in neonatal llamas. *Journal of the American Veterinary Medical Association* 206(9): 1,374–1,379, 1995.
29. Dumont, B., M. Meuret, and M. Prud'hon: Direct observation of biting for studying grazing behavior of goats and llamas on garrigue rangelands. *Small Ruminant Research* 16: 27–35, 1995.
30. Eckerlin, R. H., and C. E. Stevens: Bicarbonate secretion by the glandular saccules of the llama stomach. *Cornell Veterinarian* 63: 436–445, 1973.
31. Edmonson, A. J., I. J. Lean, L. D. Weaver, T. Farver, and G. Webster: A body condition scoring chart for Holstein dairy cows. *Journal of Dairy Science* 72: 68, 1989.
32. Engelhardt, W. von, K. Rubsamen, and R. Heller: The digestive physiology of camelids. In *The Camelid: An all purpose animal* (W. R. Cockrill, ed.) Uppsala: Scandinavian Institute of African Studies, pp. 323–346, 1984.
33. Ensminger, M. E., J. E. Oldfield, and W. W. Heinemann: *Feeds & Nutrition,* 2nd ed. Ensminger Publ Co.: Clovis, CA, 1990.
34. Fick, G. W., and R. R. Seaney: Species selection as applied to pastures, pp. 81–89, In *Proceedings Pasture in the Northeast Region of the United States.* NRAES publ. #36, April 26–28, 1988.
35. Florez, J. A.: *Rate of passage and digestibility in alpacas and sheep.* Prog Acad Med Vet, Universidad Nacional Mayor de San Marcos, Lima (BS Thesis), 1973.

36. Fowler, M. E., and J. G. Zinkl: Reference ranges for hematologic and serum biochemical values in llamas. *American Journal of Veterinary Research* 50(12): 2,049–2,053, 1989.

37. Fowler, M. E., Rickets in llamas and alpacas. *Llamas* 4(2): 92, 1990.

38. Fowler, M. E.: Rickets in alpacas. *Alpacas* (Fall): 10, 1992.

39. Fowler, M. E.: Feeding llamas and alpacas. In *Current Veterinary Therapy XI (Small Animal)* (Kirk, R. W., Bonagura, J. D., eds.). Philadelphia: W. B. Saunders, pp. 1,189–1,193, 1992.

40. Fowler, M. E.: Grasses: The staff of life. *Llamas* 7(7): 15–23, 1993.

41. Fowler, M. E.: Grasses: The dark side. *Llamas* 7(8): 25–30, 1993.

42. Fowler, M. E.: Feeding and Nutrition. *Medicine and Surgery of South American Camelids: Llama, Alpaca, Vicuña, Guanaco,* 2nd ed. Ames: Iowa State University Press, pp. 12–48, 1998.

43. Fraser, M. D.: Diet composition of guanacos (*Lama guanicoe*) and sheep (*Ovis aries*) grazing in grassland communities typical of UK uplands. *Small Ruminant Research* 29: 201–212, 1998.

44. Fraser, M. D., and D. H. Baker: A comparison of voluntary intake and *in vivo* digestion in guanacos (*Lama guanicoe*) and sheep given fresh grass. *Animal Science* 67: 567–572, 1998.

45. Fraser, M. D.: A comparison of the diet composition of guanacos (*Lama guanicoe*) and sheep when grazing swards with different clover: Grass ratios. *Small Ruminant Research* 32: 231–241, 1999.

46. Genin, D. Z. Villca, and P. Abasto: Diet selection and utilization by llama and sheep in a high-altitude arid rangeland of Bolivia. *Journal of Range Management* 47(3): 245–248, 1994.

47. Genin, D., and M. Tichit: Degradability of Andean range forages in llamas and sheep. *Journal of Range Management* 50: 381–385, 1997.

48. Gerros, T. C.: Recognizing and treating urolithiasis in llamas. *Veterinary Medicine* 93(6): 583–590, 1998.

49. Goering, H. K., and P. J. Van Soest: Forage fiber analyses (Apparatus, reagents, procedures, and some applications). *Agricultural Handbook,* No. 379, USDA, 1970.

50. Hammond, A. C.: Update on BUN and MUN as a guide for protein supplementation in cattle. *Proceedings Florida Ruminant Nutrition Symposium,* Gainesville, FL, Jan. 16–17, 1997 (http://www.ifas.ufl.edu/~dairyweb/pub/frns1997.pdf).

51. Heath, M. E., R. F. Barnes, and D. S. Metcalfe: *Forages: The Science of Grassland Agriculture,* 4th ed. Ames, Iowa: Iowa State University Press, 1985.

52. Heller, R., P. C. Gregory, and W. von Engelhardt: Pattern of motility and flow of digesta in the forestomach of the llama. *Journal of Comparative Physiology B—Biochemical systemic and Environmental Physiology* 154: 529–533, 1984.

53. Heller, R., V. Cercasov, and W. von Engelhardt: Retention of fluid and particles in the digestive tract of the llama. *Comparative Biochemistry and Physiology* 83A(4): 687–691, 1986.

54. Herdt, T. H.: Blood serum concentrations of selenium in female llamas (*Lama glama*) in relationship to feeding practices, region of the United States, reproductive stage, and health of the offspring. *Journal of Animal Science* 73: 337, 1995.

55. Hill, F. I., K. G. Thompson, and N. D. Grace.: Rickets in alpacas (*Lama pacos*) in New Zealand. *New Zealand Veterinary Journal* 42: 75 (Abstract), 1994.

56. Hilton, C. D., D. G. Pugh, J. C. Wright, B. M. Waldridge, S. A. Simpkins, and A. M. Heath: How to determine and when to use body weight estimates and condition scores in llamas. *Veterinary Medicine* 93(11): 1,015–1,018, 1998.

57. Hinderer, S., And W. von Engelhardt: Urea metabolism in the llama. *Comparative Biochemistry and Physiology* 52A: 619–622, 1975.

58. Hintz, H. F., H. F. Schryver, and M. Halbert: A note on the comparison of digestion by new world camelids, sheep and ponies. *Animal Production* 16: 303–305, 1973.

59. Hospinal, R. S. (ed): Capítulo IV. Nutrición y Alimentación de Alpacas, In *Produción de Camélidos Sudamericanos,* Huancayo, Peru: Imprenta Rios, pp. 163–203, 1997.

60. Huisa, T., R. Farfán, F. A. San Martin, F. C. Bryant, and L. C. Fierro: Composicion botanica y valor nutricional de la dieta de alpaca (*Lama pacos*) en la epoca seca en la sierra del Peru. *Revista de Camelidos Sudamericanos,* No. 3, Diciembre, pp. 19–23, IVITA/CICCS, Serie Información y Documentación No. 5, 1986.

61. Ivory, D. A.: Major characteristics, agronomic features, and nutritional value of shrubs and tree fodders. In *Shrubs and Tree Fodders for Farm Animals, Proceedings of a Workshop in Denpasar, Indonesia,* Devendra, C., ed., Ottawa, Can: IDRC, pp. 22–38, 1989.

62. Johnson, L. W.: Nutrition. *Veterinary Clinics of North America: Food Animal Practice* 5(1): 37–54, 1989.

63. Johnson, L. W.: Llama Nutrition. *Veterinary Clinics of North America: Food Animal Practice* 10(2): 187–201, 1994.

64. Jones, G. M., N. S. Wade, J. P. Baker, and E. M. Ranck: Use of near infrared reflectance spectroscopy in forage testing. *Journal of Dairy Science* 70: 1,086–1,091, 1987.

65. Jonsson N. N., and M. Rozmanec: Tick paralysis and hepatic lipidosis in a llama. *Australian Veterinary Journal* 75: 250–253, 1997.

66. Judson, G.: Survey of the mineral, trace element and vitamin status of alpacas. In *Camelid Medicine & Surgery,* Proceedings 278. Deakin University, Geelong, Victoria, Aust., pp. 311–317, July 1996.

67. Judson, G. J., and A. Feakes: Vitamin D doses for alpacas (*Lama pacos*). *Australian Veterinary Journal* 77(5): 310–315, 1999.

68. Junge, R. E., and L. Thornburg: Copper poisoning in four llamas. *Journal of the American Veterinary Medical Association* 195(7): 987–989, 1989.

69. Jurgens, M. H.: *Animal Feeding and Nutrition,* 6th ed. Dubuque: Kendall/Hunt Publishing Co., 1988.

70. Kaneko, J. J.: *Clinical Biochemistry of Domestic Animals,* 4th ed. San Diego: Academic Press, pp. 886–891, 1989.

71. Kellems, R. O., and D. C. Church: *Livestock Feeds & Feeding,* 4th ed. Upper Saddle River, NJ: Prentice-Hall, Inc., 1998.

72. Kingston, J. K., and H. R. Stäempfli: Silica urolithiasis in a male llama. *Canadian Veterinary Journal* 36: 767–768, 1995.

73. Kock, M. D., and M. E. Fowler: Urolithiasis in a three-month-old llama. *Journal of the American Veterinary Medical Association* 181: 1,411, 1982.

74. Krieger, R.: The green, green grass of home. *Llamas* 7(4): 73, 1993.

75. Lane, M. A., and B. W. Jesse: Effect of volatile fatty acid infusion on development of the rumen epithelium in neonatal sheep. *Journal of Dairy Science* 80: 740–746, 1997.

76. Langer, R. H. M.: *Agricultural Plants.* New York: Cambridge University Press, 1982.

77. Lassen, E. D., E. G. Pearson, P. Long, W. B. Schmotzer, A. J. Kaneps, and T. W. Riebold: Clinical biochemical values of llamas: Reference values. *American Journal of Veterinary Research* 47(10): 2,278–2,280, 1986.

78. Lemosquet, S., C. Dardillat, M. Jailler, and J. P. Dulphy: Voluntary intake and gastric digestion of two hays by llamas and sheep: Influence of concentrate supplementation. *Journal of Agricultural Science, Cambridge* 127: 539–548, 1996.

79. Lopez, A., J. Maiztegui, and R. Cabrera: Voluntary intake and digestibility of forages with different nutritional quality in alpacas. *Small Ruminant Research* 29: 295–301, 1998.

80. McDowell, L. R., J. H. Conrad, J. E. Thomas, and L. E. Harris: *Latin American Tables of Feed Composition.* Gainesville: University of Florida, 1974.

81. McLaughlin, B. G., and N. C. Evans: Urethral obstruction in a male llama. *Journal of the American Veterinary Medical Association* 195(11): 1,601–1,602, 1989.

82. McMillan, E., and D. Paynter: Trace element studies in Australian alpacas, In *Camelids Proceedings 257.* Deakin University, Geelong, Victoria, Aust., pp. 1–3, July 1995.

83. Mislevy, P.: Forages for grazing systems in warm climates. In *Nutrition of Grazing Ruminants in Warm Climates* (McDowell, L. R., ed.). Orlando: Academic Press, pp. 73–103, 1985.

84. Mertens, D. R.: Predicting intake and digestibility using mathematical models of rumen function. *Journal of Animal Science* 64: 1,548, 1987.

85. Miller, D. A.: *Forage Crops.* New York: McGraw-Hill, 1984.

86. Minson, D. J.: *Forage In Ruminant Nutrition.* San Diego: Academic Press, 1990.

87. Morin, D. E., F. B. Garry, M. G. Weiser, M. J. Gettman, and L. W. Johnson: Hematologic features of iron deficiency anemia in llamas. *Veterinary Pathology* 29: 400–404, 1992.

88. Morin, D. E., F. B. Garry, and M. G. Weiser: Hematologic responses in llamas with experimentally-induced iron deficiency anemia. *Veterinary Clinical Pathology* 22(3): 81–86, 1993.

89. Morin, D. E., L. L. Rowan, W. L. Hurley, and W. E. Braselton: Composition of milk from llamas in the United States. *Journal of Dairy Science* 78: 1,713–1,720, 1995.

90. Mortimer, R. G., D. A. Dargatz, and L. R. Corah: *Forage Analyses from Cow-calf Herds in 23 States.* USDA:APHIS:VS, Centers for Epidemiology and Animal Health, Fort Collins, CO., #N303.499, April 1999.

91. National Research Council: *Nutrient and Toxic Elements in Water.* Washington, DC: National Academy Press, 1974.

92. National Research Council: *Nutritional Energetics of Domestic Animals & Glossary of Energy Terms.* Washington, DC: National Academy Press, 1981.

93. National Research Council: *Nutrient Requirements of Goats: Angora, Dairy and Meat Goats in Temperate and Tropical Countries.* Washington, DC: National Academy Press, 1981.

94. National Research Council: *Effect of Environment on Nutrient Requirements of Domestic Animals.* Washington, DC: National Academy Press, 1981.

95. National Research Council, Subcommitte on Feed Composition, Committee on Animal Nutrition: *United States-Canadian Tables of Feed Composition: Nutritional Data for United States and Canadian Feeds,* 3rd rev ed. Washington, DC: National Academy Press, 1982.

96. National Research Council: *Nutrient Requirements of Sheep,* 6th rev ed. Washington, DC: National Academy Press, 1985.

97. National Research Council: *Nutrient Requirements of Beef Cattle,* 7th rev ed. Washington, DC: National Academy Press, 1996.

98. Navarre, C. B., D. G. Pugh, A. M. Heath, and A. Simpkins: Analysis of first gastric compartment fluid collected via percutaneous paracentesis from healthy llamas. *Journal of the American Veterinary Medical Association* 214(6): 812–815, 1999.

99. Oetzel, G. R.: Protein-energy malnutrition in ruminants. *Veterinary Clinics North America: Food Animal Practice* 4(2): 317–330, 1988.

100. Parker J. E., K. I. Timm, B. B. Smith, R. J. Van Saun, K. M. Winters, P. Sukon, and C.M. Snow: Seasonal interaction of vitamin D and bone density in the llama. *American Journal of Veterinary Research* 63: 948–953, 2002.

101. Pugh, D. G.: Copper nutrition in llamas. *Llamas* 7(2): 77, 1993.

102. Pugh, D. G.: Selenium nutrition for llamas: An overview. *Llamas* 7(3): 43, 1993.

103. Ralston, S. L.: Digestive alterations in aged horses. *Journal of Equine Veterinary Science* 9: 203–205, 1989.

104. Reiner, R. J., and F. C. Bryant: Botanical composition and nutritional quality of alpaca diets in two Andean rangeland communities. *Journal of Range Management* 39(5): 424–427, 1986.

105. Reiner, R. J., F. C. Bryant, R. D. Farfan, and B. F. Craddock: Forage intake of alpacas grazing Andean rangeland in Peru. *Journal of Animal Science* 64: 868–871, 1987.

106. Rübsamen K., and W. von. Engelhardt: Water metabolism in the llama. *Comparative Biochemistry and Physiology* 52A: 595–598, 1975.

107. Rübsamen K., and W. von. Engelhardt: Morphological and functional peculiarities of the llama forestomach. *Annales de Recherches Veterinaires* 10(2/3): 473–475, 1979.

108. Russel, A. J. F.: Body condition scoring of sheep. In *Sheep and Goat Practice* (Boden, E., ed.). London: Bailliere Tindall, pp. 3–10, 1991.

109. Russel, A. J. F., and H. L. Redden: The effect of nutrition on fibre growth in the alpaca. *Animal Science* 64: 509–512, 1997.

110. San Martin, F. A.: *Comparative forage selectivity and nutrition of South American camelids and sheep.* Texas Tech Univ, Lubbock, TX (PhD Dissertation), 1987.

111. San Martin, F. A.: Capítulo VII. Alimentación y Nutrición. In *Avances y Perspectivas Camelidos Sudamericanos* (S.

Fernández-Baca, ed.). Santiago, Chile: Organizacion de las Naciones Unidas para la Agricultura y la Alimentación Oficina Regional de la Fao para America Latina y el Caribe, pp. 213–262, 1991.

112. San Martin, F. A., A. Rosales, and R. Valdivia: Tasas de digestion y digestibilidad del forragje en alpaca y vacuno. *Revista de Camelidos Sudamericanos*, No. 3, December, pp. 24–31, IVITA/CICCS, Serie Información y Documentación No. 5, 1986.

113. San Martin, F. A., and F. C. Bryant: Nutrition of domesticated South American llamas and alpacas. *Small Ruminant Research* 2: 191–216, 1989.

114. Schneider, W., R. Hauffe, and W. von Engelhardt: Energie und stickstoffumsatz biem lama (Energy and Nitrogen Exchange in the Llama). *Proceedings 6th Symposium Energy Metabolism of Farm Animals,* European Animal Production Soc, Pub No. 14: 127–130, 1974.

115. Simons, J. A., D. L. Waldron, and D. P. Hennessy: Clinical biochemical reference ranges for female alpacas (*Lama pacos*). *Comparative Biochemistry and Physiology* 105B(3/4): 603–608, 1993.

116. Smith, B. B., and P. Ballerstedt: Pasture management for the llama owner (Part I). *Llamas* 3(2): 77–79, 1989.

117. Smith, B. B., and P. Ballerstedt: Pasture management for the llama owner (Part II). *Llamas* 3(3): 33–37, 1989.

118. Smith, B. B., K. I. Timm, and P. J. Reed: Morphometric evaluation of growth in llamas (*Lama glama*) from birth to maturity. *Journal of the American Veterinary Veterinary Association* 200(8): 1,095–1,100, 1992.

119. Smith, B. B., and R. J. Van Saun: Hypophosphatemic rickets in South American camelids: Interaction of calcium, phosphorus, and vitamin D. In *Proceedings 2nd European Symposium on South American Camelids* (Gerken, M. and C. Renieri, eds.). Universita Degli Studi Di Camerino, Italy, pp. 79–94, 1996.

120. Smith, B. B., R. J. Van Saun, P. J. Reed, A. M. Craig, and A. Youngberg: Blood mineral and vitamin E concentrations in llamas. *American Journal of Veterinary Research* 59(8): 1,063–1,070, 1998.

121. Smith, B. B., K. I. Timm, and P. O. Long: *Llama and Alpaca Neonatal Care.* Pine Grove Publishing Company, 1996.

122. Smith, B. B., and R. J. Van Saun: Seasonal changes in serum calcium, phosphorus and vitamin D concentrations in llamas and alpacas. *American Journal of Veterinary Research* 62(8): 1,187–1,193, 2001.

123. Timm, K.I. and B.B. Smith: Llama digestive system: Form, function and problems. *Llamas* 5 (1): 75–83, 1991.

124. Timm, K. I., and B. B. Smith: Preparing for the aged alpaca. *Alpaca Registry Journal* 5(1): 22–26, 2000.

125. Tornquist, S. J., R. J. Van Saun, B. B. Smith, C. K. Cebra, and S. P. Snyder: Histologically-confirmed hepatic lipidosis in llamas and alpacas: 31 Cases (1991–1997). *Journal of the American Veterinary Medical Association* 214(9): 1,368–1,372, 1999.

126. Tornquist, S. J., C. K. Cebra, R. J. Van Saun, and B. B Smith: Metabolic changes and induction of hepatic lipidosis during feed restriction in llamas. *American Journal of Veterinary Research* 62(7): 1,081–1,087, 2001.

127. Vallenas, A., and C. E. Stevens: Volatile fatty acid concentrations and pH of llama and quanaco forestomach digesta. *Cornell Veterinarian* 61(2): 238–252, 1971.

128. Vallenas, A., J. F. Cummings, and J. F. Munnell: A gross study of the compartmentalized stomach of two New World camelids, the llama and guanaco. *Journal of Morphology* 134(4): 399–424, 1971.

129. Vallenas, A., J. Esquerre, A. Valenzuela, E. Candela, and D. Chauca: Volatile fatty acids and pH in the first two stomach compartments in the alpaca and sheep. *Rev Invest Pecu* (IVITA), Universidad Nacional Mayor de San Marcos, Lima, 2: 115–130, 1973.

130. Vallenas, A; L. Llerena; A. Valenzuela; D. Chauca; J. Esquerre and E. Candela: Volatile fatty acid concentration along the digestive tract of alpacas and llamas. *Rev Invest Pecu* (IVITA), Universidad Nacional Mayor de San Marcos, Lima 2: 3–14, 1973.

131. Van Saun, R. J., B. B. Smith, and B. J. Watrous: Evaluation of vitamin D status of llamas and alpacas with hypophosphatemic rickets. *Journal of the American Veterinary Medical Association* 209(6): 1,128–1,133, 1996.

132. Van Saun, R. J., B. Callihan, and S. J. Tornquist: Nutritional support for treatment of hepatic lipidosis in a llama. *Journal of the American Veterinary Medical Association* 217(10): 1,531–1,535, 2000.

133. Van Saun, R. J.: Nutrient requirements of South American camelids: A factorial approach. *Small Ruminant Research* 61(2/3): 165–186, 2006.

134. Van Saun, R. J. Nutritional diseases of South American camelids. *Small Ruminant Research* 61(2/3): 153–164, 2006.

135. Van Soest, P. J.: *Nutritional Ecology of the Ruminant,* 2nd ed. Ithaca: Cornell University Press, 1994.

136. Walsh, D. J., R. G. Warner, H. R. Ainslie, M. A. Brunner, and J. M. Elliot: *Neonatal Calf Nutrition and Feeding.* Cornell University Animal Science Mimeograph No. 69, 1983.

137. Warmington, B. G., G. F. Wilson, and T. N. Barry: Voluntary intake and digestion of ryegrass straw by llama × guanaco crossbreds and sheep. *Journal of Agricultural Science, Cambridge* 113: 87–91, 1989.

138. Weaver, D. M., J. W. Tyler, R. S. Marion, S. W. Casteel, C. M. Loiacono, and J. R. Turk: Subclinical copper accumulation in llamas. *Canadian Veterinary Journal* 40: 422–424, 1999.

139. Weaver, D. M., J. W. Tyler, R. S. Marion, L. M. Wallace, J. K. Nagy, and J. M. Holle: Evaluation of assays for determination of passive transfer status in neonatal llamas and alpacas. *Journal of the American Veterinary Medical Association* 216(4): 559–563, 2000.

140. Weiss, W. P.: Estimating the available energy content of feeds for dairy cattle. *Journal of Dairy Science* 81: 830–839, 1998.

Section Three

Fiber

Overleaf Huacaya and suri offer a contrast in coat types.

Chapter 10

Fiber Processing, Characteristics, and Nomenclature

Eric Hoffman

Ancient methods of weaving survive on the shores of Lake Titicaca.

T raditionally the alpaca textile sector has not had important participation in the breeding of this species. As a result of efforts like the one made by Mr. Eric Hoffman, a huge potential was discovered in the industry through engagement with the producers in order to achieve substantial improvement in fiber quality, resulting in better prices for producers and more comfortable garments.

—*Luis Chaves, general manager, Inca Tops**

HISTORICAL PERSPECTIVE

Processing New World camel fiber on the puna (the high plains of the Andes) is an ancient phenomenon, predating even the fiber-utilizing civilizations that came before the Incas. Fiber in the form of pelts and fabrics from wild South American camels was used around 4500 BC before the domestication of alpacas and llamas. With the development of llamas and alpacas came permanent settlement, hierarchical societies, and large-scale trade. Alpaca fiber was a primary commodity, utilized by those who raised them and traded to groups outside the alpaca-growing regions that radiated from Lake Titicaca.[9,39,113]

During the long period of domestication, guard hair, which is present on both the wild guanaco, vicuña, and many of today's domestic llamas, as well as an alarming number of alpacas, disappeared from alpacas and many

*Luis Chaves, personal communication, Arequipa, Peru, April 23, 2001.

llamas. Over the centuries the alpaca's coat color became diversified, and fiber production and textile manufacturing were refined.[5] The breeding practices of the ancient pastoralists resulted in a single uniform coat: the fiber diameter of guard hair was decreased and the fiber diameter of the fleece was increased until a single, consistent, uniform fleece was produced.[20] All archeological evidence collected thus far indicates that alpacas and many llamas of the pre-Conquest cultures were generally finer fleeced and possessed greater uniformity than animals living today.[28,58]

At the time of the Conquest (1532) fiber growing had become a state-run enterprise encompassing an immense portion of the Andean region, including today's countries of Peru, Bolivia, northern Chile, northern Argentina, and parts of Ecuador. In this state system, fiber from alpacas and the cloth it was made into by master weavers was much more than just fabric. Fiber was used to build suspension bridges, record history, keep accounts (in intricately knotted *quipus*), and weave excellent textiles. The best cloth was equivalent to currency, so much so that retreating armies would destroy warehouses rather than allow victors such precious spoils.

Cloth of different qualities had specific names (see Chapter 1: Classification Prehistory, and History) and was doled out by the mighty Inca to faithful subjects for acts of loyalty and service. Though the conquering Spanish made mention of the quality of the cloth, the Spaniards' ethnocentrism and single-minded pursuit of precious metals resulted in the eradication of the world's most sophisticated state-run

235

fiber production and processing, without understanding or recording the wealth of knowledge that the Incan herding class (*llama michi*) and weavers possessed.[25,31,39,113,119]

For centuries before the Spanish Conquest, a knife or sharp object was used for shearing and the drop spindle and loom were used for processing. These tools are still used today in many areas on the puna, where about 90 percent of the shearing is done using hand shears.[33,39,45,119] The primitive appearance of alpaca management in many places on the altiplano is representative of the pervasive poverty on the altiplano today, and should not be mistaken as representative of the many-tiered, sophisticated Incan system that was entirely destroyed centuries ago. Though there are vestiges from the past, what exists today is not what was!

In the more than 450 years since the Conquest, alpaca fiber production and the sense of order that allowed it to flourish have been in constant turmoil. Hybridization of alpacas with llamas (known as *waris* or *huarizos*) is commonplace. Over the centuries a general coarsening in fiber has occurred, and it continues unabated.[39,72,113] Despite this, the procurement and marketing of alpaca fiber by large mills is a multimillion dollar industry in Peru, Bolivia, and Argentina. The bulk of alpaca fiber is still harvested, traded, and consumed by indigenous campesinos throughout the Andes. An estimated 150,000 campesino families in Peru, Bolivia, northern Chile, Ecuador, and Argentina directly or indirectly depend on some aspect of fiber production.[13,33,113,119]

The alpaca is the world's most color-diverse fiber-producing animal, and a magnificent natural asset, as measured by both fiber quality and color. The great irony about alpaca fiber is that while it is one of the greatest natural fiber resources the world has ever seen, four and a half centuries of neglect and mismanagement have made it a grossly underdeveloped resource. In South America, the export trade of fiber products has received little help or encouragement from the government, and development of the fiber has been hampered by social class divisions between people of European and traditional Quechua and Aymara ancestries.[13,33,39,43,44,46]

Alpaca fiber production is providing new investment opportunities in geographical, social, and economic contexts outside of South America. This is clearly evident in the many expensive live alpaca exportations from South America since 1983 to Australia, Belgium, China, France, Germany, Israel, Italy, Japan, Mexico, New Zealand, Poland, South Africa, Spain, Switzerland, the United Kingdom, and the United States. Undoubtedly alpacas will be found in many more countries in the years to come.* The involvement of regions outside traditional growing

areas is a significant event, the importance of which will not be entirely known for decades.

FIBER PROCESSING IN PERU

Selecting and Buying Fleeces

Social strata and social class are important factors in most large indigenous businesses in South America, and alpaca fiber production is no exception. Generally men dominate the technical areas in the processing plants, and the top echelon of administrative employees comes from the best-educated Peruvian middle and upper social classes. The fiber buyers come from the ranks of the top echelon. They often speak Spanish, Quechua, Aymara, and the European languages of the countries that commonly purchase alpaca fiber from the mills.[33,44,45,91]

Fiber buying on a large scale is both tricky and volatile, requiring considerable bartering skills and an understanding of subtle economic changes in the highlands. Weather conditions, fiber quality, mill production, market trends, overseas sales, and the behavior of middlemen who often broker large amounts of fiber all play into the final outcome. The buyers, who are responsible for purchasing huge lots of fleece for the sorting plants, must often calculate the expected yield, disallowing a percentage for fleece they suspect is wet or contaminated. At the same time they must sometimes accurately assess the average fineness of immense lots before deciding the correct price to offer. Trading in fiber also takes place weekly in community markets on a small scale throughout the year on the altiplano. Most of this trading involves small farms run by campesinos whose fiber trading is done primarily to obtain money to buy the food and tools necessary to maintain a subsistence level of existence for their families.

Every year, on the religious holiday known as the *Immaculate Concepcion* (December 8th), the large mills buy large quantities of fiber in the towns of Santa Rosa and Macusani, the traditional collection points in the southern Peruvian highlands. On this day buyers representing mills in Arequipa purchase hundreds of tons of fiber from large individual breeders, the large cooperatives, and shrewd middlemen who have acquired large amounts of fleece over the course of the year.**

Since the 1960s, price has been primarily determined by weight, but supply and demand and economic condi-

---

*Ignacio Garaycochea, Michell & CIA executive, personal communication, Arequipa, Peru, May 15, 2001; Peter Hill, businessman and alpaca exporter, personal communication, Santiago, Chile, May 19, 2001.

**Ignacio Garaycochea, personal communication, May 15, 2001.

tions are also influences. Light colors (white and light fawn) have enjoyed higher prices and, on occasion, fineness is rewarded with higher prices as well.* In the 1990s, the larger mills started to sometimes take samples from large lots for scientific assessment to determine fineness before assigning a price. By contrast, in much of the worldwide wool industry, fiber (sheep) is routinely tested in a laboratory before the sale, and the value of the fiber is calculated on the basis of the test results.**

The alpaca mills, even the largest ones, usually send a single buyer to procure raw material. Since classification of fiber is primarily a subjective exercise at this level, the single-buyer approach is thought to achieve the needed consistency in fleece, which is also the first step in grading. This approach allows for averaging; that is, the buyer may pay too much for one lot and too little for another, but as long as he or she is buying a large number of lots, the price will average out. Volume buying that takes into account this type of averaging is a purchasing system used throughout much of the world's fiber industry.

Buying on the day of the Immaculate Conception in Santa Rosa or Macusani, or from highland villagers and large co-op farms, often involves purchasing hundreds of thousands of fleeces, mostly without the aid of machines or computer technology. Yields of between 80 and 85 percent of usable fiber are generally expected and calculated with uncanny accuracy. However, because of the emphasis on weight and color, a constant contest takes place between the fiber producers and buyers from the mills that is quite sophisticated, if not entirely honest. Says Peter Kothe, who was Michell's top buyer for most of the 1990s:

> I used to spot-check the micronage [diameter measured in microns] randomly. I usually didn't have time to look at a great number of fleeces. We bought based on weight primarily with an eye out for quality. We had to watch for wet fleeces in the rainy season. Inaccuracies also occur because of a sophisticated method of spraying fleeces with a sticky mineral dust to add weight. This is nearly impossible to detect through visual inspection. We sometimes don't pick it up until the scouring stage, long after the product has been purchased. If there's a low yield and an obvious discrepancy between the raw product and scoured product, we know we've been tricked. It's a difficult problem for us.***

Problems aside, the expert buyers can usually determine the fiber's micron value by simple touch. Obviously, the expertise of professional buyers is of great importance to the mills, who rely largely on the sense of touch and vi-

Doña Augustine of the Tuqsa community demonstrates the drop spindle in central Peru.

sual acuity of a single individual for the success or failure of each year's processing.[33,43,44,45,46]

Over the years the mills' expert buyers have learned to make key distinctions between classes of fiber. It is common for buyers to find two entities in the same area producing totally different qualities of fiber. It is also common for villagers to be unaware of the quality of fiber being produced just a few miles away in another village or cooperative and to assume that the fiber they offer for sale is best. The experienced buyer learns to grade a village's fiber relative to the fiber quality throughout the puna, not just within a small region. Buyers agree that there is no substitute for experience when comparing large lots of fiber from many different areas, but buyers are also aware that in the Peruvian collection system all fiber, regardless of its fineness, will find a use in the mills. Hence, weight becomes

---

*Luis Chaves, personal communication, Arequipa, Peru, April 23, 2001; Derek Michell, executive for Michell & CIA, personal communication, Arequipa, Peru, May 15, 2001.

**Robert C. Couchman, personal communication, December 19, 1994.

***Peter Kothe, volume fleece buyer for Michell and CIA, personal communication, Chivay, Peru, May 1994.

the most important measurement when hasty decisions must be made.*

Buying fleeces in the manner just described, with little regard to fineness, fails to offer an incentive to alpaca growers for creating the best possible fleece, and therefore has been arguably the weakest link in the entire fiber production process, which needs a greater percentage of fine, uniform fleeces. In the last few years, Inca Tops and other Peruvian mills have begun paying double price for very fine fiber, which now offers an incentive for breeders to pay attention to fleece quality as well as weight. It is too soon to measure the impact of this incentive on overall fiber improvement. However, when it comes to sorting and processing fiber, the South American methods are world class and must be understood by anyone involved in breeding or production.[13,45,46]

Sorting Fleeces

After shearing and procurement, *sorting* begins the process of taking raw fleece (known as *greasy fleece* in the Peruvian mills, even though alpacas have very little naturally occurring oil compared to sheep and other fiber-producing animals)* and converting it to an end-product. There are no sorting machines or high-tech equipment in the sorting plants in Arequipa, Peru, the worldwide hub of commercial alpaca fiber processing. Instead, there are mounds of fleeces in dusty warehouses the size of high school gymnasiums. Quechua women, some of them attired in the traditional clothing of their highland villages, sit quietly among the mountains of fleeces. At first glance they appear almost motionless, until one notices that their hands are nimbly feeling and pulling at the fleeces. These women are the backbone of the Peruvian fiber industry. They sort the fleeces into various grades and colors. Derek Michell, of Michell & CIA, makes it clear how important the sorting skill is: "The whole secret of this business is the sorting process. If you have the appropriate skill to detect the correct micronage [diameter], you have the most basic part of this business in your hands."**

Microscopes and sophisticated laboratories at Michell & CIA, Grupo Inca, and other top mills make quantitative measurements of the fiber possible. However, classification (or grading) still remains primarily a tactile and visual assessment.[23,45,46,105,108] The fiber is sorted by color prior to the tactile sorting.*** To some European and Australian processors, this situation—sorting and classing by eye and hand when technically advanced methods are available—may appear to be an archaic approach being used in a developing country. This assessment fails to recognize the expertise and low cost of incorporating it into processing in the Peruvian setting. The "backwards" label brings a smile

to high-ranking Michell executives such as Ignacio Garaycochea, who points out, "Those who label hand sorting as something backward don't understand alpaca. There are no sorting machines used on alpaca anywhere in the world. Hand sorting is something unique because so much of the grading of alpaca has to do with how it feels." The Quechua women perform the sorting task entirely by hand, as it has been done for centuries. The women "inherit" their skill for sorting.† Indeed, some women have small children with them. The girls will most likely be the next generation of sorters.

Sorting for color takes place early on. The women who do the sorting are distributed in the plant according to their expertise. Some are better at sorting for dark colors, while others have a special skill for the light fawns and whites. Some have the touch for coarser qualities, while others prefer to work the *tuis* (finer-quality first shearing) or *suri*, which rarely comprise more than 5 percent of processed fiber. An accomplished sorter can sort up to 200 pounds of fiber in a single day.[45,46,106,107]

The Industrial Process

Even though industrial sorting is done on a much larger scale than that done by an individual or families living in the highland villages, the process is essentially a replication of their time-honored tactile and visual methods. Sometimes scientific assessment (airflow scanning) is also brought into the process to satisfy a client's demands. Not until the material moves from sorting and grading is it embraced by the machinery and technology of this century.

It is truly an impressive sight to visit the large plants in Arequipa when the elaborate and deafening French, Swiss, German, and Italian machines are whirling and pounding. With the machines adjusted for the special requirements of alpaca fiber (especially suri), the fiber undergoes a process similar to that of other specialty (or hair) fibers, such as mohair, cashmere, camel, wool, and angora. There are two basic types of fiber processing: worsted and woolen. Both processes are used for alpaca in Arequipa, and these processes, or modifications of them, are used for alpaca fiber worldwide (see Figure 10.1).

Worsted Process Most of the alpaca fiber that is commercially processed is subjected to the worsted process, which brings out the special qualities of good-quality alpaca. First,

---

*Ignacio Garaycochea, personal communication, May 15, 2001; Derek Michell, personal communication, May 12, 2001.

**Derek Michell, personal communication, May 28, 2001.

***Ignacio Garaycochea, personal communication, January 15, 2001.

†Raul Rivera, executive for Michell & CIA, personal communication, Arequipa Peru, April 6, 2001.

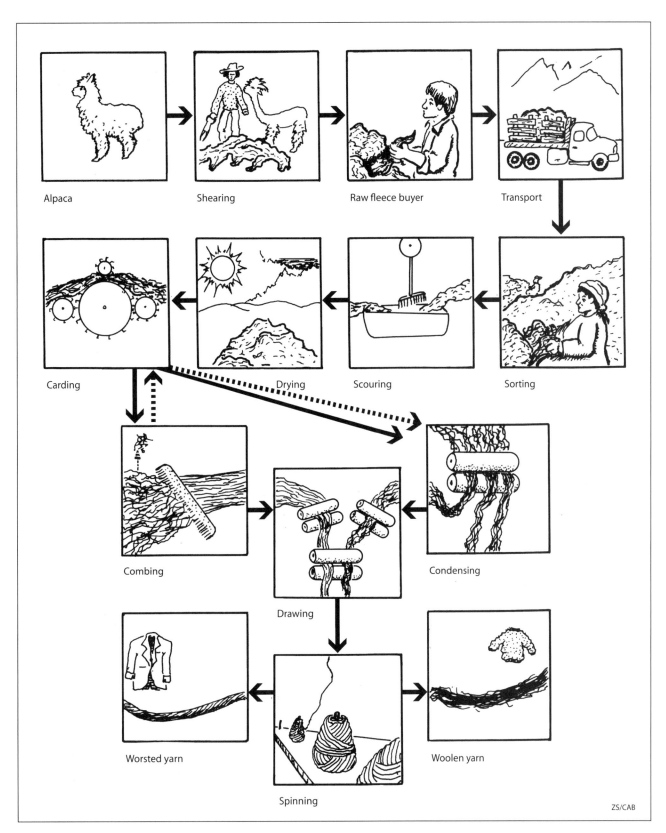

Alpaca

Shearing

Raw fleece buyer

Transport

Carding

Drying

Scouring

Sorting

Combing

Drawing

Condensing

Worsted yarn

Spinning

Woolen yarn

Figure 10.1 How alpaca fiber and its basic yarn structure are obtained.

ZS/CAB

Left Every year on the day of the Immaculate Conception (December 8th), large-scale alpaca fiber trading takes place. All the large companies trade for enormous volumes. Middlemen are major players in this process. The greatest volume, measured in tons, occurs in the towns of Macusani and Santa Rosa. The fiber is transported to mills in Arequipa by truck.

Below Women begin the process of sorting by color and fineness. The tactile skill of the sorters is the underpinning of the alpaca textile business in Peru.

Scouring commences by cleansing with three solutions. The temperature and detergents are adjusted to get the desired results. The first scouring eliminates most dirt and debris. Floating debris (seeds and straw) are the most difficult to eliminate.

Opening the fiber begins the mechanical process and readies the fiber for scouring vats.

Drying rooms or drying machines evaporate moisture from the fiber. The fiber is allowed to rest to restore its essential properties prior to bailing or further processing.

Intermediate baling (storing for future processing).

Carding parallelizes fiber (woolen process) for further processing. Carding eliminates neps and impurities.

Hydroscopic variables, especially humidity, are carefully adjusted to eliminate static electricity, which is essential to successful processing. Arequipa has a dry environment, requiring great care in creating a controlled climate for processing.

Carding forms slivers that move forward into rovings.

Tops are produced from the worsted process.

Tops are moved to baling for overseas markets or yarn plants. Bailing may not be necessary at this point, if all processing takes place in a single plant. Compression is necessary for efficient transport.

Combing (further parallelizing) and the beginning of the woolen process (felting) starts here.

Refined machinery for yarns and threads (usually made in Italy, Germany, or Switzerland) is specially made for alpaca processing.

Tops are baled for export and a quality control agent checks bail samples.

A computer-enhanced tops sampler in a Peruvian fiber mill.

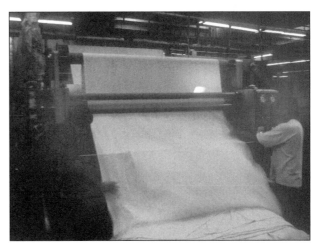

Above Processing may result in fabric manufacturing.

Below Quality control includes looking for impurities.

Dyeing can be applied at several junctures in the process. Dyeing agents made in Germany are specially made to preserve the unique touch of alpaca. Other luxury fiber processors, such as cashmere and angora, use these special dyes, too.

Above The creation of knitwear can include patterning machines.

Right A quality control expert displays samples from an established "color bank." Lot samples from processed fiber are continually matched to bank colors to assure that color consistency is maintained.

Lot samples from the week's processing.

the fiber (mostly huacaya) is manually re-sorted, and on occasion samples are laser-scanned to double-check microns. Re-sorting removes any remains of foreign material that may have been missed during the first sorting, and reclassifies any fiber that was assigned to the wrong grade. If *debris* (usually vegetable matter) or *cotts* (matted fiber) are left in, the result is a high incidence of breakage, which produces *noils** and short fiber. Short fiber is of lower quality. Debris and cotts may also damage the machinery. The short fibers are not wasted, as they can be recycled into the woolen process.

The next step is to *match* the fiber to establish consistency. In this operation, different natural shades of alpaca fiber are mixed to meet the client's color choice, usually selected from a chart showing the natural colors offered by the processor. As with sorting, matching relies on human expertise—*color technicians* with refined visual acuity (or "eye")—not machinery or computer scanning.

The first mechanical process is the *opener,* a machine that opens the fleeces and converts them into groups of *staples,* which begins the milling process and facilitates the removal of dirt, urine, and grease during the scouring process.

Scouring (or washing) is done in a series of large, long, flat-bottomed vats called *leviathans.* First, the fiber is forcibly immersed, then pushed along in the solution by pitchfork and rakelike arms. The process generally employs biodegradable soft soap and clear hot water with at least three rinsings per cycle, although solutions will vary. Eighty percent of the dirt and other impurities are removed in the first scouring. Different types of solutions can either strengthen or weaken the internal structure of the fiber. The solutions, and the conditions in which they are applied, are often guarded company secrets.

After scouring, the fiber is dried in three different chambers of a hot-air oven at 120°F (48°C) with humidity

set at desired levels. Next, the fiber is sprayed with carding lubricants and moisture in controlled amounts to reduce both static electricity and fiber breakage during the carding process. The fiber is then placed in a *resting chamber* for up to 24 hours. The interval assigned for rest is important because it allows the fiber to relax the temporary "set" it gained during scouring and drying, thus demonstrating its *resilience.* The fiber reshapes itself into its original form, only now it's clean and almost ready for carding.

Controlling static electricity is a problem that must be addressed for successful mechanical fiber processing. Before carding, the fiber's *hydroscopic* properties are adjusted with a treatment designed to enhance softness and produce the desired humidity to combat static electricity. In Arequipa (with its dry, low-humidity climate) this is especially important.

From the carding machine, the fiber is fashioned into *slivers* with no twist. A sliver looks like a thick, somewhat flattened rope, but it is loosely held together. A sliver weighs approximately 1 ounce (25–30 g) per meter. The sliver next passes through a machine called an *intersecting gill,* which evens out the fiber, or further "parallelizes" it. In most mills, gilling happens at least three times.**

Then the fiber is passed through the *combs* to eliminate noils. Fiber lengths of approximately 3 inches (7.6 cm) are processed while the shorter fiber is cast out. The humming machinery draws the fiber along until it is processed into *tops* weighing 28.6 lb (13 kg), with a distribution capability of .91 ounces (26 g) per meter and a regular *Uster factor* of 4.5 percent. The tops are the chief raw material of this process; at this stage they are either marketed or further processed into yarn or thread.

Besides tops, the mills produce many kinds of yarns and threads for a wide variety of end-products via the worsted process. With precise measurements and fine-tuned settings, the machines are programmed for the desired thinness of the yarn or thread and the number of yarn ends to be spun together. For example, yarn to be used for knitting will require less twisting and combing of threads than yarn destined for high-quality cloth. Also, different qualities of fiber are appropriate for different kinds of end-products. Average top length can be a decisive factor in the destination of a top. Long tops are usually used in fabrics.

The yarns and threads are electronically cleaned in the *winding machines,* where consistency is achieved by the re-

---

*Many terms have complete definitions in the Glossary at the end of the chapter.

**Robert C. Couchman, fiber scientist who developed standards and tests for cashmere and cashgora for the Australian Wool Testing Authority, personal communication, Melbourne, Australia, March 19, 1994.

moval of thin or thick parts. The yarn is cut and then spliced again with a *pneumatic knot,* twisted with the proper *torsion* and steamed in a vacuum chamber. This last process adds fiber "set," which ensures the desired degree of twist and prevents tangling. Yarns are then ready to be either dyed or marketed in 2.2-pound (1-kg) cones.[43,44,45] The yarn produced from this process is typically smooth and clear-faced, and possesses impressive tensile strength. Products are usually extremely durable, thin, lightweight, and capable of holding their shape well. Suits and dresses are likely products.[21,45,46,60,98,106,107]

Woolen Process The *woolen process* starts with the scouring of fiber in the same manner as in the worsted process. The woolen process employs hair as short as 1.7 to 1.9 inches (4.5–5 cm), in contrast to the desired length for worsted of 2.7 to 3.2 inches (7–8 cm). Next comes *matching,* a process in which a centrifugal machine is used to evenly distribute the different colored fiber in large blending vats. The resultant blend is left to recuperate for 48 hours.

The fiber is next put into the carding machines, and emerges as *rovings.* These are delivered on to *bobbins* to feed the *spinning machines.* The combing process, which eliminates short fibers in the worsted process, is either not done or greatly abbreviated. Twist is given to the yarn, but not with the precision that characterizes the final stages of the worsted.

Typically the woolen process produces fabric that is soft and fuzzy, and heavier than worsted fabric. Woolen products are also rougher looking and less able to hold their form than worsteds. Sweaters, tweeds, and carpets are typical woolen products. Often felted products are derived from the woolen process.

Both woolen and worsted yarns made from alpaca are often blended with other animal or synthetic fibers to manufacture knitted products, such as sweaters or different kinds of cloth. (See Figure 10.2 for more on worsted and woolen processes and Figure 10.3 for product development.)[13,45,46,68,91,92]

Survey of European Alpaca Fiber Dealers and Processors

Processors always want to know what aspects of their processing need to be fine-tuned to fulfill the needs of their largely overseas clients. The importance of both objective and subjective fiber qualities was demonstrated in a 1993 survey of key European fiber dealers and processors that was conducted by South American processors to identify strategies to further sales and production in European countries (see Table 10.1). The survey illustrates the relative importance of various criteria, according to the fiber's end use. Europe is the world's largest consumer of camelid hair, which is usually purchased as tops and yarns.[95]

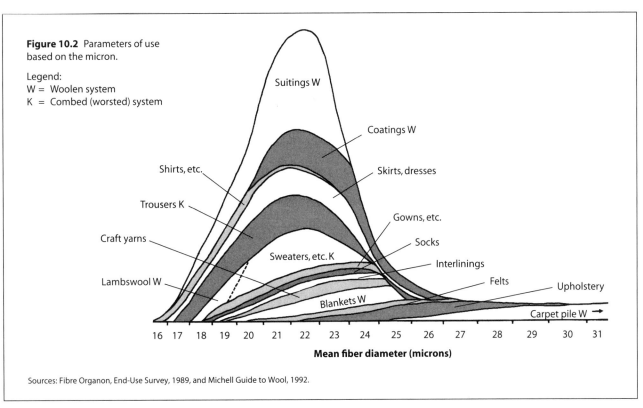

Figure 10.2 Parameters of use based on the micron.

Legend:
W = Woolen system
K = Combed (worsted) system

Suitings W
Coatings W
Shirts, etc.
Skirts, dresses
Trousers K
Gowns, etc.
Craft yarns
Socks
Sweaters, etc. K
Interlinings
Lambswool W
Felts
Upholstery
Blankets W
Carpet pile W →

Mean fiber diameter (microns)
16 17 18 19 20 21 22 23 24 25 26 27 28 29 30 31

Sources: Fibre Organon, End-Use Survey, 1989, and Michell Guide to Wool, 1992.

Figure 10.3 Sample analysis of alpaca blend products by Inca Tops.

Description	Long Fiber Spinning	Knit						
		By Hand	Rectilineo Manual	Rectilineo	Circular	Plain	Industrial Application	Socks
A Tops								
Alpaca fiber	1–2							
Wool	2							
Alpaca/wool blends	2							
Alpaca fiber semi-combed	2							
Wool superwash	2							
B Long Fiber Spinning								
Alpaca fiber								
Baby		1–2	1–2	1–2		1–2		
Suri		NA	NA	NA	NA	2		
Superfine		2	2	2	2	2		
Adults		3	3	3		3		
Wools								
Fine			1	1		1		
First quality		3	3	3		3	3	
Second quality		3	3	3		3	3	
Alpaca/Wool/Synthetic blends								
Baby/Fine		2	2	2		2		2
Superfine/First		1	1	1	1	1		1
Adults/Second		3	3	3			3	
Superfine/Acrylic			1	1	1			1
Adult/Wool/Acrylic		3	3	3			3	
Special blends								
Baby/Silk			1–2	1–2				
Superfine/Linen		2						
Suri/Mohair						2		
Superfine/Tencel		2	2	2		2		
C Short Fiber Spinning								
Pima cotton		2	2	2	2			
Tanguis cotton		3	3	3				
Organic cotton			3	3		3		
Special blends								
Pima cotton/Baby alpaca		1	1	1				1
Tanguis cotton/Fine wools			2	2		2		
Pima cotton/Silk		1						1
Pima cotton/Linen				1				
Pima cotton/Tencel				1				

Legend: 1 = Relatively high-priced products; 2 = Relatively medium-priced products; 3 = Relatively low-priced product; NA = Not available.

The relative values of various classes of fiber and blends above demonstrate the breadth of a large mill's efforts and their desire to develop new products.

Source: Thanks to Luis Chaves for sharing this material. Translated by Monica García Gamero.

Table 10.1 Alpaca fiber characteristics (in tops) as rated by European dealers and processors.

	Importance for Woven Goods	Importance for Knitwear
Fineness	4	2
Uniformity	4	2
Color	3	3
Color homogeneity	3	3
Length	2	2
Variability of length	1	1
Presence of dark hair*	3	1
Presence of dead hair*	1–3	1
Presence of impurities	2	2
Regularity of tops	2	2
Look	3	2
Feel	3	3

Legend: 4 = fundamental; 3 = very important; 2 = important; 1 = not very important

*The presence of dark or dead hair is most significant when dyeing is incorporated in processing. Black hair in otherwise white or light-colored tops causes problems, as does white or light hair in dark tops. Dead hair dyes less readily than hair that was alive when shorn. However, there are no set standards defining limits of acceptability for such factors in the alpaca industry. With cashmere, inconsistency cannot exceed 1 percent for weaving wool or .01 percent for lingerie. For alpaca fiber used by home (cottage industry) processors, standards are entirely individualistic.[60,68]

COTTAGE INDUSTRY AND SMALL-MILL FIBER PROCESSING

Alpaca fiber processing in North America, Australia, Europe, and New Zealand has been primarily a cottage industry. It is common for new alpaca owners to purchase a few alpacas and develop an interest in processing their own fleeces using their own methods.

During the early years of alpaca ownership in these countries, herd owners either sold their fleeces in raw form with no alteration, or processed the fiber themselves with their own equipment, or joined a fiber-processing cooperative made up of a large number of breeders. Of the new alpaca countries, breeders in Australia, the United States, England, and New Zealand have organized nationwide processing efforts. Pooling the annual clip helps to defray milling costs and allows alpaca breeders to meet the minimum volume (often a ton or more) of fiber that some large mills require for processing.

Of all the countries organized on a national scale, Australia may offer the most successful model because of its organization, widespread participation, and financial incentives for producing good-quality fleece. In other countries, such as the United States, the emergence of "mini-mills" that can process a single fleece or hundreds of fleeces into rovings and good-quality yarns has allowed owners of small and middle-sized herds to choose between processing their fiber as part of a cooperative or processing

their fiber with a mini-mill that tailors outcome to the specific needs of the client. Having a hassle-free way to convert raw fleece into yarn and then selling it (through retail markets, the Internet, etc.) is the desired level of involvement in processing for many alpaca owners. However, many owners who were unaware of the complexities of fiber processing when they purchased their first alpacas often find they want to become more involved in processing.

Many communities have spinning and weaving guilds, agricultural extension programs, and possibly community college courses where people can learn about different aspects of home-based fiber production. Several books on home processing are worth mentioning. The *Fiberworks Source Book* is an excellent book containing lists of weaving and spinning equipment (looms, fleece cleaners, carders, spindles, etc.), sources of many kinds of specialty fibers and dyes, lists of publications for the home processor, and names and addresses of associations and services catering to spinners and weavers throughout North America.[78]

Understanding the Spinning Wheel by Eric Corran is a detailed account of all aspects of the workings of several kinds of spinning wheels. *Small Looms in Action* by Elizabeth Jensen is excellent for novices wanting to assess their interest in using a small loom and home processing. *Turning Wool into a Cottage Industry* by Paula Simmons explains selling and marketing sheep fleece on a small scale in ways that are directly applicable to an alpaca farmer. In 1994, Coloradan Chris Switzer published *Spinning Llama and Alpaca,* which is one of the few books specific to alpacas and home processing, and she published a revised edition in 1998.[64] The book is self-published and unique because it has actual fiber samples glued to pages and many hand drawings of the general equipment needed to complete home processing. Both editions have lengthy bibliographies.[11,64,69,78,100,101,102]

Specialty manufacturers and distributors, such as Quality Llama Products of Lebanon, Oregon (fleece cleaning and shearing devices, shearing tables, restraining equipment, books, etc.), are also good resources for home processors.

Home processing is, of course, enjoyable to people who like working with fiber, but many alpaca breeders in North America and Australia have moved on to developing a "national clip," which involves a commercial processing mill that works with cooperatives. This doesn't necessarily involve new technology. In the early part of this century several small specialty mills operating in the United States processed raw alpaca shipped from South America. Alpaca processing will sustain itself in the United States and in Australia as long as it is economically feasible. A sustainable critical mass of fiber is needed. Several variables, such as volume, color, grading consistency, and degree to which fleeces are blended, will affect the approach that is adopted.[101] Breeders who organize and attempt to create a consistently high-quality fleece will find themselves benefiting the most from commercial processing.[29,95]

In some ways the approach to alpaca fiber production in Australia is similar to how cashmere and angora fiber markets were developed there. (See "The Challenge of Establishing a National Processing System in 'New Alpaca Countries'" in this chapter.)

YIELD

The *yield* is the amount of usable fiber after processing, or the difference between total and clean fleece weights. In Australia, yields from fiber animals are usually calculated after washing out impurities, drying, and adjusting moisture level to internationally accepted standards (17 percent) at 65 percent relative humidity and 20°C (68°F).* Guard hair or heavily medullated fibers that have characteristics that differentiate them from the prime fleece must be eliminated through dehairing before a yield can be calculated.

The yields of alpaca and llama fleeces, after sorting, vary according to the origin of the lot and the percentage of contamination it contains. In South America yields of 85 percent of gross weight are expected and common with huacayas and more than 90 percent with suris.[45,91] Preliminary Australian standards expect a 90 percent yield in huacayas.[29] In South America, the percentage each lot contains of a specific grade or class can vary a great deal. An outstanding lot, weighing around 121,000 pounds (55,000 kg) yielded over 39 percent baby, 46 percent superfine, 10 percent huarizo, and 5 percent coarse (see classification in Table 10.4).[45,46] An average lot will contain only about 10 percent baby, which illustrates the concern about the growing hybridization problem throughout the Andes.**

Alpacas and llamas usually produce a different quality of fleece. Llamas are generally referred to as two-coated, whereas alpacas are one-coated.[67,68,72] This generalization has exceptions. There are llamas with alpaca-quality fleeces and alpacas with coarse, two-coated fleeces of little commercial value. However, llama staple is usually composed of fine underhair intermixed with long and coarse guard hair. The range of the blanket fluctuates from 16 to 70 microns. Because of the guard hair, dehairing is necessary for optimal utilization. In South America potato sacks and ropes are often made from llama fiber that has not been dehaired.

Compared to alpaca fiber, the percentage of llama fiber processed by the textile industry in Peru is miniscule. However, this could change should dehairing technology become widespread. Llama fiber has the same smooth

scale structure that characterizes huacaya alpacas. In Bolivia, where llamas outnumber alpacas, leading camelid fiber processors are investing in specially designed European-manufactured dehairing machines, which will make llama a potentially more viable commercial fiber source.*** Guanaco, which is two-coated, has a very consistent fine undercoat and is second only to vicuña in value on the international fiber market.[59,65,67,79]

Vicuña fiber (the rarest of the world's specialty fibers) is sorted solely for fineness, because it comes in only one color and a staple length of around 2 inches (5.8 cm). Vicuña does contain some intermediate-sized medullated fiber within its downy fleece and for this reason must be dehaired by hand, a process that could be mechanized but would yield considerably less. Vicuña dehaired by machine yields approximately 65 percent and 75 percent when dehaired by hand. It used to be mechanically dehaired in Europe when there was sufficient commercial quantity available. Vicuña weighs only about 1.5 pound (500 g) per fleece.[52,53,58,59,83,90†]

The twenty-first century will most likely see limited harvesting of vicuña now that the species is recovering from near extinction and is categorized as "threatened," not "endangered," by the International Union for Conservation of Nature (IUCN). Several companies in Peru have been legally sorting vicuña fiber for the last 30 years, and Michell & CIA and other mills began harvesting fleeces in 1994.[52,53,56,68,83,90] (For a vicuña histogram, see "Histograms" in this chapter.)

Guanaco is a two-coated animal with a very fine undercoat, usually ranging between 14 and 19 microns.‡ The challenge in processing guanaco fiber is the necessity of dehairing it. Capturing and restraining wild guanacos is also costly and time-consuming. However, some attempts are underway to work with captive herds for fiber utilization. Like the vicuña, the guanaco's prime fleece is a single color. Guanaco fleece is a much underdeveloped resource, considering that guanacos are plentiful—600,000 in South America—and perhaps the most adaptable of the camelids. For more than a century young guanacos, known as *chulengos*, have been hunted for their pelts, which are often deliberately misrepresented as vicuña. In the fur trade young guanaco harvested for their pelts are known as

---

*Robert C. Couchman, personal communication, December 19, 1994.

**Luis Chaves, personal communication, October 27, 2001.

***Tito Bohrt, Bolivian minister of export and camelid fiber processor, personal communication, Arequipa, Peru, October 27, 2000.

†Robert Couchman, personal communication, December 19, 1994.

‡Adriana Maquire, guanaco researcher living in Argentina, personal communication, April 28, 2001 Angus and Margaret McColl, personal communication, Denver, Colorado, April 12, 2001.

guanaquitos,[42,65] and their pelts often have fleeces as fine as 14 microns, which is entirely comparable to vicuña.[11,42,59,65,67,68*] (For a guanaco histogram, see "Histograms" in this chapter.)

Paco-vicuña is the term used to describe offspring from the mating of a vicuña to an alpaca. Over the years several attempts have been made to cross alpacas and vicuñas, with the thought of capitalizing on the legendary vicuña fineness to create a finer-fleeced animal with an acceptable fleece weight and staple length. Vicuña fleece, though very fine, has meager staple length and minuscule fleece weight compared to most alpacas.[50]

In the United States an effort is underway to breed paco-vicuñas. Researchers at the Universidad de Nacional de Molina sampled five F-1 paco-vicuña fleeces in eight zones across the body, and declared two classes of fleeces based on average diameter ranges. The three finer fleeces comprising one class averaged 13.29 microns, while two other fleeces averaged 17.34 microns. The staple length for both paco-vicuña groups averaged 1.29 inches (3.46 cm), which is about .96 inches longer than most vicuñas. The study concluded that the differences between the two groups were due to differences in average fiber diameters in the fleeces of the alpaca mothers. This assumption was based on the fact that the vicuña fathers of the paco-vicuñas were steadfastly consistent in their micron diameters, within a very small range, usually between 12 and 14 microns. The study concluded that the best results from such crosses are achieved if the alpaca is fine-fleeced. The ages of the animals were not reported.[11]

During a trip to northern Chile, the author collected fiber samples of five animals identified as two-year-old paco-vicuñas. This group had longer fleeces (3 inches or 7.62 cm) than those described in the Universidad de Nacional de Molina study, and were somewhat coarser. The results of these histograms are found in Table 10.2.

Table 10.2 Histogram results of young adult paco/vicuñas.

Fiber Samples	1	2	3	4	5	6
Average fiber diameter in microns (AFD)	18.5	18.9	21.3	21.7	24.2	26.1
Standard deviation (SD)	4.3	4.9	4.5	4.2	4.5	6.6
Coefficient of variation (CV)	23.2	25.9	21.1	19.4	18.6	25.3
% microns >30	2.0	3.4	4.9	3.4	8.7	19.0

Source: Eric Hoffman, unpublished data, Arica, Chile, October 22, 1998.

*Adriana Maquire, personal communication, April 28, 2001.

MICROSCOPIC STRUCTURE AND CHEMICAL MAKEUP OF ALPACA FIBER

Most people working with alpacas become conversant in talking about desirable, tactile qualities of alpaca fiber. But few people expand their learning to include microscopic aspects of the fiber that make it a unique organic material.

Just as knowledge of the physical properties of metal cable allowed engineers to build the Golden Gate Bridge, an understanding of the microscopic properties and chemical bonds of fiber allows alpaca growers to analyze, assess, and intelligently breed their animals for optimal results. Compared to sheep's wool, knowledge of the complex chemistry of alpaca fiber is in the rudimentary stages.

Basic Structure

Alpaca fiber shares the basic structural characteristics of other wools (see Figures 10.4 and 10.5). The outside surface of each fiber is called the *cuticle,* which is made up of tiny *scales.* On huacaya the scales have an irregular, uneven fit. The edges of the scales are *serrated* and often slightly elevated from the fiber shaft. The nature of the scales allows huacaya fiber to grip one another during the spinning process, which results in strong threads and yarns. The cuticle and scales form a sheath around the inner structure, known as the *cortical region* or *cortex,* where the fiber's strength and elasticity lie. The cortical cells, sometimes called *fibrils,* lie parallel to each other. They usually vary from 80 to 110 microns long and 2 to 5 microns across. In

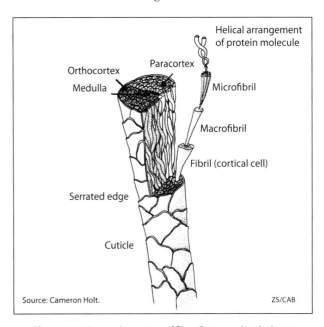

Source: Cameron Holt.   ZS/CAB

Figure 10.4 Internal structure of fiber. Cutaway sketch shows major components and subcomponents of cortical cells.

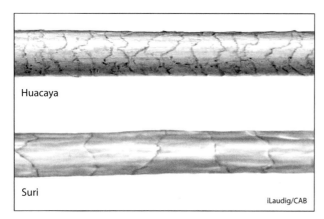

Figure 10.5 Differences between huacaya and suri fiber are readily apparent in scale structure. Longer, flatter scales typify suri. Huacaya has a more protrudent scale structure. Scales affect handling and processing characteristics. The scales on both huacaya and suri are less protrudent than scales found on sheep's wool, which is the reason alpaca fiber generally has superior handle compared to most sheep's wool.

shape they are flat, not round, and often twisted. The fibrils are embedded in an adhesive material. The chemical bonds between and within the fibrils are affected by the dietary intake of the animal, sun, scouring agents, dyes (including bleaches), and tension.[3,66,99,110,111,115]

Chemical Composition and General Health

Fiber is a protein structure, which means that the fiber's structural soundness depends on the animal's good health for the entire period between shearings. Generally, wool fibers, like alpaca, are composed of a complex protein called keratin. Common body parts of nonalpaca creatures, fingernails, hooves, and feathers also consist of keratin.[3,52,66,72,103] More than 20 different formations of amino acid have been identified in various wools, and they can unite to form thousands of combinations of bonds. The amino acids hook together in long chains called polypeptides. The appearance and physical shape of fiber and its ability to recover after deformation (tension, crushing, violent jerking, etc.) are directly related to the nature of the bonds that hold the peptide chains together in stable arrangements.

Success in working with fiber comes from understanding that many forces can destabilize these bonds and then minimizing these negative influences. During fiber processing, when attempts are made to manipulate particular qualities, other qualities may be altered as well. For example, the chemicals used in dyeing may strengthen the chemical bonds in the cortex or destabilize them. One wool researcher in the 1940s likened the study of the internal bonding agents in wool to a train wreck: "It is as though a wrecked train uncoupled into dining cars, sleeping cars,

and coaches, instead of shattering into glass, steel, and fabric."[49] In other words, the ingredients that hold fiber together can be identified, but how they interact in times of stress remains mostly a mystery. More research is needed to understand the bonding structures of alpaca fiber.

Studies have shown that the molecular configurations in fiber structure have a direct bearing on the way fibers stretch and recover—that is, the fiber's tensile strength, elasticity, resilience, and other resistant and reforming properties.[63,66] The term *tender breaks* refers to weaknesses along a section of staple or throughout a fleece, usually caused by environmental factors (poor diet, sickness, etc.) that have compromised the formation of the bonding agents within the fiber. The factors that influence fiber strength are also closely related to the fiber's softness and *handle* (feel) and the ability of a garment to adjust to the stresses of daily use. The test of a good fiber is its ability to be subjected to stress again and again and yet retain its shape. For example, ironing a fabric "sets" the fiber in a desired pattern through the use of heat and pressure, but the set will come out as soon as the fiber is wetted and the fiber will revert to its true nature.[45,46,49] A fiber that can withstand setting and resetting and still retain its original nature demonstrates the long-lasting resiliency that makes it a viable product.

The strains on the fiber's internal structure during manufacturing are also important considerations. Fiber is strained in carding, gilling, combing, drafting, and spinning. Mills in Arequipa attempt to release these strains and avoid permanent changes in the fiber by allowing it to rest at different stages in processing. Also, each method of processing presents different stress problems. In the industrial process, resting is combined with drying or increasing moisture, depending on the requirements of the next step of the process. Resting often lasts for 24 to 48 hours. The small processor who understands the benefits of minimizing stress and allowing for rests along the way may produce a longer-lasting product.

Bilateral Cortical Cells

In sheep and other fiber-producing animals that show crimp in their locks, two subcategories of cortical cells are evenly divided along the length of the fiber: the *paracortex* and the *orthocortex*. The orthocortex is always found on the outside edge of the crimp and the fiber is always crimpy (see Figure 10.6). Scientists are not entirely sure how this division of cells in the cortex causes crimp, but there is no doubt that its presence is always associated with it. Bilateral division exists in many of the finer huacayas, but not in suris or in coarse and solidly medullated fibers.

These cortical cells make up varying percentages of the fiber mass, being highest in fine fibers, where 90 percent of

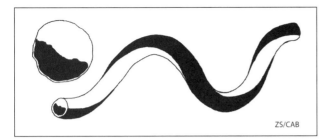

Figure 10.6 Roles of the orthocortex and the paracortex in the creation of crimp.

the fiber may be cortical material. Ian Stapleton of the Melbourne College of Textiles described the roles of the two key structural components of alpaca fiber in a talk to alpaca growers in 1992:

> Cortical cells are the load-bearing elements of fiber, whereas the cuticle imparts the inherent aesthetic qualities of the fiber such as softness of handle and luster. Other functions of the cuticle concern water repellency, felting during washing, and resistance to chemical and physical attack. The entire assembly is held together by a glue called intercellular cement.[98,99]

Medullation

Medullation is generally thought of as a characteristic accompanying coarse fiber or guard hair. In fact until recently (2004), reports from highly respected fiber scientists in South America asserted that the amount of medullation in huacaya alpacas was directly correlated to the micron, and that the lowest micron range (15–20 μm) was without medullation. There is a strong correlation between increased medullation and greater micron. However, a recent comprehensive study by Christopher Lupton, Robert Stobart, and Yocom–McColl Testing Laboratories employed a newly developed method of scanning for medullation, and proved that alpacas, more than most other kinds of fiber-producing livestock, can have medullated fibers in the lowest of micron ranges, not just in the coarser fibers where it is expected to be.

There is apparently great variability from one alpaca to the next. For example, when a fiber sample from two animals of approximately the same age and from the same herd were tested, they both had generally similar histograms in terms of AFD, SD, CV, and microns over 30, but one of the alpacas sampled possessed 32 percent medullated fiber, while the other alpaca had only 3 percent medullated fiber. (In the vicuña, the parent species to the alpaca, medullation has been detected in fiber as low as 8 microns.) It is now believed that the frequency of medullation in different micron ranges can vary a great deal between two alpacas who otherwise have very similar histograms.[58,61]

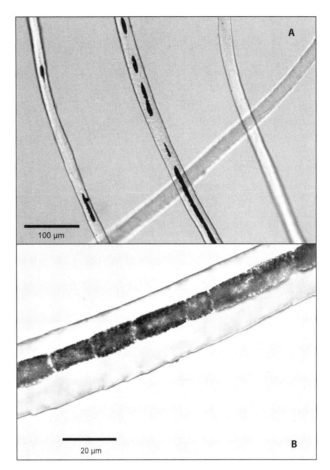

Figure 10.7 Medullation is associated with coarser fibers in most fiber-producing animals, including alpacas. However, alpacas are unique in that often fine fiber is also medullated. **A** This image shows uniform suri fibers of low microns (approximately 20). Two of these fibers are partially medullated but otherwise the same as the other fibers. **B** Fully medullated fiber in vicuñas, the parent species, occasionally occurs in fiber as fine as 8 to 12 microns, but it is more likely to occur in the coarser fibers.

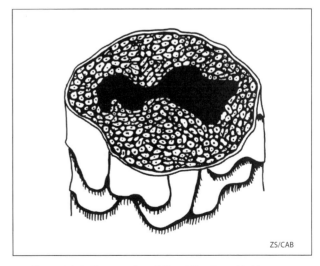

Figure 10.8 Close-up of medullated fiber (guard hair).

Hair follicles are the tiny microscopic (sometimes barely visible without magnification), porelike openings covering the surface of a fiber animal's skin. Each hair follicle is the source of a single hair. A fiber-producing animal's (alpaca, sheep, goat, etc.) fleece is made up of all the hairs produced by all the follicles. Hair follicle density is directly correlated to fleece density. Follicle distribution on the skin is inherited.

All fiber-bearing animals have two basic kinds of hair follicles: primaries and secondaries. Usually there are far more secondary follicles than primaries. Primary follicles, which include sweat glands, are often surrounded by secondary follicles. The discrepancy in size of the openings between the primary and secondary follicles has a direct bearing on the uniformity and quality of a fleece. If the primary follicles are large, they are apt to produce thick, medullated fiber (or guard hair) and contribute to a two-coated fleece. If the opening in primary follicles is small and similar in size to the surrounding secondary follicles, the overall fleece will be uniform and fine.[3,16,66,72,96,103,110]

In nature, the coarse, medullated, straight fiber produced by primary follicles is often called guard hair, because it guards the animal's undercoat by repelling debris that would otherwise cling or penetrate the undercoat and possibly inundate and irritate the animal's skin. Wild guanacos and even the fine-fleeced vicuña have guard hair and downy undercoats (see Figure 10.8).[3,13,44]

In domesticated fiber-bearing alpacas that are selectively bred to make the best possible fleece, the primary fibers are reduced in size until the hairs produced by them are no different in diameter than the surrounding secondary fibers. Selective breeding has also sought increases in the percentage of secondary fibers. (This attention to reducing the influence of primary follicles in a fleece's uniformity has occurred in sheep and goat breeding for centuries.) There is no doubt that pre-Incan civilizations bred alpacas selectively and reduced the primary follicle size substantially to produce fleeces more uniform than most fleeces being produced today. Today's alpacas often have significant size discrepancies between primary and secondary follicle sizes and therefore have significant amounts of medullated fibers in their fleeces.*

Since the Conquest (1532), nowhere is the evidence of inattention to breeding for fleece quality more glaring than the great numbers of two-coated alpacas contributing to the national clip in the alpaca heartland, Peru, and elsewhere. The hair follicle challenge for today's alpaca grower is to reduce the size discrepancies between primary and secondary hair follicles and increase the number of secondary follicles through selective breeding practices.[112,113]

*Luis Chaves, personal communication, January 24, 2001.

EVALUATING ALPACA FIBER

One of the more fascinating and elusive areas of research for this book was the assessment of fiber in measurable terms. Perhaps the biggest surprise was to learn there are no universally accepted standards for evaluating alpaca fiber, although there are generalized criteria and a general agreement that alpaca is a high-quality specialty fiber. For the newcomer to alpacas, attempting to learn about assessing fiber quality is often baffling. The spectrum of information ranges from objective (or quantitative) criteria, such as diameter, staple length, and color, to subjective factors such as the relative importance of crimp, handle, and luster.

Which of these (and other) factors are most important? This is a frequently asked question. The lack of a universally accepted official standard is partly to blame for the confusion and misunderstanding that sometimes occur in attempts to prioritize the most important qualities. The following discussion is an effort to identify fiber criteria, simplify them, and explain some of the ambiguities.

Although the often-cited evaluation criteria used by fiber processors overlaps to a large degree with the criteria that alpaca breeders use, the priorities for processor and breeder are not always the same. Moreover, information about evaluating fiber often does not distinguish between these priorities. For example, producing high-density fleeces is an important criterion for the breeder because it means greater volume and weight per animal—and therefore greater profit. To the fiber processor density produced by a particular animal is not so important, providing there is enough volume, consistency, and quality in the fleeces procured to do the job at hand. Although increasing fiber density is an important goal for all breeders, universally accepted density counts for alpacas (such as those for breeds of sheep) are practically nonexistent in South America, which adversely affects informed breeding decisions in this important area. The literature contains very little data on density, probably because processors are defining the qualities that are important, and density is not their priority.

Breeders should be aware that at times artificial criteria have been highly promoted and become popular but have little bearing on end use. For example, during the 1990s, the direction of curl in the locks of suris was promoted by some North American breeders as indicative of a superior fleece. There is no evidence to support such a claim. The amount of wool coverage (distribution of fiber between the ears and down the lower legs) and the style of crimp were promoted as ultimate traits for huacayas; however, according to many experts both criteria are only tangential to the essential qualities for processing. In this book the greatest emphasis is given to those criteria that are directly related to processing and end use—see the fiber wheel in Figure 10.9. Criteria that may be given great weight by some alpaca breeders but is of marginal or secondary importance to creating an end-product receive less coverage.[26,48,50,95,96]

When Derek Michell of Michell & CIA, the largest alpaca raw fleece buyer in the world, was asked what qualities he felt were most important in huacaya fleeces, he said, "Smooth handle, absence of guard hair, fineness, sheen, and density." The primary importance of handle was reiterated by several plant managers at various mills in Arequipa, as well as home spinners and small mill operators in Australia, Europe, and North America (see Tables 10.3, 10.4, and 10.5).

Note that the three processors, Derek Michell (Table 10.3), Luis Chaves (Table 10.4), and Gilberto Sarfaty (Table 10.5) highlighted the same key qualities, while the fiber scientist, Dr. Tumen Wuliji (Table 10.9), highlighted similar primary qualities, with mention of secondary and tertiary qualities. It is worth noting that Dr. Wuliji made

his list without ever seeing or conversing with the processors. It is not surprising that the processors did not mention the importance of fleece weight for individual animals. From their perspective the qualities of the fiber are more important than the number of fleeces it might take to fulfill an order. To the animal owner attempting to maximize the amount of good quality fleece produced from each animal, fleece weight is an important goal. (Note that when the same men were contacted in 2005, two years after the first edition of this book was printed, none of them wanted to change the essential characteristics they had pointed out for the first edition.)

FIBER VALUE AND COLOR

Perhaps the greatest gift alpacas have given to the natural fiber world is the tremendous diversity of color that was bred into them for centuries. Clearly, color diversification was appreciated and encouraged by the Inca pastoralists and their forerunners. To this day, alpacas with colored fleeces

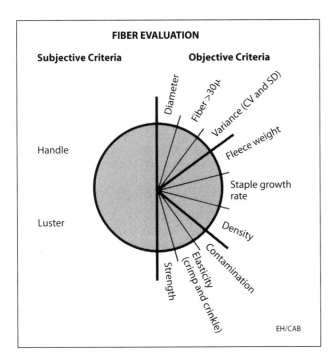

Figure 10.9 The fiber wheel identifies key components in assessing fiber. Some of these components can be measured in objective terms (right side of the wheel) and other criteria are assessed by subjective means (left side of the wheel). The standard histogram produced by laser scanning measures mostly the categories in the upper right corner of the wheel. The proportions assigned to each category don't necessarily represent the importance of that category.[47,50]

Table 10.3 Derek Michell's premium fiber characteristics.

Smooth handle
Absence of guard hair
Fineness
Sheen
Density

Source: Conversation with Derek Michell at Michell and CIA headquarters in Arequipa, Peru, October 27, 2001; reaffirmed by e-mail, September 2005.

Table 10.4 Luis Chaves's premium fiber characteristics.

Fineness
No medullation
Handle
Luster
Density
Cleanliness

Source: Phone conversation with Luis Chaves, general manager of Inca Tops, Arequipa, Peru, April 1, 2003; reaffirmed by e-mail, September 2005.

Table 10.5 Gilberto Sarfaty's primary fiber qualities.

Fineness
No medullation and reduced coefficient of variation
Handle
Luster
Density
Cleanliness

Source: E-mail from Gilberto Sarfaty, general manager of Prosur, Arequipa, Peru, April 1, 2003; reaffirmed by e-mail, September 2005.

are generally preferred for home use by the traditional Quechua and Aymara pastoralists living on the puna.

In recent years, color has played an important part in determining value in the international alpaca fiber market. But trends and fads can influence color value, and the colors that garner the highest prices have not stayed constant. For example, for most of the 1980s, alpaca growers on the puna were often paid double the price for white fiber by the large mills. Pricing favored white because it is the easiest to dye and works well in blends to lighten other colors.

This high price had a sudden impact on fleece color in herds associated with the mills. In a period of 10 years, 80 percent of the fleeces received at the mills were white or light fawn, whereas just 10 years earlier, 80 percent were dark colors and only 20 percent were white. By means of intense inbreeding and line breeding, dark colors were literally flushed from the herds (breeding white to white and culling dark) to make way for premium prices on white.[25] This breeding strategy proved to be a somewhat shortsighted response when demand in Europe increased for undyed, darker natural colors (which had been culled). Also, dyeing techniques became more sophisticated, allowing greater latitude in working with a wide range of colors.

The large mills in Peru, encouraged by these trends, began pushing the value and beauty of natural colors, because it is less costly to process fiber if dyeing can be avoided. Though Arequipa mills have made significant progress in developing organic dyes that don't affect alpaca's wonderful handle, many of the traditional dyes used around the world compromise the smooth handle unique to alpaca fiber.*

By 2001, white and light fawn were still strong colors, making up 65 percent of the inbound fiber for Michell & CIA, and 35 percent were colored fleeces.** Since the 1980s (80 percent white and light fawn), both value and demand have shifted toward a wider range of colors, with rarer colors fetching the highest prices. For example, silver grey (#401) and true black (#501) on the Michell fiber chart were in short supply in 2000. However, Derek Michell points out that, for a color to have a following in the marketplace and consistent value, there needs to be enough of it in specific classes to supply processors and other outlets on a regular basis. For colors that are rare and in demand, high value and premium prices may be the result.*** Fashion trends, clever marketing, and new technologies influence the popularity of certain colors.[1,13,43,44,45,46,50,95,119]

Breeding for a particular color is one of the more intriguing aspects of fiber production in alpacas, but any discussion of color should include the importance of color consistency.[15,32,43,46,91] Color is judged by eye, not by instruments. Business agreements with the Peruvian mills are often based solely on citing a color on a color chart. In such arrangements color consistency can make the difference between an angry customer and a satisfied one. Blending different colors to achieve a particular color is the means processors use to maintain color consistency.

In North America, Australia, New Zealand, and Europe, color diversity is great, but the number of fleeces produced annually is minuscule compared to South America. In these developing alpaca fiber markets, fiber bound for a cottage industry type of market generally embraces a variety of natural colors, but as the volume of a developing alpaca country increases, breeders usually band into fiber co-ops and processing mills become involved. At this juncture, a variety of colors makes processing more difficult and expensive. (See "The Challenge of Establishing a National Fiber-Processing System in 'New Alpaca Countries'" in this chapter.) However, emphasizing a specific rare color of the best-quality fleece may be the surest path to establish a strong niche market, based on rareness and quality. Vicuña, cashmere, and other top-of-the-market natural fibers hold high prices, providing the fiber is very fine and uniform. If a fleece's "soundness" is confirmed, value is defined by buyer preference and salesmanship—not necessarily by the color trends created by volume manufacturing for South America or European fashion houses.

Since the inception of the alpaca business in North America in 1983, top-quality fleece of all colors has sold for top dollar. To avoid repeating the color depletion that occurred in South America, breeders need to be wary of promoting a particular color at the expense of other colors, but color is a catch-22 because enough dependable volume needs to be produced to supply a market. Properly promoting color diversity allows for broader market participation and greater excitement for alpaca breeders and their customers.[43,44,45,50,91] If fiber processing were compared to a poker game, color would be the wild card.

---

*Ignacio Garaycochea, personal communication, May 15, 2001; John Callen, former executive with Burlington Industries and alpaca breeder, personal communication, Farmingham, Massachussets, April 12, 2001.

**Raul Rivera, executive at Michell & CIA, personal communication, May 12, 2001.

***Derek Michell, personal communication, May 12, 2001.

OBJECTIVE CRITERIA FOR EVALUATING FIBER

Sorting Classes Based on Fineness

Table 10.6 shows the classification system for fineness used by one of the largest processing entities in Peru, Grupo Inca. Table 10.7 shows the classifications of Michell & CIA. The South American fineness classes change from time to time. For example, for many years the finest class of alpaca was "baby alpaca," which is 20 to 22 microns. The name is derived from the fact that most of the best fleeces come from *tuis* (approximately 18 months old). At Grupo Inca, which includes many other companies, the finest category is now Royal (19.5 microns). The budding commercial entities in Australia and North America have suggested their own sorting classes for fineness that reflect an assessment of the national clip and realistic divisions within the clip. The American Society for Testing Materials (ASTM) also has a different system than the ones employed in Peru, but it is largely ignored in South America, Australia, and Europe, where most of the processing takes place.[18,29,62] Even in South America, 100 percent standardization of class names and diameter ranges is not in effect. It is common to hear two different names for the same class, even within the same consortium.

Vicuña fiber is sometimes processed and graded as a separate class, which is characterized between 12 and 16 microns and requires dehairing (removal of guard hairs). Vicuña is graded only for its fineness, since it comes in only one color phase. Also it is rarely dyed. With vicuña it is typical for about 15 percent of fleeces to be composed of medullated fiber. Even the medullated fiber is usually not greater than 30 microns.[11,68,83,88,89,90,92]

Guanaco, which isn't often processed in the Peruvian mills, is a much overlooked fiber resource. A fiber-class category for guanaco fiber does not exist in the lexicon of the Peruvian mills, where most of the world's alpaca and vicuña is processed. In part this is because guanacos have been hunted to near extinction in Peru, which means the largest concentrations of guanacos are far to the south in Patagonia. There are more than 600,000 guanacos living in South America, mostly in southern Argentina, Chile, and Tierra del Fuego.

The guanaco is two-coated with an undercoat that is very consistent in length and fineness. The undercoat, also known as "down," usually ranges between 14 and 19 microns, and even in older animals rarely exceeds 20 microns. The fleece weight is approximately 2.5 pounds (800 g). The undercoat's staple length is 3.5 centimeters (1.3 in.), which is suitable for the woolen process but below the 7.1

Table 10.6 Grupo Inca's classifications for alpaca fiber fineness.

Huacaya Grades or Classifications	Fiber Diameter in Microns (µm)
Royal	19.5
Superfine (also fleece and fine spinning)	25–26
Huarizo*	30–31
Adult alpaca	32–33.5
Coarse alpaca	34–35
Harsh alpaca	>37
Suri Classifications	
Baby suri	23
Suri	26–27
Huarizo suri	32
Coarse suri	34

Huarizo is the hybrid offspring of an alpaca female and llama male, but here the term refers to a fleece classification\ that may have no connection to an actual animal.

Source: Luis Chaves, personal communication, April 10, 2001.

Table 10.7 Michell & CIA classifications for alpaca fiber fineness.

Huacaya Grades or Classifications	Fiber Diameter in Microns (µm)
Baby	20–22
Superfine (also fine spinning)	25.5
Adult	27.5
Huarizo*	32
Llama**	34
Coarse	34–36
Suri Grade Classifications*	
Baby	21–23
Regular (average)	25–27.5
Coarse	>30

Huarizo is the hybrid offspring of an alpaca female and llama male, but here the term refers to a fleece classification that may have no connection to an actual animal.

**Llama* on fineness charts should also be considered only as a class of fiber that may or may not have originated from a llama. Llama fiber (in today's Andes) is generally two-coated and requires dehairing if it is to be used for fashionable garments. Some alpacas with poor-quality fleeces have coats that can contain both fine and coarse fiber. A poor-quality alpaca fleece may require dehairing. A dehaired product can be very fine and considered high quality.

***It is not common to sort suri because it represents a miniscule fraction of the total of commercial production compared to the volume in all other alpaca categories. (Juan Pepper, expert in suri processing at Michell & CIA, Arequipa, Peru, personal communication, March 15, 1999.)

Source: Ignacio Garaycochea, personal communication, May 15, 2001.

centimeter (2.8 in.) minimum length for alpaca in the worsted process. Yearling guanacos average an impressive 15 microns. The guard hair can be as coarse as 50 microns on adults; thus the fleece must be dehaired to utilize it properly.[39,42,65,67,68,69,79*]

*Adriana Maquire, Oscar Adot, and Sergio Heimsath, guanaco researchers, personal communication, Buenos Aires, Argentina, April 24, 2001.

Sorting and Classification of Colors

Both matching and sorting fleeces for color are based on sight, using color keys developed by processors, and can be highly accurate. This process can also be done accurately and precisely by machine, but in Peru the industry has chosen to rely on subjective appraisal.* While the fiber is being sorted into the appropriate class for fineness, it is also separated into colors.

Alpaca fiber is classified into seven basic colors: white, black, fawn, tan, red, brown, and grey. The piebald classification (sometimes called *pinto* in North America) is not a separate color, but refers to a two-colored coat in the blanket area (usually a dark color on white). There are two categories of natural colors: pure colors (occurring on an animal) and blended or streaky colors (mixed after shearing). Pure colors range from white to black, with many colors in between. Blends are usually created by adding one color to another during processing to achieve the desired color. Blends occupy the same color spectrum as pure colors. Blends are often created to ensure the color consistency and volume of a desired color.[43,44,45]

At Michell & CIA over 40 different colors can be distinguished, both solid and blended. Some companies within its Inca Group may have a color chart (or color card) with 30 colors, while others may have charts with only 20 colors. Usually about half the offerings on any color chart are blends. Peter Kothe, former volume fleece buyer for Michell & CIA, says more than 250 shades have been identified. Once fiber has been sorted according to color and fineness, it is usually packed in 220-pound (10-kg) bales with identifying tags and sent to an industrial plant for processing.[43,44,45]

Though standardization generally exists in more basic, naturally occurring solid colors, frequent changes in colors offered to purchasing agents are a source of confusion. Offerings are influenced by constantly changing market forces and fluctuating supplies of certain colors. The color identification list in Table 10.8 and the color charts in this chapter use the nomenclature of Michell & CIA and Prosur. This information expresses the color identification efforts of two of the largest processing groups in Peru, where most of the world's exported alpaca originates. Alpaca organizations in the new alpaca countries have made their own charts, and though they may not offer as many colors, they are often based on the charts originating at the mills in Arequipa. A study of the charts and list shows the attempt throughout the South American alpaca industry to standardize color identification, although significant discrepancies still exist among the various charts. (See the Michell & CIA and Prosur color charts in this chapter.)

*Raul Rivera, personal communication, May 12, 2001.

Table 10.8 Michell & CIA (Inca Group) alpaca tops color identification codes and names.

100 B white	409 GO charcoal grey
101 BMC clear stained white	404 LG4 dark grey
102 BMO-N dark stained white	510 PO dark/middle grey
201 LFX light fawn X	403 LG3 middle grey
202 LF2 light fawn (slightly darker)	402 LG2 middle silver gray
203 LFY light fawn Y (slightly darker)	401 LG1 light silver grey
204 LFR light fawn (medium fawn)	208 LT/GC light fawn/taupe
205 LFZ light fawn Z (slightly darker)	211 MRG light rose grey
209 GCC (light brown)	489 GC/GO medium rose grey
301 CC light brown	700 IG medium rose grey
302 COM dark stained brown	306 DK/GC dark rose grey
410 G brown/black	326 GA darkest rose grey
350 COM/N black/brown	408 GC dark taupe
360 CON dark brown	206 PC/Z dark/medium taupe
500 N black	267 PC medium taupe
501 NM stained black	207 PC/X light fawn

Source: Presented in a paper delivered by J. Francois Patthey Salas, Inca Group, at a specialty fiber symposium in Italy in 1993. Later, these classifications were expanded to include 22 colors now depicted on Michell's "Natural Colors MFH Tops" fiber chart and much of Prosur's fiber chart. The identifer numbers listed above can be matched to the "Natural Colors MFH Tops" chart. The color descriptions following each number were supplied by the author to assist the reader in applying the identifier number to an actual color or gradient of a color.[60]

The color list and the charts are necessary for a purchaser choosing a color. They also help breeders to identify and name the colors in their herds. By locating the letter symbol (e.g., BMC) on the chart and correlating it with the symbol and name on the color list (e.g., BMC clear stained white), you can gain a working knowledge of the most widely used color identifications.

Staple Length

The length of staple (length of fiber an animal generates between shearings) is an important criterion in judging fleece. Staple length plus density constitute volume and fleece weight. Strangely, however, the rate an alpaca regrows (or regenerates) its coat is often overlooked in judging fleeces on live animals. Breeders attempting to breed for greater fleece weights should record staple lengths each year during shearing as a means of assessing this important characteristic.

In a nutritionally consistent setting, fleece regrowth among huacayas may vary as much as 2 to 6.2 inches (5–16 cm) in a 12-month period, demonstrating plenty of room for improvement through selective breeding. An average growth rate of around 5 inches (12.7 cm) annually should be expected, although regrowth occurs more slowly with each successive shearing. Also, slower growth should be expected as the alpaca ages.[10,24,26,28,47,50,51,59,64,68,70,71,108,116,117] Consequently, in South America, as alpacas approach middle age, their diminishing productivity (when they can no longer generate enough fleece or a "sound fleece") becomes a decisive factor in butchering. Fleece productivity usually diminishes somewhere between 8 and 12 years of age.[68]

For commercial milling a minimum staple length of about 2.8 to 4 inches (7–10 cm) is sufficient for all textile purposes, including both worsted and woolen processing.[70,97,102] In South America this desired length is usually achieved on an annual basis, resulting in the yearly shearing of many large herds, but often herds are shorn at 14- to 16-month intervals as well.* Suris generally regenerate their fleeces faster than huacayas. Some suris could be shorn twice in a year.

For the home spinner living elsewhere on the planet, desirable lengths may vary a great deal, depending on the requirements of the user. The wise alpaca grower attempts to harvest fleeces with the most desirable staple length, keeping in mind that the longer a fleece stays on an animal, the more prone it is to matting, contaminants (cottings), and deterioration related to sun bleaching. Health considerations also figure into the time for shearing.[40] Breeders must consider the winter and summer coat needs of the alpaca (see Chapter 11: Fleece Preparation and Shearing and Chapter 4: Husbandry).

Density

Density refers to the number of hair follicles per square inch (or millimeter) and is usually measured by counting the follicles (with an emphasis on secondary follicles) on the skin. Tests for density are expensive, difficult, and time-consuming to carry out; they require a skin biopsy and scientific equipment.

Fiber density and staple length are the primary variables contributing to a fleece's volume and weight. Together volume and weight are often referred to as *productivity*. Besides its obvious contribution to volume, the greater impenetrability of a truly dense fleece decreases the likelihood of contaminants and tip damage in the fleece. The tightness of the locks shields the fleece's interior from the elements. For all these reasons, increasing density through breeding is a desirable goal.

Ironically, scant data exist in South America (or anywhere else) on the density parameters for alpacas, which is especially surprising because for other wool and fiber breeding programs, increasing density is a major area of emphasis. Without established parameters of acceptability based on density counts to guide breeding decisions, improving density becomes a highly subjective and inexact exercise at best.

Like sheep and goats, alpacas have both primary and secondary follicles. The primary follicles appear in rows in groups of three and the secondary follicles are grouped around them. Generally, the higher the ratio of secondary follicles to primary follicles, the greater the density. The greatest densities are usually found along the ribs (known as the prime fleece area).

Most commonly the results of follicle counts are expressed per square millimeter (mm^2). Wuliji found that crias from the same herd had a mean of 32.7 mm^2, which he attributed to the smaller body size of crias. Dr. Wuliji reasoned that crias are denser than adults because of their smaller body. As an alpaca grows in size the number of skin follicles stays the same. As the animal's skin expands its follicles spread out, resulting in a less dense fleece. The alpacas in his study came from the Putre region in northern Chile. Thirty-nine animals were used in the study.**

Dr. Jim Watts of Australia, using samples collected by Janie Hicks during a stay in Peru, reported a mean follicle density of 42.7 per mm^2. Hicks collected from skin samples of 63 live alpacas from several sources in Peru, whose owners were asked to present the best animals in their herds. The highest density in this group was an 18-month-old male (presumably not fully grown) that had a follicle density of 75 per mm^2. [88,90***]

Watts also reported that an alpaca grown in Australia had a density of 91 per mm^2, but this animal was 14 months of age and presumably about half grown.[112] The animal's adult density was not reported, but when assessing follicle density one can expect an alpaca's density to decrease by about 30 percent from cria age to adulthood, judging by the data collected by Tumen Wuliji. By comparison, adult vicuña skins have been assessed to have 72 to 95 follicles per mm^2, which is similar to top Merino sheep and somewhere between two to three times the mean follicle densities of alpacas.[88,90***] Converted from follicle counts per square millimeter to follicle counts per square inch, here's how alpacas compare to the most dense sheep breeds: Wiltshire, 7,350; Lincoln, 9,420 (like most alpacas); Corriedale, 14,800 to 19,400 (like some alpacas); and Merino (fine), 36,800 to 65,100 (most like vicuñas and the densest alpacas).

There are different views on how to increase density in alpacas. One of the more publicized approaches has been put forth by Dr. James Watts. In Australia, Dr. Watts was a

---

*Ignacio Garaycochea, personal communication, May 15, 2001.

**Dr. Tumen Wuliji, fiber scientist (formerly with Agresearch, New Zealand), personal communication, Langston University, Oklahoma, August 24, 2002.

***James Watts, PhD, MVSc, and Janie Hicks, written communication, March 28, 2001.

ASSESSING FLEECE DENSITY

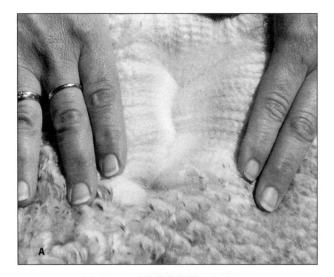

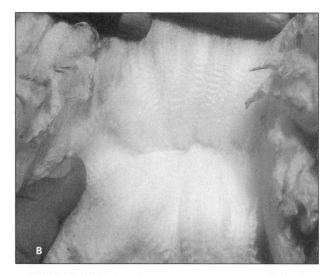

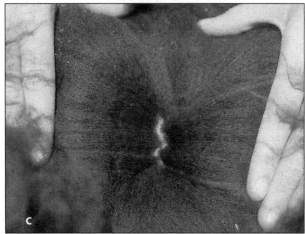

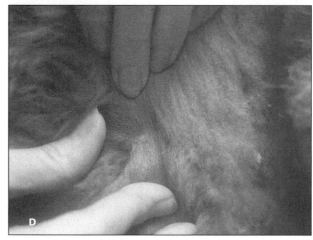

Follicle density testing indicates that alpacas are generally about 30 to 50 percent as dense as their wild progenitor, the vicuña. Usually adult alpacas have a density between 20 and 45 follicles per square millimeter, with the upper range (which is rare) of around 70 to 80 follicles per square millimeter for adults. Adult vicuñas consistently have a density of around 90 follicles per square millimeter along their neck and back. On other parts of their body, density is around 75 follicles per square millimeter. Density is predictable in different zones of their fleece; this may also be true of alpacas but at lower densities. Follicle density testing, which requires removing a plug of live skin, is not practical for most alpaca owners. Instead, density can best be judged by comparing animals. The thickness of the fleece when it is compressed on both sides of the part and the amount of visible skin at the part site are indicators of density.

A is a dense, crimpy fleece. Very little skin shows and compression is well cushioned.

B has crimp but has average density. The skin is clearly evident and cushion is moderate.

C is the least dense, judging by the amount of visible skin and the flatness of compression.

D is a vicuña fleece and predictably the densest of this group of fleeces.

consultant to a large alpaca farm. The alpaca farm's fleece quality improved under his tutelage. He basically applied an approach for improving Merino sheep to alpacas.

This approach has influenced showring criteria. Some aspects of this approach are not controversial, such as: "Follicles closely packed within the follicle group and evenly seated in the skin have a high correlation with increased density" and breeding to eliminate medullated fiber. Other assertions are controversial and doubted by fiber experts who have worked with alpaca and sheep (see Table 10.9 and interview with Dr. Tumen Wuliji; see also Chapter 26: Breeding to Improve Fleece Quality). Among the controversial assertions is that the densest Merino sheep have "soft, rolling skin" (as opposed to "heavy, tight skin" and "flat skin"), and that this rolling skin type is a desirable characteristic for greater density in alpacas.

Watts also believes that high-density fleeces can be identified by long, thin staples (*bundling*) of high-amplitude

Table 10.9a Dr. Tumen Wuliji's alpaca fiber histology chart.

Group	#	TFN	SFN	PFN	SPR	PFDum	SFDum	MeduR	NMeduR	MFDum
Adult female	22	21.9	17.2	4.8	3.6	46.1	26	87.1%	12.9%	28.2
Adult male	9	23	17.6	5.4	3.3	49.7	26.7	90.1%	9.9%	29.1
Adult mean	31	22.47	17.4	5.1	3.46	47.9	26.3	88.6%	11.4%	28.6
Female cria	4	36.5	28	8.5	3.3	33.8	19	33.5%	66.5%	20.6
Male cria	4	32.5	28	8	3.1	40.6	23	36.8%	63.5%	24.9
Cria mean	8	32.7	24.7	8.3	3.22	37.2	21	36.8%	63.3%	22.7
All means	39	34.6	26.4	5.64	3.5	45.1	25.1	77.1%	22.9%	27.3

Note: The alpacas in the New Zealand study were Quechua-owned genetic stock from the western region of the altiplano and raised in all-year pastures in a favorable climate. Because of these factors these animals may or may not be representative of herds found in other parts of the altiplano or other places in the world.

Legend: TFN = Total follicle number per sq. mm (PFN & PFN)
SFDum = Secondary follicle diameter per micron
SFN = Secondary follicle number per sq. mm
MEDUR = Medullated follicle number ratio (%)
PFN = Primary follicle number per sq. mm
NMEDUR = Nonmedullated follicle ratio (%)
SPR = Secondary and primary follicle ratio (SFN/PFN)
MFDum = Mean follicle diameter of primary and secondary
        follicles (weighted) per micron
PFDum = Primary follicle diameter per micron

Source: Research by Dr. Tumen Wuliji while working for Agresearch, New Zealand, 1990.

Table 10.9b Alpaca fiber quality assessment priorities.

Primary	Secondary	Tertiary
Fleece weight	Strength	Position of Break
Fineness	CV of fiber diameter	Crimp
No medullation	Vegetable matter contaminants	CV of length
Length	Handle	
Yield	Loft (fluffiness)	
Color		

Source: Dr. Tumen Wuliji, personal communication, September 1, 2002; reaffirmed by e-mail, September 2005.

Bundling is a term applied to fibers that grow in distinct groupings. This is an example of thick bundling. Bundling can occur in both thinner and broader fiber clusters than shown here.

(*deep crimp*) and low-crimp frequency (*bold crimp*).[110,111] Not everyone agrees. For example, vicuñas, the parent species of alpacas, are much finer and denser than alpacas; they have tight-fitting skin and clearly possess a different-appearing fleece architecture compared to the lock appearance described by Watts.[58,59,60,61,96] In huacaya alpacas there appears to be a correlation between greater curvature and fineness.[70]* Density can be assessed imprecisely by feel, and precisely by removing a small plug from the skin of an alpaca and counting the follicles.[96,112] See "Curvature: Crimp, Crinkle, and Curl."

Fleece Weighing

Fleece weights vary among animals of a given herd and among herds in different settings. Weight is defined by two different measurements: *total fleece weight* (weight of the raw fleece) and *clean fleece weight* (weight after scouring and dehairing).[62] Alpacas given ample and good-quality year-round diets produce fleeces weighing 1 to 13 pounds (450 g–5.9 kg) annually, with the weightiest fleece ever recorded being 19 pounds (8.6 kg) by Rural Alianza in an 18-month period. This wide range shows plenty of room for selective breeding to improve weights. Genetics, diet, sickness, and the amount of time between shearings all affect the outcome of fleece weight. Most of the fleece weights described in this book include the entire fleece. In many fleece shows sponsored by breed associations, only the blanket is weighed, resulting in much lower comparative fleece weights.

For accurate record keeping some experts recommend that fleece weighing be done in conjunction with grid sampling (a technique described in "Uniformity"), noting the age of the fleece (12 to 18 months is the norm for first shearing) and identifying the animal. Recording the interval between shearings (rate of staple regrowth) is an important consideration to all breeders for the purpose of comparing one animal's production to another. A thorough record of the first fleece (*tui*) is important, but recording the second fleece is more important to judge an alpaca's quality production throughout its lifetime.[26,64,115]

*James Watts, PhD, MVSc, and Janie Hicks, written communication, March 28, 2001.

DR. TUMEN WULIJI'S THOUGHTS AND FINDINGS ABOUT ALPACA FIBER*

Dr. Tumen Wuliji is a native of Mongolia who earned a doctorate from the School of Wool and Pastoral Sciences at the University of New South Wales, Australia. He has worked with fiber-producing animals his entire professional life and is one of a few scientists in the world who can converse comparatively about the strengths and weaknesses of a large number of fiber-producing animals based on his own research. While with Agresearch in New Zealand (the New Zealand government's national agricultural research institute), Dr. Wuliji conducted one of the first follicle studies ever undertaken with alpacas. He has no association with alpaca shows, or consultants or breeders involved with shows. He also worked on long-term, government-funded breeding projects aimed at improving the quality and yield of the highly refined Superfine Merino sheep. Presently Dr. Wuliji is an associate professor at Langston University in Oklahoma.

Eric Hoffman (EH) Can you compare alpacas to other fiber-bearing animals?

Dr. Tumen Wuliji (TW) Generally, the alpaca skin and fiber measured in this study were comparable to Corriedale sheep in fiber diameter and length. But comparisons to sheep are sometimes misleading and inappropriate. For example, the fleece weight of Corriedale is about 11 pounds (6 kg) per annum and alpaca fleece weight is about 5.5 pounds (2.5 kg), but alpaca has a bulky, soft handle, and is lightweight, so that the same micron of alpaca possesses better-quality textile characteristics. However, the follicle density of alpacas is low and the primary to secondary ratio is higher than in Corriedales.

EH Can you explain the significance of primary and secondary follicles in a way that is understandable to people new to fiber-producing animals?

TW The frequency of occurrence of primary and secondary follicles is an important part of any follicle study, as is the number of follicles in a square unit of measurement. The primary follicles originate in the skin and are associated with a sweat gland, and are usually much coarser than the secondary follicles. In the New Zealand alpaca study group, the ratio of primary to secondary was approximately one primary to four secondaries. In Superfine Merino sheep the ratio is 1 primary to about 30 secondaries. Secondaries usually represent the fine fibers in a fleece, while primaries are guard hairs and medullated fiber. However, the size differential between the primaries and secondaries is very important. The greater the discrepancy, the greater the variability.

With alpaca there is a significant difference in the follicle densities in crias and adults (22.47 per mm^2 versus 32.7 fibers per mm^2). It may surprise your readers to learn that crias are often denser than adults. This is a function of body surface and size. Like other fiber-bearing animals, alpacas are born with hair follicles in their skin that don't change in numbers throughout their lifetime. As the animal matures and grows in size, the skin expands and the follicles spread away from one another, resulting in lowering the follicle density per unit area.

EH You've worked both with the Superfine Merinos and alpacas. You worked on ten-year projects on Merinos with a specific focus on improving fleece characteristics. What three steps would you suggest to alpaca breeders as ways to begin the selection process of improving the quality of fleeces in their animals?

TW Alpaca fiber is a luxurious, specialty-fiber textile material, so breeders should capitalize on the fiber's special characteristics, such as softness, bulkiness, and lightness. The special qualities inherent in alpaca are fineness, low medullation, heavy fleece weight, high yield, and the color of the breeder's choosing.

EH There are alpaca breeders who believe the presence of a particular style of uniform crimp is an indicator of many desirable characteristics in alpacas, specifically greater density and low micron diameters. Is crimp a proven marker for other such qualities in sheep? Are you aware of any studies that prove there is a relationship between crimp and other important characteristics in alpacas?

TW Some 30 years ago, crimp frequency was used to estimate fiber diameter in Merino sheep indirectly. The correlation between crimp frequency and fiber diameter was about 50 to 60 percent, and it was a poor form of assessment. In other words, I don't think crimp measurements in alpacas are necessarily markers for fineness. Crimp merely means there is this type of fleece characteristic present, and not all alpacas have it, for example the suri breed.

EH Vicuña generally has more density than alpaca and is finer, plus it has curvature that is the crinkly vicuña type (high frequency, low amplitude). It has also been proven through recent DNA tests in Peru that vicuña is the wild ancestor to alpacas. Given these facts, do you think "markers" used in sheep for quality of fiber are appropriate in assessing alpaca fiber?

TW In specialty fibers, crimp is not a premium characteristic. For example, cashmere fiber has very poorly defined crimp, but attracts high values for its fineness, color, length, and uniformity. Breeders should aim for the special characteristics represented in both the vicuña and the best alpacas.

EH What are the most important areas of assessment for the alpaca breeder?

TW Maximizing fleece weight with low microns, density, and selecting toward animals genetically predisposed to hold a low micron count after subsequent shearings.

*Excerpts from interview by Eric Hoffman with Tumen Wuliji, DWPS, August 28, 2002.

Uniformity

Uniformity is one of the most important characteristics that breeders should attempt to produce in their animals. Uniformity refers to the even distribution of all the characteristics that are valued in a fleece: diameter, color, staple, crimp (or crinkle), density, handle, softness, and tensile strength. Uniformity of fineness with a very low standard deviation is particularly desirable. On a laser scan histogram, variation is most commonly expressed as coefficient of variation (CV), which is discussed under "Histograms" later in this chapter. An exceptionally desirable (possibly referred to as low or tight) CV would be 10 to 17. A CV of more than 20 is less than optimum.

In the important work of fiber scientists Christopher Lupton, Robert Stobart, and Yocom–McColl Testing Laboratories, they cited uniformity (coefficient of variation, or CV) working in concert with fineness (average fiber diameter, or AFD) as the two most important characteristics. "A change of one micron in AFD outweighs a change in staple length of 10 mm so far as spinning performance is concerned. For both worsted and woolen spinning, AFD and CV of fiber diameter are by far the most important fiber properties influencing spinning performance, yarn, and fabric."[71]

Besides the CV measurement from a single sample, as mentioned above, uniformity is tested by placing a grid with 4 × 4-inch (10.16 × 10.16-cm) squares on top of a freshly shorn fleece that has been laid out on a flat surface (see Figure 10.10). By randomly sampling fiber from these grid squares, all aspects of uniformity can be ascertained. To assess uniformity in precise terms, pioneering fiber laboratories in Australia recommended taking pencil-sized samples of fiber from each square of the grid and analyzing each sample individually and then all the samples as a whole. Grid sampling still occurs primarily with studs that will have great influence over a population of females. On most animals some areas will have finer fiber than others, but the ideal fiber is as even as possible in diameter and color throughout the fleece.[50,62,63,64] For more on uniformity, see "Histograms" and "Establishing a National Fiber-Processing System in 'New Alpaca Countries'" later in this chapter.

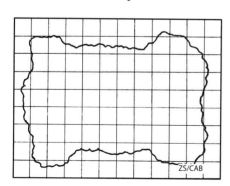

Figure 10.10 Grid for measuring fleece uniformity.

Curvature: Crimp, Crinkle, and Curl

Huacayas have waviness in their fleeces that is referred to as *curvature, crimp,* or *crinkle.* Using Sirolan LaserScan and OFDA 100 testing machines, curvature can be measured precisely by averaging measurements from individual fiber snippets, which are reported in degrees per millimeter (deg/mm).[34,35] Figure 10.11 shows the range in curvature in sheep and huacaya alpacas and how curvature is measured. Compared to sheep, huacaya alpacas do not have a great deal of curvature; their range is usually between 15 deg/mm and 52/deg/mm, with the occasional animal being higher than 52 deg/mm. In a recent study of nearly

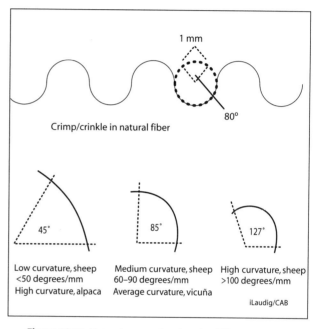

Figure 10.11 Measuring curvature in animal fibers.

Top Average fiber curvature (AFC), also known as mean curvature (MC), is determined by averaging measurements on individual snippets, and is reported in units of degrees per millimeter (deg/mm).

Bottom Typical values: Correlating curvature to other fiber characteristics varies from one species to the next and between breeds of the same species. In a 30-micron fleece of a crossbred sheep, wool typically has low curvature and broad crimp, approximately 5 crimps per inch (2 crimps/cm). This is close to the high end of curvature in many alpacas, which will likely have a lower micron (AFD) when compared to sheep in the same curvature range. Merino sheep in the 21-micron range often fall into the medium curvature range, which is about 10.2 crimps per inch (4 crimps/cm). In camelids in this curvature range, we can reliably find guanacos with 14 to 19 microns (undercoat) and vicuñas with 12 to 14 microns and a few alpacas. The curvature range is occupied by 16-micron superfine Merino sheep. Vicuñas reliably have a mean curvature of around 80 deg/mm, which is the highest among the South American camelids.

Source: AWTA Ltd. Wool Education Trust.

EXCELLENT FLEECES FOR PROCESSING MAY HAVE VARYING DEGREES OF CRIMP OR CRINKLE AND DIFFERENT LOCK FORMATIONS.

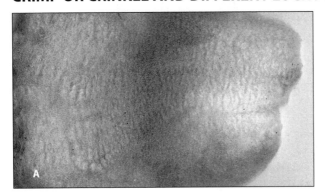

A This sample demonstrates low-amplitude, high-frequency crimp at the upper level of curvature, which is around 52 deg/mm for huacaya alpacas. Average fiber diameter (AFD),16.4; standard deviation (SD), 3.6; coefficient of variation (CV), 21.6 percent; greater than 30 (>30) microns, 0.6 percent; fleece weight, 8.0 pounds (3.6 kg); very dense, second shearing, growth period, 14 months; age of alpaca, 3 years.

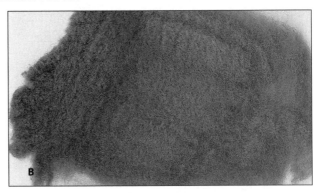

B The curvature is high frequency, low amplitude and similar to vicuña in appearance, but no curvature measurement was taken. AFD, 17.5; SD, 4.0; CV, 22.8 percent; >30 microns, .09 percent; fleece weight, 8.5 pounds (3.8 kg); very dense second shearing; growth period, 12 months; age of alpaca, 4 years.

C Uniform crimp with clearly defined upper-middle range frequency and low amplitude. This appearance is common to many huacaya alpacas, with a mean curvature measurement of 48.3 deg/mm in one study. Bundling is also evident. AFD, 17.5; SD, 3.5; CV, 20.2 percent; >30 microns, 0.9 percent; fleece weight, 10 pounds (4.5 kg); very dense; growth period, 18 months; age of alpaca, 1.5 years.

D Crimp often dissipates as an alpaca ages. However, this 6 year old still has very impressive statistics. AFD, 21.1; SD, 5; CV, 23.8 percent; >30 microns, 5.3 percent; fleece weight, 13.5 pounds (6.1 kg); very dense, third shearing; growth period, 12 months; age of alpaca, 6 years.

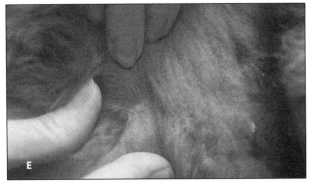

E This sample is from a vicuña. It has very high-frequency and low-amplitude curvature. The curvature is nearly microscopic. The fleece also has good loft. The mean curvature measurement is 80 deg/mm, which is much higher than for most alpacas and about mid-range for sheep. AFD, 12.5; SD, 4.2; CV, 33 percent; > 30 microns, 1.0 percent; fleece weight, 1.2 pounds (.54 kg); very dense (approx. 90 fp/mm), second shearing; growth period, 24 months; age, 2 to 5 years. Interestingly, a 9-year-old captive vicuña owned by Rural Alianza had an AFD of 13 microns, demonstrating that vicuña fleece may not change much over time, a virtue not shared by many alpacas.

F Fleece sample from the neck of a 1,000-year-old El Yaral alpaca mummy of the pre-Incan Chiribaya culture. It has high frequency and a vicuña-like appearance. AFD 17.9, SD 1.0, which is a lower SD than histograms from the best alpacas living today. The percent of fiber >30 is 0.0, which is extremely rare today. Density was not evaluated.

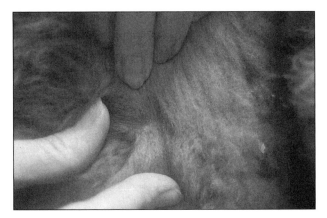

Vicuña crimp/crinkle This close-up view of vicuña fiber on a live animal illustrates very high-frequency, low-amplitude fleece, often referred to as crinkle-style fleece. The fibers appear to distribute themselves somewhat independently and do not appear to follow the uniform undulating pattern easily seen in crimpy fleece common to many alpacas. This look is common to vicuñas and many fine-fleeced alpacas. A vicuña fleece such as this has the highest curvature (approximately 80 deg/mm) of the South American camelids. This style of fleece has more than twice the curvature of the average alpaca, but it is difficult to see because it is microscopic.

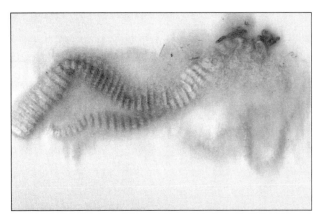

Alpaca crimp The uniform curvature or waviness of aligned fibers along the same plane, as shown above, is the popular perception of crimp. The frequency (number of curves per linear measurement) and amplitude (depth of each curve from apex to apex) can vary greatly from one alpaca to the next. This example is in the upper range for alpacas, with a mean curvature of 50 deg/mm. The sample also demonstrates bundling (clusters of fiber), which is discussed in this chapter. Some alpacas with this level of curvature display a lock that looks more like vicuña, without a corrugated look. See page 274.

600 alpacas, the mean was 32 deg/mm.[70] Vicuñas are around 80 deg/mm, possessing a higher-frequency curvature than alpacas. A vicuña's crinkly-looking fleece is characterized by very high frequency and low amplitude —curvature that is so microscopic in nature that it is not readily visible to the casual observer.

Medium curvature in sheep breeds is between 60 and 90 deg/mm.[34,35,70,103] Crimp/crinkle frequency is directly related to the resistance of compression, which results in greater bulk and loftiness in fabric. Because of its low curvature, the huacaya alpaca is not well suited to end uses that demand high resistance to compression.[70] Breeding practices can increase the amount of curvature found in alpaca fleeces. According to the late Australian fiber expert and author of *The Wool Handbook*, D. C. Teasdale, "Resistance to compression is the force (measured in kilopascals, kPa) required to compress a mass of wool to a given volume. It is largely a function of fiber diameter and single fiber crimp. Increasing fiber diameter or crimp will increase resistance to compression."[103]

In 585 huacayas tested by Christopher Lupton, Robert Stobart, and Yocom–McColl Testing Laboratories, the mean resistance in huacayas was 5.42 kPa, while the resistance in sheep ranged between 5 and 15 kPa. Superfine Merinos had a resistance of between 10 and 12 kPa, possessing more than twice the resistance of the average huacaya.[70,103] Teasdale discussed the pros and cons for crimp in sheep's wool:

Recent studies show that wools of high resistance to compression will tangle more in scouring, leading to higher processing losses. . . . However, wools with higher resistance to compression result in yarns

and fabrics of higher bulk and firmer handle. If all other properties are kept constant, decrease in resistance to compression will be associated with a softer handle and increased felting shrinkage.[103]

The role of crimp and its associative properties has been debated for years in other fiber-producing species and breeds of livestock. Even among experts there is some confusion about the terms crimp and crinkle, which are two kinds of curvature associated with huacayas. Some view crimp and crinkle as synonymous (all waviness being crimp), while others apply crimp to uniform waviness in a lock and crinkle to waviness in individual fibers. In the 1998 ALSA Show Manual, crinkle is defined as "the waviness in a single fiber, as opposed to a uniform wave in a lock," while crimp is defined as "the waviness along the length of the individual fibers throughout the blanket. The waviness in crimp occurs uniformly in the fibers of the lock in the same plane."*

The distinction between crimp and crinkle appears readily in the lock structure when one parts the fleece to assess it on a live animal. With well-defined crimp there is a clear uniform waviness with all fibers on a plane behaving the same, whereas with crinkle the appearance of waviness is not defined and individual fibers on the same plane appear independent from one another. In any case, waviness in huacayas can manifest itself in a variety of ways: locks of uniform waviness (of different amplitudes and frequencies) or very little uniform waviness with variations from strand to strand (crinkle). Variation in the type of crimp and crinkle can occur on the same animal.[19,58,59,60,61,64,68]

---

*Alpaca and Llama Show Association, Inc. Manual, 1998, p.75.

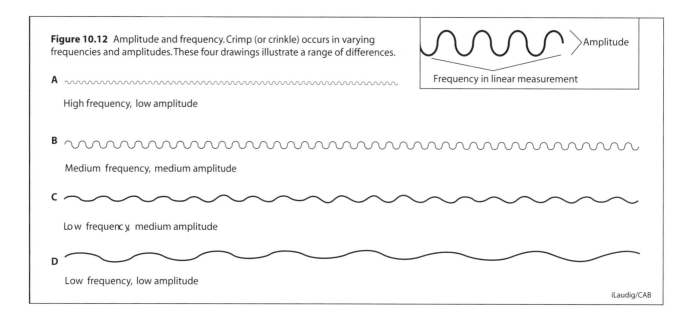

Figure 10.12 Amplitude and frequency. Crimp (or crinkle) occurs in varying frequencies and amplitudes. These four drawings illustrate a range of differences.

Amplitude

Frequency in linear measurement

A

High frequency, low amplitude

B

Medium frequency, medium amplitude

C

Low frequency, medium amplitude

D

Low frequency, low amplitude

iLaudig/CAB

Crimp/crinkle is sometimes referred to in terms of its *amplitude* and *frequency* (see Figure 10.12). Crimp/crinkle can be measured by ascertaining the distance between two consecutive apex points (*peaks*) on a lock of fiber laid out in an unstretched condition. A second measurement can be made of crimp amplitude (the height of each wave). In some sheep's wool, the more uniform and higher the amplitude of crimp, the finer and denser the fleece. In fact, in sheep's wool a value is sometimes assigned a numerical rating based on the relationship to fineness and crimp. Conversely, in some sheep breeds crimp is a poor indicator of fineness.[103] In alpaca this correlation between fineness or density and a particular type of crimp/crinkle is not precise, though higher frequency in crimp/crinkle (*curvature*) often correlates positively with finer fiber in many (but not all) fleeces.[70]

In the "new alpaca countries," opinions differ about the importance of crimp in huacaya alpacas. Some people assert that if crimp of a particular kind exists, then fineness, density, and length will follow.[58,60,61,96,111,112] But what kind of crimp? What does it look like? Australians Jim Watts, Janie Hicks, and Neil Parker, relying on Watts's copyrighted SRS (soft rolling skin) Merino sheep model, recently published their views. "Fleece length will not increase whilst breeders select for thick stapled animals and animals with high crimp frequency ('fine crimp'). Fleece length will increase rapidly when breeders select for thin staples of high crimp amplitude ('deep crimp') and low crimp frequency ('bold crimp')."[112]

One of the accompanying images in their text is a mid-side fleece sample from a high-density alpaca. Its fleece consists of long, thin staples of high-crimp amplitude

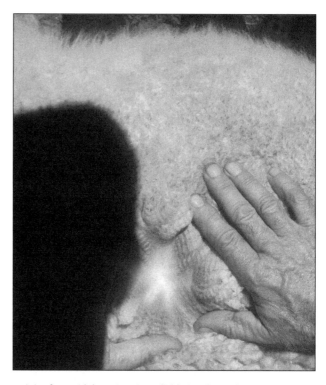

It is often said that crimp is a reliable "marker" indicating greater fleece weight, fineness, increased density, regeneration, and uniformity. This may be true much of the time. However, this photo shows a fleece with clearly defined crimp that falls short of what crimp as a marker is supposed to show. Instead of a long staple, this animal produced about 3 inches in one year, only two-thirds of the optimum for huacayas. The fleece is not uniform and is heavily medullated along the animal's back, and the fleece itself is not fine. Assessing a fleece requires more than parting it to see if crimp is present or not. Fineness, uniformity, weight (density and regeneration) are always at the top of any fleece assessment.

(deep crimp) and low-crimp frequency (bold crimp). Another photo, identified as coming from the same animal, shows follicle groups on the animal's skin that are "evenly sized and closely packed follicles and fibers." Dr. Watts's team is among the first to have pointed out that some alpacas have the follicle-grouping characteristic commonly called bundling.

Dr. Watts has many followers, particularly among breeders associated with alpaca shows. Some of them have modified his initial crimp description (deep and bold) to be one of higher frequency and low amplitude but with a clearly defined uniform "crimpy" lock structure with thin bundling. This look is often referred to as "Merino-type" fleece, perhaps because Dr. Watts was among the first to make a connection between crimp and thin bundling. (Using the Merino label is somewhat misleading because most superfine Merinos have about twice the crimp of a crimpy alpaca and the huacaya fleece type with the greatest curvature does not look like most Merino.)

Histograms (which include mean curvature measurements expressed in degrees per millimeter [deg/mm]) and close-up photos of the fibers sampled are shown in Figure 10.17.[58,59,61,70,103,111,112,114]

At the 2003 Alpaca Registry Conference in Las Vegas, Nevada, information was disseminated stating that processors in Peru thought crimp was important to processing.[*] At the time this report was made there were no internal policies concerning crimp as a de facto criteria for any of the many fiber classes processed by Prosur (Sarfaty), Michell & CIA, and Grupo Inca (Inca Tops), the three largest Peruvian mill groups.[**] According to Gilberto Sarfaty, the managing director of Prosur and president of the International Alpaca Association, "No effort is being made to breed, sort, or produce on the basis of crimp."[***] When Luis Chaves, the general manager of Inca Tops, was asked if any attempt to distinguish between varying degrees of crimp had occurred at Inca Tops or in other mills, he said:

This is not an important consideration to us. Some very fine fleeces have defined crimp; other very fine fleeces don't have it, or very little. We are primarily interested in increasing volume in fine fleeces and have introduced incentives and measurements to improve fleece quality by increasing the percentage of very fine fiber. Crimp, as a single characteristic, is not a priority and would be very difficult to monitor in any large milling system.

Inca Tops has processed vicuña and was among the first mills to institute a financial incentive for alpaca breeders who produce very fine fleeces. How

crimp does or does not relate to processing can also be ascertained by observing the women who sort and class fiber for processing in Peru. No attempt is made to classify fleeces by degree of crimp; nor are there any quality-control measures to check crimp from initial sorting on up the production line.[**]

A year after he made this statement, Luis Chaves decided to measure curvature in groups of alpacas to see how it correlated to fineness. Mr. Chaves relayed in conversation and e-mail that there was a positive correlation between curvature and fineness, but as of December 2005 his final study had not been completed. Employees of Grupo Inca have stated that even though there is no effort to sort fleeces based on styles of crimp/crinkle, there may be a correlation between fineness and types of curvature that is related to the fineness identified by the large mills' expert sorters.[†]

Christopher Lupton, Robert Stobart, and Yocom–McColl Testing Laboratories also concluded in their comprehensive study of more than 585 huacayas that in general, the greater the curvature, the lower the microns. In their peer-reviewed study, the range in curvature in the huacayas was between 15 and 52 deg/mm with a mean of 32 deg/mm.[71] Figure 10.17 shows what different types of curvatures look like.

In some alpaca show systems, a tightly defined crimp and lock are assigned value. Such hair-splitting distinctions between styles of crimp may serve the purpose of identifying differences between individual animals in high-stakes alpaca shows, but the commercial processors in Peru who move tons of fleeces through their scouring vats based on handle classing (with some recently introduced micron sampling) are not deliberately making such distinctions in the fleece used to create their high-fashion end products found in the top salons in Milan, Paris, and Geneva.

This much is known. Alpacas with high-frequency curvature are more apt to have a low average fiber diameter (fine fleeced). What this curvature looks like may vary from animal to animal, but generally it has measurable high frequency and may or may not have a uniform undulating lock structure (crimp), though not all experts agree[61,96,112] Curvature dissipates with age and coarsening.[70,112]

---

[*]Cameron Holt, Australian fiber consultant, report on "Identifying the Ideal Fibre," pp. 60–61, Alpaca Registry Inc. Conference, Las Vegas, Nevada, February 2003.

[**]Luis Chaves, personal communication, April 1, 2003; Alonzo Burgos, Grupo Inca executive and alpaca breeder, April 12, 2002; Derek Michell, personal communication, April 12, 2002.

[***]Gilberto Sarfaty, managing director of Prosur, personal communication, April 25, 2003.

[†]Luis Chaves and various employees of Grupo Inca, personal communications and e-mails, September 2005.

Many adult huacaya alpacas in the 16- to 17-micron average diameter range possess uniform fleeces with exceptional density but varying types of crimp or bundling. Huacaya and suri alpacas as low as 15.4 microns have had no or very little uniform crimp, while alpacas with clearly defined crimp have been equally as fine.* Crimp (or crinkle) contributes to the quality of resilience in a finished product. Huacayas with crinkle/vicuña-style fiber have produced fleeces of greater than 13 pounds (5.9 kg) in a year, as have alpacas with clearly defined crimp. Many huacayas lacking the corrugated look of deep crimp have a high-frequency curvature instead. If all other characteristics are desirable, a fleece with vicuña-like high frequency may be designated to the highest grade for the most refined use in the Peruvian mills.**

Low-freqeuncy, low-amplitude crimp or crinkle should not be confused with the straight lock and unique structure of suri. Suri is often compared to mohair. A pure mohair garment, although lustrous and soft, will appear flat and not hold its shape. For this reason a blend of sheep's wool (with crimp) and mohair (or suri) is often used to produce a product that contains the best properties of both.[84] Uniform crimp is often emphasized by North American and Australian alpaca breeders; but for Peruvian fiber sorters, European processors, and dealers, its importance appears to be low in priority compared to qualities of fineness, length, variability, color, handle, and consistency, among other criteria.[21,58,59,95,96,97,103]

D. C. Teasdale (*The Wool Handbook*) points out that among the many fiber characteristics to be considered, crimp is either less or more important depending on the process for which it is intended. In ranking wool properties for apparel created via the worsted process, Teasdale ranked crimp behind fineness, yield, staple length, staple strength, and color. He considered crimp more important for the woolen process, but still ranked it behind fiber diameter and yield, and only as important as many other characteristics.[103] See Figures 10.12 and 10.17.

Curl

Curl is a fiber characteristic common on most suri alpacas. The fiber parts along the spine and hangs vertically along the animal. Often the suri fiber curls in ringlets that give a suri a distinct Rastafarian look. Occasionally alpacas have been identified with both curl and broad crimp. The lack of crimp or crinkle in suri is significant for processing strategies. Among suri's distinguishing properties are smooth handle, luster, and nonprotruding scale structure and silkiness. For these qualities suri is sought after by large South American mills and occupies a special niche in value, outranked only by baby and superfine huacaya and at times surpassing them.[20,22,47,69,72,81,84,91]

Fiber curvature in suris is known as curl and is typically 10 to 15 deg/mm.

Some mills press crimp into suri fiber with specially designed machines, and suri is almost always blended with other fiber (usually Merino) to compensate for its lack of resilience. However, the straightness of the fibers is not the reason suri doesn't readily bind to other fibers to make strong yarn. Suri's amazingly tight scale structure on the fiber's surface (*cuticle*) is so smooth that the usual protruding surface scales, common to most other fiber, are not present, making suri difficult to bind.[50,81,84,91,104,107] For more on scale structure, see Figures 10.23, 10.24, and 10.25 and accompanying text.

Tensile Strength

All natural fibers have limited resistance to pulling pressure; eventually any fiber will break. The strength of a fiber is expressed in a tensile measurement of Newtons/kilotex (N/ktex), and is the force (measured in Newtons) required to break a staple of a given thickness (measured in kilotex). Obviously, if fiber is too weak to withstand the rigors of processing and the normal conditions of human use, it is not very useful.

Alpaca fiber is generally stronger than sheep fiber within the same micron range. In Lupton, McColl, and Stobart's comprehensive analysis, alpaca fiber tested between 4.42

---

*Angus and Margaret McColl, owners of Yocom-McColl Testing Laboratories, Denver, Colorado, personal communication, April 12, 2001.

**Luis Chaves, personal communication, April 12, 2006.

and 137.80 N/ktex with a mean of 50.16. This mean is more than adequate for the stresses and strains of processing; in fact, 30 N/ktex is considered adequate for processing. Only 10 percent of the 585 animals tested fell below the accepted minimum for strength. Environmental factors such as disease, poor diet, poor health, excessive sunlight, and other variables can result in individual fibers and locks being weakened throughout a fleece.[71]

Other Objective Properties

In addition to the criteria for evaluating fleece quality discussed (fineness, color, staple length, density, uniformity, crimp, crinkle, medullation, weight, and tensile strength), other properties can be readily measured that are important in judging the qualities of alpaca fiber. Among these are *hygroscopic properties, elasticity,* and *felting.*[42,43,45,47,62,70] The glossary at the end of the chapter partially explains these terms. For further information refer to one of the internationally respected wool handbooks or other references listed at the end of this chapter.

SUBJECTIVE CRITERIA FOR EVALUATING FIBER

So far I've discussed the properties of alpaca fiber that can be quantitatively measured. If measured correctly, these assessments are exact and irrefutable. But because of their nature certain properties of fiber cannot be measured in an exact and irrefutable way. These subjective criteria can be just as important as objective measurements, and without them the evaluation of fiber remains incomplete.

Handle

Handle (feel or touch) is at the top of any list of subjective criteria. It is the quality often viewed as the cumulative result of all objective and subjective properties combined. Handle was cited by many of the top management people in Arequipa as the single most important criterion in assessing fiber quality.[4,32,33,34,57,58,59,60]

Alpaca is known for its smooth handle. In part this is because compared to sheep's wool the scale structure (*cuticles*) of both huacaya and suri alpaca protrudes less from the fiber shaft than the more protrudent cuticles on sheep's wool. Typically sheep scales along the shaft of individual fibers protrude to around 0.8 micron, whereas huacaya scales protrude only around 0.3 micron and suri even less.[63,103] In suri the scales are long and tight, creating fewer ridges (or less frequent scale edges) along the shaft than occur with sheep and huacaya, which further accounts for suri's incredible slippery, smooth feel.

The scale structure not only accounts for the feel, but also affects processing. With huacaya the scales protrude enough for sufficient grip to bind the fiber strands into strong thread and yarn during processing. With suri the scale structure is so smooth that binding it into strong thread or yarn is a challenge, and sometimes blending with other fibers is required. The smoothness (or slippery feel) of both huacaya and suri reduces the likelihood of the prickle factor, allowing finer-quality products to be worn directly on human skin without itching.

It takes experience to be a good judge of handle. After feeling thousands of fleeces, the pleasantly smooth, soft, and airy feel of a top fleece becomes readily apparent. Fiber with undesirable handle might feel rough, brittle, or stiff. To acquire this skill, first attempt to differentiate between fleeces from the extremes, such as *baby* and *coarse,* or fleeces of a *tui* and a 15-year-old animal. Hold a lock or group of locks and slowly slide them back and forth between your fingers. You may notice subtle differences within the same fleece, depending on what area on the alpaca it is from. When you become adept at distinguishing between extremes, begin differentiating between fleeces belonging to the same or closely related classes. Separating strands of fiber and visually inspecting them will also help you learn to judge handle. See Chapter 7 for a recent fleece evaluation scorecard and Table 10.10.

As you develop this skill, take into account environmental factors that may affect your assessment. For example, some types of dusty soil can thoroughly penetrate an alpaca's fleece and mask its handle, giving it a gritty feel, although the dust may not be readily apparent during a visual inspection. The effect of dust should not be underrated. Alpaca usually has less than 5 percent grease, compared to 15 to 30 percent in sheep.[66,67,70,113]* The low grease content allows dust and grit to work its way into the coat more thoroughly than with sheep. The result can be an entire fleece with a deceptive feel. Washing will allow the true handle to emerge. Even though fineness is the top quantitative criterion in judging fleece, it should be remembered that a fine fleece may have substandard handle.

Other Subjective Properties

Other subjective criteria are *softness, luster,* and *brightness.* Softness, which is often considered synonymous with handle, was also cited as extremely important by the managers in Arequipa.[13,14,33,34] Luster, which refers to the amount of light reflected by a fiber, can be seen in top huacaya fleeces, and is most evident in strong suri phenotypes whose coats literally glisten. Even though luster can be measured, it is commonly judged by eye.**

---

*Ian Stapelton and Cameron Holt, personal communication, 1993.

**Robert C. Couchman, personal communication, December 19, 1994.

INSPECTING, SAMPLING, AND RECORDING FIBER CHARACTERISTICS

Scoring a Fleece

In 1994, leading members of the Australian Alpaca Association (AAA), working in conjunction with Cameron Holt of the Melbourne College of Textiles, produced a fleece scoring system. The objective was to "recognize characteristics of alpaca fiber which are required by manufacturers, processors, and producers." The key rules are:

1. Only the blanket is judged.

2. Staple length must be 4 to 6 inches (10–15 cm).

3. Record of shearing dates must be provided.

4. Fleeces are judged in classes based on age: 0 to 18 months, 18 to 30 months, 30 to 42 months, and over 42 months.

The AAA scoring system is offered as an example of an attempt to balance the relative importance of the many characteristics in fiber, being careful not to overemphasize a single characteristic while ignoring other equally important ones. The model shown in Table 10.10 is from 2001. The model is reviewed annually.[2,4,64] Similar systems have been created around the world, not always with the same criteria.

Table 10.10 Evaluation scorecard.

Categories	Maximum Points
Fineness and handle	15
Evenness of microns	10
Sheen/luster	10
Trueness of color	10
Character/Trueness to type	15
Uniformity of length	10
Impurities/Stains/Tip damage	5
Lack of medullation	10
Clean fleece weight	15
Total	**100**

Reprinted with the permission of the Australian Alpaca Association. Updating from Graeme Dickson, alpaca breeder, New South Wales, Australia, personal communication, March 21, 2001.

Notes: The AAA supplied the following explanation for the categories on its fleece scorecard: "Handle covers the fineness of the fiber and the various levels of softness. Sheen/luster takes into account the light refraction of fiber dependent on breed type. Character/style refers to wave/crimp and/or crinkle within the staple.
Impurities/stain/tip damage takes into account excessive vegetable matter, staining within the fleece, and/or excessive tip damage.

"Medullation, age, and class must be taken into account when assessing medullation. The fleece should be as free as possible from continuously medullated fibers (usually coarser fiber—hence longer-than-average length).

"Uniformity covers the evenness throughout the fleece of color, fineness, and length. Clean fleece weight relates to the percentage of clean fleece after removing extraneous matter, presuming a 90 percent yield."[45]

Visual Inspection

The assessment of a fleece begins when you first see an alpaca. As you walk around the animal you see the outer layer of its fleece. You may want to note what you see in different areas: Is the blanket free of protruding medullated fiber (guard hair)? Do medullated fibers appear on the apron or neck? If you're inspecting a juvenile or recently shorn adult, keep in mind that their medullated fiber is readily apparent as a "fuzzy" look or "halo" that appears just above the defining silhouette of the fleece. On a young animal a fleece free of coarse, medullated fiber is clearly and sharply defined when silhouetted against a bright background. In both developing animals and adults the lock fibers on the blanket should appear intermeshed but actually be relatively easy to pull apart; it should also be dense, spongy, and consistent (providing the alpaca is a huacaya).

If the fleece is uneven in appearance, further inspection may reveal sun or water damage, lack of uniformity, or matting. By parting the animal's fleece (to the skin) at three points on the blanket, the strengths and weaknesses of the fleece will become readily apparent (see Figure 10.13). Huacaya fleeces are often slightly matted at the surface (not a devaluing fault), only revealing their true nature when they are parted. Once parted, look for the following: desired staple length, uniformity, lock structure, true color and color consistency, luster, type of curvature (crimp/crinkle), density, and the devaluing and damaging

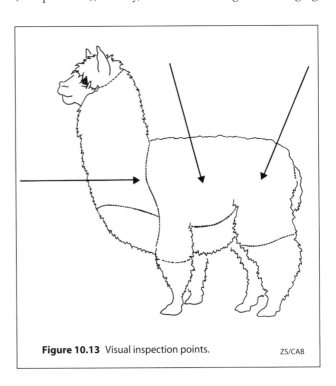

Figure 10.13 Visual inspection points.   ZS/CAB

effects of matting, debris, and lice. Requirements for the blanket are not necessarily the same as for the neck and the apron, tail, and wool cap (see Figures 10.14, 10.15, and 10.16). You may want to take notes on what you've found and include them in the animal's permanent records.[2,15,17,18,27,40,43,44,60,62,71,93,95,97]

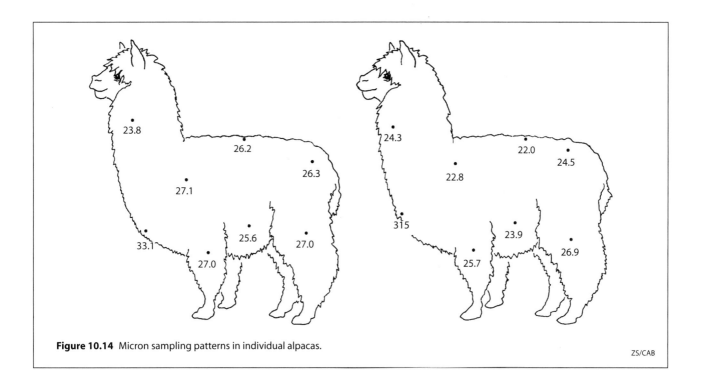

Figure 10.14 Micron sampling patterns in individual alpacas.

ZS/CAB

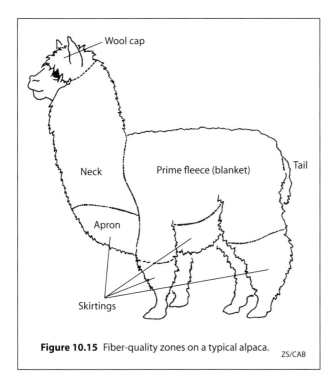

Figure 10.15 Fiber-quality zones on a typical alpaca. ZS/CAB

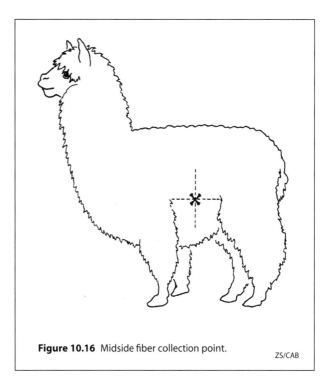

Figure 10.16 Midside fiber collection point. ZS/CAB

Histograms

The Greek *histo* means loom or web, and *gram* means anything written or drawn. In the wool industry a *histogram* has come to mean the permanent record of the quality of an animal's fiber production, as represented by samples of fiber and the statistical information (micron diameter, standard deviation, etc.) derived from them. However, the term histogram sometimes refers to something more casual—often only a sample clipped from an alpaca's prime fleece, kept safely in a filing system along with permanent health and reproductive records.

A histogram may also include measurements of tensile strength, crimp, uniformity, density (see "Objective Criteria for Evaluating Fiber" earlier in this chapter) and written comments about the subjective properties of fiber, such as handle, softness, and luster.[15,16,98]

Collection of Samples A fiber sample for a histogram is clipped from the prime fleece and from as near the skin as possible. The sample represents the fiber's key elements: handle, microns, staple length, color, and curvature (crimp/crinkle). It can also serve as a testimonial to dietary influences on fleece production.

The age of the animal, the growth period of the fleece, and the date of collection are important factors that should be recorded along with the sample. A sample taken from an 18-month-old animal should not be compared to that of a 4-year-old animal. Samples should be collected at a set time in the development of all alpacas. The first time should be shortly before an animal's first shearing between 12 and 18 months of age. A sample taken at this age will provide a record of the animal's best fleece because the *tui* (first fleece) is, under most circumstances, the best that the animal will produce.[26,59,60,117]

A sample of fiber provides a reference for judging an animal's fiber quality from the most optimal period to the end of the animal's fiber-producing days. Samples from each shearing provide a record of overall quality and show how a particular alpaca's coat weathers the aging process. This information can influence breeding decisions. In the cashmere goat business, studs that maintain a low micron count despite many shearings are the most valuable. How fast an animal coarsens will vary based on both dietary and genetic factors, with great variability within a population. Also, different species coarsen at different rates.[6,25,87]

How to go about collecting samples is a hot topic among fiber experts. The bottom line is that a sample should accurately represent an alpaca's fleece. Recommendations for sample sizes range from samples of a diameter of a pencil to samples the diameter of a person's thigh. South American experts usually check an animal at three points along its blanket before passing judgment, but actual sampling is rare. Yocom–McColl Testing Laboratories points out that the sample must be taken and packaged properly. The sample should be at least a two-inch (5.08 cm) square taken from the midside of the animal as near to the skin as possible, and at least 1.5 inches in staple length. The sample needs to be placed in a quart-sized zip-lock baggie with the staple intact and the cut end of the staple positioned at the top. Balling the sample up and squeezing it into a small baggie makes it difficult to straighten out for sampling. The inherent quality of alpaca fibers having low resistance to compression works against handling such fiber samples.[73,74,75,76*]

Generally, the larger the sample, the greater the accuracy in assessing the quality of fleece. Too small a sample may make it impossible to assess the nature of the locks, the frequency of middle-range medullation and coarse guard hairs, and other uniformity questions.

Methods of Micron Measurement Several methods exist for measuring microns. The oldest uses a standard microscope with 500× magnification and fiber samples mounted on a micron slide. This method allows a fairly accurate assessment of fiber diameter and provides some information about the degree of deviation in a fleece. But it's a slow method and the samples are small.

In the 1990s computer-aided laser technology became a permanent fixture in fiber-testing labs because it can assess much larger samples more quickly, efficiently, and for a low cost. With the new technology, which became known as Sirolan LaserScan (LS), fineness and standard deviation can be measured with ever-increasing thoroughness. A histogram that uses state-of-the-art methods will provide a much more precise, and ultimately more usable, record than a mere fiber sample. Instruments are expensive and must be operated under standard conditions for testing textiles by trained technicians, so producers must mail samples to an appropriate laboratory..

The new technologies of the last 20 years include a variety of scanning methods, or "mass counting devices," some more foolproof than others. Among these are the projection microscope (time-consuming, subject to operator error, but very accurate; the CSIRO Sirolan LaserScan; and its forerunner, the Fibre Fineness Distribution Analyser (FDA).** The FDA is a good system but has problems measuring guard hairs of more than 80 microns, and the system may omit the largest coarse hairs from its results.

As of this writing the Sirolan LaserScan, OFDA 100, and OFDA 2000 are probably the most familiar to camelid

---

*Yocom-McColl Testing Laboratories, Inc., a micron testing service, Denver, Colorado, 1994.

**Robert C. Couchman, personal communication, December 19, 1994.

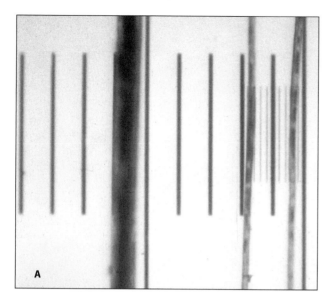

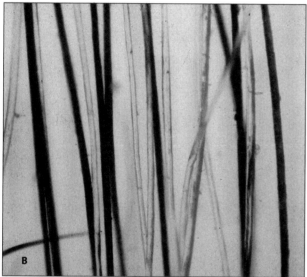

A 200× microscope makes a fairly precise measurement of fiber diameter possible. However, this form of measurement is time consuming and inefficient compared to laser scanning and other techniques. In **A**, medullated fiber is present. In **B**, the fiber appears uniform. Note that black-and-white fibers create a grey coat color.

owners in new alpaca countries. Though these are all state-of-the-art fiber-measuring technologies, they are tools with different strengths. It is important to know what each method is most apt to accurately measure.

The Sirolan LaserScan and OFDA 100 are approved by the International Wool Testing Organization (IWTO) and the American Society for Testing Materials (ASTM). The tests are performed under standard conditions for testing textiles (65% relative humidity at 70°F). The OFDA 2000 instrument, on the other hand, is not approved by

these organizations. The Sirolan LaserScan and OFDA 100 measure thousands of fibers when making a determination on average microns, standard deviation, and coefficient of variation, while the OFDA 2000 measures less than 100 fibers. The OFDA 2000 does, however, measure diameter changes along the staple and does a good job of showing the effects of environmental factors. See Figure 10.18.[74,75,76]

With the OFDA 100 and Sirolan LaserScan the results are influenced by how a sample is tested. It is generally accepted that a sample should be collected from the midside point. There are two methods of testing a sample. The method employed in the United States for the last 20 years involves taking a 2-millimeter "die-cut" (also known as a "butt cut") from the base of the sample and subjecting this cut to the laser scan.[73] The second method (more commonly used in Australia and New Zealand) involves the creation of a "minicore." The whole sample is placed in the minicore and 2-millimeter cuts are taken randomly throughout the length of the staple. The test might include fiber segments from anywhere on the staple.

The die-cut technique of sampling across the sample (where it was cut from the skin) accurately measures fibers grown in the same environment at the same time. The die-cut also accurately assesses fiber diameter and distribution at a point in time. This test of all the "ends" in a given sample is an accurate way to create a genetic picture of the animal's important hair follicle makeup.[64]

The minicore method usually increases variability in test results because of the differences in fiber diameter found along the staple. This can be especially evident if an animal has undergone severe dietary changes. Over time diameter along a staple can be affected by stress, pregnancy, lactation, age, and nutrition. In effect, the minicore technique produces a result that looks at an alpaca's fiber over the period of time it took to produce a staple. Since fiber can increase as much as 9 microns in three months, the potential for uncertain results becomes evident.[51]*

Four Common Measurements in Micron Counts A laser scan (or any kind of micron count) should result in at least four measurements: average fiber diameter, standard deviation, coefficient of variation, and microns greater than 30 (>30). Fiber diameter is merely the diameter of a fiber expressed in microns.

Standard deviation (SD) is a statistical term that indicates the amount of variation occurring in a group of fibers using the average as the starting point. For example, if an alpaca's fleece averages 22 microns and the SD is 5 microns, 68 percent of the fiber is expected to be between 17 and 27 microns. The lower the SD, the more uniform the

*Angus McColl, personal communication, May 1, 2001.

fiber distribution and the more desirable the fiber is for processing purposes. For many Australian breeders, the SD is of the utmost importance, both for assessing the fiber quality and for future breeding decisions.

The *coefficient of variation* (CV) expresses the SD as a percentage or average. It is computed by dividing the SD by the mean diameter and then multiplying by 100. A CV of 20 percent is accepted as normal in many kinds of fiber-producing animals with low microns. Low SD and CV are usually indicative of a low *prickle factor,* which is desirable in any fiber product, especially a garment.[14,37,43,56,63,77]

Microns >30 (greater than 30) indicate the probable prickle factor in a sample. The prickle factor refers to the fiber micron measurement that is the threshold of irritability to the skin. Throughout the fiber measurement world and garment industry, % >30 microns is thought to cause itching and slight discomfort to the skin in most people. In high-quality garments this discomfort is to be avoided at all costs by using fiber that can be worn directly on the skin because it has consistent and uniform fibers of <30 (less than 30) microns. Typically, a histogram measures microns >30 in a percentage. A sample with only 0.5 to 4 percent >30 microns is desirable.[61,73,76] Though 30 microns is the accepted threshold for the prickle factor, experts such as Inca Tops manager Luis Chaves put the prickle factor's threshold as low as 25 microns.*

Besides these measurements, which are common to laserscan histograms, some laboratories have expanded their assessment capabilities to include measuring the distribution and percentage of medullation (only in light-colored animals), curvature (crimp/crinkle), and spin fineness (performance measurement derived by combining variability and average fiber diameter). See examples of expanded histograms in Figure 10.17.

Alpaca Fleece Testing Services

The greatest volume alpaca fiber-testing service is Yocom-McColl, 540 West Elk Place, Denver, Colorado, USA 80216-1823, phone (303) 294 0582. This testing service has been relied on by several alpaca registries to accurately test fiber collected from inbound stock, in all more than 30,000 samples, as well as testing fiber for North American, European, and Australian breeders. The Australian Wool Testing Authority, P.O. Box 190, Guildford, NSW, 2161, phone 61 (02) 9681 1200, and Riverina Fleece Testing Services, phone 61 (02) 6925 1407, also in New South Wales, are additional wool testing resources for Australian breeders. In the United Kingdom contact Hilary Redden, The Fibre Lab, 77 Davidson Drive, Aberdeen AB16 7QS, phone 44

1224 692359, e-mail hilary@thefibrelab.co.uk. In Germany contact Universitat Hohenheim (480A), Institut fur Tierproduktion in den Tropen und Subtropen, Fachgebiet Tierhaltung und Tierzuchtung, Stuttgart–Hohenheim, Garbenstrasse 17, 70599 Stuttgart. In New Zealand contact SGS Wool Testing Service, P.O. Box 349, Timaru, New Zealand, phone (03) 688 5005, or Gribbles Analytical Laboratories, Invermay Agricultural Centre, Puddle Alley, Private Bag 50034, Mosgiel, New Zealand, phone (03) 489 9020, e-mail paul.turner@gribbles.co.nz.

These services give instructions on fiber collection and offer testing by the Sirolan LaserScan and OFDA 100 methods in all measurable aspects of alpaca fiber. Yocom-McColl employs the die-cut method of evaluation and AWTA uses the minicore method. The services have a two-fold purpose: (1) to provide reliable, accurate information to individual breeders and (2) to collect data on the national herd to assist in the development of alpaca fiber as a viable market.

Putting Histograms into Proper Perspective

A typical histogram, incorporating laser scanning of hundreds of individual fibers, contains information about average diameter, the standard deviation, and the coefficient of variation, and may even have information about what percentage of the sample was >30 microns. New technology now makes it possible to also request measurements that show the percentage and distribution of medullated fibers (in the lighter fleeces), spin fineness, and curvature. The LaserScan and OFDA 100 histograms are very much part of the evolving alpaca business in Australia, North America, Europe, and other new alpaca-growing regions. Histogram results have been used by alpaca registries around the world as criteria to accept or reject thousands of alpacas slated to be moved from one country to another.

Histograms are often affixed prominently to clipboards on the pens of animals being displayed at shows or sales at numerous venues around the world. At such events a histogram is transformed from an internal document that assists the breeder in fiber evaluation to an advertisement that seemingly attests in the most objective terms to the qualities in a particular alpaca's fiber. Used as an advertisement, the histogram assures prospective buyers of the alpaca's competitive fiber-producing powers. The unverifiable assumption of any such histogram is that it actually represents the animal it claims to represent. Most breeders listen to their consciences and submit samples for testing that are from the animal they say it came from. But because histograms have become an advertising statement, it is important to note that the testing laboratory merely tests samples

---

*Luis Chaves, personal communication, October 27, 2000.

Figure 10.17 State-of-the-art histograms showing curvature and medullation.

The six huacaya histograms in this series offer the standard measurements of average fiber diameter (AFD), standard deviation (SD), variation of coefficient (CV), and percentage of microns (>30), and the additional measurements of spin fineness and mean curvature (deg/mm). Four of these histograms show the percentage of medullated (hollow) fibers in the sample (Chaku, Chiki, Putre #1, and vicuña). This measurement can only be undertaken in light-colored fleeces. Note that in the four samples where medullation is measured and shown in dark profile on the histogram, the percentage and distribution of medullated fiber is also shown.

It was surprising to learn that some vicuña fibers as low as 8 microns and alpaca fibers as low as 11 microns were medullated. Though medullation is common in the coarser fibers, the broad distribution of medullated fibers in camelids is fairly unique among fiber-bearing animals. It is also noteworthy that three alpacas in this group with low AFDs and excellent to good histo-

grams differed markedly in percentage of medullation, from 1.1 percent (Putre #1) to 2.9 percent (Chiki) to 32.9 percent (Chaku).

The six samples are arranged in order of curvature; King Richard, the alpaca with the least amount of curvature (and worst overall histogram), appears first. The upper end in mean curvature for alpacas is around 52 deg/mm, but Putre #1 (page 275) defies this definition with a mean curvature of 63.7 deg/mm, which is close to a vicuña's curvature of 80 deg/mm. Putre #1 is a light fawn female alpaca with vicuña-like fleece in appearance and fineness. The six photos/histograms are arranged in order of mean curvature (crimp), starting with King Richard with the least curvature to the vicuña with the greatest curvature. Chaku (page 273) and Chiki (page 274) represent average curvature for an alpaca. Chimu (page 274) represents high curvature for an alpaca. The histogram of a vicuña (page 275) shows the distribution of medullation in this species, perhaps published for the first time in a book. Note the similar look and high curvature of Putre #1 and the vicuña.

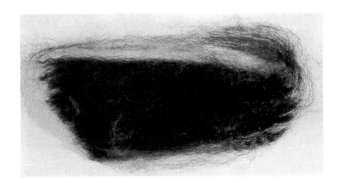

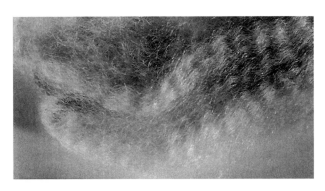

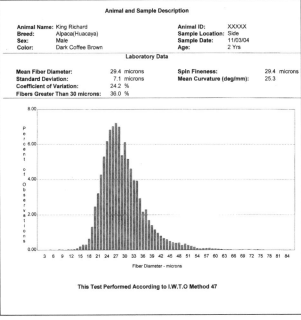

King Richard (low curvature)

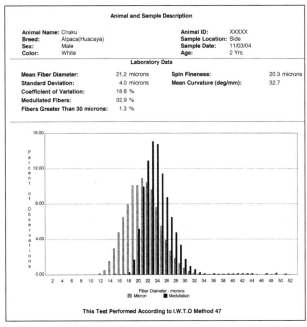

Chaku (average curvature)

Figure 10.17 continued. See page 273 for comments on these two fiber samples and their histograms.

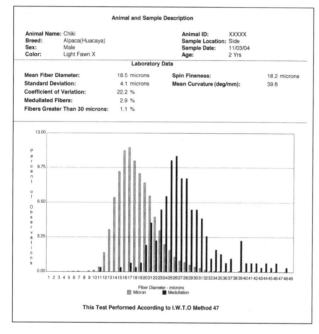

Animal and Sample Description

Animal Name: Chiki			**Animal ID:**	XXXXX
Breed:	Alpaca(Huacaya)		**Sample Location:**	Side
Sex:	Male		**Sample Date:**	11/03/04
Color:	Light Fawn X		**Age:**	2 Yrs

Laboratory Data

Mean Fiber Diameter:	18.5 microns	**Spin Fineness:**	18.2 microns
Standard Deviation:	4.1 microns	**Mean Curvature (deg/mm):**	39.6
Coefficient of Variation:	22.2 %		
Medullated Fibers:	2.9 %		
Fibers Greater Than 30 microns:	1.1 %		

This Test Performed According to I.W.T.O Method 47

Chiki (average curvature)

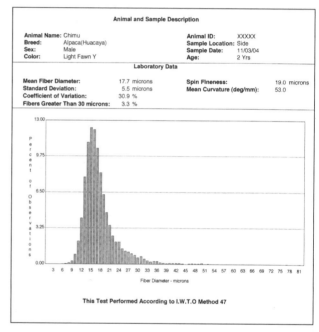

Animal and Sample Description

Animal Name: Chimu			**Animal ID:**	XXXXX
Breed:	Alpaca(Huacaya)		**Sample Location:**	Side
Sex:	Male		**Sample Date:**	11/03/04
Color:	Light Fawn Y		**Age:**	2 Yrs

Laboratory Data

Mean Fiber Diameter:	17.7 microns	**Spin Fineness:**	19.0 microns
Standard Deviation:	5.5 microns	**Mean Curvature (deg/mm):**	53.0
Coefficient of Variation:	30.9 %		
Fibers Greater Than 30 microns:	3.3 %		

This Test Performed According to I.W.T.O Method 47

Chimu (high curvature). See page 263 for an example of the same curvature result that has a different appearance.

Alpaca weaving of ancient Moche motif.

Ancient Inca weaving.

Figure 10.17 continued. See page 273 for comments on these two fiber samples and their histograms.

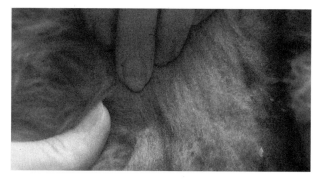

Animal and Sample Description

Animal Name:	Putre #1 (Import Group, Europe)		Animal ID:	XXXXX
Breed:	Alpaca(Huacaya)		Sample Location:	Side
Sex:	Female		Sample Date:	01/05/05
Color:	LF		Age:	18 Mos

Laboratory Data

Mean Fiber Diameter:	15.6 microns	Spin Fineness:	15.6 microns
Standard Deviation:	3.8 microns	Mean Curvature (deg/mm):	63.7
Coefficient of Variation:	24.1 %		
Fibers Greater Than 30 microns:	0.5 %		
Medullated Fibers:	1.1 %		

This Test Performed According to I.W.T.O Method 47

Animal and Sample Description

Animal Name:	Sub Adult		Animal ID:	Sub Adult
Breed:	Vicuña		Sample Location:	Neck
Sex:	XXXXX		Sample Date:	12/21/04
Color:	Lt Brown		Age:	XXXXX

Laboratory Data

Mean Fiber Diameter:	12.8 microns	Spin Fineness:	14.4 microns
Standard Deviation:	4.5 microns	Mean Curvature (deg/mm):	81.7
Coefficient of Variation:	35.3 %		
Medullated Fibers:	4.8 %		
Fibers Greater Than 30 microns:	1.0 %		

This Test Performed According to I.W.T.O Method 47

Putre #1 (exceptionally high curvature)

This histogram, from a young adult female alpaca from the Putre region of northern Chile, is an interesting study in curvature and fineness. This animal is an alpaca by all phenotypic characteristics, but its fleece type is similar to a vicuña in fineness, curvature (crimp/crinkle), and appearance. The alpaca's histogram is exceptionally fine at 15.6 AFD (microns). Its mean curvature of 63.7 deg/mm is between the upper range for alpacas (52 deg/mm) and vicuñas (80 deg/mm). This is an excellent example of what is sometimes referred to as a crinkly or vicuña-like fleece that has high frequency and low amplitude. In this instance, greater curvature correponds to very low AFD (microns).

Vicuña (highest curvature of all camelid species)

This is a close-up of vicuña fleece. The vicuña is the progenitor of the alpaca. Mean fiber diameter in vicuña typically ranges from between 12 and 14 microns with a curvature reading of 80 deg/mm, which is the highest of all the South American camelids. Because the very high-frequency curvature is also low amplitude, it is not readily visible. Individual fibers in a fleece often show independence from one another, a characteristic of crinkle.

A 2,000-year-old alpaca cloth.

and has no method of matching a sample to a particular animal, other than relying on the information provided by the sender. Relying solely on a histogram has its limitations. For this and other reasons, learning how to assess fiber quality through visual and tactile means makes good sense for anyone seriously considering entering the alpaca business.

While many alpaca breeders living in industrialized countries embrace the security and certainty that histogram results appear to offer in assessments of fiber quality, in South America (even among those with the means to use technologically advanced histograms) the traditional, often highly refined tactile method continues to be relied upon. Derek Michell, of Michell & CIA, says, "The alpaca-processing business relies on the fingers of women who sort the fiber."* The officials overseeing the international camelid festivals held annually in Peru since the mid-1990s have felt strongly enough about this tactile method to politely forbid North Americans attending the festival from taking fiber samples from champion alpacas for laser-scanning purposes. The point is well taken: What good would come of a scientific test by a bunch of gringos of animals whose owners could probably never afford such a test and who have relied on tactile assessment for centuries? The sensory experience of high-quality alpaca fiber is unquestionably a distinguishing aspect of the alpaca's special appeal to natural-fiber aficionados, especially those who have developed the tactile skill to assess it.

Still, the technology of laser scanning affords an objective insight into fiber production not available until relatively recently. There is no question that a histogram analyzing a sample of hundreds of fibers is a valuable tool for the serious breeder and a convenient aid for the novice who is "tactilely challenged" and unable to distinguish between a bear skin rug and a vicuña shawl. It doesn't take long for the novice to learn the histogram sales pitch: the lower the microns, the better the fleece. If an animal's micron average is low, the seller usually makes a quantum leap to claim that the entire animal is superior.

North American alpaca breeders are often asked, "What is a good micron count?" When a laboratory ran a histogram on a sample taken from a vicuña (the wild progenitor of the alpaca), its incredibly fine fleece registered an average of 12.7 microns, with a standard deviation of 3.4 and 0.5 percent of its fleece in excess of 30 microns. The staple was about 1.8 inch (4.54 cm), and the average vicuña produces a mere 480 grams (1.2 lb) per shearing.[11,88,89,90] These last two figures do not appear on a laser-scan histogram, but they are very important in developing a comprehensive approach to assessing the optimum productivity of an animal. For example, an impressive alpaca histogram may have an average diameter of 20 microns or below with a standard deviation of around 3, a coefficient of variation of 16, with 1 to 3 percent of the sample exceeding 30 microns, indicating that the animal is capable of annually producing a 6- to 8-pound fleece.[51]

FIBER AS A TRANSITORY MEDIUM

Relationship Between Fineness and Fleece Weight

There is much more to a histogram than a micron count, standard deviation, coefficient of variation, and the percentage of microns >30. The greatest fleece weight with the best possible histogram is what is most desirable, but you won't find an animal's fleece weight recorded on a histogram. In all domestic fiber-producing animals, achieving a high fleece weight while maintaining a low micron count is desirable and challenging. These two important fiber characteristics do not work together. In fact, they tend to undermine one another. It has been documented that when micron counts become low, the fleece weight often drops too (graphically illustrated by the statistical fiber profile for the vicuña just discussed).

Since fiber is bought and sold within certain fiber classes or structures, the answer to the optimum histogram really becomes identifying the area in which an alpaca (as a species) can maintain a substantial fleece weight while maintaining a relatively low micron count. Optimizing fleece weight while maintaining low microns is a well-known challenge to the manager of the large herds on the altiplano. Maximizing fleece weight while ignoring increases in microns is as potentially self-defeating as is ignoring low fleece weights in deference to unusually low microns. It is well known that selection for fineness alone reduces fleece weights. Per alpaca, the highest dollar return will probably not be from the alpaca with the finest fleece (and lowest fleece weight) or the animal with the greatest fleece weight (and coarse fiber). The best return will be from an animal that has substantial weight and a low enough micron count to be in the best class—20 to 23 microns in the current Peruvian systems (see Table 10.11).

In all natural fiber industries fleece weight is the primary determinant of price. However, after fleece weight, in sheep industries around the world (and fledgling commercial alpaca businesses such as in Australia and North America), differences in price for fiber are often estab-

---

*Derek Michell, personal communication, May 28, 2001.

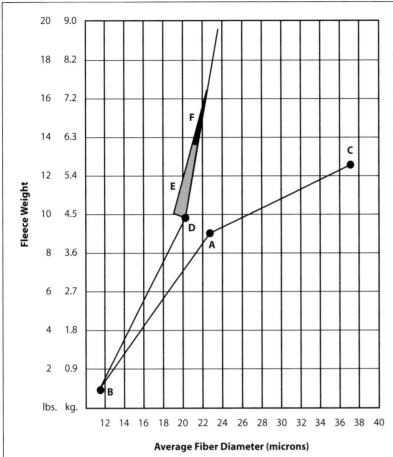

Table 10.11 Relationship between average fiber diameter and fleece weight.

A Rural Alianza's production for a prime breeding herd (22–23 microns, 9 pounds per animal) is thought to be the species optimum by experts in South America.

B Vicuña micron and fleece weight. Vicuñas are the evolutionary progenitors of the alpaca.

C Coarsening usually increases rapidly after 9 pounds.

D Breeding goal thought to be obtainable by leading experts in Peru.

E Fleece type exists, but it is rare.

F Fleece type is extremely rare.

EH/CAB

lished based on the class of the fiber. However, in Peru where commercial fiber processing occurs on a large scale, the emphasis for the last 15 years has been on fleece weight (and white and light fawn color), with little regard for fineness. In 1998 some of the large mills instituted incentives to pay more for premium fleeces that would be classed in the most desirable groupings (baby, 20–22 microns, and superfine, 23–25 microns). In developing alpaca fiber markets outside South America, such as in Australia, pricing by weight and quality (class) is instituted to encourage growers to breed for the best fiber.*

In South America buying raw fiber (or *greasy fiber*) based partially on the quality of the fiber has occurred in recent years, but not on an industrywide basis. In 1998 Grupo Inca (one of the largest mills in South America) began offering more money for better fleeces in some of its

buying to create an ongoing incentive for breeders. Before this, growers had no incentive to breed for better fleeces. In fact, with fleece weight as the main determinant of price, breeders with voluminous coarse animals would make more money. With no incentive to emphasize fineness with fleece weight, it is no wonder the impoverished campesino producers didn't pursue selective breeding of alpacas for fine fleeces with the greatest possible fleece weight.[45,51,59]

Achieving Optimum Balance Between Fleece Weight and Fineness

All fiber-producing animals have optimum parameters in which the greatest fleece weight can be achieved while maintaining an optimum fineness. For example, the wild vicuña reliably produces fleece in the 12-micron range, about 1.5 inches long (3.8 cm), and with a fleece weight of 1.5 pounds (.68 kg). In contrast, with Corriedale sheep, the optimum micron count is around 24, with a fleece weight of 11 pounds (5 kg).

*Ian Davison, an organizer of the Alpaca Fibre Marketing Organization in New South Wales, Australia, personal communication, March 22, 2001.

What is a realistic fleece weight for an alpaca while maintaining a micron count in the low 20s? Experts working with large herds in the world's most populous alpaca region of Puno in southern Peru put an optimum of between 22 and 24 microns as the lowest realistic count to accompany the optimum fleece weight of around 8 pounds (3.6 kg). Below 22 microns the fleece weight usually declines precipitously.

Dr. Isabel Quicaño works in Puno for Consejo Nacional de Camelidos Sud Americanos (CONACS), a government-funded program that works with campesinos and their herds. She keeps statistics about alpacas throughout the region. She puts the optimum expectation for the balance between fineness and fleece weight at 23 to 24 microns and 7 to 8 pounds. "Growers achieving these two basic goals are doing as well as can be expected," she states. According to Dr. Quicaño, when microns drop below 20, fleece weights also drop precipitously. Alpacas with 18-micron fleeces averaged only 2.2 pounds (1 kg), or one-third of the optimum weight of around 8 pounds (3.6 kg), with micron counts in the low 20s. Choosing between these two scenarios, the value for the breeder is clearly with the 8-pound (3.6 kg) fleece at 22 microns, rather than the 18-micron fleece at 2.2 pounds (1 kg).*

According to Julio Cuba Alvarado, president of Rural Alianza, the world's biggest alpaca operation with more than 38,000 alpacas, the optimum balance between weight and microns is obtainable with careful selection in choosing breeding animals. In time, he claims a large operation, such as the one he manages, can average an annual fleece weight of 9 pounds with a micron count of 24.** Rural Alianza may have the most comprehensive understanding of weight/micron expectations because it operates in such great volume and records fleece weights during most of its shearings. According to Alvarado, good-quality male alpacas in the prime of their lives average about 10 pounds (4.5 kg) and the females average 7 pounds (3.2 kg). The

greatest fleece weight ever recorded at Rural Alianza was a male who produced 19 pounds (8.6 kg) in 18 months.

Well-known Peruvian breeder Don Julio Barreda put the optimum balance around 22 microns with a weight of 12 to 15 pounds (5.4–6.8 kg). (The higher fleece weight reported by Barreda may be partly attributable to Don Julio's Accoyo line, which is often physically larger than the average animal.) Don Julio Barreda thinks an obtainable goal for breeders adhering to rigid selective breeding practices is to create an alpaca that produces 20 pounds (9 kg) in 18 months with a fineness of 20 microns.***

At the lower range of fleece weight, Rural Alianza culls all males who cannot produce a 7-pound (3.1-kg) fleece as a tui (14–18 months), and culls females whose tui fleece weights are below 6 pounds (2.7 kg).† Culling based solely on fleece weight also automatically culls many fine-fleeced animals whose micron counts are in the teens, but who do not have acceptable fleece weights.

The discussion offered here, from some of the most knowledgeable people in Peru, needs to be considered as a statement of the relationship between microns and fleece weight in the Peruvian setting, where animals live on native pastures that typically experience a three-month wet season (approximately 24 inches of precipitation) and a long dry season. Diet has a major influence on fiber production.[39,51,58,59,113]

Environmental Factors and Fleece Quality

Novices to alpaca raising are often surprised to find that a histogram that attracted them to an animal appears to be inaccurate when they test the same animal a year after they purchased it. It is important to remember that as long as fiber is still attached to an alpaca, it is not a static medium. For example, a 10-year-old male whose micron count has crept up to an average of 28, but with a standard deviation of 4 and a coefficient of variation of 15, and producing 6 to 8 pounds of fleece annually is also viable for breeding purposes. When evaluating a histogram, breeders must take into account many environmental factors (diet, aging, repeated shearings, pregnancy, stress, possible influences of levels of testosterone, and so forth) that affect a fleece (and the histogram) as the animal matures. This example of the older male is just one instance of many factors affecting histogram results (see Figure 10.17 shown previously, and Figures 10.18, 10.19, and 10.20).[37,39,71,113]

Quechua children capture their favorite crias to show a visitor.

*Dr. Isabel Quicaño, CONACS oversight veterinarian in Puno, personal communication, Puno, Peru, January 23, 2001.

**Julio Cuba Alvarado, president of Rural Alianza, personal communication, Ayaviri, Peru, January 25, 2001.

***Don Julio Barreda, personal communication, Arequipa, Peru, January 26, 2001.

†Julio Cuba Alvarado, personal communication, January 25, 2001.

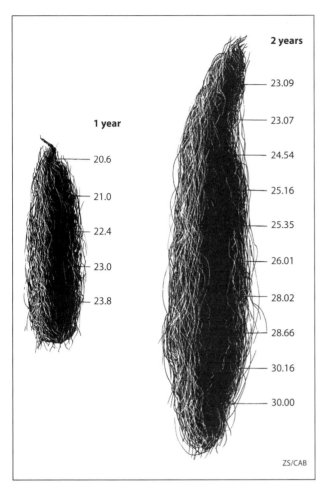

Figure10.18 Fiber diameter (shown here in microns) is influenced by diet.

1 year

— 20.6

— 21.0

— 22.4

— 23.0

— 23.8

2 years

— 23.09

— 23.07

— 24.54

— 25.16

— 25.35

— 26.01

— 28.02

— 28.66

— 30.16

— 30.00

ZS/CAB

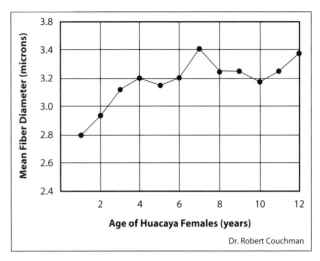

Dr. Robert Couchman

Figure 10.19 Effects of age on fleece micronage.

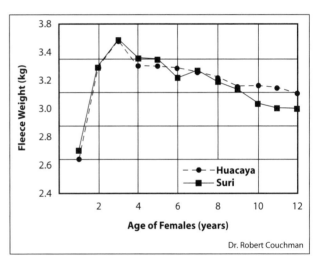

Dr. Robert Couchman

Figure 10.20 Effects of age on fleece weight of huacayas and suris.

Angus McColl, the owner and director of Yocom–McColl Testing Laboratories in Denver, Colorado, is quick to explain that while the histograms his laboratory produces are valuable information for the alpaca breeder, each histogram needs to be considered in its own special context. "Histograms should be compared to other animals in the same herd of the same age," Angus says, "not against an animal living on a different diet and of an entirely different age group." Angus notes that occasionally people send in fiber samples in the hope that the results will give them a marketing advantage over their competitors. To give histogram results greater authenticity and integrity, Angus requests the age of the animal and its registration number, which are then included on the histogram.*

Identifying an alpaca and recording its age allows a knowledgeable person scrutinizing a histogram to get a sense of how a particular animal stacks up against others in the same bracket. In addition, a potential buyer can supply the registration number to the registry to verify the animal's age. If age and registration number are not included on the histogram, the test result's worth as an advertisement is greatly diminished.[60,61,73,117]

Diet and Fleece Quality

Only a few researchers have recorded how alpaca fiber changes under various environmental conditions. George Davis of AgResearch in New Zealand reported at the Australian Alpaca Association International Seminar in 1994 that the fiber of a group of alpacas grazing on nutritious year-round pasture increased on average about 3 microns

*Angus McColl, personal communication, April 12, 2001.

a year, and individual animals had increases exceeding 9 microns.[26,27,28,37,39,51,116,117]

In 1997, while working as an alpaca screener in Peru, I was afforded the opportunity to test a group of 21 alpacas (10 huacaya and 11 suris) on two occasions four months apart during a period of radical dietary change. The animals had been taken off the altiplano when nutrition was at its poorest and fed an alfalfa hay and pellet diet. The results (Table 10.12) demonstrate that some aspects of alpaca fiber measurement commonly recited on a histogram are easily altered, while other measurements remain relatively constant.

In the test group, the first samples were collected shortly after the alpacas had been transported from the altiplano at the end of the dry season, when natural pastures are nutritionally depleted. All animals were sampled at the midpoint along the flank of the primary blanket. The animals in question arrived in relatively good body condition, with most scoring 2 or 3 on a 5-point body score. Most of the animals were tuis, in full fleece and not yet finished growing. By definition, tuis produce the best-quality fleece each animal will ever produce because it is the animal's first fleece. This group of tuis was shorn immediately following fiber sampling.

To maximize their growth potential (to meet the minimum adult weight requirement for registry screening of 105 pounds [47.7 kg]), the animals were introduced to a high-grade alfalfa and carefully regulated grain/pellet supplement. Four months later fiber samples were collected from all 21 of the animals (10 huacayas and 11 suris). In the four-month period between the original sample and second sample the animals had gained between 10 and 20 pounds (4.5 and 9 kg) and appeared to be robust and in excellent health.

Though they had experienced rapid weight gain, none of the alpacas was obese. All generally received a body score of 3 (optimum) on a 1-to-5 scale. Some had grown an inch (2.5 cm) at the withers. The weight gains in such a short time were no less remarkable than the changes in their histogram results during the same period. As a group they experienced an increase of 3 microns in diameter, moving from an average of 21.6 to 24.8 microns, with an individual animal skyrocketing 9 microns in four months. The percentage of micron counts over 30 in the sample increased by a whopping 10.7 percent, from 6.7 percent to 16 percent.

On the other hand, standard deviation and coefficient of variation proved to be much more stable measurements under the changing conditions. On average, standard deviation shifted upward by 1 micron. Coefficient of variation was practically as stable, showing a mild upward move-

Alpacas are born to be shorn. Their fleece grows continually and does not shed. The excessive staple length on these animals is a result of not being shorn for two years.

ment. Both measurements assess uniformity (consistency), which is directly related to hair follicle development on the skin, a characteristic primarily influenced by inheritance. Thus, these two measurements are usually less influenced by environmentally stimulated factors.

Identifying Alpacas Whose Fiber Diameter Is Not Affected by Diet Micron counts will likely increase with a richer diet, but that is not always the case. Of the 21 animals in the study under discussion, 5 increased in microns only slightly and 2 actually decreased ever so slightly in average microns, even though all of the animals rapidly increased in body weight during the period between the two sampling dates.[51]

Micron reductions from stress and diet are well documented, but the genetic predisposition of some animals to change to a richer diet without appreciable effect on their coat fineness is not understood. Alpacas whose dietary intake does not appreciably alter their average micron count will undoubtedly attract the attention of breeders and researchers. As should animals whose histograms change very little with the passage of time. With the emergence of DNA-based registries in which lineages can be precisely recorded, the bloodlines made up of a predominate number of animals whose micron counts (and yields) don't change as a result of dietary change, multiple shearings, and the passage of time will be sought by serious breeders.[54,55,59,115]

There is evidence that this quality of resistance to micron change is an inherited trait. A female alpaca born in California as a third-generation product of a North American breeding program of northern Chilean ancestry is one such example. This animal defied an enriched diet,

Table 10.12 Coarsening due to the difference between a low- and high-protein diet.

Alpaca ID #	Avg. Fiber Diam.	Increase	Actual Micron Increase	SD	SD After 4 mo.	SD Increase	% Over 30	Increase After 4 mo.	Increase	CV %	CV % After 4 mo.
1	20.8	25.9	5.1	5.0	5.8	0.8	5.0	20.7	15.7	24.0	22.4
2	24.4	27.2	2.8	5.4	6.6	1.2	13.0	28.8	15.8	22.1	24.3
3	21.8	22.8	1.0	4.9	5.5	0.6	6.3	9.4	3.1	22.5	24.1
4	18.1	21.3	3.2	4.5	5.6	1.1	1.9	6.9	5.0	24.9	26.3
5	23.4	22.4	−1.0	5.7	5.4	0.3	9.5	5.4	−4.1	24.4	24.1
6	20.4	24.3	3.9	5.3	7.1	1.8	5.7	12.2	6.5	26.0	29.2
7	18.8	19.9	1.1	4.4	5.1	0.7	2.1	4.3	−2.2	23.4	25.6
8	24.2	23.1	−1.1	5.6	5.5	−0.1	12.7	9.5	−3.2	23.1	23.8
9	23.0	27.0	4.0	5.6	9.2	3.4	9.1	24.0	14.9	24.3	34.1
10	23.4	25.9	2.5	5.4	6.4	1.0	9.0	20.5	11.5	23.1	24.7
11	21.6	25.4	3.8	4.9	5.9	1.0	5.3	18.4	13.3	22.7	23.2
12	19.3	20.3	1.0	4.9	4.7	−0.2	3.6	1.5	−2.1	25.4	23.2
13	20.2	23.9	3.7	5.3	5.9	0.6	5.2	14.5	9.3	26.2	24.7
14	23.2	24.6	1.4	5.0	5.9	0.9	8.3	14.4	4.1	21.6	24.0
15	24.5	28.8	4.3	5.6	7.3	1.7	13.8	40.4	26.6	22.9	25.3
16	22.5	22.6	0.1	4.0	4.8	0.8	2.9	6.7	3.8	17.8	21.2
17	21.9	25.0	3.1	4.4	5.5	1.1	4.4	16.8	12.4	20.1	22.0
18	25.2	28.0	2.8	4.3	5.3	1.0	10.2	31.1	20.9	17.1	18.9
19	18.7	27.8	9.1	3.8	6.5	2.7	1.1	31.9	30.8	20.3	23.4
20	23.3	27.6	4.3	5.1	6.7	1.6	7.5	27.6	20.1	21.9	24.6
21	20.0	26.7	6.7	5.2	5.5	0.3	4.2	23.5	19.3	26.0	20.6
Avg.	21.8	24.8	3.0	4.0		1.09			10.8		

SUMMARY

Micron Change		
Original: 21.8	Retest: 24.8	Increase: 3

SD		
Original: 5.0	Retest: 6.0	Increase: 1

CV		
Original: 22.8	Retest: 24.3	Increase: 1.5

Microns over 30	
Original: 6.7%	Retest: 16.0%

Source: "Fiber as a Transitory Medium: Factors Affecting a Histogram," by Eric Hoffman , *The Alpaca Registry Journal* 3(l) : 29–36, Winter-Spring 1998.

aging, and multiple shearings. Her average microns at 18 months of age were 18.8 with a standard deviation of 3.4. Four crias, five shearings, and six years later the micron count and standard deviation were exactly the same. The histograms of two of her crias were like hers. One cria was equally fine as a tui but, unlike his siblings, in his third year his micron count shot up 4 microns. The two males whose fleeces emulated their mother's have produced a majority of fine-fleeced offspring. Obviously, the dam's influence is a factor in these unions, too. The genetic mechanism for determining the longevity and stability of the quality of an alpaca's pelage isn't understood, but identifying animals with the trait of unchanging micron count is possible and a worthwhile pursuit.

Balancing Diet and Fineness—An Australian Experiment In the new environments outside South America, dietary and climatic conditions are often different than traditional conditions. For the most part diets will be richer, which will increase micronage, but maintaining minimum fineness is an important goal for anyone breeding a specialty-fiber animal. An experiment recounted by Australian specialty fiber expert Bob Couchman demonstrates the dilemma: "In a South American experiment that correlated diet to fiber production, a control group fed high-quality hay experienced a 6-micron increase, which amounted to a reduction in value of about US $.30 per kilogram because of downgrading. However, the production was doubled from 2.5 to 5.5 kg, which provided a 106 percent increase in income." Couchman thinks that breeders should concentrate on maximizing their alpacas' breeding potential. He sees an undesirable increase in fiber diameter as inevitable in most cases. However, careful selective breeding can counteract the effects of the rich diet and keep the increase within reasonable limits. Breeding considerations supported by an ample diet can improve production characteristics such as rate of growth, staple length, greater follicle density, and higher follicle population by increasing body size.[9,13,21,22,23,24,28,91,117,118,119]*

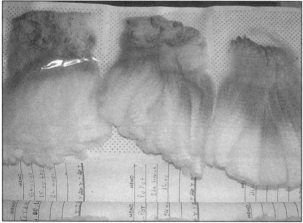

Top The author and Peruvian breeder Don Julio Barreda look through fiber samples of the well-known breeder's stud book.

Below A close-up view shows a sample from a male that produced 15 pounds (6.8 kg) of fleece. The low-micron fleece sample is characterized by crinkle with vicuña-style fleece. The other two samples are comparable in fleece weight, and have varying degrees of uniform crimp.

Variability Within the Blanket I have conducted tests in an attempt to determine how much variability existed within the blanket area of a fleece. Most people know that the skirting, bib, and to varying degrees the neck can be counted on to be coarser than the primary fleece or blanket area. Samples were taken from the same animal in different sites on the blanket at the same time, and were always procured along the skin in swatches 10 inches (25.4 cm) long from the midsection area of the blanket. The sample was then divided into three equal parts and laser scanned. The results showed a great deal of consistency, with most animals showing very slight variability of no more than 0.2 micron. However, two animals showed about 1 full micron of variability in a 10-inch (25.4-cm) swatch.

Tests were also conducted (only six animals chosen randomly from a large Peruvian operation) in which both sides (at the midpoint) of the same animal were sampled and compared. Again, most animals were consistent to less than 0.2 micron from one side to the other. However, two animals (one-third of the test group in this small sample) showed a difference of nearly 1 micron from one side to the other.[51]

Interpreting Histograms

By and large, most of the fiber test results of samples taken through the screening process (between the years 1995 and 2005) are very similar to the results of pretests conducted by importers. However, on occasion, an importer challenged a registry's test results on some animals, claiming the same laboratory performed the tests and therefore the tests should yield the same results. This notion that a histogram possesses certainty and exactness is misleading. In many cases dietary changes will account for the different results in a relatively short period of time.[26,51,116]

There are other reasons for disparate results. Sometimes the samples are taken haphazardly in an inconsistent manner. One common error is to take samples from varying places along the staple. For example, some samples might be extracted from the surface of the skin while other samples are procured 2 inches (5 cm) from the skin. Two inches (5 cm) up the staple from the skin represents 2 to 6 months' passage in time and diet, and any results from such erratic sampling will not give the tester a clear view of a herd's micron makeup.

Another common error is to collect samples from various sites on the animal rather than the recommended midside region. In one case I was involved in, an alpaca importer took pencil-sized samples rather than the 2-square-inch (5-cm) sample size recommended by Yocom-McColl and other testing laboratories. In another

*Dr. Robert C. Couchman, personal communication, December 19, 1994.

situation, recently shorn animals could not be sampled because of their inadequate staple length.

Several alpaca registries I have been employed by take samples from the midside area of the blanket. The sample is procured from as near the skin as possible with portable electric shears.[36,47,48,49,54,55] Remember that the thickness of individual fibers along the staple can vary up to 9 microns if the alpaca has undergone a significant dietary change since its last shearing. Consequently, if a sample is taken an inch (2.5 cm) from the skin, the result may be significantly different than at the skin. In fact, procuring a sample one-half inch (1.3 cm) along the staple from the skin may result in a difference of 5 microns, depending on numerous environmental factors that the animal may have experienced.

In summary, laser scanning and the resulting bar graph histogram are widely used in North America, Australia, the United Kingdom, and Europe, and are being used more and more in South America as well. Laser scanning can be a valuable tool for the breeder and fiber processor, but we need to always consider test results for what they are: the quality of the fleece at the time of the sampling. The value of the test results is that they indicate numerous factors encompassing both the genetic qualities of the fleece and numerous environmental influences. It would be a mistake to rely solely on a histogram to make comprehensive conclusions about an alpaca's fleece and the animal's ultimate value. It takes a thorough education on essential fiber characteristics in conjunction with wise use of information provided by histograms to steer a breeding program. The histograms shown in Figures 10.21 and 10.22 provide examples.

Establishing the Parameters for Huacaya Alpaca Fiber Characteristics

In the summer of 2004, North American fiber scientists Dr. Christopher Lupton, Dr. Robert Stobart, and Angus McColl of Yocom–McColl Testing Laboratories finished work on their Alpaca Research Foundation grant that was a first-of-its kind study of huacaya alpaca fiber. Their final results were published in August 2005. They sampled 585 huacayas throughout the United States. This may be the first large study that has attempted to identify the parameters of common fiber properties and record both the positive and negative correlations between important fiber characteristics.[71] See Tables 10.13 and 10.14.

For example, one of the study's many conclusions was that "the intrinsic resistance to [the] compression of alpaca [huacaya] is low because of relatively low levels of crimp. Thus, alpaca is not suited for end-uses that require high resistance to compression or bulk." It turned out that alpaca ranged between 15.4 and 52.5 curvature (deg/mm) and that curvature decreased with age. A low curvature in Merino sheep is 50 deg/mm. When it comes to crimp,

Table 10.13 Key to abbreviations in fiber characteristics of huacaya alpacas.

Abbreviations	Characteristics
Age (yr)	Age, years
BW (kg/lb)	Body weight, kg and lbs
GP (mo)	Growth period, months
AFD (μm)	Average micron diameter (μm)
SD (μm)	Standard deviation of fiber diameter, μm
CV (%)	Coefficient of variation of fiber diameter, %
PF (%)	Prickle factor, fibers >30 μm, %
CF (%)	Comfort factor, fibers <30 μm, %
AC (deg/mm)	Average curvature, deg/mm
CSD (deg/mm)	Standard deviation of fiber curvature, deg/mm
MED (per 10,000)	Medullated fibers (white and light fawn samples only), per 10,000
OBJ (per 10,000)	Objectionable fibers (white and light fawn samples only), per 10,000
LSY (%)	Lab scoured yield, %
MSL (mm)	Mean staple length, mm
LSD (mm)	Standard deviation of staple length, %
LCV (%)	Coefficient of variation of staple length, %
ADJ MSL (mm)	Adjusted mean staple length, mm
ADJ LSD (mm)	Adjusted standard deviation of staple length, mm
ADJ LCV (%)	Adjusted coefficient of variation of staple length, %
MSS (N/ktex)	Mean staple length, N/ktex
SSD (N/ktex)	Standard deviation of staple strength, %
SCV (%)	Coefficient of variation of staple strength, %
POB, tip (%)	Position of break in top third of staple, %
POB, middle (%)	Position of break in middle third of staple, %
POB, base (%)	Position of break in base third of staple, %
RTC (kPa)	Resistance to compression, kPa

Source: Special thanks to Christopher Lupton, Angus McColl, and Robert Stobart for allowing the use of this material. Reprinted from Fiber Characteristics of the Huacaya Alpaca, *Small Ruminant Journal*, in press, 2006.

sheep's wool generally starts where alpaca stops, so the species parameters are different for each. In all, 26 measurements were recorded from each animal. This study established baseline data on age, body weight, region, color, sex, and last shearing date. The baseline data allowed the researchers to assess the changes in fleece characteristics based on age, weight, and region (which are general indicators of the influences of gross diet).

The study provides valuable information for new areas of inquiry and introduced expanded types of histograms that will allow breeders to become directly involved in their own correlations of objective criteria fiber measurement. Here are some of the findings.

• For both worsted and woolen spinning, AFD (micron), and CV (coefficient of variation) measurements are by far the most important fiber properties influencing spinning performance.

• Average fiber diameter (AFD) is positively correlated with age, body weight, clean yield, and staple length, and negatively correlated with average curvature and staple length.

• Compared to wool of similar fineness, alpaca was shown to be much higher yielding, more heavily medullated, longer, and considerably stronger.

• The average level of fiber curvature in alpacas is quite low, compared to cashmere and fine wool. The aver-

age curvature is negatively correlated to age, body weight, fiber diameter, and clean yield, and positively correlated with staple length and resistance to compression.

• The range in curvature in the 585 U.S. huacaya alpacas was between 15.4 and 52.4 deg/mm, with a mean of 32 deg/mm. The bottom range for sheep is around 50 deg/mm, which is the high range for alpacas. When it comes to curvature, sheep and alpacas are quite different. Sheep and alpaca have different evolutionary paths. Not all characteristics common to one should be expected to be the same in the other. However, breeding for greater curvature (crimp/crinkle) could be advantageous for some processing requirements.

• Longer fibers produce more uniform, heavier yarns that have greater resistance to abrasion. The mean staple length was 4.6 inches (12.4 cm), which is more than adequate for processing.

• Most alpaca is medullated to varying degrees. White and light-colored fibers having medulla greater than 60 percent of the width of the fiber are chalky in appearance and also appear not to accept dyes readily. These are referred to as objectionable fibers. (Only fiber from white and light fawn/beige animals can be tested for medullation at this time; see Figure 10.17 shown previously.)

• Aging correlates to changes in fiber characteristics. Body weight, fiber diameter, and staple strength and percentage of medulla increase, while curvature and staple length decrease.

• Low AFD negatively corresponds with staple-length regeneration, which is different than most sheep breeds.

• Truly fine wool tends to have more crimp than alpaca of the same fineness.

• Fine fibers in alpacas tend to have more crimp that results in positive significant correlations in resistance to compression. However, the resistance to compression in alpaca compared to sheep is low. Thus, alpaca is not well suited to end uses that require high resistance to compression (bulk). To produce alpacas with more resistance to compression, selection should favor crimp. Less crimp in alpaca results in leaner, smoother, less bulking yarns and fabrics, which is an attribute for the worsted process.[71]

Table 10.14 Summary of data for properties measured on U.S. alpaca samples.

Property	Number	Mean	CV*	Minimum	Maximum
Age (yr)	585	4.08	68.02	1	17
BW (kg/lb)	493	65.16/143	19.25	22.68	104.33
GP (mo)	264	11.73	9.39	4	14
AFD (μm)	585	27.85	19.23	15.09	49.27
SD (μm)	585	6.52	24.42	3.81	14.34
CV (%)	585	23.48	15.11	15.06	39.24
PF (%)	585	31.61	79.23	0.68	96.62
CF (%)	585	68.39	36.62	3.38	99.32
AC (deg/mm)	585	33.16	21.10	15.39	52.51
CSD (deg/mm)	585	31.06	18.65	15.94	52.56
MED (per10,000)**	267	1,748	62.80	59	6,172
OBJ (per10,000)**	267	371	97.80	9.00	2,237
LSY (%)	584	89.77	5.01	58.27	95
MSL (mm)	583	116.28	39.97	53.80	276
LSD (mm)	583	7.74	59.46	2.06	42.28
LCV (%)	583	6.80	50.10	1.84	28.09
ADJ MSL(mm)	264	116.46	35.64	59.10	350.10
ADJ LSD (mm)	264	7.98	64.22	2.06	42.28
ADJ LCV (%)	264	6.87	51.52	2.06	28.09
MSS (N/ktex)	584	50.16	42.66	4.86	137.80
SSD (N/ktex)	584	17.33	48.65	1.25	52.53
SCV (%)	584	38.62	46.09	4.42	112.98
POB, tip (%)	584	31.25	94.98	0	100
POB, middle (%)	584	51.77	51.06	0	100
POB, base (%)	584	16.79	134.21	0	100
RTC (kPa)	575	5.42	15.44	2.89	7.80

*The CV (coefficient of variation) is a measure of variability within the property being measured. The higher the number, the greater the variability within that particular trait. For example, the growth period GP (mo)) between shearings of the samples has a low rate of variability (9.39), while the age of animals in the study was broad spectrum and more variable (68.02). More data based on color, each region, and sex can be found in the source cited below.

**NW and NLF samples only.

Source: The author expresses gratitude to Christopher Lupton, Angus McColl, and Robert Stobart for allowing the use of this data. Reprinted from Fiber Characteristics of the Huacaya Alpaca, *Small Ruminant Journal*, in press, 2006.

Yocom-McColl Testing Laboratories, Inc.
540 West Elk Place • Denver, Colorado 80216-1823 USA
PHONE (303) 294-0582 • FAX (303) 295-6944
EMAIL: ymccoll@ix.netcom.com

Sirolan Laserscan
Micron Test Report

Computer Bank (Factual) Data   4/16/01

Denver CO 80216 U.S.A.   Test No:

Animal and Sample Description

Animal Name: XXXXX   Animal ID: XXXXX
Breed: Vicuna   Sample Location: Side
Sex: XXXXX   Sample Date: XX/XX/XX
Color: XXXXX   Age: 5 Yrs

Laboratory Data

Average Fiber Diameter: 12.7 microns
Standard Deviation: 3.4 microns
Coefficient of Variation: 26.8 %
Fibers Greater Than 30 microns: 0.5 %

This Test Performed According to I.W.T.O Method 12

A Vicuña.

Figure 10.21 Interpreting histograms for a vicuña, a guanaco, and average suri and huacaya alpacas.

Histograms give us insight into the fiber characteristics of individual animals. They also tell us the characteristics of each species or breed of South American camelid. The four histograms typify the vicuña (wild progenitor of the alpaca), the guanaco, and both breeds of alpaca (suri and huacaya).

A A vicuña (*Vicugna vicugna*) sample offers a study in fineness and associated aspects in South American camelids. The average fiber diameter (AFD) of 12.7 is incredibly low compared to other fiber-bearing animals. This is the primary reason vicuña is the highest-priced fleece in the world. The standard deviation of 3.4 is also relatively low, but indicates there is variability in the fleece. The degree of variability is dramatically expressed in the 26.8 percent coefficient of variation, which testifies to the variability in vicuña fleece. Still, the medullated hairs are so fine in this sample that only .5 percent of the sample was over 30 microns, which is superior to most alpacas. Superfine animals such as vicuña (and very fine alpacas) often have diminished fleece weights. Fleece weights aren't recorded on histograms. A vicuña usually carries a fleece weighing about 500 grams (>1 lb) and has a rate of regrowth of about 1/3 inch (.8 cm) a year. Alpacas, on the other hand, are capable of an annual regrowth of 6 inches and a fleece weight of around 8 pounds (3.6 kg) or more.

B Guanaco (*Lama guanicoe*) is a much ignored resource for excellent fiber. It is considered a two-coated animal needing dehairing to utilize properly for fiber processing. Though vicuñas and guanacos generally have predicatable fiber characteristics, this guanaco is less typical in the area of medullation. Still, an AFD of 16 is very desirable and the standard deviation of 4.4 indicates some variability, which is more dramatically expressed in the high coefficient of variation of 27.5. Guanacos can be expected to produce between 350 and 800 grams of fiber annually.

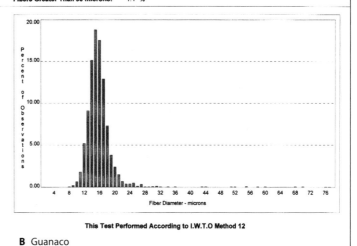

Yocom-McColl Testing Laboratories, Inc.
540 West Elk Place • Denver, Colorado 80216-1823 USA
PHONE (303) 294-0582 • FAX (303) 295-6944
EMAIL: ymccoll@ix.netcom.com

Sirolan Laserscan
Micron Test Report

Computer Bank (Factual) Data   4/16/01

Denver CO 80216 U.S.A.   Test No:

Animal and Sample Description

Animal Name: XXXXX   Animal ID: XXXXX
Breed: Guanaco   Sample Location: Side
Sex: XXXXX   Sample Date: XX/XX/XX
Color: XXXXX   Age: 6 Yrs

Laboratory Data

Average Fiber Diameter: 16.0 microns
Standard Deviation: 4.4 microns
Coefficient of Variation: 27.5 %
Fibers Greater Than 30 microns: 1.1 %

This Test Performed According to I.W.T.O Method 12

B Guanaco

Yocom-McColl Testing Laboratories, Inc.
540 West Elk Place • Denver, Colorado 80216-1823 USA
PHONE (303) 294-0582 • FAX (303) 295-6944
EMAIL: ymccoll@ix.netcom.com

Sirolan Laserscan
Micron Test Report

Computer Bank (Factual) Data   4/17/01

Denver CO 80216 U.S.A.   Test No:

Animal and Sample Description

Animal Name: XXXXX   **Animal ID:** XXXXX
Breed: Alpaca(Suri)   **Sample Location:** Side
Sex: XXXXX   **Sample Date:** XX/XX/XX
Color: XXXXX   **Age:** XXXXX

Laboratory Data

Average Fiber Diameter: 23.8 microns
Standard Deviation: 6.1 microns
Coefficient of Variation: 25.6 %
Fibers Greater Than 30 microns: 15.3 %

This Test Performed According to I.W.T.O Method 12

C Average suri at 2.5 years

Figure 10.21 continued

C The suri alpaca (*Vicugna pacos*) histogram is of an average suri, based on thousands of suris that have been tested by Yocom-McColl. The "average" animal would likely have a lower AFD if it had been tested earlier in its life. Still, an AFD of 23.8 is within the classing range of most products made of alpaca. Coarsening over time is the norm with alpacas. The AFD is somewhat high for the age of the animal (2.5 years). However, a standard deviation of 6.1 and a coefficient of variation of 25.6 percent are problem areas that are further negatively expressed in 15.3 percent of microns over 30, ensuring the fleece has considerable prickle factor. This will devalue the fleece and limit its uses for processing. Because suri fiber is soft and silky feeling (because of its flat scale structure), new alpaca owners are often surprised to learn that suri tends to have more variability than huacaya. There are, of course, individual exceptions. Many suris produce between 7 and 12 pounds (3.2 and 5.4 kg), which is an impressive yield.

D This huacaya alpaca (*Vicugna pacos*) histogram is on an average two-and-a-half-year-old huacaya, based on thousands of huacayas tested by Yocom-McColl Laboratories. Assessing this histogram is difficult because there is no information about the animal's age. For a young adult or adult the AFD is entirely within range of most end-use applications. The concern is found in the standard deviation of 5.0, the coefficient of variation of 20.8 percent, and most specifically in the percentage of microns over 30. The disparity between the average diameter and the standard deviation is reflected in the coefficient of variation. A coefficient of variation of 20 percent, and preferably lower, is desirable. There is significant medullation and prickle factor in this fleece, which would probably be much less if this sample had been taken when the animal was younger or following a year on a fairly lean diet. There is plenty of room for improvement through selective breeding practices.

Yocom-McColl Testing Laboratories, Inc.
540 West Elk Place • Denver, Colorado 80216-1823 USA
PHONE (303) 294-0582 • FAX (303) 295-6944
EMAIL: ymccoll@ix.netcom.com

Sirolan Laserscan
Micron Test Report

Computer Bank (Factual) Data   4/17

Denver CO 80216 U.S.A.   Test No:

Animal and Sample Description

Animal Name: XXXXX   **Animal ID:** XXXXX
Breed: Alpaca(Huacaya)   **Sample Location:** Side
Sex: XXXXX   **Sample Date:** XX/XX/XX
Color: XXXXX   **Age:** XXXXX

Laboratory Data

Average Fiber Diameter: 24.0 microns
Standard Deviation: 5.0 microns
Coefficient of Variation: 20.8 %
Fibers Greater Than 30 microns: 11.0 %

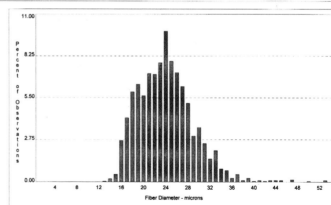

This Test Performed According to I.W.T.O Method 12

D Average huacaya at 2.5 years

Yocom-McColl Testing Laboratories, Inc.
540 West Elk Place • Denver, Colorado 80216-1823 USA
PHONE (303) 294-0582 • FAX (303) 295-6944
EMAIL: ymccoll@ix.netcom.com

Sirolan Laserscan
Micron Test Report

Computer Bank (Factual) Data   4/17/01

Denver CO 80216 U.S.A.   Test No:

Animal and Sample Description

Animal Name:	XXXXX	Animal ID:	XXXXX
Breed:	Alpaca(Huacaya)	Sample Location:	Side
Sex:	XXXXX	Sample Date:	XX/XX/XX
Color:	XXXXX	Age:	1.5 Yrs

Laboratory Data

Average Fiber Diameter:	18.6	microns
Standard Deviation:	2.7	microns
Coefficient of Variation:	14.5	%
Fibers Greater Than 30 microns:	0.5	%

This Test Performed According to I.W.T.O Method 12

A Excellent potential

Figure 10.22 Interpreting subtle difference in histograms.

A The low micron count (18.6) coupled with a low standard deviation (2.7) is very desirable, as is a coeffcient of variation of 14.5. A 0.5 percent of fibers over 30 microns is also extremely desirable. This alpaca has a very desirable histogram. However, the animal is young. The most useful time to take a histogram is several months after an animal's first shearing. If the animal's fleece weight is above 8 pounds (3.6 kg), it is indeed a superior fleece. This is an example of an exceptional and uniform fleece.

B This histogram is deceptive for predicting long-term fleece quality. The AFD of 17.2 is desirable and impressive. However, both the standard deviation (4.6) and the coefficient of variation (26.7) are high, indicating that variability is broad. This, coupled with the fact that this animal is only ten months old, means there is potential for "blow out," and a much different histogram is likely with the passage of time.

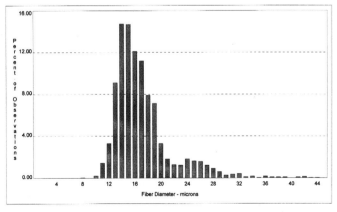

Yocom-McColl Testing Laboratories, Inc.
540 West Elk Place • Denver, Colorado 80216-1823 USA
PHONE (303) 294-0582 • FAX (303) 295-6944
EMAIL: ymccoll@ix.netcom.com

Sirolan Laserscan
Micron Test Report

Computer Bank (Factual) Data   4/17/01

Denver CO 80216 U.S.A.   Test No:

Animal and Sample Description

Animal Name:	XXXXX	Animal ID:	XXXXX
Breed:	Alpaca(Suri)	Sample Location:	Side
Sex:	XXXXX	Sample Date:	XX/XX/XX
Color:	XXXXX	Age:	10 Mos

Laboratory Data

Average Fiber Diameter:	17.2	microns
Standard Deviation:	4.6	microns
Coefficient of Variation:	26.7	%
Fibers Greater Than 30 microns:	2.2	%

This Test Performed According to I.W.T.O Method 12

B Marginal potential

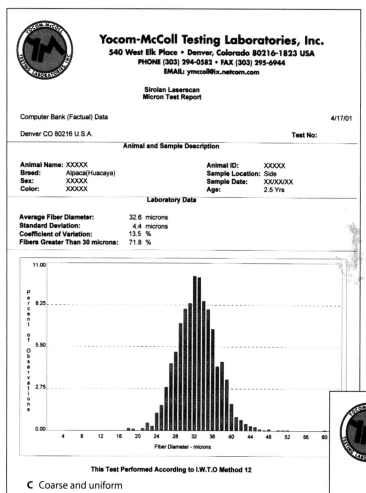

Yocom-McColl Testing Laboratories, Inc.
540 West Elk Place • Denver, Colorado 80216-1823 USA
PHONE (303) 294-0582 • FAX (303) 295-6944
EMAIL: ymccoll@ix.netcom.com

Sirolan Laserscan
Micron Test Report

Computer Bank (Factual) Data   4/17/01

Denver CO 80216 U.S.A.   Test No:

Animal and Sample Description

Animal Name: XXXXX   Animal ID: XXXXX
Breed: Alpaca(Huacaya)   Sample Location: Side
Sex: XXXXX   Sample Date: XX/XX/XX
Color: XXXXX   Age: 2.5 Yrs

Laboratory Data

Average Fiber Diameter: 32.6 microns
Standard Deviation: 4.4 microns
Coefficient of Variation: 13.5 %
Fibers Greater Than 30 microns: 71.8 %

This Test Performed According to I.W.T.O Method 12

C Coarse and uniform

Figure 10.22 continued

C This histogram is rare in that the microns are excessively high at 32.6 AFD, while the standard deviation and coefficient are low. This is a coarse, uniform fleece. The sample is from a two-and-a-half-year-old animal. If it were from 10- or 12-year-old animal, this could be considered an acceptable histogram. Many animals coarsen with time, but few animals display this degree of uniformity when they are this coarse.

D This histogram is typical of many llamas, but can occur in alpacas. It is called a bimodal distribution because instead of one spike in the histogram there are two. This shows a strongly coated (or two-coated) animal.

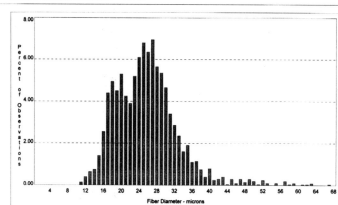

Yocom-McColl Testing Laboratories, Inc.
540 West Elk Place • Denver, Colorado 80216-1823 USA
PHONE (303) 294-0582 • FAX (303) 295-6944
EMAIL: ymccoll@ix.netcom.com

Sirolan Laserscan
Micron Test Report

Computer Bank (Factual) Data   4/16/0

Denver CO 80216 U.S.A.   Test No:

Animal and Sample Description

Animal Name: XXXXX   Animal ID: XXXXX
Breed: Alpaca(Huacaya)   Sample Location: Side
Sex: XXXXX   Sample Date: XX/XX/XX
Color: XXXXX   Age: 2.5 Yrs

Laboratory Data

Average Fiber Diameter: 25.8 microns
Standard Deviation: 7.3 microns
Coefficient of Variation: 28.3 %
Fibers Greater Than 30 microns: 19.8 %

This Test Performed According to I.W.T.O Method 12

D Bimodal histogram

Richard and Agnes Wildt, of Rich-Nes Alpacas in Minnesota, create alpaca products made exclusively from their own herd of 325 animals. All their fiber processing is done in the United States. Undyed clothing and yarn are featured in these store displays.

Joy Whitehead displays yarn and woven goods made from the fleece of her alpacas at Bozedown Alpacas, Reading, England.

Left Dyed alpaca yarns from Peru.

Right Machine-spun alpaca yarn processed at a wool mill in Taos, New Mexico.

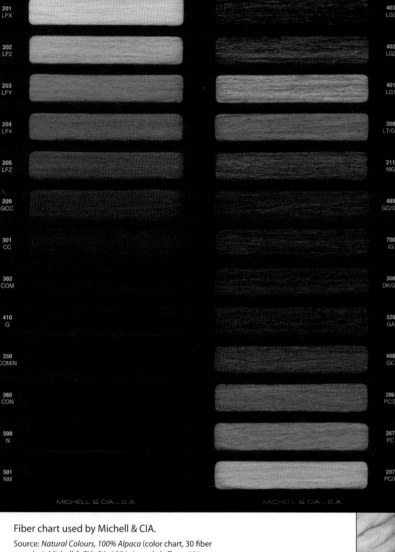

100 B			409 GO
101 BMC			404 LG4
102 BMN			510 PO
201 LFX			403 LG3
202 LF2			402 LG2
203 LFY			401 LG1
204 LF4			208 LT/GC
205 LFZ			211 MG
209 GCC			489 GC/GO
301 CC			700 IG
302 COM			306 DK/GC
410 G			326 GA
350 COM/N			408 GC
360 CON			206 PC/Z
500 N			267 PC
501 NM			207 PC/X

MICHELL & CIA., S.A.   MICHELL & CIA., S.A.

Fiber chart used by Michell & CIA.

Source: *Natural Colours, 100% Alpaca* (color chart, 30 fiber samples), Michell & CIA, SA, 1994. Juan de la Torre 101, San Lazaro, Arequipa, Peru.

Inca Tops model wearing natural-color rovings.

Rovings, yarns, and finished textiles from Michell & CIA.

An alpaca knitwear design.

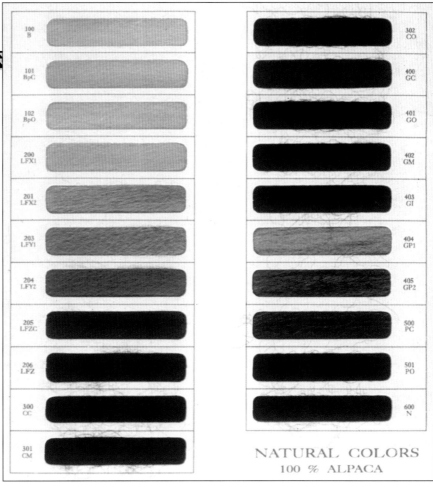

100 B		302 CO
101 BpC		400 GC
102 BpO		401 GO
200 LFX1		402 GM
201 LFX2		403 GI
203 LFY1		404 GP1
204 LFY2		405 GP2
205 LFZC		500 PC
206 LFZ		501 PO
300 CC		600 N
301 CM		

NATURAL COLORS
100 % ALPACA

Fiber chart used by Grupo Prosur.

Source: *Natural Colors, 100% Alpaca* (color chart, 20 fiber samples). Sarfatay Company, P.O. Box 1198, Lima, Peru.

A modern alpaca weaving using a Moche-inspired design.

Visitors to Victory Ranch Alpacas in Mora, New Mexico, discover a wide variety of alpaca products.

The Australian Alpaca Centre is a retail outlet for alpaca products run by Coolaroo Alpacas in New South Wales, Australia.

High-fashion alpaca clothing is shown at the International Alpaca Association Festival in Arequipa, Peru.

Canadian alpaca breeder Margaret Brewster's store, Brewster Alpacas, in downtown Banff, Canada.

INTERVIEW WITH JULIE AND DON SKINNER

Julie and Don Skinner of Snowmass Alpacas are among the most successful breeders in North America. The Skinners' ability to consistently produce extraordinarily fine-fleeced alpacas was affirmed in February 2005 when they held their public herd production auction. They sold 54 huacaya alpacas for $3 million to breeders from throughout North America, among them their toughest critics—their competitors.

Eric Hoffman (EH) Are you pleased with your sale results?

Julie Skinner (JS) We were very happy with our sale, but many people don't realize it was really the outcome of decades of work. Animal selection for initial stock was important to us. It wasn't long until our focus had turned to improving fiber, which also means understanding it. We became students of new information and tried to keep an open mind. We are continually testing theories to see if they result in improvement.

EH I know you believe strongly in testing fiber with approved scientific methods and in recording information, especially over time. When the measurement of fiber curvature became available, it is rumored you tested your entire herd of 400 alpacas.

Don Skinner (DS) The more data you collect, the better off you are to make informed decisions. Through histograms and recordkeeping, we kept track of fineness, variability, prickle factor, luster, soft handle, medullation, length, shearing weight, curvature measurements, and skin biopsies to determine densities and secondary and primary follicle ratios.

EH Your quest allowed you to assess in objective terms the changes in an animal's fleece over time and to develop data on specific lineages?

DS Creating fine, uniform, lustrous fleeces is our primary goal. The testing we have done on our herd has shown that very high-frequency crimp with low amplitude shows a consistent positive correlation to superior fineness and handle. This type of fleece consistently has the highest curvature readings of all our fleece types. We call this fleece style a vicuña type for the simple reason that it resembles a vicuña fleece in appearance and performance—except that it has a superior length and very low variability. Many people have mistakenly overlooked this style of fleece because at first glance it appears not to have clearly defined crimp, when in fact, if you part the fleece it will have an impressive fineness and handle with significant density. The fibers are tightly packed and have very high-frequency crimp, so high that it is difficult to see. When tested this fleece type proves to have high curvature and superior loft.

EH Because the crimp is not readily apparent, some breeders may describe this style of fleece as "crinkly." Is that the vicuña type?

DH At first glance it looks markedly different from what is sometimes referred to as a Merino-type crimpy fleece, but it does have consistent curvature that is very high frequency and nearly microscopic.

EH Do you see virtue in the Merino-type fleeces, too? Can you detect differences that are both subtle and significant?

JS We have seen many very good fleeces in the Merino style generally described by Watts. These are the fleeces that show high-frequency crimp with bundling clusters. These fleeces typically have a deeper amplitude than the vicuña type, but with less frequency. Both types [vicuña and Merino] can have similar follicle density measurements. The true vicuña, which does not appear to have clustered follicles, has tested much higher than both fleece types on alpacas, demonstrating that vicuña-style fleece may provide the best model for improving density.

EH Which fleece style appears to hold its fineness longer?

JS In our experience the vicuña types hold their fineness longer. The one conclusion we drew from the tests was not to be prejudiced to any one style of crimp as the primary determiner of excellence. As long as we continue to select for fineness, staple length, lack of medullation, and high luster, we are in fact creating excellence in all fleece characteristics, along with improving density and secondary to primary follicle ratios.

EH When it comes to curvature as expressed by either crimp or crinkle, do you see room for more than one approach?

DS Some people have favored high-frequency, low-amplitude crimp, best typified by the the vicuña look. Others have favored higher amplitude and high-frequency uniform crimp or deep and bold crimp. Such debates should not lose sight of the end product, which, regardless of the style of crimp/crinkle, should always keep in mind fiber fineness and low variability. If a particular style or frequency of curvature (crimp or crinkle) is associated with the essential qualities of fineness and low variability, objective scientific testing now exists to identify that style. For example, if fleeces that look more like vicuña, and prove to be very fine, dense, and uniform, test in the 52 deg/mm range for curvature, this will give us objective correlative information.[96]*

---

*Snowmass Alpacas is located in Sandpoint, Idaho. The interview with Julie and Don Skinner was held on March 10, 2005.

SURI

The word *suri* comes from a flightless ostrichlike bird, the rhea. There are two species: the lesser rhea (*Pterocnemia pennata*), which lives on the Patagonian steppes and Andean puna, and the greater rhea (*Rhea americana*), which lives primarily on the pampas of South America. Suri is the word for the lesser rhea in the Aymara dialect of the highlands. How a large, flightless bird became the namesake of the suri alpaca may never be known.[12,30,84].

Much about the suri alpaca's origins is mysterious and unknown. It is sometimes stated that suris were developed in lowland (possibly coastal) pastures prior to the Conquest, and forced to live in the inhospitable highlands after the conquerors filled the lowlands with their domestic European animals. However, the remains of pre-Conquest mummified suris have been unearthed by archaeologists in the highlands.[113] Conjecture and suris go hand in hand, since little scientific evidence about their origins exists. The silky feathers of the rhea and the fibers of suri alpaca share a common luster and smooth, silky feel. Perhaps their common name speaks to the importance of tactile stimulation among the ancient Andeans. The essential difference between the suri alpaca and the more common huacaya breed of alpaca is their coats, but otherwise the two breeds have the same physical characteristics.

Compared to all other specialty fibers on the world market, suri fiber is very rare. Estimates of the suri population in all of the altiplano vary, but literature emanating from university and government agencies commonly states that 7 percent of the entire alpaca population is suri. Judging by the number of fleeces making their way to the mills in Arequipa, the number of suris is estimated to be around

A suri grazes in the Cumbria area in the United Kingdom.

68,000 animals. About 550,000 pounds of suri fiber were received by the mills in 1999. This amount is miniscule, making up less than 10 to 12 percent of the mill processing.[84] Just how rare suris are is illustrated by comparing their numbers to the vicuña (the alpaca's wild progenitor), which, with a reported population of about 200,000 animals, is listed (2001) as an endangered species by the International Union for the Conservation of Nature. Endangered species status is reserved for species created solely by nature.[52,53,83] However, if domestic breeds could qualify as endangered species, the suri would be a candidate for such status. But suris aren't a separate species, wild or domestic.

For the past three decades, suri numbers have steadily declined, and efforts to breed them in pure form in South America have been sporadic at best. Most of the concentrated suri breeding is occurring near Nunoa in the Puno District in southern Peru. The main breeders in this area (Srs. Enriquez, Mercedes, and Cayo) are concentrating solely on the color white. Many leading alpaca breeders in South America believe the suri is in danger of disappearing if new approaches are not instituted.

Thumbnail Comparison Between Suri and Huacaya Fleeces

In many ways comparing suri and huacaya is like comparing apples and oranges. The differences in structure and characteristics are so great that processing and end use are often markedly different.

Huacaya fiber has a fluffy, spongy appearance, similar to that of Corriedale and Romney sheep's wool. The most noticeable characteristics are the crimp or crinkle along the length of the fibers and in the locks. Because of the scale configuration of huacaya fibers, it readily accepts dyes, which is an important criterion in commercial processing. The scale structure also allows huacaya fibers to grip each other efficiently so they can be processed into strong yarns and threads.

On the other hand, suri fiber is extraordinarily lustrous, soft, slippery, and pliable. It looks like mohair goat fiber, but mohair usually coarsens faster than most suris.[94] Because of the smooth feel of the fiber, suri often appears more uniform than it actually is. Suri doesn't have waviness (or crimp/crinkle). The uniform direction and tight edges of the scales account for its slippery feel and its reluctance to absorb dyes. Suri's structure does not twist and hold to make yarn as well as huacaya. To assure sufficient strength and resilience in a fabric, suri is often blended with huacaya, sheep's wool, and other fibers in ways that allow its smoothness and luster to be appreciated.[6,57,84]

Suri Lock Structure and Curl A blind person can tell the difference between suri and huacaya lock structure. The suri fibers form in locks that hang down, often in spirals or twists, known as *curl*. The fiber parts along the spine expose the animal to more direct contact with the elements than a huacaya with its spongy, puffy fleece. This increased exposure for the animal is often cited as the reason for higher mortality rates in suri crias on the harsh altiplano, where animals are usually offered no shelter from the elements. There is also a common belief, with no scientific support, that the pureness of a particular suri can be determined by examining the lock structure with regard to degree and type of curl.

The locks on suris often vary greatly in appearance from one animal to another. Some have "pencil-like" locks with tight spiraling (about the width of a pencil), giving the animal a distinctive Rastafarian appearance. Others have broader spiraling or very little spiraling in their lock structure. On some animals the locks twist to the right as they hang in ringlets, while on others the ringlets twist to the left. Some suri breeders in new alpaca countries have debated the importance of the direction of the twist and the significance of the tightness of the twist (pencil locks or broad curl). Animals with locks turning to the right are the most common. In the Quechua language such locks are called *quercas*. The direction of the twist, or spiral, of the ringlets and the variability in the twists (wide or tight pencil locks) have no known correlation to fiber quality (AFD, CV, and luster) produced by a particular animal.[104]

Unique Scale Structure The scale structure on the cortical exterior of each fiber is very different on suris when compared to huacayas. On the shaft of suri fiber the scales are long (approximately 7 scales per 100 microns as opposed to about 10 to 11 scales per 100 microns in huacayas) and very tight-fitting to the surface, often protruding no more

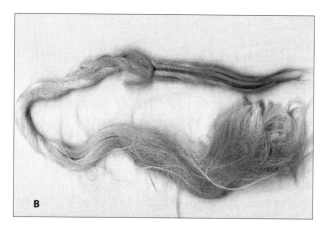

Characteristics in the lock structure of suris are often attributed to being an indicator of fineness and uniformity. In the process of taking fiber samples from hundreds of suris throughout Peru, Bolivia, and northern Chile as a screener for many different registries, I observed a wide range of lock structures and was unable to correlate a particular lock formation with fineness or uniformity. The data collected on the three examples shown here speak for the individualistic nature of suris.

A This sample came from an impressive-looking animal, whose appearance glorified the suri breed. The animal shimmered when it walked. The fleece was lustrous and was allowed to grow for two years. The staple length was 11 inches (27.9 cm). The first half of the staple does not have pronounced curl, while the exposed portion of the fleece has the characteristic suri curl. The animal's histogram is not as impressive as its visual appearance: AFD, 23.8; SD, 5.6; CV, 23.2 percent, microns >30, 10 percent; fleece weight, 12 pounds (5.4 kg); growth period, 24 months; age of alpaca, 2 years.

B This sample came from an impressive-looking animal. The fleece appeared in tight curls and was lustrous. The histogram and data are as follows: AFD, 27.3; SD, 5.8; CV, 21.3 percent, microns > 30, 22.6 percent; fleece weight, 12.5 pounds (5.6 kg); growth period, 12 months; age of alpaca, 6 years.

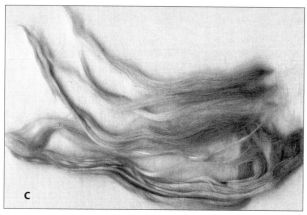

C This sample came from a two-year-old male. The lock structure was straight, without pronounced curl. The feel was superior but the luster only average. The histogram and data are as follows: AFD, 19; SD, 4.7; CV, 24.6 percent; microns >30, 2.3 percent; fleece weight, 8 pounds (3.6 kg); growth period, 12 months; age of alpaca, 2.5 years.

than .1 micron or less. A huacaya's scales are more irregular, closer together, and slightly more protrudent (.3 to .4 micron). By comparison sheep's wool scales protrude around .8 to .9 microns, which is why both huacaya and suri alpacas always feel smoother to the touch than sheep in the same micron range.

There is also a difference between suris and huacayas in the angle of the scale's edge to the cuticle. The edge of a huacaya's scale is about 65 degrees (relatively close to perpendicular), while a suri's scale edge is closer to 45 degrees—an extremely smooth transition between a scale's edge and the cuticle. The combination of barely detectable scale elevations, long scales, and mildly angled scale edges results in the extremely slick feel and is the reason suri is more challenging to process than huacaya.

It has been speculated that suri's impressive luster is influenced by its long scale structure. In fact, all four species of South American camelids (vicuña, guanaco, alpaca, and llama) can be characterized as having a tighter scale structure than sheep, with suri leading the way among all South American camelid subgroups as having the least protrudent scale structure among camelids and all domestic livestock.[104,114] However, both vicuñas (12.7 μm) and guanaco (14–19 μm) possess a more consistently fine fleece than alpacas and llamas (see Figures 10.23, 10.24 and 10.25).

Disposition of Fibers on the Body The disposition of the fibers and locks is completely different between the huacaya and suri (see Figures 10.23, 10.24 and 10.25). Huacaya fibers grow perpendicular to the body and stay this way because of the lock formation. This makes the fleece appear full, dense, and spongy. Suri grows parallel to the body, often hanging in curly ringlets. This is due primarily to the lack of waviness and less involved lock formation. Suri locks part along the spine and hang down both sides of the body.

Because of the differences in the fiber disposition, the huacaya alpaca may appear bulkier and stronger than a suri that is identical in size and structure. Strong phenotypic huacayas and suris are easily distinguishable from one another, even by a person seeing these two breeds for the first time. There are also intermediate fleece types whose fiber characteristics fall somewhere in between.[5,9] The straighter, coarser fleeces among the intermediate types are sometimes called *chilis* among North American alpaca raisers. Intermediate coat types have been identified in Australia, North America, and South America.

There is disagreement about the ultimate influence on the long-term development of both breeds when the parents are from suri and huacaya parents. Advocates of breeding suris to huacayas justify this approach based on the research of fiber scientists in Australia and New Zealand. Some of the breeders using this strategy report a high success rate in producing suri offspring from a suri sire and huacaya dams, while others report less success and intermediate coats.[5,85,86] For more on this topic, see Chapter 25, Genetics of Fiber Type and Coat Color.

Elasticity Suri fiber is usually weaker and less elastic than huacaya. In a dry state suri fiber and, even more so, huacaya fiber are more elastic and stronger than sheep's wool of a similar fineness. But when wet, suri becomes relatively weak.[107]

Softness Both huacaya and suri are softer than sheep's wool. Good-quality alpaca is considered among the softest natural fibers in the world because the scales on the alpaca fiber are less protuberant than on wool. However, compared to huacaya, the scales on suri are longer, one-directional, and smooth edged, and the only South American camelid fiber softer than good-quality suri is vicuña. Softness is a quality that cannot be measured mathematically and is best assessed comparatively by an experienced fiber handler. Fineness and uniformity (low SD) are the important quantitative criteria for judging fiber, but fineness and uniformity without a soft handle do not make top quality.[9,14,56,70,95]

Sorting Suri

As of this writing, the large mill groups in Peru, Prosur, Grupo Inca, and Michell & CIA, sort suri into several groupings based on fineness and color. Juan Pepper, who earned an MBA in International Business from the Philadelphia College of Textiles and Science before joining Michell & CIA of Peru in 1983, is the person who oversees suri production for Michell. Pepper says sorting suri is becoming more involved than it once was, and the priorities in sorting for quality from the highest to the lowest are:

1. Luster
2. Color (white and light fawn presently make up 80 percent of the suri processed commercially)
3. Fineness
4. Silkiness (feels like silk)
5. Tensile strength
6. Length*

Baby Suri As with huacaya, baby suri is the finest classification, with all fibers falling between 21 and 23 microns with a staple between 2.8 to 3 inches (7.1 to 7.6 cm). This is a much sought after class of fleece, but Pepper says, "Unfortunately, it makes up only 5 percent of suri. It is the least

---

*Juan Pepper, personal communication, Arequipa, Peru, July 5, 2000.

Figure 10.23 Microscopic view of fiber from five living camelid and other species.

Group A   Camelid family

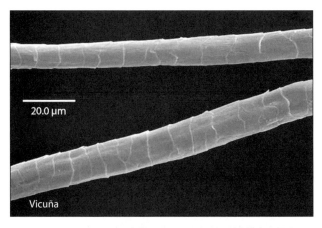

Vicuña

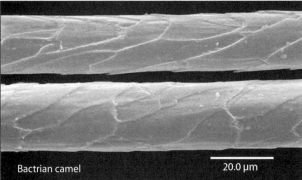

Bactrian camel

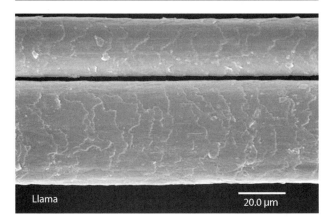

Llama

Huacaya alpaca, 30μm

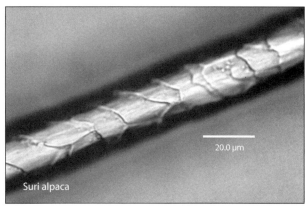

Huacaya alpaca

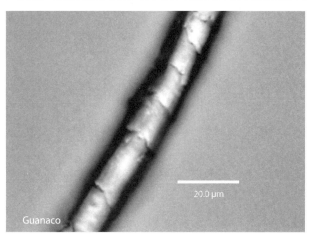

Suri alpaca

Guanaco

Alpacas' legendary smooth handle is largely attributable to a tight cuticle-scale structure, preferably in low microns.

Huacaya scale-edge height is usually 0.2 to 0.35 microns, while suri has no scale height whatsoever or usually no more than .15, which is possibly the tightest scale structure of all domestic fiber-producing animals. Suri scales are longer than huacaya scales. A tight scale structure is characteristic of the entire camelid family, giving camelids a desirable smooth feel compared to many other fiber animals.

Figure 10.23 continued
Group B Other specialty fiber animals and sheep

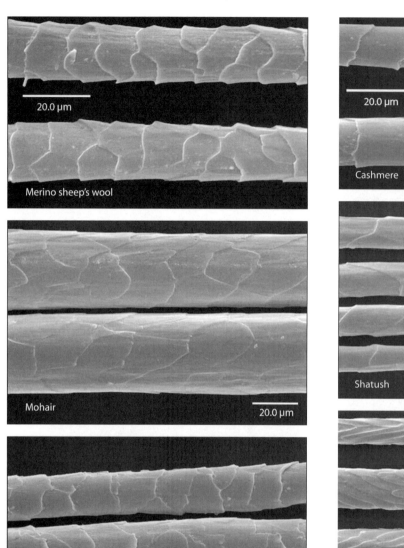

Merino sheep's wool

Mohair

Yak

Cashmere

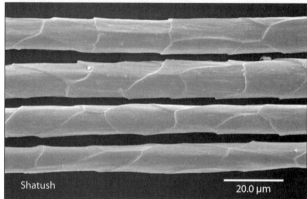

Shatush

Angora rabbit

These images are close-ups of the cuticles (scale structure) of most of the noncamelid specialty fibers. Sheep's wool scales protrude 0.8 to 0.9 microns, which is why, when comparing alpaca to sheep of the same fineness, alpaca will always have a superior handle. Note the protruding scales of the superfine Merino sheep (0.8 µm) and the even scales on cashmere, which usually has a scale height of 0.1µm higher than huacaya. However, cashmere (13–16.5 µm) is almost always finer than the finest alpaca, which gives it wonderful soft handle. Mohair looks similar to suri alpaca, but has more protruding

scales and usually coarsens rapidly after only two shearings. Shatush, a rare wild goat of the Himalayas, is around 11 µm AFD, and a very fine and sought-after fiber. Laws now forbid processing it to protect the goat from extinction. Yak is two-coated. Its undercoat is harvested. It has a scale structure elevation similar to camelids. China, South America, and France are the leading countries in the production of Angora rabbit fiber. Good-quality alpaca compete favorably with these species when it comes to annual yield per animal.

Figure 10.23 continued

Group C **Microscopic insights into camelid fibers**

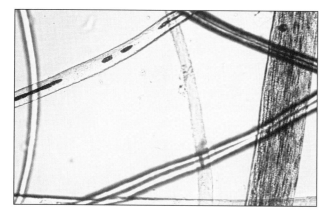

Comparison of huacaya fibers in sample with a standard deviation of 5. Note the segmented medullation in some of the fine fibers.

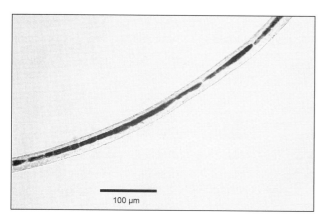

Fully medullated fiber usually occurs in the higher micron ranges, but can occur in low microns in alpacas.

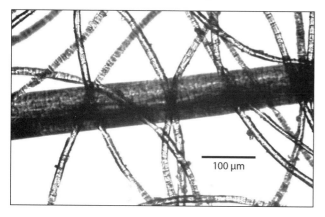

This microscopic image of vicuña fiber shows the difference between 12-micron fiber and 30-micron guard hair. The image also shows the high-frequency curvature that exists in vicuña.

Sources: The author is grateful to F. J. Wortmann of Aachen, Germany, for electron microscope imagery; and to Lee Millon of the University of California at Davis Veterinary Laboratory for 12003 magnification imagery. Found on pages 297-299.

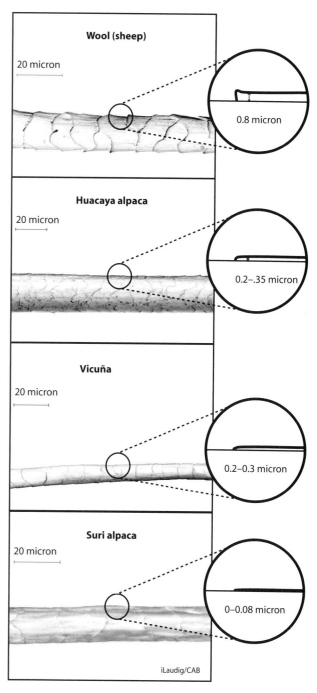

Figure 10.24 Illustrations of cuticle-scale morphologies. Notice the height of the scales and how the edges differ, all of which contribute to handle and processing properties.

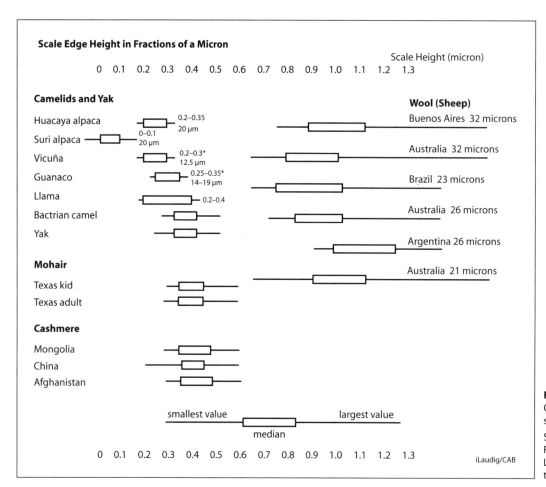

Scale Edge Height in Fractions of a Micron

Scale Height (micron)

0   0.1   0.2   0.3   0.4   0.5   0.6   0.7   0.8   0.9   1.0   1.1   1.2   1.3

Camelids and Yak

Huacaya alpaca — 0.2–0.35 20 µm

Suri alpaca — 0–0.1 20 µm

Vicuña — 0.2–0.3* 12.5 µm

Guanaco — 0.25–0.35* 14–19 µm

Llama — 0.2–0.4

Bactrian camel

Yak

Mohair

Texas kid

Texas adult

Cashmere

Mongolia

China

Afghanistan

Wool (Sheep)

Buenos Aires 32 microns

Australia 32 microns

Brazil 23 microns

Australia 26 microns

Argentina 26 microns

Australia 21 microns

smallest value   largest value

median

0   0.1   0.2   0.3   0.4   0.5   0.6   0.7   0.8   0.9   1.0   1.1   1.2   1.3

iLaudig/CAB

Figure 10.25
Comparison of scale structures.

Sources: Thanks to F. J. Wortmann and Lee Millon for some of the data.

common classification and commercially represents a minuscule fraction of total commercial production compared to the volume in other alpaca categories."[84]*

Regular Suri Fleece In the year 2000, 55 percent of suri fleece being processed was classified as average (regular) quality and fell between 25 and 27 microns with a staple of 3.4 inches (8.6 cm).

Coarse Suri Suri above 30 microns is coarse and is seen as a low-value, relatively unimportant classification. It is also characterized by lack of luster. Not much of this material ever enters the mills to be processed. It is often blended with coarse huacaya.

Colored Suri Colored suris are often much sought after in the United States, Canada, and Europe. For decades most suris have been white or light fawn. Colored suris have occurred throughout this century and earlier, but nobody knows what percentage of the suri population was traditionally colored. In today's live animal export market the

proliferation of colored suris for the export market appears to have occurred independently. Where did these animals come from? Are they predominately the progeny of colored huacaya and white suri crosses? With individual animals the origins and purity of their origins will never be known, because no precise DNA alpaca registries operate in the traditional suri-growing areas.[84,91]

Consensus About Origins of Colored Suris for the South American Export Market Most experts and growers living in the heart of suri-raising areas in southern Peru feel that white and light fawn suris are the historic color for "true suris," but no studies verify this belief. The proliferation of colored suris for exportation is seen as catering to a specialty animal market by suri breeders in South America and officials working for government agencies in southern Peru. In the Puno District, where most suris reside, esti-

*Juan Pepper, personal communication, Arequipa, Peru, July 5, 2000.

mates indicate that about 80 percent of the suris are white and 20 percent are colored. Suris exported from Bolivia and Chile often originated from southern Peru. In fact, the Quechua and Aymara herders (indigenous ethnic groups) in northern Chile have no word for suri. Alpacas are *allpachu,* which is only huacaya in the northern Chilean context.[113]

Juan Pepper won't venture many guesses about the origins of colored suris. His view of suri is through the fleeces presented to Michell & CIA in Arequipa, Peru. Based on his vantage point, Pepper says, "Suri has a smaller range of natural colors than huacaya. From our experience at Michell Group, 80 percent of suri production is concentrated in two colors—raw white and light fawn (B, LFX on Michell's standard color chart). Of the remaining 20 percent, chocolate browns (such as GCC, CC, COM, and GC) make up 15 percent, black and dark brownish shades (COM/N, CON), 5 percent."*

Processing Suri

Talk to anyone involved in processing suri and they will tell you it is difficult to process. However, those same processors will say it is worth the trouble. Suri's straight, smooth surface with lack of crinkle or crimp accounts for the challenge. Almost all aspects of the commercial process must be adjusted to successfully process suri.

The scouring process and the carding process are much like huacaya and other natural fibers. Combing presents the first problem. Combing machines must be set to a much lower speed than with huacaya, and the processing cylinders need to be carefully monitored, as fiber has a tendency to slide off the cylinder rather than bind into a loose "sliver" with its customary inch-wide (2.54-cm) loosely coiled strand. Suri binds reluctantly compared to huacaya. Extra attention to humidity and additional antistatic agents are applied to the process. The processing machines must be stopped frequently, particularly the combs. Tangles occur more frequently. Juan Pepper estimates that "yields from suri processing are somewhere around 10 to 15 percent less than that of huacaya. Double combing is required for finer yarns. Only with greater patience and proper care is a good sliver of lustrous and shiny suri fiber finally able to be transformed into a quality top, the raw material used for spinning the best yarns."*

Spinning Suri

At the industrial fiber-processing level, a high degree of expertise and skill are necessary to successfully spin suri. More than 60 years of knowledge has been accumulated in

Arequipa's mills on how to best approach spinning suri. The knowledge is carefully guarded and different mills have developed different techniques. However, all parties agree that special skills are required to successfully overcome the reluctance of suri to bind. Many of the guarded secrets have to do with careful application of the combination of humidity and antistatic oils to the processing. Pepper points out that suri has other unique properties worth mentioning:

- It has the greatest specific weight of all camelid species.

- It has a high degree of nervousness and slippage—that is, the finished product reacts to the environment, a factor that the manufacturer must consider.

- Twist-fixing the yarn during the spinning process requires more turns per inch to bind the yarn.

- Dyeing is a challenge because suri is not as porous as other fibers.

Uses of Suri

Flat knitting is not a good application of suri. The reluctance of the fiber to bind results in stitches becoming loose and the garment losing shape or unraveling. In a knitted garment suri is used in blends with other natural fibers that will enhance the strength of the garment without losing the character of suri.

Weaving suri is the best use of this rare fiber. Prestigious high-end fabric makers in Japan and Europe have developed a wide range of brushed velour-type fabrics. Women's formal coats are the most common single garment use. Japanese manufacturers such as Fuji Keori, Hosokawa, Fujimata, Nayatake, Keori, and others create high-fashion coats that retail for US $2,000 to US $5,000 in prestigious department stores in Japan. In Italy, Laneri Angnona is the world's leading manufacturer of high-quality suri products. Ricceri, Loropiana, and Piacenza are other Italian houses that produce very refined suri garments, mostly women's quality coats.[84,91]

Suri's incredibly smooth feel makes it a popular and sought-after fiber, occupying a niche at the upper end of alpaca fiber values, beneath the highest-rated huacaya classifications of baby and superfine. Suri accounts for only between 7 and 10 percent of the annual processing in the larger mills of Arequipa, where 90 percent of the world's alpaca fiber is produced for overseas markets.[91] Historically, huacaya fiber has had greater acceptance and held the highest prices in the world market. No comparative data exist on preference for or marketability of the two fleece types produced in herds outside South America.[9,108,109,110]

---

*Juan Pepper, personal communication, Arequipa, Peru, July 5, 2000.

Environmental Adaptations

Various studies and general opinions of alpacas in South America indicate that huacayas are more resistant to the severe and frigid weather conditions of the puna, whereas suris show higher rates of sickness and death in both young and adult animals. This weakness translates to a lower fertility rate.*

This difference in general health appears to be in direct proportion to the amount of protection the different fleece types provide the alpaca. It has been postulated that suris were raised in lower, more temperate regions before the coming of the Spanish (1532), who eradicated camelids from the best lower pastures to make room for European livestock. To this day suris are generally kept in high pastures (along with huacayas), where their numbers are slowly dwindling. They are often kept with huacayas, which results in suri/huacaya crosses. The crias from these unions are often huacayas, which also accounts for the suri's declining numbers.

Though the literature talks about the inability of suris to cope with the frozen world of the highest Andean pastures, in the North American, Australian, and European contexts, the problems are seasonal weather extremes and latitude rather than altitude.[4] The late Jim Vickers, a veterinarian who lived in northern Michigan, housed many huacaya and suris in subfreezing weather near sea level. He concluded that, in terms of tolerances, a shorn huacaya and unshorn suri are roughly the same. Obviously, safeguarding suris from excessive cold is an important consideration for their welfare. See Chapter 4: Husbandry, Chapter 8: Transportation, and Chapter 21: Noninfectious Multisystemic Diseases for more information on protection from and results of temperature extremes.

Comparison Summary

Both suri and huacaya have strength in the marketplace, and this trend should continue. Compared to suri, huacaya typically has greater color diversity, more tensile strength, a scale structure more easily adaptable to processing, and more impressive density.

For manufacturing purposes, huacaya is easier to process and makes a stronger yarn than suri. Huacaya is also superior to suri for felting. On the other hand, suri is incredibly soft and regenerates faster (annual growth for suri is 7.8 inches or 20 cm; huacaya, 5.9 inches or 15 cm). Suri is cleaner, and may surpass huacaya slightly in fleece weight on an annual basis.[9,17] Suri makes an extraordinarily smooth, soft, and lustrous end product. Suri's unusually tight scale structure is both a curse and an advantage. Suri is truly elite in its luster and feel, making the breeding of especially fine suri a challenge worth undertaking.[9,104,107]

*Ignacio Garaycochea, personal communication, May 28, 2001.

The Sirolan LaserScan (lower right) records fiber measurements that are then displayed on a computer (lower left). The LaserScan tests 2,000 to 4,000 individual snippets per sample and can measure average fiber diameter, diameter distribution, spin fineness, curvature, and comfort factor.

THE CHALLENGE OF ESTABLISHING A NATIONAL FIBER-PROCESSING SYSTEM IN "NEW ALPACA COUNTRIES"

Anyone who visits the large alpaca fiber-processing mills in Peru will be astounded at their complexity. Huge buildings are filled with buzzing, twirling, spinning machinery processing various classes, colors, and types of fiber into tops or end products of varying sophistication. Often machinery and humidity are specifically adjusted to accommodate a class or type of fiber. Myriad different colors are sometimes processed in a week's time, requiring the machinery to be entirely cleaned to eliminate color contaminants. With even a rudimentary understanding of the complexity of running such a mill comes the realization that establishing a consistent product on a mass scale is a daunting proposition when considering the many variables involved in processing alpaca.

Commercial processing is built on breeder cooperation and organization, coordination of efforts at every step of the way, technical expertise, investment capital, and marketing and advertising budgets. At the other end of the processing spectrum is the irony that existed (or still exists) in the "new alpaca-growing countries" such as Canada, the United States, the United Kingdom, New Zealand, and Australia.[4,29,81] Here growers probably purchased alpacas for exorbitant prices, compared to what they are sold for in South America, and to sell fiber they market via a website to home spinners who purchase fleeces to make sweaters and other "home-spun" products. As the number of animals increases in these new alpaca countries and alpaca fleece becomes more available, the cottage industry approach will eventually run into the reality of needing to organize alpaca breeders and collect a national (or regional) clip for processing to establish alpaca fiber as a bona fide fiber industry.

The initial challenge is organizing the breeders and developing parameters and standards for fleece cleanliness,

OFDA 100 software analyzes fiber images and derives AFD, SD, and CV measurements of 2,000 to 4,000 longitudinal fiber sections. OFDA 100 also measures curvature and medullation on white or light-colored animals.

staple length, preparation and correct shearing techniques, and learning how to ship fleeces in commercial quantities to a central location to be sorted and classed prior to commercial processing. This challenge is further complicated because the fiber must be sorted not only by fineness and quality, but by color as well.

The basic mathematics of the commercial processing challenge could work something like this. A country outside South America imports and breeds alpacas for a decade or so until the national herd size reaches 30,000 animals. These animals will each produce about 4.5 pounds (2.04 kg) of fleece. This results in a national clip of 135,000 pounds (61,200 kg). About 33 percent of the clip is skirtings and tertiary cuts of marginal use to the processor, which drops the prime clip to 89,000 pounds (40,500 kg) representing the most desirable blanket and neck fibers. If the entire clip is a single color, the only concern would be classing the fiber so a processor could make a run of a specific quality, but consideration of the appropriate number of classes for the volume would need to be carefully considered. The Peruvian system usually has six to nine classes (or grades). If we divide the clip into seven classes (or grades) and each is represented equally, there would be 12,714 pounds (5,767 kg) on average in each of the seven classes.[4,29]

Color diversity is much admired in alpacas, but it can create a real headache when it comes to commercial processing. Any commercial plan needs to consider the "dyeability" of the fiber, which means whites and light fawns will need to be well represented because these colors are easiest to dye. About 70 percent of the fleeces are white or light fawn. Still, in Peru mills usually offer 22 colors to customers, which is laudable considering the challenge in doing so. Most executives in the large mills steadfastly say that natural colors are part of the alpaca fiber-processing business. But in the theoretical "new alpaca country" of 30,000 animals, if all 22 colors are present in the national

clip in seven classes and all things are equal, each class for a particular color would have 577 pounds to process, providing all 30,000 animals contributed to the national clip! This is hardly the volume to excite large mills who are accustomed to contracts for processing tons, not pounds.[4,29,81]

In reality the figures used above to show the impact of fineness classes and color classes in dividing a clip into myriad subcategories is probably a somewhat pessimistic portrayal, because all classes and colors most likely will not be equally represented. However, the figures help illustrate the complexity in the challenge of establishing a commercial fiber business for alpaca. The emergence of "mini-mills" in new alpaca countries that can produce good-quality rovings and yarns allows small herd owners to process their fiber.

Classing on the Peruvian model usually includes seven to nine classes (including suri classes) of fineness without considering color. Compared to new alpaca-growing regions, Peru has the luxury of volume (with roughly 2 million alpacas contributing to the national clip) in all classes (except the suri), and thus mill managers can divide the fleeces into narrow classes of only a few microns, such as baby fiber at 20 to 22 microns. With tightly defined class criteria it's easier to produce consistent tops and end products. Even suri fiber, which is rarer than vicuña, is processed in Peru at a rate of about 190 tons a year, in three classes.

In an emerging alpaca country the existence of so many classes (both in quality and color) can become a stumbling block to establishing a commercial fiber business ready to compete on the world stage. One way to overcome the classing problem is to develop animals that produce a particular class of fiber in fineness and color. This is something to strive for in most new alpaca-growing countries, which will require a decade or more of concentrated breeding practices.

Large-, Middle-, and Small-Scale Processing

In the 1990s several alpaca breeder groups outside of South America attempted to organize fiber processing into a national or regional commercial effort. This has been attempted to varying degrees of success in North America, England and Australia. The Australian Alpaca Co-operative Ltd. has been one of the more successful national efforts, with more than 50 percent of that nation's growers shipping more than 30 tons to a central location annually.

The impetus on national efforts continues, but the entry of middle-sized privately owned processors and mini-mill technology has given fiber producers additional conduits for processing rovings and yarns. For example, there are now dozens of mini-mills throughout the United States that specialize in alpaca fiber processing. Mini-mills will process one fleece or hundreds of fleeces, which is more appealing to many small producers who like to have more control in the fiber they produce than is afforded to them in most national schemes. However, with a multitude of mini-mills in operation, working with alpaca breeders of varying degrees of expertise in classing predictable quality from one mill run to the next can become a challenging proposition.

Rachel Hebditch and Chas Brooke, of Tiverton, England, offer another model that appears to be working. Hebditch and Brooke are long-time alpaca breeders who have made fiber processing a private business. They buy raw fiber from about 50 farms and process it themselves into hand-knit yarns, which they sell in 100-gram balls with a 265-meter length per ball. In their first year of operation they processed 3 tons. Two years later they were processing 6 tons a year and selling all of it. Chas Brooke says:

We process hand-knit yarn in the worsted system. Grading is probably the most important aspect of yarn production. As production is a serial process involving at least eight major functions between raw fiber and finished balled yarn, a failure of any process will not be easily correctable, if at all. The excellent handle of our finished yarn is a reflection of the quality and consistency of our grading process.*

Brooke and Hebditch's UK alpaca company produces five colors of fiber in three grades plus dyed yarns. All of their yarns, except black, are blended with other fibers. Chas Brooke:

The blend we choose depends on the use of the yarn. For example, our sock yarn is blended with nylon or wool. Our hand-knit yarns are blended with Blue Faced Leicester wool, and our baby grade yarn is blended with silk. Nylon gives more wearability. The Blue Faced Leicester gives finished yarn more loft and helps to hold alpaca together. The silk helps emphasize the wonderful soft and silky feel. We are unable to blend the black alpaca, as there is no other natural solid black fiber available to us. All yarns are produced using a fully worsted process.*

Hebditch and Brooke have their fiber processed at a single long-established mill to assure consistency. They find themselves attending trade shows outside of the alpaca breeder community, where they are commonly competing against wool and specialty fibers from around the world. Says Brooke: "We feel we are competitive with the Peruvian yarns in price and quality. It also improves one's understanding of the fiber business to be part of events in which cashmere, mohair, and other types of high-end fibers are represented." When asked if his efforts include involvement in alpaca breed association efforts, he says, "Absolutely not. This is a private business that makes a consistent product."*

National or large operations have the advantage of establishing classes of fiber, cutting some processing costs, and bargaining with large commercial entities. How the roles these different approaches will eventually play out in new alpaca countries is a story that is still being told. At the end of the day practical solutions to improve productivity and costs are what add up to success. One example of problem solving and goal setting is encompassed in the goals of the national effort in Australia, offered here.

1. Establish regional fleece collection points throughout Australia.

2. Establish a new alpaca shearing protocol to minimize the cost of shearing, thereby reducing contamination from fiber with excessive guardhair and poor quality.

3. Seek a long-term solution to the scouring problem caused by color contamination.

4. Expand and develop the range of quality products that will be suitable for retailers and customers.

5. Work to create an annual sale of Australian products at a value of A $1 million or higher.

Getting the Most Out of a National Herd

On the surface it might appear that the new alpaca countries' attempts to establish their own competitive commercial operations is a lesson in futility because Peru and the Andean countries have the lion's share of alpacas, well-run processing mills, decades of expertise, and cheap labor. As formidable as the Peruvian situation may appear, it is not without its own serious challenges that stand in the way of refining the processing of alpaca fiber.

There is much to be learned from the Peruvian mills and their many experts. Discounting their contribution and knowledge because some processing aspect doesn't coincide with all aspects of modern sheep/wool businesses is shortsighted and ethnocentric. The Peruvian situation is unique in bringing together the impoverished alpaca growers of the altiplano and the sophisticated mills with their international contacts. Rest assured, there is more knowledge about alpaca fiber processing in Peru than anywhere else, and it will be this way for a long time. However, there are problems unique to Peru that, once understood, provide hope that alpaca fiber processing in countries with much smaller alpaca populations have a very real potential

---

*Chas Brooke, personal communication, October 15, 2005.

of evolving into independent, high-end specialty fiber markets that contribute to a world awareness of alpaca, akin to the recognition enjoyed by cashmere.[25,79,87]

The Peruvian situation is beleaguered with an often antagonistic relationship between the growers and the mills. Though there is a volume of 4,800 tons annually moving through the mills in Arequipa, only about 10 percent of that is the baby class (20–22 μm). This amounts to the tui portion of the annual clip and does not bode well for the breeding practices on the altiplano. Hybridization of alpacas with llamas and huarizos is a widespread problem among the campesinos who own approximately 70 percent of the alpacas. The hybridization problem has multiple causes, but leading the list is the often chaotic relationship between the large mills and the growers.

Raw fiber is primarily purchased by weight (and color) with little regard for fineness. Until the late 1990s, the payment system has been simple: payment by fleece weight with no other criteria. In such a system, breeding a llama to an alpaca to make a fairly large huarizo offspring might make sense to an impoverished campesino because the huarizo fleece will weigh more than the fleece produced by the smaller alpaca. This approach has changed in recent years. Executives at Inca Tops and Michell, the volume buyers in Peru, have attempted to pay premium prices for the best fiber since 1998, but intentions and reality have many obstacles. Derek Michell explains:

> We do pay higher prices for better [raw] materials. Unfortunately, this does not always get to the hand of the growers, as we would like it to, as middlemen are sometimes involved. There is no rule of thumb as to what higher percentage you would pay for normal fleece compared to tui or better fleece. It really has more to do with market prices for the finer types, compared to coarser types at a specific moment. It can be anywhere from 10 to 50 percent higher, depending on the market and prices for different types of fleece.*

The new alpaca countries will not achieve the volume found in Peru in the foreseeable future, nor will they have the availability of cheap skilled labor. However, in myriad other ways the new alpaca countries are in an advantageous position to develop first-rate national clips. Utilizing technologies like laser-scan histograms and DNA-based registries to make the most of genetic potential with precision lineage management, and strictly applying screening procedures for founder stock to assemble animals with superior fiber-producing capabilities can start the process of developing a high percentage of alpacas with fleeces that compete directly with the 10 percent of Peruvian fleece composing the highest fiber class. The combination of developing a coherent strategy and utilizing available technologies will go a long way toward becoming bona fide alpaca product producers.[4,9,23,29,54,58,81]

Developing a Fiber Standard That Makes Sense

The new alpaca countries find themselves in an interesting position compared to the source countries in the Andes. The new alpaca countries have DNA-based registries that will allow precision breeding practices to theoretically produce the most desirable fiber traits. This push to improve fiber quality to establish a commercial business must recognize the richer diet and the lack of culling due to age and coarsening (as is common in South America). Breeders must focus on producing as many fine-fleeced animals with good fleece yields as is possible. Designing a goal for breeders and adhering to it will enhance any attempts to create a truly competitive national herd. John Callen, the leading force in the Alpaca Fiber Coop, says the goal should be for each breeder to establish herds in which 75 percent of the herd possesses histograms of 26 microns with low standard deviations.** In Australia, identifying the key markers in fiber production in alpacas is underway at some of the larger farms.

Transitional Strategies to Establish a Commercial Alpaca Fiber Business

The transition of moving from a loose assemblage of a few thousand alpacas and their predominately "hobby farmer" owners to an alpaca fiber industry can be a bumpy road. Emulating the Peruvian models of 7 fineness classes and 22 colors would fractionalize the clip into so many divisions that the idea of appealing to a world market would become nearly laughable.

To maintain enough volume in its classes, the original fiber co-op in Australia decided to combine both in fineness grades and in colors. Even with fewer and combined classes, care was taken in establishing classes that were advantageous for the marketplace. Graeme Dickson:

> We established standards along existing international lines that had long been established in the sheep industry. We set in place a range of classing lines that will still be acceptable when volume increases [and more classes are created]. This didn't mean we were inflexible. We still had the flexibility to create lines to suit a particular processor.***

---

*Derek Michell, personal communication, May 12, 2001.

**John Callen, personal communication, April 12, 2001.

***Graeme Dickson, personal communication, December 2001.

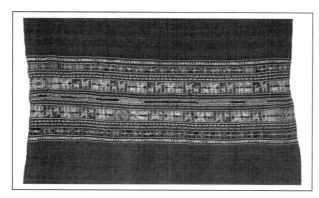

A 100-year-old Bolivian weaving featuring camelids, poultry, and cattle.

Instead of seven to nine classes (including suri classes) based on fineness, the Australian effort started with four classes: below 20 microns, Superfine (SF); 20–23 microns, Fine (F); 23.1–28.9 microns, Medium (M); and over 29 microns, Strong (S). The Australians moved to a five-class system once the volume increased sufficiently, with the creation of the following classes: SF, F, and M, as listed above; a change to 27.0–30.9 for Strong (S); and Coarse (C) for over 31 microns.

Broadening a fineness class automatically undermines uniformity. Aussie Ian Davison explains this part of the challenge:

> Consider an alpaca of 23.5 microns mean diameter with an incredibly tight CV of, say, 10 percent. If this fleece were classed with that of 50 other alpacas of the same micron and CV, the processor would have a line of 23.5 micron fiber with 10 percent CV. However, if the 23.5 fleece is classed in the same line as 28.5-micron fleece, which also has a CV of 10 percent of each of the contributing fleeces, the line reflects a much wider range of recorded diameters.[2]

It will take time and more animals to further divide classes to create greater uniformity. The pace of this transition can be greatly quickened if breeders use scientific methods. Substantial changes in fleece can be achieved in one or two generations if the correct male is used. Compared to South America, where poverty and lack of education perpetually inhibit meaningful change, alpaca breeders in most of the new alpaca-growing countries are in a position to make significant changes in fiber quality with the aid of DNA registries and laser scanning. For example, even with a broader micron range in the early classing system, breeders could pay attention to the coefficient of variation (CV) of fleeces to bring about greater uniformity within the broader micron class.

Even having alpacas grazing your paddocks with the best fleeces imaginable, maximizing the fleece won't be re-alized unless fleece preparation, shearing, and shipping are handled correctly. Dirty fleece, with matting or other forms of damage, can compromise a fleece's value partially or entirely, resulting in disappointment where there need not be any (see Chapter 11: Fleece Preparation and Shearing).[29,40]

Developing Economic Incentives to Improve Fleece

The Australian Alpaca Co-operative, which now oversees all production of alpaca growers in Australia, offered a strong financial incentive for producing fine fleece. In 2000, the Co-operative's class of superfine (less than 20 μm) was priced at A \$45 per kilogram (2.2 lb), 20–23 microns at A \$25, 23–27 microns at A \$15, 27–32 microns at A \$5, and lastly, over 32 microns at A \$1. The Co-op assigned a penalty for dark and medium fawns, browns, and rose greys of A \$5 per kilogram, because in the Australian way of doing things these colors were bleached so they could be included with the lighter fibers for processing. The difference in income was illustrated by looking at the extremes of the pricing structure: 11 pounds (5 kg) of "strong" was priced at A \$5 compared to 3.3 pounds (1.5 kg) of "fine" for A \$40. John Callen, the main mover behind the U.S.-based Alpaca Fiber Coop, expresses how the breeder can best approach the challenge of creating fine fleece animals. "The goal for breeders should be to breed selectively until 75 percent of their herd is below 27 microns."*

By concentrating on breeding practices to establish fine fleeces and rewarding the fruits of such labor with premium prices for top fleeces, the picture of establishing a non-Andean alpaca fiber business suddenly becomes a more viable proposition. The math tells the story objectively. Most of the 5,000 tons of alpaca processed in the world annually in commercial mills passes through Arequipa. About 10 percent of this tonnage is baby (20–22 microns). This amounts to 450 tons. If 75 percent of an Australian or United States national herd becomes fine enough to be classed as baby and the herd is 100,000 animals, the annual clip of 20 to 22 micron fleece will be 375,000 pounds or 167 tons (using a prime fleece weight of 5 pounds per animal). This is an achievable goal with a herd of 30,000 (national herd sizes of both Australia and the United States in 2000) in six to ten years, if there is a pervasive effort among breeders to concentrate on fleece fineness and weight. In theory, there could be 334 tons of high grade "tops" from the these two countries in the foreseeable future.

Any person studying models for organizing a national clip needs to carefully consider what to do about the myriad wonderful alpaca colors. In South America the greatest fiber-breeding effort for improving fiber characteristics (regardless of color) has occurred with white and fawn colors,

---

*John Callen, personal communication, April 12, 2001.

primarily because large breeding entities such as Rural Alianza are closely tied to the mills in Arequipa, which have offered better prices for white light fleeces for nearly 20 years. However, the unique quality of alpacas is their many rich colors. The mills in Peru have not abandoned color, but they have subdued its presence. In the 1980s the number of colored fleeces dropped by 70 percent when the mills began paying more for whites and fawns. Whites and fawns are more readily dyed, allowing for more flexibility in responding to marketing demands. However, it should always be remembered that dyeing alpaca often destroys a great deal of its wonderful handle.

The scarcity of some of the rare colors has caused them to go up in price when there is sufficient demand for them. Derek Michell of Michell & CIA sums up the color dilemma: "The problem with colored fleeces is that although they are nice, you need to have a specific demand for a given color in order to be able to sell it. Normally there will tend to be a better demand for well-defined colors, like 205 LFZ, 203 LFY, 301 CC, 302 COM, 350 COM/N, 360 CON, and 500 N, compared to streaky colors that might be used for dyeing."*

The traditional pastoralists in the Andes prefer colored animals, and home spinners in the industrialized countries often seek out colored fleeces. Some of the large mill operators have suggested to me that among the developing alpaca countries the idea of focusing breeding efforts on very fine fleeces of particular colors could lead to fiber specialization and niche market identity. Table 10.15 gives the percentage of the national clip for the various colors from Peru and Australia. Table 10.16 is the census of colors of the 38,000 alpaca Rural Alianza herd, which is a main supplier to the fiber mills in Arequipa.

Table 10.15 Colors of Peruvian and Australian national clips.

Michell & CIA, SA (large Peruvian fiber mill)

Color	Percentage of Clip
White and light fawn	65%
All other colors	35%

Australian Alpaca Co-operative Ltd. color statistics for 2000

Color	Weight	Percentage of Clip
White	4,620 lb (2,100 kg)	37.5%
Fawn	3,740 lb (1,700 kg)	20.5%
Black	2,200 lb (1,000 kg)	10.5%
Grey	833 lb (379 kg)	3.5%
Brown	2,655 lb (5,841 kg)	28.0%

Table 10.16 Rural Alianza color herd statistics.

Huacaya	Suri
20,000 white	7,000 white
10,000 color	1,000 color

*Derek Michell, personal communication, May 12, 2001.

IMPORTANT RULES AND STANDARDS, TRENDS, AND FACTS

Industry Rules and Standards

It will come as a surprise to new alpaca owners in North America, Australia, New Zealand, South Africa, China, the United Kingdom, and mainland Europe that no officially recognized product classification for alpaca fiber exists.

Official Alpaca Standards

In the sheep wool industry, specific standards describe the parameters for different grades of wool (and the method of enforcement of grade criteria). With alpaca there are no regulatory agencies and no official rules for classification. The one exception is the Standard Fineness Specification for Alpaca issued by the American Society for Testing Materials (ASTM) in 1985 (see Table 10.17).

Table 10.17 ASTM standard classification.

Type	Code	Mean Diameter (microns)
Tui, first shear, 12 months	T Extra	Under 22.00
Tui, first shear, 12 months	T	22.00–24.99
Extra-fine adult	X	22.00–24.99
Medium adult	AA	25.00–29.99
Coarse	A	30.00–39.99
Skirting	SK	Over 30.00
Locks and pieces	LP	Over 30.00

Source: Permission granted by Ian Stapleton (material modified from American Society for Testing Material, Table I: "Fineness Specifications of Types of Alpacas," April 1985).

A classification of alpaca hair based on diameter of hairs (micronage) has been suggested, but the international market has ignored this suggestion. Instead, there are only business agreements and breed and fiber association standards that help determine price. The International Alpaca Association (headquartered in Arequipa, Peru) endorses the use of "Alpaca Mark" labels in garments to distinguish 100 percent alpaca and various mixes of blends from alpaca, other natural fibers, and synthetics. See Figure 10.26. Companies such as Michell & CIA also have their own distinctive marks that attest to the quality of alpaca products. The problem is that defining standards, enforcing rules, and maintaining a regulatory system are costly,

Figure 10.26 Alpaca Mark labels.

and too little alpaca fiber is processed worldwide to cover these costs. Instead, "look" and "touch" are the chief means of classification, and contracts between large South American producers and dealers in Europe (primary user region) further define specifications.[45,46,97]

International Alpaca Fiber Market

Juan Pepper has worked in the alpaca textile business for 24 years. Juan represents the professionalism and international scope of alpaca fiber processing. He holds a B.A. from Catholic University in Arequipa, Peru, and went on to earn an MBA in textile business from Philadelphia University in the United States. He is a board member of the Peruvian Institute for Camelids and the International Alpaca Association (IAA). He is the current commercial manager for Michell & CIA, the largest vertically structured alpaca fiber processor in the world. Among Juan's responsibilities are international sales, which takes him all over the world. Most recently he has traveled extensively to Japan and other Asian countries, as well as to longtime clients in Europe. He also makes calls in Russia, Turkey, and the Middle East. Juan's efforts have helped open up the Chinese market, which now accounts for approximately 50 percent of total sales of alpaca tops for Michell & CIA.

Juan is also a specialist in suri fiber processing. He was kind enough to share international data that he and a colleague at Michell & CIA have collected. By carefully reading Tables 10.18 through 10.26, readers will have a clearer view of the interplay of the important variables that make up the international alpaca fiber market. The author is grateful for Juan taking the time from his nonstop schedule to make this data available.

Table 10.18 Speciality fiber production and population.

	Alpaca	Cashmere	Mohair	Vicuña
Fiber (tons)	5,500	15,000	7,200	4
Animals (millions)	3	7	3.5	0.103

Sources: Wool Record, 2005; Juan Pepper/Michell & CIA, 2005.

Juan Pepper in his office at Michell & CIA..

Table 10.19 Alpaca processing main end use.

Market Share by Industry	
Hand knitting	10%
Machine knitting	40%
Weaving apparel	40%
Handcrafts	10%

Source: Juan Pepper/Michell & CIA, 2005.

Table 10.20 South American camelid population.

Country	Alpaca	Guanaco	Vicuña	Llama
Argentina	400	578,700	33,791	135,000
Bolivia	324,336	54	33,844	2,022,569
Chile	27,585	25,000	19,848	703,630
Colombia	0	0	0	200
Ecuador	2,085	0	783	9,687
Paraguay	0	53	0	0
Peru	2,900,900	3,810	103,161	1,006,574
TOTAL	3,255,306	607,617	191,427	3,877,660

Sources: CONACS, Peru, 1999; Juan Pepper/Michell & CIA, 2005.

Table 10.21 Alpaca tops exports by country, 2004.

Destination	Alpaca Tops in kgs.	Percentage
China	1,230,805	51.87%
Italy	721,535	30.41%
Japan	115,328	4.86%
England	70,232	2.96%
Taiwan	68,510	2.89%
Korea	62,361	2.63%
Germany	40,047	1.69%
Hong Kong	28,679	1.21%
Chile	10,621	0.45%
Australia	7,463	0.31%
Uruguay	7,083	0.30%
New Zealand	5,640	0.24%
USA	3,222	0.14%
Various	1,120	0.05%
Total	2,372,646	100.0%

Sources: Comex, Peru, 1999; Juan Pepper/Michell & CIA, 2005.

Table 10.22 Yarn exports by country.

Destination	Alpaca Yarns Kgs.	Percentage
Syria	126,255	18.32%
Italy	89,929	16.05%
USA	71,930	10.44%
Bolivia	67,493	9.80%
Japan	59,322	8.61%
Korea	50,083	7.27%
Hong Kong	41,796	6.07%
China	33,508	4.86%
Norway	30,684	4.45%
Germany	26,497	3.85%
Spain	17,307	2.51%
Various	73,485	10.67%
Total	689,015	

Sources: Comex, Peru, 1999; Juan Pepper/Michell & CIA, 2005.

Table 10.23 Price variation, 1998–2004 (US $/kg; 1 kg equals 2.2 lbs).

Product	1998	1999	2000	2001	2002	2003	2004
Cashmere Dehaired white	58.0	115.0	145.0	82.0	76.0	67.0	92.0
Mohair tops Kid 25 microns	25.5	31.5	52.0	29.0	27.0	29.0	37.0
Baby alpaca Tops white	17.5	19.0	20.0	16.5	15.0	15.0	17.0
Angora Super quality	16.0	18.0	17.5	14.0	12.5	14.5	21.0
Camel dehaired Super baby	21.5	22.0	24.0	21.0	20.0	20.0	19.0
Yak hair	23.0	22.0	22.0	20.0	19.0	19.0	19.0
Silk mulberry Sliver	28.0	30.0	31.0	24.0	20.0	20.0	26.0

Sources: "The Wool Record Weekly," December 1998–2004; Juan Pepper/Michell & CIA, 2005.

Table 10.24 Main commercial problems.

Lack of awareness

Short supply of fiber

Restricted natural colors

Coarse alpaca

Limited end uses

Heavy specific fiber weight

Source: Juan Pepper/Michell & CIA, 2005.

Worldwide Production

Alpaca occupies a very small niche in the world textile fiber market. The whole category of "hair fiber," "specialty fiber," or "luxury fiber" to which alpaca belongs (with mohair, cashmere, angora, camel, yak, and cashgora) accounts for no more than 2.6 percent of world wool production, which itself represents 4 percent of the world textile market.

Peru produces 90 percent of the world's alpaca fiber; the rest comes from Bolivia, Chile, and Argentina. Producer companies primarily export carded or combed tops, and occasionally yarn. Raw fiber (known as *greasy* in the trade), which used to be exported in substantial quantities, is processed by Peruvian companies, most of which are located in Arequipa. Compared to other specialty fibers from domestic animals, alpaca is among the least common. Total 1992 output was 4,000 tons, which climbed to 5,000 tons by 2000.* In 1992 the world production for cashmere (China and Iran) was around 4,000 tons; mohair (South Africa, Texas, and Turkey), 22,000 tons; Angora rabbit (China, France, and Chile), 8,500 tons. Sheep's wool from Australia, New Zealand, and South Africa, however, yielded about 1,851,000 tons in the same year.[45]

*Luis Chaves, personal communication, December 14, 2004.

Table 10.25 Price fluctuations for alpaca tops, 1983–2004.

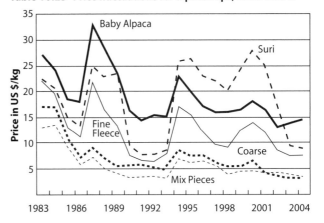

Source: Juan Pepper/Michell & CIA, 2005.

Table 10.26 Main end uses by industry.

	Hand Knitting	Weaving	Machine Knitting	Hand Crafts
Baby alpaca & fleece	•	•	•	
Suri Alpaca	•	•		
Coarse		•		•
Llama				•

Source: Juan Pepper/Michell & CIA, 2005.

ACHIEVING SUCCESS IN THE INTERNATIONAL MARKETPLACE

During the last 20 years, alpacas have been exported around the world. With this population growth and redistribution (in Australia, New Zealand, North America, and Europe), there is greater worldwide awareness of the alpaca and its ability to produce high-quality fiber in many different colors. The potential for an expanding market is great, but there are many challenges ahead.

The cashmere market may illustrate a key to future success for the alpaca industry, even though there are many differences between the two markets. For many years both produced about 5,000 tons annually. In 2005 cashmere surged to 14,000 tons, with increases in production from China. On a per animal yield basis, alpacas outdistance cashmere goats by a ratio of 6 to 1. Cashmere is collected by brushing out the downy undercoat, with a good animal yielding a mere 1.5 pounds (500 grams). It requires more work to collect 5,000 tons of cashmere than to collect the same weight in alpaca fiber. Yet the fiber mill owners in Arequipa will tell you that cashmere is a billion-dollar industry, whereas alpaca is a multi-million dollar industry. Why is this? There are many factors, which include marketing, distribution, and standards. However, fineness is one variable that stands out. Chinese cashmere is a product with fineness that challenges vicuña, making these perhaps the two softest of the readily obtainable fibers in the world.[6,25,100,114] Vicuña occurs naturally between 12 and 15 microns. Cashmere is suitable for processing between 13 and 16 microns. Alpaca is commonly processed between 19.5 and 37 microns, with only about 10 to 15 percent of alpaca occupying the top grades of 19 to 22 microns (see Figure 10.27).

Figure 10.27 Unprocessed specialty fiber chart.

Fiber	Fineness	Fiber Length	Price/kg	Source
Fine wool	21 μm	58 mm	$6	Roberto Fuchs
Alpaca	20–28 μm	4 cm	$12–$28	Wool Record IAA, Prosur
Cape mohair	25 μm (kid)	annual length	$24–$28	Wool Record
Chinese cashmere	13–15 μm	32 mm	$74–$84	Wool Record
Guanaco	14–16 μm	35 mm	$200 (not dehaired) $400 (dehaired)	European processors
Vicuña	12–14 μm	35 mm	$400–600	European processors

Notes: All monetary amounts are in U.S. dollars. One kilogram equals 2.2 pounds. Prices are for raw fleece. These price evaluations are 1999 international market approximations. Prices often fluctuate rapidly, but for comparative purposes these prices represent the ranking of specialty fiber animals with sheep's wool, the standard to which all fiber is held. There may be sidebar markets and information that are not included in these estimates.

Sources: Thanks to Adriana McGuire and the Proyecto "Ganaderia Extensiva y Sustenable del Guanaco/Lama" del Fundacion Habitat; the International Alpaca Association (IAA) in Peru; Grupo Prosur (Sarfaty) in Peru; The Wool Record; and Roberto Fuchs for information found in this chart.

From an industrywide perspective, the single greatest challenge for alpaca breeders is to create animals with low micron counts and low variability. Reducing microns might require new thinking. Traditional models for improving a fiber-producing animal include increasing the annual yield for each animal. Indeed, until recently, weight has been the most common measurement for purchasing alpaca fiber. Weight is of course an important variable, but with weight comes higher microns. Perhaps new thinking will require accepting lower fleece weights in order to achieve lower micron counts. Some of the large alpaca operations in Peru cull animals producing less than 4 pounds of fleece, even if the fleece is 15 to16 microns.

Perhaps models emphasizing other criteria for improved fiber production will emerge, but one thing is certain: Not since the Spanish Conquest in 1532 have alpaca breeders had a better opportunity to again achieve the remarkable potential for unsurpassed fiber quality of this species. Breeders, researchers, and processors from around the world must work together to make alpaca competitive with cashmere in the international luxury fiber market.

Major Commercial Entities

The international alpaca fiber trade is confined to just a few entities: Three large companies in Peru (Michell & CIA, Grupo Inca, and Prosur) and one in Argentina (Leers) control about 90 percent of the camelid export trade to areas outside of South America. Buying and selling is done through dealers who usually purchase large quantities in containers weighing 7,000 to 10,000 pounds (3,180–4,545 kg). Volume buying reduces prices. Smaller orders for tops and bales are placed for amounts weighing approximately 300 to 1,000 pounds (136–454 kg). Generally, 50 pounds (22.7 kg) is the smallest quantity sold by these large entities in tops and forms that need further processing. These companies will also sell finished products such as sweaters, women's suits, blankets, and scarves.[8,60]

Traditional Commerce

Contacts to three of the most established companies are as follows:

Michell & CIA., SA
Juan de la Torre 101, San Lazaro, Arequipa, Peru
Telephone 51 54 20 2525; Facsimile 51 54 20 2626
E-mail: michell@michell.com.pe
Website: www.michell.com.pe

Inca Tops, Grupo Inca
Miquel Forga 348, Industrial Parque
P.O. Box 94, Arequipa, Peru
Telephone 51 54 229998; Facsimile 51 54 288861
E-mail: sales@incatops.com

Grupo Prosur (Sarfaty)
P.O. Box 1198, Lima, Peru
Telephone (511) 451-1070; Facsimile (511) 452-0029
E-mail: int.sales@prosur.com.pe
Website: www.prosur.com.pe

Importing Nations

In the 1990s the following European countries imported alpaca tops or finished products: Italy, Germany, France, Spain, the United Kingdom, Austria, Holland, Belgium, Switzerland, Ireland, Hungary, Finland, Sweden, Denmark, and Norway. In the Americas the list is shorter: the United States, Canada, Venezuela, Colombia, Ecuador, Chile, and Argentina. In Asia and the Pacific Rim, China is the biggest importer, followed by Japan, South Korea, Taiwan, Australia, and New Zealand.

In volume China leads, garnering roughly 50 percent, followed by Italy, Germany, Syria, and the United Kingdom. Europe imports 40 percent of the world's alpaca fiber products.[29,46,96,109]

Worldwide, China has surged ahead in recent years. In Europe, Italy is the leading manufacturer of natural wool products, with a sophisticated textile industry. Italian manufacturers have a longtime reputation for creating imaginative high-quality products tied directly to Italy's interest in high fashion. In short, Italian textile manufacturers like to add variety to traditional products.[97,110]

GLOSSARY

Alpaca Mark One of three symbols guaranteeing quality by designating the amount of alpaca fiber existing in a textile product. The Alpaca Mark is owned and sanctioned by the International Alpaca Association headquartered in Arequipa, Peru. See page 307.

apron or bib The abundant long guard hair hanging from the chest on all species of South American camelid. The apron is most pronounced on the *Menalis* subspecies of vicuña, more subtly expressed in domestic camelids, and sometimes nonexistent on individual alpacas. The apron is not considered part of the blanket and is often of insufficient quality to be considered prime fleece.

blanket The part of the alpaca's coat that extends from the nape of the neck at the withers along the back to the tail and down the flanks nearly to the belly and haunches. Usually the best fiber on an alpaca, the blanket is the primary area for judging the quality of fleece, and is often referred to as the prime fleece.

blend Yarn obtained by mixing (blending) different colors of alpaca, usually through combing, or mixing alpaca fiber with two or more other fibers (sheep, synthetic, etc.). Alpaca blends well with sheep's wool, mohair, and cashmere, which constitute *natural blends*, because all of the fibers in the blend are produced by nature. Natural blends also include alpaca fiber of different colors that are combined to achieve another color.

bobbin A reel or spool used in spinning and weaving to wind thread or yarn.

britch Hindquarter, including the leg.

bundling The grouping of fibers into fairly distinct bundles (about the width of a human finger). This characteristic is identifiable both on the alpaca and in shorn fleeces. Some breeders believe bundling is a desirable trait, though animals without bundling have had very favorable histograms, densities, staple regeneration, and annual shearing yields exceeding 10 pounds (4.4 kg).

card (or carding) A textile machine or device that prepares fibers for subsequent operations culminating in spinning. Carding usually involves cylinders of various sizes (drums) with multitudes of iron teeth or brushlike wires protruding from them. Fiber is fed into the rotating cylinders in tangled or loose form. Fiber may be carded numerous times until the desired results are achieved. Eventually the process produces what is known as *sliver*. Home spinners often use hand carders, which are two flat brushes that are pulled across one another with fiber sandwiched between the brushes. Carding delivers fiber to a uniform condition, so that it can be drawn out and spun.

character The overall evaluation of a fleece or lock that includes important criteria such as handle, staple length, fineness, density, luster, and softness. Fleeces with good character are *sound* and reflect good breeding and husbandry. Grooming (for shows) can destroy a fleece's character.

chili A term used by North Americans to describe a fleece type that falls somewhere between huacaya and suri. Typically the term is applied to fleece with no crimp that is coarser than suri (approximately 27.5 microns). The term is not found in *Fairchild's Dictionary of Textiles* and other internatonally recognized fiber and textile glossaries.

classification (or classing) Grading or sorting fleeces according to types (color) and quality (baby, superfine, etc.). The prime fleece or blanket is of the highest class and should have the greatest uniformity. Fiber from other parts of an alpaca's body is usually classified separately and is of a lesser class.

clip All the fiber harvested by a farm or person in a single shearing season.

coarse Fiber large in diameter relative to other fiber.

combing A processing step following carding in both cotton and worsted yarn manufacturing. The process separates long, choice, desirable fibers of the same length and eliminates neps, short immature fibers, undesirable fiber, and noils. An integral part of the worsted process, combing contributes to the creation of high-quality fabric, which makes products that demand the greatest profit margin, compared to products resulting from the woolen process.

consistency Sameness or uniformity throughout a prime fleece or blanket in the important areas of handle, fineness, density, and staple length.

cortical cells The long, narrow, fibrous cells, or fibrils, that make up the inside of each fiber underneath the cuticle. Cortical cells usually measure 80 to 110 microns long and 1 to 5 microns wide; they sit next to other fibrils, interconnecting segments the length of the fiber.

cotts Small clumps of matted fiber.

coverage A term used by North American alpaca breeders to refer to abundant fiber growth on alpacas that extends to regions beyond the standard areas on the body and neck, such as between the ears (wool cap) and on the lower legs. Many breeders believe abundant fiber growth or coverage in these areas is aesthetically attractive and accentuates the phenotypic characteristics of an alpaca.

crimp Crimp is commonly known as a type of curvature that possesses an even, corrugated wave formation in the staple (lock). This characteristic can be measured by fiber-testing laboratories capable of using the expanded high-tech histogram, which measures mean curvature. In huacaya, the amplitude and frequency of crimp can vary. Among scientists and some camelid growers, crimp means any type of curvature (including crinkle) found in huacaya alpacas, vicuñas, guanacos, and llamas (and sheep, goats, etc.), all of which can be accurately measured.

crinkle Crinkle is waviness in a single fiber and a type of curvature that can be measured by scientific means. In camelids, crinkle is a term sometimes used to describe vicuña-like fleece or huacaya fleece that does not visually exhibit the uniform waviness known commonly as crimp.

curl A fiber characteristic of the strong suri phenotype. In fibers that cling to the body, curls occur in spiraling, lustrous ringlets along the length of individual fibers, giving the coat a drenched look.

curvature Curvature refers to the crimp (or crinkle) and curl that may be present in a fleece. The amount of curvature can be measured in a Sirolan Laserscan histogram that includes "mean curvature" measurement. The mean curvature is expressed in degrees per millimeter (deg/mm). Generally, huacaya alpacas range between 15 and 52 deg/mm, while suris are around 10–15 deg/mm. Vicuñas have the highest mean curvature of the South American camelids, around 80 deg/mm. Compared to most sheep breeds, huacaya alpacas have a low mean curvature.

cuticle The protective layer of cells on every fiber that encompasses the fibrous cortical cells. The outermost scales of a hair attach to the cuticle.

debris Any contaminant material found in a fleece. The amount and kind of debris can devalue a fleece.

dehairing The process of removing guard hair (or medullated fiber) from a fleece, a requirement for processing llama, guanaco, and vicuña.

density The number of fibers in a certain area on the alpaca's body. Density counts are achieved by counting hair follicles. Density of fleece varies between suris and huacayas and other species of fiber-bearing animals. Density also varies from one part of the animal to another, with ranges from 8,000 to 60,000 per square inch in fiber- and fur-bearing animals.

drawing A processing step that can occur at various stages during gilling, combing, and spinning. The purpose of drawing is to reduce the thickness of the sliver of fiber passing through a machine. This thinning is achieved by the action of two rollers moving at different speeds. The front roller moves faster than the back, hence the sliver is pulled out and stretched between the two and becomes thinner.

drying A processing step that dries the fiber either by mechanical dryers or air drying; usually occurs immediately follows scouring.

elasticity A fiber or textile product's ability to recover its original shape after being pulled or stretched.

felt A nonwoven sheet of matted material made from wool, hair, or a mix of fibers bound together in a process of heat, moisture, and pressure (felting). Felting is often the process used in making hats.

fiber The fundamental unit used in the fabrication of textile yarns and fabrics. Technically a fiber is a unit of matter whose length is at least 100 times its diameter or width. Fibers can be spun into yarn and thread. Fiber includes synthetic as well as natural material (vegetable fibers, mineral fibers, and animal fibers).

fibril One of the minute fibrous elements making up a fiber. See cortical cells.

fineness The diameter in microns of individual fibers or the overall fineness of a fleece. Fineness is one of the chief grading or classing criteria for alpaca fiber. Fineness is expressed as average fiber diameter (AFD) on histograms and as "micronage" in the Peruvian milling system.

fleece Fiber sheared from sheep or other wool-class animals. A fleece is the coat shorn from an animal at one time. Alpaca fleeces belong in the category known as *open fleeces*. Open fleeces are more apt to break apart due to the low grease content, compared to most kinds of fine sheep's wool, which is held together by abundant grease.

fleece weight The weight of a fleece after shearing. Measurement can be in total weight before impurities, dehairing, and discarding, or in clean weight after elimination of unusable materials.

fur The fine, soft, and dense hair covering a wide range of mammals. It generally consists of a double coating of hair, a layer of comparatively short, soft, curly, barbed hairs (underfur) protected by longer, smoother, stiffer hairs (guard hairs) that grow through the underfur. Alpacas are a single-coated animal and do not have fur. Fur is often associated with animals whose coats are skinned (known as pelts), such as mink, sable, and fox.

grading See classification (or classing).

guard hair Longer, smoother, stiffer, thicker hairs protruding from a coat. Alpaca guard hair is usually hollow or medullated and measures approximately 60 microns in diameter. Guard hairs in the blanket of an alpaca are considered undesirable. The absence of guard hair, especially on the blanket area, distinguishes alpacas from most llamas, which have guard hair in their blankets and are considered two-coated, whereas alpacas are one-coated.

guanaco A two-coated, llama-sized wild camelid of South America with an undercoat that usually falls between 13 and 21 microns. Parent species to the llama.

guanaquito The pelt of a *chulengo* (baby guanaco).

hair Term used interchangeably with fiber. Technically, hair is a filament growing from the skin of an animal. In a collective sense a coat is made up of individual hairs. The term often refers to a medullated guard hair, which has stiffer characteristics than the predominate fleece.

hair fibers A group of fibers classed as specialty fibers obtained from animals other than sheep. Synonymous with special fibers or specialty fibers, hair fibers are obtained from goat and camel family members that include mohair, cashmere, angora, camel, llama, vicuña, guanaco, and alpaca. These fibers, which do not include rabbit, may be included in the term wool according to the Wool Labeling Act of 1939. However, in today's fiber vernacular, wool means sheep's fiber.

handle A quality or characteristic of fabrics or raw fiber perceived by the sense of touch, e.g., softness, firmness, drapeability, fineness, resilience; in other words, its tactile qualities. Handle is synonymous with hand, feel, and touch. Handle is the primary means of classing fiber in Peru. Vicuña has the softest handle of all the camelid species.

histogram A micron test report using a histogram as the most common graphical presentation of quanititative data.

huacaya The predominate alpaca coat type, characterized by a fine fleece with an absence of guard hair (at least on the blanket); a spongy, fluffy look; and a wide range of mostly solid colors. More than 90 percent of the alpaca fleece processed in Peru is of the huacaya type.

huarizo A cross between a male llama and a female alpaca. Many Peruvian alpaca mills use the term huarizo to identify a class of fiber that is not the texture or quality of good-quality alpaca. In the context of fiber, the fiber classed as huarizo may or may not have originated on an actual hybrid animal. As a fiber classification (or grade), huarizo may be from an alpaca with less-than-perfect fiber quality or even from a llama.

hygroscopic properties Pertaining to the affinity of wool to absorb water vapor from the atmosphere. This characteristic affects weight, microns, and practically all measurable qualities. Commercial processors often control and record relative humidity for optimum processing and to measure the moisture content in the fiber they are processing.

intersecting gill A machine in the worsted process that separates and aligns fibers for the combing process.

kemp Coarse, often dead, undesirable hairs unsuitable for processing.

leviathans In the Arequipa mills, the long, shallow, scouring vats and the rakelike devices that move fiber through them.

lock A handful or tuft of fiber from an unprocessed fleece. In a lock the fibers cling and intermesh with one another in the natural state.

loft Historic term describing springiness in wool (or fiber) as it returns to normal position after it has been squeezed. Fluffiness is sometimes used synoymously for loft. In the natural fiber trade the term has come to refer to blankets made of synthetic fibers and blends, indicating bulkiness.

lot A large number of fleeces or amount of fiber, usually processed at one time.

luster A subjective quality referring to the sheen or shininess of a fleece, locks, or individual fiber. The three basic kinds of luster are *silver, silk,* and *glass.* Suri, usually more lustrous than huacaya, is closest to glass luster like mohair. The amount of luster helps determine the end use of a fleece.

matching A step in the worsted process in which fibers of different lengths are aligned to be parallel through the use of centrifugal force.

matting The tangling and binding of fiber. Matted fiber is a challenge to process, renders a fleece unfit for judging, and devalues a fleece.

medulla The generally continuous cellular marrow (or hollow space) inside the cortical layer in most medium and coarse fibers. The amount of medulla varies in fibers on the same animal. Medulla is not present at all or only to a limited extent in fine fibers but may form as much as 90 percent of the kemp or guard hair. Medulla is also referred to as *medullation*. Alpaca fiber ranges from nonmedullated to interrupted to unbroken. Usually the coarser the fiber, the greater the possibility of medullation, but it can also occur at the lowest micron levels.

micron A metric unit of length, the thousandth part of a millimeter, or the millionth part of a meter (0.000039 inch).

micronage A measurement of fineness (in microns) in the mills of South America and among alpaca fiber buyers and processors in Europe.

midside The sampling area for a histogram located on the side of the alpaca, approximately midway between the front and rear leg.

nep A small tangle or knot in fibers. In mill situations neps refer to impurities or short, incongruent fibers that cling to yarn.

noil Short fibers removed in the combing process, often associated with the creation of worsted yarns.

open fleece See fleece.

opener The initial mechanical activity of industrial processing that pulls the fleece apart.

Peruvian wool Fleeces from sheep raised by Quechua and Aymara pastoralists living in the Andean highlands. These sheep are often run with alpacas and llamas. The term is sometimes incorrectly applied to alpaca fiber.

pneumatic knot A knot made by mechanical action, usually driven by air under pressure, to rejoin a yarn broken during processing. A broken yarn can also be spliced with air jets.

prickle The quality in fleece or fabric that causes itchiness when pressed against human skin.

prime fleece The best fleece an alpaca will produce in its lifetime, usually at its first shearing when it is a tui. Prime fleece is often used synonymously with blanket, but may include other areas, and refers to the best fiber, regardless of where it occurs. See blanket.

processing The steps that transform raw fiber shorn from an alpaca to a marketable thread, yarn, tops, or finished product.

regrowth Regeneration of fiber after shearing; an important factor in assessing an alpaca's fiber productivity.

resting A step in the industrial processing of alpaca fiber that follows scouring and may coincide with or follow drying. Resting allows fiber to show its *resilience* and *recuperate* its form before further processing.

roving A loose assemblage of fiber drawn into a single strand, with very little twist. A roving is an intermediate state between a sliver and yarn.

scales Microscopic flattened ridges covering the surface of alpaca fibers. Individual scales cannot be detected by touch, although the overall texture of scale structure contributes greatly to the feel of fiber. The surface characteristics of the scales control the friction between fibers, which greatly influences the binding strength of yarns and threads made by twisting hairs together. Both frequency and height of scales of the hair's surface contribute to its adhering and interlocking potential with like fibers. Due to a greater frequency of scales and more erratic scale ridges, huacaya fiber has more exposed scaly surfaces than does suri, which gives huacaya fiber a greater resistance to pulling apart and affords suri its legendary smoothness. Looking at scale patterns under a microscope is the chief means of identifying fiber in a fabric of unknown origin.

scouring Cleaning raw fiber of dirt, vegetable matter, and other debris by mechanical or chemical methods. Alpaca fiber in Peru is generally submerged and pushed (by means of slowly rotating raking devices) through five scouring tanks. The first two tanks have solutions containing chemicals; the last three are rinses. Scouring also refers to cleaning a fabric before dyeing, especially when it is to be dyed a light color.

second cuts Short locks resulting from improper shearing in which the same area is passed over more than once.

shearing The removal of an alpaca's fleece by any of a variety of methods.

skirting Fiber of lower class or grade that is separated from the blanket or prime fleece and processed separately or discarded. Skirtings are commonly found on the belly area, legs, tail, apron, and top knot.

slippery Having a smooth, thin, snug scale structure that does not bind as well into yarn as other hair fibers with more pronounced scale patterns. Often used to describe suri fiber (or other fibers with a similar characteristic), especially during industrial processing, because machinery must be slowed to process slippery fiber successfully.

sliver A continuous, ropelike strand of loosely assembled fibers without a twist that is generally uniform in cross section. In both woolen and worsted processing, slivers are the product of carding or combing.

snowcomb (or spacer) An attachment to the shear's cutting blade that elevates the shear's cut a short distance above the skin to allow enough fiber to stay on the alpaca for protection against sunburn or frigid weather. A snowcomb is particularly necessary with older animals who are slow to regenerate their fleeces.

softness A desirable subjective quality in a fleece assessed by touch; a significant contributing factor to handle. Good-quality suri is second to vicuña in softness. Vicuña allegedly has the greatest softness of all camelid fibers and by some accounts of all natural fibers.

sorting The process of separating material into different groups of comparable characteristics and quality, determined by standards in color, fineness, feel, etc. Also referred to as classing or grading.

sound fleece A fleece that is not compromised with tenderness or excessive kemp or matting.

speciality fiber Fiber from the goat, rabbit, musk oxen, and camel families, including mohair, cashmere, angora, alpaca, vicuña, guanaco, llama, and Bactrian and dromedary camels. See hair fibers.

spinning The process of making yarn by any of numerous methods that involve drawing and twisting. Traditional Andean methods use the drop spindle; a spinning wheel with a foot pump is another common method. Industrialized processing uses spinning machines following carding, drawing, and combing.

spindle A slender, tapered rod held in a vertical position on the side of a spinning frame. A bobbin is placed on the spindle to receive yarn as it is spun at high speed, giving a twist to the yarn.

staple Synonymous with fiber but commonly used to indicate the length of fiber either on the alpaca itself or for processing. In such usage it is more accurately called staple length.

strong A term used to describe coarse fiber.

style See character.

sun bleaching Color change in the outer fleece due to sunlight. In some colors such as black, distinctions are made between fading black and nonfading black that appears not to be affected by sunlight. Prolonged exposure to sunlight on a two- or three-year-old fleece will likely result in brittleness at the tips of the locks.

suri The least common of the two alpaca coat types. Suri is similar to mohair and characterized by lustrous, silky fiber with an absence of crimp, but possessing curl on the most representative phenotypes. A suri coat appears to hang from the the animal as if it were wet. About 90 per-

cent of suris are white or fawn; only 5 percent (in 2000) of the fiber processed at Michell & CIA in Arequipa was suri.

tenderness Weakness in a fiber or fleece that causes breaks when the fiber is pulled. A sound alpaca fleece is generally less tender than sheep's wool and is usually rated as "increasingly sound" and "very sound" in Australian testing standards. These ratings are at the middle/upper range for sheep's wool.

tensile strength The ability of fiber to resist breaking under tension from a pulling motion, not to be confused with tearing or bursting strengths, which involve other forms of measurements.

tensometer A device that measures tensile strength.

textile fiber Any fiber with the properties necessary for the manufacturing of textiles.

texture A term describing yarn or textile appearance, character, and handle. It may relate to the composition, structure, or finish of the yarn or fabric.

thread A thin, continuous cord that is usually a derivative of the combing process. Specifically smooth and compact yarn, generally plied, characterized by combination of twisting and finishing semisolid. Similar to yarn, though generally thinner and more often used for needlework.

tops An untwisted strand of staple after it has completed the combing process (from the English word tuft, which means a "bunch of fiber"). It is often associated with the worsted process, which requires fiber to have been straightened, parallelized, and separated from short fiber (noils). Often tops are wound into a ball weighing between 5 and 15 pounds (2.27–6.80 kg) for the purpose of trading.

torsion State of being twisted.

uniformity Consistency or sameness throughout a fleece with regard to handle, color, density, staple length, waviness (huacaya) or lack of it (suri), and other important criteria.

Uster factor A machine measurement to describe yarn evenness. If a yarn has weak points or bulky points in its construction, it has a poor Uster reading. Yarn evenness is important in both yarn breakage and fabric/garment appearance.

wool Usually the fine, soft, scaly fiber covering on sheep. Under the U.S. Wool Products Labeling Act of 1939, "wool" is defined as: "The fiber from the fleece of a sheep or lamb, or hair of the Angora or Cashmere goat (and may include so-called specialty fibers from the hair of the Camel, Alpaca, and Vicuña) which has never been reclaimed from any woven or felted wool product."

wool cap The wool on an alpaca's head between its ears, also known as the top knot. A wool cap is an aesthetic quality appreciated by many alpaca owners.

woolen system One of the two chief processes for making yarn (spelled woollen in the UK). Usually the woolen process amounts to carding fiber two or three times, condensing, drawing, and spinning. In general, the fiber used is shorter and of varying lengths compared to the worsted system. In the woolen process it is possible to blend fibers (sheep, cashmere, synthetic), readily creating textile properties other than alpaca and lightening or darkening a color. Rustic-looking yarns such as tweeds are a product of this system. The cloth produced is usually soft. Products include overcoats, suits, blankets, and industrial felts.

worsted system One of the two chief processes for making yarn, commonly associated with commercial processing of alpaca and mohair. Worsted yarns are made of medium and long fibers that are carded, parallelized, and combed (to remove the noils), drawn, and spun. The removal of the noils helps achieve the main objective of producing a compact yarn made of parallel, smooth fibers.

yield The amount of usable fiber produced by an alpaca after processing. Yields are usually measured after the washing process and are thus known as washing yields. Alpaca yields are usually between 85 and 90 percent, while sheep are usually around 43 to 76 percent. The amount of loss from raw weight to yield weight is known as shrinkage.

REFERENCES

1. Anonymous: *From Fleece to Fashion*. Alpaca Owners and Breeders Association, Estes Park, CO 80517, p. 26, 1994.
2. Anonymous: *Fleece Preparation, Recording and Standards Manual*. Australian Alpaca Fibre Marketing Organization Pty Ltd., P.O. Box 764, Seymour, Victoria, Australia 3661, pp. 1–10, November 1997.
3. Appleyard, H. M.: *Guide to the Identification of Animal Fibres*, 2d ed. Leeds, England: Wira, the Research and Services Centre for Textiles and Clothing, p. 124, 1978.
4. Barns, S.: Breeding for Fiber, Aussies Explore a Serious Market. *Llama Life* 2(48): 6–12, Winter l998.
5. Billington, W.: Suri vs. Huacaya and the Opportunity for Cross Breeding. *Alpaca Association New Zealand,* Palmerston North, New Zealand, pp. 12–14, 2005.
6. Bishop, D. S, and N. R. Wray: "Genetics of Fibre Production in Cashmere Goats." Commission of European Communities, Doctorate-General XIII, Luxembourg, pp. 33–49, 1993.
7. Bravo, W.: Small Ruminant Production: Alpacas. *Alpacas,* p. 55, Fall 1993.
8. Bruford, M.: Genetic Analysis and the Ancestors of the Llama and Alpaca. *The Alpaca Registry Journal* 6(1): 42, Spring 2001.
9. Bustinza, V. C.: *Razas de Alpaca del Altiplano: Suri y Huacaya.* Puno, Peru: Universidad del Altiplano, Instituto de Investigaciones para el Desarrollo Social del Altiplano, p. 34, 1982.
10. Carpio, M.: Fibres de Camelidos Alpacas. In *Produción de Rumiantes Hemores: Alpacas* (C. Novoa and A. Florez, eds.), Lima, Peru: Rerumen, pp. 295–356, 1996.
11. Carpio, M., C. Leyva, S. Solari, P. Santana, and J. Sumar: Diameter and Length Variations in Different Types of Alpaca Fibre and Fleeces of Llama, Vicuña, and Paco-Vicuña. *Universidad Nacional Agraria*, La Molina, Apartado 456, Lima, pp. 76–91, 1990.
12. Carvajal, J., A. H. Salles, and N. R. Pizarro: *Diccionario Illustrado, Aymara* (Español/ Ingles), Maiten Editores, p. 130, 2001.
13. Chaves, L.: The Alpaca Fibre Faces the XXI Century. Grupo Inca presentation at International Camelid Festival, Arequipa, Peru, pp. 1–20, October 27, 2000.
14. Chepolis, T.: Fiber Evaluation on the Alpaca. *Fiberfest Magazine* 2(1): 30–33, 1994.
15. Chepolis, T.: Selecting an Alpaca Fleece. *Llama Life* 18: 30, Summer 1991.
16. Collins, K.: Spinning Suri Alpaca. *Spin Off,* pp. 40–45, Fall 2000.
17. Condorena, A. N.: Algunos Indices de Producción de la Alpaca Bajo el Sistema de Esquila Establecido en La Raya. *IVITA*, Lima, Peru: Universidad Nacional de San Marcos 5(1): 50–54, 1980.
18. Couchman, R. C.: Characteristics Given Highest Value in Specialty Fibers. *Llama Life* 19: 28, 1991.
19. Couchman, R. C.: South American Camelid Fibers. *Llama Life* 18: 32, 1991.
20. Couchman, R. C.: Base Levels for Fiber Production. *Llama Life* 21: 32, 1992.
21. Couchman, R. C.: Processing Fine Animal Fibers. *Llama Life* 23: 32, 1992.
22. Couchman, R. C.: Price Volatility of Specialty Fibers, *Llama Life* 24: 28,1992–1993.
23. Couchman, R. C.: Alpacas in the Wider Textile World. *Llama Life* 26: 28, 1993.
24. Couchman, R. C.: Identifying Better Genetic Stock. *Llama Life* 28: 26, 1993–1994.
25. Dadal-Jakes, S.: The Golden Fleece. *Time Style and Design*, pp. 45–47, Fall 2005.
26. Davis, G., T. Wuliji, G. Tumen, G. Moore, J. Pollard, and C. Mackintash: Alpaca Research in the South Highland High Country. Australian Alpaca Association, International Alpaca Industry Seminar, 1994 Proceedings, pp. 1–4, 1994.
27. Davis, G.: Alpacas Are Just Fine—Should They Be Finer? *The Alpaca Registry Journal* 1(1): 43–44, Winter-Spring 1996.
28. Davis, G.: Achieving High Fleece Weights—the Key to Successful Fiber Production. *The Alpaca Registry Journal* 2(1)1: 45–52, Spring 1997.
29. Davison, I.: Alpaca: Fiber of the Future; the Future of the Fiber. *The Alpaca Registry Journal* 4(1): 23–31, Spring 1999 (originally published in *Town and Country Farmer* in Australia, 1998).

30. De la Pena, M., and M. Rumboll: Birds of Southern South America and Antarctica. Princeton University Press, New Jersey, p. 11, 1998.
31. Dever, J.: Spinning an Exotic Yarn. *Alpacas Australia,* pp. 31–36, Summer 1992–1993.
32. D'Harcourt, R.: *Textiles of Ancient Peru and Their Techniques.* Seattle: University of Washington Press, p. 185, 1962.
33. Fernandez-Baca, S. (ed.): *Avances y Perspectivas del Conocimiento de los Camelidos Sudamericanos.* Santiago, Chile: Oficina Regional de la FAO para America Latina y el Caribe, pp 7–10, 41–429, 1991.
34. Fish, V. E., T. J. Mahar, and B. J. Crook: Report CTF01. Commercial Technology Forum, IWTO Meeting, Nice, France, November/December 1999.
35. Fish, V. E., T. J. Mahar, and B. J. Crook: Report CTF06. Commercial Technology Forum, IWTO Meeting, Christchurch, New Zealand, April/May 2000.
36. Fowler, M., E. Hoffman, and B. Smith: Fibre Characteristics Evaluation. *British Alpaca Society,* p. 1, October 1999.
37. Francis, P.: Wool. *Australian Farm Journal,* p. 11, December 1994.
38. Gordon, J. I., and M. D. Fraser: Foraging Ecology of Fibre Producing Ruminant Species. Commission of European Communities, Directorate-General XIII, Luxembourg, pp. 63–77, 1993.
39. Hoffman, E.: Ships of the Andes. *Pacific Discovery* 42(3): 7–15, 1989.
40. Hoffman, E.: Joe Mattingly, Master Shearer. *Llama Life* 19: 30, 1991.
41. Hoffman, E.: First Suris Arrive in North America. *Llama Life* 21 (32): 1, Spring 1992.
42. Hoffman, E.: The Many Ways Guanacos Talk. *International Wildlife,* pp. 6–11, July 1993.
43. Hoffman, E.: The Most Colorful Fiber Animal in the World. *Llamas* 8(1): 111–112, 1994.
44. Hoffman, E.: Ruminations on Fiber Color from the Backroads of Peru. *Llamas* 8(6): 18–19,1994.
45. Hoffman, E.: Meet Peter Kothe, the World's Greatest Volume Buyer of Alpaca Fiber. *Llamas* 8(7): 19–20, 1994.
46. Hoffman, E.: Previously Undisclosed Facts and Thoughts About the International Alpaca Fiber Market. *Llamas* 9(1): 91–92, 1995.
47. Hoffman, E.: Evaluating Alpaca Fleece Through Objective Criteria. *Llamas* 9(2): 27–30, 1995.
48. Hoffman, E.: ARI Publishes Alpaca Registry Screening Manual. *The Alpaca Registry Journal* 1(2): 13–34, Summer-Fall 1996.
49. Hoffman, E.: The Screening Process Critiqued and Praised at UC Davis Conference—Top Camelid Vet and Registry Officials Refine Screening Criteria. *The Alpaca Registry Journal* 1(2): 11–12, Summer-Fall 1996.
50. Hoffman, E.: The Kaleidoscope and Fiber Evaluation. *The Alpaca Registry Journal* 2(1): 39–44, Winter-Spring 1997.
51. Hoffman, E.: Fiber as a Transitory Medium: Factors Affecting a Histogram. *The Alpaca Registry Journal* 3(1): 29–36, Winter-Spring 1998.
52. Hoffman, E.: Vicuñas: Bearers of the Golden Fleece. *Animals,* pp. 30–33, May-June 1999.
53. Hoffman, E.: Protecting the Golden Fleece. *Wildlife Conservation,* pp. 36–41, October 1999.
54. Hoffman, E.: Creating Registries That Can Operate Internationally. International Alpaca Association: Alpaca Fiesta 2000, pp. 1–10, October 27, 2000.
55. Hoffman, E.: How Alpaca Registries Facilitate the Improvement of Alpacas. *The Alpaca Registry Journal* 6(1): 25–41, Spring 2001.
56. Hoffman, E.: Chaku: Capturing the Golden Fleece. *Living Planet,* pp. 24 –34, Winter 2001.
57. Hoffman, E.: Looks Fine to Me. *Alpaca World,* pp. 38–40, Spring 2004.
58. Hoffman, E.: Studying the Vicuña to Better Understand Alpaca Fiber. *Llama Life* 2 (7): 14,15, 28, Summer 2004.
59. Hoffman, E.: The World Fiber Market, Vicuñas May Be the Key. *International Camelid Quarterly* 3(3): 8–13, September 2004.
60. Hoffman, E.: Thoughts About Evaluating Alpaca Fiber. *International Camelid Quarterly* 2(3): 8–13, September 2004.
61. Hoffman, E.: Histogram Measurements Now Include Spin Fineness, Curvature and Medullation. *International Camelid Quarterly* 3(1): 1–3, March 2005.
62. Holt, C., ed.: *Alpaca Production.* Melbourne College of Textiles, pp. 1–66, 1994.
63. Holt, C.: Alpaca Fibre Characteristics. *Alpaca Press,* pp. 1–9, 1996.
64. Holt, C.: Using Measurement in Selection. Cameron Holt, pp. 1–21, 1996.
65. Hook, M. M.: Guanacos in Wales. *Llama Life* 23: 4, 1992.
66. Hopkins, G. E.: The Structure of Wool Fiber. *Textile Research Journal* (Textile Research Institute, New York), pp. 3–7, December 1949.
67. Hopkins, W. H.: Specialty Fiber Markets. Commission of the European Community, Directorate General XIII, Luxembourg, pp. 5–9, 1993.
68. Hospinal, R:, *Producción de Camelidos Sudamericanos.* Imprenta Rios, S.A., pp. 285–324, 453–540, 1997.
69. Krieger, M., and R. Krieger: *Secrets of the Andean Alpaca* (video recording), 1995.
70. Laker, J.: Wildlife or Livestock. *Alpaca World,* pp. 22–25, Spring 2005.
71. Lupton, C. J., A. McColl, and R. H. Stobart: Fiber Characteristics of the Huacaya Alpaca. *Small Ruminant Journal,* in press, 2006.
72. Mauersberger, R. H.: *Matthews' Textile Fibers,* 5th ed. New York: John Wiley and Sons, pp. 1,283, 1947.
73. McColl, A.: Understanding and Interpreting Micron Testing. *The Alpaca Registry Journal* 1(2): 50–56, Summer-Fall 1996.
74. McColl, A.: Fiber Sampling. *International Camelid Quarterly* 2(3): 70–71, September 2003.
75. McColl, A.: Methods of Measuring Microns. *Llama Life* 2(68): 20, Winter 2003–2004.
76. McColl, A.: Objective Fiber Diameter Measurement Methods for Measuring Microns. *International Camelid Quarterly* 3(2): 67–69, June 2004.
77. McColl, A., and M., McColl: "Fiber Testing Terminology." Yocom–McColl Testing Laboratories, Inc., p. 1, 2005.
78. McRae, A. B.: *The Fiberworks Source Book: Your Mail Order Guide to Supplies and Services for the Fiber Arts.* White Hall, VA: Betterway Publications, 223 pp., 1985.
79. Milne, A. J.: Economics of Fibre Production. Commission of European Communities, Directorate-General XIII, Luxembourg, pp. 95–103, l993.

80. Moyhnihan, L.: Alpaca Fleece Collection in Australia. Australian Alpaca Association National Conference, Hobart, Australia, pp. 189–192, 2004.

81. Morgan, G.: Fibre Growth. Australian Alpaca Association: International Alpaca Industry Seminar, 1994 Proceedings, pp. 49–54, 1995.

82. Owens, J.: Working with Alpaca. *Threads,* pp. 46–48, December-January 1992.

83. Perez, W.: La Saga de la Vicuña. *Auspiciado por el Nacional y Technologia,* 1st ed., 345 pp., 1994.

84. Pepper, J.: Suri Fiber Processing. *The Alpaca Registry Journal* 4(1): 37–40, Spring 1999.

85. Ponzoni, R. W., D. J. Hubbard, and R. V. Kenyon, et al.: Phenotypes Resulting from Huacaya by Huacaya, Suri by Huacaya, and Suri by Suri Alpaca Crossings. Proceedings of the 12th Annual Conference of the Association for the Advancement of Animal Breeding and Genetics, pp. 136–139, 2002.

86. Pope, S.: Genetics of the Suri. Australian Alpaca Association National Conference, Hobart, Australia, pp. 145–155, 2004.

87. Porter, V.: *Goats of the World.* Ipswich, UK: Farming Press, 179 pp., 1996.

88. Pino Carpio, M., and Z. Solari Escobedo: Estudios Preliminaries sobre Foliculos Pilosos en la Piel de la Vicuña. Universidad Nacional Agraria, La Molina, Programa de Ovinos y Camelidos Americanos, 1978.

89. Pino Carpio, M., and Z. Solari Escobedo: Diametro de la Fibra en el Vellon de la Vicuña. Unversidad Nacional Agraria, La Molina, Programa de Ovinos y Camelidos Americanos, l978.

90. Pino Carpio, M., and P. Santana Chavez: Estudiar de Longitud y Analisis Cuticular en la Fibra de Vicuña. In *Informes de Trabajos de Investigacion en Vicuñas,* Vol. 1, Universidad Nacional Agraria, La Molina, Programa de Ovinos y Camelidos Americanos, l982.

91. Pringle, H.: Secrets of the Alpaca Mummies. *Discover,* pp. 58–65, April 2001.

92. Pumyalla, A., and C. Leyva: Production and Technology of the Alpaca and Vicuña Fleece. Proceedings of the First International Symposium on Specialty Fibres, DWI, Aachen, Germany, pp. 234–241, 1988.

93. Quigg, G.: Choosing Alpaca Fleece. *Fiber Network* 1: 6–7, December 1990.

94. Russel, A.J.F.: Development of Management Systems. Commission of European Communities, Directorate-General XIII, Luxembourg, pp. 83–88, 1993.

95. Salas Patthay, F. J.: Textile Process for South American Camelids. Paper presented by Inca Group to the Italian National Agency for Technology, Energy and the Environment, Rome, 1993.

96. Skinner, J., and D. Skinner: Advancements in Fleece Types (draft form). Snowmass Alpacas, Sandpoint, ID, 36 pp., 2005.

97. Sporle, P. J.: Elite Natural Fibre. Australian Alpaca Association: International Alpaca Industry Seminar, 1994 Proceedings, pp. 66 –77.

98. Stapleton, I. W., and C. Holt.: *A Survey of Alpaca Fleece Characteristics.* Textile and Fibre Institute, School of Agriculture, La Trobe University, Bundoora, Victoria and Melbourne College of Textiles, Victoria, Australia, 1993.

99. Stapleton, I. W., and B. B. Steadman: It's a Fine Way to Use Fibre. *Alpacas* (Australia), pp. 37–38, Summer 1992–93.

100. Sutherland, L.: From Animals to Textiles; From Expense to Profit. *International Camelid Quarterly* 2(3): 75, September 2003.

101. Switzer, P., and D. Switzer: Enter: The Paco-Vicuña. *Llama Life* 2(70): 10, 35, Summer 2004.

102. Switzer, C.: *Spinning Llama and Alpaca,* 2nd ed., 1998.

103. Teasdale, C. C.: *The Wool Handbook, The A to Z of Fibre Top,* 9th ed. Australia: Fast Books, 121 pp., 2001.

104. Tillman, A.: Surface Scanning Electron Microscopy of Suri Fiber. *Purelysuri* 3(1): 28–42, Summer 2005.

105. Tuckwell, C.: A Brief Look at the Peruvian Alpaca Industry. Australian Alpaca Association. International Alpaca Industry Seminar, 1994 Proceedings, pp. 5–15, 1995.

106. Tuckwell, C.: The Peruvian Alpaca Industry. *Alpacas* (Australia), pp. 3–10, Summer 1994.

107. Villarroel, J.: Las Fibras. In *Avances y Perspectivas del Conocimiento de los Camelidos Sud Americanos* (S. Fernandez-Baca, ed.). Santiago, Chile: Oficina Regional de la FAO para America Latina y el Caribe, pp. 363–387, 1991.

108. Villarroel, J.: Medullated Fiber Types. In *Alpaca Production* (Cameron Holt, ed.). Melbourne College of Textiles, pp. 1–66, 1994.

109. Vinella, S.: *The European Market for South American Camelid Wool.* Italian National Agency for Technology, Energy and the Environment. Rome, 1993.

110. Von Bergen, W.: *Wool Handbook,* 3rd ed., Vol. 1. New York: Interscience Publishers (John Wiley and Sons), p. 450, 1963.

111. Watts, J. E.: Elite Alpaca Production Breeding from Fibre to Fabric. *Coolaroo Alpaca Stud.* Mittagong, Australia, pp. 1–12, 2001.

112. Watts, J., J. Hicks, and N. Parker: Observations of the Fibre Density and Length of Huacaya Alpacas. Australian Alpaca Association National Conference, Hobart, Tasmania, pp. 129–134, 2004.

113. Wheeler, J:. Evolution and Origins of Domestic Camelids. *The Alpaca Registry Journal* 3(1): 37–51, Winter-Spring 1998.

114. Wortmann, F. J., and G. Wortmann: Fibre Properties and Their Management: Methods for Analyzing Textile Animal Fibre. Commission of the European Communities, Doctorate General XIII, Luxembourg, pp. 11–24, 1993.

115. Wingate, I. B.: *Fairchild's Dictionary of Textiles,* 6th ed. New York: New York University Press, p. 688, 1967.

116. Wuliji, T. H.: Alpaca Fiber, Fiber Growth Seasonality and Fiber Characteristics Variation in a Cool-Temperature Environment of New Zealand. Proceedings of the Seventeenth International Grasslands Congress, pp. 1,494–1,495, 1993.

117. Wuliji, T., G. H. Davis, K. G. Dodds, P. R. Turner, R. N. Andrews, and G. D. Andrews.: Production Performance, Repeatability and Heritability Estimates for Live Weight, Fleece Weight and Fiber Characteristics of Alpacas in New Zealand. *Small Ruminant Journal* 37, pp. 189–200, December 19, 1999.

118. Wuliji, T.: Fibre Production and Measurement for Alpacas in New Zealand. *Alpacas Australia,* pp. 24–29, Winter 1993.

119. Young-Sanchez, M.: Textile Traditions of Ancient South America. *Alpacas* (focus on fashion), pp. 10–20, Fall 2000.

Chapter 11

Fleece Preparation and Shearing

Eric Hoffman

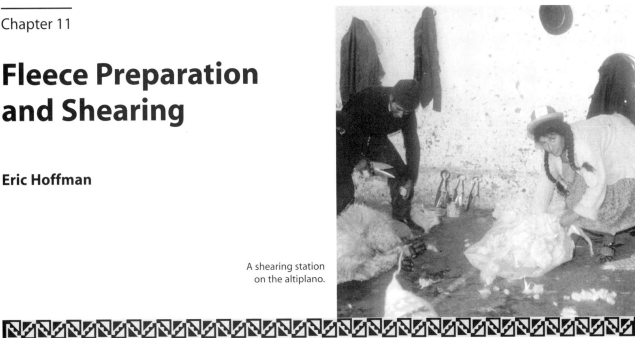

A shearing station
on the altiplano.

SHEARING ON THE PUNA

Today the region known as *Puna Humeda* (wet grasslands) north of Lake Titicaca in southern Peru is the primary alpaca-growing area in the world. Most of Peru's 2 million alpacas live here on the vast treeless plain (the *puna*) 2 miles above sea level, where it freezes about 300 nights a year. Most of the alpacas are owned by campesinos (70 percent), and the 40,000-alpaca strong Rural Alianza Cooperative operates here along with well-known private breeders Accoyo and the experimental breeding herd known as Mallikini owned by the large processor Michell & CIA. To the south of Lake Titicaca and into northwestern Bolivia lies the *Puna Seca* (dry grasslands), where alpacas are also raised, but with less success due to much less rainfall and corresponding marginal forage, lower stocking levels, and high mortality rates in crias. Growing alpacas and fiber collection in these areas incorporates the ancient ways of the Incas and the cultures before them as well as methods arriving with the Spanish five centuries ago.[4,6,8]

Shearing is usually done in late November and early December, just before the rainy season. However, it is also common for shearing to occur during the rainy season, from January through March. Shearing during the rainy season may seem unfair to the alpacas, but in Peru at this time of year, temperatures are usually at their warmest and the pastures are green. Though alpacas are often shorn at

the same time each year, some herds wait 18 months between shearings.*

Shearing techniques are generally with manual sheep clippers, scissors, or sharp implements. Animals are often rolled off their feet onto their side and then held to the ground as the hand shearing commences. This is a noisy, stressful process, with animals protesting through squeals and screams, and men struggling to control each animal's legs (as the means of restraining the animal) while women collect the fleece in burlap bags. By and large the shearing done on the puna is not the technique that is used by North Americans, Australians, New Zealanders, and Europeans.[8]

PRESHEARING ACTIVITIES

In any setting shearing requires preparatory activities to maximize fiber production and to ensure that both shearer and alpaca go through the process unscathed.

Seasonal Considerations

When to shear is a decision that shouldn't be taken lightly. Shearing too early or too late can jeopardize the lives of alpacas. Animals shorn too early in the spring may be exposed to wet and cold weather that they are ill equipped

---

*Ignacio Garaycochea, executive with Michell & CIA, personal communication, Arequipa, Peru, May 15, 2001.

Vicuñas are hand held in a truss position for shearing.

The vicuña's fleece is dense and usually each side of the blanket can be removed without it pulling apart.

to cope with in their shorn state. (See Chapter 4: Husbandry and Chapter 21: Noninfectious Multisystemic Diseases for the relationship between coat and frigid conditions.) Shearing too late may result in insufficient regrowth and too short a coat for the onset of winter, especially in the northern regions of the United States, Canada, England, Europe, New Zealand, and many of the states of southeast Australia.[1,3,7,10]

In North America spring shearing allows alpacas comfort from the heat throughout the summer. Also, shearing before the onset of the dry season, when paddocks become dusty, helps to maintain the fleece quality and reduces wear and tear on electric shear motors and blades.

If possible, shearing should be timed to avoid pasture-seed contamination, which damages and devalues a fleece. Most pasture grasses go through the same annual cycle: new growth, stalk maturation, flower and seed head development, total plant maturation, and seed drop. If a type of seed that clings to fleece is prevalent, owners should shear before the plant's seed production or move the alpacas to an enclosure where the threat doesn't exist. Shearing may

also need to be adjusted to avoid contamination by non-seed debris dropped from trees and shrubs.[1,3,7]

Grooming and Coat Preparation

Alpacas should not be groomed (deeply brushed) prior to shearing. Washing or excessive brushing of an animal breaks down the lock formation and can damage the fleece's character. In many alpaca show rules, an animal with washed fleece is disqualified, because the lock formation has been altered and the all-important criterion of "handle" can no longer be assessed accurately. During the shearing process any preparatory measures that seriously disrupt the lock structure may also negatively impact the skirting process, where the fragile lock structure is relied on to hold the fleece together when it is bundled following skirting. For all of these reasons an undisturbed lock formation and natural handle are important in evaluating and harvesting a fleece. Overpreparation in the form of washing and brushing can devalue a fleece's potential.[1,3,7]

In ideal conditions preparation should be limited to housing alpacas in paddocks and pastures with minimal fleece contaminants in the weeks prior to shearing. Just before shearing a superficial dusting and picking of the outer layer is normally necessary. Unfortunately, however, even the best efforts to keep an alpaca's fleece free of contaminants is not always successful. A number of tools and techniques can aid you in preparing a fleece prior to shearing. Having a pair of scissors on hand will allow you to cut away mats, dung, and caked muddy patches. Metal wands (specifically designed for alpaca fleeces) are effective for removing surface debris, especially hay and straw. Metal wands, used properly in a fast flicking motion, create static electricity in the fleece, causing debris to come to the surface and fall from the fleece.

An electric blower is probably the most useful tool because it blows away debris on and below the surface quickly. A blower is the most effective way to remove dust and sand that have accumulated during the year from the dust baths that alpacas partake in several times a day. Removing this gritty material is not necessary for processing fiber at this stage, but it minimizes wear and tear on the shears and prolongs the sharpness of the cutting blades.

Grit in a fleece dulls blades quickly, causing the shearer to continually stop the shearing process to change blades. Dirty fleeces can dull a comb and blade after only 1 to 3 animals, where clean fleeces may allow 11 to 15 animals to be shorn before a blade change is needed.[3,7] If fleeces prove to be laden with debris or matted, the alpaca's paddock environment should be evaluated and improved. A well-cared-for fleece should have a veneer of dust and debris on the outer surface, but be clean and free of debris when opened up.

Paddock Preparation

The cleaner the pasture or paddock, the cleaner the fleece. This may require moving alpacas to a clean area prior to shearing or more diligence in keeping pens clean by removing any form of debris (straw, twigs, seeds, leaves, etc.) that might become embedded in an alpaca's coat. Alpacas should be separated weeks prior to shearing from muddy areas that will contaminate a fleece. If alpacas are to be transported to a shearing place, make sure the conveyance is clean and free of contaminants that will collect on fleeces.

Alpacas need to be shorn in a dry state. If their fleeces are wet from rain, fog, or dew, they should be allowed to dry out entirely. If rain is predicted on shearing day, put animals in dry shelter to protect their fleeces. If there is not enough shelter to protect the animals adequately, reschedule the shearing day.[1,3,7]

Final Preparation and Equipment

Long before the first alpaca is rounded up to be shorn, the shearing station should be planned and equipped. This checklist can serve as a guide for what you need.

1. *Scale.* A hanging-hook scale for bagged fleeces, accurate to 1 ounce (or ground scale equally accurate with a broad enough weighing surface to support an entirely full 30-gallon garbage bag). The weight of a fleece (measured annually) is one of the most important assessments for a particular alpaca's productivity. If the fleece is sorted on sight into blanket, neck, skirtings, etc., the separate bags need to be weighed together in the "weighing bag" that is attached to the scale. This way you can record the total fleece weight produced by an alpaca. The blanket should make up about 60 percent of the overall fleece's weight. Breeders may want to weigh both all of the fleece and the sorted portions to more precisely assess the percentage of good-quality fiber being produced by a particular animal.[7]

2. *Ruler or measuring tape.* The weight of a fleece is largely a measurement of what rate the fleece regenerates in a year's time and its density. Therefore, measurement of staple length should be part of any record system designed to assess the productivity of a particular animal.

3. *Fiber production record book.* Minimum records (histograms) include fleece weights, age of animal, staple length, growth period (months since previous shearing), color, and tactile handle assessment. This means you need to develop a fleece recording form and have a color chart available. Accurate recording of color will

Eileen Ausland prepares an alpaca for shearing by air-blowing dust and debris from its coat.

aid in future breeding decisions and in developing color-specific lineages.

4. *Work bench and chair(s).* If a substantial number of animals are involved, shearing day will be a full day or more. Having a place to sit and record is important. A table and comfortable chairs set up in the shearing theatre, in shade with ample amounts of drinking water and soft drinks, contributes to the attitude and working conditions of the support people.[1]

5. *Small zippered plastic bags.* Make sure the sample is taken in the prescribed manner (see Chapter 10: Fiber Processing, Characteristics, and Nomenclature), the lock structure is kept intact, and the zipper is firmly sealed. Use indelible-ink felt-tip pens to write the animal's identity on the bags. To compress the air from the bag, poke a small hole in it.

6. *Fiber-handling table.* This mesh-surfaced table is essential for skirting the blanket (main part of fleece) prior to rolling it into a bundle and placing it in a bag or box for storage. Several manufacturers make lightweight portable tables. Should you decide to build your own handling table, it should stand at least 4 feet (1,200 cm) high and the surface dimensions (table top) should measure 3 × 5 feet (900 × 1,500 cm). The actual surface should be 1 inch (2.54 cm) wire or plastic mesh.[7]

7. *Fleece storage bags.* Paper, cardboard, or tightly knit cloth bags (not hemp or fabric that will contribute to contamination) are best for fleece storage. (Plastic bags do not breathe, which can result in fleece damage when condensation occurs. Plastic bags can store fleeces successfully, but not for long-term storage; they should be used only for short-term storage or bagging on the day shearing occurs.)[1,3,7,10]

Adopting a fleece color coding system is also a good idea. You can use different-colored labels, different-colored bags (or boxes), or use a clear plastic bag, so a fleece's color can be seen without needing to open it to see the fleece.[1,3]

8. *Shearing tools and accessory parts.* Besides the shears, you need sharpening devices, extra parts (especially extra cutters and combs), water or oil to cool electric shears, and a generator for power shears, if electricity is not on the site. Double-checking electricity sources and shearing equipment prior to shearing day is important. Nothing is more frustrating than assembling a supporting cast and readying the animals, but all for naught because the shears quit functioning or the cutter and comb become dull and sharp spares aren't available.

Bagging fiber.

9. *Restraint system.* Human handlers, or a combination of handlers and restraining devices, including halters, lead ropes, leg restraints, and shearing tables, need to be carefully considered. If your human helpers are new to the task, explain carefully what is expected and assign roles to participants.[3]

10. *Sufficient people power.* A smooth shearing operation must have enough people to restrain the animals, clean up after each shearing, keep up with record keeping, and separate out skirtings. If more than a half dozen animals are to be shorn, four to five capable people are optimum: shearer, record keeper, two alpaca handlers, and a cleanup person. Some of these people may also help in the "rough" sorting and bagging of fleeces.

11. *Clean and safe working space.* It is essential that the working place be clean. The shearing floor (preferably wood or rubber mat) should be as free from dust as possible and swept after each shearing. If a solid floor is not available, spread a tarp (canvas, not plastic, which is slick and noisy to walk on) on the ground. It should be large enough for the alpaca, shearer, handler, and laid-out fleece. The working area should be carefully scrutinized for sharp nails and wires that could harm an alpaca, as well as other hazards. After each shearing the working areas should be carefully cleaned.[1,3,7]

12. *Sufficient lighting.* Bright light is essential for safety and preliminary sorting. Shearing often takes place outdoors, which works well if there is very little wind and no precipitation.[1,3,7]

13. *Wind-free environment.* Shearing operations should not be susceptible to wind, which can create havoc to all aspects of the shearing process. One of the main

Scott Anderson holds while shearer Joe Mattingly removes blanket.

A tail hold and two holders are required for this cantankerous alpaca.

reasons large shearing sheds were created throughout Australia was to prevent wind or rain from disrupting shearing activities for millions of sheep each year. It's no different when it comes to alpacas, only the scale is different[1,3,7]

14. *First-aid kit.* Cuts and nicks are sometimes the by-product of a shearing operation to both alpaca and human participants. A first-aid kit should be stocked with compresses, topical antibiotics, and other means to clean wounds and stop bleeding should an alpaca or a person become injured. Alpacas can sustain substantial lacerations.[1,3]

15. *Fleece grid (optional).* To obtain an average measurement of uniformity, use a grid with 4 × 4-inch (10 × 10-cm) squares.[10]

Electric Shears and Attachments If you count yourself among the alpaca owners who don't hire a shearer, you need to carefully consider buying the correct electric shears and accessories. Several manufacturers make powered electric shears (known as handpieces). Handpieces carrying the brand names of Oster-Sunbeam and Heiniger are used throughout the world by sheep and goat operations.

Handpieces work most efficiently if the clippers have two running speeds. Because alpaca fleece contains so little grease, clippers run hotter than they would with sheep fleece. A slower speed is needed to prevent overheating. Using water to cool blades may be necessary.[9]

Handpieces consist of a powerful electric motor whose most essential moving parts are the comb and blade. The selection of combs and blades is important. The comb is the stationary part of the head and the blade is the moving part. Generally the larger the spacing between the teeth on the comb and the blade, the greater the chance of nicking an alpaca. Alpaca fiber is harder to cut through than most kinds of sheep wool, so you want the industrial model shears.[2,5,6,7,11,12,13]

Picking the Right Comb The type of comb you choose is very important. Combs of varying designs have between 9 and 20 teeth. The fewer the teeth, the less the resistance and the faster the cut. However, the combs with fewest teeth (nine, for instance) are a safety risk to alpacas because the distance between teeth is great enough for skin to be caught in the shears, resulting in serious injury to the alpaca. Some shearers I've talked with prefer a 12- or 13-tooth comb because the teeth are close enough together to

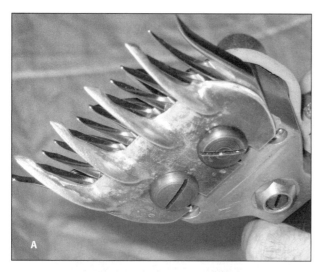

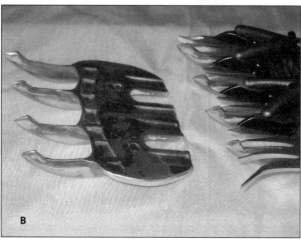

These two types of shearing spacers allow a cut to be elevated from the skin by about the thickness of a finger. Spacers are a valuable shearing aid for animals that need protection from sunburn or need a head start in growing their fleece back for cold weather.

A and **B** New Zealander Russell Gent's custom-designed spacers.

C Wood dowling fashioned as a spacer. Note the 13-tooth comb, which many shearers prefer.

avoid slicing the alpaca's skin and the cutting resistance is not so great as to slow the shearing process.[7]

Even though they are the safest, some shearers don't use 17- to 20-tooth combs because the resistance to the shears moving through a fleece is so great that it takes an inordinate amount of time to shear an alpaca, increasing the total shearing time and stress to the alpaca. Other shearers say there is less hazard in taking a little longer, and doing so means less chance of cutting an animal. The individual shearer's skill and comfort zone play a part in tool preferences.[9]

Spacers Most shearing heads are designed to do the cutting on the surface of the skin. In most cases, cutting the fleece from the alpaca's body right on the skin is the correct approach. But in areas in which cold or onset of a harsh winter can be anticipated, shearing ½ inch (1.3 cm) above the animal's skin may be warranted to allow the alpaca to retain enough coat to better combat the elements. This may also be necessary in hot, sunny areas where the alpaca is likely to receive a severe sunburn if shorn to the skin.

When an alpaca's environment dictates shearing above the skin, achieving this isn't as easy as it may seem. Holding a handpiece out from the alpaca's skin while shearing is challenging and often results in "second cuts" or a sloppy job. Though some shearers claim they don't exist, there are specially designed spacers that can be attached to the cutting surface of an electric shears to allow the shears to be pressed onto the skin in the correct fashion while the actual cutting occurs ½ inch (1.3 cm) above the skin. By attaching a spacer you can achieve an even, smooth cut and leave a protective layer on the alpaca.[7]

Know Your Shears Well Shearing day is too late to learn the intimate details of how to successfully work your shears. Never buy a handpiece and attempt to shear an animal without first watching an experienced shearer work. There are many ways to injure an alpaca with shears, so learning the correct way to shear an alpaca is essential before trying it yourself.

Knowing the intricacies of your particular kind of shears is as important as knowing how to shear. Each handpiece has settings that need to be maintained or changed depending on the type of comb being used, the density of the animal being shorn, and other variables. A handpiece needs to be continually checked during the shearing process to make sure the correct settings haven't changed. Good handpieces have two speeds and knowing the appropriate speed for the job is important. A handpiece needs to be continually lubricated with the recommended type and weight of oil. The basic information will be part of the owner's manual that comes with a new handpiece, but most manufacturers talk about shearing sheep, not alpacas. So, before you subject your first alpaca to your new handpiece, talk with someone who is experienced in shearing alpacas with your brand of handpiece to find out about the nuances of establishing the best settings.[7,9]

SHEARING RESTRAINTS

All shearing operations have two objectives: (1) to remove fleece in an economical way that does not damage it and (2) to do it in a way that minimizes stress to the alpaca. Alpacas experience different degrees of stress during shearing, depending on the animal's temperament, its newness to the process, its pregnancy status, its treatment by human handlers immediately before and during the shearing, and its previous interactions with people. Proper handling and shearing techniques will minimize stress and eliminate the possibility of injury.

Getting "in and out" in a safe, efficient manner should be the goal of any shearing team. An experienced shearer and handler can usually remove a fleece in five to seven minutes and release the alpaca with no ill effects. Prolonged restraint, in which an inordinate amount of time passes or struggling isn't controlled, increases the chances of shearing-related health risks. Health problems, such as stress-induced diseases and abortions, may not show up until days after shearing. A traumatic experience may create an animal fearful of the process, making subsequent shearings all the more stressful and difficult.

Importance of Restraint

Struggle and movement must be controlled throughout the shearing operation, but manhandling alpacas, as is sometimes done with sheep, is counterproductive and degrading to both the alpaca and shearer. Keeping an alpaca calm before shearing is important. Moving animals familiar with one another in groups of two to four into holding areas near the shearing site is reassuring to alpacas who rely on herd mates for their sense of security. Crias should accompany their mothers to shearing. A mother separated from her cria often becomes very agitated. Even when using a shearing table, allowing a cria to be close to its mother is calming to both of them.[1,3,7]

If you elect to shear an animal in standing position, a trained alpaca familiar with a halter and human contact often needs minimal restraint and will stand quietly throughout the entire process. Familiarizing animals with the noise of shearing, moving slowly, and eliminating stressors (dogs, loud talking, and gesticulating people) also help. Animals usually make it clear how they will respond within the first minute. The rare alpaca that reacts badly to the noise and feel of electric shears may be better off shorn by hand. Usually, first-time animals (and young animals) react the most unpredictably.

Restraining and shearing alpacas is not for everyone. Some alpaca owners will do themselves and their animals a favor by hiring an experienced shearing team. The best way to learn is to watch and participate with an experienced team. The handler and shearer should be working as equal partners and be cognizant of one another's actions and of the peculiarities of each animal.

Three chief means of restraint are: the *freestanding*, the *trussed-prone on-the-ground*, and *shearing-table prone* positions. All three methods have their proponents and work well if implemented properly.

A homemade fiber cleaner: Two electric dryer motors blow air through a slotted stove pipe as the drum turns slowly. The drum turns about one revolution per second.

Shearing a standing alpaca. Tail and head restraints are applied to minimize movement.

Freestanding Restraint

This method, the one I prefer, requires a skilled handler as well as a shearer. The alpaca is sheared in the standing (or sitting) position. The handler(s) holds on to the alpaca while the shearer removes its fleece. The handler must try to "read" the alpaca's response to head off violent struggles and "sit-downs." Many alpacas will stand throughout shearing with only minimal reaction, providing the shearer is careful not to nick them. Others will react by spinning, sitting, screeching, bucking, rearing, kicking, and spitting. In general, an alpaca whose head is held close to the handler's chest in a calm but secure fashion tends not to struggle, even if it is predisposed to do so. When alpacas are held securely, they are generally less apt to try escape options. The handler who stands away from an uncooperative alpaca, allowing a slack lead rope and free moving head, is asking for trouble.

All of the responses in an alpaca's repertoire can be controlled by an experienced shearer and handler with only momentary interruptions in shearing activities. For example, spinning can be stopped by placing the alpaca against a fence or wall or by having a third person hold the animal's tail. Spitting can be dealt with by directing the head away or by draping a cloth over the animal's mouth and tucking it into the halter. Rearing up or bolting can be stopped by controlling the head (sometimes by "earing," with a firm grip but no twisting or lifting, while simultaneously applying some downward tension on the halter) and placing a

hand on the withers. A half-wrap with a lead rope around a post secures an alpaca to a stationary object. The post absorbs the struggle, and a half-wrap (as opposed to a full wrap) allows instantaneous release should the animal twist its neck or otherwise endanger itself. If the alpaca begins to sit (kush) and it seems steadfast in its resolve, allow it to sit and then continue shearing. In the case of a particularly strong and uncooperative animal, two handlers may be necessary, but this is rare with an experienced team.

An alpaca's body has some universal control points:

1. *Head.* Use halter, lead rope, earing, or post with half-wrap if an animal's strength is too much.

2. *Withers.* The handler's grasp and use of body positioning control bucking and rearing.

3. *Tail.* A convenient handle to control spinning, bolting, bucking, and sitting, provided someone else is working the front end.

4. *Sternum.* An alpaca that is prone to sit can be grasped under its conveniently narrow sternum and lifted. Also, a handler's knee pushed under the sternum and against a wall or fence prevents the animal from sitting.

5. *Fiber.* Controlling an animal by holding fiber is not advisable and should only be used to grasp, not to pull or jerk.

These three young suris have not yet received their first shearings.

All behavioral responses should be dealt with firmly and calmly. Striking an alpaca or losing one's temper creates a worse situation. Subtle body positioning, not fast-paced wrestlinglike maneuvers, is the correct style. In time, the handler and the shearer will become familiar with all of the animals' responses and react spontaneously.

Caution: To avoid serious injury, the shearer must know the whereabouts of the handler's hands, particularly his or her fingers. The handler must anticipate the shearer's actions and adjust holds to accommodate the shearer. Shearing should stop if an animal cannot be controlled.

Trussed-Prone Restraint

This technique is preferred by many South American and large Australian entities. It is applicable to animals that are seldom handled and does not take into account a particular animal's disposition. This technique involves reaching over the alpaca's back, grasping locks of fiber, and pulling the animal onto its side or lifting the animal off the ground and dropping it onto one side. Almost simultaneously the back and front legs are secured so the alpaca can't flail or regain its feet. A particularly strong person is needed to do the lift; another person must grasp the back legs; and a third person secures the front legs.

Australian alpaca growers have modified this technique with the use of ropes. Each foot or pair of feet is placed in a lasso, which is pulled snugly (with care not to injure the animal) and secured to a cleat. The rear legs are pulled to the rear of the animal, and the front legs are pulled far forward. With all four legs secured in this fashion the alpaca is rendered immobile. A handler must sometimes hold the alpaca's neck to the ground to prevent it from struggling. The shearer removes the clip from one side. Then the animal is rolled to its back and onto its other side to complete the process. This method is efficient, taking less than five minutes to complete. However, if not performed correctly, the restraint can be injurious and overly stressful.

When I saw the trussed-prone on-the-ground restraint performed on about 20 animals, I noted that most animals took the ordeal in stride, but some fought and had to be manhandled to the ground to be kept off their feet. An occasional animal struggled throughout the process, regurgitating stomach contents. The risk of aspiration inhalation was readily apparent, especially when regurgitating animals were rolled onto their backs either to shear their undersides or to reposition them for shearing the unshorn side. Some Australians, aware of this risk, roll their animals over belly down to avoid problems. The primary advantage of the trussed-prone technique over the standing technique is control. With animals that are prone to kick or "dance," a shearer may want this control to avoid a serious leg injury.[3,10]*

---

*Grey Morgan, former president of the Australian Alpaca Association, personal communication, 1994.

THE TRUSSED-PRONE RESTRAINT METHOD OF SHEARING

1 An alpaca fitted with leg restraints.

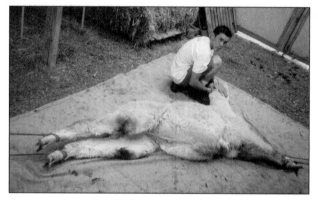

2 An alpaca on its side, "stretched," with a head attendant.

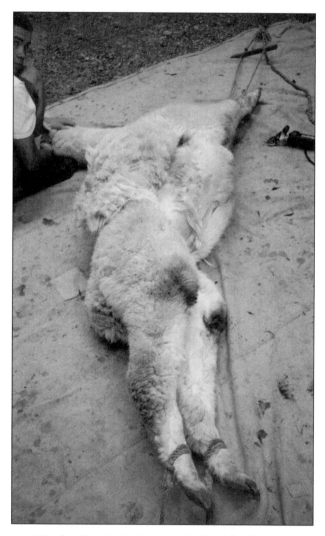

3 The first "blow" on the bottom right side of the blanket.

4 The right side of the blanket removed.

5 Collecting the right side of the blanket.

7 One side finished.

6 Shearer Steve Murray continues shearing the belly, neck, and legs.

8 The alpaca is rolled over (sternally) and the sequence is repeated.

New Zealander Russell Gent's invention, the alpaca shearing table, takes the fight out of shearing.

Shearing Table

New Zealander Russell Gent is credited with inventing the shearing table, for which he holds a U.S. patent. A shearing table is one of the most significant inventions to help alpaca owners humanely remove the fleece without struggle and without the kinds of stress that can occur with other methods of restraint and shearing.

Gent's alpaca shearing table is easy to operate. The table is rotated into a vertical position and the large padded door that sits atop the table is opened, leaving a space between the table (now in a vertical position) and the door (also in a vertical position). The alpaca is walked between the table and door, the door is closed against the alpaca holding it in place as the table is rotated back to a horizontal position.

Two people are needed to work a table. A handler holds the animal's neck to combat any thrashing about, while the other attendee attaches leg ropes and mild tension and the alpaca finds itself strapped to a table, where shearing commences. First one side is shorn, then the alpaca is gently rolled over and the other side is shorn. The pad (door) is then lowered back onto the alpaca to hold it in place. The table is rotated back to the vertical position, the door is opened, and the alpaca is released. The table does such a good job of holding an animal in place that many devotees use it to hold an animal for worming or toenail or teeth trimming.[7]

NOTES FROM TWO SHEARERS

Joe Mattingly, of Salinas, California, is a professional sheep shearer who has shorn alpacas in California for nearly 20 years. For the bulk of his career he has shorn alpacas in a standing position, though he often shears using leg restraints or a table. Here are his views on the optimum equipment and comb:

I use an Oster-Sunbeam Shear with a 3-inch head. It's one of many models designed to shear herds of sheep. For alpacas I've found a 20-tooth comb on a 3-inch blade does a good job. The greater the number of teeth on the comb, the smoother the job and the less likely there will be nicks. Tension adjustment is essential to creating a smooth cut. If there is tearing or jerking the tension needs adjusting. I oil the blade about every 10 minutes to compensate for lack of natural grease. I always take several sets of combs and blades. I don't hesitate to

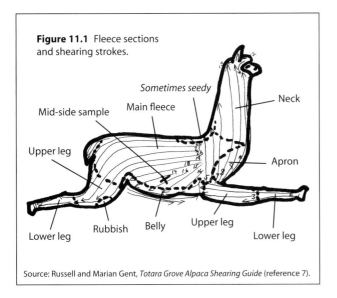

Figure 11.1 Fleece sections and shearing strokes.

Sometimes seedy

Neck

Main fleece

Mid-side sample

Apron

Upper leg

Upper leg

Lower leg

Rubbish

Belly

Upper leg

Lower leg

Source: Russell and Marian Gent, *Totara Grove Alpaca Shearing Guide* (reference 7).

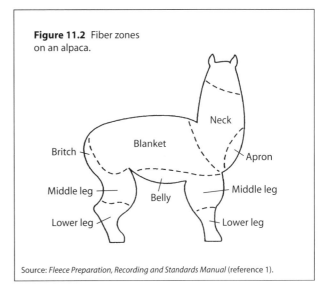

Figure 11.2 Fiber zones on an alpaca.

Neck

Britch

Blanket

Apron

Middle leg

Belly

Middle leg

Lower leg

Lower leg

Source: *Fleece Preparation, Recording and Standards Manual* (reference 1).

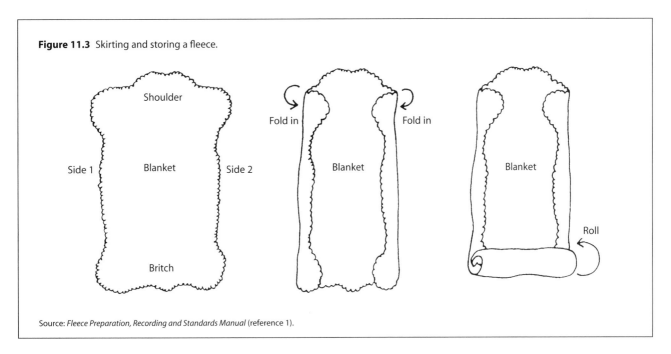

Figure 11.3 Skirting and storing a fleece.

Shoulder

Side 1

Blanket

Side 2

Britch

Fold in

Blanket

Fold in

Blanket

Roll

Source: *Fleece Preparation, Recording and Standards Manual* (reference 1).

change them when they become dull. Cutting edges become dull sooner than with sheep because alpacas have a little more debris due to their open fleeces and lack of natural grease. Alpacas are tight-skinned compared to sheep. There are no wrinkles or folds. If an alpaca is properly restrained and the shearer is aware of an alpaca's anatomy, nicking is entirely avoidable. Care must be taken where the legs meet the body. Running a shear into an armpit will make a mess.[9]

Alpacas shorn too close to the skin can become sun-burned. Lifting shears along the back so that fiber the depth of a pencil's width remains is a sufficient safeguard against sunburn.[9]

Russell Gent feels strongly that the shearing pattern is very important to separate the fleece into its naturally oc-curring grades: skirtings (belly, leg, apron), neck (often not the quality of the blanket), and blanket (running from the withers to the tail and along both sides of the rib cage). Gent suggests a stroke sequence that collects the fleece along the lines of the naturally occurring grade sections on most alpacas (see Figure 11.1).

Like Gent, Mattingly also stresses that shearing should be done in sections along classing lines to help the sorting process go smoothly. Preliminary sorting should take place as soon as the fleece is taken from the animal, with the separation of fleece sections into different bags. For example, the blanket area should be taken off and kept separate. The neck is often treated separately, although it may be of the same quality as the blanket. The skirtings (which usually include the legs, belly, apron, and the area around the tail) are almost always separated into its own class.

Both Gent and Mattingly agree that each area on the alpaca has different shearing requirements (see Figure 11.2). For example, the withers usually collect a great deal of vegetable matter, which can dull shears. The area around the tail is often matted and stained, and thus not always usable. The legs are usually coarse and may carry a wide range of contaminants, including dried mud and vegetable matter. Every effort should be made to extract the blanket area in one or two complete pieces. The neck usually contains a shorter staple than the blanket and may be of a lesser quality. Judgment on classing the neck needs to be exercised from one animal to the next.

STORING THE BLANKET

When the blanket is removed from the alpaca, keeping it intact is desirable for storage and future use. The general steps are as follows. Lay the blanket out on a flat surface with the cut side facing up. This should be done on a wire mesh table (skirting table) that allows debris to fall from the fleece. Spend some time looking over the edges of the fleece and remove debris or coarse fibers that would devalue the fleece's consistency. Fold the sides in to the middle and roll the fleece up gently, much in the manner of rolling up a sleeping bag (see Figure 11.3). Place the fleece in a bag or storage area that is insect proof but not entirely airtight.

REFERENCES

1. Anonymous: *Fleece Preparation, Recording and Standards Manual*, pp. 1–11. Seymour, Australia: Australian Alpaca Fibre Marketing Organisation Pty Ltd., 1997.
2. Appleyard, H. M.: *Guide to the Identification of Animal Fibres*, 2d ed., p. 11. Leeds, England: Wira, the Research and Services Centre for Textiles and Clothing, 1978.
3. Blake, L., and B. Kitson: *New Zealand Alpaca Fibre Manual*, pp. 1–20. Alpaca and Llama Association of New Zealand, 1999.
4. Bustinza, V. C.: Razas de Alpaca del Altiplano Suri y Huacaya, p. 34. Puno, Peru: Universidad del Altiplano, Instituto de Investigaciones para el Desarrollo Social del Altiplano, 1982.
5. Couchman, R. C.: South American Camelid Fibers. *Llama Life* 18: 32, 1991.
6. Fernandez-Baca, S. (ed.): *Avances y Perspectivas del Concocimiento de los Camelidos Sudamericanos,* p. 429. Santiago, Chile: Oficina Regional de la FAO para America Latina y el Caribe, 1991.
7. Gent, R., and M. Gent: *Totara Grove Alpaca Shearing Guide,* pp. 1–23. Picton, New Zealand: Blenheim Printing Ltd., 2001. (In North America the guide can be purchased by contacting Stevens Llama Tique & Suri Alpacas, 29581 U.S. Hwy. 59/60, Worthington, MN 56187. Telephone: (507) 376-4230 or (800) 469-5262 (toll free in the U.S and Canada); e-mail: llamatiq@rconnect.com. In Australia or New Zealand contact Russell and Marion Gent, Totara Grove, Koromiko, P.O. Box 57, Picton, New Zealand. Telephone: (64) 3 573 7480; fax: (64) 3 573 7483; e-mail: totaragrove@xtra.co.nz.)
8. Hoffman, E.: Ships of the Andes. *Pacific Discovery* 42(3): 7–15, 1989.
9. Hoffman, E.: Joe Mattingly, Master Shearer. *Llama Life* 19: 30, 1991.
10. Holt, C.: *Alpaca Production*, pp. 1–66. Melbourne College of Textiles, 1994. (To order, write AFTS, Wool and Fibre Testing Laboratory, 25 Dawson Street, Brunswick, Victoria 3056, Australia.)
11. Hopkins, G. E.: The Structure of the Wool Fiber. *Textile Research Journal*, pp. 3–7. New York: Textile Research Institute, December 1949.
12. Mauersberger, R. H.: *Matthews' Textile Fibers,* 5th ed., p. 1,283. New York: John Wiley and Sons, 1947.
13. Von Bergen, W.: *Wool Handbook*, 3rd ed., Vol. 1, p. 450. New York: Interscience Publishers (John Wiley and Sons), 1963.

Reproduction and Neonatology

Overleaf A mother and her newborn are ready for light rainfall.

Chapter 12

Male Reproduction

Ahmed Tibary, DMV, PhD, Dipl ACT

An adult male alpaca.

The reproductive system of the male camelid presents several anatomical and physiological peculiarities compared to other more common kinds of livestock.[80,81] Breeders and clinicians working with camelids should become familiar with these peculiarities in order to conduct a thorough examination of a male. This chapter covers various aspects of reproductive anatomy, physiology, and behavior, as well as the most common reproductive abnormalities affecting alpacas. Emphasis is given to breeding soundness examinations, with special reference to semen characteristics and factors that may affect semen quality.

ANATOMY

Male reproductive organs have been thoroughly described in the llama, alpaca,[15,17,19] guanaco, and vicuña.[18,86] An illustration of the anatomy of the reproductive organs in the male alpaca is given in Figure 12.1.

The Scrotum and Testicles

The scrotum is situated high in the perineal region in the area of the ischial arch with the testicles directed caudodorsally.[3,29] The mechanism of testicular descent remains unstudied in the camelid. The testes are generally present in the scrotum at birth, but they are usually soft and difficult to palpate.[29,67] The testicles are relatively small compared to those of other species. They are ovoid and present a great variation in size (see Figure 12.2). Size of the testicles is an important trait, as it is highly correlated with sperm production and fertility. In yearlings, the testes measure on average 1.1 to 1.4 centimeters in length. Testicular size increases until about four years of age. No seasonal variation of the size of the scrotum has been described in alpacas. Average testicular sizes at specific ages are presented in Table 12.1. From a histological point of view, the camelid testis has a general organization similar to that of most species.[18,19,27,39,57,63,80]

The epididymis, an anatomical structure that collects sperm and fluid from the testicles, is composed of three distinct parts: the head (caput), body (corpus), and tail (cauda) (see Figure 12.2). Regional differences with respect to metabolism and biochemical activity exist within the epididymis and represent different secretory functions that may play a role in the process of sperm maturation.[17,80,81]

The tail of the epididymis is the main storage area of spermatozoa. During ejaculation sperm cells are propelled from the tail of the epididymis to the penis via a ductus deferens (deferent duct). The ductus deferens is 0.5 to 1 millimeter in diameter at the junction of the epididymis. It widens a little bit in the abdominal cavity toward the pelvic urethra. The length of the ductus deferens is about 30 to 40 centimeters.[65]

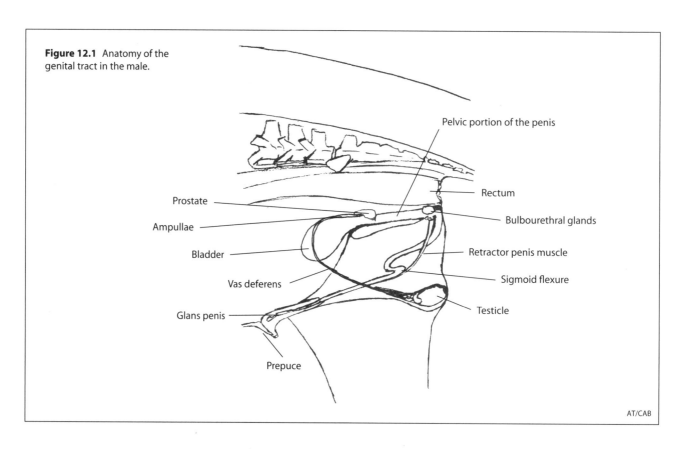

Figure 12.1 Anatomy of the genital tract in the male.

Pelvic portion of the penis

Rectum

Prostate

Bulbourethral glands

Ampullae

Bladder

Retractor penis muscle

Vas deferens

Sigmoid flexure

Glans penis

Testicle

Prepuce

AT/CAB

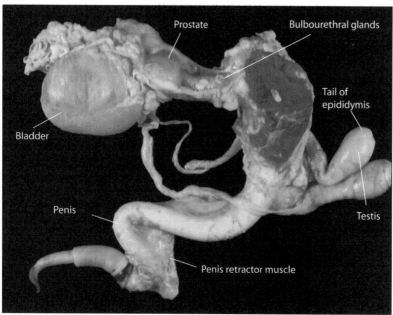

Prostate

Bulbourethral glands

Tail of epididymis

Bladder

Testis

Penis

Penis retractor muscle

Figure 12.2 Male reproductive anatomy.

Table 12.1 Average alpaca testicular size at different ages.

Age (months)	Length × Width (cm)
	1.0 × 0.4
12	2.3 × 1.5
18	2.8 × 1.9
24	3.3 × 2.2
30	3.6 × 2.4
36	3.6 × 2.4
Adult sire	3.7 × 2.5

Source: P. W. Bravo, Camelid Medicine, Surgery and Reproduction Conference. Ohio State University, 2000.

Exceptional testicular development in both size and symmetry.

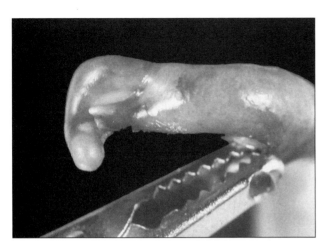
Anatomy of the glans penis in alpacas. Note the corkscrew cartilaginous end that allows penetration of the cervix.

The Prepuce and Penis

The prepuce (foreskin) is located in the inguinal region. It is flattened from side to side and triangular in shape when viewed laterally. In the absence of sexual arousal, the small preputial orifice is directed caudally. The prepuce is adherent to the glans penis until two or three years of age, making exteriorization of the penis impossible and negating successful breeding efforts.[73] The prepuce has a well-developed muscular apparatus, which allows movement of the preputial orifice needed for changing its direction during erection and mating behavior. These muscles are identified as the cranial, the lateral, and the caudal preputial muscle.[29]

The penis is a fibroelastic organ. In the absence of erection, the penis is retracted into its sheath via a prescrotal sigmoid flexure. The length of the penis ranges from 35 to 40 centimeters.[65] The alpaca penis is cylindrical, gradually decreasing in diameter from its root (ischial arch) to the neck of the glans penis.

The penis is composed of the root of the penis, the body of the penis, the free end of the penis, and the glans penis. The glans penis is long and cartilaginous, and has a slight clockwise curvature.[3,80] The urethral orifice is located at the base of the cartilaginous shaft, not at the tip. These anatomical features (curved and cartilaginous) of the camelid penis allow penetration of the cervical rings and intrauterine deposition of semen using a combined rotational and thrusting movement.

The Accessory Sex Glands

One of the most important features in the anatomy of male camelid genitalia is the absence of seminal vesicles. The only accessory sex glands described in the literature as significant are the prostate and the bulbourethral glands.[29] These glands secrete fluids that are added to semen during ejaculation. These secretions have mechanical and biological function. They increase the volume of semen and allow delivery of sperm cells into the uterus, but also contain several substances that help protect sperm cells and increase their viability. Accessory sex gland secretions may also contain ovulation-inducing substances.

PHYSIOLOGY

Understanding the reproductive physiology of the male alpaca is fundamental in the selection of a potential herd sire and the management of breeding. Decision making concerning age at breeding and the number of matings allowed in a certain time frame depend on factors such as puberty, sexual maturity, sperm production ability, and senile changes.

Puberty and Sexual Maturation

An exact age of puberty is difficult to determine because of the wide variety of definitions given to the term and the progressive nature of this event. Puberty is usually defined as the age at which a male is capable of completing the mating act and producing enough spermatozoa to successfully impregnate females. This definition supposes the presence of normal sexual behavior, spermatogenesis, penetration, and ejaculation. For camelids, as for many other species, the variability of the age at puberty is probably due to factors such as genetics, nutrition, climatic changes, and season of birth.

Testicular growth in this species is slow. The testicles should be 4 to 5 centimeters in length and 2.5 to 3 centimeters in width by five years of age.[72] A study in Australia showed that half of males may be able to produce spermatozoa and impregnate females between 13 and 24 months of age. The other males will not be capable of reproduction until 24 to 36 months of age.[31] When asked to comment on this possibility, a number of long-term North American volume breeders reported that it is extremely rare to find a male capable of impregnating a female before 21 months of age.

Male alpacas can display mounting behavior at a very young age (less than one year).[20] However, they will not be able to complete erection and intromission until the penis is completely freed from its preputial attachment. The process of detachment from the preputial adhesions begins at 11 to 13 months of age and is probably regulated by testosterone levels, because this age coincides with an increase in plasma testosterone concentration.[3] Plasma testosterone concentrations in 11-month-old alpaca males have been

Mounting behavior.

Breeding behavior: the mating position in alpacas.

reported to be similar to those found in adult males.[49] Preputial adhesions are lost (allowing the penis to extend) in only 8 percent of males at one year of age, 70 percent of the males will have detached by age two, and all males will have detached by age three, which corresponds to the recommended age to begin breeding.[20,72] Alpacas reach sexual maturity at five years of age, when they have achieved a weight of about 62.5 kilograms (130–140 lb).

Spermatogenesis and Sperm Production

Spermatogenesis is similar to that described for other species.[19,76,81] The effect of season on sperm production is poorly understood in alpacas, but seems to be present in wild South American camelids. In South America, the size of the testicles (longitudinal and transverse testes diameters) in the male vicuña is affected by season: The diameter of the seminiferous tubules is larger in February (163.5±29.6 µm) than in August (137.9±25.2 1 µm) and Leydig cell nuclei diameters are also greater (5.9±0.97 µm vs. 4.2±0.03 µm).[84–86] Based on these observations, it appears that February is an active spermatogenetic phase and August a regression phase.[85,86] Spermatogenesis is not completely arrested during August because all germ cell types can still be observed at this time. The increase in testicular size is attributed mainly to increases in the diameter of the seminiferous tubules, and the enlarged Leydig cells appear similar to those found in the one-humped camel during the rutting season.[86] An effect of season on sperm production was also reported for the llama, with high sperm concentration in fall and low sperm production in summer.[34]

In the male vicuña, individual testosterone values tend to be higher in summer, but some high values are also noted in August.[86] Seasonal changes in plasma testosterone concentrations have also been reported in alpaca males; samples taken in March have the highest monthly mean value and June the lowest.[49,86] The higher plasma testosterone levels in vicuña in summer are probably responsible for the behavioral changes observed in males at this period of the year. High levels of testosterone are consistently found in dominant males and young males that are trying to recruit their own harem. Dominant males (leaders) invariably have higher hormonal plasma concentrations than those that do not.[86]

As in other domestic species, sperm production is highly correlated with testicular size.[11] Selection of a herd size should take this parameter into consideration.

Mating Behavior and Ejaculation

Mating takes place with the female sitting in a sternal position. The male, squatting with his hind limbs completely flexed, sits on the ground using the surface of his heels and hocks. His forelimbs are extended on each side of the female with his feet rarely reaching the ground. The duration of copulation is variable, ranging from 5 to 65 minutes. Most matings, however, average 18 to 25 minutes. Among

A male alpaca displaying flehmen.

Note that the male's cheeks are puffed out as he orgles noisily.

factors affecting the length of copulation are breed, age, sire, season, and frequency. Duration of copulation tends to be shorter for younger males and decreases in all males with increased frequency of mating.

Length of copulation is longer for multiparous females (21.5 min) than for maiden females (14.7 min). Also, when several males are present in the same herd, copulation will be less than when no other males are present (8 versus 21.5 min).[67]

All South American camelids display flehmen behavior after smelling fresh female dung. They lift the head, elevate the upper lip without curling it, and open the mouth slightly.[29] According to some authors, South American camelids do not sniff the female perineal area during courtship. However, I have observed sniffing behavior by many males.

When introduced into a herd, the male will chase a female and try to force her down by mounting her and putting pressure on the pelvis. Even if females are receptive (presence of a mature follicle), they do not automatically sit down in response to male advances. Some females may spit and run for a while, but will sit later if the male is persistent. Other females may "drop" immediately when the male approaches them. Some of this apparently receptive behavior may in fact be a submissive behavior rather than readiness for breeding. This behavior is generally very confusing to beginning alpaca breeders and may lead to overbreeding.

Erection is achieved after the female is mounted in a sitting position. The perineal area is probed by the partially extended penis to locate the opening of the vulva. The penis will be fully extended upon successful vaginal penetration. At this point the male moves his pelvis close to the pelvis of the female and begins short pelvic thrusts. The activity of the penis is accompanied by a rotational movement (corkscrew) of the glans penis. The rotation of the glans penis helps to dilate the cervix, allowing in utero ejaculation. During copulation, the male may shift position from side to side and alternate between getting very close to the female and sliding slightly backward. This copulatory behavior is believed to help redirect the penis so that ejaculation occurs in both uterine horns.

There is no correlation between copulation time and conception rate. Ejaculation in camelids appears to occur throughout the entire duration of copulation, which can vary from 5 to 65 minutes. Conception rates are the same, regardless of copulation length. In addition, semen can be collected from alpacas as early as five minutes after copulation commences.[9,25,42]

The male will attempt to breed the same female again the same day or a day later unless she ovulates, in which case she will "spit off." Vigorous males can breed several females in one day for the first four to five days after introduction into a group of nonmated females. This activity decreases sharply after the first two weeks when the males lose interest even in females that are returning to estrus.

One male orgles and mounts, stimulating a nearby male to do the same.

Seventy percent of the breeding takes place in these first days, with a conception rate of 50 percent.[67] In a free mating system, it is generally recommended to change males every two weeks, so that all females can be bred during a short interval of time.[70] In alpacas, length of copulation and fertility drop off when the number of matings increases to more than four times per day.[5] Breeding with a male whose sperm count has dropped has a higher likelihood of stimulating ovulation without conception than if he had bred the same female in the first two breedings that day.

Although mature males may sustain good sperm production even if ejaculated four times a day for a few days, for efficient reproduction the mature herd sire should not be used for breeding more than twice a day. Younger males should be used less frequently. No studies have been conducted to thoroughly investigate optimum use of young males, but it is generally recommended not to breed them more than two or three times a week.

Urethral pulsations increase after four minutes of copulation and occur in clusters every one minute. Urethral contractions are evenly distributed during copulation, suggesting that ejaculate is dribbled throughout the length of copulation. The average number of pulsations during one copulation is 40.[9] In llamas, each cluster lasts 20 seconds and is composed of four to five rapid urethral pulses followed by a tremor of the whole body. Each cluster is preceded by 2 repositions and 38 pelvic thrusts. Researchers have interpreted the urethral pulses accompanying the whole body strain as a single ejaculation.[46] Thus, ejaculation in the llama starts at about four minutes after the beginning of copulation and occurs every minute (18 to 19 ejaculations per 22 min). These observations (multiple ejaculation and straining during ejaculation) are confirmed by the pattern of ejaculation observed during semen collection by artificial vagina.[48] In alpacas, sperm cells can be found in the seminal fluid as early as five minutes after the beginning of copulation.[9]

During the chase and copulation, alpacas produce a special guttural sound (orgling) as air is expired through the mouth while the cheeks are inflated. Males can display all copulatory behavior without achieving intromission.[20] Vocalization increases as a warning when another male or a handler approaches the breeding pair. Often when one male begins to orgle, other males in the vicinity will begin to orgle and mount females, stimulated by the initial orgling. This behavior can be used to stimulate a male who is reluctant to breed. Vocalization tone may be very high pitched in some males.

Alpaca males exhibit different sexual behavior patterns if they are maintained with females year round than if they are run in separate groups. In the former, they show distinct seasonal variations in activity, while in the latter, they show continuous libido and breeding capability, servicing females whenever they have an opportunity.[26] Higher plasma testosterone levels have been found in the latter situation,[49] but no related changes in fertility rate have been reported.[86] Aggressive behavior toward other males has been observed, culminating in direct confrontations such as biting, necking, and chest ramming that can lead to serious injuries, especially if the fighting teeth are well developed. To curtail this behavior, some breeders house their males in bachelor herds, well away from females, and only allow the males to be with females during the act of breeding (see Chapter 2: Behavior and Communication).

REPRODUCTIVE DISORDERS IN THE MALE ALPACA

There are limited reports on the pathology of the male reproductive tract in camelids.[83] The most comprehensive study on abnormalities of the reproductive tract in alpacas was reported by Sumar.[66] This author examined 3,015 males and 792 slaughterhouse reproductive organs. The incidence of pathology in breeding alpacas was 18.1 percent (testicular hypoplasia, 10%; cryoptorchidism, 5.7%; and ectopic testis, 2.5%). In the slaughterhouse animals, the incidence of abnormalities was 30.5 percent (hypoplasia, 10.8%; cryoptorchidism, 3%; ectopic testis, 1.9%; cysts, 14.5%).

Diseases of the Penis and Prepuce

Diseases of the prepuce and the penis are relatively rare because these organs are well protected due to their anatomic position. Swelling of the prepuce may be due to local inflammation caused by contact with a chemical or physical irritant, parasitic infestation, or rupture of the urethra.

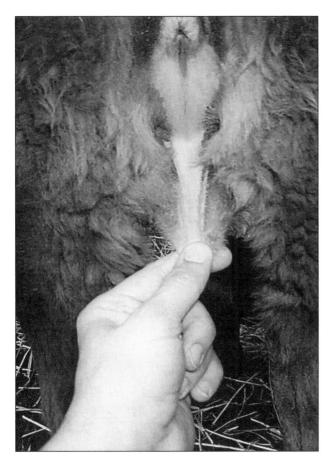

Testicular degeneration.

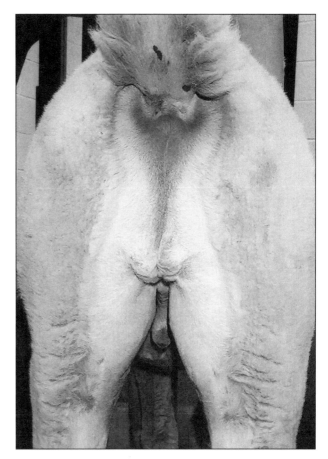

Testicular hypoplasia.

Preputial swelling can also be part of a large ventral edema in some animals suffering from heat stress.[53] If the preputial swelling is due to urethral rupture, the urine accumulated in the subcutaneous space should be drained and a urethrostomy performed.

Preputial prolapse was reported in at least one alpaca.[43] This condition can lead to paraphymosis or the inability to retract the penis into the prepuce. This condition can become complicated by dirt in the preputial opening and lead to a balanoposthitis (inflammation of the penis and prepuce), sometimes with necrosis of the tip of the penis. Early detection of paraphymosis and treatment will avoid these complications. Paraphymosis and balanoposthitis can be due to the presence of "hair rings" if the females are not clipped before breeding.[29]

Urolithiasis (urinary stones) has been reported in male camelids, especially llamas.[40,41,51] Most of these calculi occur at the level of the distal part of the urethra or at the level of the sigmoid flexure. The affected animals initially show signs of colic, which become more and more frequent. At later stages of the disease, the animal becomes lethargic and anorexic. Deterioration of the animal's health usually signals rupture of the bladder and peritonitis. Relief

of the condition can be attempted via a urethrostomy. Recurrence of obstruction is common even after a urethrostomy. Prevention of urolithiasis can be accomplished by better nutritional management (well-balanced diet, salt supplementation, and access to fresh water), assuming that the cause of the condition is similar to that seen in sheep.

Diseases of the Testicles

The testicles and surrounding tissue can be affected by several congenital or acquired conditions. Congenital disorders of the testicles include abnormal development (testicular hypoplasia), lack of testicular descent (cryptorchidism), abnormal location (ectopic testicles), and the presence of cystic formations. Acquired conditions of the scrotum and testicles include trauma, testicular degeneration, orchitis, and neoplasm.

Testicular Hypoplasia Testicular hypoplasia is the lack of normal development, resulting in hard, smaller than normal testicles. Partial or total testicular hypoplasia has been reported to have an estimated incidence of 10 percent.[66] Most hypoplasia cases are bilateral. The left side seems to be more affected than the right in unilateral cases.[66]

Microscopic study of the testicular tissue shows small seminiferous tubules with absence of spermatogenesis (see Figure 12.3). Testicular biopsy is helpful in the diagnosis and prognosis of fertility in such cases.[74,83] The causes of testicular hypoplasia in alpacas are not well understood. Severe bilateral hypoplasia results in complete sterility because of the lack of sperm cell production (azoospermia). Less severe hypoplasia may cause substandard semen quality and poor fertility.

Cryptorchidism Cryptorchidism or the failure of testicular descent into the scrotum is a relatively rare condition in South American Camelidae.[62] Cryptorchidism can be unilateral or bilateral and is suspected when inspection of the perineal region shows a flat or absent scrotum. In Sumar's study, cryptorchidism was found in approximately 3 percent of the population examined.[66] The undescended testicles are usually found close to the internal inguinal opening, but can also be found intraabdominally, caudal to the kidney, or within the inguinal canal.

Cryptorchidism was reported in related vicuñas (3 cases in a population of 60 individuals), which suggests that the affection may be hereditary.[62] Differentiation between abdominal cryptorchidism and castration can be achieved using hormonal diagnosis.[59] Testosterone is measured before and two hours after intravenous administration of 5,000 IU units of hCG (human chorionic gonadotropin). Castrated males will show very low testosterone, whereas cryptorchid males will show a two-fold increase in testosterone. Unilateral cryptorchid males will continue to show male behavior and will breed any receptive female. It is therefore important to identify these animals and castrate them.

Testicular Cysts Testicular cysts are found in various numbers, sizes, and locations on a testicle. Their diagnosis requires ultrasonographic examination. I have seen cases of testicular cysts with a reproductive history ranging from normal to subfertility to complete sterility. Cysts may be found in the mediastinum testis or at the level of the head or tail of the epididymis.[74]

Testicular Trauma Scrotal trauma due to bites from other males is relatively common. Prognosis for the reproductive life of the individual male depends on the extent of the injury and the time elapsed until detection. The trauma should be differentiated from orchitis or hydrocele. Deep lacerations are frequently complicated by testicular hemorrhaging and infection, and the development of a schirrous cord requiring urgent surgical intervention (castration). Scrotal dermatitis or keratosis is seen in some animals with mange, a tick infestation, or a zinc deficiency.

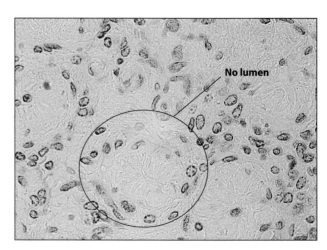

Figure 12.3 Histology of hypoplastic testicles from an alpaca. Note the absence of any spermatogenesis.

Testicular Degeneration Testicular degeneration is probably the most common cause of infertility in adult male alpacas. The degenerated testicles are smaller than normal and either soft or hard and fibrous. Testicular degeneration results from exposure to high temperatures (heat stress) or following severe systemic illness. A testicular biopsy may be of value for the diagnosis of this condition and to differentiate it from testicular hypoplasia. Males with testicular degeneration may become completely azoospermic or produce very few sperm cells with increased abnormalities. Most males will maintain normal libido. There is no effective treatment for testicular degeneration. Prevention requires excellent management and care of sires in terms of nutrition, prevention of exposure to excess heat or cold, and rational productive use.

Hydrocele Hydrocele is the abnormal collection of various quantities of fluid between the visceral and parietal layers of the tunica vaginalis. The scrotal sacs become pendulous and increased in size. This condition can be due to an inflammatory or noninflammatory edema. Initial diagnosis is based on palpation of the scrotum and its content. The scrotum is not painful, the testes are usually free within the scrotal sac, and fluid can be isolated in one area. Confirmation is easily done by visualization of the fluid by ultrasonography of the scrotal sac. The nature of the fluid varies from anechoic (clear serous fluid) to slightly echoic (snowy). I have observed several cases of moderate hydrocele in old animals during the peak of the summer. The condition resolves progressively with decreasing ambient temperatures.

Hydrocele can develop following obstruction of normal blood flow in the spermatic cord. A case of hydrocele in a llama was attributed to the presence of an abscess in the area of the external inguinal ring. Long-standing hydrocele may affect the thermoregulation of the testes and decrease the quality and quantity of semen.

Orchitis Infectious conditions affecting the testicles in alpacas are relatively rare. Infectious orchitis may occasionally occur following septicemia. Treatment with systemic antibiotics may be attempted, but in most cases this treatment is not effective. Castration of the affected testicle in valuable males may increase the chance of salvaging the nonaffected testicle and the reproductive life of the animal.[2]

Testicular Tumors Testicular tumors are rarely reported in camelids. Reports of this pathology may increase in the future as more alpacas are kept in the herd for a long time. I am aware of three cases of seminomas in alpacas. Diagnosis of a testicular tumor is based on palpation and ultrasonographic and histopathological changes in the testicle.

Diseases of the Epididymis

There are very few reports of disease of the epididymis in camelids. Epididymal cysts have been reported in alpacas.[66] Cystic structures were found in 14.5 percent of slaughtered animals, mainly on the anterior portion of the head of the epididymis and near the ventral border of the testis. The majority of these cysts were 1 to 5 millimeters in diameter, although in one case the cyst was 50 millimeters.[66] Epididymal cysts may be due to segmental aplasia (lack of development) of the duct. In these cases, males will show oligozoospermia or azoospermia (little or no sperm cell production).

Diseases of the Accessory Glands

To date no diseases of the accessory sex glands have been described in alpacas. I have seen two cases of abnormally large prostates, but a definitive diagnosis of the cause of this enlargement was not possible. Both males were presented for persistent straining and dysuria. Both cases resolved spontaneously.

Behavioral Problems and Infertility of Unexplained Origin

Many other reproductive problems are reported in camelids, but their exact etiology is not known. Among the most commonly reported problems are lack or reduced libido, ejaculatory problems, and unexplained subfertility or infertility. Lack of libido may be associated with hormonal imbalance, high temperature, stress, age, and the presence of debilitating diseases. Substandard semen quality can be involved in male infertility, especially in overused or old

animals. However, in one case at our clinic, all seminal parameters were normal and yet no pregnancies could be obtained after mating. This suggests that other factors (immunological or genetic) may be involved in male infertility in camelids.

Aggressive behavior is associated with high testosterone. However, this trait is not correlated to fertility and may even hinder fertility in the long run. Aggressive behavior and female savaging is not a desirable trait and should be discouraged. Males should be selected for strong libido without overaggression. Techniques for behavioral modifications used in other species may be applied to reduce aggressive behavior in male alpacas.

EVALUATION OF THE MALE SEXUAL FUNCTION

The male breeding soundness examination (BSE) is an important part of the evaluation of herd infertility and decision making concerning selection or purchase of a herd sire. Unfortunately, little data are available on the incidence and types of infertility in male camelids. This is due in part to the lack of routine examinations of males under extensive management, and in part to the lack of standardization in many clinical examination procedures, especially semen collection and evaluation, which thus give variable results and make interpretation very difficult.[77,82]

Examination of the male alpaca should be conducted methodically to avoid the oversight of any problem that may affect reproductive performance. A complete breeding soundness examination should include the following:

- Identification of the animal
- History
- Detailed description of the reason(s) for examination
- General health examination
- Special examination of the genital system

The reasons for examination can generally be divided into two categories: examination for purchase or selection of a herd sire and examination for infertility or obvious genital lesions. It is important to define the problem in exact terms, such as the existence of visible lesions, the suspicion of infertility due to many unsuccessful matings, or a change in reproductive behavior (reduced libido). An approximate date of the onset of the problem should be obtained, as well as conditions surrounding the onset of the problem: Did the problem appear suddenly or was it a slow, progressive process?

SAMPLE FORM
Alpaca Male Breeding Soundness Evaluation

Case Number _____ Date _____

Name _____ Client _____

Registration number _____

Color_____ Address _____

Date of birth _____

Picture profile taken: _____ lateral _____ facial

History

Reason for evaluation: _____

Previous significant illness: _____

General Physical Exam

Temperature: _____ Pulse: _____ Respiration: _____

Body weight: _____ Body Condition Score: _____

External Genitalia

Prepuce: Normal _____ Abnormal _____

Penis: Free/detached _____ Preputial attachment _____ Abnormal _____

Scrotum: Normal _____ Abnormal _____

Testis:

Presence: Normal _____ Abnormal _____

Palpation: Normal _____ Abnormal _____

Size (right testis): Length (cm) _____ Width (cm) _____

Size (left testis): Length (cm) _____ Width (cm) _____

Ultrasound: Normal _____ Abnormal (Photos) _____

Sexual behavior (in presence of a receptive female)

Time from introduction to attempting to mount: _____

Time from introduction to mount: _____

Time from introduction to copulation (verify that penis is extended): _____

Length of copulation: _____

Source: Washington State University, Veterinary Teaching Hospital, Pullman, Washington 99164, USA.

Animal Identification and History

It is the responsibility of the veterinarian to identify the animal examined and to make adequate records for future reference. Many animal identification systems are used in alpacas (name, electronic ID). Electronic identification remains the best system, because it is unique and permanent. The increased interest in alpacas, especially in North America, Australia, New Zealand, and Europe, has led to the development of breed registries kept by various organizations. These organizations can be contacted to verify the identity and lineage of individual animals.

An animal's history is very important in establishing examination criteria and identifying potential problems. This history should cover at least the following: age, origin and type of management, breeding records, previous health problems, vaccinations, recent treatments, and the reason for examination.

Age is important in order to establish whether the animal is sexually mature or not. Problems such as inability to mount or exteriorize the penis, or even substandard fertility can be due to sexual immaturity. If the animal is registered, age is easily obtained from birth records that are included in registration certificates. In the absence of an accurate written record, the most common approach of estimating age is through evaluation of the teeth (see Chapter 15: On-Farm Assessment and Diagnosis). Guidelines have been published for aging alpacas.[20,29] They are helpful in giving a rough estimate of age, and can at least place the animal in one of three categories: young/immature, mature, and old.

Breeding history should include breeding management: free mating or hand mating, breeding frequency, and conception rate (number of pregnant/bred females).

Diseases of systems other than the genital tract can seriously affect the reproductive performance of the male. Lesions of the musculo-skeletal system can impair the physical ability of the male to copulate. Poor conformation or weakness of the hind legs may compromise the mating ability of the male alpaca. A prolonged fever or debilitating disease can seriously affect testicular function and spermatogenesis.

General Physical Examination

A general physical examination should be performed on all animals whenever they are presented for examination. First, the general appearance and body condition of the animal should be noted. During the sire selection process, particular attention should be given to the presence of congenital or potentially heritable conditions.[29] Each system should be thoroughly examined, with special attention to signs of contagious diseases and neuromuscular, vision, and locomotion problems. A sound musculoskeletal system is critical for a breeding male camelid because of the position and extreme strain during copulation. Complete blood cytology and biochemistry should be done on all recently introduced males. In addition, these animals should be quarantined or tested for major contagious diseases and parasites before introduction into the herd. Ideally, a breeding soundness evaluation should be done on all males before each breeding season and results reported in a clear form (see the sample form on the facing page).

Examination of the Genital Tract

It is desirable to conduct this examination in two steps: examination in the resting animal and examination during breeding. Examination of the genitalia includes inspection and palpation of the different parts of the external genitalia, ultrasonography of the testicles, behavioral evaluation, and semen evaluation.[79,81,82]

Examination of the Penis and Prepuce Detailed examination of the prepuce may require restraint or even sedation of the animal. This should be done when there is an obvious problem, such as an abnormally pendulous prepuce, presence of edema, or laceration. The first evaluation should establish whether or not the animal is able to exteriorize the penis. The penis is normally extended when the male assumes the breeding position, but full erection is completed intravaginally. Penile attachment to the prepuce is normal in young, prepuberal animals, but can signal the presence of adhesions in the mature male. The penis should be completely free at three years of age. Examination of the penis during copulation is difficult, but may be attempted in order to observe the erect organ. In the young male, preputial detachment can be verified by placing the male on his side and gently pushing the penis from the sigmoid flexure with one hand while the other closes the preputial orifice by pushing the prepuce toward the back. In the adult male, exteriorization of the penis requires sedation.

Examination of the Testis and Epididymis Examination of the testicles and epididymis includes inspection, palpation, measurement, and ultrasonography of the scrotum and its content. This examination can be completed when the male is restrained in a standing or sitting position. Both testes should be present and visible within the scrotum in the perineal region. In old males, the scrotum may sometimes be pendulous with a longer neck. One of the testicles is usually situated slightly lower than the other, but both should be nearly equal in size.

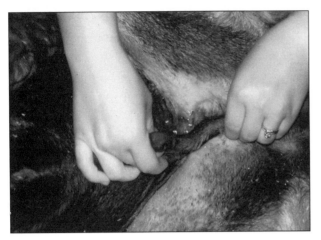

Examination of the prepuce by applying traction.

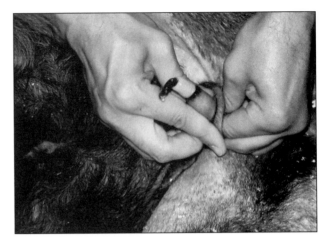

Exteriorization of the penis by pushing the sigmoid flexure and extending the penis.

Inspection and Palpation of the Scrotum The scrotal region is examined from a distance to evaluate the size and shape of the scrotal sacs, their symmetry, and integrity of the skin in the area. Palpation of the scrotum and its content allows the veterinarian to assess the regularity of the contour of the testicles as well as their consistency. Absence of visible testicles in the scrotum may be due to severe testicular degeneration, ectopic testicles, or cryptorchidism. The scrotal skin is thin and smooth, but can become thick and folded in older males, in males with testicular degeneration, and in cases of skin problems such as dermatitis or hyperkeratosis. The scrotum should be examined for bite wounds (by other males), insect bites, and tick infestation.

The testicles should be examined carefully if there is evidence of asymmetrical development. The surface of the testes should be smooth and regular. The testicles should be freely movable within the scrotal sac, resilient, and not painful or hot. The testicles become hard and fibrotic or very soft when there are degenerative changes. The scrotal sac should be free of large accumulations of fluid or obvious edema and thickening of the scrotal skin. The tail of the epididymis is palpable as a small, hard structure.

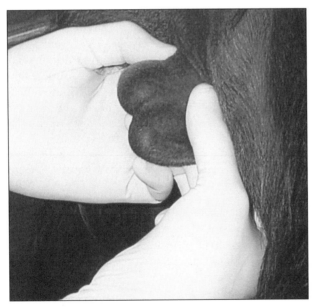

Examination of the testicles: palpation for consistency, mobility, and sensitivity.

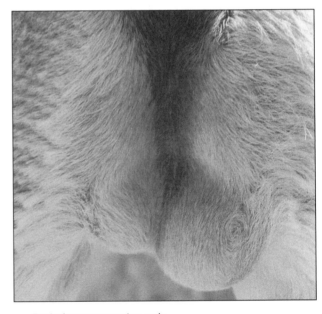

Testicular asymmetry in a male.

Testicular Measurements Testicular size is a very important indicator of sperm production ability and fertility.[11,71] Size of the testis can be evaluated by measuring its axis, the scrotal circumference, or the total scrotal diameter. These measurements can be obtained with precision calipers or by ultrasonography. Average testicular size for alpacas at various ages is reported in Table 12.1. The difference in size between the testicles should not be greater than 15 percent. Australian studies show that testicular length is highly correlated with body size, but there is a wide variation in testicular sizes among animals of the same age. Spermatogenesis was lower in animals with testicular length smaller than 30 millimeters,[31] so it is not recommended to use males with testicles less than this size. Measurements should be taken regularly (every four to six months) on all sires and potential herd sires to monitor testicular growth and potential problems.

Pathological changes affecting testicular size include orchitis, hematoma, or reduction in size due to hypoplasia or degenerative atrophy .[2,66,78,83]

Testicular Ultrasonography Ultrasonography can help to evaluate testicles as well as the surrounding tissues. Ultrasonographic examination of the scrotum and its content can be done on a standing animal. The scrotum is cleaned and a layer of coupling gel is applied to the area in order to have a good contact with the transducer. As an alternative to coupling gel, the probe can be fitted with a stand-off pad in order to provide maximum contact with the scrotum and avoid imaging problems. I prefer to use a 7.5 megahertz linear transducer to evaluate an alpaca scrotum.[74] The testicle is examined by placing the probe in a vertical position and sweeping it along the whole surface of the organ. The scan is repeated on the same testicle in the horizontal position. The image obtained shows a peripheral area of homogenous tissue corresponding to the testicles and a central more echogenic area corresponding to the fibrous mediastinum testis. Ultrasonographically visible lesions are of two natures: increased echogenicity (testicular fibrosis, with or without mineralization) and fluid-filled lesions.

Testicles lose their homogenous appearance in the presence of localized lesions such as cysts, fibrosis, or neoplasm. Increased echogenicity is usually due to degenerative changes. Testicular fibrosis consists of hyperechogenic and patchy scar-tissue areas with single or multifocal mineralized lesions. Fluid-filled ultrasonographic lesions are of four types: cysts, hydroceles (without circumscribing wall), abscesses, and sperm granulomas (with circumscribing wall). Accumulation of fluid in the testicular envelopes (hydrocele) is usually easy to identify because of the good contrast obtained between testicular parenchyma and the

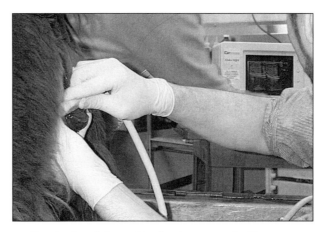

Examination of the testicles by ultrasonography. The transducer of the ultrasound machine is externally applied to the scrotum. This technique allows visualization of abnormalities that might otherwise go unnoticed.

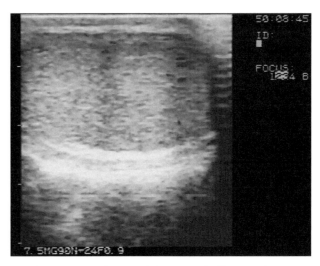

Ultrasonogram of a normal alpaca testicle. The testicular tissue looks grayish and homogenous, with the central part markedly more dense (the whitish line is more echogenic), which corresponds to the mediastinum of the testis.

fluid. Hydrocele is observed frequently and with varying degrees of intensity in heat-stressed camelids.

Over the past decade, I have seen numerous cases of intratesticular (mainly in mediastinum testis) cysts and epididymal cysts that may have been missed without the use of ultrasonography. These cysts are very significant in subfertility or infertility of the male camelid and may be associated with segmental aplasia of the epididymis. The size, number, and distribution of these cysts are variable. I have observed epididymal and mediastinal cysts in animals with poor semen concentration, with poor semen quality but normal concentration, and with complete azoospermia. Ultrasonography is very helpful in differentiating between hematoma, orchitis, and some testicular neoplasms.

In the case of localized lesions, the technique can be used to perform ultrasound-guided needle aspiration or biopsy.

Evaluation of Mating Ability

A male's mating ability is best observed in the presence of a receptive female. During this evaluation the succession of the normal behavioral pattern is recorded, as well as the times needed for each step: chasing, forcing down, mating, intromission, and duration of copulation. Behavioral problems at mating can be due to shyness, inexperience, or lack of libido. Young inexperienced males are particularly difficult to assess for mating ability. It is important that these males be presented to receptive females with good dispositions. A completely strange environment may inhibit sexual behavior in some males. Breeders use a wide range of stimulation techniques or positive reinforcement to encourage mating. One of these techniques is to let the male observe breeding by a more experienced male.

In my experience, most herd sires that are experienced have no problem performing as soon as they are presented to a female. Poor libido is a relatively uncommon complaint, but does exist. Loss of libido can be due to systemic illness, painful conditions, excessive use of hormones, and behavioral problems if several males are housed in the same area. Determination of the cause of poor libido can be very difficult and unrewarding in many cases.

Semen Collection

Several semen collection techniques described for other species have been modified and adapted to the male Camelidae with variable degrees of success. Semen collection in alpacas presents many difficulties, due mainly to the nature of their copulatory behavior and the slow (dribbling) process of ejaculation. The main techniques used nowadays for collection of semen in this species are with an artificial vagina (AV) or by electroejaculation. See the sample form on semen collection and evaluation on the facing page.

Semen Collection with an Artificial Vagina Successful collection of semen from alpacas by artificial vagina has been reported since the late 1960s.[23,69] Semen is collected using a dummy mount fitted with a collection apparatus or while the male is mounting a receptive female.[28] The dummy is made of a wooden frame mimicking the sitting position, covered with an alpaca hide.[7,32,73] Males are trained by getting them used to being touched on the penis in the presence of receptive females. When this phase is accomplished, they are trained to serve the dummy fitted with the artificial vagina by using a receptive female as a stimulus.[32] The artificial vagina is made of a PCV pipe (20–25 cm long and 4 cm in diameter) fitted with an inner lining, with annular constrictions to simulate the cervical rings (electrical cord coiled in a 2.5-cm band) in the female and stimulate ejaculation.[5,7,30] The outer chamber of the artificial vagina is filled with warm water and kept at 45°C during ejaculation and attached to the dorsal and lateral walls of the dummy.[32,60,69]

Various modifications have been made in the design of the artificial vagina. In some the inside of the AV cylinder is lined with a natural latex tube and sealed to the PVC pipe at both ends by means of elastic rubber bands. The AV chamber is filled with water at 40°C, and a polyethylene bag 8 centimeters wide and 30 centimeters long is placed to receive the semen sample.[28] This technique prevents direct contact with rubber and its effect on semen motility. One of the most challenging factors in semen collection with an AV is the ability to maintain the inside at alpaca body temperature (39±0.5°C) during the whole process of collection. Some authors have suggested covering the AV with high-density plastic foam as a thermal insulator or an electric blanket. Others maintain a constant flow of hot water through a peristaltic pump.[9]

Semen collection (presence of spermatozoa) is successful in 80 to 90 percent of the attempts using an artificial vagina. The average collection time varies between 18 to 20 minutes, but can range from 2.5 minutes to 30 minutes.[7,28]

Semen Collection by Electroejaculation Electroejaculation (EE) is an alternative method for semen collection in the Camelidae. The use of ram electroejaculators has been reported under various degrees of sedation or anesthesia in alpacas.[21,23] Response to the electrical stimulus is highly variable from one individual to another. Erection is possible, but failure to obtain an ejaculate or only a few sperm cells is common. In many cases, the ejaculate is of poor quality and contaminated with urine and cellular debris.

I prefer the technique in which a ram probe with a variable voltage of EE is used.[37] The animal is anesthetized with xylazine (0.3 mg/lb intravenously) or 10:1 ketamine: xylazine (for example, 2 mg/lb ketamine: 0.2 mg/lb xylazine, intramuscularly). The rectum is emptied of fecal material and thoroughly lubricated before insertion of the EE probe. The three electrodes of the rectal probe should face ventrally for stimulating the nerve supply for erection and ejaculation. To prevent gross contamination of the semen sample, grasp the penis and extend it out from the prepuce prior to ejaculation. When using fixed-voltage EE, try applying stimulation for four to six seconds followed by a four-second rest period, during which the accessory sex glands are massaged with the rectal probe. The EE technique does not work in all males. Electroejaculation is considered controversial by some experienced

SAMPLE FORM
Semen Collection and Evaluation

Method of collection: Artificial vagina ___   Electroejaculation ___   Vaginal aspiration ___

Semen parameters	First ejaculate	Second ejaculate	Third ejaculate
Volume (mL)			
Color			
Consistency			
Liquefaction time			
Motility (%)			
Concentration			
Morphology (%)			
Normal			
Pyriform heads			
Tapered heads			
Microcephalic			
Macrocephalic			
Detached heads			
Crater/Diadem			
Vacuolated			
Detached acrosome			
Knobbed acrosome			
Incomplete midpiece			
Coiled midpiece			
Proximal droplets			
Distal droplets			
Coiled tail			
Bent tail			
Medusa			
Spheroids			
WBC			

Diagnostic and Breeding Recommendations

Examination performed by Dr. _____

Source: Washington State University, Veterinary Teaching Hospital, Pullman, Washington 99164, USA.

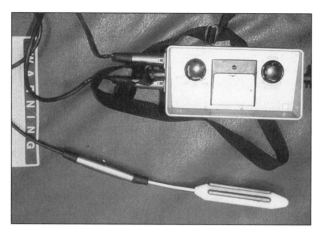

A typical electroejaculator for semen collection in alpacas. This technique needs to be done under general anesthesia.

Semen collection: aspiration of the semen from the vagina after coitus.

camelid veterinarians. It is not a procedure that should be undertaken lightly, and should only be attempted by a qualified veterinarian.

Other Methods of Semen Collection In practice, vaginal aspiration is the most commonly used technique for collecting alpaca semen. It is less stressful to the male than electroejaculation. The male is allowed to breed a receptive female. Upon completion of mating, a pipette is introduced deep into the vagina/uterus and fitted with a 12 milliliter syringe for the aspiration of seminal fluid. An alternative method is to use a speculum or vaginoscope to scoop the seminal fluid from the vagina. This method presents a major problem for determining the total volume and sperm count in the ejaculate. However, it is a simple and quick method to verify presence of semen, activity, and semen morphology.

Other techniques for semen collection yield variable results. They include the use of an intravaginal condom or sponges and vaginal aspiration[37,54,56,64] and even urethral fistulation.[42]

Semen Evaluation

Physical and biological characteristics of semen are determined following collection. These characteristics may be quite variable depending on the condition of the collection. See the sample form on semen collection and evaluation.

Volume Ejaculate volume ranges from 0.4 to 12.5 milliliters.[22,32,69] Ejaculates obtained by electrical stimulus are usually smaller in volume than ejaculates obtained by artificial vagina. Ejaculate volume does not vary significantly with repeated collection using the artificial vagina.[5,7,23,32,60,69] The volume of semen collected by postcoital aspiration may be very small (0.25–1 ml).

Color The color of alpaca semen varies according to sperm concentration. It is predominately milky white whether it is collected by electroejaculation[23] or by artificial vagina.[28,32,60] It can sometimes be creamy white[32] and in a smaller proportion yellowish.[28] Seminal plasma and sperm cells represent respectively 88.5 percent and 11.5 percent, of the ejaculate with no significant differences among ages.[32] Ejaculate may be heterogeneous with some translucent material mixed with cloudy areas. Semen collected using postcoital vaginal aspiration method may be pinkish to red due to contamination with blood.

Consistency and Liquefaction One of the main physical characteristics of camelid semen is its high viscosity, which makes it very difficult to manipulate (pipetting, preparation of slide) and mix with extenders.[32,52] The degree of viscosity depends on the individual male and on the proportion of seminal gelatinous fluid, and tends to decrease with the number of ejaculations. Ejaculates collected with the artificial vagina method are generally frothy.

Liquefaction may happen to some degree after incubation at 39°C. However, some ejaculates may not liquefy completely until 23±1.2 hours (range 8–48 hours).[32,45] The viscosity of semen and the time required for liquefaction vary from one male to another and from one ejaculate to another. The viscosity of alpaca semen collected by artificial vagina tends to decrease on the third ejaculate.[5] The viscosity of the semen is usually attributed to the presence of mucopolysaccharides from secretions of the bulbourethral glands or the prostate.[32] The physiological role of this semen characteristic is not clear. Liquefaction of alpaca semen can be obtained by adding enzymes such as trypsin or collagenase to the ejaculate. The fertility of semen, liquefied in this manner and used for artificial insemination, remained normal.[10]

Sperm Concentration Concentration of semen is estimated using a hemocytometer technique. The semen sample is diluted 1:100 or 1:200 in a buffered formol saline solution using a standard red blood cell dilution pipette. The total number in the ejaculate can be measured by a commercial WBC (white blood cell) Unopette system (Becton Dickinson, Rutherford, NJ). The semen is drawn up into the capillary pipette (20μL) provided with the kit and dispenses it into the second diluent container according to kit instructions. This technique works best when the semen is totally liquefied.

In nonliquefied semen, the sample is not homogenous and clumping may occur, making the sperm cell counting difficult and estimation of concentration erroneous. The diluted semen is loaded into the two counting chambers of the hemocytometer and sperm are counted under the microscope (×10). The number of sperm in the center 1-millimeter square equals the number of million sperm per milliliter in the ejaculate. Other rapid methods for determining sperm concentration include using an electronic blood cell counter and a spectrophotometer. A great variability in the concentration of ejaculates is reported in the literature. Reported sperm cell numbers per milliliter of ejaculate range from 2 to 250 million and is affected by age, method of collection, and ejaculate rank.[5,7,8,23,28,68]

pH The pH of semen is between 7.5 and 8.0.[5,42] In a study on llamas, the pH of semen collected by artificial vagina did not differ significantly in fractions taken at different moments of the copulation.[47] This is probably due to the fact that camelid ejaculate is not emitted in distinct fractions.

Biochemical Components The biochemical composition of alpaca semen is similar to that reported for other species. Chloride is the main anion and calcium the main cation.[32] These electrolytes could be of importance in the biology of the sperm cell (motility, capacitation). Glucose is found in high concentration in the seminal plasma and could be the main substrate for energy.[33] Glucose concentrations are higher in younger animals than in adult males.[32,33]

Other components of semen such as lipids, phospholipids, and proteins have been quantified in the seminal plasma of the alpaca.[32] Their function has not yet been studied in these species, but they certainly play a role in maturation and protection of sperm cell membrane integrity (prevention of cold shock). Proteins give protection to spermatozoa against harmful effects of high dilution.[32] An ovulation-inducing factor may be present in alpaca semen.[58]

Semen Motility Semen motility is usually evaluated on undiluted samples (mass activity) and on diluted samples (individual sperm motility). Mass motion depends upon sperm concentration, percentage of progressively motile sperm, and the speed of sperm progression. Mass activity is ascertained by rating the intensity of swirling motion.[32] Mass activity is generally poor in camelid semen unless the ejaculate is constituted exclusively by the sperm-rich fraction.[22,32]

Individual sperm motility is estimated by placing a drop of semen diluted in a citrate buffer or other suitable semen extender on a prewarmed glass slide and examining the slide under a cover slip at ×40 power. Initial motility is very low (5%) and increases as the ejaculate becomes more fluid. Progressive motility, as observed in other species, is very difficult to appreciate because of the viscous nature of semen. Individual motility ranges from 20 to 95 percent in llamas and alpacas.[5,7,47]

The motility of spermatozoa can be objectively determined using a computerized semen motion analyzer. Although this new method has been thoroughly investigated and proven to be valuable in many domestic species,[77] its use in camelids is limited due to the difficulty in preparing semen samples and the low sperm motility due to its gelatinous nature. In our laboratory, we have established that this technique can be used accurately when semen are completely liquefied and diluted. In addition to the percentage of motility, computerized semen analysis offers the advantage of electronically determining the sperm concentration in the ejaculate and the morphology of the head as well as other motion characteristics.[77] These parameters can be valuable for the objective evaluation of different treatments, such as the effects of freezing, extenders, and in-vitro capacitation treatments. The accuracy of the technique largely depends on the calibration (setup) of the machine and on the purity of the extender.

Semen Morphology The mature sperm of alpacas consists of a head, midpiece, and tail. The total length of the camelid sperm cell is smaller than that of the bull, buffalo, ram, ass, and stallion, but larger than that of the boar.[75]

The head of camelid spermatozoa is described as elliptical as opposed to ovoid. Lengths of the head and midpiece of the camelid spermatozoon are shorter than those of other animals, while the tail is longer than that of the boar and stallion spermatozoa and shorter than all others.[52] Head size and morphology may vary. In one study, 50 percent of the sperm cells in the ejaculate had normal head sizes, 26 percent had small heads, and 24 percent had large heads.[12]

Spermatozoa morphology can be evaluated by stained smears. Two staining techniques are commonly used: eosine-nigrosin and Diff Quick (Giemsa) stains. Diff Quick staining is done on a dried smear prepared from liquefied, diluted semen. The smears are observed under a phase-contrast microscope at high magnification (×100 oil). A total of at least 200 sperm cells from different fields should be evaluated for each sample. Morphological evaluation is done according to the parameter given for other species. The morphological abnormalities should be reported according to type and location.

All sperm abnormalities found in other livestock species can be found in alpaca semen. These include abnormalities of the head, midpiece, and tail, and proximal and distal droplets. The effects of these types of abnormalities on fertility have not yet been determined. Most of the ejaculates collected from fertile males have fewer than 30 percent total abnormalities. The incidence of abnormal heads, cytoplasmic droplets, and abnormal tails and midpiece are 9 to 12 percent, 3 to 9 percent, and 14 to 25 percent, respectively. Midpiece defects seem to be more prevalent in alpacas than in other species. The incidence of abnormalities is not affected by the rank of ejaculate.[5,8] Incidence of cytoplasmic droplet in alpacas between 15 and 20 months of age can be as high as 90 percent.* Ejaculates collected from fertile males after 45 to 90 days of sexual rest may contain up to 50 percent abnormal sperm cells.[12,28] Various abnormalities of alpaca sperm are presented in Figure 12.4.

The major problem in interpreting semen analysis in the Camelidae is the lack of standard methods, not only for collection but also for examination. A thorough investigation on the best methodology for semen collection from alpacas and the physiological and pathological factors that may affect semen quality is greatly needed before a sound evaluation methodology can be recommended for implementation. Some of the physiological factors that may affect quantity and quality of semen, such as age, nutritional status, and season, need to be critically evaluated. The study of these factors will allow clinicians to make recommendations concerning the frequency of use of a male based on clinical examination.

OTHER METHODS OF INVESTIGATING MALE INFERTILITY

Hormonal Analysis

Thorough studies are lacking on the use of endocrinological evaluations of male alpacas to diagnose fertility and subfertility. A few researchers have used plasma testosterone changes after hCG (human chorionic gonadotropin) injection to differentiate between gelded and cryptorchid males.

*A. Tibary, unpublished.

Testicular Biopsy

A testicular biopsy is not a routine procedure for the evaluation of breeding soundness in the male. However, in some cases a diagnosis or prognosis of male fertility cannot be reached solely on the basis of physical examination, ultrasonography, and semen evaluation. This is particularly true for camelids, in which semen collection is very difficult and gives inconsistent results. A testicular biopsy should be considered in males that have low fertility, testicular asymmetry, or an abnormal testicular ultrasonography not consistent with hematoma or orchitis. This technique is useful for the diagnosis of spermatogenic arrest, oligospermatogenesis, hypogonadism, and neoplasm.

Experimentation with different biopsy techniques and their long-term effects on testicular tissue showed that the surgical wedge biopsy technique was not desirable since it is hard to perform and can cause bulging of testicular tissue because of the incision in the tunic. Wedge biopsy is deemed to be unsafe because it is associated with complications such as hematoma, hemorrhage, adhesions, inflammation, autoimmune reactions, and degeneration of germinal epithelium and tubules. Also, a biopsy may cause a transient decrease in sperm output that lasts for several months.

The fine-needle aspiration technique is preferred because it is easy to administer, but samples are difficult to interpret.[38,74] A testicular biopsy using a fine-needle aspirate or a self-firing 14-gauge instrument was found to be safe in llamas.[36]

Fine-needle aspirate cytology is a commonly used technique for the evaluation of azoospermia and testicular neoplasm in humans. It is rapid, simple, and inexpensive. Cytological smears are interpreted based on the different types of spermatogenic cells. The relative frequency of types of cells can allow the differentiation between hypospermatogenesis, spermatogenic arrest, and normal spermatogenesis. Also, the fine-needle aspirate does not have long-term effects.[74]

I recently conducted a preliminary study at Washington State University on samples from 12 normal (5 to 9 years of age) and 8 abnormal (2 azoospermic, 1 oligospermic, 3 with questionable infertility, and 2 atrophic testicles) animals. All animals were subjected to a Trucut and a fine-needle aspirate before castration, after general anesthesia.[74]

The needle aspiration technique used is similar to that common for dogs. After anesthesia and surgical preparation, the testicles are aspirated with a 20-gram needle and 12 milliliter syringe. A midline puncture is made and constant suction aspirates are taken in three to four directions, making sure not to include the epididymis. The

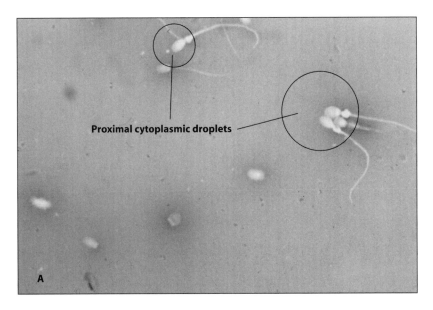

A

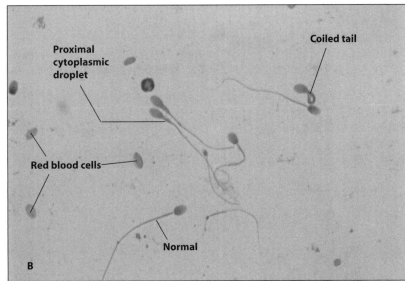

Proximal cytoplasmic droplets

Proximal
cytoplasmic
droplet

Coiled tail

Red blood cells

Normal

B

Figure 12.4 Normal spermatozoa and various semen abnormalities.

A Sample sperm cell shows proximal cytoplasmic droplets from a young male (cytoplasmic droplets are typical for immature sperm). Proximal droplets appear as a "blob" just behind the head of the spermatozoa.

B and **C** Note the presence of red blood cells, which is normal for samples collected by postcoital vaginal aspiration. Untrained persons may mistake red blood cells for detached sperm heads because they look very similar.

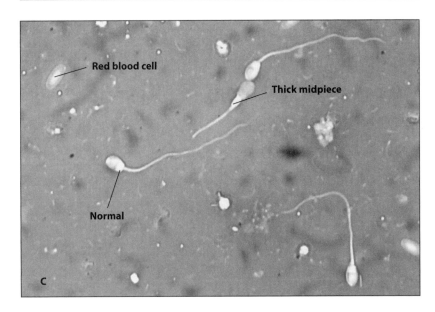

Red blood cell

Thick midpiece

Normal

C

whole aspirate is smeared onto a microscope slide, air dried, and stained with Diff Quick stain.

This technique has some major flaws, particularly the difficulty in obtaining a sufficient amount of material for cytological examination in cases of severe degenerative changes. The amount of aspirate material obtained depends on the consistency of the testicles. Very low cell population is obtained when the testicles are soft or hard. Twenty-five percent of the samples obtained are not satisfactory.

Trucut biopsies were performed according to a technique used for dogs. After general anesthesia and surgical preparation of the testicles, the scrotum is incised using a sterile #10 surgical steel blade. The Trucut biopsy needle is inserted in the testicle through the tunica albuginea. The scrotum is closed with two skin sutures using 2-0 Vetafil. Results obtained with this technique are more reliable, but hemorrhage at the biopsy site is more frequent.

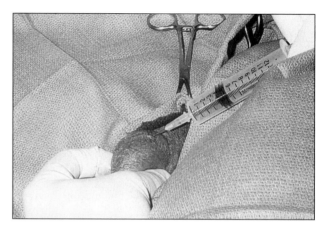

Technique for testicular biopsy by fine-needle aspiration.

SEMEN PRESERVATION AND ARTIFICIAL INSEMINATION IN THE ALPACA

Artificial insemination (AI) is a technique that has been used to bring about rapid genetic change in different forms of livestock. The use of artificial insemination in alpacas has been reported since the late 1960s.[13,21] Since their creation in the 1980s, the llama and alpaca registries in North America have not allowed the registration of animals conceived by artificial insemination (see Chapter 27: Maintaining a DNA Registry for the Good of the Breed).

Semen Preservation Technology in Camelids

Semen is usually used immediately after collection or after dilution. The use of undiluted semen offers medical advantages in breeding difficult females, young females with narrow or small genital tracts, and females with behavioral problems. It is also used to eliminate behavioral problems and size incompatibility due to interspecies crossbreeding (vicuña with alpaca). More efficient use of artificial insemination requires dilution of the ejaculate and its preservation. Diluted semen can be used within minutes (fresh), after short-term preservation (a few hours), or after long-term preservation (months or years).

Short-term Semen Preservation Short-term preservation (a few hours) of camelid semen has been attempted at different temperatures (25°C, 30°C, or 4°C). Semen is collected by electroejaculation, artificial vagina, or flushing of the epididymis with heat-treated milk. Several extenders are used to dilute freshly collected semen (skim milk, sodium-citrate-EY, lactose egg yolk).[75] Most of these ex-

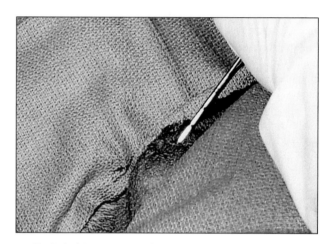

Testicular biopsy, trucut technique.

tenders are adapted from studies in other species and contain a buffering system, a source of energy (glucose or fructose), and a protein for protection against cold shock such as lipoprotein from egg yolk or casein from milk. There are no studies concerning the effects of physical and chemical proprieties (i.e., pH, ionic strength, and osmotic pressure) of the extender on the motility and fertilizing ability of preserved semen. Studies on llama and alpaca semen showed that egg yolk-citrate is a suitable extender for short-term preservation in these species. Tris-citric acid-fructose extender was used successfully for insemination with fresh semen in llamas.[1]

Cryopreservation of Alpaca Semen Cryopresevation of camelid semen has been used successfully for over three decades.[35] A variety of extenders used for deep freezing semen from other species have been adapted to camelid semen. The cryoprotectant of choice is glycerol (3–7%). Llama and alpaca semen have been frozen in tris-egg-yolk-glycerol or sodium citrate-egg yolk-glycerol.[35,50] Dilution rates of semen vary from 1 to 1:8 (semen: extender) in the llama.[35]

The freezing procedure depends on the packaging method used. Semen can be packaged as pellets in plastic straws with different volumes (0.25 ml, 0.5 ml). Llama and alpaca semen have been frozen successfully using a technique similar to that used for bull semen. Semen is collected by artificial vagina and liquefied by collagenase treatment in sodium citrate-egg yolk. Semen is extended with the same extender containing 7 percent glycerol, then loaded in 0.25 milliliter straws and frozen in liquid nitrogen vapors after two hours' equilibration at 4°C.[4]

Thawing rates vary according to the packaging technique used. Pellets are usually thawed by dropping them into heated receptacles or by mixing them in a warm thawing extender. Small straws are thawed in a water bath at 37°C for 30 to 40 seconds or 40°C for 8 seconds. Semen from llama frozen in pellets and thawed in warm extender showed 45 percent postthaw motility (prefreezing motility 50%). The motility of frozen semen remains acceptable even after eight years of storage. Factors that influence the quality of camelid semen after freezing and thawing have not been yet thoroughly investigated. There is a large male-to-male variation in postthaw motility.

Artificial Insemination (AI)

Successful insemination depends on timing, site of semen deposition, and quality and quantity of semen. Ovulation in camelids is induced by copulation and semen deposition in the female genital tract. The best alternative is to inseminate at known intervals following the induction of ovulation by hormonal treatment (hCG, GnRH). Behavioral signs of estrus should be combined with ultrasound assessment of follicular activity before insemination. AI is generally performed 35 to 45 hours after inducing ovulation with GnRH, hCG, or a vasectomized male.[6] The conception rate decreases if insemination is performed less than 24 hours or more than 48 hours after treatment. In llamas, the conception rate is higher in females inseminated 24 hours after the injection of GnRH (40%) than those inseminated twice at 24 and 48 hours (13.6%) or once at 48 hours (20.0%). However, the overall pregnancy rate after AI is lower compared to natural service.[1]

Semen is deposited into the uterus using an AI gun or a pipette. In alpacas, the method of choice for AI is direct deposition of semen inside the uterus using a vaginoscope. The rectovaginal method is possible in llamas.[1,14] Semen is deposited in the uterine body or deep into the uterine horns. Although some veterinarians prefer to place semen in the horn ipsilateral to the side of ovulation, this may not be critical for the success of AI. I believe that semen should be deposited deep inside the horn because the body of the uterus is very small. Laparoscopic insemination has been tried on alpacas, but did not result in higher conception rates compared to cervical insemination.[7]

Pregnancy rates following AI with fresh unextended or extended semen vary from 12 to 75 percent (see Table 12. 2). The deposition of semen by rectovaginal manipulation resulted in a pregnancy rate of 38 percent. Fertilization rates are highest when insemination is carried out 35 to 45 hours after treatment for the induction of ovulation (breeding to vasectomized males or injection of hCG (500–1,000 IU iv or im) or GnRH (50 μg im).[24] No difference in the conception rate has been observed between alpacas inseminated with cervical methods and those inseminated by laparoscopy.[7] No study has been conducted to determine the minimal number of spermatozoa to be used for insemination in camelids. In alpacas, conception has been achieved following AI of 8 million sperm cells.[7]

There are few reports on AI with frozen-thawed lamoid semen. Pregnancy rates with frozen-thawed semen in South American camelids vary from 25 to 70 percent. In one trial, insemination of 19 females with semen frozen in

Table 12.2 Artificial insemination trials with fresh semen in camelids.

Extender	Method*	Site	Timing	Fertility % (n)	Ref.
PBS	C	Uterine body + uterus	After teaser male	40 (133)	[16]
None	C	Uterine body + uterus	Immediately or 18 hours after hCG	12.5	[14]
None	C	Uterine body + uterus	35 and 45 hours after hCG	75	[14]
None	C	Uterine body + uterus	52 hours after hCG	58.3	[14]
None	C	Uterus	hCG immediately following AI	66.7	[7]
None	L	Uterus, ipsilateral to follicle	hCG immediately following AI	72.7	[7]
Egg yolk-citrate	C	Deep uterus	After hCG	57 (80)	[61]

*Method : RV= rectovaginal, C= cervical, L = Laparoscopic.

sodium citrate-egg yolk-glycerol (0.25 ml straw) resulted in five pregnancies.[4]

Further research is needed in the area of semen physiology to determine the best conditions for freezing and utilizing frozen-thawed semen with conception rates approaching those of natural mating.

Interspecies Insemination

Because of the close phylogeny of different species of camelids, interbreeding is possible. Cross-species insemination has been performed for a long time in South America (see Table 12.3). Studies using vicuña semen and paco-vicuña semen with female alpacas and llamas have yielded variable results.[21,44] A pregnancy rate of 2.3 percent was obtained in alpacas following intracervical insemination with vicuña semen. This low fertility rate was explained by the poor quality of the semen used.[21,24] In general, conception rates and embryonic survival are low. In recent years, interspecies breeding between the Old World camelid (dromedary in particular) and New World camelid (guanaco and llama) has been attempted successfully using artificial insemination (see Chapter 1: Classification, Prehistory, and History).

Table 12.3 Hybrid species obtained by artificial insemination in camelids.

Male Species*	Female Species*	Cross	Fertility of the Cross
V. pacos	L. glama	Misti	Yes
V. pacos	V. vicugna	Paco-vicuña	Yes
V. pacos	L. guanacoe	Paco-guanaco	??
L. glama	V. pacos	Huarizo or pacocha	Yes
L. glama	V. vicugna	Llamo-vicuña	Yes
L. glama	L. guanacoe	Llamo-guanaco	Yes
L. guanacoe	V. vicugna	Guanaco-vicuña	??
L. guanacoe	C. dromedarius	**	
C. dromedarius	L. guanacoe	Cama***	??
C. dromedarius	C. bactrianus		low
C. bactrianus	C. dromedarius		low

*Species: V.=Vicugna; L.=Lama; C.=Camelus.

**2 pregnancies resulted from 50 inseminations of 30 females, one aborted at 260 days, and one had a stillborn female at 365 days.

***6 pregnancies in 9 females inseminated a total of 34 times. Two reabsorbed at 25 and 40 days, two female fetuses aborted at 291 and 302 days, one female was stillborn at 365 days. One premature male (328 days) is still alive.

Source: Tibary, A. *Semen Preservation in Camelids* (reference 75).

Males on the lookout on the altiplano.

GLOSSARY

atrophy Reduction in size generally due to degenerating tissue.

azoospermia Absence of spermatozoa in the ejaculate.

caudo-dorsally Backward in high position.

dermatitis Skin inflammation.

dysuria Abnormal urination (difficulty in urinating or dribbling of urine).

ectopic testicles Testicles that are not located in the normal anatomical area.

epididymis Tubelike structure that collects sperm cells from testicles. Sperm cells are matured and stored in the epididymis.

hair rings Hair from the tail of a female may become wrapped around the penis, forming rings that may lead to traumatic injury and inflammation of the surface of the organ.

hematoma Blood clot.

histological From histology, describing cellular arrangement of a tissue.

hyperkeratosis Skin thickening.

hypoplasia Low development.

inguinal Region of the groin, high inner thighs.

intromission Penetration into the vagina.

oligospermia Low volume of ejaculate.

oligozoospermia Low sperm count in the ejaculate.

orchitis Inflammation of a testicle.

ovoid Egg shaped.

mediastinum testis Central core of the testicle.

parenchyma The tissue forming the organ.

prepuce Foreskin.

preputial orifice Opening of the prepuce.

process Extension of an organ.

seminoma Special testicular tumors affecting the germinal tissue.

septicemia Dissemination of bacteria in the general blood circulation.

tunica vaginalis Envelope of the testicle that has two layers: an inner layer called visceral and an outer layer called parietal.

urolithiasis Urinary stones, also known as urinary calculi.

REFERENCES

1. Aller, J. F., et al.: Semen Collection in Llamas *(Lama glama)* from the Argentinian Puna. *Veterinaria Argentina* 14(132): 104–107, 1997.
2. Aubry, P., et al.: Septic Orchitis in an Alpaca. *Canadian Veterinary Journal* 41: 704–706, 2000.
3. Bravo, P. W., and L. W. Johnson: Reproductive physiology of the male camelid. *Veterinary Clinics of North American, Food Animal Practice* 10(2): 259–264, 1994.
4. Bravo, P. W., C. Ordonez, and V. Alarcon: Semen Processing and Freezing in Llamas and Alpacas. Proceedings of 13th International Congress on Animal Reproduction, Sydney, Australia, 1996.
5. Bravo, P. W., D. Flores, and C. Ordonez: Effect of Repeated Collection on Semen Characteristics of Alpacas. *Biology of Reproduction,* 57(3): 520–524, 1997.
6. Bravo, P. W., J. A. Skidmore, and X. X. Zhao: Reproductive aspects and storage of semen in Camelidae. *Animal Reproduction Science* 62(1–3): 173–193, 2000.
7. Bravo, P. W., et al.: Collection of Semen and Artificial-Insemination of Alpacas. *Theriogenology* 47(3): 619–626, 1997.
8. Bravo, P. W., et al.: Fertility of the Male Alpaca—Effect of Daily Consecutive Breeding. *Animal Reproduction Science* 46(3–4): 305–312, 1997.
9. Bravo, P. W., et al.: Ejaculatory Process and Related Semen Characteristics. *Archives of Andrology* 48(1): 65–72, 2002.
10. Bravo, P. W., et al.: Degelification of Alpaca Semen and the Effect of Dilution Rates on Artificial Insemination Outcome. *Archives of Andrology* 43(3): 239–246, 1999.
11. Bravo, P. W.: Relationship Between Testicular Size and Fertility. *Alpaca Registry Journal* 1(1): 45–46, 1996.
12. Buendia, P., et al.: Morphometric Characterization and Classification of Alpaca Sperm Heads Using the Sperm-Class Analyzer® Computer-Assisted System. *Theriogenology* 57(4): 1,207–1,218, 2002.
13. Calderon, W., K. Sumar, and E. Franco: Advances en la inseminacion de las alpacas. *Revista de la Facultad de Medicina Veterinaria* (Lima) 22: 19–35, 1965.
14. Calderon, W., K. Sumar, and E. Franco: Advances en la inseminacion de las alpacas. *Revista de la Facultad de Medicina Veterinaria* (Lima) 22: 19–35, 1968.
15. Collazos, V. G. D.: Estudio de la irrigacion superficial del pene y prepucio de la alpaca, *Lama pacos.* B.S. Thesis, Facul-

tad de Medicina Veterinaria. Universidad Nacional Mayor de San Marcos, Lima, pp. 1–20, 1972.

16. De la Vega, A.: Effecto de la concentration espermatica y la hora de insemination artificial con semen fresco sobre el porcentaje de gestation en alpacas. MVZ Thesis, Facultad de Medicina Veterinaria. Universidad Nacional, Altiplano, Peru, 54 pp., 1996.

17. Delhon, G., I. V. Lawzewitsch, and I. Von Lawzewitsch: Ductus epididymidis Compartments and Morphology of Epididymal Spermatozoa in Llamas. *Anatomia Histologia Embryologia* 23(3): 217–225, 1994.

18. Delhon, G., et al.: Estudio citologico de las gonadas de guanaco *Lama guanicoe*, Macho, en las estudios prepuperales, sexualmente maduros y seniles. *Rev. Fac. Cienc. Vet.*, 1(1): 47–60, 1983.

19. Delhon, G. A., and I. von Lawzewitsch: Reproduction in the Male Llama *(Lama glama)*, a South American Camelid. I. Spermatogenesis and organization of the intertubular space of the mature testis. *Acta Antiqua Academiae Scientiarum Hungaricae,* 129(1): 59–66, 1987.

20. Escobar, R. C.: *Animal Breeding and Production of American Camelids.* Lima, Peru: Talleres Graficos de ABRIL, 1984.

21. Fernandez-Baca, S.: Inseminacion artificial en alpacas y vicuñas. *Bol. Extraordinario* 1:104–105, 1966.

22. Fernandez-Baca, S., and W. Calderon V.: Metodos de coleccion de semen de la alpaca. *Revista de la Facultad de Medicina Veterinaria* (Lima) 18–20: 13–26, 1963–66.

23. Fernandez-Baca, S., and W. Calderon: Metodos de coleccion de semen de la alpaca. Annale Universidad Nacional Mayor de San Marcos Facultad de Medicina Veterinaria 9:18–20, 1966.

24. Fernandez-Baca, S., and W. Calderon: Primer ensayo de inseminacion artificial de alpacas (Lama pacos) con semen de vicuñas *(Vicugna vicugna) Revista de la Facultad de Medicina Veterinaria,* Universidad Nacional Mayor de San Marcos, (Lima, Peru) 22: 9, 1968.

25. Fernandez-Baca, S., D. H. L. Madden, and C. Novoa: Effect of Different Mating Stimuli on Induction of Ovulation in the Alpaca. *Journal of Reproduction and Fertility,* 22(2): 261–267, 1970.

26. Fernandez-Baca, S., C. Novoa, and J. Sumar: Actividad reproductiva en la alpaca mantenida en separacion del macho (Alpaca reproductive activity maintained separate from the male). Assoc. Latinoamericana de Produccion Animal. Memorias, 7:7–18, 1972.

27. Flores, F. R. F.: *Estudio histologico del testiculo de alpacas aparentemente inaptas para la reproduccion.* B.S. Thesis, Facultad de Medicina Veterinaria, Universidad Nacional Mayor de San Marcos, Lima, pp. 1–29, 1970.

28. Flores, P., et al.: Alpaca Semen Characteristics Previous to a Mating Period. *Animal Reproduction Science* 72: 259–266, 2002.

29. Fowler, M. E.: *Medicine and Surgery of South American Camelids: Llama, Alpaca, Vicuña, Guanaco,* 2nd ed. Ames: Iowa State University Press, 1998.

30. Franco, E., J. Sumar, and M. Varela: *Eyaculacion en la alpaca (Lama pacos).* Proc. IVth Int. Conf. South American Camelids, Punta Arenas, Chile, 1981.

31. Galloway, D. B.: *The Development of the Testicles in Alpacas in Australia.* Proceedings of Australian Alpaca Association National Conference, pp. 21–23, 2000.

32. Garnica, J., R. Achata, and P. W. Bravo: Physical and Biochemical Characteristics of Alpaca Semen. *Animal Reproduction Science* 32: 85–90, 1993.

33. Garnica, J., E. Flores, and P. W. Bravo: Citric Acid and Fructose Concentrations in Seminal Plasma of the Alpaca. *Small Ruminant Research* 18(1): 95–98, 1995.

34. Gauly, M.: Seasonal Changes in Semen Characters and Serum Concentrations of Testosterone, Oestradiol-17beta, Thyroxine and Triiodothyronine in Male Llamas *(Lama glama)* in Central Europe. *Journal of Camel Practice and Research* 163(147), 1997.

35. Graham, E.F., et al.: Semen Preservation in Non-Domestic Mammals. Syp. Zool. Soc. Lond., 1978(43): 153–173, 1978.

36. Heath, A. M., et al.: Evaluation of the Safety and Efficacy of Testicular Biopsies in Llamas. *Theriogenology* 58: 1125–1130, 2002.

37. Johnson, L. W.: Llama Reproduction. *Veterinary Clinics of North America, Food Animal Practice* 5(1): 159–182, 1989.

38. Johnson, L. W., and M. E. Fowler: *Infertility Evaluation in Llamas and Alpacas.* Zoo and Wild Animal Medicine, 1993.

39. Johnson, L. W., and P. C. Schultheiss: *Results of Testicular Biopsies in Llamas.* In Symposium on the Health and Disease of Small Ruminants. Kansas City, Missouri, 1994.

40. Kingston, J., and H. Staempfli: Silica Urolithiasis in a Male Llama. *Canadian Veterinary Journal* 36(12): 767–768, 1995.

41. Koch, M. D., and M. E. Fowler: Urolithiasis in a Three-Month-Old Llama. *Journal of the American Veterinary Medical Association* 181: 1,411, 1982.

42. Kubicek, J.: Samentnahme beim Alpaca durch eine Harnrohrenfistel (Semen collection in alpaca with an urethral fistula). *Zeitschrift fur Tierzuchtung und Zuechtungsbiologie* 90: 335–351, 1974.

43. Lane, D.: Preputial Prolapse in an Alpaca. *Canadian Veterinary Journal* 40(4): 260, 1999.

44. Leyva, V., E. Franco, and J. Sumar: *Artificial Insemination in South American Camelids.* I. Resion. Assoc. Per Prod. Anim. (APPA), Lima, Peru, 1977.

45. Leyva, V., J. Sumar, and E. Franco: *Estudio preliminar de la concentracion de espermatozoides del semen de alpaca obtenido con vagina artificial.* Proc. VIII Reunion Cientifica Anual del APPA, Huancayo, Peru, 35 pp., 1984.

46. Lichtenwalner, A. B., G. L. Woods, and J. A. Weber: Ejaculatory Pattern of Llamas During Copulation. *Theriogenology* 46(2): 285–291, 1996.

47. Lichtenwalner, A. B., G. L. Woods, and J. A. Weber: Seminal Collection, Seminal Characteristics and Pattern of Ejaculation in Llamas. *Theriogenology* 46(2): 293–305, 1996.

48. Lichtenwalner, A. B., G. L. Woods, and J. A. Weber: Pattern of Emission During Copulation in Male Llamas. *Biology of Reproduction* 56: 298–298, 1997.

49. Losno, W., and J. Coyotupa, *Testosterona serica en alpacas macho prepuberes.* Res. Proyectos de Investigacion, Periodo 1975–1979, Universidad Nacional Mayor de San Marcos, Lima, Peru, p. 116, 1979.

50. McEvoy, T. G., et al.: Collection, Evaluation and Cryopreservation of Llama Semen. *Journal of Reproduction and Fertility,* 9 abstract 81, 1992.

51. McLaughlin, B.G., and N.C. Evans: Urethral Obstruction in a Male Llama. *Journal of the American Veterinary Medical Association* 195(11): 1,601–1,602, 1989.

52. Merlian, C. P., et al.: Comparative Characteristics of Spermatozoa and Semen from a Bactrian Camel, Dromedary Camel and Llama. *Journal of Zoo Animal Medicine* 10: 22–25, 1986.

53. Middleton, J. R., and S. M. Parish: Heat Stress in a Llama *(Lama glama)*: A Case Report and Review of the Syndrome. *Journal of Camel Practice and Research* 6(2): 265–269, 1999.

54. Mogrovejo, S. D.: *Estudios del semen de la alpaca.* B.S. Thesis, Facultad de Medicina Veterinaria, Universidad Nacional Mayor de San Marcos, Lima, 1952.

55. Montalvo, C., E. Cevallos, and M. Copaira: *Estudio microscopico del parenquima testicular de la alpaca durante las estaciones del ano.* Res. Proyectos de Investigacion, Periodo 1975–1979, Universidad Nacional Mayor de San Marcos, Lima, p. 37, 1979.

56. Neely, D. P.: *Reproductive Aspects of the Male Llama.* Proceedings 4th Hudson-Walker Theriogenology Conference, pp. 29–37, 1993.

57. Pacheco Ibanez, O.: *Biopsia testicular en alpacas.* B.S. Thesis, Facultad de Medicina Veterinaria, Universidad Nacional Tec. Altiplano, Puno, pp. 1–54, 1968.

58. Paolicchi, F., et al.: Biological Activity of the Seminal Plasma of Alpacas, Stimulus for the Production of LH by Pituitary Cells. *Animal Reproduction Science* 54(3): 203–210, 1999.

59. Perkins, N. R., G. S. Frazer, and B. L. Hull: Endocrine Diagnosis of Cryptorchidism in a Llama. *Australian Veterinary Journal* 74(4): 275–277, 1996.

60. Quispe, F.: *Evaluacion de las caracteristicas fisicas del semen de la alpaca durante la epoca de empadre.* B.Sc. Thesis, Facultad de Medicina Veterinaria, Universidad Nacional del Altiplano, Puno, Peru, 75 pp., 1987.

61. Quispe, G.: *Inseminacion artificial en alpacas* (Lama pacos) *con semen diluido a different concentraciones.* I. Zootec. Thesis, Facultad. Agron. Zootec., Universidad Nacional San Antonio, Abad, Cusco, Peru, 103 pp., 1996.

62. Rietschel, W.: Cryptorchidism in the Vicugna *(Lama vicugna).* Tierärztliche Praxis 18: 459–461, 1990.

63. Ruiz, R. L.: *Biopsia testicular en alpaca mediante el uso de la aguja de Vim-Silverman.* B.S. Thesis, Facultad de Medicina Veterinaria, Universidad Nacional Mayor de San Marcos, Lima, pp. 1–22, 1970.

64. San Martin, M., et al.: Aspects of Reproduction in the Alpaca, *Lama pacos. Journal of Reproduction and Fertility* 16(3): 395–99, 1968.

65. Smith, C. L., A. T. Peter, and D. G. Pugh: Reproduction in Llamas and Alpacas: A Review. *Theriogenology* 41(3): 573–592, 1994.

66. Sumar, J.: *Studies on Reproductive Pathology in Alpacas.* M.S. Thesis, Dept. Obstet. and Gynaec., College of Veterinary Medicine, Swedish University of Agricultural Science, Upsala, 1983.

67. Sumar, J.: Reproductive Physiology in South American Camelids. In *Genetics of Reproduction in Sheep* (R. B. Land and D. W. Robinson, eds.), pp. 81–95. London: Butterworths, 1984.

68. Sumar, J.: Present and Potential Role of South American Camelids in the High Andes. *Outlook on Agriculture* 17(1): 23–29, 1988.

69. Sumar, J., and V. Leyva: *Coleccion de semen mediante vagina artificial en la alpaca.* Proceedings IVth Int. Conf. South American Camelids, Punta Arenas, Chile, 12 pp., 1981.

70. Sumar, J., and M. Garcia: *Fisiologia Reproductiva en Los Camelidos Sudamericanos: Alpaca y Llama.* IAEA-SM-292/16, pp. 26–27, 1984.

71. Sumar, J., and W. Bravo: *Fertility of Female Alpacas Based on the Size of Testicles of Breeding Males.* 7th Annual Rep. CRSP, University of California, Davis, 1986.

72. Sumar, J., and M. Garcia: Reproductive Physiology of the Alpaca. *Fisiologia de repoduccion de la alpaca,* 1986.

73. Sumar, J. B.: Reproduction in Llamas and Alpacas. *Animal Reproduction Science,* 42: 1–4, 1996.

74. Tibary, A.: *Testicular Ultrasonography and Biopsy in Small Ruminants and Llamas.* Proceedings of the Annual Conference of the Society for Theriogenology, September 12–15, 2001, Vancouver, BC, Canada, pp. 369–378, 2001.

75. Tibary, A.: *Semen Preservation in Camelids.* Proceedings of the Annual Conference of the Society for Theriogenology, September 12–15, 2001, Vancouver, BC, Canada, pp. 369–378, 2001.

76. Tibary, A., and A. Anouassi: Reproductive Physiology of the Male. In *Theriogenology in Camelidae: Anatomy, Physiology, BSE, Pathology and Artificial Breeding* (A. Tibary, ed.). Actes Editions, Institut Agronomique et Veterinaire Hassan II. pp. 49–74, 1997.

77. Tibary, A., and A. Anouassi: Male Breeding Soundness Examination. In *Theriogenology in Camelidae: Anatomy, Physiology, BSE, Pathology and Artificial Breeding* (A. Tibary, ed.). Actes Editions, Institut Agronomique et Veterinaire Hassan II. pp. 79–111, 1997.

78. Tibary, A., and A. Anouassi: Pathology and Surgery of the Reproductive Tract and Associated Organs in the Male Camelidae. In *Theriogenology in Camelidae: Anatomy, Physiology, BSE, Pathology and Artificial Breeding* (A. Tibary, ed.). Actes Editions, Institut Agronomique et Veterinaire Hassan II. pp. 115–132, 1997.

79. Tibary, A., and A. Anouassi: Breeding Soundness Examination of the Female Camelidae. In *Theriogenology in Camelidae: Anatomy, Physiology, BSE, Pathology and Artificial Breeding* (A. Tibary, ed.). Actes Editions, Institut Agronomique et Veterinaire Hassan II. pp. 243–310, 1997.

80. Tibary, A., and A. Anouassi: Anatomy of the Male Genital Tract. In *Theriogenology in Camelidae: Anatomy, Physiology, BSE, Pathology and Artificial Breeding* (A. Tibary, ed.). Actes Editions, Institut Agronomique et Veterinaire Hassan II. pp. 17–44, 1997.

81. Tibary, A., and M. A. Memon: Reproduction in the Male South American Camelidae. *Journal of Camel Practice and Research* 6(2): 235–248, 1999.

82. Tibary, A., and A. Anouassi: *Breeding Soundness Examination in the Male Camelid.* Proceedings Camelid Medicine, Surgery

and Reproduction Conference, Ohio State University, Columbus, pp. 409–423, 2002.

83. Tibary, A., A. Anouassi, and M. A. Memon: Approach to Diagnosis of Infertility in Camelids: Retrospective Study in Alpacas, Llamas and Camels. *Journal of Camel Practice and Research* 8(2): 167–179, 2001.

84. Urquieta, B., and J. R. Rojas: An Introduction to South American Camelids. In *Livestock Reproduction in Latin America*. Proceedings of the Final Research Coordination Meeting, Bogota, 1988.

85. Urquieta, B., and J. R. Rojas: Studies on the Reproductive Physiology of the Vicuña *(Vicugna vicugna)*. In *Livestock Reproduction in Latin America,* Proceedings of the Final Research Coordination Meeting of the FAO/IAEA/ARCAL, Vienna, pp. 407–428, 1990.

86. Urquieta, B., et al.: Seasonal Variation in Some Reproductive Parameters of Male Vicuña in the High Andes of Northern Chile. *Journal of Arid Environments* 26: 79–87, 1994.

Chapter 13

Female Reproduction

Ahmed Tibary, DMV, PhD, Dipl ACT

A normal birth.

The alpaca industry has seen tremendous development in North America, Australia, and many European countries starting in the 1980s. During the same period because of this interest in camelids, huge progress has been made in understanding the physiology of these species. In the field of reproduction, in addition to original work done since the late 1950s by South American scientists, the scientific literature has been tremendously increased. The aim of this chapter is to provide the reader with complete information on the normal reproductive process in the female alpaca, as well as to review the causes of reproductive disorders.

ANATOMY

The reproductive system of the female camelid is composed of the ovaries, uterine tube or oviduct, uterus, cervix, vagina, and vulva (see Figure 13.1). The function of all these organs is regulated by hormones originating from different structures in the ovary, which are themselves controlled by the hypothalamus and the pituitary glands.

Editor's note: I realize some of this chapter's material will be difficult for readers without strong scientific backgrounds. Nevertheless, it is included as a detailed resource for breeders and veterinarians because of the complexity and importance of reproduction. No procedure or treatment stated or implied in this chapter should be undertaken without the diagnosis and supervision of a licensed veterinarian.—E.H.

Ovaries

Alpaca ovaries are suspended by the mesovarium within the abdominal cavity in the area of seventh lumbar vertebrae about 15 to 20 centimeters from the vulva. The ovary is attached to the broad ligament by a well-defined strong ligament (ovarian ligament or proper ligament) that extends from the hilus of the ovary to the tip of the corresponding uterine horn. Both ovaries are enclosed within a fold of the mesosalpinx: the ovarian bursa (see Figure 13.2).

The ovary can be easily exteriorized from its bursa. It is oval (almond shaped) and flattened laterally with slightly convex lateral and medial surfaces. The general appearance and size of the ovaries vary according to the activity and age of the animal. They are small and have a smooth and glistening surface in noncycling prepubertal animals. The ovaries increase in size and become more irregular and lobulated in older animals. The active ovaries measure 1.6±0.3 centimeters in length, 1.1±0.2 centimeters in width, and 1.1±0.2 centimeters in thickness. The weight of the ovaries in the alpaca averages 1.87±0.94 grams.[26,49,96] Several raised, small, blisterlike vesicles can be seen throughout the surface of the ovary and correspond to follicles, giving the ovary a granular appearance. Both left and right ovaries are equal in size and activity.

Two major parts form the ovary: an external part (cortex) and an internal part (medulla). The organ is surrounded by a tunica albuginea, except in the region of the hilus. Follicular activity takes place in the cortex and ovulation can

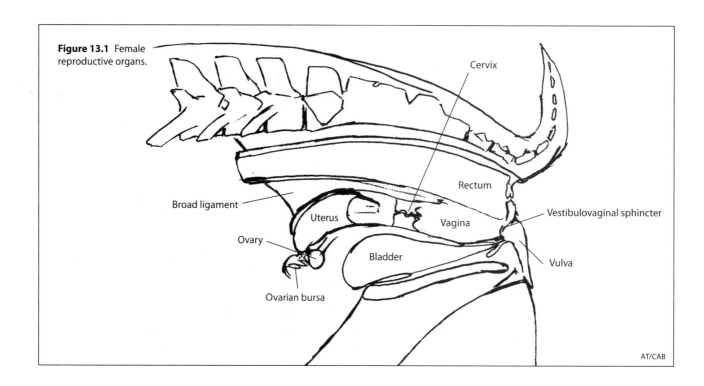

Figure 13.1 Female reproductive organs.

Cervix

Rectum

Broad ligament

Uterus

Vagina

Vestibulovaginal sphincter

Ovary

Bladder

Vulva

Ovarian bursa

AT/CAB

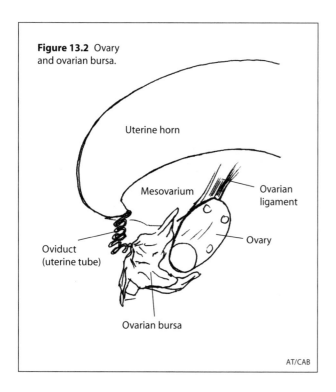

Figure 13.2 Ovary and ovarian bursa.

Uterine horn

Mesovarium

Ovarian ligament

Oviduct (uterine tube)

Ovary

Ovarian bursa

AT/CAB

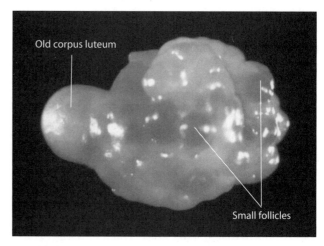

Old corpus luteum

Small follicles

Figure 13.3 Ovary with an old corpus luteum and several small follicles.

occur anywhere on this surface. As in other mammals, the exterior of the ovary is continuously modified by the type and number of structures present on its surface. These ovarian structures are of two types: follicles and corpora lutea, at different stages of development or regression.

Follicles Follicular activity in camelids occurs in waves displaying four types of follicles: small growing follicles, mature pre-ovulatory follicles, regressing follicles, and sometimes large anovulatory follicles.[96]

The small growing follicles emerge as a group (cohort) within a new follicular wave. Their number varies from four to eight. They are visible at the surface of the ovary as small, 2 to 4 millimeters, slightly raised vesicles (see Figure 13.3). The mature pre-ovulatory follicle emerges from the follicular wave after establishing dominance. It measures 8 to 12 millimeters.[11,27,81,97] The follicles are spherical and have a thin, clear, translucent wall. They are turgid and protrude markedly from the ovarian surface. The surface of the mature follicle is sometimes richly vascularized.

The appearance of the regressing (atretic) follicles varies according to the stage of regression. At the beginning of regression, the follicular wall becomes opaque and thick and the ovarian diameter regresses slowly until most of the follicles recede into the ovarian mass.

Large anovulatory follicles may be present on the ovary in nonbred females. Their size and appearance are highly variable and depend on the stage of their evolution. They can have a thin, richly vascularized wall or an opaque, thick wall and contain various amounts of serous or hemorrhagic fluid or organized blood clots and fibrin. Other follicular structures can be observed on the surface of the ovary or even on the surface of the anovulatory follicles.

Corpus Luteum The corpus luteum (yellow body or CL) forms after ovulation, which occurs 24 to 48 hours after mating. The ovulating follicle becomes increasingly hemorrhagic and collapses at ovulation. The follicular cavity is then filled with blood to form a corpus hemorrhagicum. The mature corpus luteum is spherical or oblong and protrudes distinctly from the ovarian surface. It has a liverlike consistency. A sagittal section of the corpus luteum shows a reddish brown, richly vascularized luteal tissue, which has a fibrous central zone or sometimes a central cavity.[96]

In the pregnant female, the corpus luteum continues to grow during the first two months of gestation, becomes more spherical, and protrudes markedly from the ovarian tissue. The corpus luteum of pregnancy has a dark red color with an irregular highly vascularized surface. A section of the corpus luteum shows a thin capsule enclosing the luteal tissue. A central fibrous area is usually observed in a noncavitary corpora lutea. The size of the

mature corpus luteum varies from 12 to 16 millimeters in diameter.[26,37,51,79]

Regression of the corpus luteum occurs on the ninth to eleventh day following a sterile mating.[96,97] It is characterized by a decrease in size and vascularization and a change in color to pale or light brown.

Regression of the corpus luteum of pregnancy starts just before parturition, and continues during the next few days. The regressing corpora lutea are light brown in color and firm. The corpus albicans originating from the complete regression of the corpus luteum of pregnancy is hard, laterally compressed or button shaped, and bluish-white or grayish-white in color, with no blood vessels on the surface. These structures present a dark central zone surrounded by a thick, fibrous capsule with a fibrous central area. Corpora albicantia of different sizes remain on the surface of the ovary of the female for a long time and give the organ its characteristic lobulated appearance, especially in old multiparous females.

Ovarian Bursa

The camelid ovary is completely surrounded by a large ovarian bursa formed medially by the mesovarium and laterally by the mesosalpinx (see Figure 13.2).[96] The bursa measures 2.5 × 2.5 × 5 centimeters.[49] This anatomical structure is capable of stretching several centimeters to accommodate large anovulatory follicles. The bursa is blind on its lateral aspect and presents a large circular orifice that leads to the uterine tube. The fimbria of the uterine tube are located on the floor of the bursa and form a funnel-shaped organ that collects the oocytes (eggs) after ovulation and takes them to the oviduct.[96]

Uterine Tube (Oviduct)

The uterine tube (or oviduct) is a duct that goes from the bursa to the uterus. It plays an important role in the storage of semen (sperm reservoir), fertilization, and early embryo development. In guanacos (*Lama guanacoe*) 20 to 25 percent of the sperm cells in the ejaculate are found in this area 120 hours after a single breeding.[76] The uterine tube is capable of these functions because of its peculiar macro- and microscopic characteristics.

The uterine tube is long and tortuous. Its length ranges from 15 to 20 centimeters in the alpaca.[26] It starts with a wide abdominal end located close to the medial opening of the ovarian bursa and ends in the corresponding uterine horn at a protruding utero-ovarian junction (isthmus or papillae). The ampullary end is soft and flabby and presents a wide opening into the bursa. The uterine tube becomes harder and smaller in diameter and becomes straight before entering the isthmus region. The

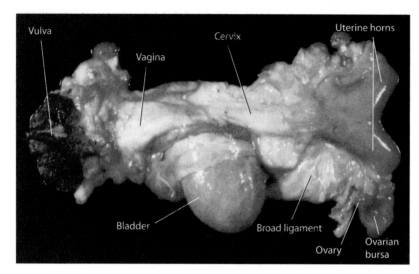

Figure 13.4 Anatomy of the female genital tract in alpacas.

uterine tube papillae are conical and protrude 2 to 4 millimeters into the uterine lumen. The oviduct is covered by a fold of the peritoneum: the mesosalpinx, which is continuous with the broad ligament. The utero-ovarian artery runs parallel to the long axis of the oviduct within the mesosalpinx.

The uterine end of the oviduct (isthmus) is quite peculiar in camelids in that it is well developed. The uterine tube extends into the uterine cavity by conical or pyramidal papillae. The papillae are very muscular and present a sphincter muscle at their apex. The reason for this peculiarity has not been fully investigated. It is possible that the papillae play an important role in the selective transport of fertilized embryos.

Uterus

The alpaca uterus is bicornuate (two uterine horns). In the mature nonpregnant female, this organ is located in the abdominal cavity. In maiden females the uterus is very small and can be found entirely within the pelvic cavity. The position of the uterine horns gives the organ a "Y" or a "T" shape depending on the reproductive history of the animal (number of pregnancies, age, etc.).

The uterus shows two distinct parts externally: a cranial transverse part formed by the free portions of the uterine horns and a caudal longitudinal part formed by the fused parts of the horns and the body to the cervix (see Figure 13.4). Internally, a long intercornual septum divides the longitudinal part of the uterus into two distinct horns, which join briefly into a small uterine body before reaching the cervix. The dorsal and ventral intercornual ligaments found in the bovine and small ruminant species are absent in camelids.

The size of the uterine horns varies greatly among animals depending on their reproductive history. Uterine horn lengths range from 6 to 8 centimeters and their diameter from 1.2 to 1.6 centimeters. Both uterine horns are comparable in size in the nulliparous female.[52] In general, the left horn is always longer and has a larger diameter than the right one. This discrepancy in size between the two uterine horns increases with number of pregnancies because nearly all are carried in the left uterine horn. The length of the free portion of the right horn (from the external bifurcation to the tip of the horn) measures one-third to four-fifths that of the left uterine horn. The uterine body is relatively short and measures 2 to 3 centimeters in length and 1.5 to 1.7 centimeters in diameter.

The major means of fixation of the uterus, the broad ligament, is attached to the lateral and caudal mesometrial borders of the longitudinal and transverse parts of the uterine horn, respectively.

Cervix

The cervix measures 2 to 3 centimeters in length and 0.5 to 1.5 centimeters in diameter in a nonpregnant and non-postpartum female. It presents two to four rings, a uterine orifice, and a vaginal orifice. The cervix is widely open in a receptive female and becomes very tight in a pregnant female. The cervix increases in tone in response to increased estradiol during the period of receptivity, allowing the penis to penetrate and deposit semen inside the uterine horns.

One of the characteristics of the cervix in camelids is that it is difficult to identify by rectal palpation.

The cervical canal presents longitudinal folds, which extend on annular muscular projections and form the cervical rings. The internal cervical orifice is well demarked from the uterine body by a clear fold of the cervical mucosa. The caudal cervical ring protrudes slightly into the vaginal cavity forming a small fornix. The cervical os (opening) toward the vagina can easily be identified by vaginoscopy in most females.

The cervical lumen traverses in a clockwise direction. Others have described the cervix as having a single spiral fold that makes two to three turns, appearing like rings. During estrus, these folds become soft and pliable, rendering the cervix less distinct and more difficult to palpate. The cervix is tight during the luteal phase. During pregnancy, the cervix becomes very tight. In advanced stages of pregnancy, it is pulled forward and downward beyond the pelvis brim.

The size and protrusion of the vaginal portion of the cervix increase during the immediate postpartum period. Normal size and position of the cervix are regained within the first two weeks following parturition.

Vagina and Vestibulum

The vestibulum measures 3 to 6 centimeters and is separated from the anterior vagina by the hymen and vestibular sphincter muscle (see Figure 13.1). The vagina measures 15 to 25 centimeters in length and 3 to 5 centimeters in diameter. There is a clear transition from the vestibulum to the vaginal cavity. The urethra opens above a very shallow suburethral diverticulum. The bulb of the vestibulum is covered by the constrictor muscle of the vestibulum. This structure is very tight in nulliparous or young animals and makes speculum and manual examination of the vaginal cavity very difficult. The anterior vagina and the vestibulum are separated by a strong band of tissue and the hymen.

Vulva and Clitoris

The vulva opens directly below the anus in a vertical plane and measures 2 to 4 centimeters. The space between the dorsal commissure of the vulva and the anus, called the perineum or perineal body, is very small (0.5 and 1.5 cm). The clitoris can be felt as a hard structure at the tip of the ventral labial commissure of the vulva. There is no distinct clitoris fossa. The corpus clitoris consists of a central cartilaginous core surrounded by the corpus cavernosum clitoridis. During the follicular phase, edema of the vulva can be present but is very discrete. The vulva becomes relaxed and edematous during the last week of prepartum.

Mammary Glands

The udder consists of four glandular quarters, each with its own teat. The left and right halves of the udder are sep-

A normal alpaca udder.

arated from each other by fibroelastic tissue extending from the linea alba and prepubic tendon. A groove is generally visible between the left and right halves of the udder. The lateral aspect of the quarters is covered by tissue from the abdominal tunic and the caudal abdominal wall. The anterior and posterior quarters are independent, but there is no visible separation between them. Each quarter is in fact composed of two totally separate glands opening into the same teat. The teats are directed cranioventrally and possess two openings (streak canals). Each streak canal leads to a separate teat and glands cistern. Conformation of the udder changes according to breed, age, and stage of lactation.

Malformation of the mammary glands includes supernumerary teats, short teats, a large bulbous teat, and introverted teats. Teat abnormalities may make it difficult for a cria to nurse.

PHYSIOLOGY OF REPRODUCTION

The reproductive patterns of female camelids are quite peculiar when compared to other farm animals. Understanding these peculiarities, such as induced ovulation, predominately left-horn pregnancies, the importance of the corpus luteum during pregnancy, and the behavioral responses to the male, is very important in breeding management and the diagnosis of infertility.

Puberty

Laparoscopy studies show normal follicular waves by the end of the first year of age.[62,63] However, ovarian activity does not reach its fullest potential until 17 months of age.[13] I have documented ovarian activity in some females as early as four months of age. Breeders have reported accidental mating and pregnancy in four- to six-month-old females. Most alpaca breeders wait for young females to develop sufficiently before breeding, generally around one and a half to two years of age.[57,79] Nutritional status and body development are more important than age in the decision to start breeding. Females are considered ready to breed once they reach 60 percent of their adult weight (100 lb; 40 kg).[63,64] In North American rearing conditions, some female alpacas may be ready to breed as early as 12 to 14 months of age.

Reproductive Cycle

Seasonality of Reproduction Seasonality of reproduction has long been suggested for the female camelid. This is based on the seasonal distribution of birth, both in the wild and in domesticated animals, and on the status of ovarian activity in slaughtered females.[104] The seasonal pattern of reproduction in female camelids probably developed largely because of nutritional conditions. In the domesticated alpaca, this apparent seasonality is due to management decisions by breeders to ensure births during the most appropriate time of the year in terms of nutrition and climatic conditions compatible with good survival of cria.[38,44,74,75,88,97]

Alpacas show follicular activity throughout the year.[44] Absence of seasonality in the female alpaca is also confirmed by laparoscopic observations, which show no significant effect of the season on the number of large follicles present on the ovary.[13] However, in a recent study, sexual behavior of the female alpaca was found to be affected by both season and time elapsed since parturition.[69,71] Female alpacas in this study were less receptive in spring than in fall and when the time from parturition until mating was increased. More research is needed to further clarify seasonality in alpaca reproduction and its effect on ovulation and early embryonic survival.

Ovarian Cycle Definition of the estrus cycle in camelids is different from that used in other species because of the induced nature of ovulation in camelids. In fact, the use of the term estrus cycle may not be appropriate for camelids because cyclic ovarian activity and estrous behavior depend largely on the presence or absence of an ovulation-triggering stimulus. In the absence of mating there is a succession of follicular waves with a highly variable rhythm, whereas in the presence of a nonfertile mating followed by ovulation, a true estrus cycle is displayed.

Ovarian Activity in the Absence of Mating or Ovulation-inducing Stimulus Early attempts to study follicular activity in the alpaca were based on postmortem examination or behavioral observations and therefore were not very precise.[36,43,75] More recently, techniques such as ultrasonography and laparoscopy have allowed repeated examinations on the same animal and led to a better understanding of the follicular wave dynamics in camelids.[5,12,93,94]

In the absence of an ovulation-inducing treatment (mating or hormone injection), the ovarian activity is limited to a succession of follicular waves. These follicular waves tend to overlap and therefore the follicular phase is very difficult to define. Each follicular wave can be divided into four distinct phases: follicular recruitment, follicular growth and establishment of dominance, pre-ovulatory follicles, and follicular regression. The duration of each of these phases of the follicular cycle in nonbred females is variable. The duration of the whole follicular wave varies between 7 and 19 days in alpacas.[13]

The follicular recruitment phase is the time lapse between an examination, which does not show any follicular activity (state of quiescence), and the emergence of several follicles (2 to 3 mm) on the surface of the ovary. The quiescent ovary of the female camelid is usually small, smooth, and deprived of any follicular activity, but can be irregular in older females because of the presence of old corpora lutea. Little is known about the mechanisms of recruitment of each follicular wave, but it is possible that it constitutes a response to an increase in the follicle stimulating hormone (FSH) from the pituitary gland. Recruitment of the follicular wave occurs before any follicles are visible on the ovary and can only be thoroughly investigated by histological techniques. Many small follicles (less than 3 mm in diameter) are always present on the surface of the ovaries. These follicles occur in waves and grow to 5 millimeters in size within 6 to 12 days. Dominance by one or two follicles is established when the diameter of the follicle reaches 6 millimeters.[11]

The follicular maturation phase encompasses growth of the dominant follicle or follicles from the time they establish dominance until the time they become capable of ovulation (pre-ovulatory follicles). Laparoscopic studies show that ovulatory size is reached after four days of growth (range three to five days). The pre-ovulatory follicles remain at the same size for four days (range two to eight days).[13] Establishment of dominance and regression of subordinate follicles are probably under the control of the in-situ production of inhibin by the dominant follicle.

In the absence of ovulation-inducing treatment, such as mating or injection of human chorionic gonadotropin hormone (hCG) or gonadotropin-releasing hormone (GnRH), the fate of the mature follicle follows one of two possible courses: atresia or "cystic degeneration." Atresia, or the slow regression of the follicles due to cell death, occurs in the majority of follicles. Cystic degeneration, which is the development of large follicles incapable of ovulation (anovulatory), occurs in some cases. Regression of the mature follicle takes between four and six days. Regression of the anovulatory follicle is a relatively slow process, especially if it becomes very large.

Follicles larger than 12 millimeters are generally considered pathological cysts by some researchers.[21,81] It is possible that a large proportion of these "cysts" are large anovulatory follicles. Some research has suggested that the anovulatory follicle inhibits follicular development in the llama.[16,21] However, based on estrogen plasma levels, these cysts do not appear to be active.[21] According to studies in the llama, the negative effect of these cysts on the emergence of a new follicular wave tends to disappear after eight days. Partial luteinization of anovulatory follicles associated with significant plasma levels of progesterone is possible, as reported in the llama.[18,103]

Copulation can take place over a wide range of follicular sizes.[18,45,85] Estrus signs are variable both in young and adult females and are not well correlated with ovarian status. Sexual receptivity can also be displayed in the presence of anovulatory follicles. The relationship between behavior and ovarian status in alpacas is controversial. In one study, sexual receptivity was found to be positively correlated with follicular size, with the "strongest estrus" behavior observed when the follicular size was between 8 to 12 millimeters.[13] However, alpaca females can display sexual receptivity whenever there is at least one follicle >6 millimeters. Others can be nonreceptive even when a 7-millimeter follicle is present, and some females may display sexual receptivity in the presence of a corpus luteum in one ovary and an 8-millimeter follicle on the other.[13] Some females allow breeding even during pregnancy.[70]

Ovarian Activity in the Presence of an Ovulation-inducing Stimulus Camelids are induced ovulators—meaning that copulation must take place for ovulation of the dominant follicle to occur. The hypothesis that camelids may be induced ovulators was proposed as early as the 1950s.[37,62,65,73] Coitus-induced ovulation was first described in alpacas.[73] Further studies indicated that penile intromission provides the stimulus necessary for release of gonadotropin(s), particularly luteinizing hormone (LH), and subsequent ovulation.[42] Recent endocrinological studies have established that mating causes the hormonal changes (luteinizing hormone surge) necessary for ovulation in all species of Camelidae.[17,94,97]

In South American rearing conditions, the incidence of ovulation following mating is very high at the height of the breeding season, but tends to be lower at the beginning and end of the breeding season.[37] Ovulation does not occur if breeding takes place when the follicular size is between 4

and 5 millimeters or in the presence of a regressing follicle.[18] Ovulation incidence increases when the size of the mature follicles is 7 millimeters and is at its maximum (100%) when follicular size is between 8 and 12 millimeters.[18] Breeding does not affect the normal growth of the small follicles. Incidence of ovulation does not increase with multiple matings.[20] This suggests that LH is released after the first copulation and the pituitary becomes refractory for at least 24 hours.[11] Incidence of ovulation after mating can be affected by the age of the female. In one study, 34.8 to 40 percent of yearling females failed to ovulate following breeding, compared to only 8.1 to 15 percent of adult females.[79]

Ovulation occurs 24 to 26 hours after mating or human chorionic gonadotropin (hCG) injection.[20,42] In one study, none of the females ovulated before 24 hours after breeding, but by 28 hours postmating all follicles had ovulated.[75] Others have found that the majority of ovulations occurred by 30 hours, but some females did not ovulate until 72 hours following breeding.[86,88]

Mechanism of Ovulation Induction Although it is now well established that ovulation is caused equally by mating with a normal or vasectomized male, the detailed mechanism by which this occurs is not known. Several theories have been proposed, but none has been fully tested. Some researchers have proposed a neurohormonal pathway as the triggering mechanism, whereas others have cited a hormonal substance present in the semen and acting directly as GnRH.

The ovulation-inducing mechanism in the alpaca was thought to be neural and caused by several factors (penile intromission into the cervix, semen deposition, leg clasp of the male, and probably the characteristic orgling sound of the male) acting synergistically. Mounting and intromission are essential for inducing ovulation.[42] There is no relationship between the occurrence of ovulation and the duration of copulation (interruption after five minutes). This study was the first to show clearly that coitus and probably ejaculation are necessary to ensure ovulation in camelids. The fact that 33 percent of the mounted and inseminated females ovulated, an intermediary response compared to mounted only and bred, suggests that a seminal factor could be involved in the mechanism of ovulation in this species. In another study, sterile mating (vasectomized male) or fertile mating resulted in an 80 to 100 percent incidence of ovulation, whereas intravaginal deposition of alpaca semen resulted in only a 60 to 67 percent incidence of ovulation.[82]

The role of semen or seminal plasma in the mechanism of inducing ovulation has been thoroughly investigated in the Bactrian camel by Chinese scientists over the last 15 years.[94,100] In-vitro evaluation of the biological activity of alpaca seminal plasma suggests that it may contain factor(s) different from GnRH but having a GnRH-like activity that is responsible for LH release.[66,67]

The occurrence of spontaneous ovulation in the female camelid is a controversial and confusing subject. Spontaneous ovulations have been reported in alpacas on the basis of laparoscopic, laparotomy, and hormonal studies. Their incidence was reported to range from 3.5 percent to more than 10 percent.[5,13,37,42,82] In one study, the incidence of "spontaneous" ovulation was reported to be 40 percent.[57,58] According to earlier studies, spontaneous ovulations are more frequent during the height of the breeding season.[37] It was suggested that spontaneous ovulation is caused by audiovisual stimulus or direct contact with the male during teasing.[13,42] Spontaneous ovulation was confirmed in a few animals by the visualization of an ovulation depression (or ovarian stigma). However, in many animals no stigma was found, which suggests that in many cases the ovarian structures observed are not corpora lutea but just luteinized follicles.[13]

I have observed a "real" ovulation in the absence of copulation in only a handful of cases in more than a 1,000 examinations. However, luteinization of follicles without ovulation is commonly observed. In most studies, spontaneous ovulation is suspected when plasma progesterone levels are high in a nonbred female. This could simply be luteinization of anovulatory follicles, as suggested by other researchers.[7,70] The mechanism of LH release and luteinization of large anovulatory follicles remains unstudied.

Ovulation occurs equally on the left and right ovaries.[13,27] The predominance of left horn pregnancy is not due to a difference in activity between ovaries or increased embryo mortality for right ovary ovulations, as originally postulated.[75] The predominance of pregnancy in the left uterine horn is due to a difference in the mechanism of release of prostaglandin F2 alpha, a hormone re-

sponsible for the destruction of the corpus luteum and initiation of a new cycle in the absence of pregnancy.

Corpus Luteum (CL) Activity and Regression Endocrinological as well as clinical studies show that the camelid corpus luteum has two main characteristics: a slow development and an early demise in the absence of conception. The CL develops within a few days after ovulation, reaches a maximum size in 8 days, and then regresses if no conceptus is present by day 10 to 12.

Depending on the examination method used, the CL is first visualized two to six days after mating or hCG treatment.[100] Its presence is easily ascertained by direct observation of the ovary or by determination of plasma progesterone levels. Visualization by ultrasonography is more difficult in the early stage of its development (the first four days).

The CL reaches its maximum size between 7 and 8 days postbreeding then starts to regress by 9 to 10 days and is completely absent by 12 days.[2,4] Luteolysis (destruction of the corpus luteum) is brought about by a release of prostaglandin F2 alpha (PGF2α) from the endometrium (uterus).[39,41,87] Partial hysterectomy prolongs the lifespan and secretory activity of the corpus luteum ipsilateral (on the same side) to the missing horn.[48]

There seems to be a difference in the luteolytic effects of the right versus left uterine horn. When the CL is on the left ovary, surgical removal of the ipsilateral uterine horn results in a marked prolongation of luteal function (high plasma progesterone levels, large corpora lutea, and lack of sexual receptivity for a period up to 70 days).[48] In contrast, removal of the right uterine horn in females with a functional corpus luteum in the right ovary causes only a slight delay in luteal regression. When a CL is present on each ovary, removal of the left uterine horn results in persistence of the corpus luteum on the left ovary and normal regression of the CL on the right ovary, while removal of the right uterine horn results in regression of corpora lutea on both ovaries.[48] These experiments suggest that the luteolytic activity of the right uterine horn is local, while that of the left uterine horn has both a local and a systemic effect.[48] A recent study on uterine blood vessels in llamas and alpacas showed that venous drainage from the left uterine horn crosses to the right side. A large vein originating in the left horn and sending branches to the right uterine horn is present in these species, even in uteri from fetuses.[35]

The lifespan of the CL seems to depend on the stage of follicular development at breeding. Corpora lutea formed following breeding when the follicle is at the growing stage (7 mm) last 10 to 12 days, whereas those obtained following mating when the follicle is regressing last only 5 to

Table 13.1 Mating stimuli and ovulation rate.[42]

Stimulus	Ovulation Rate
Unmated	5%
Mounted only	15%
Mounted and inseminated, service interrupted after 5 minutes	33%
Bred by vasectomized male	66%
Bred by vasectomized male and inseminated	77%
Bred once	82%
Bred several times	70%
Given hCG or hCG with insemination	80–90%

A female rejects a male by spitting.

The male behavioral response may be complicated by inexperience and the presence of crias.

7 days. Short-lived corpora lutea could be the results of a luteinization rather than ovulation of the regressing follicles.[18]

Follicular activity continues even in the presence of an active corpus luteum. In the absence of pregnancy, the return to receptivity and presence of a mature follicle is expected 12 to 14 days following mating and ovulation.[41,79,97] A new pre-ovulatory follicle was found on the ovary opposite to the corpus luteum in 80 percent of females, suggesting that ovarian activity alternates between the two ovaries during successive cycles.[13]

Reproductive Behavior

Receptive females assume a mating position (kush) in the presence of the male. Some estrous females can also display interest, approach a mating couple, kush, or try to mount other females.[85] Nonreceptive females will react to the male's approach by spitting, kicking, or running away.[36,75,85,88] The receptivity period can last from 1 to 36 days in alpaca females.[36,75] Long periods of receptivity can be interrupted by occasional 48-hour periods of refusal.[38,85]

Sitting behavior, kushing, which is considered by many observers as a sign of sexual receptivity, is in fact part of a submissive behavior by nondominant females.[70,71] The most indicative signs for reproductive status are spitting and attempting to escape from the male, which are frequently displayed by mated females with a corpus luteum.[70] This confirms reports that receptivity to the male can be almost continuous in the absence of a corpus luteum.[85]

In most breeding operations where the male is led to the female in a controlled manner, "reading" female alpaca behavior may be complicated by other factors. An aggressive male may attempt to force a young female down even if she is not receptive; on the other hand, females that are very submissive may sit for a male even if they are pregnant.

FERTILIZATION AND PREGNANCY

Fertilization and Early Embryo Development

The process of fertilization has not been thoroughly investigated in alpacas. Due to the induced nature of ovulation in these species, it is likely that oocyte maturation is completed during the phase immediately following copulation and LH release, and shortly after ovulation. Cumulus dispersion is observed in cumulus-oocyte-complex (COC) recovered by aspiration from follicles 18 to 24 hours after hCG injection.

Semen is deposited deep inside the uterine horns. No detailed studies are available on capacitation and acrosome reaction of camelid sperm. The period required for these two important changes to be completed is unknown in these species, but since ovulation does not usually occur in these species until 24 to 48 hours after breeding, one can speculate that sperm is mature and remains viable at least during this time lapse.

Shortly after ejaculation, sperm cells are transported to the utero-tubal junction, which acts as a sperm reservoir in camelids. In the guanaco, as much as 20 to 25 percent of the ejaculated sperm cells are found in this area up to 120 hours after breeding.[76] In the llama, sperm cells stored in the isthmus (utero-tubal junction) can remain viable up to five days.[89] In a study on alpacas, a population of spermatozoa formed a reservoir in the utero-tubal junction within 6 hours of mating and remained present up to 30 hours postcoitus.[22] It is possible that sperm cells are released progressively from this site of storage to guarantee fertilization when the oocyte is shed and transported into the uterine tube.

After ovulation, the ovum is picked up by the fimbria of the large infundibulum and carried to the site of fertilization (the uterine tube) where the initial stages of embryo development are found. Fertilization rates are high and range from 66.6 to 85.7 percent.

Left-side ovulation seems to result in higher fertilization rates (100%) than for right-side ovulations (81%), though this difference is not statistically significant.[40] Multiple matings during the same receptivity period do not increase conception rate.[54] I have recorded a 100 percent pregnancy rate at 12 days following a single mating in the presence of an 8- to 10-millimeter follicle.[91]

Little information is available on the chronology of early embryonic development. Embryo collection results suggest that the development of the embryo from one cell to a hatched blastocyst (embryo in the process of hatching) takes five to six days. In the alpaca, it was reported that the embryo reaches the uterine cavity three days after ovulation. However, a recent study showed morulae and compacted morulae collected from the oviduct at four and seven days, respectively, postmating, and blastocysts (see Figure 13.5) were collected from the uterus ten days postmating.[22] In the llama, flushing of the uterine tube at regular intervals after breeding yielded 1 to 2 cell embryos, 4 to 8 cell embryos, 8 to 16 cell embryos, and morulas at 48 hours, 72 hours, 96 hours, and 96 hours, respectively.[75] Collection of embryos from the uterus yields mainly hatched blastocysts.[22,91,92]

The embryo sheds its envelope (zona pellucida) and enters the uterus around day six to seven postovulation. The freshly hatched embryo is usually spherical. The embryo expands rapidly and loses it spherical shape between day nine and ten postbreeding, and starts to elongate. It is presumed that the conceptus remains free within the uterus for the first 20 days of its life, because no firm attachment between the trophoblast and the uterine wall is observed at this time in the alpaca. This period is characterized by a high incidence of early embryonic death.[40,75] The morphology (fetal heartbeats) and estrone sulfate profiles suggest that implantation in the alpaca and llama begins around days 20 to 22 postbreeding.[14] Implantation is believed to be complete around 25 days and the placenta is usually well developed and shows a vascular connection with the uterus at 60 days.

In spite of the fact that both ovaries are equally active, the pregnancy is almost always carried in the left uterine horn.[14,47,48] In one study, 98.4 percent of a total of 928 pregnancies in alpacas were carried in the left uterine horn with corpora lutea located in the right ovaries in 50.4 percent of the cases.[46,47] These observations indicate the need for embryos originating from ovulations in the right ovary to migrate to the left uterine horn in order to survive. In another study, only 1 fetus out of 48 (2%) was located in the right uterine horn at 120 days of pregnancy.[14] The exact mechanism of embryo migration and embryo signaling to prevent luteolysis is not yet known.

Placentation and Fetal Growth

Placentation in camelids is microcotyledonary diffuse epitheliochorial, similar to that of horses.[30,50] An extra-fetal membrane, called the epidermal membrane, epithelion, or fourth membrane, is found in all species of camelids.[50,94] This membrane is made up of a layer of epithelial cells that cover the entire fetus. It is connected to the mucocutaneous junction of the lips, nose, eyes, and coronary

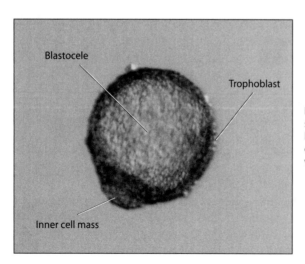

Blastocele

Trophoblast

Inner cell mass

Figure 13.5 An alpaca embryo at the blastocyst stage, seven days after mating. There are three regions: a central blastocele; an outer layer of cells (trophoblast), which will evolve into the placenta; and the inner cell mass, which will differentiate into the fetus.

bands. It is not known exactly when this membrane first appears. The epidermal membrane is thought to play an important role as a lubricant during parturition because of its slippery nature, as well as protection from dehydration for the newborn.

Alpaca gestation is approximately 11.5 months. Development of the fetus throughout pregnancy was investigated in one study.[14] Morphogenesis is completed by 60 days of pregnancy. Macroscopic fetal sex determination is not possible at 30 days but is easy at 60 days and thereafter. The presence of hair on the lips, eyebrows, and tail is observed at seven months of gestation, and the body is completely covered by fiber by eight months of gestation.

Fetal growth is very slow during the first six months of pregnancy; 65 percent of fetal weight increase occurs during the last trimester. During the last four months the fetus is the major contributor to the total mass of the gravid uterus. Eighty-five percent of the weight gain occurs from 210 days until parturition. Fetal weight of alpacas at eight months, nine months, and ten months of gestation is respectively 30 percent, 51 percent, and 65 percent of that at birth. At 11 months, a fetal weight of 18.9 pounds (8.6 kg) is not significantly different ($P > 0.06$) from a weight of 19.3 pounds (8.8 kg) at birth.[14] Regression equations to determine age of pregnancy based on fetal measurement have been published. One such equation is based on fetal crown rump length ($Y = 2.8 + 0.08X + 0.002X^2$), where Y is the gestation age in months and X is crown-rump length in centimeters.[14] These regression equations may be helpful in the diagnosis of abortion, but are not very accurate.

Pregnancy Diagnosis

Early pregnancy diagnosis is an important management practice in alpaca breeding. Pregnancy can be detected based on behavioral changes, hormonal assays, per rectum palpation of the uterus, abdominal ballotment, or ultrasonography.

Behavioral Indicators of Pregnancy Behavioral rejection (spitting off, refusal to sit) of the male is the first suggestive sign of pregnancy. However, this technique is not 100 percent reliable. Spitting behavior is usually a good indicator of the presence of high progesterone. Spitting behavior may be due to persistent luteal activity or behavioral problems. This behavior is seen at about 1 week after ovulation, becomes more intense at about 14 or 15 days postmating, and continues throughout pregnancy. This is a good, quick test, but should always be followed up by a more precise technique such as ultrasonography. A small proportion of females may sit as a sign of submissive behavior while they are pregnant.

Hormonal Diagnosis of Pregnancy The main hormone test for pregnancy diagnosis is the determination of the level of progesterone in the blood. High progesterone levels (>2 ng/ml) are significant and indicate the presence of a luteal structure. These levels of progesterone are observed eight days after mating and remain high in pregnant alpacas. Progesterone assay can therefore be used to determine whether the alpaca has ovulated after mating (>2 ng/ml at 8 days postmating) and if it is possibly pregnant (maintenance of approximately 2ng/ml beyond 14 days postmating). A small proportion of false positive diagnoses may result from the presence of a persistent luteal structure. Pregnancies with a progesterone level of between 1 and 2 ng/ml have consistently been reported, but in my experience all pregnancies were associated with levels of 3 ng/ml or higher. Differences in levels of progesterone may be due to sample handling or the method of progesterone measurement. Progesterone levels lower than 2 ng/ml warrant monitoring of the pregnancy with repeated progesterone tests or ultrasonography.

Palpation Palpation per rectum is possible only if the hand of the operator is small. Pregnancy can be detected by transrectal palpation as early as 35 days (presence of fluid in the uterus). The fetus is not palpable per rectum until three months of gestation. The fetus may be too low in the abdominal cavity and difficult to reach during mid-pregnancy.

The fetus can be balloted (felt by pushing upward against the uterine wall and feeling the return impact of the displaced fetus) externally in late pregnancy, with the alpaca either in a standing or lateral position.

Ultrasonography Ultrasonography is the gold standard for accurate pregnancy diagnosis and evaluation of the growth and viability of the fetus in alpacas. Two methods are used depending on the stage of pregnancy: trans-rectal or trans-abdominal.

Pregnancy diagnosis by trans-rectal ultrasonography is possible as early as nine days postmating if a 7.5 MHz transducer is used. This diagnosis is based on two main criteria: (1) visualization of an embryonic vesicle and (2) visualization of a corpus luteum of pregnancy. Early diagnosis of pregnancy by ultrasonography requires a methodological approach. The uterus should be investigated along all its length and findings should be compared to the ovarian situation. Visualization of a functional corpus luteum in one of the ovaries is a must to confirm pregnancy status.

The embryonic vesicle in camelids is relatively difficult to visualize in early pregnancy because it is elongated, the embryonic fluid is dispersed, and the uterus is relaxed. In the early stage (14 to 16 days postmating), the embryonic vesicle appears and a cross section of the uterine horn is a star-shaped anechoic (not echo-producing) area. In a longitudinal view, the embryonic vesicle is very difficult to recognize at this stage because it is represented by a thin line of fluid. Diagnosis is best made by trying to visualize the vesicle at the tip of the horn where most of the embryonic fluid is likely to have accumulated. The vesicle is almost always present in the left uterine horn.

As the stages of pregnancy progress, the embryonic vesicle increases in size and becomes more visible and round in cross section and oblong in longitudinal views of the uterus. At 18 days of pregnancy, diagnosis of embryonic vesicles should not pose any problem for an experienced examiner. The embryo becomes visible within the embryonic vesicle around day 20 postmating. It appears on the ultrasonogram as a small echogenic area fixed at one pole of the vesicle.

The embryonic mass continues to grow and the fetal heartbeats become visible between days 22 and 25 of pregnancy. All parts of the fetus and its envelopes are easily identifiable by 50 days of pregnancy. Visible fetal parts and their ultrasonographic appearance depend greatly on the orientation of the fetus and that of the transducer.

The corpus luteum is the major source of progesterone during pregnancy in camelids and its presence is required throughout the gestation period. Therefore, visualization of the corpus luteum adds to the accuracy of the early pregnancy diagnosis. In addition, the size and echotexture of the corpus luteum is a good indicator of risks of embryonic loss. All pregnant animals should have at least one functional corpus luteum. The presence of two corpora lutea during pregnancy has been reported in camelids.

Accuracy of early pregnancy diagnosis using ultrasonography depends on the stage of diagnosis, the number of criteria used to make the diagnosis, and the expertise of the operator. It is important to remember that accurate early pregnancy diagnosis does not guarantee a birth approximately 11 months later. Pregnancy diagnosis should be confirmed at later stages because of the high level of embryonic loss in the first two months of pregnancy.

Trans-abdominal ultrasonography is possible after 40 days of pregnancy. The ultrasound frequency of choice is 5 MHz between 40 and 90 days and 3.5 MHz for more advanced stages. In alpacas, the highest accuracy rate (92%) is recorded at 80 days, compared with 90 percent at 70 days of gestation. The accuracy rate falls to 50 to 65 percent at 155 to 165 days of gestation. The increased size of the fetus may make visualization more difficult. Detailed ultrasonographic examination of the fetus is very helpful in determining the gestation stages (measurement of fetal parts) and its viability (movement or cardiac activity).

Determination of the stage of pregnancy is very important to breeders, so they will have a projected parturition date and be ready to monitor the expectant female closely. The practitioner is often asked to determine the approximate stage of gestation, especially in cases of mismating or group breeding. The age of the fetus can be determined by measuring some of its parts. In the llama and alpaca, the formula for determining gestation stages is to measure fetal head and trunk diameter. This formula can be used with relatively good accuracy (error of 10 to 18 days) if four measurements are made between 60 to 75 days after mating until 250 days of pregnancy.

Pregnancy Length

Pregnancy length in alpacas varies between 335 and 359 days.[34,38,75,88] However, I have documented pregnancies of up to 378 days without any effect on the dam or newborn. Breeders have also reported pregnancies of up to 386 days. Possible factors that may affect pregnancy length are breed, sex of the fetus, season, nutrition, and sire and dam. Pregnancy length is 12.5 days longer in spring-mated than in fall-mated alpacas.[34]

DISORDERS OF PREGNANCY

Disorders associated with pregnancy in alpacas include loss of pregnancy due either to early embryonic death or to abortion, stillbirth, uterine torsion, or metabolic disorders such as pregnancy toxemia.

Embryonic Death

Early pregnancy loss is probably the most common form of reduced fertility in alpacas. The incidence of early embryonic death in camelids can be as high as 57.8 percent.[8,25,40,81] In general, early embryonic loss is higher in very young maiden females and in females with a history of infertility or who are more than ten years of age.

A study in New Zealand showed that about one-fourth of all pregnancies will be lost between day 30 of pregnancy and parturition.[55] Pregnancy loss is even higher if pregnancy diagnosis is started earlier (day 10 or 12 postbreeding). In my experience, most fetal losses occur before day 90, with an increased risk around day 12 to 15 and day 35 to 45 of pregnancy. Therefore, it is important to perform a pregnancy diagnosis several times during the pregnancy to determine the viability of the fetus. Unfortunately, many breeders do not suspect fetal loss until the female fails to show external signs of pregnancy or is overdue. Many criteria are used to determine the health of a pregnancy, including shape and growth of the embryonic vesicle, echogenicity of embryonic fluids, cardiac activity of the fetus, growth of the fetus, and finally, movement of the fetus.

In the early stages of pregnancy, the most used criterion is the size of the embryonic vesicle in relation to breeding date and the echogenicity of its contents. The normal embryonic fluid is anechoic. It becomes slightly echoic or contains echogenic debris in case of embryonic death. Fetal heart rate is a good indicator of fetal viability at all stages of pregnancy where the rib cage can be visualized without a problem. Normal fetal heart rate is usually one and one-half to two times that of the dam.

Some of the possible etiologies of embryonic death in camelids include genetic or environmental factors (heat stress), corpus luteum dysfunction, uterine pathology such as infection or fibrosis, and general debilitating diseases. Determination of the exact cause of the embryonic loss may be hard to achieve. Although progesterone insufficiency is always incriminated in these losses, this etiology is probably not the most common. Progesterone decline results from other factors that may affect maintaining the corpus luteum function. Therefore, progesterone supplementation in the form of implants or injection may not work in all cases.

The most common cause of pregnancy loss that I have encountered is uterine fibrosis, which prevents implantation and normal placentation around day 35 to 45 of pregnancy. Attempts to "treat" pregnancy loss with progestogen implants or injection remain anecdotal and not thoroughly and scientifically investigated. There are no precise guidelines on the use of progesterone for pregnancy maintenance in the alpaca. It is important to check the viability of the fetus if this hormone is used on pregnant females, as dead fetuses will be retained as long as the treatment is continued because the cervix will remain closed. Progesterone therapy should be stopped two to three weeks before the expected due date.

Abortion and Stillbirth

Abortion is defined as the expulsion of a nonviable fetus before term. Stillbirth is the delivery of a dead fetus at term. Abortion is usually not clinically visible until about 80 days of pregnancy. In early abortion (day 80 to 100), the aborting dam may show a bloody discharge from the vagina, a dirty tail, or fetal membranes hanging from the vulva. Later in the pregnancy, the aborting dam may show discomfort, development of the udder, and typical signs of first stage labor. The incidence of abortion is probably between 2 and 20 percent.[55] In my practice, the incidence of abortion is about 3 percent. It is important to take each

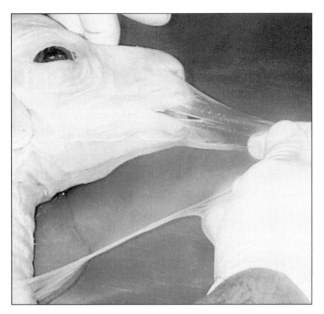

Mucocutenous adhesion of the fourth or epidermal membrane on an alpaca fetus.

abortion seriously, as it may be the beginning of a series of abortions (an abortion storm). Abortion storms are usually due to the introduction of an infection or toxin in the herd. The breeder should collect all tissue (fetus and placenta) and contact a veterinarian or a veterinary diagnostic laboratory for the best method to submit the tissue for an abortion panel.

Many factors can lead to abortion in alpacas. These causes are usually grouped as infectious or noninfectious. Infectious agents that have been associated with abortion include nonspecific bacterial placentitis, brucellosis (*Brucella meltensis*), leptospirosis, toxoplasmosis, and chlamydiosis.[49] Leptospirosis has been associated with abortion storms in llamas and alpacas. Vaccination against leptospirosis is commonly practiced in some areas.

Many factors may contribute to a noninfectious abortion. Intoxication and some treatments, for example, corticosteroids—particularly dexamethasone, even when applied topically in very small doses (eye ointment)—causes abortion. Other drugs associated with abortion include prostaglandin F2 alpha products and eight-way vaccines. Because an alpaca pregnancy depends on the corpus luteum for progesterone secretion, any factors that may induce luteolysis will result in abortion.

Diagnosis of the cause of abortion can be very challenging, and in the best-case scenario, less than half of all cases of abortion will be solved. This rate is even lower in the case of isolated sporadic abortions. To increase the chances of determining the cause of abortion, fresh and frozen or fixed samples of the fetus and the placenta, as well as a blood sample from the aborting dam, should be rushed to a veterinary diagnostic laboratory as soon as possible.

Uterine Torsion

Uterine torsion is probably the most common disorder observed at or shortly before term. Uterine torsion refers to a condition associated with a twisting of the uterine horns around the body of the uterus. The degree of torsion can range from 180 degrees to more than 520 degrees, (a twist and half). Causes of uterine torsion are largely unknown. Factors such as genetic predisposition, rolling, right-side ovulation, and increased fetal motility have been hypothesized, but none has been scientifically demonstrated.[32] The intensity of the clinical signs associated with this condition depends on the severity of the torsion. Torsions are described as either clockwise or counterclockwise depending on the direction of rotation looking from behind the animal. Uterine torsion should be considered in any pregnant female that shows colicky signs, increased straining and vocalization, and a prolonged first stage of labor. As the condition progresses, the female may become severely depressed. Initially the female may show increased heart rate and respiration. In some cases, females may develop stress diarrhea.

Definitive diagnosis is made by trans-rectal palpations, if possible. The objective of this examination is to determine the location and displacement of the broad ligaments that suspend the uterus on each side. In clockwise torsion, which was found by some as the most common direction of torsion in camelids, the broad ligament on the left side runs diagonally from left to right as a tight band over the uterus, while the right broad ligament is shorter and trapped under the uterus (see Figure 13.6). Determination of the direction of torsion may be very difficult if the torsion is very severe and obviously if palpation per rectum is not possible.

Nonsurgical or surgical options are available to correct uterine torsion. The most common nonsurgical method is rolling. This technique may be done only if the direction of the torsion is determined. The alpaca is placed on her side with the side of torsion on the floor. Pressure is maintained on the fetus/uterus by placing both hands on the abdominal wall. The alpaca is then rolled gently toward the direction of the torsion. After each rolling attempt, the alpaca is palpated to determine the location and tightness of the broad ligament. Rolling is repeated until the situation is resolved. Trans-vaginal manipulation may be used to correct the torsion if the cervix is open.

Surgical correction of the torsion requires laparotomy under general anesthesia. Delivery of the fetus by Cesarean

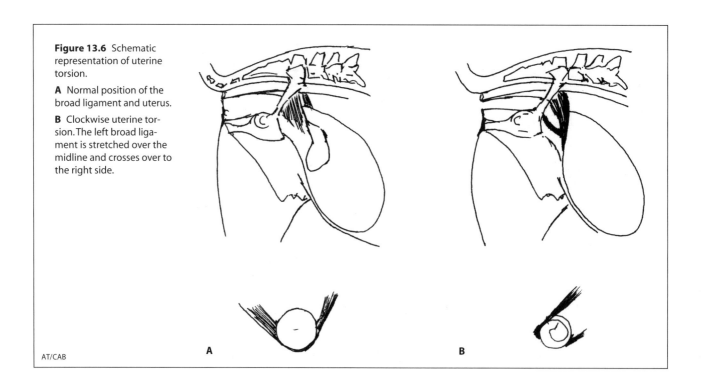

Figure 13.6 Schematic representation of uterine torsion.

A Normal position of the broad ligament and uterus.

B Clockwise uterine torsion. The left broad ligament is stretched over the midline and crosses over to the right side.

AT/CAB

A

B

Uterine torsion is rare, but is an emergency if it occurs. This condition is corrected either by rolling or surgery.

A Correction of uterine torsion by rolling. The veterinarian attempts to hold the fetus in place while the dam is rotated.

B Rolling was unsuccessful in this 300-degree torsion. A surgical left-flank approach was performed to remove the fetus and correct the torsion. The fetus did not survive, but the dam and her reproductive ability were saved.

section may be indicated in some cases, but the viability of the cria may be severely compromised.

Vaginal Prolapse

Vaginal prolapse is a condition characterized by the appearance of various amounts of vaginal tissue at the vulva. In most cases this occurs in thin older alpacas near the end of pregnancy. The bulging of vaginal tissue out of the vulva is more pronounced when the alpaca is kushing. Exposed tissue may become necrotic or infected and may lead to other complications such as complete prolapse or even abortion. This condition is best managed by reducing the vulvar opening using a truss (or shoelace) suture pattern after replacement of the prolapsed tissue. Replacement of the prolapsed vaginal mucosa may require epidural anesthesia if the amount of tissue is very large. It is important to monitor all females with vulvar suture around the time of parturition!

Overdue Alpacas

Most breeders consider 340 days as a standard pregnancy length in alpacas and establish due dates based on this. Pregnancies lasting longer raise the concern of having large crias and increased risks of dystocia. In such cases of prolonged pregnancy, it is important to first verify if the alpaca

is still pregnant. Fetal well-being may need to be evaluated by trans-abdominal ultrasonography.

In general, nothing should be done as long as the dam is well and not showing any sign of distress. Induction of parturition is possible but generally not recommended. Induction of parturition is relatively simple and can be accomplished by injection of PGF2α. In one study, injection

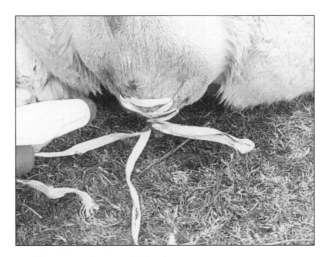

Truss suture closes vaginal prolapse.

of PGF2α after day 330 of pregnancy resulted in the induction of parturition within 20 to 30 hours with no effect on the neonatal behavior of crias or their viability.[24]

PARTURITION

In the traditional South American rearing systems, the majority (93.5%) of births take place between 7:00 am and 1:00 pm, and none are observed at night.[38,79,81] This is probably an adaptation feature of these animals to ensure birth of the young (cria) in the most favorable time of the day for ambient temperatures and protection against predators.

Parturition (birthing), referred to by some alpaca enthusiasts as "creation," "umpacking," or labor, is the culminating point of almost 11.5 months of the process of fetal growth, maturation, and preparation of the dam for delivery and nursing. Becoming familiar with the normal events that occur during different stages of labor is a must for every breeder and is the first step in preserving the well-being of both the dam and the newborn cria. The first step in planning for a healthy birth is the accurate determination of the fertilization date, pregnancy status, and the calculation of the due date based on the average length of pregnancy. During the last few weeks of pregnancy the female should be vaccinated with clostridium CD and T to provide good colostral antibodies for the cria at birth. In the last few days of pregnancy, the pregnant female should be checked regularly for any signs of impending parturition.

Duration of parturition is short in all camelids.[24,28,61,88,100,105] The premonitory signs of parturition include the development of the mammary glands, relaxation of the sacro-pelvic ligaments, and development and relaxation of the vulva. Relaxation of the ligaments can be verified by gentle palpation of the pelvic and perineal areas. Relaxation of the pelvic ligaments can be visible two weeks prior to parturition and can sometimes lead to a bulging of the perineal area when the female is sitting, defecating, or urinating. Relaxation and bulging of the vulva occurs during the last few days or hours of pregnancy and may be the only sign of imminent parturition. However, none of these signs can precisely predict the time of parturition.

Most of the udder development takes place during the last month of pregnancy. Udder development is variable and can be visible as early as two to three weeks prior to parturition, especially in multiparous females, and as late as five days after parturition in primiparous. The weight of the mammary glands increases from 71.1 to 97.1 grams during the first 240 days of pregnancy, and to 143 grams, 192 grams, 453 grams, and 672 grams at 270 days, 300 days, 330 days, and at birth, respectively.[14] Some females may show ventral edema, swelling of the nipples, and waxing (dried colostrum on the nipples), a week before parturition. For better observation of the birthing process, the tail of the female should be wrapped as soon as dilation of the vulva is noticed. Tail wraps should not be tight and should be changed every other day.

Relaxation and bulging of the vulva and perineal area are observed from a few days to only a few hours before birth, due to relaxation of the ligaments.

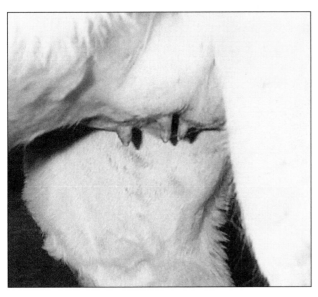

Development of the mammary glands prior to birth.

In the second stage of labor, the fetus appears shortly after the rupture of the second water bag.

First Stage of Labor

The first stage of labor lasts two to four hours and may be controlled to some extent by the female. During this period the frequency of urination increases. The dam can show signs of anxiety, seek solitude, and frequently visit the dung pile. Some females go off feed and show signs of colic.[29,31]

Moderate amounts of rolling or lying on one side is frequently observed during the first stage of parturition. The rolling and alternating of position are believed to help the fetus get into a normal birthing position. Excessive signs of rolling, kicking at the belly, and vocalization or grunting should be taken seriously, as they may signal uterine torsion.

Second Stage of Labor

The second stage of labor (expulsion of the fetus) is very short, lasting 15 minutes on the average (5 to 40 minutes).[31,49] Uterine contractions occur every ten minutes at the beginning of the second stage and become more frequent and intense as the fetus is expelled. Nearly all fetuses are born in an anterior presentation and dorso-sacral position (head and front legs first and the back of the fetus toward the back of the dam). Most (65–73%) of the fetuses are delivered while the dam is standing, and the umbilical cord ruptures 5 to 15 centimeters (2–8 in.) from the fetal abdominal wall.[31,49]

Chronologically, the fetus will appear at the vulva shortly after the rupture of the first water bag. The second water bag is recognized by its white translucent color. It forms a small balloon at the vulva before breaking. In most

A normal anterior presentation in the second stage of labor; both front legs and head are now visible.

The mother may alternately stand and lie down during the birth process.

Second stage is completed. A cria, just minutes old, rights itself while the placenta emerges.

Third stage of labor is complete. The placenta is expelled and the cria struggles to stand.

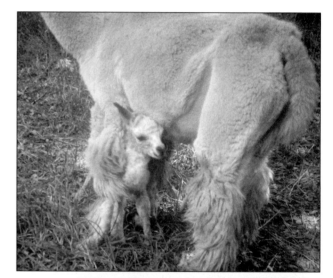

Middle right The cria begins its search for teats, which can take a while.

Right The cria finds its mother's teats and begins nursing.

cases, only the nose will be visible, then progressively the whole head and the front legs will pass through the slowly dilating vulva. The fetus is expelled due to the combined contraction of the uterus and abdominal muscle. During this process, the dam may alternate between a lateral and standing position. Obstetrical intervention should be planned if the female has broken the first water bag and nothing is appearing at the vulva within 20 minutes or if she is showing signs of distress. Once the cria is on the ground, it should show an interest in nursing within the first hour. It should immediately be cared for and examined, as explained in Chapter 14: Obstetrics and Neonatology.

Third Stage of Labor

Expulsion of the placenta usually occurs within one hour of delivery of the fetus, but may take up to three hours without noticeable complication in the dam. The placenta is sometimes delivered inside out. Placenta weight and size vary with the size of the dam and parity (number of births). The placenta generally weighs 800 grams to 1,000 grams (1.75–2.2 lb).

Examination of the fetal membranes (placenta) is very important to detect any infectious processes that may have contaminated the fetus and to ensure that there is no partial retention. The placenta should be inverted so one can thoroughly examine its chorionic surface for lesions. The chorionic surface is the side of the placenta that was in contact with the uterine wall. It usually has a dark red (burgundy) color and a velvety texture due to the presence of microvilli. It may show some areas of bare tissue but no necrotic tips. These bare areas are usually found in a regular pattern on the surface of the placenta and probably correspond to a zone of high stress and ripped tissue, which occurs during invagination (folding so that it becomes inside out) within the uterus. Small protein and mucus concretions, 1 to 3 centimeters in length, called "hippomanes," may be present within the allantoic sac. These are perfectly normal and are believed to be an aggregation of dead cells and proteins.

POSTPARTUM

Postpartum is the period from delivery to reestablishment of a uterine and ovarian condition compatible with the ability to be pregnant. In the alpaca this period is relatively short. Normal postpartum vaginal discharge, called lochia, is minimal in camelids and only a small amount of reddish or tan mucoid discharge is noticed during the first few days after parturition. In normal cases, this discharge becomes thick and scant after four to five days. Uterine involution (decrease in uterine size) is rapid. A rapid change in the

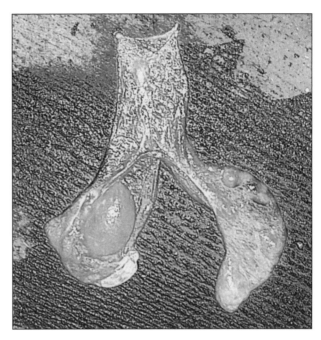

Examination of the placenta is very important. The complete placenta shows both uterine horns.

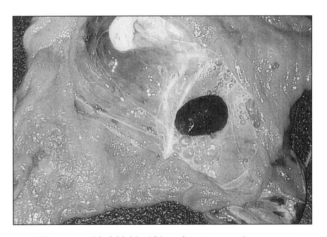

A hippomane (dark blob) within a placenta sometimes causes alarm, though it is a normal occurrence.

weight of the uterus is observed during the first ten days postpartum. Uterine weight decreases from 883 grams (about 1.9 lb) at 24 hours to one-third of that at 5 days and one-fifth at 10 days postpartum.[15] The diameter of the left horn decreases from 15 centimeters (7 in.) at delivery to 3.5 to 3 centimeters (1.5–1 in.) at 10 and 20 days postpartum, respectively.[84]

The CL, now changing to a corpus albicans or CA, decreases rapidly in size during the first 10 days postpartum and then slowly decreases between 10 and 20 days postpartum.[84]

The interval from parturition to resumption of ovarian follicular activity is about five days and mature follicles are present by ten days. Females can accept males as early as 24 hours after parturition but these matings are never followed by ovulation.[75,84] Ovarian follicles are less than 3 millimeters in diameter 24 hours after parturition and increase steadily during the next 10 days.[15,88] First postpartum ovulation has been observed at five days with a conception rate of 30 percent.[15,84] Fertile mating can occur as early as day 15 postpartum. However, ovulation and conception rates are low before ten days after parturition.[15,84] All females should have at least two follicular waves by day 18 postpartum.[15]

The interval from parturition to breeding has a significant effect on the incidence of ovulation and on embryo survival beyond day 40. In one study, the proportion of alpacas ovulating 10, 20, and 30 days postpartum was respectively 64.5 percent, 76.9 percent, and 83.9 percent, with conception rates of 62.5 percent, 87.5 percent, and 90.4 percent, respectively. However, the proportion of females that experienced pregnancy loss by day 40 was 24 percent, 11.4 percent, and 6.4 percent for breeding at 10, 20, and 30 days postpartum, respectively.[15]

POSTPARTUM DISORDERS

The postpartum period is very critical in the reproductive life of a female alpaca. Complications during or immediately after birth can lead to compromised future fertility, as well as severe consequences to the newborn cria if the female is unable to nurse. Most postpartum complications stem from dystocia or metabolic diseases.

Retained Placenta

The placenta is generally considered retained if not delivered in its entirety within the first three hours after parturition, and your local veterinarian should be consulted. Placental retention may be due to several factors, including uterine inertia (lack of contractions), placentitis, and exhaustion. Factors that may increase the risk of placental retention include dystocia, abortion, or stillbirth, delivery by Cesarean section, adhesions due to placentitis, and hypocalcemia. If left untreated, placental retention may lead to severe uterine infection and toxic shock in the female.

Thorough evaluation of the dam for any signs of toxemia or underlying metabolic diseases should always be considered. The severity of a retained placenta should be evaluated by tugging gently on the part of the placenta showing from the vulva. In many cases the placenta is completely detached and not expelled because of the lack of uterine contraction.

If the placenta seems to be firmly attached, a first treatment would be administration of 10 to 20 IUs of oxytocin. This treatment can be administered as a single dose, in two doses of 5 IUs at 10-minute intervals, or in a lactate ringer IV drip over a 15-minute period. Most animals will respond within one hour. If the placenta proves difficult to remove manually or if no response is obtained following administration of oxytocin, an intravenous catheter should be inserted and systemic antibiotic and nonsteroidal anti-inflammatory therapy started. Retention of the placenta for more than 24 hours has been very rare in my experience.

Uterine Prolapse

Uterine prolase is the complete protrusion of the uterus from the vulva. This condition has been associated with long, difficult births; excessive vaginal manipulation; and excessive pulling on the placenta. However, prolapse of the uterus may occur in females that had otherwise normal, nondifficult births and delivery of the placenta. This seems to occur more frequently in the older female. Uterine prolapse may also occur following the induction of abortion.

Replacement of the prolapsed uterus is not difficult if the condition is seen early. The placenta should be peeled off gently before replacing the uterus; this prevents recurrence of the condition. The uterine wall should be thoroughly cleaned with clean, warm water and repositioned by gentle massage starting at the vulva and working toward the tips of the uterine horns. In some cases, uterine edema may have developed by the time the condition is noticed, which will make correction more difficult. Wrapping the uterus in a wet towel and compressing it may help reduce its size and facilitate replacement. Replacement of the uterus may be easier if the female is sedated and placed in a kush position with the hindquarters elevated. The replaced uterus can be kept in place by truss suture on the vulva. The female should be observed frequently for the first 12 hours for signs of straining. Epidural anesthesia or sedation may help reduce straining.

Postpartum Metritis

Postpartum metritis can be a complication of prolonged inadequate obstetrical manipulations, nonhygienic conditions in the birthing area, and contamination of the uterus with partial or total placental retention. Excessive malodorous vaginal discharge may be noticed a few days after parturition. Some females may develop fever and toxic shock if the infection is severe. Postpartum metritis with systemic signs of illness requires intensive care with fluid therapy and systemic antibiotics. Uterine lavage may be required to rid the uterine cavity of debris.

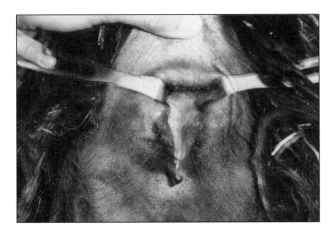

Perineal body laceration and trauma to the vulva are common injuries following a difficult birth.

Uterine Hemorrhage/Rupture

Rupture of the uterine wall or large uterine blood vessels within the broad ligaments is possible but relatively rare. Uterine rupture may occur following a severe dystocia or trauma in late-term pregnancy. Hemorrhage may lead to severe anemia and shock. Rupture of the uterus leads to peritonitis.[9] Surgical repair of the uterus via laparotomy may be attempted if the condition is diagnosed early. Uterine rupture may also occur as a sequel to Cesarean section.

Laceration and Trauma

Trauma to the birth canal, the vulva, and the perineal area are commonly seen after a difficult birth or inappropriate obstetrical manipulation. Laceration to the birth canal may lead to complete adhesions and loss of reproductive ability. The most common traumatic lesion is third-degree perineal laceration and formation of a cloacae. Reconstruction of the area may be attempted surgically within two to three weeks after birth.

BREEDING MANAGEMENT OF THE FEMALE ALPACA

Management errors account for a significant number of infertility cases. Management errors include breeding with a young male, overuse of males, lack of verification of intromission during copulation, breeding females at the wrong phase of the cycle, inadequate protocol for testing for pregnancy, and inadequate management of the pregnant female. Table 13.2 summarizes the management procedures needed to improve reproductive efficiency. If the stage of the cycle is not known, females should be teased and bred if they are receptive. Each bred female should be teased three days later and bred again if receptive. Females that are not pregnant after two breeding cycles with a proven male should be thoroughly evaluated for infertility. Table 13.3 covers the steps to follow in managing pregnant and parturient alpaca females.

Table 13.2 Management procedures for improved reproductive efficiency.

When	What to Do
Before target breeding date	
Months before	Design a mating plan for genetic improvement. Contact potential sire owner for breeding contracts.
One month before	Make sure all vaccinations are current and body condition is evaluated. Examine sires for breeding soundness. Evaluate maiden females for breeding soundness.
During the breeding season	
Day 1 (day of receptivity)	Breed female if receptive. Record breeding date and length of breeding.
Day 3	Check again for receptivity (spit check). Breed if receptive. Wait 6 days and recheck if not receptive.
Day 9	Tease. If receptive, breed and start over from day 1. If spitting, wait another 5 days.
	Perform progesterone test. If positive, wait until days 12–14. If negative, continue to tease.
Days 12–14	Tease. If receptive after spitting on day 9, breed and start over from day 3. If spitting, perform ultrasound exam.
	Perform ultrasound exam (gold standard). If pregnant, recheck in 15 days unless female becomes receptive again. If negative, tease or breed according to follicle size.
	Perform progesterone test. If high, wait another week and recheck or do ultrasound exam.
Day 30	Perform ultrasound exam. If pregnant, wait another 30 days and recheck. If open, evaluate the female for early pregnancy loss.
Day 60	Perform trans-abdominal ultrasound exam. If pregnant, no further exam is needed (see Table 13.3). If open, evaluate for cause of early embryonic death.

Table 13.3 Management of the pregnant and parturient female.

When	What to Do
First month of pregnancy	Check with ultrasound for confirmation, check body condition score
Second or third month of pregnancy	Recheck pregnancy status and fetal viability
Last trimester	Adjust nutrition, check body condition score
Last month of pregnancy	Vaccinate (CDT), check body condition score
Last week of pregnancy	Close observation
Parturition	Observe and intervene if necessary
Postparturient First day	Provide neonatal care Check for any abnormalities in placenta, treat if retained placenta Check udder for abnormalities
First week	Check for abnormal discharge Check for abnormal cria growth Evaluate and treat any uterine infection
Second week	Reevaluate if a complicated birth or retained placenta
Third week	Breed a normal receptive female and proceed as in Table 13.2

DIAGNOSING FEMALE INFERTILITY AND REPRODUCTIVE DISORDERS

Outside of routine health care, the diagnosis and treatment of reproductive disorders is the most common veterinary act in individual alpaca medicine. This does not mean that alpacas have a lower reproductive potential than other species, but rather reflects the complexity of breeding management. The methodology for the diagnosis of causes of reproductive disorders relies on several types of procedures, commonly called a breeding soundness evaluation.

Breeding Soundness Examination

A breeding soundness evaluation of the female consists of an examination protocol covering all aspects of the medical history, health parameters, and reproductive behavior, and a detailed examination of reproductive organs. Using this protocol, the veterinarian is able to arrive at a diagnosis of the reason for infertility and institute a therapy. Or an informed decision can be made to remove the animal from the breeding program, which will avoid distressing sterile females and unnecessary owner expense.

History and General Physical Examination A general and reproductive history is an important tool for determining causes of reproductive failure and prognosis. The history should cover all parameters that may have an impact on reproductive performance, including, age, type of animal, breeding record and breeding management system. A history of previous illnesses and treatments is important because of the possible effect on reproductive performance and it helps identify females with high-risk pregnancies. Most alpaca breeders keep detailed health and breeding records. Complete clinical evaluation of the female, including body condition, should be done before any manipulation of the genital tract.

Evaluation of Sexual Behavior Female behavior provides a relatively accurate and inexpensive means for pregnancy diagnosis (see "Reproductive Behavior"). One important aspect to remember is that the possibility of pregnancy should not be based on behavior alone.

Examination of the Perineum and Vulva The vulva is inspected for any discharge or lesions and its size and conformation is evaluated. The size of the vulva in camelids is relatively small compared to other species. Females presenting increased size and edema of the vulva should be examined for recent parturition or abortion.

Abnormal size and position of the vulva in maiden females may suggest the presence of congenital problems or

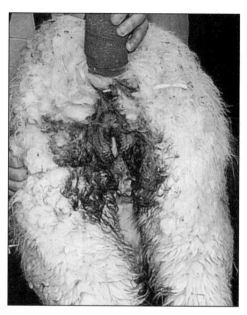

The vaginal discharge indicates a uterine infection. Infections can also be present without discharge.

intersexuality. Intersexed animals present ambiguous external genitalia, sometimes with a rudimentary penis. Copious vaginal discharge beyond seven days postpartum is almost always pathological. Vaginal discharge is suspected upon observation of dried material on the ventral side of the tail or by matting of the fiber around the tail and perineal area.

Palpation per Rectum Per rectum palpation of the genitalia is an essential part of the examination of the female camelid. Rectal tears or colonic injuries can result from rectal palpation by nontrained persons.[77] Per rectum palpation should only be attempted if the hands of the operator are small and can easily be inserted in the rectal cavity. A lubricant containing a local anesthetic such as lidocaine 2 percent at a rate of 10 percent volume (1 part lidocaine to 10 parts lubricant) helps dilate the anal sphincter and reduce peristaltic activity of the colon and rectum. Epidural anesthesia provides relaxation of the anal sphincter but will not inhibit rectal peristaltic activity. Ovarian structures (corpus luteum, follicles) are palpable in large alpacas. The cervix is difficult to differentiate from the uterine body by palpation. However, its posterior orifice can be felt per rectum if the uterus is contracted. Uterine tone and edema increase during the follicular phase and become maximal in the presence of a mature follicle. The uterus is flaccid and thin walled during pregnancy.

Increased size of the uterus in the absence of pregnancy can be due to pyometra or mucometra. Palpation of the uterine horn can reveal some localized pathological processes such as peri- or intrauterine abscesses, peri- or

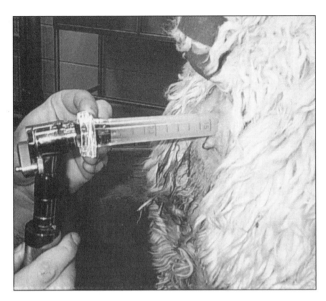

A vaginal examination using a sigmoidoscope.

intrauterine cysts, and peri-uterine adhesions. Other types of abnormal uterine content that can be felt by palpation per rectum are fetal parts (especially bones in case of maceration), mummification, foreign bodies, and cysts.

Vaginal Examination A digital examination of the vestibulo-vaginal area should be performed on all maiden females (persistent hymen and segmental aplasia) and females with pyometra or hydrometra (vestibular or vaginal adhesions). Open (slit) specula are helpful if a biopsy punch or a culture swab needs to be guided into the cervix. The most frequent abnormalities encountered in the vagina and cervix are inflammations or adhesions. Vaginal adhesions are a frequent cause of pyometra and inability to copulate. The most frequent developmental abnormality of the cervix in camelids is the presence of a double cervix. Several types of specula may be used for this examination. A sigmoidoscope provides a good visualization of the vaginal cavity and cervix.

Ultrasonography of the Female Genital Tract

The veterinarian should conduct all ultrasonographic examinations of the camelid genital tract with the animal in a standing position and restrained in a chute. This initial examination allows the practitioner to determine the general position of the genital organs so that the ultrasound probe can be positioned appropriately. Trans-rectal ultrasonography of the genital tract is performed using a 7.5 MHz or 5 MHz linear transducer. The transducer is mounted on a long handle to allow manipulation without inserting a hand in the rectum.

The different parts of the genital tract are examined in the following order: the cervix, the body of the uterus, then each uterine horn, followed by the ipsilateral uterine tube, ovary, and ovarian bursa. Ultrasonography allows a precise evaluation of follicular and luteal activity within the ovary. In the nonpregnant female, the ovaries are scanned by following the uterine horn all the way to its tip, then by moving the probe slightly caudally and laterally. The ovary is usually easy to identify if it has some follicular activity. Determination of ultrasonographic characteristics of ovarian structure and the uterus, and their relationship to each other at different stages of the cycle have allowed better and more efficient management of reproduction in alpacas. The uterus is also examined for size, echogenicity of the wall, and content.

During the follicular phase, the uterus is contracted and the uterine horns are straight, especially in the presence of a mature follicle. The echotexture of the uterus is usually heterogeneous and shows increased edema and endometrial folds giving the uterine horn a characteristic appearance. The degree of edema increases toward the end of the follicular phase and disappears slowly (over a two- to three-day period) following mating. The uterine cavity can show increased echogenicity due to the presence of thick mucus. During the luteal phase (presence of a mature corpus luteum, plasma progesterone ≥2 ng/ml), the uterus is homogeneous with a medium degree of echogenicity, and shows some curling.

Evaluation of the uterus after parturition is a good practice for the management of early postpartum breeding in the alpaca. The early postpartum period is characterized by a highly vascularized uterus and a large diameter of the uterine horns. The uterine cavity usually presents some fluid up to five days postpartum. The uterus is contracted and has a heterogeneous echotexture in the early postpartum period, then becomes more homogeneous after the evacuation of all fluid and a decrease of uterine edema.

The echotexture of the cervix varies in the same manner as that of the uterus during the different phases of the pregnancy cycle. During the follicular phase, the cervix is contracted and dark due to the presence of intercellular fluid (edema). Its contour is not very clear. It becomes tight and more echogenic during the luteal phase. The cervical fold becomes more and more hyperechogenic with advancing pregnancy.

Pathological changes of the ovaries detected by ultrasonography include hypoplasia, cystic changes (anovulatory or hemorrhagic follicles), inflammation, and tumors. Hypoplastic ovaries are very small and cannot be found by palpation or ultrasonography. In camelids, development of large anovulatory hemorrhagic follicles is quite common in the absence of ovulation-inducing stimulus. Peri-ovarian cysts are not rare and should be differentiated from enlarged oviducts (hydro or pyosalpinx). Ovarian inflammation (oophoritis) is suspected when the ovarian size is normal or slightly increased and does not show clear delineation from the rest of the tissue. Ovarian tumors are suspected when the ovary is enlarged and does not show the normal follicular dynamic. The ultrasonographic appearance of the ovary depends on the type of neoplasm.

Abnormalities of ultrasonographic appearance can be of two types: abnormal uterine echotexture (endometritis, metritis, neoplasm) and abnormal uterine content (pyometra, mummification, maceration, embryonic death).[93,95] Evaluation of the uterine wall can be facilitated by ultrasonography during the uterine flushing process.

The uterus is heterogeneous and presents several degrees of echogenicity in cases with chronic inflammatory processes. The contour of the uterus becomes less well-defined in the presence of peri-uterine adhesions. Abnormal uterine content can vary from free fluid to localized cysts or abscesses. Ultrasonography is also a valuable tool for the study of pathological conditions during pregnancy, such as early embryo loss. The presence of a large amount of fluid in the uterus of camelids, in the absence of pregnancy, is usually due to cervical adhesions or segmental aplasia.

Uterine Cytology and Culture

Endometritis is a common cause of infertility in alpacas and can be confirmed by uterine cytology or culture. Samples should be taken from the uterine cavity using a double-guarded swab. Swabs are examined routinely for aerobic and anaerobic bacteria. Uterine culture may be negative in many cases of chronic endometritis.

Uterine Biopsy

Uterine biopsy is used to detect inflammatory, degenerative, or neoplastic changes in the endometrium.[72] The technique may present some difficulty because of the smallness of the animal. I prefer to use a small biopsy punch when the cervix is totally open. The cervix can be opened by administration of estradiol (1–2 mg) 12 hours before biopsy; however, this treatment does not always help. Evaluation of the specimen should be done by a person familiar with the normal histology of the camelid endometrium. Degenerative changes are mainly due to the presence of peri-glandular or peri-vascular fibrosis. In severe cases, nesting with cystic dilation of the endometrial glands or lymphatic cysts is observed. A classification of lamoid (alpacas and llamas) endometrial biopsies has been proposed.[72]

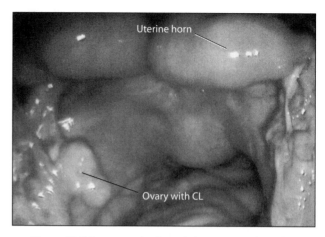

Figure 13.7 Laparoscopic view of the uterus and ovaries. Note the right ovary with a corpus luteum.

Laparoscopy

Laparoscopy consists of the introduction of a rigid laparoscope into the abdominal cavity under general anesthesia and visualizing all internal genital organs. This technique is invaluable for the confirmation of lesions suspected as a result of ultrasonography or palpation (ovarian hypoplasia, hydrosalpinx, segmental aplasia, peri-uterine adhesions), particularly when palpation is impossible.[102] This technique requires general anesthesia (see Figure 13.7).

Hysteroscopy

Hysteroscopy is a technique allowing close examination of the uterine cavity. A flexible videoendoscope is introduced into the uterus via the cervical canal. The uterine cavity can be evaluated for the presence of adhesions, cystic dilation, or abnormal content. Targeted biopsy can be performed in combination with hysteroscopy.[93,106]

Cytogenetic Evaluation

All camelids have the same number of chromosomes ($n=74$). Abnormal karyotype has been associated with different forms of reproductive problems in camelids.[93,99] Cytogenetic studies should be considered when external sexual characteristics are ambiguous.

Hormonal Evaluation

Determination of progesterone levels in the blood is probably the most widely used hormone assay in alpacas. Progesterone levels above 2 ng/ml indicate the presence of a functional corpus luteum or luteinized anovulatory follicle. This assay is used to determine occurrence of ovulation in bred females. Pregnancy is suspected if the progesterone level remains high in a second sample taken two weeks after breeding. This method of pregnancy diagnosis is relatively precise if the breeding history is accurate. A plasma estrogen level above 10 pg/ml in plasma is a good indicator of follicular activity in the female.

ENDOCRINOLOGY

Endocrinology of the Reproductive Cycle

Understanding the relationship between various hormones and ovarian and uterine function is fundamental to understanding the use of hormone assays in the investigation of reproductive function. The main hormones involved in the reproductive function come from the ovary (estrogen and progesterone), the uterus (prostaglandin F2 alpha), and the pituitary gland or hypophysis (LH, FSH, and oxytocin). The interaction of these hormones is illustrated in Figures 13.8 and 13.9.

Estrogen (estradiol-17ß and estrone sulfate) profiles during the cycle show that both urinary estrogen levels and estradiol-17ß plasma levels correlate well with follicular waves and give a good indication of ovarian follicular status.[18,20] Plasma estrogen levels decrease rapidly just be-

fore ovulation.[16] Urinary estrogen falls sharply 24 hours after ovulation.[11,18,68] Levels of urinary estrone sulfate and plasma estradiol-17ß peak at 20 to 30 pg/ml and 10 to 15 pg/ml, respectively, when the diameter of the follicle reaches its pre-ovulatory size (8–12 mm).[11] Another increase in urinary estrogen is observed five to six days after ovulation and corresponds to the emergence of a new follicular wave.[68] Estrogens are responsible for receptive behavior and cause increased tone and edema of the uterus.

Luteinizing hormone (LH) is secreted by the pituitary gland and is responsible for the ovulation of the largest follicle. LH and prostaglandin F2 alpha (PGF2α) increase immediately after mating.[2] An LH surge is observed within 30 minutes of copulation in camelids and lasts 7 to 8 hours.[18,59,60,100] Significant LH release can be observed as early as 15 minutes after the onset of copulation and increases three- to five-fold within 2 to 3 hours.[18,20] This pituitary response to coitus is similar to species in which the induction of ovulation by copulation is due to LH release via a neural reflex (e.g, cats).

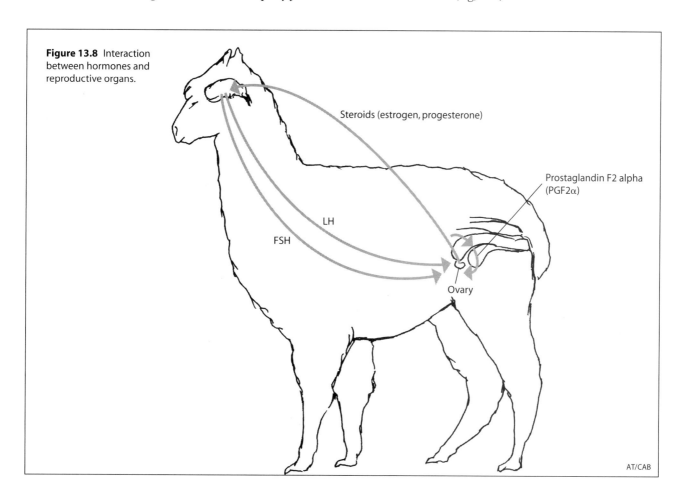

Figure 13.8 Interaction between hormones and reproductive organs.

Steroids (estrogen, progesterone)

Prostaglandin F2 alpha (PGF2α)

LH

FSH

Ovary

AT/CAB

Stage 3 of the Reproductive Cycle	Behavior	Uterus	Ovary	Pituitary Gland
Folllicular recruitment	Variable		Multiple small follicles	FSH is released and induces follicular growth
Follicular dominance	Very receptive	Uterus toned and cervix open	One dominant follicle mature at 8 to 12 mm; produces estrogen	
Ovulation 24 to 48 hours after mating	Receptive	Mating occurs; semen is deposited inside the uterus; triggers LH release	Ovulation	LH released 30 minutes after mating and causes ovulation
Day 5 to day 9 after mating	Spitting	Uterus is relaxed; cervix is closed	Corpus luteum produces progesterone (>2 ng/mL)	
Nonpregnant day 12 after mating	Receptive	Uterus releases prostaglandin F2α if no embryo is present	Corpus luteum regression; new follicle; progesterone low; estrogen high	FSH is released and induces folliculur growth
Pregnant day 12 and beyond	Spitting very strongly	Presence of embryo	Corpus luteum maintained; no PG2α released from uterus; progesterone remains high	

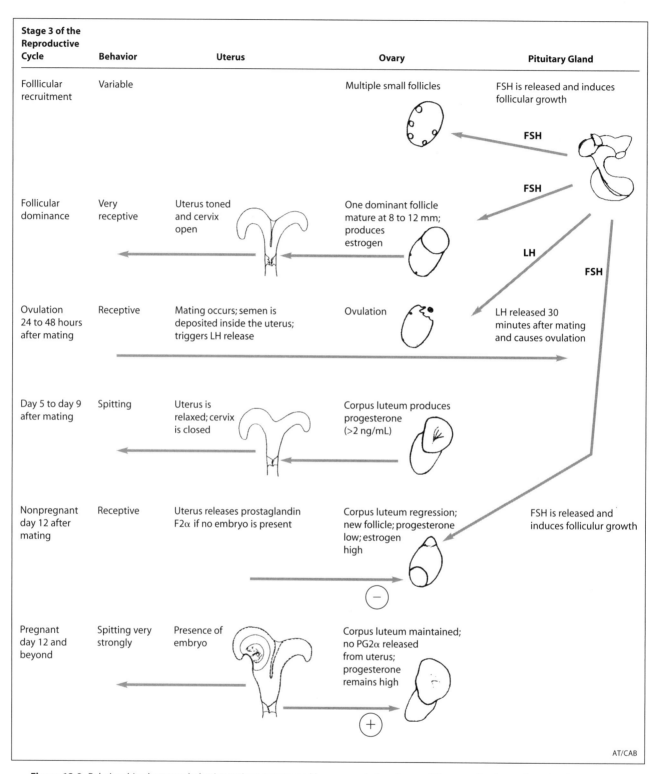

AT/CAB

Figure 13.9 Relationships between behavior, various organs, and hormones during stages of the reproductive cycle and early pregnancy.

Measurement of LH and FSH following copulation showed that an adequate LH surge is obtained only in females with growing or regressing follicles, while only a small LH release is obtained when small follicles (4–5 mm) are present.[18] The LH surge that follows mating induces ovulation in alpacas with growing follicles (7–12 mm) and luteinization in regressing follicles.[18,20] It is important to note that a second and third mating 6 and 24 hours after the first do not cause another peak of LH. This suggests that all pituitary LH is released after the initial breeding.[20] Therefore, increasing the number of matings does not necessarily decrease the incidence of ovulation failure, which can be as high as 30 percent.[38,42]

FSH, another hormone secreted by the pituitary gland, is responsible for follicular growth. Little information is available on the FSH profile during the cycle in alpacas. FSH levels present high individual variability. These levels are generally independent of follicular size and mating stimulus.[17]

Progesterone is a steroid secreted by the corpus luteum. In the absence of ovulation, plasma concentrations of progesterone remain low (<1 ng/ml) throughout the follicular cycle. In the presence of ovulation, progesterone appears in the blood two to three days after ovulation or three to four days after mating.[2,41] Progesterone levels reach a maximum on the eighth day after hCG treatment, then decrease sharply by day 13.[39] More precise (daily) measurements of progesterone in alpacas after mating to vasectomized males show an increase at five days, a maximum at seven to eight days, and a return to basal level at ten days.[83,87]

Prostaglandin F2 alpha (PGF2α) is secreted by the nonpregnant uterus and is responsible for the destruction of the CL (luteolysis). This effect produces a decrease in blood progesterone and a return to receptivity. Nonpregnant alpacas will become receptive again 12 to 14 days after ovulation.

In summary, the luteal phase, determined by plasma progesterone profile, lasts nine days. The progesterone level remains very low during the first 4 days after mating, then increases significantly on day 6, reaching a maximum between days 8 and 9 (10–14 ng/ml) before decreasing to basal levels (<1 ng/ml) on day 11. Luteolysis is associated with a significant increase in PGF2α.[2,87] The concentration of progesterone does not exceed 0.4 ng/ml in nonovulating females.[2] Progesterone levels during the cycle can be affected by the type of ovulatory stimulus and on the quality and number of corpora lutea. Plasma levels of progesterone are positively correlated to the size of the corpus luteum.

Endocrinology of Pregnancy

Hormonal activity during pregnancy is important for the development of the uterus, fetus, fetal membrane, and maintenance of pregnancy. Hormonal changes are also responsible for adequate preparation of the mammary glands for lactation and the uterus for proper delivery of the fetus. Changes in the hormonal profile during pregnancy are presented in a simplified scheme in Figure 13.10.

Estrogen Estrone sulfate concentration remains low during the first 17 days of pregnancy, then increases rapidly between days 21 and 25, probably as a result of the aromatizing activity of the trophoblast.[2,3,23,56] Another increase is seen from the eleventh month of pregnancy until delivery.[23]

In the pregnant llama, estradiol-17ß varies between 10 and 46 pg/ml during most of pregnancy and does not peak (196±10 pg/ml) until the final third of pregnancy.[3] During the first nine months of pregnancy, the combined estrone + estradiol-17ß and estradiol-17ß concentrations range between 6 and 274 pg/ml and 4 and 114 pg/ml, respectively. In the llama, after the ninth month of pregnancy these levels increase to peak at 827±58 pg/ml for estrone + estradiol-17ß and 196±10 pg/ml for estradiol-17ß during the last week of pregnancy.[56] Similar changes

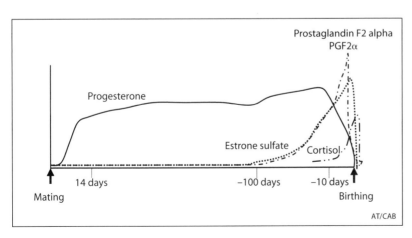

Figure 13.10 Hormonal changes during pregnancy. Progesterone remains elevated past day 14 after mating. Estrone sulfate and prostaglandin F2 alpha start increasing slowly in the last three months (–100 days). Ten days (–10) before birth, progesterone starts to fall and is very low just before parturition. Cortisol increases in the last few days prior to labor. Graph is not to scale.

Progesterone The corpus luteum is the primary gland secreting progesterone during pregnancy. The role of this hormone is to prepare the uterus for the embryo and to maintain the pregnancy. The first increase in plasma progesterone is observed by day three to four following mating. Progesterone secretion by the corpus luteum becomes significant five days after mating, as evidenced by the increase in levels of this hormone in the plasma and its metabolite in the urine.[1,2] Levels of plasma progesterone usually remain above 2.0 ng/ml throughout pregnancy.[23] Since the main source of progesterone during pregnancy is the corpus luteum, administration of luteolytic doses of PGF2α or its analogues, or surgical ablation of the corpus luteum, results in abortion if done before the tenth month of pregnancy, and in premature birth or induction of parturition if done later.[24,80]

The diameter of the corpus luteum of pregnancy varies between 12 and 16 millimeters. No further significant increase in the weight of corpora lutea or progesterone levels above the values reached on day eight have been observed in pregnant females. A transient decrease in progesterone has been described between days 8 and 18 in pregnant females.[1,2,6,41] This stage corresponds to the time for release of PGF2α in nonpregnant females and embryo elongation, and may represent a critical period for embryo survival. A rise in PGF2α, similar to that observed in nonpregnant females, occurs between day 8 and day 11 but is of lower magnitude.[1] A high incidence of double corpora lutea on the same ovary has been reported for alpacas,[14] but no secondary corpora lutea have formed following a single ovulation.

During the last month of pregnancy, plasma progesterone concentrations varies between 5 and 9 ng/ml.[81] Progesterone starts to decline about 2 weeks before parturition, drops markedly during the final 24 hours before parturition, and returns to basal concentrations (<0.5 ng/ml) by the day of parturition. A similar decline is found in the urinary metabolite of progesterone (pregnediol glucoronide) during the last five days of pregnancy.[3] However, complete withdrawal of progesterone does not occur prior to delivery.[3] The regulatory mechanisms associated with the gradual decline in progesterone concentrations during the two weeks before parturition are unknown and could be due to the conversion of progesterone to estrogen by 17-hydroxylase, synthesized in response to fetal cortisol secretion.

Prostaglandin F2 alpha (PGF2α) PGF2α metabolites increase steadily during the last 100 days of pregnancy. A surge in PGF2α is observed on the morning of the day of parturition and coincides with a decrease in progesterone. PGF2α concentration returns to basal levels three days after delivery.[3]

Relaxin The relaxin level is low during the first months of pregnancy, then increases significantly at three and a half months. A decrease in this hormone is observed between five and a half and seven months of pregnancy, followed by a steady increase until parturition. Relaxin is probably secreted by the feto-placental unit and is implicated in the growth of the uterus during pregnancy and relaxation of the ligaments and cervix at the end of pregnancy.[23]

Endocrinology of Parturition

An increase in estrogen is observed during the last days of pregnancy. Urinary estrone sulfate concentrations increase before parturition and remain high through the initiation of parturition, declining only at the end of delivery.[3] Increased concentration of estrogen one week before parturition could be due to increased contractions of the uterus and the beginning of dehiscence of the placenta. Estrone sulfate starts to increase 80 days before parturition, peaks immediately before parturition, and drops sharply on the day of parturition or one day later.[3] Estradiol-17ß is high during the last 45 days of pregnancy, decreases on the day of parturition, and is very low two days postpartum.[3]

PGF2α increases massively on the day of parturition, then decreases three days after delivery.[3] Progesterone drops in response to this increased PGF2α release. The cortisol concentration is elevated at parturition and the day preceding labor.[3]

Postpartum Endocrinology

The endocrinology of the immediate postpartum period is characterized by a fall of progesterone due to regression of the corpus luteum. Progesterone levels are very low as early as 24 hours after parturition.[3,11] Progesterone levels remain low until the female is bred. As expected, an increase is observed four to six days following breeding and ovulation and formation of a normal corpus luteum.[3,11]

Plasma estradiol and urinary estrone sulfate concentrations closely follow follicular activity in the postpartum period. In the llama, significant estrone sulfate levels compatible with the presence of a normal dominant follicle were observed between five and ten days postpartum.[3,19,56]

Studies on pituitary hormone secretions during the postpartum period are not available. However, from observation of the ovarian function and steroid hormone profiles, one can assume that pituitary activity (FSH and LH secretion) are reestablished very early during the postpartum period. Lower response of the pituitary to copulation is to be suspected during the first ten days postpartum. Low LH in response to breeding is suspected to be the cause of the low ovulation response in early postpartum breeding. Suckling does not seem to have a great impact on pituitary and ovarian function in New World Camelidae. More detailed endocrinological studies on the effect of lactation and suckling on ovarian function are needed.

DISEASES OF THE REPRODUCTIVE SYSTEM

Reproductive function may be altered or completely lost in the female due to either congenital abnormalities or acquired lesions in different areas of the reproductive tract. All females with a history of infertility should undergo a thorough reproductive examination by a qualified veterinarian.

Diseases of the Ovaries and Ovarian Bursa

Ovarian pathology reported in animals with a history of infertility include cystic follicles, lack of ovarian activity (hypoplastic ovaries or failure of follicles to grow beyond 6 mm), ovulatory failure, and tumors.[78,101,102]

Cystic Ovarian Disease Cystic conditions of the ovaries have been described in llamas and alpacas.[21,78] The role of ovarian cysts in infertility is not known. An incidence of 4.7 percent was reported in a random sample of slaughtered alpacas, while a higher frequency of 8.3 percent was reported in specimens collected from infertile animals.[78]

There are few studies dealing with the endocrinology of cystic conditions of the ovaries. In one study on llamas and alpacas, animals with cystic follicles showed a decrease in estrogen secretion with the appearance of the cystic follicle (>12 mm).[21] Large anovulatory follicles are present in many nonbred females. The effect of these structures on fertility is not known. Some of the anovulatory follicles may become hemorrhagic. I have seen several cases of large anovulatory luteinized follicles with significant progesterone production.[99,103]

Ovulation Failure Failure of ovulation is a frequent problem in camelids.[21,78,101] Ovulation failure may be due to inadequate LH release after copulation.[21] Assessment of ovulation by ultrasonography or progesterone assay should be an integral part of the reproductive management of the female camelid.

Para-ovarian Cysts Para-ovarian cysts are single or multiple, unilateral or bilateral, fluid-filled structures located in the broad ligament near the ovary or uterine tube. They could be remnants of the mesonephric (Wolfian) or paramesonephric (Mullerian) duct system. They measure 0.5 to 5 centimeters in diameter (0.25–2.5 in.) and their effect on

fertility is not known. These cysts should be differentiated from a distention of the uterine tube with fluid (hydrosalpinx) or a collection of fluid within the bursa.

Ovarian Hypoplasia Ovarian hypoplasia is the absence of the development of the germinal epithelium, leading to very small ovaries devoid of any follicular activity. Ovarian hypoplasia was found in 16.8 percent of 155 infertile alpaca females in postmortem examinations.[78] Ovarian hypoplasia should be ruled out in any maiden female with repeat breedings and lack of ovulation.

Diagnosis of ovarian hypoplasia can be made based on failure to observe follicular waves in serial ultrasonography or a persistently low estradiol level. Definitive diagnosis can be reached by laparoscopic examination of the ovaries.[101] Follicular development may be seen in some females, but the follicles fail to develop to an ovulatory size.[21] Reduced follicular activity may be observed in females that have had crias in the past. This condition is generally due to poor body condition, systemic metabolic diseases, or endocrinological problems, and should not be confused with congenital ovarian hypoplasia or aplasia. There is no treatment for congenital ovarian hypoplasia.

Persistent Luteal Activity Persistent corpora lutea are rare in the female camelid. However, the condition has been suspected in llamas on the basis of prolonged periods of high progesteronemia without pregnancy.[5,7] Some of the persistent luteal structure may be due to the development of luteinized hemorrhagic follicles.[103] Persistent luteal activity may be responsive to treatment with a luteolytic dose of prostaglandin F2 alpha. Treatment may require repeated use of the drug. Careful monitoring of ovarian activity by ultrasonography is highly recommended during and after treatment.

Other Ovarian Abnormalities Other ovarian abnormalities such as tumors, inflammation (oophoritis), or periovarian adhesion have been described but are usually rare. Ovarian tumors have been reported in infertile alpacas.[78] Teratomas are the most common ovarian tumors reported in camelids.[33,90] Unilateral teratomas are usually managed by removing the affected ovary. Successful surgical management of a bilateral teratoma with dissection and excision of the affected tissue from the ovary has been reported.[33]

Diseases of the Uterine Tube (Oviduct)

The most common disorders of the uterine tube in camelids are aplasia (congenital anomaly of development), inflammations with occlusion, and accumulation of fluid in the form of pyosalpinx or hydrosalpinx.[78,101] The enlarged uterine tube can be visualized by ultrasonography. In severe cases, the ovary and ovarian bursa may be involved and adhere to each other. Other reported uterine tube pathologies include mucosal cysts and micro-abscesses. Diagnosis requires endoscopic evaluation of the uterine tube papillae and laparoscopy. Prognosis for all these diseases is poor if bilateral and guarded if unilateral.[95,101]

Diseases of the Uterus

The uterus can be the site of congenital conditions, most commonly segmental aplasia, or acquired conditions such as endometritis, metritis, uterine fibrosis, or pyometra.

Congenital Abnormalities The most common congenital abnormalities of the uterus reported in camelids are segmental aplasia, uterus unicornis, and infantilism.[53,78,95,101] Segmental aplasia may affect any part of the genitalia from the vestibulum (or hymen) to the oviduct. Aplasia of the posterior part of the tubular genitalia (from the cervix to the hymen) is usually associated with mucometra or pyometra and detected by ultrasonography.

Another type of developmental abnormality described in the llama is the presence of only one uterine horn (uterus unicornis). Pregnancy is possible, but breeding of animals presenting such a condition is strongly discouraged because of the risk of genetic transmission of the abnormality.

Uterine Infection (Endometritis and Metritis) Uterine infections are the most common acquired reproductive problem resulting in infertility.[52,98,101] Little is known of the pathogenesis and evolution of this infection in camelids. Uterine infection should be suspected in animals that have a history of repeat breeding or early embryonic death following at least one normal pregnancy. Diagnosis is initially confirmed by the results of clinical examination of the animal (vaginal discharge, uterine wall thickening, presence of intrauterine fluid). Diagnosis is further confirmed by uterine culture, uterine cytology, and eventually uterine biopsy.

Endometritis is best managed by prompt appropriate treatment, sexual rest, and management of breeding to limit the number of matings. Treatment of uterine infection consists of uterine lavage followed by intrauterine administration of antibiotics for three to five days. The choice of antibiotics will depend on the organism isolated and its sensitivity. Uterine lavage can be accomplished using a Foley catheter and repeated flushing of the uterine cavity with a sterile lactate ringer solution. Some practitioners prefer placing an indwelling infusion catheter into the uterus to prevent repeated attempts to catheterize the cervix. Cervical catheterization may be difficult at times. The administration of 2 milligrams of estradiol cypionate

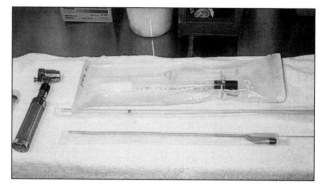

Uterine flushing equipment.

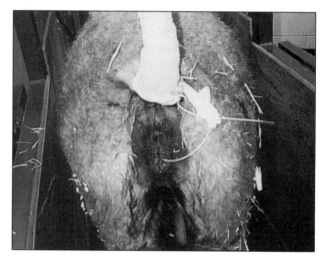

Indwelling catheter for infusion.

(ECP) may help to open the cervix. However, ECP may lead to cervical edema and more difficulty in catheterization. Catheterization of the cervix is easier during peak follicular development (open cervix).

Severe postpartum metritis may be seen following dystocia, infectious abortion, retained placenta, or injury to the birth canal, which can be life threatening if not treated promptly and adequately. A systemic antibiotic as well as supportive treatment (fluid therapy and a nonsteroidal anti-inflammatory) should be given immediately. Uterine lavage should not be attempted unless a uterine rupture is ruled out.

Prevention of uterine infection can be achieved by carefully monitoring each female, avoiding excessive breeding, and strictly observing the rules of hygiene during breeding and obstetrical manipulation.

Pyometra Pyometra has been reported in all types of camelids. Pyometra with an open cervix and vaginal discharge is observed primarily in the puerperium period and is due to a postpartum complication (retained placenta, dystocia, uterine prolapse) resulting in delayed involution due to infection and accumulation of fluid. A closed pyo-metra is usually associated with cervical adhesions or prolonged progesterone therapy. All diagnosed cases of pyometra that I have seen were associated with either cervical or vaginal adhesions or prolonged progesterone treatments.[101]

Other Diseases of the Uterus Other reported diseases of the uterus include uterine cysts, uterine abcesses, peri-uterine adhesions, polyps, and uterine neoplasms.[72,78,95,101] These adhesions are usually a consequence of peritonitis. Uterine neoplasia (adenocarcinoma) has been described in the llama.[72] Diagnosis of these conditions requires tech-niques such as uterine biopsy, laparoscopy, and hysteroscopy.

Diseases of the Cervix

A double cervix with some degree of didelphia (double va-gina) has been described in llamas and alpacas.[10,78,101] The major complaint is infertility with a persistent vaginal dis-charge. Diagnosis of the condition is made after vaginal examination using a speculum and confirmed by direct ex-amination of the genitalia after ovario-hysterectomy. A complete vaginal septum (double vagina) may also be pres-ent in some cases.

Cervicitis (inflammation of the cervix) is relatively common in overbred alpacas or following injuries during parturition or gynecological manipulations. Cervicitis is usually associated with uterine infections and vaginal mucopurulent or bloody discharge. Other acquired anom-alies of the cervix include cervical adhesions or lacerations resulting from a complication of birth or excessive trauma during manipulation.

Diseases of the Vulva and Vagina

Abnormalities of the vagina and vestibulum reported in camelids include segmental aplasia, persistent hymen, vagi-nal stricture, and presence of vaginal septum. Vaginal stric-ture or tight hymen can be enlarged by progressive manual dilation. Complete imperforation of the hymen is usually associated with an accumulation of various amounts of fluid within the vaginal cavity and uterus. These anomalies should be suspected when there is difficulty in penile pene-tration. A persistent hymen is usually suspected if penile penetration is impossible and if there is an apparent mem-brane in the vulva.

Abnormalities of the external genitalia can arise from chromosomal abnormalities.[107] Ambiguous external geni-talia with a long prepucelike structure was described in a case of XX sex reversal in a llama with urinary inconti-nence.[107] The animal was genotypically female, but the gonads were composed entirely of testicular tissue.

A well-nourished suri at one month of age is alert, curious, and highly interactive with members of the herd.

Vaginitis is relatively common and associated with bad breeding management or inadequate manipulation of the vaginal cavity. Traumatic injuries of the vagina can lead to the formation of complete adhesions between the vaginal wall and the development of pyometra.[101]

CONCLUSIONS AND RECOMMENDATIONS

The reproductive process in alpacas is very different from other domestic species and needs to be well understood both by the breeder and the attending veterinarian. Errors in management or delayed recognition of a reproductive problem can seriously affect the reproductive life of the fe-male or her welfare. Reproductive management programs should be designed with the help of a veterinarian to assure good monitoring of reproductive phenomena, particularly for animals that have a high-risk pregnancy. Maiden or re-placement females should undergo a complete veterinary examination, including a thorough reproductive tract eval-uation for any congenital malformation. Prevention and early treatment of acquired reproductive diseases are both important to increase the reproductive life of the female alpaca.

GLOSSARY

ablation Surgical removal.

acrosome reaction Biochemical reaction involving a region of the spermatozoa called acrosome that enables fertilization.

allantoic sac Sac formed by one of the fetal membranes or placenta that collects fluid from fetal metabolism.

ampullary Region of the ampullae.

anechoic Does not produce echoes.

anestrus Lack of estrus or lack of ovarian activity.

annular Has a ring shape.

anovulatory Follicle that failed to ovulate but did not regress and is no longer able to ovulate.

anterior Front.

aplasia Lack of development of an organ.

aromatize Special biochemical transformation of a molecule.

assay Test.

blastocyst A stage in the development of the embryo characterized by the presence of a central cavity surrounded by cells.

ballottment, balloted A sharp upward pushing with a finger against the uterine wall for diagnosing pregnancy by feeling the return impact of the displaced fetus.

brucellosis Disease due to a bacteria (*brucella abortus*).

bursa Saclike structure that surrounds the ovary and helps collect eggs after ovulation.

carpus Knee.

corpora lutea Plural of corpus luteum or yellow body.

corpus albicans White body, old corpus luteum of pregnancy that is no longer active.

commissure A joining, a point or line of union of the vaginal lips.

cranio-ventrally Front and toward the abdomen.

cumulus dispersion Dispersion of the cumulus cells that usually surround a freshly ovulated egg.

capacitation Biochemical reaction making sperm cells capable of fertilizing the egg.

conceptus Product of conception, refers to an embryo or very young fetus.

chorionic Belonging or referring to the surface of the placenta that is in contact with the uterus (chorion).

cloacae Anatomical defect joining the vagina and rectum into a single cavity.

chlamidiosis Disease due to chlamydia.

cytogenetic Study of chromosomes.

diverticulum A pouch formed by the lining of a mucous membrane.

dystocia Difficult birth.

echogenicity Ability to produce an echo.

endocrinology Hormonal patterns.

endometritis Inflammation of the endometrium (uterine epithelial lining).

epithelium Cellular lining.

estradiol Steroid, estrogenic hormone produced by the follicle.

fibrin Protein substance.

follicle Small vesicle with blisterlike structure containing the female egg.

fornix Region formed between the vaginal wall and the cervix.

fossa Crater.

gravid uterus Pregnant uterus.

hilus Region of the ovary where all blood vessels and nerves converge.

hormone Chemical substance produced by an endocrine gland. Each hormone has a specific role (progesterone, estradiol, FSH, and LH are all hormones with specific functions).

hydrosalpinx Collection of fluid within the oviduct.

hyperechogenic Produces a large amount of echo.

hypocalcemia Low blood calcium.

hypoplasia Lack of development of an organ.

infundibulum Region of the oviduct.

in-hand mating Live cover where the female and male are brought together under direct human supervision.

inhibin Hormone secreted by the large follicle, which causes regression of the other follicles.

ipsilateral On the same side.

intercornual Between the uterine horns.

invagination Folding of a structure such that it becomes inside out.

karyotype Number of chromosomes.

leptospirosis Disease due to leprospira.

linea alba White line, middle line of the abdominal wall where all muscles converge.

luteinization Transformation of a cell within the wall of the follicle into a specialized luteal cell, which forms the corpus luteum and produces progesterone.

luteolysis Destruction (lysis) of the corpus luteum.

maceration Degradation resulting in softening and loss of shape.

mesometrial Relative to the ligament (meso) holding the uterus (metrium).

mesosalpinx Ligament (meso) holding the oviduct (salpinx).

mesovarium Portion of the broad ligament that holds the ovary in place.

metabolite By-product of metabolism.

metritis Inflammation of the whole uterine wall.

morphogensis Development of different parts of the body.

morulae Stage of embryonic development characterized by the presence of 64 or more cells.

mucoid Mucuslike.

mucocutaneous Junction between a mucous membrane and the skin.

mucometra Accumulation of mucus in the uterine cavity.

multiparous Has had several births.

neoplasm Cancer, tumor.

nonechogenic Does not produce echoes.

nulliparous Female that has never had a birth.

oocyte Egg released by a follicle after ovulation.

oviduct Uterine tube that goes from bursa to uterus.

palpation Touching and feeling structures with the hands.

parity Number of births.

parturition Birthing process.

peritonitis Inflammation of the peritoneum or abdominal cavity.

placentation Formation of a placenta.

placentitis Inflammation of the placenta.

papillae Small projection of tissue.

pyometra Accumulation of pus in the uterine cavity.

pyosalpinx Accumulation of pus within the oviduct.

sagittal Through the middle.

serous Liquid in nature.

taxoplasmosis Disease due to toxoplasma.

tease Teasing or checking the behavior of a female by presenting her to a male.

teratoma(s) Type of tumor, usually in the ovary, that contains different types of tissues (bone, cartilage, hair, etc.).

transducer Part of an ultrasound machine (sometimes called a probe) containing crystals that generate ultrasound waves.

trophoblast Special cell that will form the placenta.

tunica albuginea Capsulelike anatomical structure surrounding the ovary.

ultrasonography The technique of using an ultrasound machine to image organs.

vestibulum Anatomical structure separating the vulva from the vaginal cavity.

videoendoscope Medical instrument that allows examination of body cavities.

REFERENCES

1. Aba, M. A., et al.: Endocrine Changes During Early-Pregnancy in the Alpaca. *Animal Reproduction Science* 47(4): 273–279, 1997.

2. Aba, M. A., et al.: Endocrine Changes After Mating in Pregnant and Non-pregnant Llamas and Alpacas. *Acta Veterinaria Scandinavica* 36(4): 489–498, 1995.

3. Aba, M. A., et al.: Plasma-Concentrations of 15-Ketodihydro-PGF (2-Alpha), Progesterone, Estrone Sulfate, Estradiol-17-Beta and Cortisol During Late-Gestation, Parturition and the Early Postpartum Period in Llamas and Alpacas. *Animal Reproduction Science* 50(1-2): 111–121, 1998.

4. Aba, M. A., et al.: Levels of Progesterone and Changes in Prostaglandin F-2 Alpha Release During Luteolysis and Early Pregnancy in Llamas and the Effect of Treatment with Flunixin Meglumine. *Animal Reproduction Science* 59(1–2): 87–97, 2000.

5. Adams, G. P., P. G. Griffin, and O. J. Ginther: In Situ Morphologic Dynamics of Ovaries, Uterus, and Cervix in Llamas. *Biology of Reproduction* 41: 551–558, 1989.

6. Adams, G. P., J. Sumar, and O. J. Ginther: Form and Function of the Corpus Luteum in Llamas. *Animal Reproduction Science* 24: 127–138, 1991.

7. Adams, G. P., J. Sumar, and O. J. Ginther: Hemorrhagic Ovarian Follicles in Llamas. *Theriogenology* 35(3): 557–568, 1991.

8. Alarcon, V., et al.: Comparison of Three Methods of Pregnancy Diagnosis in Alpacas and Llamas. *Theriogenology* 34(6): 1,119–1,127, 1990.

9. Bedford, S. J., et al.: Peritonitis Associated with Passage of the Placenta into the Abdominal-Cavity in a Llama. *Journal of the American Veterinary Medical Association* 209(11): 1,914–1,916, 1996.

10. Belknap, E. B., A. R. Schmidt, and C. L. Carleton: Double Cervices in Two Llamas. *Journal of the American Veterinary Medical Association* 197(8): 1,049–1,050, 1990.

11. Bravo, P. W.: Reproductive Endocrinology of Llamas and Alpacas. *Veterinary Clinics of North America, Food Animal Practice* 10(2): 265–279, 1994.

12. Bravo, P. W., and M. E. Fowler: *La aplicacion de la tecnica de ultrasonografia en llamas y alpacas.* VII Convencion Internacional sobre Camelidos Sudamericanos. Potosi, Bolivia, 1986. Abstr. 12, p. 12.

13. Bravo, P. W., and J. Sumar: Laparascopic Examination of the Ovarian Activity in Alpacas. *Animal Reproduction Science* 21: 271–281, 1989.

14. Bravo, P. W., and M. H. Varela: Prenatal Development of the Alpaca (*Lama pacos*). *Animal Reproduction Science* 32: 245–252, 1993.

15. Bravo, P. W., D. Pezo, and V. Alarcon: Evaluation of Early Reproductive-Performance in the Postpartum Alpaca by Progesterone Concentrations. *Animal Reproduction Science* 39(1): 71–77, 1995.

16. Bravo, P. W., et al.: Ovarian Follicular Dynamics in the Llama. *Biology of Reproduction* 43(4): 579–585, 1990.

17. Bravo, P. W., et al.: Endocrine Responses in the Llama to Copulation. *Theriogenology* 33(4): 891–899, 1990.

18. Bravo, P. W., et al.: The Effect of Ovarian Follicle Size on Pituitary and Ovarian Responses to Copulation in Domesticated South American Camelids. *Biology of Reproduction* 45(4): 553–559, 1991.

19. Bravo, P. W., et al.: Urinary Steroids in the Periparturient and Postpartum Periods Through Early Pregnancy in Llamas. *Theriogenology* 36(2): 267–278, 1991.

20. Bravo, P. W., et al.: Pituitary Response to Repeated Copulation and/or Gonadotropin-Releasing Hormone Administration in Llamas and Alpacas. *Biology of Reproduction* 47(5): 884–888, 1992.

21. Bravo, P. W., et al.: Ovarian and Endocrine Patterns Associated with Reproductive Abnormalities in Llamas and Alpacas. *Journal of the American Veterinary Medical Association* 202(2): 268–272, 1993.

22. Bravo, P. W., et al.: Transport of Spermatozoa and Ova in the Female Alpaca. *Animal Reproduction Science* 43: 2–3, 1996.

23. Bravo, P. W., et al.: Hormonal Indicators of Pregnancy in Llamas and Alpacas. *Journal of the American Veterinary Medical Association* 208(12): 2,027–2,030, 1996.

24. Bravo, P. W., et al.: Induction of Parturition in Alpacas and Subsequent Survival of Neonates. *Journal of the American Veterinary Medical Association,* 209(10): 1,760–1,762, 1996.

25. Bravo, W., and J. Sumar: Factores que determinan la fertilidad en alpacas. In *Anales de la V Convencion Internacional sobre Camelidos Sudamericanos.* Organizado por IVITA de la Universidad Nacional Mayor de San Marcos y Universidad San Antonio Abad del Cusco, Lima and Cusco, Peru, p. 4, 1985.

26. Bravo, W. M., and J. K. Sumar: *Some Anatomical Parameters of the Reproductive Tract in Alpacas.* Resumenes Invest., Universidad Nacional Mayor de San Marcos, Lima, 1984.

27. Bravo, W. M., and J. K. Sumar: *Actividad folicular del ovario de la alpaca.* Proceedings 5th Conv. Int. Camelidos Sudam., Cuzco, Peru, p. 7, 1985.

28. Bucher, F.: Haltung und Zucht von Vikunjas *(Vicugna vicugna)* im Zürcher Zoo. *Der Zoologische Garten (NF)* 36(1/3): 153–159, 1968.

29. Bustinza, A. V., P. J. Burfening, and R. L. Blackwell: Factors Affecting Survival in Young Alpacas (*Lama pacos*). *Journal of Animal Science* 66(5): 1,139–1,143, 1988.

30. Bustinza, J. A.: *Estudio macro y microscopio de la placentacion en Lama pacos (Alpaca).* B.S. Thesis, San Marcos University, Lima, Peru, 1961.

31. Bustinza, M. J., M. Gallegos, and M. A. Santos: *Observaciones del parto de alpaca.* 1st Conv. Camelidos Sudam., Puno, Peru, pp. 153–55, 1970.

32. Cebra, C. K., et al.: Surgical and Nonsurgical Correction of Uterine Torsion in New-World Camelids—20 Cases (1990–1996). *Journal of the American Veterinary Medical Association,* 211(5): 600, 1997.

33. Cotton, T.: *Bilateral Ovarian Teratomas in an Alpaca.* Proceedings Camelid Medicine, Surgery and Reproduction Conference. The Ohio State University, Columbus Ohio, pp. 437–439, 2002.

34. Davis, G. H., et al.: Seasonal Effects on Gestation Length and Birth-Weight in Alpacas. *Animal Reproduction Science* 46(3–4): 297–303, 1997.

35. Del Campo, M. R., C. H. Del Campo, and O. J. Ginther: Vascular Provisions for a Local Utero-ovarian Cross-over Pathway in New World Camelids. *Theriogenology* 46(6): 983–991, 1996.

36. England, B. G., A. G. Cardozo, and W. C. Foote: A Review of the Physiology of Reproduction in the New World Camelidae. *International Zoo Yearbook* 9: 104–109, 1969.

37. England, B. G., et al.: Ovulation and Corpus Luteum Function in the Llama (*Lama Glama*). *Journal of Endocrinology* 45: 505–513, 1969.

38. Escobar, R. C.: *Animal Breeding and Production of American Camelids.* Lima, Peru: Talleres Graficos de ABRIL, 1984.

39. Fernandez-Baca, S.: *Luteal Function and the Nature of Reproductive Failures in the Alpaca.* PhD Thesis, Cornell University, Ithaca, New York, 1970.

40. Fernandez-Baca, S., W. Hansel, and C. Novoa: Embryonic Mortality in the Alpaca. *Biology of Reproduction* 3(2): 243–251, 1970.

41. Fernandez-Baca, S., W. Hansel, and C. Novoa: Corpus Luteum Function in the Alpaca. *Biology of Reproduction* 3(2): 252–261, 1970.

42. Fernandez-Baca, S., D. H. L. Madden, and C. Novoa: Effect of Different Mating Stimuli on Induction of Ovulation in the Alpaca. *Journal of Reproduction and Fertility* 22(2): 261–267, 1970.

43. Fernandez-Baca, S., C. Novoa, and J. Sumar: *Actividad reproductiva en la alpaca mantenida en separacion del macho (Alpaca reproductive activity maintained separate from the male).* Assoc. Latinoamericana de Produccion Animal. Memorias 7: 7–18, 1972.

44. Fernandez-Baca, S., C. Novoa, and J. Sumar: Seasonal Variations in the Reproduction of the Alpaca. *Animal Breeding Abstract* 40: 336, 1972.

45. Fernandez-Baca, S., J. Sumar, and C. Novoa: Comportamiento sexual de la alpaca macho frente a la renovacion de las hembras (Sexual behavior of the male alpaca with females changing). *Revista de Investigaciones Pecuarias* 1: 115–128, 1972.

46. Fernandez-Baca, S., et al.: Relacion entre la ubacacion del cuerpo luteo y la localizacion del embrion en la alpaca. *Revista de Investigaciones Pecuarias* (IVITA) Universidad Nacional de San Marcos, 2: 131–135, 1973.

47. Fernandez-Baca, S., et al.: *Localizacion del cuerpo luteo y la ubicacion del embrion en la alpaca.* Mem. ALPA, Guadalajara, Mexico, 9: 87–88, 1974.

48. Fernandez-Baca, S., et al.: Differential Luteolytic Effects of Right and Left Uterine Horns in the Alpaca. *Biology of Reproduction* 20(3): 586–595, 1979.

49. Fowler, M. E.: *Medicine and Surgery of South American Camelids: Llama, Alpaca, Vicuña, Guanaco,* 2nd ed. Ames: Iowa State University Press, 1998.

50. Fowler, M. E., and H. J. Olander: Fetal Membranes and Ancillary Structures of Llamas (*Lama glama*). *American Journal of Veterinary Research* 51(9): 1,495–1,500, 1990.

51. Fuertes, Q. J., *Formacion del cuerpo luteo y algunas observaciones en el endometrio de alpacas jovenes durante los primeros dias de la gestacion.* B.S. Thesis, Facultad de Medicina Veterinaria, Universidad Nacional Mayor de San Marcos, Lima, pp. 1–37, 1961.

52. Johnson, L. W.: Llama Reproduction. *Veterinary Clinics of North America, Food Animal Practice* 5(1): 159–182, 1989.

53. Johnson, L. W., and M. E. Fowler: *Infertility Evaluation in Llamas and Alpacas.* Zoo and Wild Animal Medicine, 1993.

54. Knight, T. W., et al.: *Effects of GnRH and of Single Versus Multiple Mating on the Conception Rate in Alpacas.* Proceedings of the New Zealand Society of Animal Production 52: 311–312, 1992.

55. Knight, T. W., et al.: Foetal Mortality at Different Stages of Gestation in Alpacas (*Lama pacos*) and the Associated Changes in Progesterone Concentrations. *Animal Reproduction Science* 40: 1–2, 1995.

56. Leon, J. B., et al.: Endocrine Changes During Pregnancy, Parturition and the Early Post-partum Period in the Llama (*Lama glama*). *Journal of Reproduction and Fertility* 88(2): 503–511, 1990.

57. Leyva, V., and J. Sumar: *Evaluacion del peso corporal al empadre sobre la capacidad reproductiva de hembras alpacas de un ano de edad.* Proceedings 4th Conv. Int. Camelidos SudAm., Punta Arenas, Chile, 1981.

58. Leyva, V., and J. Sumar: *Determinacion del patron anual de presentacion de celo y ovulacion expontanea en alpacas.* Investigaciones en Camelidos Sudamericanos y ovinos. Programa Colaborativo de Investigacion en Rumiantes Menores. Titulo XII-AID. IVITA-Universidad Nacional Mayor de San Marcos, Lima, 1981.

59. Marie, M., and A. Anouassi: Mating-induced Luteinizing Hormone Surge and Ovulation in the Female Camel (*Camelus dromedarius*). *Biology of Reproduction* 35(4): 792–798, 1986.

60. Marie, M. A., and A. Anouassi: Induction of Luteal Activity and Progesterone Secretion in the Nonpregnant Onehumped Camel (*Camelus dromedarius*). *Journal of Reproduction and Fertility* 80: 183–192, 1987.

61. Merkt, H., et al.: The Presence of an Additional Fetal Membrane and Its Function in the Newborn Guanaco (*Lama guanacoe*). *Theriogenology* 30(3): 437–439, 1988.

62. Novoa, C.: Reproduction in Camelidae [Camels, llamas, alpacas]. *Journal of Reproduction and Fertility* 22(1): 3–20, 1970.

63. Novoa, C., et al.: Pubertad en la alpaca. *Revista de Investigaciones Pecuarias.* (IVITA), Universidad Nacional San Marcos 1: 29–35, 1972.

64. Novoa, C., et al.: Incremento reproductivo en alpacas de explotaciones comerciales mediante metodo de empadre alternado. *Revista de Investigaciones Pecuarias.* (IVITA), Universidad Nacional de San Marcos 2: 191–193, 1974.

65. Novoa, C. A., and J. Sumar: Coleccion de heuvos in vivo y ensayos de transferencia en alpacas. *Bulletin Extraordinario* 3: 31–34, 1958.

66. Paolicchi, F., et al.: Biological Activity of the Seminal Plasma of Alpacas, Stimulus for the Production of LH by Pituitary Cells. *Animal Reproduction Science* 54(3): 203–210, 1999.

67. Paolicchi, F., et al.: The Activity of the Seminal Fluid of Alpaca: Estimation of the Production of LH Released During an Assay of Pituitary Cells. *Revista Argentina de Produccion Animal* 16(4): 351–356, 1996.

68. Paul-Murphy, J., et al.: Urinary Steroid Evaluations to Monitor Ovarian Function in Exotic Ungulates: VII. Correspondence of Urinary Plasma Steroids in the Llama (*Lama glama*) During Nonconceptive and Conceptive Cycles. *Zoo Biology* 10: 225–236, 1991.

69. Pollard, J. C., G. H. Moore, and R. P. Littlejohn, The Sexual Behaviour of Alpacas Imported to New Zealand from Chile. *Proceedings of the New Zealand Society of Animal Production* 51: 43–46, 1991.

70. Pollard, J. C., R. P. Littlejohn, and I. C. Scott: The Effects of Mating on the Sexual Receptivity of Female Alpacas. *Animal Reproduction Science* 34: 289–297, 1994.

71. Pollard, J. C., R. P. Littlejohn, and G. H. Moore: Seasonal and Other Factors Affecting the Sexual Behaviour of Alpacas. *Animal Reproduction Science* 37: 349–356, 1995.

72. Powers, B. E., et al.: Endometrial Biopsy Technique and Uterine Pathologic Findings in Llamas. *Journal of the American Veterinary Medical Association* 197(9): 1,157–1,162, 1990.

73. Rodriguez, A. R. P.: *Ovulacion en las Alpacas.* B.S. Thesis, San Marcos University, Lima, Peru, 1959.

74. San Martin, H. F.: Nutrition of South American Camelids and Its Relation with Reproduction. *Revista Argentina de Produccion Animal* 16(4): 305–312, 1996.

75. San Martin, M., et al.: Aspects of Reproduction in the Alpaca, *Lama pacos. Journal of Reproduction and Fertility* 16(3): 395–399, 1968.

76. Steklenev, E. P.: Anatomic Morphological Peculiarities of the Structure and Physiological Function of Fallopian Tubes of Camelids. 6th International Congress on Reproduction and Artificial Insemination, Inst. Nat. Rech. Agron. 1: 71–74, 1968.

77. Stone, W. C., et al.: Rectal and Colonic Injury in the Llama: Anatomic Considerations and Surgical Management in Four Llamas. *Veterinary Surgery* 22(1): 62–66, 1993.

78. Sumar, J.: *Studies on Reproductive Pathology in Alpacas.* MS Thesis, Dept. of Obstetrics and Gynaecology, College of Veterinary Medicine, Swedish University of Agricultural Science, Upsala, 1983.

79. Sumar, J.: *Reproductive Physiology in South American Camelids,* pp. 81–95. In *Genetics of Reproduction in Sheep* (R. B. Land, D. W. Robinson, eds.). London: Butterworths, 1984.

80. Sumar, J.: Removal of the Ovaries or Ablation of the Corpus Luteum and Its Effect on the Maintenance of Gestation in the Alpaca and Llama. *Acta Veterinaria Scandinavica* 83 (Suppl): 133–141, 1988.

81. Sumar, J.: *Reproductive Physiology in the Female Alpaca and Llama.* Proceedings of the Workshop: Is it possible to improve reproductive performance in the camel?, Paris, 1990.

82. Sumar, J., Effects of Various Ovulation Induction Stimuli in Alpacas and Llamas. *Journal of Arid Environments* 26(1): 39–45, 1994.

83. Sumar, J., and M. Garcia: *Determination of Progesterone Levels in Peripheral Blood Plasma in Alpacas by Solid-phase RIA Technique.* Seminario destinado a la America Latina para mejorar la eficiencia reproductora y la sanidad del ganado por medio del RIA y tecnicos Conejas in Caracas, Venezuela, IAEA, Vienna, 1987.

84. Sumar, J., C. Novoa, and S. Fernandez-Baca: Fisiologia Reproductiva Post-Partum en la Alpaca. *Revista de Investigaciones Pecuarias* (IVITA) 1: 21–27, 1972.

85. Sumar, J., P. W. Bravo, and W. C. Foote: Sexual Receptivity and Time of Ovulation in Alpacas. *Small Ruminant Research* 11: 143–150, 1993.

86. Sumar, J., et al.: *Laparoscopy in Alpacas, Llamas and Vicuñas.* In Proceedings of the International Convention on South American Camelids, p. 11, 1985.

87. Sumar, J., et al.: Levels of 15-keto-13, 14-dihydro-PFG2α, Progesterone and Oestradiol-17ß after Induced Ovulations in Llamas and Alpacas. *Acta Veterinaria Scandinavica* 29: 339–346, 1988.

88. Sumar, J. B.: Reproduction in Female South American Domestic Camelids. *Journal of Reproduction and Fertility Supplement* 54: 169–78, 1999.

89. Thibault, C.: Sperm Transport and Storage in Vertebrates. *Journal of Reproduction and Fertility Supplement* 18: 39–53, 1973.

90. Tibary, A.: *Approach to Diagnosis of Infertility in Camelids.* Proceedings of the Annual Conference of the Society for Theriogenology, September 12–15, 2001, Vancouver, BC, Canada, pp. 407–416, 2001.

91. Tibary, A.: *Fertilization, Embryo and Fetal Development in Camelids.* Proceedings of the Annual Conference of the Society for Theriogenology, September 12–15, 2001, Vancouver, BC, Canada, pp. 387–396, 2001.

92. Tibary, A.: *Embryo Transfer in Camelids.* Proceedings of the Annual Conference of the Society for Theriogenology, September 12–15, 2001, Vancouver, BC, Canada, pp. 379–386, 2001.

93. Tibary, A., and A. Anouassi: Breeding Soundness Examination of the Female Camelidae. In *Theriogenology in Camelidae: Anatomy, Physiology, BSE, Pathology and Artificial Breeding* (A. Tibary, ed.). Actes Editions, Institut Agronomique et Veterinaire Hassan II. pp. 243–310, 1997.

94. Tibary, A., and A. Anouassi: Reproductive Physiology in the Female Camelidae. In *Theriogenology in Camelidae: Anatomy,* *Physiology, BSE, Pathology and Artificial Breeding* (A. Tibary, ed.). Actes Editions, Institut Agronomique et Veterinaire Hassan II, pp. 169–242, 1997.

95. Tibary, A., and A. Anouassi: Reproductive Disorders of the Female Camelidae. In *Theriogenology in Camelidae: Anatomy, Physiology, BSE, Pathology and Artificial Breeding* (A. Tibary, ed.). Actes Editions, Institut Agronomique et Veterinaire Hassan II, pp. 317–368, 1997.

96. Tibary, A., and A. Anouassi: Anatomy of the Female Genital Tract, In *Theriogenology in Camelidae: Anatomy, Physiology, BSE, Pathology and Artificial Breeding* (A. Tibary, ed.). Actes Editions, Institut Agronomique et Veterinaire Hassan II, pp. 135–164, 1997.

97. Tibary, A., and M. A. Memon, Reproductive Physiology in the Female South American Camelidae. *Journal of Camel Practice and Research* 6(2): 217–233, 1999.

98. Tibary, A., and A. Anouassi: Uterine Infections in Camelidae. *Veterinary Science Tomorrow.* An online current awareness journal 1(3), 2001.

99. Tibary, A., and A. Anouassi: *Camelid Infertility/Sub-Fertility: Clinical Cases.* Proceedings Camelid Medicine, Surgery and Reproduction Conference. The Ohio State University, Columbus, pp. 427–428, 2002.

100. Tibary, A., and A. Anouassi: *Comparative Reproductive Physiology in Different Species of Camelids.* Proceedings Camelid Medicine, Surgery and Reproduction Conference. The Ohio State University, Columbus, pp. 271–291, 2002.

101. Tibary, A., A. Anouassi, and M. A. Memon: Approach to Diagnosis of Infertility in Camelids: Retrospective Study in Alpaca, Llamas and Camels. *Journal of Camel Practice and Research* 8(2): 167–179, 2001.

102. Tibary, A., C. Ragle, and S. Thompson, *Abdominal Endoscopy in Clinical Camelid Theriogenology.* Camelid Reproduction and Production Twin Conference, Paper 43, Reproductive Health Center, Charleston, SC, October 13–15, 2001.

103. Tibary, A., A. Anouassi, and J. Bowman: *Investigation on the Persistently Elevated Progesteronemia in Non-pregnant Camelid.* Proceedings Camelid Medicine, Surgery and Reproduction Conference. The Ohio State University, Columbus, pp. 381–388, 2002.

104. Urquieta, B., and J. R. Rojas: *An Introduction to South American Camelids.* In *Livestock Reproduction in Latin America.* Proceedings of the Final Research Coordination Meeting, Bogota, 1988.

105. Urquieta, B., and J. R. Rojas: Studies on the Reproductive Physiology of the Vicuña (*Vicugna vicugna*). In *Livestock Reproduction in Latin America.* Proceedings of the Final Research Coordination Meeting of the FAO/IAEA/ARCAL, Vienna, pp. 407–428, 1990.

106. VanSaun, R. J., Endoscopic Evaluation of the Female Camelid Reproductive Tract. Proceedings of the Society for Theriogenology Conference, Nashville, TN, 1999, pp. 206–210, 2000.

107. Wilker, C. E., et al.: XX Sex Reversal in a Llama. *Journal of the American Veterinary Medical Association.* 204(1): 112–115, 1994.

Chapter 14

Obstetrics and Neonatology

Ahmed Tibary, DMV, PhD, Dipl ACT

Newborn and mother
rejoin the herd.

The objective of this chapter is to present the essential elements of obstetrics and neonatal care, as well as to discuss some of the neonatal disorders in alpacas. Most neonatal loss occurs at the time of birth or shortly thereafter. Proper birthing procedures, immediate neonatal care, and close observation of the newborn are the most effective ways to reduce neonatal losses.

BIRTHING IN ALPACAS

Anatomical Considerations

To better understand and evaluate the progress of labor, three terms are used to describe fetal orientation during birth: presentation, posture, position.

Fetal position is described by the orientation of specific parts of the fetus (withers, head, and pelvis) to the different components of the birth canal of the dam (sacrum, ilium, and pubis) (see Figure 14.1). The posture of the fetus describes the position of the head, limbs, and neck in relation to its body. The head and neck can be extended or deviated laterally, ventrally, or dorsally. The limbs can be extended or flexed at different degrees above or under the fetus.

Fetal presentation describes the orientation of the dorsal (back) axis of the fetus in relation to that of the dam, as well as the part of the fetus that is presented to the birth canal. Thus, fetal presentation can be:

1. Anterior longitudinal presentation—the dorsal axis of the fetus and dam are in the same plane and the head and forelegs are presented first (see Figure 14.2).

2. Posterior longitudinal presentation—the dorsal axis of the fetus and dam are in the same plane and the hind legs are presented first (see Figure 14.3).

3. Transverse ventral presentation—the fetal dorsal axis is perpendicular to that of the dam and the abdomen of the fetus is presented to the pelvic canal.

4. Transverse dorsal presentation—the fetal dorsal axis is perpendicular to that of the dam with the back presented to the pelvic canal.

Obstetrical Manipulations

Obstetrical manipulations require a thorough knowledge of the anatomy of the birth canal and the position of the pregnant uterus and the fetus in relationship to the bony structures of the pelvic area (see Figure 14.1). The alpaca birth canal is very small even for people with small hands, and any error in manipulation may lead to permanent damage of the genital tract and loss of fertility.

The health and well-being of both the dam and the fetus should be considered when contemplating obstetrical intervention. Low-risk interventions such as helping with vaginal dilation, retrieving carpal flexure (retrieving a retained foot at the knee), or minimum traction on an otherwise normally presented cria may be handled by a breeder who has enough experience with birthing. All other cases should be left to professional veterinary help.

A hands-on birthing course is highly recommended for breeders who would like to gain experience with birthing. Breeders should also consider having an obstetrics kit on

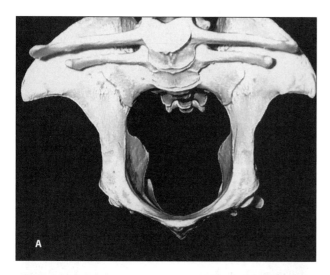

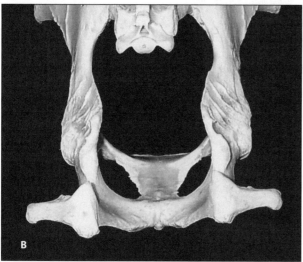

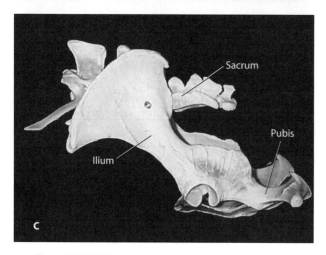

Figure 14.1 Pelvic area.
A Cranial view from the front.
B Caudal view from the back.
C Lateral view from the left side, with head of animal toward the left.

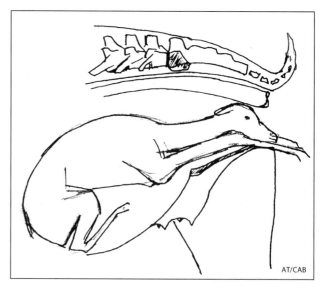

Figure 14.2 Anterior longitudinal (normal) presentation.

hand (see Table 14.1). Obstetrical manipulations that require sedation of the alpaca or appear to be complicated should be left for the veterinary practitioner.

Examination of the parturient (birthing) female should be routine practice for all animals showing signs of first-stage labor. History of the parturient should include age, number, and normalcy of previous births, the exact breeding date, and signs suggesting the beginning of labor. It is very important to make sure that the female is not in the process of aborting.

Any female that shows signs of distress or increased duration of labor should be examined to assess the position, posture, and presentation of the fetus. This veterinary examination is ideally accomplished with the animal standing. However, in some situations, this is not possible and the animal has to be examined while restrained in the sitting position.

Providing analgesia (pain control) in the form of epidural anesthesia and administration of butorphenal may facilitate the examination. Examine the parturient alpaca with extreme care to avoid causing injuries to the birth

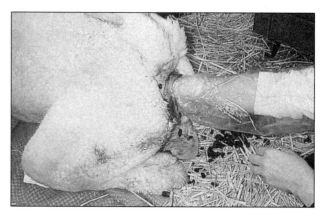

Examination of a parturient alpaca.

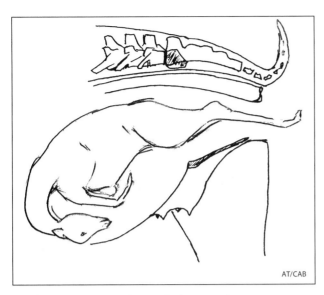

Figure 14.3 Posterior longitudinal presentation.

canal or rectum. Expect expulsive efforts from the female in response to the examination. The tail should be wrapped and held up. If no fetal parts are showing at the vulva, it is important to start with trans-rectal palpation to rule out uterine torsion. Also, rectal palpation allows emptying the rectum of fecal material, determination of fetal position (feel for the head or pelvic area), and assessment of uterine contractions.

Continue the examination with vaginal palpation. After thoroughly cleaning the perineal region with soap and water or scrubbing with betadine, introduce a well-lubricated and disinfected hand into the vagina. Examine the birth canal for the presence of twists (uterine torsion) or le-

sions from previous examinations or injuries. Evaluate the size and dilation of the pelvic canal. If the cervix is open and the fetus is accessible, evaluate its tone and viability. If the cervix is closed, the viability of the fetus can be judged by its movements by palpation or trans-abdominal ultrasonography, which will permit detection and evaluation of fetal heart activity.

From this examination you should be able to determine the extent of cervical dilation and the presentation, posture, position, and viability of the fetus. This information will guide your course of action.

DYSTOCIA IN ALPACAS

Dystocia is the abnormal progress of the process of birth resulting in a prolongation of either stage one or stage two of parturition.

Fetal manipulations in case of dystocia are based on three principal actions: repulsion of the fetus, reduction of the cause of dystocia, and extraction of the fetus. In all dystocia that can be corrected by vaginal delivery, the fetus should first be pushed gently back into the uterus to allow more space for manipulation. The reduction phase depends on the fetal part that needs to be retrieved and placed in the correct position before traction is applied. Ample lubrication should be provided during these manipulations. Traction should be moderate in force and should take advantage of the normal anatomy of the pelvis and the fetus. The body of the fetus should be rotated to about 45 degrees to take advantage of the widest diameter of the

Table 14.1 Obstetrics and neonatal kit.

Item	What For
Thermometer	Check rectal temperature of dam, check rectal temperature of cria
Stethoscope	Determine heart rate of cria
Antiseptic soap	Clean perineal area
Clean towels	Dry cria
Flashlight (need to move animal near a source of electricity or well-lit barn)	Examine the parturient and afterbirth
Scale	Determine birth weight
Betadine scrub	Scrub the perineal area before any manipulation of the birth canal
Cotton or gauze pads	Clean the perineal area
Lubricating gel	Preferably sterile, large amounts for obstetrical manipulations
60 ml catheter tip syringe	Inject lubricant into birth canal (be careful not to force lubricant into cria's nose or mouth)
Vet wrap or brown bandage	Tail wrap
Bulb syringe	Clear cria airway
0.5% chlorhexidine (Nolvasan)	Disinfect umbilicus
Heavy string or navel clamp	Tie off the umbilical cord in case of bleeding
Stomach tube	Colostrum feeding
Warm water and mild soap	Enema
Frozen colostrum (preferably goat)	In case of agalactia or failure to nurse
Frozen llama plasma	In case of agalactia or failure to nurse

pelvis. Traction should be applied with the hands (no chains are necessary) and in a manner that the cria is pulled in an archlike fashion, with the body curving downward and toward the hocks of the dam. Pulling straight on the cria is absolutely inappropriate obstetrical manipulation.

Incidence of Dystocia

The incidence of dystocia in camelids is very low. In llamas this incidence has been estimated at 2 to 5 percent.[19,20,22,26] However, early diagnosis of dystocia is very important because it can evolve very rapidly to a critical situation endangering the life of both the fetus and the dam.

It is critically important that owners be knowledgeable about the normal birth process, including the duration of each stage, so that they will be able to recognize signs of abnormal parturition and know when to call for veterinary help. There is no replacement for frequent monitoring of the preparturient female to detect early signs of birth complications.

Lack of an exact breeding date is the most common problem when dealing with the parturient in a free mating system. Development of reliable methods based on biochemical changes in mammary secretion such as those used in the equine would be very helpful for managing parturition in camelids. Experience in identifying animals with dystocia and handling them can only be gained by careful observation of several births. Therefore, many owners with only one or two animals will always be lacking the expertise needed to deal with parturition and tend either to overlook problems or to be easily alarmed.

Signs of Dystocia

Dystocia can occur anytime during the process of parturition. The most important indication of trouble is the increased duration of one of the stages of labor and a colicky syndrome in the dam. Dystocia should be suspected if the first or second stages of labor exceed respectively six hours and one hour. In addition to this increased duration of labor, the dam may show signs of distress with frequent alternation between a standing and sitting position, with frequent side-to-side rolling, frequent vocalization, and excessive straining.

Dystocia of Maternal Origin

Types of dystocia are generally classified into two groups: dystocia of maternal origin and dystocia of fetal origin. Dystocia of maternal origin is due to a displacement of the uterus (torsion), uterine inertia, or disproportion between fetal size and size of the pelvic canal. Dystocia of fetal origin is due to abnormal fetal position or posture such as carpal flexion, and lateral deviation of the head, as well as hip and hock flexion in posterior presentation. Feto-pelvic disproportion, monstrosities, and transverse presentations are rare.

Uterine torsion is probably the most common serious cause of dystocia of maternal origin. For management of uterine torsion see Chapter 13: Female Reproduction.

Uterine Inertia Dystocia may be due to weak or absent contractions of the uterus (uterine inertia). This is occasionally seen in older animals or females with prolonged pregnancy. Primary uterine inertia may be due to hypocalcemia. Secondary uterine inertia is mainly due to exhaustion and muscle fatigue. Uterine inertia should be differentiated from failure of abdominal expulsive effort. I have seen the lack of abdominal contractions in older females, females that had previous abdominal surgeries, and two females with uterine-intestinal adhesions that resulted from previous Cesarean sections. Primary uterine inertia may predispose the female to retained placenta or uterine prolapse.

Uterine Rupture Uterine rupture is relatively rare in alpacas and is generally the consequence of delayed recognition of dystocia. The prognosis in these cases is guarded at best. Surgical intervention is required to deliver the fetus and repair the uterus.

Failure of Dilation of the Vulva or Cervix Dystocia due to the small size of the dam is not frequent if breeding management is adequate and the females are not bred until they reach the appropriate size. Although rare, cases of feto-maternal disproportion have been described in South American camelids.[16,26] These conditions are diagnosed after lengthy unsuccessful second-stage labor. The external genitalia may be swollen and the vulva lacerated due to prolonged expulsive efforts. Difficulties of fetal expulsion are usually due to the failure of the vulva to stretch sufficiently to allow passage of the head of the fetus. Management of this type of dystocia consists of evaluating the birth canal and helping the vulva to stretch or performing an episiotomy. If these procedures are unsuccessful and the fetus is alive, the female should be prepared for an immediate Cesarean section.

Failure of cervical dilation requires delivery by Cesarean section. It is important to confirm that the dam is at term and rule out uterine torsion.[31]

Dystocia of Fetal Origin

Dystocia of fetal origin occurs most commonly as a result of malposition (abnormal position) or malposture (abnormal posture) of the fetus and to a lesser degree from the presence of a malformation, twins, or a large-size fetus. Fetal malposition or malposture most often involves the retention of one limb (flexion) or a head deviation.

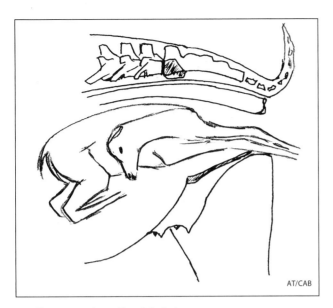

Figure 14.4 Lateral head deviation.

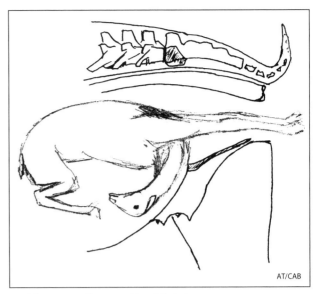

Figure 14.5 Downward head deviation.

Fetal Abnormalities Fetal monstrosities are rare in camelids. However, *Schistosoma reflexus* (failure of closure of the abdominal wall with bowel exposed to the outside), contracted tendons, ankylosis of the hind limbs, and complete stiffness of the neck are possible.[33] Other anomalies that may complicate delivery include fetal anasarca and emphysematous fetus resulting from fetal death and the production of gas from decomposition.

Twin Delivery Although twinning is extremely rare in alpacas, a few twin births have been reported. Delivery of twins may be complicated by presentation of both fetuses to the birth canal at the same time. Not all twin births are complicated. Twin delivery can be recognized if a front and a back leg are presented in the birth canal at the same time. The legs should be pushed back and the fetus (or fetuses) assessed. Each cria can then be brought into the pelvic inlet separately.

Head and Neck Deviation Head deviation may occur as a result of failure of the mechanism responsible for orientation of the fetus during the birth process or due to ankylosis. The long neck of the species predisposes to two types of head deviation: lateral head deviation (see Figure 14.4) and downward head deviation (see Figure 14.5). Head deviation is recognized by the absence of the head in the birth canal, although both forelimbs can be reached. Correction of head deviation depends on the ability of the veterinarian to reach and manipulate the head into a longitudinal position.

Retention of a Forelimb Retention of a forelimb may be due either to a flexion at the knee (carpal flexion, see Figure 14.6) or a flexion at the shoulder. Carpal flexion can be corrected by gently grasping the flexed limb and bringing it slowly into alignment with the birth canal, making sure

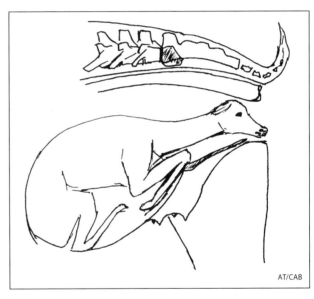

Figure 14.6 Carpal flexation (leg bent at the knee).

not to cause any laceration of maternal tissues in the process. Correction of shoulder flexure requires first a reduction to a carpal flexure and then alignment of the limb.

Retention of a Hindlimb Retention of a hindlimb may be due to a flexion of the hock. The fetus should be gently pushed back into the uterus, and then the flexed limb should be grasped at the hock and pulled gently until it is in a normal position.

Breech Breech presentation describes a situation in which both hindlimbs are flexed and the fetus is in a posterior and dorsosacral position (Figure 14.7). Upon examination of the birth canal, only the tail and buttocks of the fetus are

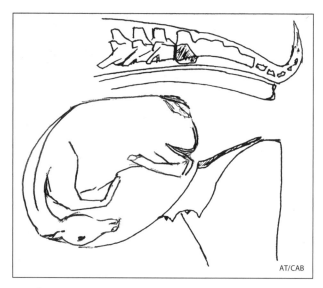

Figure 14.7 Breech presentation.

identified. Breech is a very difficult form of dystocia to correct if one's hands are too large. The principal for correction of breech dystocia is to push the fetus back into the uterus. Reduce one side by bringing one leg then the other from under the fetus into a normal posterior presentation. Cesarean section should be considered if the cria is alive.

Other Forms of Dystocia Fetal malposition/malpresentation may include failure to rotate properly in the uterus, resulting in an upside-down (facing-up) fetus or a transverse presentation with all limbs presented at once. An upside-down fetus may be corrected by gently rotating it into the correct position.

Surgical Management of Dystocia (Cesarean Section)

Delivery of the fetus by Cesarean section should be considered if vaginal delivery is impossible. The operation is relatively simple in the hands of a trained veterinarian. The surgery may be accomplished under general anesthesia or regional block, depending on the medical situation of the patient. Two types of approaches are possible: ventral midline or left lateral flank. The principles of surgery are similar to those used for other small ruminants.

CARE AND EVALUATION OF THE NEONATE

An epidemiological study in the United Kingdom showed that 4 to 11 percent of the deaths among llamas and 17 to 33 percent of deaths in alpacas occur during the first six months of life. A high proportion of these deaths occurs within the first week of life.[10] In South America, cria mortality rates can be as high as 50 percent, mostly due to *Clostridium perfringens* types A and C.[15] Neonatal care and early recognition and treatment of neonatal ailments are of the utmost importance in reducing these fatalities.

Care of the neonate begins during the long gestation, where the strength and viability of the newborn are greatly influenced by the health of the dam.[35] The normal rate and growth pattern of the fetus can be altered by numerous factors, including abnormal hormonal environment, nutrition, genetics, and infectious conditions. These factors can cause either a chronic or an acute disruption of the development of the fetus, resulting in either a stillborn or a newborn that is slow to adapt to extrauterine life without any obvious clinical problems. With this in mind, prenatal care of the dam, with proper nutrition, vaccinations, and knowledge of any concurrent health problems, is important to enhance survival of the newborn.

Early diagnosis and aggressive treatment of neonatal disease is important when the newborn has an active infection at birth. The clinical signs are often nonspecific and vague, resulting in a cria that is slow to adapt to extrauterine life or that dies suddenly in the first few days of life. If there is an intrauterine infection, the fetus may be born alive or may die in utero. Intrauterine infections of bac-

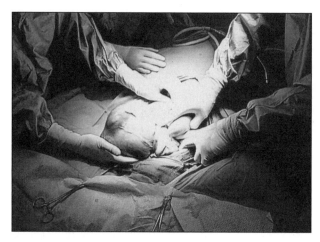

Ventral midline Cesarean section.

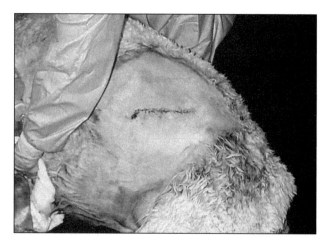

Left-flank Cesarean section.

terial origin in the newborn cria are recognized more commonly than viral infections. Infections acquired in utero rather than postpartum should be suspected if the newborn had elevated plasma fibrinogen in the first 12 to 24 hours of life, the placenta appears abnormal, or the dam exhibits uterine discharge peripartum.[1]

The newborn is subjected to severe stresses and some degree of oxygen deprivation during parturition, even with an optimal uterine environment, and it undergoes a tremendous transition during the postnatal period. During parturition it is possible that the neonate may suffer from a damaging degree of asphyxia, secondary to hypoxemia or ischemia. Several mechanisms help the neonate adapt to extrauterine life. The first is an increase in fetal cortisol concentration that triggers parturition and allows adequate levels of surfactant to be produced by the type II alveolar pneumocytes (to enable breathing). In addition to elevated cortisol concentration there is a catecholamine surge. A negative side effect of this physiological feature is that it may allow potential problems to be masked and the newborn to appear normal immediately postpartum, even though it may have substantial physiologic impairment.

The most important aspects of the care and evaluation of the neonate can be summarized in the following points:

1. Establish that the cria is normally developed and that it has adjusted to extrauterine life.

2. Establish that the behavior of the cria is within the normal range.

3. Prevent infection by supplying a clean environment, disinfecting the umbilical cord, and ensuring adequate colostrum intake (passive transfer of immunity).

The Newborn Cria

Each newborn cria should be evaluated within the first hours of life to detect any abnormalities of development or maladjustment to extrauterine life. Physical parameters of the normal newborn cria are presented in Table 14.2. The

Disinfection of the umbilicus by dipping it into a small container of solution of tincture of iodine.

epidermal membrane should be removed by gently rubbing with clean towels. Assessment of the newborn cria should include evaluation of the epidermal membrane, respiration, heart function, and presence of obvious congenital abnormalities. The epidermal membrane, which is normally translucent, may become yellow or brownish due to meconium staining in cases of fetal stress due to dystocia.

The cria should be weighed immediately after birth to monitor daily weight gain accurately. Birth weights usually range from 12 to 22 pounds (5.5–10 kg) in alpacas. Regular weighing the cria (daily for the first two weeks and every other week thereafter) is warranted to determine adequacy of milk production and intake.

Many congenital abnormalities have been described in alpacas. Among the most important are angular limb deformities, cleft palate, choanal atresia, atresia ani, and heart defects. The initial examination of the cria should establish if any of these abnormalities are present (see Table 14.3).

Prevention of infection once the cria is born entails several key components. If the birth is observed or occurs in a clean birthing area, the umbilicus should be trimmed

Table 14.2 Biological parameters of normal, healthy alpaca crias.

Parameter	Normal Range
Birth weight	5.5 to 10 kg (12.0–22 lb)
Temperature	37.7 to 38.9°C (100–102°F)
Pulse	60 to 100 beats per minute
Respiration	10 to 30 breaths per minute
Time to standing	30 minutes (10–120 minutes)
Time to nursing	45 minutes (20–180 minutes)
Nursing frequency	Once an hour for 1 to 2 minutes
Meconium passage	18 to 24 hours
Urination	18 hours

Table 14.3 Congenital abnormalities seen in newborn crias.

Type of defect	References
Reproductive tract defect including intersex	25
Urinary tract defects	16, 23
Atresia ani	6, 11
Cleft palpate	16, 23
Choanal atresia	14, 17, 18
Angular limb deformities	2, 7, 14, 19, 20
Umbilical hernia	16, 23
Heart defects	16, 23
Polydactyly	16, 23
Ear defects	9
Eye defects	8, 32
Esophageal defect	16, 23
Skin defects	4

Nose-to-nose touching and nuzzling is important for bonding between dam and cria.

A one-hour-old newborn demonstrates its ability to sit sternally and hold its head up.

and dipped in 7 percent tincture of iodine. If the birth did not occur in a clean area, it is advisable to clean the umbilicus with chlorhexidine solution or soapy water, and dip or spray the umbilicus with regular-strength betadine solution.

After the initial evaluation, the cria should be observed from a distance. The mother-cria bond is established through humming, nose-to-nose touching, and nuzzling the cria.[16] The cria should be able to sit sternally 5 to 15 minutes after birth, stand within 15 to 60 minutes after birth, and nurse by 60 to 90 minutes after birth. If the cria is not up and nursing by three hours after birth, then a problem may exist and intervention may be needed. Some healthy crias are more adept than others in finding their mother's teats for their first milk. Sometimes it is helpful to gently direct the cria in its search. Meconium should be passed within 24 hours after birth.

Signs of Prematurity

Since exact breeding dates are not always known, it is important to recognize the signs of prematurity in crias to prevent additional complications. Signs include weakness, inability to stand or difficulty in standing, depressed suckling reflex, silky fiber coat, nonerect ears (floppy ears), nonerupted incisors, increased passive range of motion of the limbs (joint laxity), and difficult or slow respiration.

Premature crias tend to adapt to extrauterine life more slowly than normal-term crias. Due to the normal elevated fetal cortisol levels, the premature cria may appear healthy initially, but there is a high risk of developing metabolic problems, and the cria may quickly decompensate several hours after birth.

Problems that are most frequently encountered by premature crias are due to hypoxemia, acidosis, hypoglycemia, and limited body reserves or poor thermogenic ability. Alpaca crias less than 12.7 pounds (5.5 kg) should be monitored for signs of prematurity or maladjustment. In normal circumstances, the cria is left with the dam once it has been determined that the dam has colostrum. Maternal bonding enhances absorption of colostrum, but in these situations it is hard to determine if adequate colostrum is consumed by the cria. The pair should be carefully monitored to ensure that the cria learns to latch onto the teats, especially if it is a primiparous dam or a dam with an engorged, painful udder. Even with a pregnancy of normal length, the cria may show signs and complications indicating prematurity due to in-utero growth retardation.

Importance of Colostrum (Passive Transfer of Immunity)

The placental arrangement in camelids does not allow passage of antibodies (immunoglobulins or IgG) from the dam to the fetus. Therefore, crias are born agammaglobulinemic (without immunoglobulins) and cannot fight off infections. Immunoglobulins are acquired with the ingestion of first milk (colostrum). This transmission of immunoglobulin via colostrum is called passive transfer of immunity.

Increased incidence of illness and death from infections in neonates is associated with inadequate passive transfer of immunoglobulin as measured by low serum immunoglobulin concentrations in sick or dead neonates. Conversely, successful immunoglobulin transfer is associated with low infection rates and the high likelihood of survival.[3] Even though this is true, there are great differences among farms for immunoglobulin concentrations of healthy neonates. The effect of between-farm variations could involve factors such as management practices, nutrition, exposure to pathogens, herd bloodlines, geographic location, and climate that would enable a cria with failure of passive transfer to remain healthy.

Need for Colostrum in Alpacas There are indications that unlike other livestock species, camelids do not selectively transfer immunoglobulin (specifically IgG_1) from the sera to the mammary glands just prior to parturition.[5] Current data support the theory that periparturient llamas and alpacas may produce and store IgG from sera in the mammary glands in a gradual manner near term. The concentration of IgG drops quickly from mammary secretion after parturition.[5]

The cria is able to absorb colostral antibodies for only a short period of time (18 hours). The amount of colostrum a cria needs to ingest is not known and recommendations are made based on research done in calves.[35] Using information extrapolated from calves, which require 100 grams of IgG_1, an average cria of 22 pounds (10 kg) would require 20 grams of IgG. The average colostral IgG concentration in llamas is 170 milligrams per milliliter, which means that the cria needs (120 ml) of colostrum, or 12 percent of body weight. This is a very small amount of colostrum; in reality, the amount received should be much greater to take into account the inconsistent absorption of immunoglobulins.

Many factors can negatively affect the absorption of immunoglobulin, such as cold weather or heat stress, lack of mothering, delivery by Cesarean section, and metabolic disturbances. A cria should receive 10 percent of its body weight in colostrum, preferably within the first 12

A mother and her baby rest after birth and first nursing.

hours after birth, with 5 percent given in the first 6 hours after birth.

Colostrum Requirements for Alpacas Colostrum production and quality depend on the normal preparation of the mammary gland to concentrate antibodies during pregnancy and its ability to lactate after birth. The quality of colostrum depends on the immune status of the dam. In many situations colostrum production or quality may be compromised, putting the cria at risk of contracting infections in the first weeks of life.

Agalactia (lack of milk production) or poor mammary gland development is frequently seen in young females or following dystocia. If the dam does not have enough colostrum, a strategy for colostrum supplementation should be immediately instituted. The best approach is to provide colostrum from another alpaca or llama. If this is not possible, the second best choice is goat colostrum (up to 20 percent of body weight). Whenever colostrum from another species is used, the total amount is increased to make sure that the cria will get the mount of IgG needed.[27]

If colostrum is collected from healthy dams and stored properly (kept frozen at −20°C), it should be usable for at least one year. Frozen colostrum should be thawed slowly and brought up to body temperature before administering. Rapid thawing at high temperature or in a high-power microwave may denature the antibodies. Thawing is best accomplished by placing small quantities of colostrum-containing bags in a water bath. If thawed in a microwave, liquid portions should be removed progressively during the thawing process, so that they are not exposed to high temperature for a long time.

As a rule, colostrum administration should be started if an agalactia problem has been identified, if the dam suffers from mastitis, or if the cria is not seen suckling by three hours after birth. If the cria is able to suckle, the best way to administer colostrum is by bottle feeding. If the cria has a poor suckling reflex, administration of colostrum should be done via orogastric intubation using a 24-French catheter. Care should be taken while intubating not to inject milk into the respiratory tract (trachea). The tube should be felt by palpation as it goes down the left side of the neck. It should be kept within the esophagus to provide closure of the esophageal groove and avoid depositing milk within the first stomach compartment, increasing the risks of fermentation. Crias should receive 20 percent of their body weight in colostrum divided into four to six feedings (one feeding every four to six hours).

Testing for Passive Transfer of Immunity The IgG status of a newborn alpaca is the most important factor in the prevention of infectious diseases. Most insurance companies require a determination of the passive immunity status of a cria. Therefore, determination of IgG levels in the blood 24 hours after birth has become standard practice for newborn crias.

Many different methods are available to evaluate serum immunoglobulin concentrations in calves and foals, with some methods more appropriate than others for use in the cria.[36] Single radial immunodiffusion (SRID) is a quantitative test that specifically measures serum IgG concentrations.[12,37] The SRID is species-specific with high sensitivity and specificity, and two kits are commercially available.* Each kit is meant to be independent of the other, and reference values for levels of adequate passive transfer are specific for each kit. Since the SRID is species-specific, if colostrum other than llama is used there will be negative results. If these tests are not available, total protein can be determined and should be less than 5 milligrams per deciliter.

Dealing with Failure of Passive Transfer If failure of passive transfer is confirmed, a plasma transfusion is indicated. Plasma (10–25 ml/kg) can be given either intravenously (IV) or intraperitoneally (IP) at a rate of 100 to 200 milliliters per hour (IV). If the cria is dehydrated and requires IV fluids, this is the preferred route for the plasma transfusion. If the cria is still healthy, the IP route is preferred, especially in a field setting. Several sites have been reported for IP administration: right or left lower ventral abdomen or right paralumbar fossa. A 16- or 18-

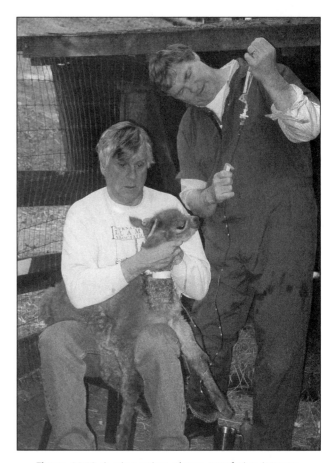

Figure 14.12 A cria receives plasma transfusion intravenously because of incomplete passive transfer.

gauge, 3-inch catheter should be aseptically placed at a shallow angle to avoid puncturing or lacerating the intestinal tract. The cria should be kept warm during the administration and the plasma warmed to 37°C. The plasma should be given over a 30 to 60 minute timeframe, so both the cria and holder should be in comfortable positions to prevent shock. Hyperimmune llama plasma is commercially available.** Alternatively, a healthy male donor can be kept for the routine harvesting of plasma.

Administration of plasma is not without risk and the cria should be observed for any signs of shock. Pain associated with intraperitoneal injection of plasma may be managed by administering a low dose of nonsteroidal anti-inflammatory drug. If the cria is determined to be at high risk for developing infection, prophylactic broad-spectrum antibiotics should be administered.

---

*Llama IgG Test Kit, Triple J Farms, Redmond WA 98054; Llama Vet-Rid Kit, Bethel Laboratories, Montgomery, TX.

**Triple J Farms, Redmond WA, 98054.

THE ORPHANED CRIA

A cria may need to be cared for following rejection by the dam, agalactia, sickness, or death of the dam. Caring for orphaned baby animals is not an easy task. In addition to managing the possible failure of passive transfer of immunity, which was discussed earlier, the care for the first few weeks of life includes thermoregulation, appropriate nutrition, and social insertion into the herd. Most of these tasks are left to the breeder as the only person in continuous contact with the baby.

The challenge in caring for orphaned crias is to get them to a point where they can readily be bottlefed. Delivery of milk by stomach tube, although seemingly simple, should be limited to the first feeding to guarantee colostral intake, and should not be considered a method for continuous feeding of the orphaned cria. Deliberate use of stomach-tube feeding may compromise the health of a cria, particularly if large quantities of milk are delivered into compartment one (C1) of the gut, resulting in fermentation and digestive upset.

Getting a cria to accept the bottle takes a lot of time and patience. The cria should be fed often and in small quantities to reach a total of 10 percent of its body weight in an 18- to 24-hour period. The feeding bottle should be fitted with a small human baby nipple or a lamb nipple with a crosscut. Milk outflow should be just right—not too overwhelming and also not too slow. Good results have also been reported by breeders who use a large syringe to gently dribble milk into the cria's mouth. The cria should be encouraged to hold its head high to prevent aspiration.

Although no product can completely mimic the dam's milk, several types of milk replacement may be considered for orphaned crias. They include pasteurized, homogenized cow milk, pasteurized goat milk, and commercial milk replacers for goats and lambs. I prefer the use of pasteurized goat milk or goat milk replacers because they are more energy dense. Preparation of milk replacers from powder should be done carefully, following to the letter the preparation guidelines of the manufacturer. Lamb milk replacers may be too concentrated for alpacas and may need to be diluted.

Crias should be encouraged to live with the herd, preferably with other crias. Although they will start eating hay and grass on their own, they are not capable of sustaining themselves without milk until they reach a minimum of three months of age. With male crias great effort should be taken not to have them associate feeding with people. A male cria who is imprinted to expect people to feed him will at first act submissive, but will later become aggressive and probably dangerous. To avoid this kind of imprinting, alternate methods of feeding can be used.

Correct method to feed an orphaned neonate. It is important to avoid too much contact with humans, which can result in undesirable imprinting and aggressive behavior as the alpaca matures, especially in males.

NEONATAL CONDITIONS

Neonatal cases are often presented with a wide variety of nonspecific complaints based on deviations from normal appearance and behavior. The minimum database used to evaluate the cria covers evaluation of maternal transfer of immunogobulins; complete blood cell count, including determination of plasma fibrinogen and differential count; arterial blood gas analysis; serum chemistry; and anaerobic blood cultures. Contrast radiographs of the nasopharyngeal area may be indicated if choanal atresia is suspected to be the cause of dyspnea.[35]

The First Few Days

Diseases seen in the first 24 hours of life are usually associated with congenital abnormalities, digestive problems (meconium retention), urinary problems (urine retention), exposure, or malnutrition.

Congenital Abnormalities Heart defects, choanal atresia, atresia ani, and atresia coli are some of the most common congenital abnormalities that affect the well-being of the cria. Severe heart defects result in the cria's death within a

Choanal artresia confirmed with radiograph.

An example of choanal artresia. This cria is gasping for air trying to breathe from the mouth.

Wry face.

few hours, but most affected crias will survive for a few days or months with the only visible abnormality being a failure to grow normally. Episodes of syncope or fainting have been observed in crias with severe heart defects.

Choanal atresia is the inability of the nasal air passages to open, resulting from the presence, at the choanae, of a membranous or osseous separation between the nasal and pharyngeal cavities (can't breathe through its nostrils).[14,18] This condition is extremely serious if it is bilateral, because the cria cannot breathe and nurse simultaneously. The affected cria is usually observed gasping for air, with the mouth partially open and the nostrils flared. Choanal atresia may be associated with other defects of the skull and jaws. Absence of air movement through the nostril can be verified by placing a cold mirror in front of the nasal openings and watching for fogging. Diagnosis can be confirmed by mouth to nose artificial breathing or by radiographs of

the head after injection of a radio-opaque substance in the nasal cavity. Surgical correction of this abnormality has been described, but should not be considered in breeding animals because of the potential of hereditary transmission of the defect. Animals with unilateral or partial choanal atresia can survive.

Wry face is a head deformity characterized by various degrees of deviation of the maxilla. This abnormality may be associated with choanal atresia. There is no treatment for this condition and crias with severe deviation should be euthanized.

Atresia ani and atresia coli are respectively the lack of opening of the anal sphincter and lack of connection between the colon and rectal cavity. These abnormalities result in the blockage of intestinal transit and the accumulation of fluid in the gastrointestinal tract. The cria becomes progressively bloated and depressed. Ultrasonographic and radiologic examinations of the abdominal cavity allow confirmation of the diagnosis. Atresia coli may be mistaken for meconium retention. In the female cria these abnormalities may involve the genital tract. Surgical correction of atresia ani and other congenital abnormalities have been described.[6]

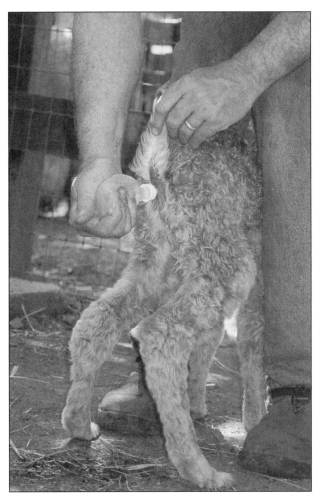

An enema is used to help this cria pass meconium.

Digestive Problems Meconium is the amniotic fluid ingested by the fetus during pregnancy. Meconium is usually passed with 18 to 24 hours after birth in dark pasty feces (meconium). Meconium retention is usually overdiagnosed by breeders. Some breeders systematically give enemas to every newborn cria—this practice is to be discouraged. Clinical signs of meconium retention include straining, squatting, tail wagging, anorexia, and signs of abdominal discomfort. Initial treatment consists of one or two warm soapy-water enemas (20–40 ml). If the meconium has not passed after two enemas, intravenous fluids may be indicated, as multiple soapy water enemas may irritate the rectal mucosa, resulting in severe straining and rectal prolapse.[27] Crias that have retained meconium may have other abnormalities and should be examined closely.

Urinary Problems Urine retention may be associated with congenital abnormalities of the urinary and genital tracts.[25] In males, urethral blockage (aplasia) results in bladder rupture. In females, lack of opening of the vulva results in an accumulation of large quantities of urine in the uterus. Diagnosis of this condition requires ultrasonography.

Exposure Hypothermia and depression due to exposure or starvation are probably the most common acquired problems of the newborn cria in the first 24 hours of life. These problems can be easily prevented by closely monitoring near-term alpacas and providing a clean, warm

Meconium.

A blanket protects the cria from cold or wet weather.

environment for birthing. Crias who are housed out of doors should be protected from the cold and rain by wearing well-fitting waterproof jackets. Resuscitation of the compromised cria requires providing a warm environment, dealing with the failure of passive transfer, and dehydration. Hypothermia and depression may also be seen in crias with severe blood loss from the umbilicus or a rupture.

Infections in the Neonate

Most medical problems seen in the newborn cria stem from lack of initial care or failure of passive transfer. Lack of proper care of the umbilicus may lead to severe infection of the umbilical cord (omphalophlebitis, or navel-ill) due to contamination with opportunistic organisms. The infection can be localized with the cria showing only swelling of the umbilicus. In some cases the infection may enter the abdominal cavity via the veins and arteries, and cause peritonitis or an internal swelling that is seen only by ultrasonography. Affected crias may show loss of weight, depression, and colic. Septicemia and death can occur if the condition is not treated. Treatment of early cases requires administration of broad-spectrum antibiotics. Complicated cases that have abscessed may require surgical removal of affected tissues. Chronic infection may develop if treatment is not adequate. Chronically infected crias may show growth retardation and painful swollen joints due to septic arthritis.

Crias with compromised immune systems, due to the failure of passive transfer or to an overwhelming contamination with gram-negative and gram-positive bacteria, may also develop respiratory problems, diarrhea, and meningitis or meningoencephalitis following septicemia.[1,34] Initial signs of septicemia are weakness, depression, and anorexia. Blood culture should be attempted to determine the exact microorganism involved. Broadspectrum antimicrobial therapy may help if exact determination of the microorganism is not possible. Septicemia may be suspected if crias show hypopyion, uveitis, or conjunctivitis.

Dehydrated sick crias may show hyperglycemia, hypernatrenemia, and hyperosmolarity. If necessary, fluid therapy should be delivered by intravenous catheter either in the jugular or saphenous vein. Intraosseous fluid therapy may also be used. Nonsteroidal anti-inflammatory therapy Ketoprofen (4 mg/kg, IV SID) is helpful in reducing pain and toxemia. Use of this drug may be associated with the development of gastric ulcers.

Cria diarrhea has been associated with giardiosis, coccidiosis (*Eimeria*), or cryptosporidium.[30] Viruses (coronavirus, rotavirus, Bovine Viral Diarrhea virus, and a parvovirus) may also be involved in enteritis in crias. Nonspecific diarrhea is observed in some crias and may be due to changes in the gastrointestinal flora. Probiotic agents have been used by some breeders with claimed success after ten days of therapy.

Limb Deformities

Angular limb deformities are very common in camelids. Less severe cases will improve with time. Severe cases (>10°) require surgical correction.[7,24] Polydactyly (extra number of toes) has also been noted in alpacas.

PREVENTIVE CARE FOR THE NEWBORN CRIA

Vaccination

The most common infections of the cria are clostridial diseases due principally to *Clostridium perfringens* types C and D and *Clostridium tetani* (tetanus). Pregnant alpacas should be vaccinated and boosted four to six weeks before parturition. Administration of clostridial antitoxin should be considered if the cria did not have adequate passive transfer. Some veterinarians also recommend vaccinating crias in their first week of life. Clostridiosis due to *Clostrid-*

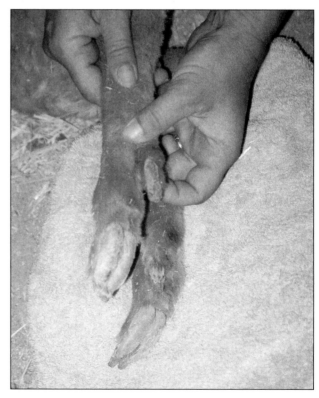

This cria was born with extra toes (polydactylism).

ium perfringens type A has been reported to cause severe losses among some populations of crias.[13, 28,29] Autologous vaccines may help reduce the effects of *Clostridium perfringens* type A.

Vaccination of dams against *E. coli* may provide some protection if a farm is experiencing an increased incidence of neonatal diarrhea.

Vitamins and Trace Minerals

Crias should receive vitamins A, D, and E, as well as selenium in areas where it is needed. Crias not given a vitamin D supplement have a reduced growth rate during winter and may show clinical signs of rickets if born in winter. A dose of 1,000 IU D3 per kilogram of body weight subcutaneously has been suggested for crias in late autumn and again in midwinter, and to adult females in midwinter, to prevent vitamin D inadequacy.[21]

CONCLUSION

An understanding of birthing, obstetrical manipulations, and care of the newborn cria is critical to successful breeding. Informed breeders may be able to handle many situations that avoid losing the fruit of more than 11 months of care and waiting. The principles that have been described in this chapter are somewhat straightforward and not complicated. However, for them to be accomplished in a timely and correct manner, a great deal of practical experience is needed. It is important to plan for access to quick assistance until one reaches a certain level of confidence. Even for the experienced breeder, it is important to know when more advanced help is needed. Fortunately, alpacas do not have a high incidence of birthing complications compared to many other domestic species.

GLOSSARY

alveolar pneumocytes Special cells of the lungs.

analgesia Pain control.

angular limb deformities Deformities resulting in increased angles of the limb joints.

ankylosis Stiffness of joints resulting in crooked cria.

asphyxia Lack of oxygen or increased carbon dioxide in the body caused by respiratory arrest.

Bovine Viral Diarrhea virus (BVD) Virus that causes a disease characterized by diarrhea in cattle.

catecholamine A group of substances including epinephrine that acts on the nervous system.

cleft palate Failure of closure of the roof of the mouth resulting in inability to suckle.

coccidiosis (*Eimeria*) Disease caused by coccidian.

coronavirus Virus that causes diarrhea in young stock.

cortisol Hormone of stress.

cryptosporidium Bacteria.

dyspnea Abnormal breathing.

emphysematous Enlargement due to buildup of gases from decomposing tissue.

enteritis Inflammation of the bowels.

escherichia coli Bacteria that live in the gut.

fetal anasacra Fluid buildup in the fetal tissue resulting in swelling.

giardiosis Disease caused by giardia.

hypopion Collection of pus cells in the aqueous humor of the eye, forming a white layer between the cornea and the iris.

hypothermia Abnormally low body temperature.

hypoxemia Low level of oxygen in the blood.

ilium Bone that forms the side of the pelvic (birth) canal.

intraosseous Inside the bone.

intraperitoneal Inside the peritoneal (abdominal) cavity.

ischemia Lack of blood flow due to blockage of a blood vessel.

orogastric intubation Placing a tube from the mouth into the stomach.

parturient Female about to give birth or in the process of giving birth.

parvovirus Type of virus associated with diarrhea.

primiparous Female at her first birthing.

pubis Bone that forms the floor of the pelvic (birth) canal.

rotavirus Type of virus.

sacrum Bone that continues the spine and forms the roof of the birth canal.

saphenous vein Vein of the hind leg.

septicemic Suffering from septicemia or blood contamination with microorganisms.

uveitis Inflammation of the middle part of the eyeball called the uvea.

REFERENCES

1. Adams, R., and F. B. Garry: Gram-negative Bacterial Infection in Neonatal New World Camelids: Six Cases (1985–1991). *Journal of the American Veterinary Medical Association* 201(9): 1,419–1,424, 1992.
2. Alyakine, H., et al.: Surgical Treatment of a Congenital Flexural Deformity of the Tarsal Joint in a Llama. 6(2): 203–208, 1999.
3. Barrington, G. M., S. M. Parish, and F. B. Garry: Immunodeficiency in South American Camelids. *Journal of Camel Practice and Research* 6(2): 185–190, 1999.
4. Belknap, E. B., and R. W. Dunstan: Congenital Ichthyosis in a Llama. *Journal of the American Veterinary Medical Association* 197(6): 764–767, 1990.
5. Bravo, P. W., J. Garnica, and M. E. Fowler: Immunoglobulin G Concentrations in Periparturient Llamas, Alpacas and Their Crias. *Small Ruminant Research* 26: 1–2, 1997.
6. Carraro, D. B., et al.: Surgical-Correction of Anorectal Atresia and Rectovaginal Fistula in an Alpaca Cria. *Australian Veterinary Journal* 74(5): 352–354, 1996.
7. Cashman, T., et al.: Management of Bilateral Flexural Deformity of the Metacarpophalangeal Joints in Three Alpaca Crias. *Australian Veterinary Journal* 77(8): 508–510, 1999.
8. Cullen, C. L., and B. H. Grahn: Congenital Glaucoma in a Llama *(Lama glama). Veterinary and Comparative Ophthalmology* 7(4): 253–257, 1997.
9. Davis, G. H., et al.: *The Inheritance of Fused Ears in an Alpaca Family.* Breeding . . . responding to client needs. Association for the Advancement of Animal Breeding and Genetics. Proceedings of the Twelfth Conference, Dubbo, NSW, Australia, April 6–10, 1997, 1: 131–135.
10. Davis, R., et al.: South American Camelids in the United Kingdom: Population Statistics, Mortality Rates and Causes of Death. *Veterinary Record* 142(7): 162–166, 1998.
11. Del Campo, C. H.: et al.: A Case of Atresia Ani with Rectovestibular Fistulae in an Alpaca *(L. pacos). DTW Dtsch Tierarztl Wochenschr* 100(12): 495–497, 1993.
12. Drew, M. L., B. M. Alexander, and R. G. Sasser: Pregnancy Determination by Use of Pregnancy-Specific Protein-B Radioimmunoassay in Llamas. *Journal of the American Veterinary Medical Association* 207(2): 217–219, 1995.
13. Ellis, R. P., et al.: *An Overview of Clostridium Perfringens Type A Enterotoxemia in Alpacas and Llamas.* Symposium of Diseases of Small Ruminants. Corvallis, Oregon, June, 1990. pp. 2–3.
14. Fenwick, B. W., and M. Kock: Complete Choanal Atresia in a Llama. *Journal of the American Veterinary Medical Association* 181(11): 1,409–1,410, 1982.
15. Fernandez-Baca, S.: Alpaca Breeding in the High Andes. *World Animal Review* 14: 1–8, 1975.
16. Fowler, M. E.: *Medicine and Surgery of South American Camelids: Llama, Alpaca, Vicuña, Guanaco,* 2nd ed. Ames: Iowa State University Press, 1998.
17. Fulton, I. C., J. P. Caron, and P. Le Blanc: Surgical Repair of a Bilateral Choanal Atresia in a Llama. *Journal of Zoo and Wildlife Medicine* 20(44): 488–490, 1989.
18. Gerros, T., and W. Stone: What Is Your Diagnosis? Complete Bilateral Choanal Atresia. *Journal of the American Veterinary Medical Association* 205(2): 179–180, 1994.
19. Jessup, D. A., and W. R. Lance: What Veterinarians Should Know About South American Camelids. *California Veterinarian* 11: 12–18, 1982.
20. Johnson, L. W.: Llama Reproduction. *Veterinary Clinics of North America, Food Animal Practice* 5(1): 159–182, 1989.
21. Judson, G. J., and A. Feakes: Vitamin D Doses for Alpacas *(Lama pacos). Australian Veterinary Journal* 77(5): 310–5, 1999.
22. Lang, E. M.: Geburtshilfe IM Zoologischen Garten (Embryotomy in a Guanaco in a Zoo). *Zoologische Garten* 14: 29–32, 1945.
23. Leipold, H., T. Hiraga, and L. Johnson: Congenital Defects in the Llama. *Veterinary Clinics of North America, Food Animal Practice* 10(2): 401–420, 1994.
24. Livingston, C. K., et al.: Surgical Correction of Carpal Valgus Deformity in Three Alpacas. 79(12): 821–824, 2001.
25. Lopez, M. J., M. D. Markel, and R. Dubielzig: Urinary Obstruction in a Hermaphroditic Llama. *Journal of the American Veterinary Medical Association* 212(5): 710, 1998.
26. Paul-Murphy, J.: Obstetrics, Neonatal Care, and Congenital Conditions. *Veterinary Clinics of North America, Food Animal Practice* 5(1): 183–202, 1989.
27. Pugh, D. G., and E. B. Belnap: Perinatal and Neonatal Care of South-American Camelids. *Veterinary Medicine* 92(3): 291–295, 1997.
28. Ramirez, A., A. Payne, and R. P. Ellis: *Immunoaffinity Purification of Clostridium Perfringens Type A (alpaca) Enterotoxin.* Abstracts of the Annual Meeting of the American Society for Microbiology 88: 48, 1988.
29. Ramirez, A., et al.: *Monoclonal Antibodies to Enterotoxin Derived from Clostridium perfringens Type A Isolated from Enterotoxemia Neonatal Alpacas.* Abstracts of the Annual Meeting of the American Society for Microbiology 87: 62, 1987.
30. Rickard, L. G., and J. K. Bishop: Prevalence of *Eimeria* spp. (Apicomplexa: Eimeriidae) in Oregon Llamas. *Journal of Protozoology* 35(3): 335–336, 1988.
31. Saltet, J., et al.: Ventral Midline Caesarean Section for Dystocia Secondary to Failure to Dilate the Cervix in Three Alpacas. *Australian Veterinary Journal* 78(5): 326–328, 2000.
32. Schuh, J. C. L., J. G. Ferguson, and M. A. Fisher: Congenital Coloboma in a Llama. *Canadian Veterinary Journal* 32(7): 432–433, 1991.
33. Tibary, A., and A. Anouassi: Obstetrics and Neonatal Care. In *Theriogenology in Camelidae: Anatomy, Physiology, BSE, Pathology and Artificial Breeding,* (A. Tibary, ed.) Actes Editions, Institut Agronomique et Veterinaire Hassan II, pp. 391–409, 1997.
34. Tsur, I., et al.: Meningoencephalitis and Brain Abscessation Due to Escherichia-Coli in a 2-Week-Old Alpaca-Cria. *Australian Veterinary Journal* 74(6): 437–438, 1996.
35. Walker, P. and A. Tibary: Neonatal Care of Camelids: A Review and Case Reports. 6(2): 255–263, 1999.
36. Weaver, D. M., et al.: Evaluation of Assays for Determination of Passive Transfer Status in Neonatal Llamas and Alpacas. *Journal of the American Veterinary Medical Association* 216(4):559–63, 2000.
37. Weaver, D.M., et al.: Passive Transfer of Colostral Immunoglobulin G in Neonatal Llamas and Alpacas. *American Journal of Veterinary Research* 61(7): 738–741, July, 2000.

Section Five

Medicine
and Herd Health

Overleaf Young suris balance shyness and curiosity near the Thames River in England.

Chapter 15

On-Farm Assessment and Diagnosis

Ty McConnell, DVM, and Eric Hoffman

Ty McConnell, DVM, establishes rapport with his patient.

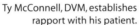

The ability to assess the health status of an alpaca may be the single most important skill that a successful alpaca owner needs to learn. Alpacas will often show very few clinical symptoms before they become gravely ill. In other species, running a fever, lethargy, vomiting, and diarrhea are telltale clinical symptoms. Those symptoms may be absent in the alpaca.

To make a health assessment of an alpaca, you need to develop a critical eye for subtle changes. Looking for an early symptom that can lead to an early diagnosis and successful treatment is the key to successful intervention.

A daily pen check is an excellent way to observe animal behavior. This needs to be done at least once a day and better yet twice daily. Knowing your animals as individuals and each animal's idiosyncrasies is important. In this way, subtle changes become readily apparent. As you make your daily walk through the pen or pasture, observe the alpaca's reaction to your presence. If an animal's behavior is not convincing, a cursory assessment is in order. This assessment should follow a checklist similar to the one below.

BEHAVIORAL INDICATORS

Observe the alpaca's behavior from a distance during the daily pen check. A sick animal may be slow to get up or move away. It may walk a short distance and sit again. Or it may not get up at all. Another sign is a usually social animal that has separated itself from the group or reacts slowly to group behavior. Other signs include the dominant alpaca that suddenly behaves submissively, or an aggressive eater who becomes disinterested in food. Body posture can also be a strong indicator. Does the usually alert and proud-acting animal seem drowsy and stand hunched over with its neck arching out and away from its body?

Just as importantly, the way an animal walks says a lot about how it is feeling. Is its movement fluid and like other animals in the pen, or does it walk oddly with an unusual gait? Does it limp or favor a leg? Does it walk without vigor and alertness? Does it trail behind the herd?

SEVEN-POINT QUICK VISUAL ASSESSMENT

Before you call your veterinarian, you can make observations that will assist him or her should a call be warranted. Here's what you can do.

1 Symptoms of the Head

If you sense something is wrong, look at specific areas starting with the head. Look at the eyes for discharge (watery eye), a closed eyelid, or partially closed eyelid. Is the alpaca squinting? Does it seem alert? Does it track what's going on around it? Does it hold its head to one side? Does it shake its head ?

Do both ears move in concert with one another, or is one ear held down regardless of what is happening? Is there any discharge from the ears? Is there sneezing or nasal discharge? Are the nostrils flared while the animal is resting? Is the animal distressed and breathing through its mouth for no apparent reason (like exertion after fighting or a hierarchical battle)? Anytime you have a sense that the animal is disoriented or is in respiratory distress that can't be explained by exertion, you have reason for major concern and immediate diagnosis.

If the nostrils are flared, look at the animal's sides and see how rapidly it is breathing. Is it working hard to breathe? Is breathing shallow, slow, and difficult to detect? Is the breathing more rapid than in nearby animals? Animals may have different respiration rates that are normal, but rates that are different than the animal's normal rate or clearly different than the other members of the herd are important signs. Factor in the ambient temperature. On a hot day you can expect some animals to be breathing harder than they normally do. If it's a cool day and an animal is breathing hard, chances are something other than the weather is causing elevated respiration.

2 Ears

Ears are great indicators of a problem. Ear flagging means that one or both ears are held down, indicating pain or discomfort. A closer look may reveal injury or discharge. If the alpaca is a male housed with other males, check to see if the ear is lacerated from fighting (males with fighting teeth can shred another male's ear and in some cases have entirely severed an ear as a result of fighting.) If it's a female or a male and there is no laceration, catch the animal and look into the ear orifice for a waxy buildup, discharge, or raw skin. Ear problems can range from foxtails or foreign debris to a variety of mites, some requiring lengthy treatment. Ear problems can become serious and should not be neglected or treated lightly.

3 Abdominal Pain

Learn to detect abdominal pain, commonly called colic. Your ability to do this will sooner or later literally make the difference between life and death in an alpaca you own. Colic is a general symptom for "gut" problems that can be mild in nature to life threatening. Often these signs are at first very subtle. The animal may merely sit a little off center with its hind legs out to one side. This may mean nothing at all (late pregnancy, mild indigestion, or just sitting preference), or it may mean the animal is experiencing some pain. In warm weather alpacas will often lie with their legs to one side, rather than in a true sternal position, with all four limbs tucked up under the animal in a kushed position. In cold weather the healthy alpaca is less apt to sit askew and let its underside be exposed to cold weather.

Alpacas also sun themselves and often sprawl on one side as if they are dying or dead. The breeder can learn to distinguish between abdominal pain and an animal whose daily habits sometimes mimic preliminary symptoms. Often owners become so well acquainted with their animals they will know when one animal sits with its rear legs out to the side it means nothing at all, while with another animal it may mean the animal is ill. When you are unsure if you are looking at true abdominal pain, look for other danger signs: elevated respiration, groaning, grinding teeth, lack of appetite or bowel movements, diarrhea, and reaction to your approach (see Chapter 21: Noninfectious Multisystemic Diseases).

4 Walking Motion and General Movements

How an animal moves indicates a lot about its conformation and health. Is there lameness? Will the animal run or just walk? Can it run and keep up with the herd? Does the walk appear normal? Or does the animal walk gingerly or abnormally slowly? Does it stagger or seem unsteady on its feet? What is the placement of the legs when the animal is standing? Does it put weight on all four legs? Does it stand oddly with the legs far to the rear (possibly indicating abdominal pain)?

Locomotion anomalies can indicate a variety of problems. If there is a limp, attempt to ascertain if the affected limb is swollen by visually inspecting the leg. This can be challenging on a leg covered with fiber. Look at the leg's profile. How does it compare to the next nearest leg? Look carefully at the inside of the leg and areas not covered in fiber to assess the leg's conformation. If palpating the leg is possible, start by looking at the bottom of the foot and move your hand up the leg. Watch for signs of pain that may help locate the problem area. Are the bones where they belong? Are there lumps or misalignments? Is the animal in pain? Avoid pressuring the animal into struggling or further damaging the affected limb.

If the animal is young and begins walking gingerly, i.e., taking short steps, carefully examine the legs. Has the leg conformation changed? Is there exaggerated angulation at knee, pastern, or hock on the rear legs? The combination of deteriorating conformation and a gingerly walking motion often indicates that an animal is suffering from a vitamin D deficiency. The animal may be experiencing pain in its joints and not be able to run or walk in a normal manner. If the animal can't keep up with a herd that runs, watch the slow animal's movement. Are its pasterns strong and supportive of the legs?

5 Appetite

Alpacas spend much of the morning and late afternoon eating. Watch to see if each animal is eating. Generally, all animals react to the daily dispersal of hay or forage. Watch for the animal that does not come to food or is slow to react. Some animals prefer to wait until a feeding area has cleared out before eating. Know the habits of your individual animals. Be alert to submissive animals who are intimidated from feeding by more dominant animals. Make sure food is distributed so all animals have access to it.

Alpacas continually kept from food may become emaciated, or develop ulcers or other life-threatening maladies. An animal without an appetite is often a sick animal.

If an animal is not eating, further assessment and immediate diagnosis are warranted. Start by offering a variety of feeds to see if there is any interest in feed.

6 Body Condition (Body Scoring)

Knowing the body condition of your animals is extremely important and easy to do. Body scoring is generally used as an indicator of general health. Body scoring is simple to perform. While holding an animal, place your hand over its spine about 6 inches (15 cm) behind the withers. The amount of flesh an animal is carrying can be easily felt in this area. Simply feel the area by pushing downward, compressing the fiber until you can clearly feel both sides of the spinal area, with your thumb on one side of the dorsal spinous process area and your fingers on the other side. Generally, if you feel a pronounced spinal ridge and the flesh from the spine to the top of the ribs is concave, the animal is thin. If the flesh in this area is straight (neither concave nor distinctly convex), the animal's weight is optimum. A convex bulge here indicates excess weight. A flat area across the back (rather than sloping) indicates the animal is obese.

Body scoring adults on a regular basis should be part of any management plan. Often owners are surprised to find that a sick animal is also emaciated, because its thick coat has hidden the animal's decline to poor body condition from view. A body score can't be guessed from afar. It requires feeling the alpaca in the manner described. Some breeders and veterinarians use a ten-point body scoring system, but all screenings and most veterinarians use a five-point system:

> 1 is emaciated (an immediate health risk).
>
> 2 is thin and normal for some animals, but may also signal a decline in health if the animal is in the process of shedding weight.
>
> 3 is optimum and recognized as the ideal.
>
> 4 is somewhat overweight and may be normal for some animals, or be an indicator an animal is eating its way to obesity.
>
> 5 is obese, an undesirable condition for an alpaca.

Table 15.1 shows typical body scoring profiles. Also see Chapter 9: Feeding the Alpaca.

A change in body score is often the first sign that something is wrong. Often nothing more is required than adjusting the diet or social setting for the affected alpaca. Body scoring adults is a more accurate means to assess general condition than weighing. The correct weight is relative to the animal's size, pregnancy status, and other variables. A body score indicates the condition of the animal, regardless of its height and other weight-affecting variables.

Body scoring is the most useful tool for assessing the general condition of older crias (greater than three months), juveniles, and adults. Body scoring crias is problematic. They tend to be born without much body fat and will often feel thin. The more accurate assessment on how well a cria is progressing is to weigh it with an accurate scale. It should average about one-half pound of weight gain per day.

Even a healthy alpaca's body score will change through its lifetime. Usually between 12 and 14 years of age an alpaca's muscle and tissue begin to decline and its body score

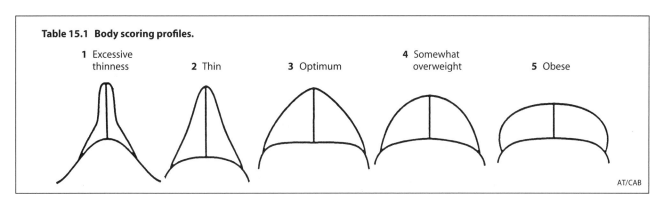

Table 15.1 Body scoring profiles.

1 Excessive thinness   2 Thin   3 Optimum   4 Somewhat overweight   5 Obese

AT/CAB

Copious amounts of fiber can hide body condition. Peruvian/Californian Ale Revilla demonstrates proper hand placement. The alpaca on the left is emaciated (see hand grasp), while the alpaca on the right has optimum body condition.

drops. An older animal's teeth are often worn, making it more difficult to chew food efficiently. Many older animals have body scores of 2 or lower.

If the feeding situation is competitive, the social setting may also work against this animal (see Chapter 22: Geriatric Alpacas).

Body scores on lactating females also often decline during lactation. Some females experience very little decline, while others have severe declines and slow recovery periods after the cria is weaned. Some breeders assess their females' reproductive vitality by how well they maintain a good body score during lactation and how quickly they gain weight back after weaning. With older females lactation has a more severe impact, and recovery to a healthy body condition takes longer than with young females. Pregnant females with low body scores (1 or 2) are at risk because they may not be able the meet the physical demands on their body when lactation begins in earnest. It is common for females older than 14 years to die during the first two months of lactation due to the energy demands on their tiring bodies. Breeding older females that cannot maintain a credible body condition becomes a philosophical and ethical decision for the breeder.

7 Coat Condition

Any initial assessment of an alpaca will be visual. The condition of the coat may be the first telltale sign of a problem.

Wool loss can be a result of stress, poor nutrition, metabolic disorders, external parasites, or fungal and bacterial infections. There is often a delayed response time of up to two months from when the stress takes place and the wool

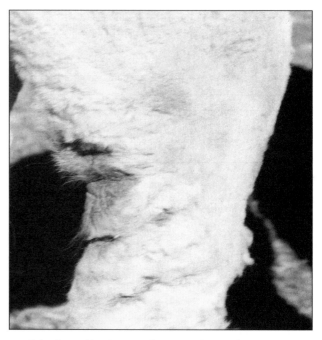

Flaky skin and hair loss are often signs of zinc deficiency.

loss occurs. In crias that go through a period of severe nutritional stress, the loss may be dramatic and quick.

Hair loss from rubbing and itching very likely indicates a parasite problem. By parting the fiber you can sometimes see lice or mites. If a quick visual inspection is inconclusive, taking a skin scraping for a microscopic evaluation may identify the cause.

Brittle hair that breaks at the same place throughout the staple (tender breaks) indicates a period of stress or sickness sometime in the fairly recent past. Hair loss that occurs on the bridge of the nose, especially on dark-pigmented animals during summer months, may be a result of biting insects.

Dermatology lesions can be a challenge to diagnose and treat. Sometimes the general symptoms have a discrete source. For example, abscesses on the head can result from a bacterial infection of the lymph nodes, possibly "lumpy jaw" (a large bony swelling on the mandible), or wounds from shearing or fighting. Serious wounds from fighting often go undetected because they are hidden under thick fleece. Biting insects on a young cria's ears or on the bridge of an adult's nose can cause significant dermatitis. Besides treatment for a particular animal, an overall insect control program may be the remedy.

Dermatitis and wounds on the skin can result in excessive serum production that leads to thick, crusty scabs.

HANDS-ON ASSESSMENT

Once you've assessed the seven areas outlined, you may want to expand your assessment prior to calling your veterinarian. The information you collect may greatly assist your veterinarian in diagnosing the problem.

Temperature

Take the alpaca's temperature. Use a rectal thermometer or an electronic (battery powered) one. Normal temperature is 99.0 to 102.5°F (37–39°C). Though it may seem obvious, remember to shake down the thermometer to its lowest reading before inserting it. Always use a lubricant.

Generally, young animals will be on the higher side of normal and older animals on the lower side, but there are exceptions. The ambient temperature also affects an alpaca's body temperature. Look for temperatures at the higher end of normal on hot days and at the lower end of normal on cold days.

Most commonly an elevated temperature indicates heat stress (or heat stroke), pneumonia, or other infectious diseases. A normal temperature does not mean the alpaca is healthy. Often an alpaca with a severe infection will have a normal temperature. It remains a mystery why some very sick alpacas remain in a normal temperature range.

A very low body temperature can be the result of cold or freezing weather, especially in young or recently shorn alpacas. It may also mean an animal is gravely ill and the alpaca has a poor prognosis for survival. Warming the animal as soon as possible is very important. It is also important to realize that dropping temperature, with no obvious reason for it, is commonly a sign an alpaca is dying.

Weight

Weighing is a helpful tool to assess changes in an animal that may be initially difficult to detect. To do this you must have an accurate scale (see Chapter 4: Husbandry). Periodic weighing of a herd of animals is a valuable means of assessment. A cria or adolescent who stops gaining weight or begins losing weight should be investigated thoroughly. Perhaps the milk supply is inadequate. In a recently weaned animal, perhaps its lowly status in the pecking order is affecting its food consumption. In an adult who has had an inexplicable weight loss, perhaps the diet needs to be assessed, especially if a group of animals has all lost weight. Weight loss can also mean a parasite problem, renal disease, liver disease, nutritional insufficiencies, or behaviorally based problems. If an adult is overweight, weighing will tell you how a weight reduction program is progressing.

Crias should be weighed daily for the first week of life. They should be gaining between one-quarter to one-half pound (0.6–1.3 kg) a day. The weight should continue to increase as the animal ages, but not as dramatically as during the first few weeks. A cria in the first 90 days of life has the highest mortality rate of any age group, except the very old. Weighing and finding no weight gain or weight loss may precede other symptoms. Early detection of a problem is essential for the effective treatment of crias.

Respiration Rate

Normal respiration should be between 10 and 30 breaths per minute. This rate needs to be taken from a distance by watching the abdomen go up and down with each breath. Once a person approaches, the alpaca's respiration rate may increase rapidly, which is a situation that may not be helpful for diagnostic purposes.

A second method of assessing respiration is with a stethoscope. Listen for airway sounds in the middle neck area and side of the chest. A third place to always look is the nose. Look for nasal discharge or flared nostrils.

Palpation of Body Parts

Body score was covered in detail earlier in this chapter and in Chapter 9: Feeding the Alpaca. Knowing an animal's body score is, of course, essential to any overall evaluation. However, other body parts also deserve scrutiny and

Veterinarian Ty McConnell (middle) checks for a luxating patella (loose knee cap) during a screening examination in South America. Veterinarian Pat Long (left rear) explains the technique to an attending Chilean veterinarian.

Because front legs are covered in fiber, assessing leg conformation sometimes requires wrapping the legs to depress the fiber and expose the true shapes of the legs.

palpation. Check for discharges from the eyes, mouth, ears, vulva, penis sheath, and anal area (including the back legs). If you suspect an injury from fighting or other sources, the common areas to find lacerations are the ears, feet, tail, head, neck, scrotal area, and rectal area.

If an animal is lame or favoring a limb, examine the limb systematically. Begin with the foot and work upward. Check the bottom of the foot for puncture wounds, lacerations, or swelling. Slowly examine the other joints of the lower leg. Extend the leg and flex it, and see if there are signs of pain or sensitivity in any joints. Be sensitive to a loose or unstable joint or any grinding sounds (crepitant). If you are able to feel crepitant, there is likely a bone fracture. Careful handling is needed not to further damage the underlying tissues. A full examination of a leg requires slowly working along the leg, working each joint, until the leg attaches to the body.

Teeth

Examination of the teeth can be a challenge. The molars are deeply seated in the jaw and they are difficult to observe. The front incisors (only on the bottom jaw) are easy to see. The incisors can easily be checked for the presence of deciduous teeth (baby teeth) and permanent teeth. In the alpaca the central and intermediate permanent teeth erupt at around two and one-half to three and one-half years of age, and the corners at four to six years of age.

An alpaca skull found on the altiplano has top and bottom molars but incisors only on the bottom mandible. An adult also has fighting teeth (canines), three per side—two on the bottom and one on the top.

What do the teeth say? By pulling back the lower lip, alpaca dentition often reveals everything from approximate age to serious defects. Here are some examples.

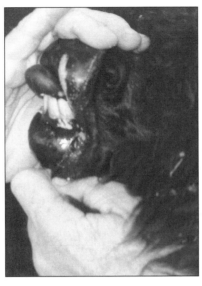

In a correct bite, the incisors intersect the dental pad about the thickness of a coin behind the front of the upper mandible.

In this severe underbite, the incisors intersect the upper mandible behind the dental pad. This defect went undetected until the alignment was examined.

Incisors are deciduous and are replaced by permanent teeth as an alpaca ages. The central incisors are replaced first, usually between two and a half to three years of age. However, assessing an alpaca's age by teeth alone is not always accurate because there are numerous exceptions to the norm.

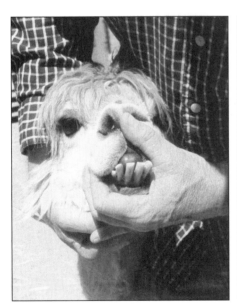

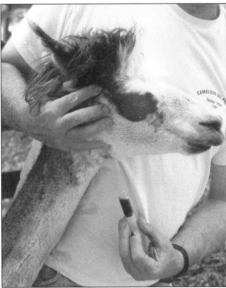

Here, incisors miss the upper mandible entirely. This defect is common in alpacas and is usually referred to as an overbite. In this instance, signs of previous tooth trimming are in evidence. The thickness and quality of the teeth indicate that the alpaca is fairly old.

Molar abscesses are usually discovered when they begin to discharge puss and blood. A radiograph can confirm the cause of these telltale signs. In this case, debris is removed by flushing with an antiseptic solution.

During a routine prepurchase examination, it was discovered that this six month old had no central incisors. This proved to be a rare congenital defect, and the animal never produced the teeth.

Fighting teeth erupt in the males between two and six years, with two and one-half years of age the most common (see Table 15.2).

Once the permanent teeth fully erupt, the deciduous teeth should have fallen out. If one is still present, the condition is called a "retained deciduous tooth," and a veterinarian should be contacted to extract it.

Alignment is important. The incisors should intersect the bottom of the dental pad. See Chapter 3: Anatomy and Conformation for details. Other tooth abnormalities that are readily apparent if you roll the lower lip down and take a look are broken teeth (due to trauma) or entirely missing teeth due to a congenital defect.

Another relatively common malady found in the area of the teeth is "lumpy jaw." In this condition the mandible is swollen due to the presence of actinomyces bacteria. Tooth abscesses are also fairly common in alpacas and llamas. Usually the first sign of an abscess is a draining tract below the molars. The tract usually discharges pus. Radiographs are necessary for a definitive diagnosis. Usually, alpacas between four to ten years of age will develop the abscesses on the mandibular molar and premolar teeth.

OVERALL ASSESSMENT

Often an owner or veterinarian is asked to assess an alpaca's overall quality. A veterinarian doing this type of exam for a prospective alpaca buyer may call it a prepur-

Table 15.2 Age of dental eruption.

Teeth	Age
Central incisors	2½ years
Intermediate incisors	3 to 3½ years
Corner incisors	4 to 6 years
Canines	2 to 6 years

Note: There are many exceptions to the timetable described here, but these are the most common eruption intervals as an alpaca ages.
Source: Ty McConnell, DVM, 20 years of experience in alpaca/llama medicine.

chase exam. This involves assessing not only the animal's general health but also its conformation and fiber quality. Such an assessment needs to be objective and may be used by an insurance company to determine an alpaca's general worth. Again, a systematic approach works best. (See the next page for a sample assessment form.)

VETERINARIAN'S COMPREHENSIVE HEALTH ASSESSMENT

Although some experienced alpaca owners are adept at making the assessments already outlined in this chapter themselves, there are assessment areas where a veterinarian's expertise is absolutely necessary .

When a veterinarian pulls onto a ranch, he is often first bombarded with the owner's impressions and feelings about an animal's health. This type of anecdotal evidence can be helpful but is often misleading if the areas outlined

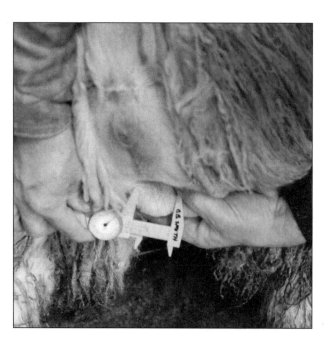

Measuring a testicle during a prepurchase examination.

Veterinarian Brad Smith watches an alpaca walk during the screening process.

Sample Prepurchase Examination/Alpaca Assessment Form.

Date: _____

Alpaca Identification:

Name: _____ Registration ID #: _____ Microchip: _____ Age: _____ Sex: _____ Color: _____
Owner: _____ Address: _____

Physical & Stethoscopic Assessment:

Withers height:_____ Weight:_____ Body score (1–5): _____ Temperature:_____ Motility: _____
Heart: _____normal rate Murmur: _____yes _____no Respiration (tracheal/chest): ____normal ____airflow through both nostrils
Explain problem areas _____

Head, Eyes, and Dentition:

Skull: _____alpacalike _____llamalike _____symmetry
Ears: _____spear shaped _____llama shaped _____intermediate _____abnormality
Eyes: _____presence of cataract _____scarring _____tearing _____blindness Other_____
Teeth: Condition of teeth_____ Presence of fighting teeth (males)_____
Bite: _____correct _____undershot _____overshot (measured in mm) Tooth trimming needed: _____yes _____no

Detailed Conformational Assessment:

General appearance: _____above average _____average. Obvious defect(s):_____
Front view: straight_____ degree of angulation_____ Side and rear view: correctness of front and back legs_____
Assessment of joints: pasterns_____ knee_____ hock_____
Presence of: knock-knee_____ cow-hock_____ sickle-hock_____ luxating patella_____ calf-knee_____ fused toes_____
Abnormal or neglected toenails_____ Other limb defects:_____
(See Chapter 3: Anatomy and Conformation; enter angle of defect in blanks above.)

Neck and Spine:

Palpation of neck, back, and tail: Neck vertebrae: _____normal Spine (cervical and lumbar) vertebrae: _____normal Tail: _____normal
Do any of the following conditions exist: _____scoliosis _____lordosis _____kyphosis _____crooked tail

Reproduction:

Female: Appearance of vulva: size_____ position_____ discharge_____ If maiden female, is there evidence of intersex? ____yes ____no
Reproductive history: abortions, absorptions, prolapsed uterus, hormone implants, difficulty in conceiving, inadequate milk production?
Explain problem areas _____
_____
Is there a detailed written reproductive history? _____ yes _____ no Behavior: _____easy breeder _____difficult behavioral read
Number of cria_____ Number of teats_____

Male: Testicle measurements: length_____ width_____ Testicle abnormalities:_____ Scrotum: ___normal ___abnormal
No. of registered cria_____. Explain known defects in cria_____
Libido: _____untested _____nonaggressive, persistent breeder _____easily discouraged/selective breeder Other_____
Abdominal exam: _____no hernias present _____umbilical hernia present, size_____ _____abdominal or scrotal hernia present, size_____

Fiber Assessment:

Age:_____ Fleece weight for last shearing:_____ Interval between shearings _____ (months)
Histogram after second shearing (attached) or take sample and send to fiber lab
Density: _____very dense _____average _____below average
Staple length_____ Condition of fleece_____

Temperament and Training:

Is animal lead trained? _____yes _____no Will animal easily load into vehicle? _____yes _____no
Interaction with herd members: _____fights _____dominant occasionally _____belligerent _____gets along with others _____submissive
_____special housing requirements. Explain:_____

Signature of Examiner: _____

previously have not been assessed. Often the owner will continue to spew forth ideas even when the veterinarian has donned a stethoscope and is attempting to listen to bodily functions to begin diagnosing a problem. Panic, though understandable, doesn't usually help. What the veterinarian needs is a written history with information about behavior and vital signs. Accuracy and detail in reporting are the most important contributions an owner can make.

Once this information has been exchanged, a veterinarian performs a physical examination. Additional clinical tests are often needed to reach a definitive diagnosis. Common tests include radiographs (X-rays), skin scrapings, blood tests, biopsies, fecal collection, and ultrasound examinations.

The complete blood count (CBC) is a commonly used test (see Table 15.3). It will show anemia (a low red blood cell [RBC] count) or infection (a high white blood cell [WBC] count). It may also show inflammation with a high fibrinogen value, or the presence of a bacterial infection with a left-shift WBC (immature neutrophils).

The CBC includes a chemistry panel that indicates organ function (see Table 15.4). To understand these common associations, talk to your veterinarian:

• Liver disease with elevated ALP, SGGT, SGPT, SGOT

• Renal disease with elevated BUN and creatinine

• Rickets with a low phosphorus value

• Third compartment ulcer with low protein and albumin

• Dehydration—electrolyte imbalances with potassium(K), sodium (Na), and chloride (Cl).

Table 15.3 Complete blood count (CBC).

Component	Normal Range
Red blood cell (RBC) 10⁶/μL	9.9.–17.7
Packed cell volume (PCV) %	25–44.5
Hemoglobin g/dl	10.8–18
Leukocytes (white blood cells, WBC) 10³/μL	7.2–22
Neutrophils 10³/μL	2.9–15.0
Lymphocytes 10³/μL	0–7.4
Monocytes 10³/μL	0–1.1
Eosinophils 10³/μL	0–4.7
Basophils 10³/μL	0–0.3

Source: Fowler, M. E.: *Llama/Alpaca Clinical Pathology*. Llama Medicine Workshop for Veterinarians, Colorado State University, 1993.

Table 15.4 Serum biochemistry.

Component	Normal Range
Total protein g/dL	4.7–7.3
Albumin g/dL	2.9–5
Globulin g/dL	1.1–3
A:G ration	1.1–1.6:1
Calcium mg/dL	7.6–10.9
Phosphorus mg/dL	4.0–11
Sodium mEq/L	148–158
Potassium mEq/L	3.6–6.2
Chloride mEq/L	98–120
Total CO^2 mEq/L	14–34
T-3 ng/dL	0–423
T-4 ng/dL	9.8–30
SGOT IU/L (AST)	128–450
SGPT IU/L (ALT)	0–14
SGGT IU/L (GGT)	3–28
SDH IU/L	0–15
LDH IU/L	10–695
ALP IU/L (AP)	0–610
CPK IU/L	0–137
Creatinine mg/dL	0.9–2.8
BUN mg/dL	9–36
Cholesterol mg/dL	0–128
Glucose mg/dL	76–176
Total bilirubin g/dL	0–0.1

Source: Fowler, M. E.: *Llama/Alpaca Clinical Pathology*. Llama Medicine Workshop for Veterinarians, Colorado State University, 1993.

Additional testing can give further understanding of some organ functions. But with South American camelids there are sometimes mysteries. Every test known to science can be run and no cause will be determined. This is when educated guesswork comes into play.

Sometimes the "next step" in diagnosis involves consulting a veterinary specialist. Moving on to a specialist should be a joint decision and involve communication between the attending veterinarian, the owner, and the specialist. A team effort works best.

WHEN DOES A HEALTH EMERGENCY EXIST?

Emergencies That Require Urgent Care

Many maladies discovered by owners are not emergencies, but many are. Knowing what constitutes an emergency is important. Here are signs that a serious condition exists:

• High body temperature and lethargy (especially when heat stroke or acute infection is suspected)

Alert and active alpacas are usually healthy alpacas. The animals on the left enjoy life high in the Swiss Alps.

• Low body temperature from cold ambient temperature or metabolic shock

• Unusual respiratory rate (too slow or too fast) that cannot be explained from strenuous activity. Pneumonia, severe stress, heart failure, or collapsed lung are all possibilities.

• Mouth breathing in a newborn (check for choanal atresia and other causes)

• Rapid swelling, especially on the nose or head (snake bite, fracture, trauma)

• Evidence of fracture (a sudden change in angle of limbs, acute lameness, protruding bone)

• Head injuries manifested by unusual head tilting, circling, wobbly balance, falling (check ear for foreign bodies).

If any of these conditions exists, keep the alpaca "quiet" in a small pen and contact a veterinarian. If a bro-ken leg is readily apparent and a long wait is anticipated before a veterinarian arrives, it may be necessary to wrap the broken limb. The wrap should include a layer of roll cotton. The support for the wrap should be above the joint of the suspected break. If a splint is attempted, it should extend past the leg and transfer the animal's weight above the joint of the break. Handling a broken bone should be done by professionals, unless none are available and the animal's condition appears to need immediate attention.

Other Emergency Situations

Predator Attack Even if there appears to be no injury, serious injury may exist. Examine the victim carefully. Part the hair in areas where fiber has been pulled from the body. Wounds may be present. Carefully check the hindquarters, legs, and underside of the animal. Uncontrolled bleeding needs to be arrested quickly. It is important to keep the animal calm and apply pressure to a serious wound until a veterinarian arrives.

Leg Strangulation This occurs when wire or rope becomes wrapped around the animal so tightly that circulation stops to the involved appendage or circulation is greatly reduced. Free the animal immediately from the restriction. Gently massage the leg to promote circulation. Use warm compresses to return the affected tissue to normal temperature.

Burns Some camelids are very slow to react to fire. Don't assume an alpaca will keep a safe distance from a brush fire or controlled burn. If an animal is burned, smother the fire and apply cold water to the burned area immediately after the burn occurs. Shock is a possibility. Call a veterinarian.

Gunshot Wounds Unfortunately, livestock of all kinds often fall victim to hunters, especially in deer hunting regions. In deer hunting season, keep animals near a barn and in sight of your house. If an alpaca is shot, control bleeding, take vital signs, and call a veterinarian.

Toxin Ingestion See Chapter 23: Poisons for types of poisons and symptoms. If poisoning is suspected, try to identify the toxic agent and call a veterinarian immediately. Treat with activated charcoal by oral "tubing" to bind up the toxin.

Chapter 16

Routine Herd Health

**Ty McConnell, DVM,
and Eric Hoffman**

A healthy herd in an *ichu* grass
environment, southern Peru.

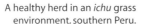

This chapter presents the routine husbandry and medical practices your alpacas may need to remain healthy. The specifics of a program are likely to be different from one farm to the next, depending on a number of factors: population density, age groups, irrigated pasture, dry lot, presence of ponds and lakes, and disease risks in the general area.

Routine herd health addresses maintenance, such as toenail and incisor teeth trimming. It also includes a regular schedule of inoculations and vaccinations against disease risks in your area, assesses dietary needs, and monitors the herd's overall condition and well-being. These tasks often include understanding and minimizing stress factors, both subtle and overt (see Chapter 2: Behavior and Communication and Chapter 4: Husbandry). If you are just starting an alpaca operation, you should meet with a local veterinarian who is experienced with camelids to assess the the routine herd health needs of your animals.

QUESTIONS TO ASK THE VET

What are the recognized parasites, infectious diseases, and metabolic disorders in your area? You'll find that diseases are associated with particular conditions. For example:

- Liver flukes are associated with wet (irrigated or naturally occurring marshy) pastures with poor drainage.

- Rickets is often common in areas of heavy cloud cover, short days, and generally meager amounts of sunshine.

- Low levels of selenium in soil and hays are often associated with weak babies and white muscle disease.

- Heat stroke is common in chronically hot or hot and humid areas.

- Coccidioidomycosis is a systemic fungal disease common to camelids living in the Southwest United States where this fungus is found.

Other diseases are associated with specific environmental conditions and regions. The point here is to learn what they are and to set up a program that addresses them before they occur, not after. This requires implementing a routine health plan, to which there are several important components.

RECORD KEEPING

Keeping records is essential. When it comes to regular health care, much of what happens needs to be recorded. Each animal should have its individual health history. It is important to record the date and amount of any medications or inoculations. Narrative comments about behavior are also helpful (see Chapter 4: Husbandry).

427

ESTABLISHING A ROUTINE

The farm that is run with specific routines in mind catches health problems more consistently than the farm that does things on a sporadic basis. Important routines include:

• Walk through the pen a minimum of once a day, preferably twice a day. Take this time to quietly watch your animals and investigate any aberrant or unusual behavior.

• Feed at set times daily. Alpacas are early risers. In pasture settings they will graze most vigorously early in the day and in the late afternoon. In dry lot settings they often establish early and late eating habits as well. Having quality forage in front of alpacas during their preferred eating times is important (see Chapter 9: Feeding the Alpaca).

• Weigh all animals semiannually. Though often neglected, weighing is worthwhile because it is often the first alert that a particular animal or herd of animals has a problem. Watch for weight losses and attempt to understand why.

• Clean pens regularly. In large operations with plenty of land, this is not as important or as necessary as in small dry lot situations with limited space. Excessive manure is an invitation for diseases of many kinds. Remove it daily in crowded situations (see Chapter 4: Husbandry).

• Scrutinize the dung piles, looking for diarrhea or other telltale signs of gastrointestinal or reproductive problems. Learn to distinguish between a loose stool and outright diarrhea. Aborted fetuses are sometimes found near or on dung piles.

• Have a plan for housing animals in times of life-threatening weather. Know the weather conditions in your area and design your farm to best accommodate your animals for these conditions.

TRIMMING TOENAILS AND CUTTING TEETH

Trimming Toenails

Many alpacas need their toenails and teeth trimmed on a regular basis. The entire herd's toenails should be checked every three months. You'll find that some animals require trimming every three months, while others never need toenail trimming. Some bloodlines produce animals whose nails grow faster than other bloodlines. Also, older animals

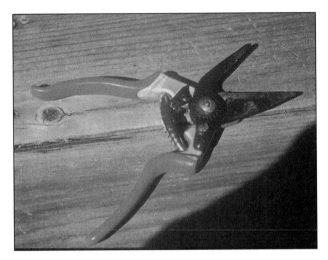

Toenail trimmers are available at camelid industry suppliers. It is important to use cutters specifically designed for camelids.

who become more sedentary often require more trimming because they are less active.

When trimming toenails, be careful to cut only the toenail and not the bottom of the foot. Carefully look at the angle of your intended cut before cutting. The cut should be parallel to the bottom of the foot and not angled upward, to avoid unnecessary injury and copious amounts of blood. Attempt to learn from an experienced toenail cutter before attempting this procedure on your own.

Cutting Canine Teeth

Canine teeth, also known as fighting teeth, are present on all adult male alpacas. Older females may also have canine teeth, but usually not as pronounced as those found in males. The canine teeth are found in the jaw between the incisors and the molars. There are two canine teeth on each side of the maxilla (upper jaw bone) and one canine on each side of the mandible (lower jaw), making a total of three per side or six per animal. These teeth curve backward, are razor sharp, and are designed to lacerate an opponent during a fight. Serious and permanent injuries result from males fighting and biting with their canine teeth.

The canine teeth need to be disarmed after they have erupted into the oral cavity. The fighting teeth are cut at the gum line using a variety of techniques. The use of OB wire (also known as wire saw) is the preferred method to cut all six fighting teeth at the gum line. This procedure should be attempted only by a veterinarian or experienced and trained alpaca handler.

Proper restraint is important. The head must be held still and the lip retracted and kept out of the way through-

The orientation of the toenail ridges indicates whether further investigation and possible trimming are needed. This alpaca's toenails probably don't need trimming, judging by the perpendicular, nontilting orientation of the ridge of each nail.

out the entire procedure. Failure to do this correctly can result in failure to cut the teeth quickly and correctly, or cuts to the gum or lip.

Using the OB wire, care must be taken in setting the wire around the back of the tooth and cutting along, but not into, the gum line. The cutting motion should be gentle but steady, making sure not to apply too much pressure and splinter or damage the tooth or surrounding tissue. If the tooth is large and requires more than a few strokes, it will be necessary to irrigate the tooth with water (usually from a 60 cc syringe) to prevent overheating.

Canine teeth continue to grow for several years, and it may be necessary to cut them again at a later date.

Cutting Incisor Teeth

As the permanent incisor teeth erupt into place, check the alignment. The top of the incisors should fit squarely into the bottom of the dental pad. An alpaca with the correct dental alignment of the incisor teeth (with the dental pad of the upper mandible) will gradually wear them in normal chewing motion as the teeth come in contact with the dental pad. If the alignment is not good and teeth miss the dental pad and upper mandible, they will continue to grow and need to be trimmed periodically.

Cutting incisors involves more factors than cutting canines. With incisors the teeth need to be cut where the tooth would touch the dental pad. Incisors neglected for a long period of time can be quite large and even those that are not neglected can be thick. Usually a cut involves four teeth at once.

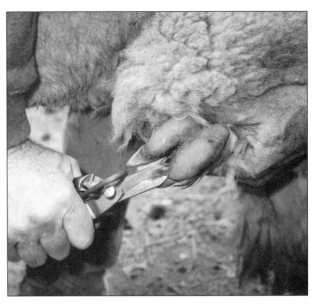

Work with your veterinarian to learn the correct technique of toenail trimming before attempting the procedure on your own. Nail trimming is a routine chore for most owners. Make a cut parallel to the bottom of the foot. Be careful not to cut the footpad or through the quick in the nail. If the nails have been badly neglected and are curled or twisted, the quick will extend below the footpad, requiring consultation with a veterinarian and possible incremental trimming to restore correct profile and length.

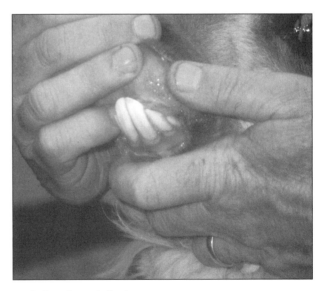

Incisors in need of a trim.

Care needs to be taken in assessing the teeth to avoid cutting and exposing the roots. A tooth is cut with OB wire much in the same manner as the canines, taking care to apply enough pressure—but not too much—to cut the tooth rather than dislodge or damage it. During this procedure the tooth should be irrigated with water to keep it from overheating. Incisor trimming should be

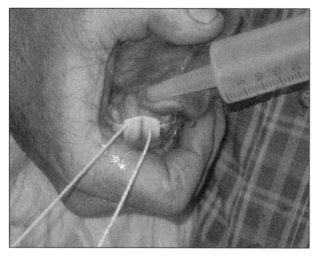

Teeth are cut with OB wire, and water is applied to cool the cut.

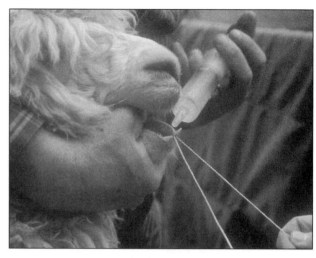

A correct technique for restraint while cutting incisors.

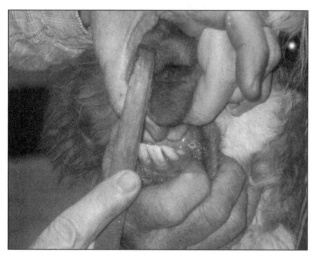

Dull sharp edges with a file.

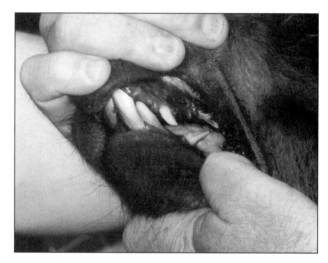

Male fighting teeth (canines) are razor sharp and can inflict serious permanent injury on another alpaca.

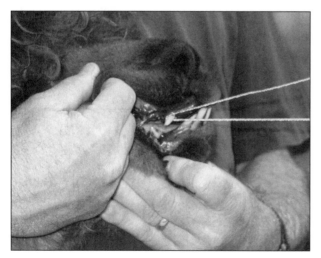

Use OB wire to cut male canines just above the gum line.

This male's ear is cut in half from the base to the tip, damage caused by another male's use of his fighting teeth. Expect other alpacas to receive lacerations to ears, legs, neck, tail, and testicles from a male whose canines have not been removed.

done by a veterinarian or under the direct supervision of a veterinarian.

VACCINATIONS

Basic Considerations

Though alpacas and llamas have been vaccinated for years, there are no scientifically approved vaccines for llamas and alpacas. All vaccines used on camelids were developed for other species of livestock. The effectiveness of vaccine protocols for llamas and alpacas has not been determined, though it is known that they are susceptible to diseases common to all livestock.

In general, the smaller the herd size and the less movement of animals in and out of a herd, the less frequent the need to vaccinate. Also the more space per animal, the less the need for frequent vaccinations.

Widely Used Vaccines

Before adopting a vaccine regime for your herd, consult a veterinarian in your area, because the specific diseases endemic to your area may influence the amount, kind of vaccine, and intervals at which it will be administered. The common vaccines are:

CDT CDT is really two vaccines in one. The "C" and "D" parts of the vaccine are *Clostridium perfringens* types C and D, two common problem diseases with all livestock. The "T" part of the the vaccine is tetanus toxoid.

The recommended vaccination schedules are:

• Crias should be vaccinated at 8 and 12 weeks of age, and then vaccinated every 3, 6, or 12 months depending on the size of the herd and other health risk factors.

• For animals six months or older, vaccinate two to four times yearly depending on the stocking levels and

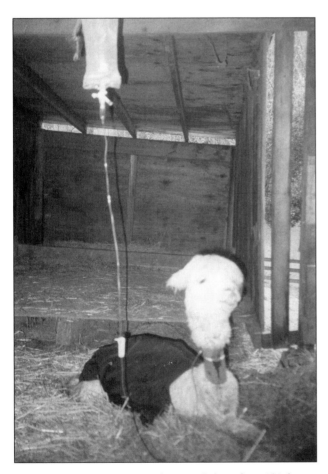

Emergencies occur sooner or later on all alpaca farms. This female is being fed intravenously after developing an ulcer and becoming a reluctant eater. Intravenous intervention saved the animal's life; she went on to produce a beautiful female cria. Setting aside a dry space for such emergencies should be part of any management plan.

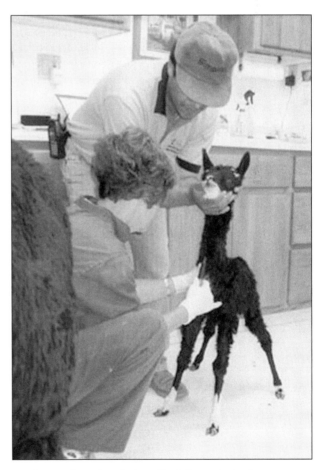

Oregon alpaca breeder Lona Frank demonstrates the proper technique for drawing blood from a cria. Blood analysis is a helpful diagnostic tool.

coming and goings of animals. Often CDT is simply given twice yearly during the spring and fall as a means of assuring consistency in vaccinating the entire herd on a regular basis.

Rabies Camelids can contract rabies. Check with your veterinarian to see if you are in a rabies-endemic area. The vaccine is usually given annually from the Meriux vaccine product, which has the most species-approved labeling.

Leptospirosis Known commonly as "lepto," this bacterium is associated with cattle. Camelids in cattle-raising areas, particularly where they share common pastures, are vaccinated. Flies are the vector. The vaccine is given annually or biannually. The amount of protection camelids receive from the vaccine is questionable.

Eight-way Clostridium This vaccine is in widespread use in the United States. It includes tetanus, *Clostridium* C and D, *Clostridium chauvoei*, *Clostridium speticum*, *Clostridium novyi*, *Clostridium sodelli*, and *Clostridium haemolyticum* type B. It is uncertain whether any of the above clostridials are an actual pathogen to camelids. A large-volume vaccine of this kind can be irritating to the animal, and so many antigens in a single injection may act to dilute one another. This vaccine group may be responsible for abortions or premature births following vaccinations, especially in late-term females.

Equine Herpes 1 Alpacas kept in close proximity to horses, especially zebras, are advised to be vaccinated. Central nervous system blindness with a very sudden onset has occurred in alpacas kept in close proximity to equine stock.

Malignant Edema This is associated with snake bites. Learn what poisonous snakes live in your area and keep species-specific anti-venom on hand in case of snake bite.

PARASITE CONTROLS

Basic Considerations

There are no approved dewormers for camelids. However, dewormers developed for other livestock are in wide use for camelids and are known to combat numerous species of parasites.

It is important to try to determine if a herd's environment puts it at high risk for contracting parasites, or if it is a low-risk herd. A number of variables must be weighed to make this determination. The approach to a high-risk herd can be substantially different than to a low-risk herd.

The variables to consider are: number of animals in the herd; concentration of animals; dry lot versus pasture fed; age of animals; pasture management and field rotation; shared pasture with sheep, goats, or other species; overall body condition of the herd; and hygiene (dung-pile removal).

Frequency of Worming

Worming or deworming are widely used terms meaning to medicate for any of a number of internal parasites. In herds of two to four alpacas with little or no contact with outside animals, two times a years is recommended. With groups of four to eight, three times a year is recommended, and with groups larger than eight, four times a year is recommended.

Fecal Testing for Parasites

The most common way to determine if parasites exist is to collect a fecal sample and take it to your veterinarian for testing. The McMaster flotation test works well with camelids. If a fecal test is done just before worming, and repeated in two weeks, the effectiveness of the worming can be obtained. As a matter of responsible management, a herd's fecal output should be sampled once or twice a year to test for the existence of parasites.

Internal Parasite Medicines (Anthelmintics)

Medicines to treat internal parasites include ivermectin, doramectin, fenbendazole, and pyrantel pamoate. These anthelmintics must be administered in the doses and methods recommended by your veterinarian for them to be effective. See Chapter 17: Parasitology for specific parasite treatments.

ADDITIONAL INFORMATION

For meningeal worm, see Chapter 18: Unusual Parasitic Diseases. For questions on neonate health, see Chapter 14: Obstetrics and Neonatology. For diseases or conditions related to reproduction, see Chapter 12: Male Reproduction and Chapter 13: Female Reproduction.

Chapter 17

Parasitology

Ty McConnell, DVM

Periodic fecal sample analysis can reveal internal parasites.

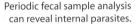

P arasites are one of the most important considerations in the overall health of the alpaca. It is imperative to learn what parasites are common to your particular area by consulting with local veterinarians and other livestock owners. A parasite prevention program should be based on what parasites actually exist as a significant risk and not on rare parasites never seen in your area.

One parasite risk factor is the number of animals that share a common pen space. The higher the density of animals that are kept together in the same pen, the higher the risk for parasites and other infectious diseases.

A second risk factor is pasture grazing. Since most intestinal parasites gain entry into a host through oral ingestion, pasture grazing represents a higher risk of exposure than dry lot feeding. Pasture rotation management is important to reduce parasite exposure and to prevent overgrazing. Sharing the pasture with other animal species such as sheep and goats can also increase the parasite risk. Several intestinal parasites are shared between sheep, goats, and camelids.

In dry lot management, controlling parasites and other infectious agents may be easier, especially if the dung pile is cleaned out regularly.

Alpacas that are thin or in poor condition may represent animals with a heavy parasite load and in their stressed state are more susceptible to parasite infestation. Animals that are sick will often be positive for parasites, but it may not be the only reason the animal is ill.

Frequency of worming should be decided based on the risk factors and number of animals owned. With a very small herd of two to four animals, worming twice yearly may be all that is needed. With four to eight animals, three wormings may be needed. Alpaca herds of eight or more may need worming every three months.

It is important to have your herd checked for internal parasites by running fecal exams on a regular basis. This needs to be done not only when animals are having diarrhea, but also periodically on selected individuals from a herd. If the size of the herd is small, every individual can be done; on larger herds this may not be practical and only a few representative animals should be chosen for testing. A representative of each production stage should be randomly selected: young preweaning crias, yearling crias, pregnant females, adult males, and older geriatric alpacas.

A fecal sample submitted just before worming and two weeks after worming will be an excellent way to judge parasite control effectiveness.

The rest of this chapter describes common parasites and their treatment.

NEMATODE PARASITES

Gastrointestinal Nematodes

Parasites found primarily in the rumen third compartment are *Camelostrongylus mentulatus*, *Ostertagia ostertagi*,

Expect an increase in parasite problems with overcrowding.

Teladorsagia circumcinta, *Trichostrongylus axei*, *Marshallagia marshalli*, and *Haemonchus* species.

The strongylus worm is the most often observed, and larval migration of this and other parasites can cause gastritis. These parasites do not generally cause death, but they can be debilitating.

Small intestinal parasites include *Trichostrongylus* species, *Nematodirus* species, *Cooperia* species, *Capillaria*, and *Strongyloides*. Most of these parasites, although encountered frequently on camelid parasitology exams, are not considered pathogenic unless they are present in high numbers.[3]

Parasites found in the cecum and colon include *Oesophagostomum venulosum* and *Trichuris* species. *Trichuris tenius* is the predominate camelid whipworm.

Clinical symptoms of camelids infested with gastrointestinal parasites are most dramatically seen in young alpacas: poor growth, diarrhea, anemia, dehydration, and emaciation. Anthelmintics used to treat gastrointestinal parasites include ivermectin, fenbendazole, levamisole, thiabendazole, pyrantel pamoate, and mebendazole (see Table 17.1). Ivermectin and fenbendazole are considered the safest and most effective of the anthelmintics used on camelids.[1]

When selecting an anthelmintic, you need to consider the effectiveness of the medication toward a particular parasite. Fenbendazole is more effective against *Trichuris* than ivermectin, for example.

Lungworm

Dictyocaulus is the lungworm parasite common in sheep and cattle. It is contracted by grazing on pasture containing the infective larvae. Camelids sharing pasture with sheep and cattle are at risk for this parasite. Mature worms living in the nasal passages are coughed up and swallowed. The worms are passed through in the feces as larvae. If this parasite is suspected, a fresh fecal sample should be obtained rectally or immediately after defecation and inspected for lungworm larvae. Fenbendazole, levamisole, and ivermectin are all effective against lungworms.

Meningeal Worm

Parelaphostrongylus tenuis is the meningeal worm found in North America. The natural host for this parasite is the white-tailed deer. Alpacas living in white-tailed deer habitat are at risk to contract this parasite. You do not want to wait until clinical symptoms appear to treat this parasite (see Chapter 18: Unusual Parasitic Diseases).

Tapeworms

Moniezia is a tapeworm found in camelids, sheep, and cattle. It is believed to cause very little harm, but it can be very alarming in appearance. The tapeworm is passed in large quantities and often gets a dramatic reaction from the owner. The treatment usually consists of administering fenbendazole at triple the normal dose. A second round of treatment may be needed in two weeks or even higher doses of fenbendazole may be needed.

Liver Flukes

Fasciola hepatica and *Fascioloides magna* are the liver flukes that affect alpacas and llamas. The adult fluke resides in the bile duct of an infected animal. The eggs are passed down the bile duct and into the intestinal tract. The eggs are shed in the feces and need to be deposited in damp water conditions for further maturation. The snail becomes a biological vector for the infective larvae to further develop. The larvae are ingested while grazing on wet pasture, and they finally migrate to the liver after a prolonged period of time. Diagnosis of liver flukes is made by demonstrating the presence of eggs in the feces or by performing an ELISA test that can indicate an infection two weeks

Table 17.1 Anthelmintics.

Generic Name (Brand Name)	Treatment*
Fenbendazole (Panacur)	11–15 mg/kg PO 1–3 days
Ivermectin (Ivomec)	.2 mg/kg SQ 1 day
Thiabendazole (Omnizole)	55–110 mg/kg PO 1–3 days
Levamisole (Levasol)	5.5–8.5 mg/kg PO or SQ 1 day
Mebendazole (Telmin)	22 mg/kg PO 3 days
Albendazole (Valbazen)	6.5 mg/kg PO 1 day
Clorsulon (Curatrem)	6.5 mg/kg PO 1 day
Praziquantel (Droncit)	2.2–3.3 mg/kg PO or SQ 1 day
Pyrantel (Strongid-T)	8.5 mg/kg PO 1 day

*PO = by mouth (Latin *per os*); SQ = subcutaneously
Source: Johnson, L. W.: *An Orientation to Llama Medicine or What Every Veterinarian Has Always Wanted to Know About Llamas But Was Afraid to Ask.* Llama Medicine Workshop for Veterinarians, Colorado State University, 1993.

after larvae exposure and before the fluke matures in the liver.[3] Treatment is usually done with Clorsulon 6.5 mg/kg PO (by mouth), but the effectiveness of this medication has not been established.

Eyeworms

Thelazia species is the eyeworm that effects alpaca eyes. The nematode may be seen swimming on the surface of the eye and residing in the conjunctival sac. This parasite is transmitted by flies and is most prevalent during the fly season. With a large number of eyeworms, conjunctivitis may develop. Application of ivermectin drops into the conjunctival sac is an effective treatment for eyeworms.[2]

PROTOZOAN PARASITES

Coccidia

Eimeria species is responsible for a prevalent diarrhea seen in young crias under one year of age. When exposed to the parasite, crias already under stress (crowded conditions with poor nutrition, cold, travel, or weaning) may present symptoms of coccidia as an acute diarrhea. Many crias may contract coccidia showing very few clinical signs. If the diarrhea is very mild or not present at all, treatment of coccidia is not recommended. In more severe cases Albon or Corid is used to treat coccidia diarrhea. Management is the key to control—good diet, no overcrowding, clean environment, and reduction of stress will control this parasite to subclinical status. Table 17.2 lists drugs for use in coccidia prevention and treatment.

Toxoplasmosis

Toxoplasmosis gondii is the protozoan parasite responsible for toxoplasmosis. Toxoplasmosis usually presents itself as a cause of abortion in the last trimester of pregnancy. The alpaca is exposed to the parasite by ingesting hay or pasture contaminated with cat feces that contain the infective oocysts. Young cats will shed the infective oocysts for two weeks in the feces after exposure to toxoplasmosis from

In small farm settings, where a paddock may become saturated with urine and fecal matter, in addition to daily cleaning some owners cover dung-pile areas with absorbent soil or replace it altogether. Doing this can reduce the buildup of parasites and other manure-associated diseases.

eating rodents. Keeping young cats out of the hay barn and preventing access to the pasture may help to prevent toxoplasmosis. There is no treatment for toxoplasmosis in camelids.

ARTHROPOD PARASITES

Mites

Sarcoptes, chorioptes, and *psoroptes* are the mange mites that affect camelid skin and ears. Sarcoptes skin lesions usually begin on the legs and then spread all over the body. The lesion will first show up as a red papule, but then quickly change to a profound, deep, crusty, scaly skin lesion and wool loss over the body. The mite burrows deeply into the skin. Deep skin scrapings are needed to find the mite. Treatment with ivermectin 0.2 mg/kg, SQ (subcutaneously) twice two weeks apart is usually effective. All animals having contact with infected animals need to be treated, since the parasite is highly contagious.

Chorioptes mange are mites found on the surface of the skin. The skin lesions appear on the feet and on the base of the tail. The mange may spread to other parts of the body but at a slower rate. There will be much less itching, and this mange usually does not cause wool loss. The mite is easier to find in a skin scraping because the mite is

Table 17.2 Coccidial drugs.

Generic Name (Brand Name)	Treatment*
Prevention	
Amprolium (Corid)	5 mg/kg PO 21 days
Decoquinate (Decox)	0.5 mg/kg PO 28 days
Therapy	
Sulfadimethoxine (Albon)	55 mg/kg SQ day 1
	22.5 mg/kg SQ day 2–5

*PO = by mouth (Latin *per os*); SQ = subcutaneously
Source: Johnson, L. W.: *An Orientation to Llama Medicine or What Every Veterinarian Has Always Wanted to Know About Llamas But Was Afraid to Ask*. Llama Medicine Workshop for Veterinarians, Colorado State University, 1993.

on the skin surface. It needs to be differentiated from the sarcoptes mange mite and treated differently. Ivermectin is not as effective on chorioptes mange mite. Chorioptes is difficult to eradicate from a herd and needs to be treated aggressively. Several types of treatment can be tried:

• a 2 to 3 percent lime sulfur spray used weekly for six weeks.

• Coumaphos as a dip or spray every two to three weeks.

• a combination of ivermectin and DMSO applied topically.[3]

The treatment may need to be repeated several times to finally clear up the infection.

Psoroptes is the ear mange seen in alpacas. It is restricted to the ear and ear canals. The ear will become very itchy and develop a large amount of ear wax that has a bad odor. The mite can easily be found by making a smear of the ear discharge. Treatment consists of cleaning out the excess ear wax debris and placing 0.5 ml of ivermectin into each ear two weeks apart.

Lice

Damalinia breviceps (biting lice) and *Microthoreis cameli* (sucking lice) are found on camelids. Lice are species-specific and infect only one species. Lice are found near the surface of the skin and can be seen with the naked eye. Biting lice have a blunted head while sucking lice have an elongated head. A microscope is needed to make positive identification.

The shoulder area, lateral thigh, and along the sides of the animal are the most likely place to find lice. You need to part the hair and very carefully look for small moving lice near the skin level. They may closely resemble debris on the skin. The alpaca may or may not have itchy skin. If sucking lice are found, treat all exposed animals with ivermectin 0.2 mg/kg SQ twice two weeks apart. Biting lice require a topical organophosphate pour-on product such as fenthion twice two weeks apart. Dusting with 5 percent carbaryl is also effective but labor intensive.

It is important to control lice infestation by preventing exposure to the lice. Careful screening of new animals arriving on your farm will help to reduce lice exposure.

Ticks

Otobius megnini, the spinose ear tick, is found in the ear canal of alpacas. Head shaking and ear flagging are the common clinical signs. The ticks can cause a lot of ear inflammation. The adult tick will lay several hundred eggs in the barn or feeding areas. The eggs will hatch into six-legged larvae and find a host. The larvae will find the ear and may reside there for seven months, molting twice, then drop to the ground to lay eggs. Treatment consists of manually removing the ticks with alligator forceps or applying mild ear insecticide and ivermectin 0.2 mg/kg SQ. Barn areas and feeding areas may need inspection and cleaning if the tick problem recurrs.

Dermacentor species has been identified as the tick causing tick paralysis. The female tick feeding on a host may emit a neurotoxin, causing paralysis. This tick resides primarily in the western United States. The paralysis begins as a rear leg weakness, causing difficulty walking and knuckling over at the feet (the feet collapse so the front of the fetlock touches the ground). The weakness will progress to a flaccid paralysis involving the legs, throat, and facial muscles. If the tick does not get removed or fall off, the animal will die as the muscles of respiration, chewing, and swallowing are affected. It may be a challenge to find a tick under all the wool, and shearing the entire animal may be needed. Once the tick is removed, the animal can return to normal in two hours. Ivermectin should not be the sole treatment of tick paralysis, as it may take several days to kill a tick.[1]

Nasal Bot

Cephenemyia species is the fly larva that causes nasal bot. The primary host for the nasal bot is deer, but it can also affect camelids. The adult fly lays eggs at the nasal opening, and the hatching larvae migrate up the nasal passages and into the nasal pharynx area. The larvae develop into pupae in the deer and are eventually sneezed out. Alpacas that contract nasal bot develop a lot of nose and throat irritation that leads to sneezing, coughing, gagging, and sometimes difficulty breathing. Seeing the parasite in the nose is very difficult to witness and can only be done endoscopically or sometimes with radiographs. Treatment consists of ivermectin double the normal dose 0.4 mg/kg body weight SQ. A second treatment in two to four weeks may be needed.

REFERENCES

1. Cheney, J. M., and G. T. Allen: Parasitism in Llamas. Veterinary Clinics of North America. *Food Animal Practice* 5(1): 218, 1989.
2. Fowler M. E.: Parasites. In *Medicine and Surgery of South American Camelids*, p. 132. Ames: Iowa State University Press, 1989.
3. Rickard, L. G.: Parasites. *Veterinary Clinics of North America. Food Animal Practice* 10(2): 420, 1994.
4. Rickard L. G.: Development and Application of a dot-ELISA Test for the Detection of Serum Antibodies to *Fasciola hepatica* Antigens in Llamas. *Vetetrinary Parasitology* 58: 9–15, 1995.

Chapter 18

Unusual Parasitic Diseases

Colored herd, Cañar Province, Ecuador.

SARCOCYSTOSIS: A DISEASE ENDEMIC TO ANDEAN ALPACAS

Stuart White, PhD

Many alpaca breeders outside the Andes are relatively new to alpacas and to alpaca husbandry, but their inexperience is offset by an avid desire to comprehend the biology, environment, and production parameters of these animals. The management of internal parasites is one subject that has received considerable attention in both technical and trade journals, so very few breeders are unprepared to deal with roundworms, *Eimeria*, liver flukes, or meningeal worms. But there is one parasite that receives only passing mention, even though it infects virtually all adult alpacas imported to the industrialized world from the Andes. Because it encysts in muscle, it is unaffected by deparasitizations, either as part of the quarantine procedures or later in the hands of new owners. This masked rider is the single-celled parasite *Sarcocystis*.

The genus *Sarcocystis* is related to the *Eimeria* (coccidia) that infect alpacas, but unlike *Eimeria* it requires two hosts to complete its life cycle. Of the two hosts one is a predator, the other its prey. In the case of South American camelids, the predator role is assumed by the dog or fox, and the prey is the alpaca, llama, guanaco, or vicuña. The parasite is species specific—that is, a species that infects cattle, *S. cruzi*, will not infect sheep; nor will *S. tenella*, which infects sheep, infect camelids. But the close relation-

ship of South American camelids may allow all four to be infected with the same species of *Sarcocystis*. All evidence suggests that those species of *Sarcocystis* infecting alpacas can also infect the llama and perhaps the wild South American camelids, and vice versa.

The parasite lives and sexually reproduces in the intestine of the dog and eliminates large numbers of sporocysts* in the feces—between a half million and 2 million per day, depending on the species of *Sarcocystis* and the evolution of the dog's infection. Shedding continues for a period of four to eight weeks, when a spontaneous recovery occurs. Because sporocysts may survive in pasture for six months or more, and given the extended patent period (the period during which the infection is active and eggs are being produced) and the large number of sporocysts excreted per day, the contamination resulting from one infected dog is potentially severe. In the dog there may be no manifestation of infection, or a mild or fatal enteritis** may be present.

An alpaca eating the grass contaminated by infected dog feces becomes the intermediate host. The parasite

---

*Each egg (oocyst) contains two sporocysts, and within each sporocyst four sporozoites develop—the actual infective agents. A thin membrane enclosing the oocyst may rupture, releasing the two sporocysts even before feces are expelled by the dog. Thus, the sporocyst and not the entire oocyst is more likely to be identified under a microscope.

**Leguía and his colleagues[15, 16, 22] observed the following symptons in fatal infection in a dog: anorexia, fever (106°F; 41°C), dyspnea, anemia, bloody diarrhea, trembling incoordination, prostration, and death 12 days postinfection. The infection was induced by feeding heavily burdened heart tissue.

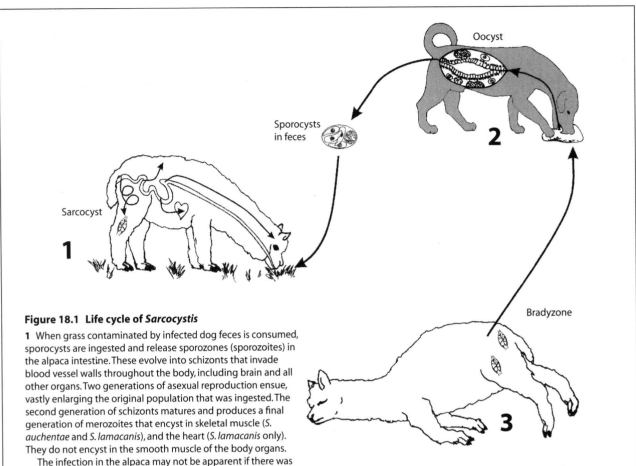

Figure 18.1 Life cycle of *Sarcocystis*

1 When grass contaminated by infected dog feces is consumed, sporocysts are ingested and release sporozones (sporozoites) in the alpaca intestine. These evolve into schizonts that invade blood vessel walls throughout the body, including brain and all other organs. Two generations of asexual reproduction ensue, vastly enlarging the original population that was ingested. The second generation of schizonts matures and produces a final generation of merozoites that encyst in skeletal muscle (*S. auchentae* and *S. lamacanis*), and the heart (*S. lamacanis* only). They do not encyst in the smooth muscle of the body organs.

The infection in the alpaca may not be apparent if there was recent exposure and thus immunity to *Sarcocystis*, but if immunity is lacking or the alpaca is immune suppressed or has ingested a large dose of sporocysts, then symptoms of acute disease (anemia, abortion, wasting, weakness, hair loss, death) are possible.

2 Upon consuming raw camelid meat, bradyzones (bradyzoites) contained in sarcocysts are released in the dog's stomach and intestine, and then invade the intestinal wall and divide into male or female form (gamonts). The infection may or may not produce gastrointestinal disturbance. Sexual reproduction and sporula-

tion take place within the intestine. Nine to 20 days after ingesting meat, the dog begins to shed sporocysts and continues to shed for 20 to 72 days. These sporocysts contaminating the pasture are immediately infective and may survive for six months or longer.

3 An alpaca dies from any cause or is sacrificed. The meat is butchered or abandoned to dogs. Sarcocysts in skeletal muscle and heart are the cumulative result of (perhaps many) prior and likely subclinical infections. Within each sarcocyst are large numbers of bradyzones, which are the infective agent for the dog.

migrates from the alpaca intestine to blood vessels throughout the body, where it reproduces asexually. Two generations[12] are produced in the endothelial tissue of the blood vessel walls and cause anemia. A now much increased number of parasites migrates to the skeletal or heart muscles, where they produce a third generation and then encyst.

With each ingestion of eggs, another population of cysts establishes itself in skeletal or heart muscle. As mentioned, there is no treatment that will eliminate them. The cysts survive for years* before eventually degenerating and

becoming reabsorbed. But if the alpaca dies before this occurs and its raw meat** is consumed by a dog, the viable cysts are released in the intestine and the life cycle begins again.

In camelids at least one species of *Sarcocystis* produces microscopic cysts (*S. lamacanis*), and another (*S. aucheniae*)

*The precise number of years and factors affecting sarcocyst longevity have not been determined for camelid species of *Sarcocystis*. In other farm animals sarcocysts may remain viable for the life of the host.[5]

**Cooking, drying, or freezing at −4°F (−20°C) (but not at 14°F, −10°C) kills the sarcocysts.

produces macroscopic cysts. In natural infections it is common for both species to infect an intermediate host simultaneously.* Microscopic cysts are found especially in the heart and diaphragm, but also throughout the skeletal muscles. The macroscopic cysts are white and about the size of small or broken grains of rice, and are often concentrated in the esophagus and neck but may be anywhere in skeletal muscle, although never in the heart. These cysts, whether macro or micro, cause little or no local inflammatory reaction once they find their resting place in striated muscle,** though over time, as the concentration of cysts increases, they may interfere with muscle efficiency. In appears, for example, that heart tissue malfunctions when burdened with massive numbers of microcysts and results in a condition that mimics Brisket disease, which is induced by hypoxia or high altitude.***

Available information on these two camelid-specific species, derived from the South American literature and conversations with some *Sarcocystis* researchers, is summarized in Table 18.1.

Another species, *S. tilopodi*, has been described in guanacos in Argentina[19] and may be the same as that found in Chilean guanacos.[8] There appears to be no published information comparing *S. tilopodi* to the two common domestic camelid species of *Sarcocystis*, nor to the macrocyst species noted in vicuñas.[18]

As with other internal parasites, the potential of *Sarcocystis* to cause harm is a function of various factors. The principal ones are the number of viable eggs consumed, the period of time during which this burden is assumed (a given number of eggs ingested over a short period of time

Camelid macrosarcocysts (*Sarcocystis aucheniae*).

is usually more damaging than the same number when ingested over an extended period), and the host's specific immunity to this parasite, which is, in turn, a function of previous exposures. There are also great differences in the pathogenicity of different species of *Sarcocystis*. For cattle, *S. cruzi* may cause acute disease, but *S. hirsuta*† does not. For domestic camelids, *S. lamacanis* is apparently more

---

*This is the universal impression of lab workers who examine camelid meat (R. Sam, Facultad de Medicina Veterinaria, Universidad Nacional Mayor de San Marcos, Lima, interviews, November 24–26, 1993).

**Striated muscle refers to cardiac or skeletal muscle, as differentiated from the smooth muscle of, for instance, the internal organs, hair follicles, and blood vessels.

***Vicente Carrion, DVM, personal communication, Cotopaxi, Ecuador, 1992.

†The definitive host for *S. cruzi* is the dog, and for *S. hirsuta*, the cat.

Table 18.1 Characteristics of two camelid species of *Sarcocystis*.

Characteristic	S. aucheniae	S. lamacanis
Definitive host	Dog;[12,15] fox also likely[15]	Dog;[12,15] fox also likely,[15]*
Prepatent period in dog (definitive host)	11–20 days[15]	9–14 days[15]
Duration of sporocyst shedding by dog	20–41 days[15]	60–72 days[15]
Number of spororcysts shed per day	Up to 560,000[15] (max. at 15 DPI)	Up to 2 million[15] (max at 22 DPI)
Size of sporocysts	13.1–15.7 × 9.0–11.3 μm[5] 13.2–15.84 × 9.9–10.56 μm[15] 15.63±0.47 × 10.84±0.36[1]	13.10–15.55 × 9.08–11.15 μm[15]
Survival of sporocysts in pasture	Prolonged;[12] may be 4–5 months* or more	Prolonged;[12] may be 4–5 months* or more
Prepatent period of acute sarcocystosis in alpaca (intermediate host)		21–25 days;[12] 19–22 days[16,17,20]
Speed of maturation of sarcocysts in alpaca	Slow;[12] 14–18 months	Rapid,[12] 4–5 months*
Primary location of sarcocysts	Skeletal muscles;[12] never in heart*	Heart[12] and other striated muscles*
Toxicity for humans and dogs of sarcocysts in uncooked meat[15]	Low*	High*
Lethal dose of sporocysts		>40,000 and <160,000[12,16,17,20]
Size of mature sarcocysts	Macroscopic;[12] 3–6 mm × 1.5–2.5 mm	Microscopic;[12] 12–14 μm × 30–32 μm[11]

*In humans and monkeys, consumption of uncooked contaminated meat results in malaise and gastrointestinal disturbance, including cramps and diarrhea, which resolve spontaneously in 24 to 72 hours. Illness apparently results from cyst endotoxins. Heart muscle is especially toxic, even for the definitive host.[15,23]

pathogenic than *S. aucheniae.* Thus, the manifestations of sarcocystosis* range from virtually no clinical signs or loss of productivity to acute signs and death. It behooves us to be aware of this parasite if we are to limit its incidence and avoid its potentially serious consequences.

CAMELID *SARCOCYSTIS* IN THE CENTRAL ANDES

The vast majority of alpacas in the Andes of Peru, Bolivia, and Chile graze on the puna, which is high (12,800–17,000 ft; 3,900–5,200 m) and dry to quite dry across large areas, and further characterized by an annual rainless period. Because vegetation is sparse and seasonal, herds often range over wide areas at low stocking rates (0.2–1.3 per hectare; 0.5–3.2 head per acre). Often alpacas are brought to the shepherd's house each night as a defense against predators. In these cases, the corrals or areas where the alpacas sleep are generally devoid of vegetation because of trampling and overgrazing, except during the rainy season. In other cases, the grazing locations are rotated over a large territory, distant from the home site, and alpacas are herded together at night near the shepherd's temporary shelter. Dogs are always kept by herders and roam freely with the alpaca herd. Dead alpacas may be eaten by dogs before shepherds discover the carcasses, and scraps of uncooked alpaca meat are often fed to dogs or scavenged by them when alpacas are butchered.

Thus, dogs may shed *Sarcocystis* eggs more or less continually, but most of their shedding will be in areas near the home site, where grass is absent or limited for most of the year, and where, consequently, most of the eggs are not ingested by alpacas. Shedding of eggs over areas of extensive grazing will expose the herd to but continuous levels of infection. The dry climate, intense solar radiation, and perhaps nightly freezes of the puna kill the sporocysts, so that in the dry season decontamination is in some balance with new contamination by dogs. In contrast, during the rainy season (December to March in most of the puna), the climate is warmer, wet, and often cloudy, aiding sporocyst survival. Simultaneously, grass growth is abundant, even near the dwelling and areas of intense grazing, favoring consumption of eggs by alpacas. Perhaps for these reasons the peak of *Sarcocystis* sporocyst ingestion is reported to occur during the rainy season.[12]

Within this seasonal climate regime and extensive management, infections with *Sarcocystis* are usually subclinical, although almost universal. Of domestic camelids greater than two years of age in Peru, virtually 100 percent harbor sarcocysts in muscle.[1,4,9,21] Although most cases are subclinical, the continual exposure of alpacas over their lifetimes to waves of *Sarcocystis* infection causes declines in production and increases susceptibility to other diseases.**

CLINICAL SARCOCYSTOSIS

We have seen that infection with one or more species of *Sarcocystis* is common in the central Andes, as evidenced by the high incidence of sarcocysts in the meat of animals sacrificed for market. Although cumulative infections result in cumulative losses in production, this parasite is generally not associated with acute disease, and perhaps for this reason receives little attention. Nevertheless, in other farm animals death can be induced experimentally for pathogenic species of *Sarcocystis* when a large number of sporocysts are ingested over a short period of time, or when the intermediate host is stressed or has no recent exposure to homologous challenge species.[5,6] It can be assumed that under certain field situations and management schemes one or more of these conditions may be fulfilled. Such natural outbreaks have been reported for cattle (*S. cruzi*) and sheep (*S. tenella*).[3,5] An experimental infection carried out in Peru has shown that acute disease may also be induced in alpacas.

Leguía and colleagues[14,17,20,23] inoculated three young alpacas free of prior exposure to *Sarcocystis* with 160,000 sporocysts of *S. lamacanis* each.*** Beginning at 21 days postinfection (DPI), they showed incoordination, loss of appetite, weakness, and recumbence, fever, weight loss, excessive salivation, dyspnea (labored breathing), and pale mucous membranes. Death occurred at 23, 24, and 28 DPI. Necropsy and histopathological findings included:

- Hemorrhage of perivascular tissue (surrounding the blood vessel) and interstitial tissue of heart, liver, kidney, and lung

- Moderate-to-severe infiltration of mononuclear cells (immune cells, termed "monocytes" in blood or "macrophages" in tissue)

---

*Four terms are used to describe infection by *Sarcocystis* species. They reflect both author preference and a desire to emphasize the character of the infection. I have used *sarcocystosis,* following Dubey et al.,[5] to refer to infection in its range of clinical manifestations. *Sarcocystiosis* is often employed for subclinical, chronic infections (this is the term, spelled *sarcocistiosis,* that is most often used in Spanish). *Sarcosporidiosis* (spelled the same in Spanish) is an older term seen in the literature. *Sarcocystiosis* is preferred by Fowler.

**Sarcoystosis in other farm animals is commonly associated with immunosuppression.

***At the time this experiment was conducted, *S. auchemiae* was considered to be the species employed. Nevertheless, in 1990 Leguía proposed that the microcysts contained in meat and used in the inoculation to infect dogs, and from which sporocysts were obtained, be termed *S. lamacanis,* a designation now universally accepted.

- Edema and hemorrhage along the entire gastrointestinal tract

- Formation of hyaline (a glassy substance that may reflect degeneration of tissue) on striated muscles and a mottled appearance to the muscle

- Pleurorrhea (liquid in the chest cavity), hydropericardium (liquid in the heart sac), and ascites (liquid in the abdominal cavity)

In the brain and cerebellum, findings included:

- Hyperemia (abnormal accumulation of blood), hemorrhage, and mononuclear cell infiltration

- Perivascular edema and death of Purkinje cells (a specific kind of brain cell) and other brain neurons

In this experiment another alpaca inoculated with 40,000 sporocysts showed severe anemia, appetite suppression, fever, and weight loss, but recovered. A control alpaca that received no sporocysts remained healthy.

Immunity in camelids appears to be solid after exposure to small numbers of sporocysts but is of relatively short duration. In an unpublished experimental inoculation,* Leguía selected three field alpacas of 3, 4, and 5 years of age that were presumably exposed for most of their lives to *Sarcocystis*, isolated them for approximately 14 months, and then inoculated them with doses of 250,000, 500,000, and 1 million sporocysts of *S. lamacanis*. All died between 21 and 35 DPI. Similarly limited durations of protective immunity are reported in other farm animals, from more than 80 to less than 120 days in pigs, at least 90 days in sheep, 250 days in cattle, and 270 days in goats.[5]

Symptoms of naturally occurring and induced clinical sarcocystosis are relatively consistent for different farm animal intermediate hosts. (Immunological detection in camelids is possible[20,21] but has not be standardized.)** Table 18.2 summarizes those symptoms reported for clinical *S. cruzi* infection in cattle and those observed by Leguía and colleagues for *S. lamacanis*.

IMPLICATIONS FOR ALPACA MANAGEMENT

Over the last decade alpacas have expanded their range to include lower altitudes and wetter conditions, both in the Andes and on other continents.*** New and more amenable environments are usually combined with higher stocking rates and intensities of management. These displacements result in new disease exposures and new disease entities for alpacas. But traditional diseases have also

Table 18.2 Symptoms reported for clinical sarcocystosis.

Symptom	S. cruzi[a]	S. lamacanis[b]
Anemia	X	X
Decrease or cessation of lactation	X	N/A[c]
Hypersalivation	X	X
Hair loss	X	
Abortion and stillbirth	X	N/A[c]
Anorexia	X	X
Weight loss	X	X
Fever	X[d]	X
Diarrhea	X	X[c]
Neurologic signs	X	X

X = symptom observed
a. From both natural and experimental infections.[5]
b. From an experimental infection of three alpacas.[14,23]
c. Not applicable; only males were used in the experimental inoculation.
d. Fever equal to or greater than 40°C (104°F).
Source: Guillermo Leguía, Facultad de Medicina Veterinaria, Universidad Nacional Mayor de San Marcos, Lima, interviews, November 26–27, 1993.

shown new levels of morbidity and mortality and have sometimes altered clinical manifestations.

For example, fascioliasis (liver fluke infestation) is present as a chronic disease on the altiplano of the central Andes, but is of limited economic significance in the average herd. When, however, alpacas were first transported to the lower and wetter northern Andes of Peru, liver flukes produced illness and became a leading cause of death.† Similarly, clinical sarcocystosis appears to be unusual in the central Andes, but may represent a major threat to future alpaca husbandry in environmentally more benign conditions and under more intense management, both in the Andes and elsewhere.

Four factors increase the likelihood of clinical sarcocystosis in these new areas:

- Climates that are humid, cloudy, of low elevation, and not subject to deep or frequent freezes allow sporocysts in pasture to survive for extended periods.

- When care is taken not to overgraze, sporocysts are provided greater protection from ultraviolet (UV) light

*Guillermo Leguía, Facultad de Medicina Veterinaria, Unversidad Nacional Mayor de San Marcos, Lima, interviews, November 26–27, 1995.

**A group led by Dr. Teresa López at the Facultad de Medicina Veterinaria Universidad, Nacional Mayor de San Marcos, is working on standardizing an ELISA test for *Sarcocystis* infection.

***In South America alpaca herds are being established in northern Peru, central and southern Ecuador, and central Chile, locations considerably wetter and of lower elevation than their places of origin.

†Nelson Clavo, Facultad de Medicina Veterinaria, Universidad Nacional Mayor de San Marcos, Lima, personal communication, 1993.

and desiccation, and grass provides a year-round means of conveyance to the mouth of the alpaca.

• In intensely managed operations, proximity of the owner's or caretaker's residence (and thus of dogs) to pastures may result in more concentrated contamination of grass.

• A higher stocking rate, in which pastures are closely and uniformly grazed, may be reflected in greater herd exposure because relatively few sporocysts will escape ingestion.

The fundamental decision of an alpaca manager is whether or not infection with *Sarcocystis* can be eliminated from the herd and its reintroduction prevented. In the traditional alpaca-raising zones of south central Peru, northern Chile, and Bolivia, this goal is unattainable. Where all neighbors keep camelids and dogs, where grazing areas are contiguous and sometimes communal, and where dogs reign freely and foxes exist, it would be impossible to maintain a *Sarcocystis*-free herd or zone. The objective then is to limit exposure to sporocysts, which in turn will reduce the amount of meat condemned at slaughter and the losses in production from chronic, cumulative infections.

Controlling the infection in dogs and their contamination of pastures is problematic for various reasons. In the Andes, the elimination of dogs is not possible where they provide protection against predators or are needed by shepherds or ranching families for other reasons. Preventing dogs from consuming camelid meat is made difficult by large herds, broken terrain, and severe weather conditions, which limit supervision, especially when combined with a small number (and sometimes the tender age) of shepherds. Dogs do not acquire significant immunity after infection and so are capable of shedding sporocysts almost continually if their consumption of infected raw meat is frequent. Also, the infection in dogs may easily go undetected. Treatment is reported to be ineffective once production of oocysts has begun,[13] though it may be attempted with anticoccidials.

Nevertheless, Peruvian extensionists recommend various management changes that should, in theory, reduce exposure for the camelid host.[2,12] No study that measures the relative value of these actions or the real reduction of pasture contamination has been published. To the extent that they are undertaken simultaneously by all families in a community or grazing area, the effects of each additional action may be synergistic. They include reducing numbers of dogs per family, eliminating foxes and feral dogs, not permitting dogs to eat uncooked meat from sacrificed

camelids, avoiding home butchering for commercial sale, providing dog control at established slaughterhouses, burying carcasses that will not be eaten, keeping dogs out of and away from night corrals or sleeping areas if these have a grass cover, and avoiding pasturing near home sites where dogs are fed and spend most of their time and where they are thus more likely to defecate.

For alpaca herds in areas of recent introduction, where these herds are isolated from other camelids, where the areas dedicated to grazing can be well supervised, where dogs and wild canids are absent or can be controlled, and where personnel responsible for shepherding are educated in the role of canids in *Sarcocystis* transmission, it may be possible to eliminate infection completely. The major risk of this strategy, of course, is that future contamination of pasture with camelid *Sarcocystis* sporocysts may be manifested as an outbreak of acute disease because the alpacas will lack immunity.

Managers of alpacas in North America who decide to attempt to eliminate *Sarcocystis* from a herd must assume that all herd members raised in the Andes harbor at least two species of this parasite. As mentioned, cysts in meat eventually age, degenerate, and become noninfectious, but this process occurs over years. Elimination of the parasite from a herd thus requires, at minimum, the lifespan of the last-living introduced alpaca. Meanwhile, those born on the premises must not become infected. Where no dogs are kept, where no canids from neighbors or the wild have access to alpacas or their grazing areas, and where there is complete assurance that no raw alpaca or llama meat will be consumed by canids, eradication is feasible in principle.

If the possibility remains that dogs will on occasion consume raw camelid meat, but the herd is under minimal threat from wild predators (or predators can be fenced out from pastures), alpacas could be left uncorralled at night, and thus at greater distance from the house and the principal activity areas of dogs. In cases where household dogs consume, or are suspected of having consumed, raw camelid meat, they should be removed from the premises for at least three months and tested for the presence of *Sarcocystis* eggs.* If results are positive, pastures frequented by the dogs one week or more after meat consumption should not be grazed by camelids for at least six months, and considerably longer if ambient conditions are cool and humid.

---

*Because the dog may be infected with noncamelid species of *Sarcocystis*, a distinction must be made between camelid and noncamelid sporocysts found in fecal samples.

THERAPY

There is consensus that acute sarcocytosis is unresponsive to therapy.[10] Although there is no doubt that in an affected herd those individuals that do not have immunity and that have consumed large numbers of sporocysts of pathogenic species of *Sarcocystis* will die, nonetheless others whose dose has been lower or whose level of protective immunity is higher may survive if given appropriate supportive and specific therapy. For camelids that have been transferred outside of their Andean homeland, and on which high economic value is placed, therapy will no doubt be attempted.

From the literature, as well as field experience in response to an outbreak in Ecuador,* the following tentative recommendations are made regarding management of acute sarcocystosis.

1. Begin specific therapy immediately. A few agents have shown activity against *Sarcocystis* species. Oxytetracycline given intravenously (30 mg/kg body weight) is reported to have prevented death in acutely ill sheep, as has halofuginone (0.67 mg/kg b.w. given once) in sheep and goats. In another study, excellent activity was obtained against *S. muris* with various drugs, including Zoalene®, primaquine diphosphate, sulfaquinoxaline plus pyrimethamine, and Bay® G7185.[5]

2. Deparasitize if fecal analysis shows even moderate parasite loads, both to eliminate an additional stress and to prevent buildup of loads, as immune protection is compromised due to *Sarcocystis* infection.

3. Correct anemia, which is regenerative, with whole blood transfusions, iron, and vitamin B complex.

4. Provide physical therapy for recumbent and uncoordinated individuals, including help in standing, passive exercise, and sling support.

5. Consider the application of prophylactic antibiotics to protect from secondary bacterial infections.

6. Provide nursing offspring with supplemental feed, because milk production of the dam is severely compromised.

Where an outbreak of sarcocystosis can be anticipated (for example, dogs are known to have consumed raw camelid meat or discovered to be shedding sporocysts), application of *Sarcocystis*-appropriate chemoprophylactics should be begun. These may include halofuginone (0.22 mg/kg body weight), amprolium (100 mg/kg b.w.) and salinomycin (1–2 mg/kg b.w.).** It appears that the use of these drugs does not inhibit the acquistion of immunity induced by exposure to the parasite.[5] In small herds it is advisable to obtain packed cell volumes of all members. Because anemia is apparent after only one week postingestion of a lethal number of sporocysts, and two weeks before manifest illness,[20] infected individuals can be identified and chemoprophylaxis begun. An additional experimental possibility for alpacas under threat of infection is to stimulate immunity by inoculating them with a limited number (as yet undetermined for camelid species of *Sarcocystis*)*** of sporocysts at least one month before natural exposure.

REFERENCES

Many articles derived from Leguía et al.'s experimental *Sarcocsystis* infection repeat the same information. All are mentioned here, however, because access to these articles varies and some differences in emphasis and data among the articles exist.

1. Alva, J., H. Bazalar, C. Guerrero, and A. Nuñez: Observaciones del Ciclo de Vida del *Sarcocystis aucheniae* de Alpacas (*Lama pacos*). *Resumen del Quinto Congreso Peruano do Microbiologia y Parasitologia*. Arequipa, Peru, p. 75, 1981.
2. Barcena, E., and F. Amachi: *Sarcocystiosis en los Camélidos Sudamericanos*. Puno, Peru: Universidad Nacional del Altiplano, Facultad de Medicina Veterinaria y Zootecnia, and Centro Experimental de Camélidos La Raya, 1993.
3. Carrigan, J: An Outbreak of Sarcocystosis in Cattle. *Australian Veterinary Journal* 63(1): 22–24, 1986.
4. Castro, J.: *Sarcocystis aucheniae* en Llamas (*Lama glama*). *Revista de Investigaciones Pecuarias* (IVITA and Universidad Nacional Mayor de San Marcos, Lima) 3(1): 91–92, 1974.
5. Dubey, J. P., C. A. Speer, and R. Fayer: *Sarcocystosis of Animals and Man*. Boca Raton, FL: CRC Press, 1989.
6. Ford, G.: Immunity of Sheep to Homologous Challenge with Dog-Borne *Sarcocystis* Species Following Varying Levels of Prior Exposure. *International Journal for Parasitology* 15 (6): 629–634, 1985.

*On my ranch in Ecuador there was an outbreak of disease whose clinical manifestations closely resembled those reported by Leguía, Sam, and colleagues for experimental inoculations with *S. lamacanis*.[12,17,20,23] Evidence for the role of *Sarcocystis* is being studied.

**Amprolium and salinomycin appear to be ineffective in treating acute disease, but function in prevention.[5]

***Summaries of LD[100] in different species, compared with numbers of sporocysts needed to establish protective immunity,[5,6] suggest that between 0.2 and 2 percent of LD[100] will provide protection without producing illness, depending upon the species of *Sarcocystis* involved.

7. Fowler, M.: *Medicine and Surgery of South American Camelids: Llama, Alpaca, Vicuña, and Guanaco.* Ames: Iowa State University Press, 1989.

8. Gorman, T., H. Alcaino, H. Muñoz, and C. Cunazza: *Sarcocystis* sp. in Guanaco (*Lama guanicoe*) and Effect of Temperature on Viability. *Veterinary Parasitology* 15: 95–101, 1984.

9. Guerrero, C., J. Hernández, and J. Alva: *Sarcocystis* en Alpacas. *Revista de la Facultad de Medicina Veterinaria* (Universidad Nacional Mayor de San Marcos, Lima) 21: 69–72, 1967.

10. Howard, J. L.: *Current Veterinary Therapy, 3: Food Animal Practice.* Philadelphia: Saunders, 1993.

11. Instituto Nacional de Higiene "Leopoldo Izquieta Pérez." Analyses by Oswaldo Albornoz, Clímaco Egas, Bolívar Ricaurte, and Luis Vasco Quito, Ecuador, 1993.

12. Leguía, G.: Enfermedades Parasitarias. In *Avances y Perspectivas del Conocimiento de los Camélidos Sudamericanos,* S. Fernandez-Baca, ed., pp. 331–334. Santiago, Chile: FAO, 1991.

13. Leguía, G., and N. Clavo: Sarcocystiosis o 'Triquina,' *Boletin Técnico no. 7.* Lima: Centro de Investigación Científica Camélidos Sudamericanos and Instituto Veterinario de Investigaciones Tropicales y de Altura (IVITA), 1989.

14. Leguía, G., C. Guerrero, R. Sam, and R. Rosadío: Patología del *Sarcocystis aucheniae* en Alpacas Infectadas Experimentalmente. *VI Convencion Internacional Sobre Camélidos Sudamericanos.* Oruro, Bolivia, pp. 225–226, 1988.

15. Leguía, G., C. Guerrero, R. Sam, and A. Chávez: Infección Experimental de Perros y Gatos con Micro y Macroquistes de *Sarcocystis* de Alpacas (*Lama pacos*). *Revista de Ciencias Veterinarias* (Lima) 5(3): 10–13.

16. Leguía, G., C. Guerrero, A. Chávez, F. Arévalo, and R. Sam: Estudio de la Sarcocistiosis en Alpacas. *Avances Sobre Investigación en Salud Animal, Camélidos Sudamericanos* (Universidad Nacional Mayor de San Marcos, Lima), Boletín de Divulgación 23: 43–46, 1990.

17. Leguía, G., C. Guerrero, R. Sam, and R. Rosadío: Patología del *Sarcocystis lamacanis* n. sp. en Alpacas Infectadas Experimentalmente. *Revista de Ciencias Veterinarias* (Lima) 6 (3): 11–13, 1990.

18. Paucar, A., J. Tellez, L. Neyra, and J. Rodriguez: Estudio Tecnologico del Beneficio de Vicuñas. In *La Vicuña,* Lima: Editorial Los Pinos, pp. 33–48, n.d.

19. Quiroga, D., O. Lombardero, and R. Zorilla: *Sarcocystosis tilopodi* n. sp. en Guanacos (*Lama guanicoe*) de la República de Argentina. *Gaceta Veterinaria* 31: 67–70, 1969.

20. Sam, R.: *Sarcocystis aucheniae:* Caracterización Parcial de Componentes Antigénicos y Patología Experimental en Alpacas. PhD Thesis, Facultad de Ciencias Biológias, Universidad Nacional Mayor de San Marcos, Lima, 1988.

21. Sam, R.: Caracterización de los Componentes Antigénicos de Alpacas Infectadas con *Sarcocystis aucheniae. Avances Sobre Investigación en Salud Animal, Camélidos Sudamericanos* (Universidad Nacional Mayor de San Marcos, Lima), Boletín de Divulgación 23: 47, 1988.

22. Sam, R., R. Oré, and G. Leguía: Cambios Hematológicos y Serológicos en Alpacas Experimentalmente Infectadas con *Sarcocystis aucheniae. Resúmenes del 11th Congreso Panamericano de Ciencias Veterinarias.* Lima, p. E.11.4, 1988.

23. Sam, R., C. Morales, and A. Ramírez: Toxicidad de Lisados de Macroquistes de *Sarcocystis aucheniae.* Unpublished manuscript, n.d.

MENINGEAL WORM

Karen Baum, DVM

Known as the deer worm, meningeal worm is a parasite called *Parelaphostrongylus tenuis (P. tenuis)*. Its geographic distribution is associated with the white-tailed deer (*Odocoileus virginianus*), which live throughout eastern North America. The white-tailed deer is the definitive natural host to this parasite. Deer carrying the parasite often have no clinical signs. Snails and slugs are also required for *P. tenuis* to complete its life cycle.

In llamas and alpacas, meningeal worm can cause serious neurological problems in the spinal cord and sometimes the brain. Signs are typically asymmetric (unequally affecting the two sides of the body). A meningeal worm infection can lead to death due to complications from paralysis.

LIFE CYCLE OF THE PARASITE

The infective larvae (L3) are consumed by deer, where they develop into adults. Eggs are laid and develop into larvae (L1), which migrate within the deer. L1 larvae can be coughed up, swallowed, and passed in the feces of infected deer. The *P. tenuis* larvae are shed in the feces of clinically unaffected white-tailed deer as L1 larvae. The survival of free-living L1 larvae is reduced by repeated freezing or drying. The L1 larvae are extraordinarily long-lived in optimal conditions, surviving on average between 200 and 300 days! It is a very hardy parasite.

Snails and slugs (gastropods) are the intermediate hosts in which development of the *P. tenuis* larvae occurs. L1 larvae gain entry into snails and slugs through ingestion or through penetration of the soft foot or other body surface. Two molts occur in the gastropod, resulting in the infective L3 larvae.

The gastropods prefer a moist environment with plenty of organic material (leaf litter, live and decaying plants) plus available dietary calcium carbonate. Terrestrial gastropods experiencing these conditions in moderate temperatures, with long days, thrive. Once the snail or slug molts, the survival of the L3 larvae outside the snail is thought to be short-lived, especially if not in water or moist spongy conditions. It is not known how long the larvae can remain in the gastropod and what triggers its exit.

When unnatural hosts (e.g., alpacas, llamas, goats, elk, moose, and reindeer) ingest the infective L3 larvae, migration through the body occurs. Clinical signs usually involve the central nervous system, especially the spinal cord—paresis (weakness), ataxia (incoordination), staggering, inability to rise, etc. Migration to the central nervous system in white-tailed deer takes a minimum of ten days, while experimental data on llamas (and presumably alpacas) indicates it takes a minimum of two to eight weeks to see clinical signs following ingestion of L3 larvae. There is a variable period between ingestion (consumption) and clinical signs due to variable lengths of migration (wandering) within the body of the camelid before arriving at the spinal cord. Not all animals that ingest larvae display signs. Signs depend on the location of the parasite, but signs can change as larval migration in the central nervous system continues. Asymmetrical spinal cord lesions causing paralysis or paresis are common.

DIAGNOSIS AND TREATMENT

Presumptive diagnosis is based on clinical signs, history (exposure to white-tailed deer and terrestrial gastropods), elimination of other diseases, and response to treatment. Definitive diagnosis is based on identification of the parasite under a microscope. This means collecting tissue samples of the nervous system after death.

Treatment depends on the duration and severity of clinical signs. Anti-inflammatories are indicated to reduce the reaction to the parasite. Phenylbutazone (bute) has been safely used in camelids, especially if the patient is eating. Dewormers should be effective against migrating parasites before they penetrate the central nervous system. Ivermectin at double the cattle dose orally or subcutaneously repeated, and fenbendazole at 15 mg/kg orally daily for three to five days, with concomitant use of anti-inflammatories, seems to be beneficial. I usually give one dewormer then the other dewormer, i.e., ivermectin followed by a regime of fenbendazole. Supportive treatment is important, along with dewormers, anti-inflammatories, and possibly DMSO (dimethylsulfoxide) as a 5 to 10 solution in 5 percent dextrose intravenously (IV).

Physical therapy needs to be diligent and persistent. Recovery may take several weeks or months. Central nervous system cells heal very slowly. Some residual signs may persist. These may be permanent if they persist a year following the onset of signs.

PREVENTION

There is no commercial vaccine currently available. Therefore, prevention is based on management principles. Elimination of exposure to deer, snails, and L3 larvae is ideal but often impractical. Reduction of exposure along with frequent deworming to kill the parasite before penetration into the central nervous system seems to be more feasible. Prevention of deer and gastropod cohabitation can be difficult.

Alpacas housed in white-tailed deer habitat receiving monthly dewormings have avoided the parasite. Ivermectins and fenbendazole will kill the parasite prior to entry into the central nervous system. Once migration into the central nervous system is complete, treatment can be difficult. Anthelminthics should be utilized. Anti-inflammatories, such as bute, Ketofen (ketoprofen), or Banamine (flunixum meglumine) are useful in alleviating inflammation due to death of larvae in the central nervous system. *Steroids should be avoided.*

Deworming every four weeks or once a month apparently is efficacious in killing *P. tenuis* larvae before the central nervous system is penetrated. Prevention is the key: Deworm monthly, alternating between ivermectin and fenbendazole. This also takes care of regular intestinal and stomach worms. Coccidiosis, a common intestinal tract parasite in camelids, needs to be treated with a species-specific deworming medication. The regime I just mentioned would not prevent coccidia problems. Tapeworms also require a different protocol. Ivermectin can be given two months in a row, then fenbendazole (Safeguard or Panacur) the third month.

Monthly dewormings are the key to prevention. Scheduled monthly dewormings seem to be very effective in preventing new animals from being infected. Dectomax injections can be reserved for potential resistance problems with gastrointestinal parasites. Year-round deworming is best where winters are mild and extended droughts do not occur. Fall and winter are common times of the year to see new cases of meningeal worm. Do not stop deworming too early in the fall. In the Southeast, deworm monthly all year. An ounce of prevention is worth a pound of cure, and may save a life!

Chapter 19

Husbandry and Care on the Altiplano

Rufino Quilla, DVZ
Translation by Lucrecia Bianchi-Salvadó

Father and son capture alpacas to show a visitor.

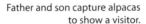

The important characteristic of the Andean *puna* (high plain) is that it offers a broad selection of native vegetation appropriate for raising alpacas, specifically the *bofadales* (wet areas, typified by a variety of green vegetation and pockets of shallow standing water).

The people of this region usually breed a variety of domestic animals, including cattle, sheep, and camelids. The puna is more than 4,000 meters (13,000 ft) high, and the harsh conditions at this elevation make it a difficult place for many creatures to live. It freezes most nights and can be warm during the day. It is a land of extremes. Of the domestic livestock the only species that show consistent profitability are the llamas, vicuñas, and alpacas. This is their world, for which they are well adapted.

Camelids to this day continue to demonstrate their productive potential and genetic adaptation to this region, even though they are largely raised by low-income, undereducated breeders using traditional methods. The government of Peru has not been active in educating and promoting the development of South American camelids. Camelids are an underdeveloped resource.

The importance of the seasons for reproduction, feeding, and health of the herd is very important to alpaca growers on the puna. Domestic and wild camelids have adapted to the puna climate of two seasons: rainy and dry.

During the rainy season, January through March, there is an abundance of healthy, green vegetation and water. This is the ideal condition for reproduction, and a high number of births occur during these months. A low percentage of births happens during the dry season when animals have difficulty finding food, making them weak and susceptible to infection, parasites, and an early death.

FORAGE ON THE PUNA

On the Humeda puna (the best part of the puna for alpacas), four grass communities grow at different times of the year. Alpacas rotate through the different grass communities during the dry and wet seasons, feeding on what is available. In ideal conditions there is a great deal of nutritious food. In drought or heavy snow, animals that are weak or that need better nutrition don't survive, or may be culled to leave more food for the remaining animals. If nature is good to us, the animals do well. If nature is bad to us, the animals are stressed and have difficulties. The weather is the biggest factor affecting the health of alpacas in Peru.

Outside of South America there is a common misconception that the alpacas of the puna have a narrow range of plants to choose from in the course of each day's grazing. Though the vast puna may look as if it lacks variety, it is rich in a variety of plant communities and a wide assortment of wild plants suitable for grazing.

The puna is often discussed in terms of three plant communities: the preferred bofadales and the drier or sloped areas, the Pajonales and the Cresped de puna. Table 19.1 shows what alpacas eat in the different parts of the puna.

447

Table 19.1 The wild pastures of the puna.

Common Name (Spanish/Quechua)	Botanical Name
Bofadales	
Champa estrella	*Plantago rigida*
Kunkuna	*Distichia mucoides*
Taruca pasto	*Oxychloe andina*
Nappa pasto	*Calamagrostis ovata*
Sora pasto	*Calamagrostis eminens*
Tullo pasto	*Calamagrostis rigescens*
Pilli	*Hipochoeris taraxacodes*
(No common name)	*Werneria pigmaenum*
Cresped de puna	
Yareta	*Azorella pulvinata*
Pampa yareta	*Liabum ovatum*
Pilli mojado	*Werneria nubigena*
Pasto lloron	*Stipa hans-meyeri*
Ojotilla	*Geranium* spp.
Ichu	*Stipa* spp.
Grama ichu	*Stipa brachyphylla*
Pajonales	
Llama pasto	*Festuca rigida*
Iruichu	*Festuca orto phylla*
Ichu	*Stipa ichu*
K'hena	*Calamagrostis amoena*
Tisna	*Stipa obtusa*
Llama ichu	*Calamagrostis rigida*

Andean pastoralism, a timeless way of life.

Often a newcomer to the Andes will see a herd of alpacas grazing on unfenced land and assume the animals are wild. There are no wild alpacas in the Andes. Instead of fences, traditional pastoralists keep a watchful eye over their herds to prevent predation or theft. In this instance, the herder and his guard dogs relax as alpacas peacefully graze under the midday sun.

When it comes to fleece color, alpacas (*Vicugna pacos*) have tremendous diversity. This Peruvian herder has selected black-and-white animals, which represent both ends of the color spectrum. White is common in herds whose fleece are sold to the large fiber mills in Arequipa. True black is quite rare.

COMBATING ILLNESS

Alpacas are generally strong and resistant to this harsh land if they have enough food. But alpacas, like all living things, are susceptible to a number of diseases. There are two basic approaches to fighting disease on the altiplano. Those breeders who are better educated tend to use antibiotics and medicines designed to combat parasites and common diseases. The breeders in the low-income brackets with very little education often apply "folk cures" to their animals. Often these breeders experience high mortality rates, which keep their herd sizes at no more than 50 animals. These breeders often lack an understanding of basic biology and how diseases attack alpacas. Even when mortality is high, there is usually no attempt to change herding practices to benefit the animals.

Often, poorly educated herders don't notice symptoms, so disease goes unnoticed and untreated, and the consequences aren't good. A number of folk cures are used, but many of them are not effective and they are often applied to general symptoms (diarrhea, colic) that are not diseases at all, but are signs of any of a wide range of diseases, each requiring a different treatment. Table 19.2 lists some of the common folk cures.

DEALING WITH PREDATORS

On the puna the main predator of the alpaca is the fox, which is a coyote-sized animal that is usually larger than foxes found in many other parts of the world. Female foxes are a bigger problem than males because the females must feed their litters. They become bold and will kill crias and drag them to their dens.

Breeders try to protect their herds in different ways. Many breeders build a fenced pen of either wire or stone. The stone corrals are called *canchones* and some of them have been around since Incan times. The animals are herded into the pens at night for safety. Sometimes lighting is placed over the pens so that predators can be

This Quechua healer and alpaca herder has traditional cures for ailing animals. Notice the small stone suri figurine with burning incense.

The *ichu* grass plant community is drier than bofadales and dominates much of the altiplano.

Table 19.2 Folk cures on the puna.

Illness/Symptoms	Folk Cure	Affected Animal
Colic symptoms	Chamomile; mint	Young
Diarrhea	Chachamoca (*Baccharis, microphylla launth*)*	Young
Conjunctivitis	Available milk (from any species)	Young
Fleas	Ashes	Adult and young
Mange	Lard; oil	Adult and young
Parasites (internal)	Wormwood	Adult and young

*Matico, a medicinal plant from the jungle, may actually be several different plants.

Left A Quechua woman with her *zunca*, the guard dog of the altiplano.

Right Foxes (*Vulpes* spp.) on the altiplano are coyote-sized animals that prey efficiently on crias during the night.

Shearing day in a village.

In times of drought, alpaca herders cull their animals, starting with the oldest first.

detected easily. Other people rely on watchdogs. A favorite is the *zunca*, which is an ancient breed on the altiplano. A good dog can be very valuable to a breeder.

If fox attacks occur, breeders often resort to making traps or using poisons such as strychnine (outlawed in many places in the world).

Breeders also combat foxes by organizing a *chaku*. Most people think chakus refer only to vicuña roundups, but this method can be used for other animals as well, including foxes.

During a chaku, all of the people in a village or several villages form a huge circle, often holding hands. The atmosphere is festive with dancing and singing as the people move across the puna. The noise and motion scare the fox into the open, and the circle closes and the fox is killed.

STRATEGIES DURING DROUGHT

During drought, a low-income breeder will pull out and sacrifice the older alpacas from the herd so the main herd can eat the remaining food. As the drought continues, young animals not old enough for reproduction will be sacrificed, so the females that can reproduce and the lactating females have a chance to live. If the drought persists, more difficult decisions must be made to reduce the herd so the core can live. A severe drought causes economic hardship that may be felt for many years. The meat from the sacrificed animals is often dried and made into jerky.

The limited funds of a low-income breeder will not allow him to buy hay or alfalfa to supplement his animals through a drought. Breeders with adequate economic resources can buy hay to help their animals survive. The poorest breeders always suffer the most.

SHEARING AND SALE OF WOOL

During the shearing season, 80 percent of the breeders utilize hand shears or scissors to remove the wool from their alpacas. The other 20 percent use a knife or tin-can lid to remove the fiber.

Breeders who are more commercially oriented will usually shear during the months of November and December, which is summer in South America. The low-income or subsistence breeders will shear throughout the year, depending on their economic needs. This group will often sell their fiber for the lowest price. Many of the poorest breeders make handicrafts such as potato sacks, ropes, and clothing to sell in small village markets.

The commercial selling of alpaca wool usually involves selling to a middleman, who is known as a speculator. These speculators attend local markets and try to get the

A family goes to market with alpaca skins to sell.

lowest possible price for wool. When the speculator gets a large enough quantity, he sells it to large merchants in the district capitals, who in turn sell it to the large fiber mills in Arequipa, who make fashionable garments for the world market. This method of moving fiber to the large mills makes it difficult for the mills to know which breeders are producing the best fiber.

SELECTION OF ALPACAS FOR REPRODUCTION

There are different levels of selection for breeding animals. Some of the poorest breeders hardly select at all and allow alpacas and llamas to breed and create huarizo offspring. Many breeders generally apply the following criteria to males (machos):

• White is the premium color selected in both huacaya and suri breeds.

• Breeding begins at three years of age.

• Testicles must be healthy, large, and equal in size.

• Animals should be free of obvious defects.

• Animals should be of adequate size.

Some breeders apply stricter criteria to selection. This group keeps long-range goals in mind and tries to improve the fiber and general health of large populations of alpacas.

A Peruvian herder and his employees.

The llama is an all-purpose pack animal. This one shows its displeasure at being conscripted as a riding animal.

Herders mark their alpacas with distinctly colored tassels.

Traditional dress is worn on market day by the women on the alitplano.

Chaku is an ancient method involving an entire community. Chaku is used to capture wild vicuñas for shearing or to round up foxes whose predation is hurting the herds.

This group utilizes the following selection criteria for male alpacas:

- Must be three years to be eligible for selection.
- Must be a solid color for either huacayas or suris.
- Density must be above average.
- Fiber must be fine and without guard hair.
- Must have good height and gait.
- Conformation must be strong and sound.
- Must be healthy.
- Must be free of physical defects.

For females the selection is much less strict. The *machorras* (sterile females) and females with poor density and poor fleece are often eliminated from the herd.

ECONOMICS OF ALPACA BREEDING ON THE ALTIPLANO

The demand from foreign markets determines whether wool prices are high or low. When wool prices are high, the alpaca breeder has enough income to purchase new breeding stock and medicines for the herd. He is also able to travel to large cities to buy goods for the family.

When the price of fiber is low, the profit received from selling fiber is drastically reduced. The only option for many breeders is to use the money for living expenses. A breeder is no longer able to purchase breeding stock, visit areas outside of his pastures, or buy medicine for the herd. Instead he has to rely on folk medicines to combat diseases and on trade for essential goods.

A breeder has one other recourse when things become difficult. He can sell his alpacas for their meat as a way to get enough income to survive. Often this is the way a small breeder gets enough money to upgrade his farm and herd with the addition of new breeding stock. For the last several years alpaca meat has sold for about 20 to 25 percent less than the price of mutton. This is partly because people in the cities are more familiar with the characteristics of European livestock than they are of their own native species, like the alpaca. Sarcocystosis is also a problem with alpaca meat in the Andes (see Chapter 18: Unusual Parasitic Diseases).

Three problem areas facing alpaca breeders in the Andes could be changed:

- The high cost of veterinary products.
- The lack of any kind of credit from the national bank system. Breeders must survive through hard times from their own savings.
- A severe lack of technical support from government agencies, allowing ignorance about raising alpacas to be pervasive among many alpaca owners.[*]

CHANGES TO IMPROVE ALPACAS AND FIBER PRODUCTION IN PERU

According to records from the textile industry, as much as 70 percent of the fiber being processed is 28 microns or higher. This indicates that it is essential to focus on alpaca genetics by creating a National Program for Genetic Improvement of the Alpaca, under the supervision of CONACS (Consejo de Camelidos Sudamericanos). INIA (Instituto de Investigacion Agraria, National Institute of Agrarian Investigation) and the universities also need to become involved. We need to change our thinking in Peru to embrace a program that will increase density, lower micron count, and highlight good conformation. We have it in our power to do this if we try hard enough.[**]

[*]Teodosio Huanca, professor of agriculutre, personal communication, Universidad de Puno, Puno, Peru, August 15, 2002.

[**]José D. Choquehuanca, agronomy engineer, personal communication, Juliaca, Peru, August 15, 2002.

Chapter 20

Infectious Multisystemic Diseases

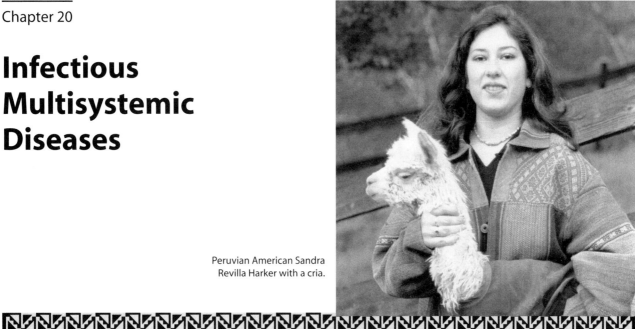

Peruvian American Sandra Revilla Harker with a cria.

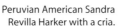

INTRODUCTION
Eric Hoffman

An infectious disease is the result of a replicating agent invading a body, often resulting in illness. Infectious diseases are categorized into three groups: bacterial, viral, and fungal. Some infectious diseases are highly contagious and are apt to appear throughout a herd once one animal has contracted the disease; foot-and-mouth disease is an example.

Many diseases are common to all forms of livestock. Others are more prevalent in particular kinds of livestock, and still others are strongly linked to regional and environmental factors. For example, the bacterium *Clostridium perfringens* type A is particularly lethal to crias in South American alpaca herds.

The same disease may behave differently in different regions and on different continents. Anyone familiar with the history of the colonization of the Americas knows about the ravages of smallpox and other diseases brought from Europe. Native Americans, having never been exposed to these diseases, had no resistance to them and perished by the thousands once the diseases were introduced by Europeans. Alpacas, more than most forms of livestock, are often moved from one continent to another and in the process are exposed to new diseases. Often a disease will be combatted by resistance or immunity that has evolved over many centuries.

Infectious diseases often operate in balance with their host. Often the host, in a healthy condition, can resist the disease entirely or be infected but show no sign of illness. Infectious diseases are often opportunistic. They assert themselves following stress or other problems that compromise an immune system. Animals of all kinds, including alpacas, live in environments that always have dangerous infectious diseases present. When this balance is upset, the disease may suddenly appear.

Alpacas are more prone to infectious disease in environments favoring disease. Poor sanitation, dietary deficiencies, exposure to carrier animals, social situations causing increased stress and depression of the immune system, and inherited or environmentally induced immunodeficiencies are all likely precursors to the onset of infectious disease. For example, prolonged harsh, wet weather is likely to result in pneumonia in some members of an alpaca herd whose immune responses have been compromised.

Describing every infectious disease that might infect an alpaca is neither possible nor appropriate. This chapter is dedicated to the diseases most common to the species and those diseases that could cause serious harm to alpacas. The chapter has three authors: Linda Carpenter, DVM, a USDA veterinarian with extensive knowledge and experience with infectious diseases; Robert Ellis, PhD, an expert in clostridial diseases; and Nancy Carr, MD, a Canadian alpaca rancher who has helped expose the dangers of bovine viral diarrhea virus to alpacas.

BACTERIAL, VIRAL, AND FUNGAL DISEASES

Linda V. Carpenter, DVM

Besides categorizing infectious diseases by their agent of infection, we can also divide them into those of concern to the alpaca owner because they affect herd health and occur naturally within a livestock population and those of national and international concern that are controlled by state and federal regulations.

The latter group of diseases are of concern, often not because they are common in a population, but because they have serious consequences when they do appear or because they cause serious human health hazards. Foreign animal diseases (FADs) that enter a country will have serious economic consequences, including production loss, death loss, and international trade restrictions. When an FAD enters a country, all species affected by the disease may be under regulatory action. To prevent introduction of FADs, import testing is required. Each country defines what testing it will require for importing or exporting. A foot-and-mouth-disease outbreak in the United Kingdom caused the destruction of almost seven million cloven-hoofed animals, including several hundred llamas and alpacas. The cost was in the billions of dollars.

Those infectious animal diseases that can cause human disease are *zoonotic diseases* (transmittible from animals to humans). To prevent serious human disease, efforts have been underway to eradicate those diseases in the animal population. Mandatory testing for selected zoonotic diseases is usually required for international and interstate movement. Brucellosis and tuberculosis are the major zoonotic diseases that are closely regulated. Other zoonotic diseases of importance are anthrax, leptospirosis, tetanus, rabies, and West Nile virus.[18]

SIGNIFICANT BACTERIAL DISEASES

Anthrax

Anthrax is an acute febrile (fever-producing) disease of almost all warm-blooded animals including humans. Anthrax is caused by a spore-forming bacterium *Bacillus anthracis,* which is endemic to the United States and many other countries throughout the world. The disease occurs sporadically as environmental conditions allow. The United States reports outbreaks almost yearly—Texas, North Dakota, and Nebraska reported outbreaks in 2000, 2001, and 2002. When cells of *B. anthracis* escape from the animal's body and are exposed to oxygen, they form spores. These spores are highly resistant to heat, cold, chemical

disinfectants, and long, dry periods. *B. anthracis* spores are reported to survive for years in the environment.

Animals are usually infected by ingesting soil-borne spores, such as in contaminated food or water. Spores can also be picked up directly from the soil through grazing or from feed grown on infected soil. When periods of drought cause livestock to forage much closer to the ground, animals may ingest spores in soil they accidentally eat along with forage. Although rare, it is possible for animals to inhale dust-harboring anthrax spores. The incubation period of natural infection in animals is typically 3 to 7 days with a range of 1 to 14 days, or more.

Symptoms Anthrax is associated with a peracute form (very short and severe) where the course of illness may last about one to two hours. In the acute form, there may be clinical signs, such as fever up to 107°F, muscle tremors, respiratory distress, and convulsions that often go unnoticed. After death, there may be bloody discharges from the natural openings of the body, rapid bloating, a lack of rigor mortis, and the presence of unclotted blood. This failure of blood to clot is due to a toxin released by *B. anthracis.*

Diagnosis Diagnosis is based on a laboratory examination of a blood sample, because diagnosis based on clinical signs can be difficult.

Treatment When an outbreak of anthrax is recognized, early treatment and vigorous implementation of a preventive program are essential. Antibiotics should be used for the sick animals. Vaccine is available for cattle.[5]

Brucellosis

Also known as Bangs disease, brucellosis is caused by several *brucella* species, the most common being *Brucella bovis.* This disease has great economic importance worldwide because of loss of animal production and concern over its significant human health hazard (the human form is known as undulant fever or Malta fever). It occurs in many mammalian species, predominately as a reproductive disease normally associated with abortions. It can cause sterility in males through infection in the testis. Brucellosis is very important because the United States and many of its trading partners are free or close to being free of this disease. It is one of the two major diseases that requires a negative test for interstate or international movement (the other is tuberculosis).

Llamas and alpacas are not readily susceptible to brucellosis, but could become infected if they are exposed to other infected species such as bison or elk when those animals are giving birth. The disease is significant as a regulatory disease and because of movement restrictions.

Symptoms Usually the only symptom of brucellosis is midterm to late abortion.

Brucellosis is one of the infectious diseases that should be included in the differential diagnosis whenever there are a series of unexplained abortions in a group of pregnant animals.

Diagnosis The diagnosis of brucellosis is by blood testing for titer and culture of the organism in milk or tissue.

Treatment and Prevention There is no successful treatment for brucellosis or any vaccine for alpacas. Brucellosis is present in several wildlife species, so it is advisable to avoid contact with wild ruminants and feral swine.[6,7,23*]

Johne's Disease

Johne's disease is caused by the bacterium *Mycobacterium paratuberculosis*. This chronic, contagious disease of the intestinal tract is characterized by persistent and progressive diarrhea, weight loss, debilitation, and eventually death. Johne's occurs in a wide variety of animals, most often in ruminants such as cattle, sheep, goats, alpacas, llamas, camels, deer, antelope, and bison, but is most commonly reported in dairy cattle. The organism is shed in the feces, and transmission occurs when an animal is exposed to feed or pasture contaminated with infected feces. Young animals seem to be more susceptible than older animals. It appears that the younger an animal is when exposed to the organism, the more likely it will become infected. The time from exposure to onset of clinical disease may be months to years. Johne's disease has been diagnosed in alpacas in Australia.

Symptoms The clinical signs of Johne's disease are primarily diarrhea and rapid weight loss. In some animal species, such as sheep, goats, and alpacas, diarrhea is less common. In general, animals with Johne's disease "waste away" despite their continuing to eat well. Infected animals maintain a normal temperature but may appear unthrifty and can become weak in later stages of the infection. Because of the slow progressive nature of the infection, signs of Johne's disease are usually not seen until animals are adults, although onset of the infection occurred when they were young.

Diagnosis Since the signs of Johne's disease can be confused with those of several other diseases, a diagnosis can be confirmed only by laboratory tests. Three common methods are available to test animals for Johne's disease: culture of fecal samples, DNA probe on fecal samples, and blood tests for antibodies to *M. paratuberculosis*.

Treatment and Prevention The major source of infection is contamination of pastures and feed with cattle manure. Prevention is based on pasture management. Avoid pasturing alpacas on fields that have been grazed by cattle or had cattle manure spread on the fields. Animals with subclinical cases may contribute to contamination of the pastures. There is no treatment or vaccination.[9,29**]

Leptospirosis

Leptospirosis or lepto is caused by the spirochete *Leptospira*, of which there are several important serovars, the most common being *L. pomona*. Lepto is commonly associated with abortion and is an important zoonotic disease (a disease acquired by humans from animals). Leptospirosis is generally contracted by the direct splashing of urine from infected or carrier animals into the eyes of susceptible animals. It can also be spread through the skin and mucous membranes from contact with water contaminated with leptospires. Transmission may also occur during breeding through residual urine in the genital tract or through infectious semen. Once infection has occurred, the leptospires multiply in the kidneys, lungs, reproductive organs, and brain. Uterine penetration of pregnant animals results in infection of the fetus with resulting death of the fetus and abortion.

Leptospires can survive outside the body if environmental conditions are favorable. The bacteria prefer moist, slightly alkaline soil, stagnant ponds, and low-flow, slow-moving, slightly alkaline streams. In these conditions the organism can survive for weeks.

Symptoms The most common symptom of leptospirosis is abortion. Abortion will usually occur within two to five weeks after initial infection. Although abortions may occur earlier, they usually occur in the last three months of pregnancy. Infections can be inapparent, very mild with few signs of illness, and occasionally severe with fever, loss of appetite, and dark urine. The inapparent infections can be a significant cause of abortions.

Because of the nature of the disease, it should not be considered a problem of the individual animal but a problem of a population, either a herd or a species within the area. Several alpacas in a herd may develop serologic titers without apparent clinical signs and be a source of infection to other animals.

Diagnosis Leptospirosis diagnosis in all animals must be confirmed by laboratory tests, demonstrating significant levels of antibodies to leptospires in the serum of recovered animals.

---

*Personal experiences as a designated brucellosis epidemiologist for 25 years. Continuing education on the subject of brucellosis conducted biannually by USDA-APHIS Veterinary Services.

**Training for designated Johne's epidemiologist, USDA-APHIS Veterinary Services, Ames, Iowa, 2002.

Treatment and Prevention Antibiotic therapy has been effective in reducing the numbers of circulating spirochetes in the blood and the severity of clinical signs if administered during the acute stage of the infection. Administration of leptospiral bacterins can result in the development of protection for 6 to 12 months.

When an outbreak has occurred, animals should be fenced away from ponds, marshes, and streams that may be contaminated by leptospires.[17,25]

Mastitis

Mastitis is defined as an inflammation of the mammary gland or udder. Mastitis is the reaction of milk-secreting tissue to injury produced by physical force, chemicals introduced into the gland, or most commonly from bacteria and their toxins or viruses.

Symptoms Mastitis may be subclinical where swelling of the udder is not detected and abnormalities in the milk are not observable, or it can be clinical. Clinical mastitis can be mild or acute, with leukocytes (white blood cells) present in the milk. Mild clinical mastitis involves abnormality in the milk, such as flakes, clots, and a watery or other unusual appearance. A hot or sensitive udder may be slight or absent; however, there may be signs of swelling.

Severe clinical mastitis involves a hot, hard sensitive udder that is quite painful to the nursing female. The onset is sudden and the female may become ill, showing signs of fever (105–107°F), rapid pulse, depression, weakness, and loss of appetite. When the whole system of the female is affected, the condition is referred to as acute systemic mastitis or bluebag. Milk production by a female with a bluebag has usually ceased and the cria will need to be reared as an orphan.

Chronic mastitis is a persistent udder infection that exists most of the time in the subclinical form, but occasionally can develop into the clinical form before returning to the subclinical. The results are hard lumps in the udder from the "walling off" of bacteria and the formation of connective tissue.

Diagnosis Often the first symptom of mastitis is failure of the cria to nurse or frequent attempts to nurse without appearing satisfied. The udder should be palpated for abnormal hardness that is painful to the dam and evaluated for the presence of heat or lumps in the udder tissue. The milk should be carefully examined for the consistency and presence of flakes.

Treatment When mastitis is diagnosed, antibiotics are indicated.[27]

Necrobacillosis

Necrobacillosis, commonly known as lumpy jaw, is caused by the bacterium *Actinomyces bovis*. The disease is characterized by an infection of the bone of the head, particularly the mandible and the maxilla (lower and upper jaw), with abscesses forming in or near the lower jaw bones. The organism generally enters the body through cuts and abrasions in the mouth. The eruption of teeth may play an important part in this regard. Although not generally considered economically important, the disease has the potential to spread within a herd from affected animals. Alpacas are susceptible to this condition.

Symptoms Lumpy jaw can occur in bony and soft tissues, but is predominately seen in the bones of the upper and lower jaw. The first symptom is usually swelling as the bone becomes enlarged and honeycombed and fills with pus. In most cases, but not always, the swelling will break out, the discharge being very thick.

Diagnosis In most cases, diagnosis can be made by close inspection of the animal. Laboratory confirmation is by examination of microscopic smears or culturing the organism. X rays of the head will help differentiate between lumpy jaw and tooth abscesses.

Treatment Necrobacillosis has the potential to be fatal but can be treated. Treatment consists of the oral or intravenous administration of iodide compounds and surgical drainage of the affected areas. The response to treatment is generally quite successful if started early in the course of the disease.[4,14]

Tetanus

Tetanus, commonly known as lockjaw, is caused by a toxin produced by the bacterium *Clostridium tetani*. *C. tetani* is a spore-forming bacteria that persists in the environment for years. *C. tetani* grows in wounds, especially closed wounds like punctures, and produces a toxin that paralyzes the muscles—thus the term lockjaw. In the worst case tetanus can kill by paralyzing the breathing muscles. Although *C. tetani* itself can be treated easily with penicillin, antibiotics will not destroy or neutralize the toxin. Antibodies to the toxin can bind to and inactivate the toxin before it attacks muscles and nerves.

Symptoms An affected animal moves with a stiff-legged gait, often with the tail held out stiffly and the ears pricked. As the disease progresses, the muscles become so rigid and stiff that the animal can fall and not be able to get up again. Convulsions may occur and death is caused by paralysis of the breathing muscles.

Diagnosis The diagnosis of tetanus is usually made by observation of clinical signs. It may be possible for a laboratory to demonstrate the presence of the neural toxin in serum.

Treatment and Prevention Treatment is difficult, time-consuming, very expensive, and often unsuccessful. Tetanus antitoxin neutralizes unbound circulating toxin; penicillin prevents further growth of *C. tetani*; muscle relaxants relax the rigid muscles; and supportive therapy is needed until the toxin is eliminated or destroyed.

Vaccination is the only way to provide safe, effective, long-term protection against tetanus.[19]

Tuberculosis

Tuberculosis (TB) is caused by *Mycobacterium bovis (M. bovis)* or other *Mycobacterium* species. This disease causes granulomas within the body, most commonly in the lymph nodes of the head and respiratory system. South American camelids are resistant but can become infected. This disease is a chronic condition with clinical symptoms developing over a period of time from months to years. Severely affected animals rarely show any symptoms other than slow weight loss.

Once a group of animals is exposed to TB, it may be years before the disease is recognized as being present. For this reason there are strict testing requirements for movement of animals internationally. Since TB is a herd disease and a serious zoonotic disease, the status of the herd of origin must be known and dictates the testing requirements for movement. This required testing has a major economic impact by restricting the movement of many animals at once.

The live animal test is a skin injection that must be read by a qualified veterinarian. A positive response to the first test means that a comparative cervical test must be done by a qualified state or federal veterinarian to determine if the initial reaction was due to exposure to bovine TB or to another group of organisms that caused the tested animal to give an avian response.

Symptoms There are rarely any clinical symptoms other than slow weight loss.

Prevention Prevention is accomplished by mandatory testing before movement. There is no treatment or vaccine.[18,22]*

---

*Based on 20 years of personal experience in eradication, control, and training on tuberculosis.

VIRAL DISEASES

Contagious Ecthyma

Other common names for contagious ecthyma are soremouth, orf, and scabby mouth. This disease is caused by a member of the pox virus family. These viruses are very contagious and can be easily transmitted to humans. This disease occurs worldwide and is very common in the United States.

Symptoms Lesions start with the formation of small blisters around the mouth, on the lips, and sometimes in the mouth or on the tongue. Blisters and scabs may also occur in other areas such as the udder, prepuce, and hairline of the feet. The blisters break, and scabs form around the lips and nose, which may have underlying reddening of the area. The scabs around the lips are often all that are noticed. These sores are painful, and sometimes a young animal will not nurse, especially if the sores are in its mouth. Dams with udder or teat lesions are much more susceptible to staphylococcal mastitis, which often results in loss of half the udder or in death of the dam.

This virus can persist for months in dried scabs in the environment. The virus can be transmitted to susceptible animals by direct contact with other animals having signs of this disease. The soremouth virus can also be spread by contact with equipment, fences, feed, and bedding that have previously been in contact with infected animals.

Diagnosis Diagnosis of soremouth is generally based on clinical signs alone. Laboratory testing of animals is usually not of much use or not available.

Treatment and Prevention Treatment of soremouth infection is of limited use. Control is more important: Limit exposure to affected animals, which should be kept in isolation until the scabs fall off. Most common disinfectants work well to limit environmental exposure. A vaccine available for sheep and goats can be used in the face of an outbreak.[16,26]

Foot-and-Mouth Disease

Foot-and-mouth disease (FMD) is a highly contagious viral disease of all cloven-hoofed animals. It is regarded by the OIE (Office of International Epizootics) as one of the most severe epidemic animal diseases. FMD is widespread, especially in the major livestock-producing countries of the world. It is well established in the Commonwealth of Independent States, including Russia, Turkey, and the Middle East, Asia, Africa, and some areas of South America. Most of Western Europe is now free of it, but recent outbreaks have occurred in the United Kingdom, the Republic of Ireland, France, and the Netherlands (2001), Italy (1993), and Greece (1994).

Although not lethal in adult animals, it causes serious production losses. On an individual animal basis, the loss is in reduced production of milk, abortions, loss of appetite and thus weight in growing animals, and loss associated with lameness. The real loss is to the international market and to the exporting nation associated with the presence of the disease. Camelids are not highly susceptible, but if they are in an area where FMD breaks out, they are just as susceptible to regulatory controls as any other cloven-hoofed animals in the area.

Symptoms This virus affects all cloven-hoofed animals, including llamas and alpacas, although the symptoms in those species are mild. One of the key signs is fluid-filled blisters on the tongue and in the mouth, causing the animal, particularly cattle, to salivate excessively. Lameness is a frequent sign as a result of blisters on the feet above the claw and between the digits. Blisters may also occur on the teats and udder. Milk yield drops considerably in dairy cattle.

Mortality does not exceed 5 percent in adults, but may be very high in young animals. However, even in FMD-free countries the first cases may not show dramatic clinical signs. The disease is usually mild in sheep and goats, with few lesions, and can be easily missed.

FMD is one of the most contagious animal diseases. Infected animals excrete the virus in the fluid from ruptured blisters, exhaled air, saliva, milk, semen, feces, and urine. Virus transmission can commence up to ten days before the appearance of blisters. The primary method of transmission within herds and flocks is by direct contact or via respiratory particles and droplets. Pigs are potent excreters of airborne virus. The spread of infection between properties and areas is frequently due to the movement of infected animals or contaminated vehicles, equipment, people, and products. The windborne spread of infected aerosols can occur for many miles under the right conditions.

Diagnosis Presumptive diagnosis may be made on the appearance of excessive salivation, evidence of vesicles, or lameness with evidence of ruptured vesicles on the feet. Confirmation must be done in a laboratory and differential diagnosis must be made to distinguish FMD from other vesicular diseases.

Prevention In countries that are unable to eradicate the disease, vaccination programs are used.[8,28]

Rabies

Descriptions of rabies go back thousands of years because rabies has been one of the most feared infections of all time. Rabies is a fatal viral disease of the central nervous system caused by a rhabdovirus. The rabies virus is relatively unstable in the environment, requiring fresh contact with mucous membranes to establish infection. In most cases, disease is transmitted via bite wound. Rabies in bats is widely distributed throughout the United States. Rabies is most often seen among wild mammals such as raccoons, bats, skunks, and foxes. Most warm-blooded animals, including humans, are susceptible to rabies. There have been at least two occurrences of rabies in llamas in the United States. Once signs of illness appear, rabies is 100 percent fatal. It is currently found in every continent except Australia; most countries free of the disease are islands.

Symptoms The first sign of rabies is usually a change in the animal's behavior—it may become unusually aggressive or unusually tame. The animal may lose fear of people and natural enemies. It may become excited, irritable, and act aggressively to anything in its path. Or it may appear affectionate and friendly. Staggering, convulsions, spitting, choking, frothing at the mouth, and paralysis are sometimes noted. Many animals have a marked change in voice. "The atypical is typical" describes rabies symptomatically in any species of animal.

Animals with furious rabies exhibit aggressive signs early in the disease and then become paralyzed. Those with dumb rabies simply become paralyzed and die shortly thereafter. Animals with furious rabies usually have an excitation phase lasting several days. The animal is restless and soon becomes vicious, biting at anything and everything. This action gradually subsides; incoordination and tremors are often apparent. Convulsions, paralysis, and prostration occur just prior to death. Death occurs within one week after showing signs of rabies.

Diagnosis These clinical signs are so varied and overlapping that limited confidence should be placed on a clinical diagnosis of rabies. The only sure way to diagnose rabies is with laboratory tests of the brain.

Prevention Prevention is accomplished by vaccination. There is no treatment. The death rate is 100 percent after clinical symptoms appear.[2,13,15,24]

Vesicular Stomatitis Virus

Vesicular stomatitis virus (VSV) is a disease that affects a large variety of species. It causes vesicles (blisters) to form on the mouth (on the tongue, dental pad, and lips), in the nostrils, on areas around the hooves, and on the teats.

Aside from its economic impact, vesicular stomatitis is significant because its outward signs are similar to (although generally less severe than) those of foot-and-mouth disease. The only way to differentiate the two diseases is through laboratory tests. Anyone noting signs of a vesicular condition, excessive salivation, lameness, loss of weight, or drop in milk production should immediately report these signs to a veterinarian and state or federal animal health officials.

Symptoms VSV is characterized by vesicular lesions on the tongue, oral mucosa, teats, or coronary bands of cattle, horses, and swine. Vesicular stomatitis is most likely to occur during warm months in the southwestern United States, particularly along rivers and irrigation canals. VSV affects horses as well as cloven-hoofed animals.

Diagnosis VSV will affect horses, which helps differentiate it from FMD. Confirmation is by laboratory testing, confirming antibodies present in the blood and actual virus isolation.

Treatment and Prevention Treatment is usually not required as lesions heal rapidly. There is no prevention other than moving animals away from an area where outbreaks are occurring, particularly away from waterways. A vaccine is available for horses.[22]

Viral Diarrhea

Viral diarrhea (dysentery) is a term that covers a wide variety of virus-caused diseases. Included is this group may be adenovirus, togavirus, rotavirus, and corona virus. In most instances there will be profuse watery diarrhea, white to yellow in color. There will be a significant inability to absorb fluids. Viral diarrhea is most common between days 5 and 15 days of age. It is important to remember that most viral infections of this type include a large number of potential symptoms including respiratory distress and weakness. Bovine viral diarrhea virus (BVDV) is discussed at the end of this chapter.

Treatment In viral disorders the treatment is palliative. Try to maintain fluid levels, and watch for secondary infections (coughs, etc.). Use kaolin pectin or some form of antidiarrhetic.[11]

West Nile Virus

West Nile Virus (WNV), a viral encephalitis that was first reported in North America in 1999, has been known in the Old World for many years. It first appeared in New York in crows, horses, and humans. By 2002 it had spread across the entire continent. This virus has a natural host in birds and is transmitted from bird to bird by many species of mosquitoes. A mosquito bites an infected bird and then another animal. Many animals, including mammals, birds, reptiles, and humans, have been found to have a positive blood test to this virus. Most deaths have occurred in birds, horses, and humans, although in 2002 some deaths were confirmed in species as diverse as reindeer and alligators. The number of species reported to be infected continues to expand. By fall of 2002, WNV was declared endemic to the United States and it was recognized that eradication will not be possible.

Symptoms Clinical symptoms include ataxia (muscle incoordination) or abnormal way of moving, loss of appetite, and signs of disturbance of the central nervous system. Some horses will show increased sensitivity of the face. Unexplained deaths in animals of diverse species have been confirmed as having died of WNV.

Diagnosis Diagnosis is by laboratory testing to confirm the presence of antibodies. The antibodies present in the early stages of the infection can be differentiated from those of vaccination.

Treatment and Prevention A vaccine is licensed for horses. Many animals have survived infection with strong supportive treatment.[3,10]

Miscellaneous Viral Infections

Most camelids are seropositive (antibodies in the blood) for a presumptive nonpathogenic adenovirus that is specific to llamas. Occasionally, an animal will develop antibodies to bovine viral diarrhea virus, and a few animals have developed a mild diarrhea or respiratory disease, presumably in response to the virus. Equine herpes virus 1 infections with associated neurologic signs and blindness have been seen in a small number of alpacas. Although an occasional animal will develop a serologic response to the bluetongue virus, all seropositive animals have been asymptomatic.

FUNGAL DISEASES

Aspergillosis

The disease aspergillosis or fungal pneumonia is caused by a fungus from the genus *Aspergillus*, especially *A. fumigatus*. *Aspergillus* is found worldwide and has the potential to infect a wide range of mammalian, avian, and reptilian species, including humans, and is probably the most common fungal infection found in birds. *Aspergillus* is widespread throughout the environment, and where conditions are suitable it will grow and multiply to give a localized high concentration of the fungus.

Aspergillus species organisms are capable of living both a saprophytic and parasitic way of life, and susceptible hosts have numerous opportunities to contact this agent. Favored environments for the mold are on damp litter in stubble fields, moldy grass along riverbanks, moldy grain or meal, and rotting plant and animal material, especially damp hay and straw. Aspergillosis is primarily a respiratory infection that may become generalized.

Symptoms In ruminants aspergillosis may be asymptomatic, occur in bronchopulmonary form, or cause mastitis, placentitis, and abortion. The chronic nodular pulmonary form of the disease is characterized by areas of consolidation and the coalescence of several nodules, or the enlargement of single nodules to form masses of necrotic or granulomatous lesions. Calcification of the masses may result from these changes, with death being the usual termination of the mycotic pneumonia. *Aspergillus* may cause abortion, with evidence of the fetus being dead prior to the abortion.

Diagnosis A diagnosis of aspergillosis can be demonstrated by microscopic examination of fresh or preserved tissue and by cultural methods. It is possible to demonstrate the presence of the characteristic organisms in typical respiratory tract lesions.

Treatment Treatment has been by various combinations of drugs, usually unsuccessfully.[12, 21]

Coccidioidomycosis

Coccidioidomycosis, known most commonly as valley fever and caused by *Coccidioides immitis,* is a dust-borne, noncontagious fungal infection usually of the lungs. The spores become airborne when uncultivated soil is disturbed, and are inhaled into the lungs where the infection starts. The disease is not contagious from animal to animal, and it appears that after one exposure the body develops immunity. The only route of infection is by inhalation of the spores, which causes most cases of valley fever to be primary lung infections. Lesions are discrete, variable-sized nodules with a firm grey-white cut surface, and resemble those of tuberculosis. Valley fever is limited geographically to arid and semiarid regions of the southwestern United States and similar areas of Mexico and South America.

Symptoms Symptoms are usually that of a chronic respiratory disease with shortness of breath and coughing. Valley fever may become disseminated anywhere in the body and will form pyogranulomas bodywide, including the skin. In those cases symptoms will vary depending on what body system is involved.

Diagnosis Diagnosis is based on serological testing and identification of the fungal organism in pus samples or on histopathology.

Treatment Treatment is based on long-term antifungal agents, although the prognosis is not good.[21]

Dermatophytosis

Dermatophytosis, known as ringworm, is an infection of the skin and hair by one of several genera of fungi—*Microsporum* and *Trichophyton*. They are found worldwide and most species of animals are susceptible. In most cases, these fungi are obligate parasites of the skin and hair. They are highly contagious from animal to animal—particularly in dense population conditions. The infections not only transmit readily to other animals, but often transmit to human attendants of the animals and cause severe skin lesions. Infection results from direct contact with infected animals, as well as by indirect contact through clippers, brushes, combs, blankets, and contaminated pens. Unless vigorously disinfected with a commercial fungicide, these materials may remain infectious for several years.

Symptoms Symptoms include discrete, scaling patches of hair loss.

Diagnosis Presumptive diagnosis is based on the appearance of scaley skin and patchy hair loss. Diagnosis is based on laboratory confirmation of the presence of the fungus in skin scrapings and spores on the hair. Culture attempts to grow the organism can be made to identify the fungus present.

Treatment and Prevention Treatment is based on the application of appropriate topical ointments; occasionally systemic therapy is indicated.

Prevention is based on avoiding animal contact with infected animals and avoiding the use of equipment that has been used on infected animals. It is extremely difficult to disinfect items like brushes and clippers once they have been contaminated.[1, 21]

REFERENCES

1. All Creatures Virtual Veterinary Clinic: Dermatophytosis (Ringworm). http://www.appspring.com/ACVC/ringworm.htm
2. American Veterinary Medical Association: Compendium of Animal Rabies Prevention and Control, 2002. http://www.avma.org/pubhlth/rabcont.asp
3. American Veterinary Medical Association: What You Should Know About West Nile Virus. Updated November 5, 2002. http://www.avma.org/communications/brochures/wnv/wnv_faq.asp

4. Anderson, David E.: Contagious Abscesses in Camelids. Columbus, OH: College of Veterinary Medicine, The Ohio State University. http://www.vet.ohio-state.edu/docs/Clin Sci/camelid/abcess.html

5. Animal and Plant Health Inspection Service (APHIS, part of USDA): USDA 2002 Anthrax Fact Sheet—Clinical Signs and Diagnosis; General Information and Vaccination; Safety Aspects. http://www.aphis.usda.gov/oa/pubs/anthrax.html

6. Animal and Plant Health Inspection Service: National Center for Animal Health Programs, Brucellosis. http://www.aphis.usda.gov/vs/disease_eradication.htm

7. Animal and Plant Health Inspection Service: Brucellosis, USDA-APHIS Veterinary Services. http://www.aphis.usda.gov/vs/nahps/brucellosis/

8. Animal and Plant Health Inspection Service: USDA 2001 Foot-and-Mouth Disease (FMD) Fact Sheet—Travel Information; Emergency Response; Information for Producers, Importers, and the Military; General Information. http://www.aphis.usda.gov/lpa/issues/fmd/fmd.html

9. Animal and Plant Health Inspection Service: Johne's Disease, USDA-APHIS Veterinary Services. http://www.aphis.usda.gov/vs/nahps/johnes/

10. Animal and Plant Health Inspection Service: West Nile Virus (WNV): West Nile Virus in the United States, 2000; West Nile Virus in the United States, 1999; Factsheet on the West Nile Virus; Q&A's on the West Nile Virus. http://www.aphis.usda.gov/lpa/issues/wnv/wnv.html

11. Belknap, E. B., J. K. Collins et al.: Bovine Viral Diarrhea Virus in New World Camelids. Fort Collins, CO: Colorado State University, College of Veterinary Medicine and Biomedical Science, *Journal of Veterinary Diagnostic Investigation* 12 (6): 568–570, 2000. http://ae.inno-vet.com/articles/2001/0601/26.htm

12. Centers for Disease Control and Prevention (CDC): Aspergillosis. http://www.cdc.gov/ncidod/hip/pneumonia/1_asper.htm

13. Centers for Disease Control and Prevention (CDC), National Center for Infectious Diseases: Rabies. http://www.cdc.gov/ncidod/dvrd/rabies/

14. Chapman, Del: Cattle Diseases: Lumpy Jaw and Wooden Tongue. Animal and Plant Health Service, Queensland Government Gateway. http://www.dpi.qld.gov.au/health/3566.html

15. Department of Primary Industries, Queensland Government, Australia: Rabies. http://www.dpi.qld.gov.au/health/3952.html

16. Hopkins, Fred M., and Warren Gill: Soremouth in Sheep. University of Tennessee. http://www.agriculture.utk.edu/ansci/sheep/soremouth_in_sheep.htm

17. Hudson, Donald B.: Leptospirosis of Domestic Animals. Lincoln, NE: Nebweb, Cooperative Extension, Agriculture and Natural Resources, University of Nebraska. http://www.ianr.unl.edu/pubs/animaldisease/g417.htm

18. Institutional Animal Care and Use Committee, University of Santa Barbara: Zoonotic Diseases. (Created by Brent Martin, modified from document created by Michael S. Rand.) http://research.ucsb.edu/connect/pro/disease.html

19. Little, Peter: Tetanus Information Page. Victoria, Australia: CSL Limited. http://www.cyberhorse.net.au/csl/tetanus.htm

20. *The Merck Veterinary Manual,* Eighth Edition. Whitehouse Station, NJ: Merck & Co., 1998.

21. *The Merck Veterinary Manual,* Eighth Edition. Sec. 13, Ch. 158, Systemic Fungal Diseases (Systemic Mycoses). Whitehouse Station, NJ: Merck & Co., 1998.

22. *The Merck Veterinary Manual* (electronic version). Whitehouse Station, NJ: Merck & Co., 2002. http://www.merckvetmanual.com/mvm/index.jsp

23. Michigan Department of Natural Resources: Brucellosis Fact Sheet. http://www.michigan.gov/dnr/0,1607,7-153-10370_12150_12220-26503—,00.html

24. Michigan Department of Natural Resources: Controlling the Spread of Rabies in Wildlife and Transmission to Humans. Wildlife Division Issue, Review Paper 6, May 10, 1999.

25. Michigan Department of Natural Resources: Leptospirosis: Description and Distribution, Fact Sheet. http://www.michigan.gov/dnr/0,1607,7-153-10370_12150_1222026943—,00.html

26. Peacock, Andrew: Contagious Ecthyma (Orf) in Sheep and Goats. Newfoundland and Labrador Department of Agriculture, October 1999. http://www.gov.nf.ca.agric/pubfact/orf.htm

27. Swartz, Helen A.: Mastitis in the Ewe. Lincoln, NE: State Sheep, Goat and Small Livestock Specialist Extension, University of Nebraska.

28. United States Animal Health Association: Foreign Animal Diseases, 1998. http://www.vet.uga.edu/vpp/gray_book/FAD/index.htm

29. United States Animal Health Association: National Johne's Working Group (NJWG) Subcommittee on Small Ruminants. Paratuberculosis (Johne's Disease) in Sheep and Goats: Recommendations for Diagnosis and Control. http://www.usaha.org/njwg/njwgssmr.html

CLOSTRIDIUM PERFRINGENS ENTERITIS

Robert P. Ellis, PhD

TYPES, TOXINS, AND VACCINES

Clostridium perfringens is ubiquitous worldwide. There is no place in the world where humans and livestock live that has not seen a case of disease caused by *C. perfringens*. Countless documented reports describe the destruction that *C. perfringens* has caused among humans and animals.

Clostridium perfringens is a gram-positive, nonmotile, spore-forming anaerobe, which means that it lives and grows best in an environment without oxygen. Although defined as an anaerobe, *C. perfringens* is not a strict anaerobe. This *Clostridium* species can survive long periods (hours) of exposure to oxygen and remain viable in a vegetative state. Spores are very resistant to degradation and can remain viable in the soil for decades.

Typing of *C. perfringens* Strains

Clostridium perfringens strains are divided into five types, designated A, B, C, D, and E according to the lethal toxin combinations produced by the strains alpha, beta, epsilon, and iota. Table 20.1 illustrates the typing scheme based on the toxin(s) produced by the different types. Enterotoxin and the recently discovered beta 2 toxin may be produced by any of the five types.

Thousands of soldiers died in the Civil War in the United States and in World War I due to wound infections that led to gas gangrene caused by *C. perfringens* type A. Animals are often the victims of fatal intestinal disease caused by types B, C, D, and E. Evidence is growing that type A is an important cause of intestinal disease in animals. Humans and animals are also victims of *C. perfringens* enterotoxemia, a food-borne disease caused by the enterotoxin produced by *C. perfringens*.

The toxin typing system, based on the production of alpha, beta, epsilon, and iota toxins, was established in the

1930s. In the late 1990s, the system was changed to base detection on the genes that produce the toxins rather than on the previously used assays done on mice. The current system, termed genotyping, is much more accurate and less expensive. In addition to the six toxins listed in Table 20.1, about 15 to 20 other toxins and enzymes may contribute to the pathogenicity of strains of *C. perfringens*. Most certainly other toxins and enzymes are produced by *C. perfringens* that have not been defined. We may not be able to develop strategies that adequately control losses due to *C. perfringens* until these toxins are detected. In fact, the major reason for limited progress in control of *C. perfringens*-caused disease in the past decade may be that several as yet unidentified toxins are virulence factors.

Clostridial Disease in South American Crias

In the 1950s, Dr. Manuel Moro, a Peruvian veterinarian, observed an enteric disease that affected young alpacas and that almost always ended in the death of crias. Dr. Moro began to compile observations of these acute deaths and continued to do so over the next 20 years. His observations were that young alpacas were commonly between three and six weeks of age when affected, the onset of disease was very rapid, and the disease almost always caused death of the animal. These observations were confirmed and extended to llamas as well as alpacas by many other animal disease investigators in Peru, Bolivia, and a few other South American countries. The initial investigations of this disease indicated that the disease was caused by *C. perfringens*, originally called *C. welchii*.

The most recent and in-depth investigations have been conducted by Dr. Antonio Ramirez, a Peruvian veterinarian. Dr. Ramirez, like Dr. Moro, observed the rapid onset of the disease and the nearly 100 percent mortality in affected crias. He confirmed that the disease rarely affected crias younger than three weeks of age and seemed to have run its course when the crias reached six weeks of age. Adults were rarely if ever affected.

Over a period of about 15 years, Dr. Ramirez and others observed that the cria death loss would gradually rise during the first year of a cycle to 15 to 20 percent, then 30 to 40 percent the next year, and after a steady rise over a 3- to 5-year period, the loss would peak at 50 to 60 percent of the crias within a given herd. In the year immediately following the extremely high loss of crias in a given herd, the percentage would usually drop abruptly back to the 6 to 10 percent that was observed when enterotoxemia was not a significant cause of death.

Dr. Ramirez and I observed this pattern of the rise and fall of the death rates of alpaca crias at La Raya High Altitude Camelid Research Center, located at an altitude of

Table 20.1 Types of *C. perfringens* as defined by the toxins they produce.

Clostridium	Toxins				Strain of *C. perfringens*	
	alpha	beta	epsilon	iota	enterotoxin	beta 2
Type A	yes	no	no	no	yes or no	yes or no
Type B	yes	yes	yes	no	yes or no	yes or no
Type C	yes	yes	no	no	yes or no	yes or no
Type D	yes	no	yes	no	yes or no	yes or no
Type E	yes	no	no	yes	yes or no	yes or no

A victim lies in a field for 24 hours after being stricken by the deadly *Clostridium* bacteria.

slightly over 14,000 feet and situated almost midway between Cuzco and Puno. Although I was able to work in Peru for portions of only an eight-year period, from 1981 to 1988, Dr. Ramirez and others have continued the research. They have observed this pattern of increasing death rates and abrupt dropback to low death rates several times. The cycle is usually five years (plus or minus one year) in an individual herd. Factors such as weather affect the cycles, but the main factor is the current immune status of the dams, and thus the ability of the dam to pass colostral antibodies through the colostrum to the cria. The higher the concentration of antibodies that are specific to the *C. perfringens* enterotoxin, the better the protection of the cria against enterotoxemia.

We were studying this disease in Peru because the loss of crias has a significant effect on the socioeconomic well-being of the *campesino* (peasant) families who reside in the altiplano areas of South America. These families, estimated to number at least 200,000 in Peru alone, rely heavily on the alpaca as a source of food and fiber. In addition, they use alpacas extensively for bartering at local markets to obtain other items necessary for their existence. Peru has an estimated 3.2 million alpacas, and more than 80 percent of the alpacas are owned by campesino families.

Clinical Studies and Assays *C. perfringens* type A produces only the alpha lethal toxin; type B produces alpha, beta, and epsilon toxins; type C produces alpha and beta toxins; type D produces alpha and epsilon toxins; and type E produces alpha and iota toxins. In our research, we were able to type many *C. perfringens* isolates of alpaca origin. The isolates from typical cases of *C. perfringens* enterotoxemia were type A.

The method used to type the isolates, called biotyping, involved injecting mice with the toxins produced by each strain, then injecting the mice with antitoxins produced specifically for biotyping applications. This typing had been the only technique available until DNA-based typing methods were recently developed. I have been using a DNA-based method developed by Dr. Glenn Songer at the Department of Veterinary Science at the University of Arizona. This DNA amplification technique allows us to identify genes for the toxins listed above, as well as the enterotoxin gene. The gene typing method is much more accurate than the biotyping technique formerly in use.

Dr. Ramirez and I also developed assays for the detection of the enterotoxin that is produced by some strains of *C. perfringens*. It had been hypothesized that the enterotoxin, and not other toxins produced by *C. perfringens* type A (alpha toxin and other toxins referred to as minor toxins), was the primary toxin involved in alpaca enterotoxemia. In our experimental research with enterotoxin-producing strains of *C. perfringens*, we were able to reproduce the clinical signs of enterotoxemia in a limited number of three- to four-week-old alpacas and llamas. We surgically exposed the intestine of the crias and injected the live organism directly into isolated loops of intestine. This was done to prove that the strains that were isolated from cases of enterotoxemia were the causative agents of the disease. In our studies, strains that did not produce enterotoxin did not cause the same disease that occurred when enterotoxin-producing strains were used.

Limited Vaccine Trial We were able to conduct a limited vaccine trial using enterotoxin produced and partially purified at Colorado State University when Dr. Ramirez visited in 1989. He vaccinated some dams with the toxoid and a control group of dams with culture broth that did not contain enterotoxin. The dams that were vaccinated with the enterotoxoid had significant levels of antienterotoxin in their serum, colostrum, and milk in comparison to the control dams. The year that we conducted the vaccine study, there was a low death loss, and essentially no death loss due to enterotoxemia, so our vaccine was not given an adequate challenge to determine whether it was effective in preventing neonatal enterotoxemia. The amount of enterotoxoid that we produced was very limited and was all used in this vaccine study.

Since enterotoxin is produced only under sporulation conditions and is produced in very low concentrations, it does not lend itself well to large-scale production. There have been reports of production of *C. perfringens* enterotoxin by genetically engineered *E. coli* strains, and perhaps strains such as these could be used to produce enough enterotoxin to produce adequate vaccine to vaccinate adult alpacas and llamas in Peru and other South American countries.

Prior to embarking on such a production project, research must be done to ensure that the enterotoxoid will stimulate protection that is passed from the dam to the cria. In theory, the reason the death losses due to enterotoxemia abruptly drop in the year immediately following a severe outbreak of enterotoxemia is that during the outbreak, dams are exposed to higher than normal levels of *C. perfringens* enterotoxin-producing type A strains. The dams are thus naturally "vaccinated" against the pathogen, and in the subsequent years pass antibodies on to their crias. As the exposure wanes, because fewer animals are exposed and dying, the antibody levels in the dams also wanes. Over the observed five-year period of the enterotoxemia cycle, fewer and fewer antibodies are passed from the dam to the cria, until a major outbreak occurs. Then high exposure leads to stimulation of the dams' immune responses and the disease is again on the decline.

Another contrast between the enterotoxin and the lethal toxins is that enterotoxin is not produced by *C. perfringens* strains when they are grown using methods that yield good production of the lethal toxins. The enterotoxin is produced when the bacteria sporulate, which can occur in the intestine of crias after they ingest spores of *C. perfringens* that are ubiquitous in the environment. For reasons as yet undefined, the intestine of the crias is an ideal environment for the production of enterotoxin. After its production by *C. perfringens* in the intestine, the enterotoxin enters the circulatory system of the cria and causes the many signs associated with enterotoxemia. There are neural signs, such as prostration and loss of consciousness, plus edema of the mucosal surfaces and hyperemia in the intestinal tract.

Clostridial Diseases Outside South America

The cyclic episodes of enterotoxemia, as seen in South America, have not occurred to my knowledge in North America. I have been asked repeatedly why we don't see such outbreaks in other parts of the world where camelids are now being raised. My response is that the conditions under which camelids are raised in South America by campesino families is very different than conditions under which they are raised elsewhere. Crowded, unsanitary conditions are the norm for the campesinos, while in other parts of the world the camelids are afforded clean environments with very little crowding. These conditions limit the buildup of *C. perfringens* and help prevent the spread of the bacteria among susceptible animals. However, outbreaks have been reported in clean-appearing environments.[2]

There have definitely been outbreaks of clostridial diseases in North American camelids, but to my knowledge the cause has not been confirmed as enterotoxin produced by *C. perfringens* type A. This is not to say that disease caused by *C. perfringens* type A has not occurred in North America, only that outbreaks of enterotoxemia caused by enterotoxin-producing *C. perfringens* type A have not been documented. I have heard of several instances where *C. perfringens* type A has been the cause of disease and death of many crias in North America. Some of the disease outbreaks caused the death of nearly all of the crias born in the year of the outbreak.

Most camelid owners routinely vaccinate their adults with *C. perfringens* C and D toxoids, which assist in preventing disease due to types C and D. In both beef and dairy calves, we see minimal death loss due to *C. perfringens* types C and D because the dams are routinely vaccinated with those toxoids. We see several foals each year, and hear of many more, that are victims of type C enteritis. The foals invariably die due to extensive destruction of the intestinal mucosa by the beta toxin, and likely other toxins, produced by type C strains. In addition, we have been finding many strains of type A (from horses and cattle) and C (from foals), and occasionally type E (from calves), that are beta 2 toxin positive.

Beta 2 Toxins Beta 2 toxin is the latest *C. perfringens* toxin to be discovered and defined. Its discovery and characterization were first published in December 1997 by a French group whose primary research focus is pigs. It has since been cited as a contributing factor to *C. perfringens* disease in horses, pigs, and cattle in Europe and North America. The action of the beta 2 toxin, destruction of the cell membrane, is very similar to that of the beta toxin; thus it was named beta 2. However, the gene that is responsible for production of beta 2 toxin is 85 percent different from the gene that is responsible for the production of beta toxin, so beta 2 is not a derivative or mutant of beta, but is in fact a newly discovered toxin. It appears that type A strains that possess the beta 2 toxin gene in addition to the alpha toxin gene are more likely to cause disease than strains without the beta 2 toxin gene. During the past five years we have genotyped several isolates of *C. perfringens* from alpacas that have been type A and possess the beta 2 toxin gene.

Pathogenic Type A Strains The current dilemma from a diagnostic and vaccine development standpoint is how to assess the significance of type A. Types C and D are proven pathogens, that is, highly capable of causing disease. In most cases where *C. perfringens* type A is isolated, and the pathologists can see associated intestinal lesions typical of *C. perfringens* type A, there is adequate reason to give credit (or blame) for the disease to type A, especially if the beta 2 toxin gene is also present in the strains identified.

However, many pathologists are reluctant to recognize all type A strains as pathogens. It is thought, with some evidence, that most type A strains are nonpathogenic and a small number of type A strains are pathogenic.

C. perfringens type A is easily isolated from the feces of normal horses. In a study we completed last year with colleagues at Colorado State University, we found that 90 percent of the 124 foals in our study were shedding *C. perfringens* type A at three days of age. These foals were normal, since there was no sign of disease due to the presence of type A. On the other hand, we have had well over 40 cases of foal enteritis over the past 4 years from which we have isolated *C. perfringens*, and the disease in the foals (usually 3 to 5 days of age) has been attributed to *C. perfringens*. Almost 75 percent of the cases have yielded type A, and the other 25 percent type C. Almost 100 percent of the foals who contracted type C and 50 percent of the foals with type A die, even with intensive care. In addition, we have had three cases where the clinical signs are those of type C (bloody diarrhea, collapse, and death), but only type A was recovered from the patient. Informal reports indicate that the mortality rate in cria alpacas who contract type A is close to 100 percent.

Obviously certain type A strains differ in their ability to cause disease. We and others are currently seeking a method to distinguish nonpathogenic type A strains from the type A strains that are very definitely causing disease. The differences may be in the toxins produced, in the amount of toxin produced, or in other mechanisms that are contributing to overall pathogenicity.

Custom Vaccines Custom toxoids or bacterins, also called autogenous toxoids or bacterins, are those products produced specifically for an individual owner from bacteria isolated from that owner's diseased animals. Do they work? Anecdotal evidence indicates that the autogenous toxoids do help. However, there is no clear answer because no controlled studies on individual premises have objectively answered the question of efficacy for autogenous toxoids.

I encourage owners and veterinarians to consider each case from an in-depth diagnostic standpoint before requesting autogenous toxoid production. I believe that in some cases the custom vaccines do help. In other cases the vaccines appear to help, but may have been a small factor in the overall resolution of the disease. Other factors in resolution of such disease are weather, immune status of the dam, age of the remaining crias, feed changes, and other factors that are unique to each farm or ranch. If we were able to better define the toxins that make a type A strain a definite pathogen, we could search for those toxin genes, and for the means of producing toxoids that would induce better immune protection in alpaca populations.

CONCLUSIONS

We in the research laboratories admit that we do not know everything there is to know about *C. perfringens*, and definitely not all there is to know about *C. perfringens* type A. Many of us in laboratories around the world are in contact with each other regarding our progress with *C. perfringens*. Vaccines under development may be valuable management tools in suppressing disease due to *C. perfringens*.

Since *C. perfringens* is a spore-forming bacterium that remains viable in the soil indefinitely, it will always remain a potential pathogen, so when suppression does occur, it may be only a temporary respite. *C. perfringens* is a very complex bacterium that will undoubtedly acquire new genes through mutation or from other bacteria, which will allow them to circumvent the controls that we impose. Greater understanding of this disease and the development of vaccines are both extremely important for all camelid breeders.

REFERENCES

1. Ellis, R. P., and A. C. Dennison: Enteric Disease and Death Due to *Clostridium perfringens*. *The Alpaca Registry Journal*, pp. 21–24, Spring 2000.
2. Skinner, J.: *Clostridium perfringens* Type A Enterotoxemia: One Ranch's War. *The Alpaca Registry Journal*, pp. 16–20, Spring 2000.

BOVINE VIRAL DIARRHEA VIRUS (BVDV)

Nancy Carr, MD

Bovine viral diarrhea virus (BVDV) is an important cause of abortions and illness in cattle, and until recently was thought not to cause significant problems in camelids.[5,6,7] However, research in 2004 has shown that BVDV does cause abortions and illness and, most importantly, can cause the persistently infected (PI) state in alpacas.[2,3] This information likely applies to other camelids as well.*

The most important aspect of BVDV is its effect on the developing fetus. It can cause abortions at all stages of gestation, from early embryo loss to stillbirth at term. Abortion may occur months after the infection. A unique feature of BVDV is that if a pregnant female is exposed to the virus in early gestation and does not abort, she may

Editor's Note: I consider the recent evidence suggesting that alpacas infected with BVDV may suffer more clinical and reproductive diseases than previously thought important enough to present in this book, with the warning to the reader that information is only now starting to be gathered about this disease, and that findings may need to be amended in future editions.

produce a PI offspring. Because the fetus is not immune-competent in early gestation, it does not make an immune response to rid itself of the virus. Once the PI offspring is born, it sheds huge concentrations of virus from every secretion (tears, nasal discharge, urine, and feces), and is the main source of the spread of BVDV. The only way to be PI is to be born PI. In cattle some PI animals appear normal; however, many are "poor-doers," with low birth weight, poor weight gain, and susceptibility to other diseases such as pneumonia. Most die before they are two years old.

In cattle an acute infection with BVDV commonly results in a subclinical illness. When present, signs of clinical illness can include fever, nasal discharge, oral erosions, and diarrhea that can be severe and bloody. Some animals may contract other diseases, such as pneumonia, because the virus depresses the immune system. Acute infection with BVDV occurs through the nose and mouth by contact with secretions from an infected animal (usually a PI animal)—either directly from the infected animal or from items that have been contaminated by those secretions, such as water troughs. An acutely infected animal sheds the virus for a relatively short length of time (two weeks), in contrast to a PI animal, which sheds the virus its whole life. The virus can survive a maximum of two weeks in the environment.

Knowledge about alpacas and BVDV is evolving. The range of gestation that results in the birth of a PI cria has not yet been determined. The first verified PI cria was from a dam that had been subclinically infected with BVDV at approximately 65 days of gestation.[2,3] The majority of alpacas exposed to BVDV have a subclinical infection. Known manifestations of clinical illness in alpacas from acute infection with BVDV include sore mouth, lethargy, and decreased appetite (with resultant hepatic lipidosis).[2,3] Abortions or stillbirths and the prevalence of BVDV serum antibodies may be the only sign that BVDV has been present in the herd. Possible presentations of PI alpacas are low birth weight at full term, very premature birth, a weak newborn, or a poor-doing cria with repeated infections. It is also likely that PI alpacas can appear normal.

BVDV has probably been in alpaca herds for a while and responsible for some unexplained abortions, stillbirths, and poor-doing crias.[1,4] Routine pathology testing does not show the virus; it must be specifically tested for. Testing for BVDV should be part of the routine workup for aborted or stillborn fetuses, all poor-doing crias, and alpacas with unexplained illnesses or death. If BVDV is found, then testing to find any PI animals must be done and the PI animals euthanized. Females who were pregnant while BVDV was present in the herd must have their crias tested soon after birth to make sure they are not PI. Testing for BVDV, especially for detecting the PI state, should be done in consultation with a veterinary virologist or a lab experienced in BVDV testing.

Biosecurity measures will be important for preventing BVDV in alpaca herds. All animals arriving at a farm (females coming for breeding with their crias at their side, or new purchases) should be tested before arrival to ensure they are not PI. Quarantining new arrivals or animals who have been off the farm should be routine. Activities such as shows, auctions, and the commercial transportation of alpacas need to be considered. There should be no fence-line contact with other livestock. Research is needed into the potential role of BVDV vaccines for alpacas.

It will be difficult to know how prevalent BVDV is in alpacas until awareness of the disease increases and testing for it becomes common. Dr. Edward Dubovi, whose work focused on BVDV in alpacas in 2005, warns, "This virus is being transmitted from alpaca to alpaca. The problem is continuing to grow, and I think it is more serious than anyone originally suspected."*

REFERENCES

1. Belknap, E. B., and J. K. Collins, et al.: Bovine Viral Diarrhea Virus in New World Camelids. *Journal of Veterinary Diagnostic Investigation* 12(6): 568–570, 2000.
2. Carman, S., and N. Carr, et al.: Bovine Viral Diarrhea Virus in Alpacas: Abortion and Persistent Infection. *Journal of Veterinary Diagnostic Investigation* 17: 580–584, 2005.
3. Carr, N., and S. Carman: BVD Virus: A Newly Recognized Serious Health Problem. *Alpacas,* pp. 146–151, Summer 2005.
4. Goyal, S. M., and M. Bouljihad, et al.: Isolation of Bovine Viral Diarrhea Virus from an Alpaca. *Journal of Veterinary Diagnostic Investigation* 14a(6): 523–525, 2002.
5. Larson, R.: A Medical Marvel. *Alpacas,* p. 122, Winter 1999.
6. Mattson, D. E.: Viral Diseases. *Veterinary Clinics North America: Food Animal Practice: Update on Llama Medicine* 10 (2): 346–347. W. B. Saunders Co., Philadelphia, 1994.
7. Wentz, P.A., and E. B. Belknap, et al.: Evaluation of Bovine Viral Diarrhea Virus in New World Camelids. *Journal of the American Medical Association* 223(2): 223–228, 2003.

*Dr. Edward Dubovi is director of the virology section of the Diagnostic Laboratory of the New York State College of Veterinary Medicine, Cornell University.

Chapter 21

Noninfectious Multisystemic Diseases

Achieving homeostasis decreases disease.

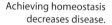

THE RELATIONSHIP BETWEEN STRESS AND DISEASE

Eric Hoffman

STRESSORS AND HOMEOSTASIS

Before discussing several common and some not so common noninfectious diseases in alpacas, the concepts of homeostasis and stress need to be defined. These concepts are central to preventive strategies in combating many diseases. For the alpaca manager here is a truism worth internalizing: With homeostasis and minimal stress there will be less disease.

You may recall the concept of homeostasis in a dull biology class somewhere in your distant past. It may not have seemed relevant then. *Homeostasis* has to do with the optimum conditions for a living thing. From one creature to the next the optimum won't be the same. For example, an emperor penguin that lays an egg in winter in Antarctica and fasts for months to raise its young would not survive in an alpaca pasture in central California or on the altiplano. Nor would an alpaca survive long in ice-covered Antarctica in the middle of winter. For homeostasis each species has an ideal diet, an ideal kind of social interaction, an ideal outdoor temperature, an ideal environment, and an ideal for many of life's variables. In this way living things of all shapes and sizes share a common undeclared goal: to live

as best they can. With domestic livestock like alpacas, the "best they can" is almost entirely under the control of human managers.

Homeostasis occurs when the physiological functions of the body are at optimal levels and all organ functions are as they should be. *Stressors* are things that contribute to a body being forced from the homeostatic state. Too much heat, too much cold, too little food, too much of the wrong food, too aggressive companions, and too crowded living conditions are examples of stressors.

In many species the impact of stress has been studied in both individuals and entire groups. Depending on the variables at work, subgroups within a population are often subject to more stress than the group. A great deal of evidence points to prolonged stress as contributing to the onset of many diseases in many species. Stress impacts immune response, hormone secretions, sexual function, growth, gastrointestinal function and health, the formation of ulcers, cardiovascular health, and basically part or all of the physiological system. Put simply, too much stress impacts the quality of life. With alpacas and llamas there are few studies specific to stress, but there is ample evidence of stress's impact on rats, zebras, baboons, birds, fish, and dogs.

In social animals such as alpacas, stress is constant and can be considered healthy at certain levels, but harmful at others. In many ways animal management of any kind has as much to do with stress management as anything else.[9]

"My alpaca arrived in good shape, but became sick three days later" is a common circumstance in which an alpaca is declared sick. Transitions of all kinds require greater vigilance on the part of the manager because homeostasis is disrupted. Often all seems well during and immediately after a transition. The problems usually occur two days to two weeks after a stressful transition.[6] The influences of stressors often don't make themselves known right away. Events like taking alpacas to shows or sales, transporting animals, changing an animal's pen assignment, removing the alpaca from its companions and relatives, the onset of a dramatic change in weather, and numerous other changes may directly impact the alpaca.

MAJOR STRESSORS

Heat Stress

Alpacas evolved in a cool and dry climate—a high-altitude environment where it freezes more than 300 nights a year and rarely reaches 85°F (30°C) during the day.[5] The climate is generally dry with low humidity. By comparing these parameters to the annual averages and seasonal fluctuations in your area, you can determine how important combating high temperatures is for your herd. Alpacas have been introduced to many new environments outside their native land that challenge their tolerances, especially in areas of severe heat and humidity. In general, annual shearing, constant access to drinking water, providing shade, and exposure to air currents (which may mean electric fans) will allow most animals to withstand warm temperatures and generally high humidity.

Body Temperature Heat stress or *hyperthermia* occurs when the body temperature increases significantly above the accepted average (99°–102.5°F or 37°–39°C). In hot or humid conditions the body temperature may be two or three degrees above normal without any adverse consequences to the alpaca. However, when the temperature rises to 104.2°F to 106°F (40°–41.1°C), there is danger of permanent damage to organs in most animals, including alpacas. Animals experiencing significant heat stress may have temperatures between 106° to 108°F (41°–42°C). Animals with temperatures higher than this are in critical condition. Besides organ damage the central nervous may be impacted. The animal may stagger, not respond to stimuli properly, and lapse into a coma. Obviously immediate action is warranted if heat stress is underway.[1,3*]

Alpacas seem to be able to cope fairly effectively with short-term rises in body temperatures that occur due to a hot afternoon, but in areas with prolonged heat and warm nights, an alpaca's ability to cope may become severely challenged. High humidity compounds the risk. The man-

An alpaca thermoregulating on a hot day.

ager's responsibility is to know the weather conditions that are likely to bring about heat stress and have a plan in place to combat it. Having no plan and reacting after the fact are irresponsible.

Thermoregulation *Thermoregulation* refers to an animal's ability to maintain the correct life-sustaining body temperature. Without the ability to self-regulate body temperatures within correct parameters, most mammals would die. A number of variables affect thermoregulation: high ambient temperatures, high humidity, fever from sickness, drugs that adversely impact thermoregulation, dehydration, poisons, and exertion such as running, fighting, mating, labor while giving birth, and struggling while being restrained.

Often several of these variables will conspire to push an alpaca to the point at which it can no longer thermoregulate itself within safe limits. In overheating, the animal's rate of liquid loss through evaporation (sweating) isn't at a sufficient rate to allow the animal to discharge excess heat. Dehydration is also often at work at the same time. Liquids lost through evaporation must be replaced for the animal to continue to thermoregulate. When the intake of liquids and the discharge of liquids through sweating and urination don't result in maintaining thermoregulation, human intervention is warranted.[1,3,5,8]

80–80 Rule Researcher David Pugh, DVM, previously with Auburn University in Louisiana, has come to know the tolerances of alpacas to heat and humidity. Pugh operates in the Southeast United States, in the heart of the most humid and often hottest part of the country. The region often sees summer temperatures over 90°F (32°C) with 95 percent humidity, a climate type unknown to alpacas in their native Andes.

---

*Ty McConnell, DVM, personal communication, Scotts Valley, California, August 2002.

In 1988, Dr. Pugh and I were hired to visit the quarantine facility in Key West, Florida, that had been experiencing heavy losses due to heat stress on imported animals. After surveying the facility, a protocol was developed for coping with heat. Pugh proposed that anytime the combined temperature (Fahrenheit) and humidity (percent) exceeded 160, water would be turned on to cool the animals. This became known as the "80–80" rule: 80°F (27°C) and 80 percent humidity were designated as the threshold levels at which to actively combat overheating in humid and hot climates. Because animals differ from one another, water was made available for animals to cool off in if they so chose.[8]

In most ranch situations, soaker hoses or plastic kiddy pools can be used. It is important that the water comes in contact with the underside of the alpaca because the stomach area is generally hairless, the skin is thin there, and it is very near many of the vital organs.

In dry heat, with low humidity, the threshold for risk is higher than 80°F (27°C). Alpacas have successfully been raised in excessively hot areas such as California's Central Valley on farms where preventive measures for heat stress are farm policy (shearing, access to water and shade, air currents). As a rule, when temperatures in a low-humidity area exceed 90°F (32°C), alpacas should be scrutinized several times a day to assess their response to the heat. Pay special attention to late-term pregnant animals, young animals, and old animals. These groups are often more susceptible to heat stress. Check respiration rates (nostril flare) relative to other animals in the same enclosure. Often the first visual sign of hyperthermia is an animal in a resting position that is mouth breathing for no apparent reason. I have known of births in 106°F (41°C) temperatures that were successful. The crias were moved to shade with fans shortly after birth. When in doubt about how a particular animal is coping with heat, watch it, evaluate its respiration rate and alertness, and if necessary poke a thermometer in the animal's rectum and take its temperature.

Heat Stress and Sperm A few really hot days can kill sperm and render breeding males infertile for 30 to 60 days. If heat is chronic, a male may be affected for the summer season. A telltale first sign is loose and extended skin in the testicular area. More severe signs may include swelling in the scrotum area and fluid buildup in the scrotum.

Heat Stress and Pregnancy Heat stress can affect fetal development in numerous ways. Congenital defects, brain damage, and abortion are all possible. Heat has different effects on various stages of fetal development.[1,3]

Treating Acute Heat Stress Elsewhere in the text, soaker hoses, electric fans, and wading pools were described as

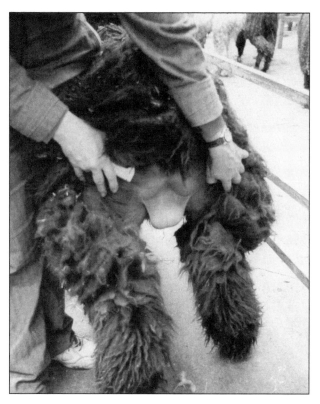

These testicles are showing heat stress. If heat is severe enough, a male can be infertile for 60 days or longer.

elective ways to help an alpaca cope with high temperatures. But what do you do when you find an alpaca that is clearly suffering from heat stress who elected not to cool off on its own or lacked the opportunity to do so?

Acting swiftly is important. Take the animal's temperature. This important starting point determines which other critical decisions must be made. Water is your friend. If possible, run a hose on the animal's underside in the belly area and on the open area under the tail. If two hoses are available, use them both. Another method is to slide the animal into a child's wading pool. This might necessitate moving the animal to the water or the pool to the animal.

After ten minutes of cooling off, take its temperature and see if it has begun to drop. If it has dropped, continue with the therapy. In extreme cases consider a cold-water enema. If this is done with a garden hose, be extremely careful to use low pressure and allow water that enters the rectum to flow freely back out. Death can be rapid if heat conditions are severe enough. Heat stress is an important concern when transporting alpacas during heat waves.

With overheated crias the goal is the same, but the animal's body mass is much smaller. Moving the animal to water is easier. Cold-water enemas (children's Fleet enema) are also effective.

Once an animal's condition has stabilized and the temperature is in the normal range, attempt to keep the animal

Stress-related diseases are probable from overcrowding like this.

in a cool (not refrigerated) place and monitor the situation until a veterinarian can examine the animal.[1,2,3,4,6,8]

Cold Stress

Cold stress, or *hypothermia*, is a serious consideration in the higher latitudes in North America, parts of Victoria and New South Wales, New Zealand, and Europe. In most instances alpacas cope well with cold conditions. Though it freezes more than 300 nights a year on the altiplano, the temperature usually doesn't drop far below freezing, so alpacas are not used to the severe cold found in northern latitudes.

Numerous variables affect an alpaca's ability to cope with cold. Among them are quality of food, availability of water, length of coat, body condition, breed type, age, shelter, wind chill, amount and kind of precipitation, and other factors (see Chapter 4: Husbandry and Chapter 8: Transportation). It need not be freezing for hypothermia to occur. Alpacas experiencing prolonged cool rains can easily become hypothermic. Shearing and subsequent cool weather can result in a herd being exposed to hypothermia they wouldn't have experienced under full fleece.

Symptoms Body temperature is the surest indicator for how cold an alpaca really is. Most thermometers don't record below 92°F (33°C). Any animal this cold is in grave danger. An animal whose temperature is 98°F (36°C) or below should be monitored. If it dips to 97°F (35°C), the animal is chilled. At some point during the downward movement of the temperature, basic metabolic processes may become compromised. Signs that hypothermia is progressing include dullness, shallow breathing, inability to

stand, and coma. When attempts are made to make a hypothermic animal stand, it will often feel limp and cold.[3,7]

Variables Influencing Response to Cold Suri and huacaya alpacas differ significantly in their ability to withstand cold. Generally, cold without precipitation is less of a risk than cold with precipitation and wind. The latter two variables can compound cold-related problems rapidly and always need to be taken into consideration. Due to their fleece's construction, huacayas are better designed to withstand both rain and snow. Suris are a different story. Their fleece is more open and parts along the spine where water can penetrate to their skin. As a result, they are more susceptible to becoming chilled quickly due to cold precipitation. Basically, a fully fleeced suri should be thought of as a recently shorn huacaya when considering housing needs and avoiding cold-related problems.* Energy needs increase with cold weather. Ample good-quality feed and water are essential. The importance of a reliable water source is sometimes overlooked. Without water, digestion may be impaired and dehydration is a possibility (see Chapter 4: Husbandry).

How to Combat Hypothermia Moving adults to dry space with abundant forage out of the wind is often all that is needed to allow an adult to regain its normal temperature. Neonates are a different story. Due to their small body mass, they are the often the first stricken and the first to perish if not discovered. They often have a difficult time warming themselves and need to be assisted. The fastest way to warm a cria is to put it in a garbage bag with its head sticking out of the top and immersing the animal (in the bag) in a warm bath that is around 108°F (42°C). If you have no plastic garbage bag, put the cria in the tub anyway. The plastic bag allows you to warm the animal without making it wet, which will be a problem if you must reunite it with its mother.

Combinations of heating pads and sleeping bags have also been used. It is important to monitor the heating process. More than one cria has died by being overheated or burned. The idea is to warm the animal gradually, not broil it.

Frostbite One of the associated problems of hypothermia is frostbite. Ears are particularly vulnerable—more than one alpaca has lost part or most of one or both ears due to frostbite. Frostbite can also occur on the nose, tail, and feet. Frostbite usually occurs when an animal begins to become hypothermic and the blood flow increases to the vital organs and decreases to the outer appendages. If the ear

---

*Jim Vickers, DVM, personal communication, Charlevoix, Michigan, 1994.

becomes cold enough and freezes, the tissue not receiving blood will die. In the early stages the affected tissue is white, later it becomes brown and leathery, and eventually it falls off. If caught early, warm the appendage slowly and some tissue may be saved.*

Digestive Tract Problems

Numerous maladies involve the digestive system, ranging from mild in importance to life threatening. Unfortunately, alpacas are slow to show signs of a problem until it is fairly well advanced. The alert owner learns to look for certain signs, such as reluctance to eat, reluctance to stand, diarrhea, constipation, gut ache, self-isolation, change in eating habits, and food preference. Often the subtle signs may be animal specific, because, though each animal is a member of a herd, it may have idiosyncratic behaviors that distinguish it. For example, hiccuping may just be a passing thing, or it may be symptomatic of something else. Refusal to eat and cessation of defecation are serious signs that something is wrong.

Disorders can be a result of environmental changes, stressful social situations, and just plain bad luck. Changes in the weather or the herd can trigger digestive disorders of one kind or another. Stress is a significant factor in many kinds of digestive disorders. Disorders of the digestive tract deserve immediate attention. Often fairly subtle signs can be something life threatening. Some of the possibilities are colic, constipation, urinary tract problems, parasite-related problems, ulcers, and intestinal torsion.

Colic This term is borrowed from horse medicine and is often applied to alpacas and llamas with digestive tract upset. Remember that a horse is not a ruminant, and though alpacas and horses can both have intestinal flare-ups, ruminants and horses are different and the generalities for what to do for a horse don't necessarily hold for a camelid.

In general, colic refers to the expression of discomfort and pain in the abdominal area that is digestive in nature. Usual signs are groaning, shifting from one side to another while sitting in a sternal position, grinding teeth, biting at the hindquarters or stomach, strange stances, and unusual (hunched) walking styles. Colic of any kind indicates that something is wrong, so these symptoms demand further investigation.

Constipation Constipation, impaction, and blockage are often used interchangeably when they really mean different things. There are many reasons for constipation. If constipation is the sole cause for difficulty in producing

bowel movements, the problem can be corrected with oral medications or simply making sure that the alpaca has a source of clean water and good forage.

With cessation of bowel movements, something more serious may be underway. On a gradient, impaction is worse than constipation. Where constipation may be a slow bowel, impaction is a plugged or stopped bowel with a probable obstruction somewhere in the digestive system. Impaction will likely require a veterinarian's assistance and may require surgery.

Blockage is another term confused with constipation. Blockage can be from external sources, such as pregnancy pressing against a portion of the intestines, or be something as dire as intestinal torsion. Torsions can be terminal if they are not corrected and the blood flow to the affected area is cut off. Blockage simply means the digestive system is blocked.

Terms aside, if you suspect an animal is ill, spend the time to see if it is able to produce a bowel movement. If it can't, call a veterinarian. Since alpacas are stoic and slow to show a digestive tract problem, the problem may have been at work for days before the alpaca manager realizes it. Fast action is often required to prevent losing an alpaca.

Urinary Tract Problems Urinary tract obstruction is usually the most serious urinary problem encountered by most veterinarians and owners. This is almost exclusively a problem in male or adolescent crias and luckily it's relatively rare. Typically the affected alpaca will visit the manure pile, strike the defecation pose, and strain for a prolonged period time. The animal may or may not defecate but will continue straining. Instead of a steady (pulsating) stream, urine may instead drip from the animal or not come out at all. These are symptoms of a urinary tract obstruction. The alpaca will need to see a veterinarian immediately. The cause can vary—buildup of salts, abnormally narrow urethra, injury, and other reasons. If the alpaca can't urinate, its bladder may burst. Passing a catheter may relieve the immediate problem, but doing this, even for a skilled veterinarian, can be difficult. Surgery may be necessary. In some cases the best efforts fail to correct the problem.

Parasite-related Problems An animal whose intestinal tract has significant parasitic loads may develop chronic diarrhea, anemia, and poor body condition. Diagnosis is usually easily done through fecal samples. A regular worming program should take care of parasites (see Chapter 17: Parasitology).

Ulcers In llamas and alpacas ulcers are often very serious and result in death if not remedied. Symptoms may vary, but waning appetite is often the first sign. Ulcers in the early stages can be treated by injectible and oral medications.

*Jim Vickers, DVM, personal communication, 1994.

Ulcers further along may require surgery. Depending on how advanced the ulcer is, surgery may not succeed. C-3 (third stomach chamber) ulcers are usually the deadliest and the hardest to treat. The actual cause of ulcers is not known. They may be a result of one or more kinds of stress. (See page ___ for more details.)

Intestinal Torsion This life-threatening condition affects the ability of the animal to defecate, but more importantly may result in blood flow being blocked to a portion of a twisted intestine. The result is often catastrophic. A portion of the animal's intestines may literally die and begin to necrotize. Surgery (involving the cutting out of the affected section) has saved some animals, but without early detection the prognosis is very poor.*

Common Dental Problems

An alpaca's dentition is not complicated. Upper and lower molars are used to chew food. These are the alpaca's most important teeth, and without them they could not chew food or cud and they would perish. The incisors occur only on the bottom jaw close against the dental pad on the front of the upper jaw. The incisors function to hold grass against the dental pad and tear it free to chew. Alpacas also have six canine teeth that become razor-sharp weapons in mature males.

The four common dental problems in alpacas are poor bite, abscesses, aged teeth, and retained incisors.

Poor Bite (Undershot or Overshot Jaw). This condition occurs in different degrees of seriousness and is a common problem in alpacas. A condition in which the front teeth pass by the dental pad (instead of resting on it) is often called an overbite. In this condition the front teeth must be cut periodically. Incisors aligned correctly to the dental pad (shutting into it) don't continually grow and don't require periodic trimming. An underbite occurs when the lower jaw falls short and the teeth close against the roof of the mouth instead of the dental pad (see Chapter 3: Anatomy and Conformation). Minor deviations of the incisors (slight overbite or a slight underbite) will probably not impact the animal's ability to eat and enjoy life. However, occasionally a severe overbite or underbite indicates that the molars are not aligned properly, causing problems in chewing food. This type of malocclusion can be a serious problem and result in the alpaca not being able to maintain a correct body condition.

Abscesses Alpacas in middle and late life sometimes develop painful tooth abscesses, usually in the molars and most often in the lower jaw. To many owners the first sign

---

*Ty McConnell, DVM, personal communication, August 2, 2002.

of an abscess is the presence of bloody or pussy drainage along the bottom mandible below the abscessed tooth. An abscessed tooth needs to be addressed immediately because it may affect eating, though it often doesn't. A portable X-ray unit is usually used to ascertain the severity of the abscess. Some abscesses involve the mandible and pose a serious health risk. Tooth extraction is sometimes necessary to clean up an abscess. Because of the design of an alpaca molar's roots and its positioning in the jaw, extracting a tooth requires anesthesia and a veterinarian schooled in the correct technique. Inexperience and bad luck in tooth extractions have resulted in broken jaws.

Aged Teeth Often an alpaca more than 15 years of age will slowly lose weight and waste away. There can be multiple reasons for loss of body condition, but a common one (and one often overlooked) is that the molars are no longer functioning properly. Several things can be wrong. The teeth may simply be worn to the gum line and no longer capable of doing their job, or they may have worn unevenly. The latter condition can sometimes be corrected by a veterinarian who is experienced in filing teeth and correcting dental problems.

Retained Incisors This condition occurs when the permanent incisors erupt and grow, and the deciduous teeth are supposed to fall out—but don't. The permanent incisors appear between two and three years of age. If you open an alpaca's mouth and see two sets of teeth (usually the front-most teeth), you are looking at retained incisors. In some cases the deciduous teeth are slow to fall out but eventually do. In other cases the deciduous teeth are permanent. You can tell if the tooth is apt to depart by feeling it. If it is loose, it will eventually fall out. If it is rock hard and the new tooth is fully erupted behind, chances are you will need to have the unneeded deciduous tooth removed. If two sets of teeth are allowed to exist side by side, expect dental problems from food collected between the two sets of teeth.

Fractures

Alpacas are agile, calculating animals most of the time. They are not prone to injury, but on occasion they will fracture bones. Fractures of the legs and neck are usually easy to detect. Some fractures (pelvis, ribs, skull) may be more difficult to detect. A veterinarian with a portable X-ray unit can diagnose a fracture. The good news about alpacas and fractures is that their bones usually have great capacity to heal, if treated properly. Unlike horses, a broken leg is not a death sentence. I have seen camelids with compound fractures, or a bone protruding outside of the body, or a foot crushed and broken in 12 places that have all healed, and the animals have gone on with a normal life. A veterinarian with a good understanding of orthopedics can work wonders on badly broken legs.

When a fracture is suspected or detected, the first step is to contain the animal in a safe place where there is food and water. If veterinary help is not nearby, the limb should be splinted in the position the fracture is found. If the fracture is on the leg, weight will adversely affect the fracture. Place the leg in a splint that extends past the foot to the ground, so the alpaca's weight is transferred to the splint. Knowledge of basic first aid will help do this successfully (see Chapter 8: Transportation).

IMPORTANCE OF BLOOD TESTS

Blood is essential to life and it is the medium in which scientific assessments are taken. Blood tests can tell a veterinarian a great deal about an alpaca: progesterone level (ovulation or pregnancy), elevated white blood count (infection), enzyme assays and other tests for specific organ function, relative fitness of the immune system (IgG), low red blood cell count (anemia), low phosphorus/calcium (Vitamin D deficiency), and numerous other measurements. Blood tests provide the window for accurate diagnosis and cure. Taking a blood test at the onset of an alpaca's illness will often make the difference between life and death, because the forthcoming information will often focus the diagnosis and cure.

REFERENCES

1. Baum, K.: Heat Stress in Camelids. *Large Animal Medicine*, pp. 23–24, 2002.
2. Fowler, M. E.: Hyperthermia in Llamas and Alpacas. Veterinary Clinics of North America. *Food Animals* 10(2): 309–318, 1994.
3. Fowler, M. E.: *Medicine and Surgery of South American Camelids*, pp. 1–387. Ames: Iowa State University Press, 1989.
4. Freeman, P.: Coping with Heat Stress at Oak Hill. *Llama Life* 14: 11, 1990.
5. Hoffman, E.: Ships of the Andes. *Pacific Discovery* 42(3): 7–15, 1989.
6. Hoffman, E.: Facility at Key West Adapts to Receive Imports. *Llama Life* 7: 1–26, 1990.
7. Price, T.: The Faiks Like Challenges: Raising Alpacas in Arctic Weather and Exporting Alpacas to Australia. *Llama Life* 9: 2, 1989.
8. Pugh, D. G.: Heat Stress in North American Camelids. *Proceedings of the North American Veterinarian Conference*, Auburn University, Orlando, Florida, 1995.
9. Sapolsky, R.: *Why Zebras Don't Get Ulcers: Guide to Stress Related Diseases and Coping*, pp. 1–368. New York: W. H. Freeman and Company, 1994.

DIGESTIVE DISORDERS
Christopher K. Cebra, VMD, MA, MS, DACVIM

The digestive system plays an important role in providing alpacas with nutrients. It also acts as a portal for many undesirable factors, including parasites, bacteria, and viruses. Most alpacas are generally healthy and have an intact, functional digestive system, but disorders of this system are also common. Awareness of digestive disorders and their signs will aid alpaca owners in recognizing them at an early stage and minimizing their impact on both individual and herd.

DIGESTIVE TRACT SYMPTOMS

Some disease signs relate more specifically to the digestive tract than others. Among the more specific signs are losing food or saliva out of the mouth, swellings of the jaw or throat, misaligned teeth, colic, diarrhea, and straining to defecate. Among the less specific signs are inappetence, weakness or decreased activity, weight loss, abdominal distention, lack of feces, and changes in heart rate or body temperature. Identifying any of these abnormalities may be enough cause for a veterinary investigation, with the more specific signs at least giving hints about how to start correcting the problem. This section covers the more specific signs of digestive disorder.

Losing Saliva or Food Out of the Mouth

Resembling ruminants, alpacas thoroughly chew roughage and mix it with copious saliva. Boluses of chewed feed are swallowed and descend the esophagus to the stomach, and are also regurgitated back up the esophagus for more chewing. Most alpacas conduct this entire process without losing anything out of their mouth. Others will lose saliva or possibly regurgitated feed.

Small amounts of salivary loss may occur due to irritation of the mouth or tongue, general dullness of the alpaca leading to a down-turned head, or occasionally poor esophageal function. A quick assessment may be made by watching the alpaca eat and drink, and by lifting the lips to look at the gums. If the alpaca eats and drinks readily without drooling and the inside of the mouth looks healthy, small amounts of salivary loss may be forgiven. Alpacas that are weak for any reason tend to have a down-turned nose. This allows small amounts of saliva to drain forward and hence be lost. Correction of the primary problem will correct salivary loss.

The loss of saliva is of most concern if a large amount is lost. If an alpaca eats sluggishly, a veterinary investigation may be advisable. If the inside of the mouth looks raw, the environment should be examined for caustic material, especially acids, lye, and plants like rhododendron, azalea, or laurel. Incorrectly mixed medications are another cause of oral irritation.

Loss of chewed feed material is even more of a concern. Dropping a few stalks of unchewed hay after taking a mouthful is of no consequence, but aside from spitting, chewed feed should not be dropped. Observe the alpaca to determine if the feed is lost due to an active (retching, choking) or a passive process. If no abnormalities are noted during eating or in the hour after eating, no abdominal distention is noted, and the alpaca appears bright and alert, the process is more likely to be passive. Possibilities for an active process include irritation of the digestive tract by one of the aforementioned plants, choke (blockage of the esophagus), megaesophagus, or intestinal blockage.

Choke is relatively rare in camelids, unless another problem is present, such as megaesophagus. The major sign is acute copious, continual salivation with chewed feed mixed in, particularly after eating. Resolution frequently requires veterinary attention. Specific diagnosis is usually made when resistance is encountered by trying to insert a stomach tube. Persistence of choke can lead to complications including pneumonia.

Megaesophagus occurs secondary to chronic blockages of the esophagus or weakening of the esophageal muscles.[15] As a result, the esophagus is less capable of moving boluses of feed between the mouth and the stomach. Initial signs are salivation when a bolus to be rechewed fails to make it to the mouth. Later signs include weight loss and a fluid wave visible at the base of the neck on the left side. Alpacas that choke on more than one occasion should be examined for megaesophagus. Specific diagnosis requires endoscopy or radiography. Megaesophagus can occur for a variety of reasons, including neck trauma and abscesses or other tissue masses that constrict the esophagus. Often a specific cause cannot be identified.

Megaesophagus tends to affect two different age groups: adults and juveniles near weaning. In juveniles, the disorder may have been present for a longer time, only becoming apparent with the shift from milk to solid feed. Some juvenile cases may reflect congenital lesions, though the specific cause for the lesions may not have been identified.

Intestinal blockages rarely lead to active regurgitation unless they occur near the origin of the intestine.[2] Abdominal distention, inappetence, and lethargy should be accompanying signs. Blockages are usually due to wads of plant material, except in weanlings, where alpaca fiber is commonly found. It is thought that attempts to nurse each other leads to fiber ingestion in these weanlings.

Night regurgitation is an infrequent syndrome marked by finding pools of feed-tinged saliva on the ground in the morning. Careful observation or isolation can lead to identification of the culprit, usually a juvenile 4 to 15 months old. The cause is unknown, and may relate to the transition to the fermentative digestive system. Most alpacas cease the behavior within 3 months. As far as we know, night regurgitation is not detrimental.

Swelling of the Jaw or Throat

One of the most common serious digestive ailments of alpacas is having a tooth root abscess, which results from an infection of the tooth root that spreads to adjacent bone.[4] The primary sign is a hard swelling that usually appears midway along the lower jaw, but also occasionally on the upper jaw, at other places on the lower jaw, or at multiple places at once. The swelling usually enlarges with time, and may occasionally break open and release pus. Pus drainage may come from directly over the affected tooth, further back on the jaw, or between the bones of the lower jaw. If the infected tooth is on the upper jaw, pus may come out the nose. Surprisingly, affected alpacas rarely appear to have difficulty chewing or suffer weight loss, and the infection rarely spreads to other sites in the body.

A presumptive diagnosis can be made after identifying a bony swelling. Other causes of such hard swelling include fractures, tumors, and bone cysts, all of which are rare. Confirmation of a diagnosis requires radiography. In some cases, pus drainage is more obvious than the swelling. Since other causes of pus drainage from the face or between the jaw are uncommon, alpacas with these signs should always be examined for the presence of a tooth root abscess. A variety of treatment options are available, including long-term antibiotics, complete or partial tooth removal, and root canal surgery. If left untreated, the abscess will enlarge, may spread to affect other teeth, and in rare cases, may seed bacterial infections in other parts of the body.

Soft swelling around the face or jaw is rarely a digestive disorder. Some possibilities are snakebite or insect bite, tumor, abscesses, or edema (rare). Fluctuant swelling around the base of the throat may indicate megaesophagus.

Misaligned Teeth

Malocclusion is one of the most common conformational disorders of alpacas. Incisors should meet with the dental pad in order to shear off pasture grass. The most common abnormality involves incisors that protrude beyond the pad (overbite). Affected alpacas commonly show no problems with malocclusion, especially on hay diets, although some decline in body condition may be seen in pastured alpacas. If considered necessary, correction involves filing, grinding, or cutting the teeth to a more proper conformation. Care must be taken with power tools to avoid overheating the teeth. Given the constant growth of alpaca teeth, this procedure may have to be repeated yearly.

Misalignment of molars is less common and usually involves either a more serious facial defect, such as wry face, or distortion due to a chronic tooth root abscess. Correction is difficult in any case, and is probably only necessary if there is firm evidence of dropping feed out of the mouth or trauma to the tongue or cheeks. Correction is through filing or grinding down sharp points. Normal alpaca molars have a very irregular grinding surface, so points should be ground down only if there is associated trauma to the soft tissue of the mouth.

Colic

Colic is the general term given to abdominal discomfort, and may arise through problems with the liver, urinary tract, pancreas, reproductive tract, peritoneal lining, or digestive tract.[3] Alpacas tend to show colic by lying down in an unusual posture (on one side or upright with one or more pairs of legs sticking out to the side), appearing restless (not maintaining a posture for more than 5 minutes at a time), lying down quickly in spite of adequate strength to stand, or maintaining the "elimination stance" (squatting to urinate and defecate) longer or more frequently than normal.[2] In most cases, they will also have decreased appetite and fecal passage.

Alpacas suspected of having colic should be observed carefully. Many, particularly late-pregnant females, will have transient episodes that last less than an hour. Unless these occur repeatedly over the course of a day or two, they can usually be ignored. Veterinary examination should be considered for alpacas that have episodes lasting longer than an hour, have multiple serious episodes in one day, or have repeated bouts over several days.

The major digestive causes of colic are an intestinal blockage, twist, or irritation. Transient gas colic, like that occurring in horses, is rare in alpacas beyond the nursing period. Blockages are indicated by the eventual (over 3 to 5 days) cessation of fecal passage and progressive abdominal distention. Causes are listed in the previous discussion of intestinal blockages. Twists progress much more quickly (within 1 day) and the alpacas are generally notably in pain. Irritation is often marked by diarrhea. Fermentation of milk may lead to gas colic and abdominal distention in crias. Note that ulcers are not included on the list of digestive causes of colic. Contrary to popular belief, there is minimal evidence that camelids with nonruptured gastric ulcers show signs of colic.

The major nondigestive causes of colic are uterine torsion or other fetal malpositions in late-pregnant females,[6] bladder or urethral stones in males (more straining than other signs of colic), or infections within the abdomen (al-paca fever, navel infections, or ruptured gut). Fatty liver, liver flukes, inflammation of the pancreas, abdominal tumors or abscesses, and kidney infections or stones are less common. The myriad possibilities as well as the severity of some of the individual diseases bespeak the need for careful assessment by a veterinarian. For transient mild colic, an assessment may consist of no more than the observation of eating and elimination behavior, and the general impression that the alpaca is bright. For more persistent or violent colic, the assessment may need to extend to a complete physical examination, ultrasonographic evaluation, analysis of blood or other body fluid samples, and even exploratory surgery. In general, alpacas assessed early in the course of their disease by a veterinarian are more likely to have their discomfort alleviated.

Diarrhea

Being adapted for harsh, dry conditions, all camelid species have the capacity to extract most water from their feed. Thus their feces are dry and pelleted. Disorders that cause diarrhea in species with a simpler gut result in no fecal abnormality in camelids. This leads to a high level of concern when alpacas actually develop diarrhea.

Diarrhea results from oversecretion of fluid from the gut, underabsorption of fluid, undigested or undigestible feed, or leakage of blood or blood proteins. Oversecretion has not specifically been identified in alpacas. Underabsorption may occur due to overingestion of fluid, mainly in the form of lush pasture (benign) or damage to the intestinal lining. The most common causes of damage are parasites, bacteria, viruses, and chemical irritants.[5,7] Because of the nature of the alpaca gut, all of these are most likely to cause diarrhea if they affect the colon versus the stomach or small intestine. For example, whipworms, "regular" coccidia, coronavirus, and in crias, *Giardia* and *Cryptosporidia*, are more likely to cause diarrhea than stomach worms and *Eimeria macusaniensis*.

Identification of whipworms and coccidia may be done by normal fecal flotation, though centrifugation techniques may be necessary to find whipworm eggs when they are present only in small numbers. Identifying coronavirus, *Cryptosporidia*, and *Giardia* may require the services of a diagnostic laboratory. It is rare for specific bacteria (*Salmonella*, *E. coli*, *Clostridia*) to cause diarrhea in alpacas, although *Clostridia* may have regional "hot spots." Since most chemical irritants originate in the diet or stomach, they must cause considerable gastrointestinal damage before they cause diarrhea. Among the culprits are the previously mentioned caustic plants and the acid formed on high grain or sugar diets.

Treatment of parasitic enteritis depends on the severity and also the specific parasite involved. The different classes of parasite respond to different medications, so identification is important. Coronavirus and bacterial enteritis are most dangerous when they damage the gut lining enough to allow gut bacteria into the blood. Fluid and electrolyte loss can also be significant and should be addressed with oral or intravenous fluids. Antibiotics may also be useful to treat primary and secondary infections.

Undigested or undigestible feed particles draw water into the bowel and soften the feces. This is more likely to result in poorly formed, clumped pellets than outright diarrhea. Undigested feed may pass through the digestive tract in alpacas that are sick for another reason and have lost their population of gastric microbes or suffered damage to the lining of the gut. Such diarrhea is not likely to be profuse or significant, and correcting the underlying problem is the best approach to resolving the diarrhea.

Transfaunation of stomach microbes from healthy alpacas or ruminants may speed recovery. Probiotics are a poorer substitute, but may have some benefit. Undigestible feed is most common in crias, who begin to eat forage before they fully form their fermentative digestive system. Poor fibrous forage containing strawlike material or seed husks can defy fermentation even in adults. Provided the alpacas receive adequate nutrition, the resulting soft feces are unlikely to be deleterious.

Alpacas fed high-grain or sugar-rich diets are occasionally prone to bouts of diarrhea, most likely due to a die-off of the normal stomach microbes, chemical injury to the lining of the gut, and the intestinal formation of lactate, which is poorly absorbed. The definition of "high grain" is subjective. Guidelines for feeding grain are given in Chapter 9. Suffice it to say that alpacas have relatively delicate guts in this regard compared to sheep or cattle.

Leakage of blood or blood protein into the bowel is possibly the most severe cause of diarrhea, because it represents a higher level of gut damage than the other forms. The underlying causes are similar: parasitic, microbial, or chemical injury. Generally, the alpaca is sicker, with possible signs including fever, weight loss, inappetence, weakness, and recumbency. Diagnostic evaluation, including fecal analysis and possible blood culture, may reveal the cause of the problem and the likelihood that it is an individual animal problem or possibly of herd significance. Affected alpacas may respond to treatment, but the level of care required is often considerably more than with the other causes of diarrhea.

Straining to Defecate

Straining to defecate (tenesmus) is an uncommon finding in alpacas, and should be differentiated from straining to urinate (stranguria). Because alpacas perform their elimination functions simultaneously, careful observation is necessary to tell the two disorders apart. Straining to defecate usually reflects irritation or blockage of the hind portions of the digestive tract. Causes for irritation include whipworms, coccidia, and rarely coronavirus or inflammation of the gut lining. Straining in those cases usually results in the passage of diarrhea.

Causes for obstruction include birth defects in crias, meconium impaction in crias, fecal impaction in any age of alpaca, and compression of the gut by an abscess, hematoma, or tumor. The most common birth defect leading to straining is atresia ani or lack of an anus.[10] This defect can usually be detected simply by looking under the tail. Some affected female crias will pass feces through a communication with the vagina, but most require some form of surgical repair within the first few days of life. Atresia ani is commonly linked with other defects of the pelvic bones or urogenital tract, and may be heritable in alpacas, although heritability has not been established in this species.

Blockages lead to straining without the passage of feces. Meconium impaction is relatively infrequent in alpaca crias compared to foals. Affected crias frequently posture to defecate, grunt and strain, and occasionally show more severe colic signs. The impaction can usually be managed by administering gentle soapy-water enemas. However, if the impaction lasts longer than one day, the cria's nursing behavior is inhibited by pain, or abdominal distention develops, more intensive treatments, such as intravenous fluids and pain medication, may be necessary.

Similar signs may be due to constipation in older crias fed goat's milk, or in camelids of any age due to feed impactions. Weaning crias are also prone to develop impactions if they ingest each other's fiber. Feed and fiber impactions may be managed similarly to meconium impactions, but if they are not resolved relatively quickly (within a day, at most), more intensive interventions should be considered. In my experience, most feed impactions are resolved within a few hours if they are going to respond to conservative treatment. The majority require veterinary intervention that may extend to surgical exploration.

Partial obstruction due to compression of the bowel is an infrequent finding. The most common causes are pelvic hematomas or abscesses due to breeding or birthing trauma in females. Lymph node abscesses due to alpaca fever, tumors, and shrinkage of the hole created after surgery for atresia ani are also possibilities. Affected alpacas will develop intermittent, partial obstructions with signs that wax and wane. Palpation, ultrasonography, radiography, or exploratory surgery may be necessary to diagnose the problem.

OTHER DIGESTIVE DISORDERS

Many of the most important or best-known digestive disorders of alpacas do not lead to specific digestive tract signs. This does not make them any less serious, only more difficult to diagnose. Among the most important disorders on the list are ulcers, grain overload, and endoparasitism. Other diseases of importance include clostridial infections and Johne's disease.

Gastric Ulcers

Gastric ulcers are one of the best-known disorders of alpacas and also one of the most frustrating for owners and veterinarians. Ulcers, which are deep erosions of the lining of the stomach or intestine, are usually clinically silent until they catastrophically rupture. Reports of colic signs, inappetence, or tenderness to abdominal palpation prior to rupture are probably unfounded. Blood changes are equally unreliable. Unfortunately, that means there are no good criteria for assessing which alpacas could be treated in the early stages of the disease when treatment would theoretically be most efficacious. To compound this problem, there are no good oral medications for the treatment of ulcers: every single oral anti-ulcer medication tested (duration of action <1 hour for cimetidine and ranitidine; no change with either the human or equine preparations of omeprazole)[9,11,12,14] in camelids has been shown to be ineffective. Intravenous omeprazole has shown more promise,[14] but is not widely available. Gastric protectants such as sucralfate or bismuth subsalicylate are very difficult to assess experimentally, so it is unknown whether they help or not.

Once ulcers rupture, the abdomen becomes contaminated with bacteria and feed material, and the alpaca is effectively beyond the reach of curative treatment. Clinical signs appear abruptly (anorexia, lethargy, recumbency, possible fever, blood work changes). The usual history is that an alpaca that looked completely healthy the day before now refuses to rise or eat, and appears to be in distress. These signs resemble other severe diseases, including systemic bacterial infections and various poisonings, so veterinary assessment is still required to make a firm diagnosis. Ruptured ulcers account for about 3 to 6 percent of all adult alpaca deaths. Mini outbreaks are not uncommon. Because of the severity of this disorder, the ideal strategy is to prevent ulcers or treat them before they rupture, but again, we are left trying to guess which alpacas have ulcers and with no proven medication.

A legion of theories has been presented on why camelids get ulcers. The bulk of this material is extrapolation and of questionable pertinence. Only one scientific study has been conducted investigating why ulcers might occur in camelids.[8] That study, although not in any way de-

finitive, suggests that ulcers may form in an alpaca whose stomach empties poorly into the intestine. This at least gives some framework for prevention and determining at-risk alpacas. A poorly emptying stomach retains its acid, which may cause chemical injury to its lining. While little is known about gastric emptying in camelids, here some extrapolation from other species may be useful. The herbivore stomach usually empties in response to moderate distention, moderate amounts of fermentation products, and adequate plant fiber. A decrease or increase of any of these factors outside of the beneficial range will inhibit emptying.

Ruptured ulcers occur most commonly in breeding alpacas—either in males who are in a competitive environment or in females who are transported for breeding. Ruptured ulcers also occur in alpacas newly introduced into a herd, weanlings grouped together for the first time, and alpacas feeding on fresh, lush pasture. Overcrowding exacerbates any stressful situation, and the adjustment period during the establishment of the group hierarchy is the most dangerous time. In many of these situations, it is likely that feed intake decreases, hence decreasing distention, the amount of fermentation products, and the amount of plant fiber. Stress or anxiety, while harder to measure, may also contribute to the reduction in gastric emptying. On the other side of the coin, higher carbohydrate feeds such as lush grass, cereal grains, and sugar supplements may increase gastric acidity and decrease fiber content enough to inhibit gastric emptying. Given this, the simplest strategy to prevent ulcers may be to maintain alpacas on a diet that is high in roughage and low in soluble carbohydrate, and also to make sure that alpacas exposed to stressful environments such as competitive breeding, transport, and introduction to new herds are allowed rest periods and time to adapt gradually to a new environment.

Grain Overload

Already mentioned in the previous discussion on diarrhea, grain overload is the result of overingestion of grain or sugar-containing feeds. The carbohydrate in those feeds is rapidly fermented to acids in the stomach, and these acids damage the lining of the stomach, are absorbed to alter blood pH, allow stomach microorganisms into the blood, and leave unabsorbed particles in the bowel to cause diarrhea. Severity depends on the type and amount of feed ingested. Large amounts at one time lead to acute grain overload, whereas smaller amounts lead to subacute or chronic grain overload.

Acute grain overload is an immediately life-threatening condition.[5] It usually results from accidental overingestion: alpacas gain access to the feed room, a novice overfeeds grain, or a few greedy or dominant alpacas eat grain put out for an entire group. The signs are more neurologic than digestive: a wobbly gait, weakness, recumbency, head tremors, and the head arching over the back. Some degree of fluid distention of the stomach may be present, and over the first two days the alpaca may develop diarrhea. Diagnosis can be made by gaining a history of access to grain or measuring the stomach pH. Other blood tests may be suggestive. Treatment involves intravenous or oral alkalinizing fluids to correct the pH imbalance. Antibiotics, antiinflammatory drugs, and thiamine are useful adjuncts.

Subacute or chronic grain overload is less severe, and more likely to lead to diarrhea and weight loss than to neurologic signs. The history is similar, though occasionally as simple as a skinny alpaca fed additional grain to improve its condition. Definitive diagnosis is by determining stomach pH. Treatment follows the same guidelines as acute grain overload, but may frequently be less intensive.

These disorders are better prevented than treated. When formulating rations for alpacas, it is best to remember that they are not adapted and appear to have poor adaptability to high-carbohydrate rations. When feeding grain to groups, it is best to assure that there is enough feeder space and space between feeders so that all alpacas get relatively equal shares.

Endoparasitism

Endoparasites are covered in detail elsewhere in this text. The most important digestive parasites are stomach worms, intestinal worms, and coccidia. Crias are additionally confronted by *Giardia* and *Cryptosporidia*. Liver flukes are somewhat different, in that they move from the bowel into the liver, where they cause their principal damage.

Except in neonates, most internal parasites can cause severe gut damage before diarrhea develops. The most common signs of endoparasitism are weight loss or lack of weight gain, poor body condition, weakness, and lethargy. The most common blood abnormalities are anemia and loss of blood proteins. Diagnosis involves fecal analysis. For most of the stomach and intestinal worms and regular coccidia, the standard float test works well. For some specific parasites, namely *Nematodirus battus*, *Eimeria macusaniensis* (the large coccidia called E. mac or Big mac), and *Trichuris* (whipworms), small numbers of eggs may be present, so centrifugation techniques may be necessary to demonstrate the presence of the parasite. For almost all of them, but particularly *E. macusaniensis*, signs of disease may precede the shedding of eggs in the feces, so repeating negative fecal exams 7 to 10 days later may be necessary to confirm the parasite.

These parasites damage the gut lining, impairing the absorption of nutrients and possibly leading to loss of protein and blood. Generally, the more that are present, the worse the damage will be, but it is also true that the younger stages tend to be more damaging than the adult ones. Therefore, reduction of adult parasite loads and reduction of new infestations are important in preventing disease. Most parasites can be tolerated at low levels, and it is also thought that exposure to small amounts may help the alpaca develop immunity, so complete obliteration of parasite infestations is rarely the goal, and even more rarely achievable. Factors that increase the danger of problems due to endoparasitism include mild, damp weather; feeding on the ground; underuse, misuse, or overuse of deworming medications; accumulation of feces; high stocking density; and high density of naive alpacas (usually youngsters). Each herd is unique and conditions may change dramatically from month to month or year to year. Thus each herd requires an individual herd health strategy to prevent loss due to endoparasitism. Periodic fecal analysis is often the best way to determine the current status of a herd.

Most parasitic problems are controlled through a combination of management and antiparasitical medications. Different medications work better against different classes of parasite, and resistance issues to certain popular dewormers are becoming widespread. Improved hygiene, lowering stocking density, and greater separation of the naive young alpacas from older herdmates may help reduce the problem.

More severely infested alpacas may require more intensive care, including fluid administration, blood or plasma transfusions, and other supportive care. Around one-third of the heavily parasitized alpacas seen at our clinic also have bacteria in the blood, and hence are treated with antibiotics.

Liver flukes are a different class of parasite with more complex life cycles involving snails and other hosts. They are regionally very important, depending mainly on the correct environment for the snail, and also on the presence of other hosts including cattle, sheep, and deer. Large liver flukes (*Fasciola hepatica*) exist almost everywhere, but regions known to be favorable include the Pacific Northwest, the Gulf Coast and southern Mississippi River valley, and southern Florida in North America; the southeastern coastal and irrigated regions in Australia, including most of Victoria, the eastern third of Tasmania, and New South Wales within about 175 km of the ocean; and the western side of Great Britain. Smaller pockets are found almost anywhere there is swampy ground with a moderate climate. The small or lancet liver fluke (*Dicrocoelium dendriticum*) is theoretically more widespread, because its intermediate host is a land snail instead of an aquatic snail. To date, it has been identified as a serious health threat to alpacas only in central Europe.

Liver flukes damage the liver and bile ducts. As with other parasites, small numbers are tolerated but large numbers lead to sufficient tissue damage to result in clinical disease. The major signs are weight loss and weakness. Lab abnormalities include anemia and loss of blood proteins. Additionally, blood tests may reveal evidence of liver damage. The parasite is best identified on fecal sediment analysis. Fluke eggs do not float in conventional solutions. Some antiparasiticals have efficacy against flukes, and there are certain medications designed especially for fluke control. Additionally, snail control through drainage or fencing off of wet zones, introduction of snail predators (fowl), or application of molluscicides may be helpful.

Clostridial Infections

Clostridium perfringens is handled separately in this text. It is an important bacterium under some conditions, but also has the potential to be afforded more importance than is warranted. *Clostridia* are often present in the healthy gut, and multiply under favorable conditions, which in other species usually reflect slow gut transit and highly soluble carbohydrate (see ulcers and grain overload, previously discussed). *Clostridia* secrete powerful toxins that destroy the lining of the gut and blood vessels. However, they also have a tendency to overgrow once the gut is damaged, or indeed, the alpaca is dead. Thus, finding *Clostridium* postmortem does not necessarily indicate that it was the cause of death—a common way its importance is overestimated.

Clostridium perfringens has several subtypes. Type A is reported to be a cause of fatal gastritis, mainly in crias (and also piglets, calves, horses, and a variety of other species). Type C is an important cause of fatal gastroenteritis in young lambs, and type D is an important cause of fatal gastroenteritis and neurologic disease in somewhat older calves, kids, and lambs. Vaccines commonly recommended for use in alpacas may provide some protection against types C and D but not against type A.

Reports from South America that *Clostridium* accounts for the majority of deaths in crias have not been confirmed by investigations in North America, Australia, or Great Britain. In the United States, coronavirus, *Giardia*, and *Cryptosporidia* appear to be far more important gut pathogens, and may be required to damage the gut enough for *Clostridium* to proliferate. That being said, we can attribute a certain number of cria and adult deaths to *Clostridium*, and in some cases, *Clostridium* may kill an alpaca that might otherwise have survived an original disease. The most important syndrome we see is sudden death in crias between 1 and 5 months of age. Some show colic signs or a small amount of diarrhea shortly before death. Our most common isolates are type C, although some are type A. Crias that die after several days of diarrhea and then are found to have *Clostridium* postmortem usually have a different pathogen that caused the diarrhea (and

presumably created the favorable environment for *Clostridium*). We see a similar syndrome in adults: alpacas with severe parasitic infections or grain overload may eventually die of a clostridial infection.

In all cases, we believe early effective treatment of the first infection or infestation is the best way to eliminate clostridial disease. Vaccination may be helpful in preventing the disorders, but commercial vaccines provide no protection against type A or against some of the newly identified toxins found in type A and other types of *Clostridia*. Antibiotic coverage may be helpful in preventing clostridial proliferation in at-risk alpacas. Prevention may be achieved by general measures to protect gut health, such as good nutrition and a good parasite and infectious disease control program.

Johne's Disease

Johne's disease is another disease that has received more attention than its importance seems to warrant. The disease is caused by a *Mycobacterium* related to the tuberculosis organisms, and is best known as a cause of chronic wasting and diarrhea in cattle and to a lesser extent in sheep and goats. It has been identified in camelids in North America,[1] Australia,[13] and Europe. Alpacas probably get infected through contact with infected ruminants or ruminant products (milk or colostrum), or possibly by grazing on pastures previously grazed by infected ruminants. The organism is very hardy and can survive in the environment for years.

Johne's disease predominantly presents as a wasting disease, with diarrhea in the last stages. Other differentials for wasting, including endoparasitism, ruptured gastric ulcers, cancer, and chronic infections, should be considered, as they are all more common than Johne's disease. Diagnosis is by culture of the feces and blood testing with the caveats that the fecal culture takes several months and serologic tests are not particularly reliable in alpacas. Most diagnoses are made postmortem. The disease is generally believed to be untreatable and infections are believed to be lifelong. The risk to the rest of the herd of maintaining an infected alpaca on the property should be considered before beginning a treatment course.

REFERENCES

1. Belknap, E. B., D. M. Getzy, and L. W. Johnson, et al.: *Mycobacterium Paratuberculosis* Infection in Two Llamas. *Journal of the American Veterinary Medical Association* 204 (11): 1805–1808, 1994.
2. Cebra, C. K., and M. L. Cebra: Assessment of Colic in New World Camelids. *Journal of Camelid Practical Research* 6: 171–176, 1999.

3. Cebra, C. K., and M. L. Cebra: Gastrointestinal Causes of Colic in New World Camelids. *Journal of Camelid Practical Research* 6: 171–176, 1999.

4. Cebra, M. L., C. K. Cebra, and F. B. Garry: Tooth Root Abscesses in 23 New World Camelids (1972–1993). *Journal of the American Veterinary Medical Association* 209: 819–822, 1996.

5. Cebra, C. K., M. L. Cebra, and F. B. Garry, et al.: Forestomach Acidosis in Six New World Camelids. *Journal of the American Veterinary Medical Association* 208: 901–904, 1996.

6. Cebra, C. K., M. L. Cebra, and F. B. Garry, et al.: Surgical and Nonsurgical Correction of Uterine Torsion in New World Camelids: 20 Cases (1990–1996). *Journal of the American Veterinary Medical Association* 211: 600–602, 1997.

7. Cebra, C.K., D. E. Mattson, and R. J. Baker, et al.: Potential Pathogens in Diarrhea from Unweaned Llamas and Alpacas. *Journal of the American Veterinary Medical Association* 223: 1806–1808, 2003.

8. Cebra, C. K., S. J. Tornquist, and R. J. Bildfell, et al.: Bile Acids in Gastric Fluids from Llamas and Alpacas with and without Ulcers. *Journal of Veterinary Internal Medicine* 17: 567–570, 2003.

9. Christensen, J. M., T. Limsakun, and B. B. Smith, et al.: Pharmacokinetics and Pharmacodynamics of Antiulcer Agents in the Llama. *Journal of Veterinary Pharmacology Therapeutics* 24: 23–33, 2001.

10. Del Campo, C.H., L. Vits, and M. R. Del Campo, et al.: A Case of Atresia Ani with Rectovestibular Fistulae in an Alpaca (*L. pacos*). *Deutsche Tierarztliche Wochenschrift* 100: 495–497, 1993.

11. Drew, M. L., E. Ramsay, and M. E. Fowler, et al.: Effect of Flunixin meglumine and Cimetidine hydrochloride on the pH in the Third Compartment of the Stomach of Llamas. *Journal of the American Veterinary Medical Association* 201: 1559–1563, 1992.

12. Poulsen, K. P., G. W. Smith, and J. L. Davis, et al.: Bioavailability and Pharmacokinetics of Oral Omeprazole in Llamas. *Journal of Veterinary Internal Medicine* 19: 412, 2005.

13. Ridge, S. E., J. T. Harkin, and R. T. Badman, et al.: Johne's Disease in Alpacas (*Lama pacos*) in Australia. *Australian Veterinary Journal* 72 (4): 150–153, 1995.

14. Smith, B. B., E. G. Pearson, and K. I. Timm: Third Compartment Ulcers in the Llama. *Veterinary Clinics of North America Food Animal Practice* 10: 319–330, 1994.

15. Watrous, B. J., E. G. Pearson, and B. B. Smith, et al.: Megaesophagus in 15 Llamas: A Retrospective Study (1985–1993). *Journal of Veterinary Internal Medicine* 9: 92-99, 1995.

FATTY LIVER DISEASE (HEPATIC LIPIDOSIS)

Christopher K. Cebra, VMD, MA, MS, DACVIM

Most alpaca owners will first encounter hepatic lipidosis as the cause of death on a postmortem report. This usually raises more questions than it answers, as hepatic lipidosis (fatty liver) in New World camelids is a complex, poorly understood disorder. Our understanding is additionally hampered by the well-known but only distantly related condition of the same name in sheep, goats, and cattle, and attempts to equate the camelid condition with the ruminant condition are not likely to be helpful. The ruminant condition is essentially a mathematic imbalance: insufficient dietary energy to meet demands in early lactation or late pregnancy, commonly referred to as "negative energy balance," whereas the camelid condition strikes all ages and genders, herds or individuals, often in the face of adequate nutrition.[6]

As best we understand it, hepatic lipidosis in camelids usually results from a collapse of the camelid's ability to mobilize its body stores of energy, process them in the liver, and deliver them to other cells around the body. The cause of the collapse varies. In rare cases, it is due simply to not eating enough energy, especially in pregnant or lactating camelids that have a higher energy demand—this approximates the ruminant disorder. More frequently, the condition develops in camelids that are already suffering from severe endoparasitism, stress of some kind, or inadequate dietary protein. Causes of stress include extreme weather, dominance interactions with herdmates, overcrowding, transport, dysmaturity, and a variety of other poorly understood factors. Stressors may act in different ways, but the end result is that fat builds up in the liver, and if the condition is not recognized in a timely fashion, the liver fails and the alpaca dies.

NUMBERS

We have seen hepatic lipidosis in camelids ranging from 2 days to 15 years of age. Camelids with a definitive diagnosis (liver tissue collected by biopsy or postmortem) account for only 4 percent of our camelid hospital and postmortem submissions;[5] but we see a far greater number with a prelipidosis syndrome diagnosed by blood tests that we believe would progress to fatty liver if left untreated, or with undiagnosed lipidosis, because we tend not to perform liver biopsies on many critical patients. Adding the undiagnosed and at-risk camelids means that probably closer to 15 percent of our camelid patients are treated therapeutically or prophylactically for hepatic lipidosis.

Twelve percent of live-born crias that died and were examined postmortem at our facility had hepatic lipidosis, reinforcing the finding that this disorder is found in all ages.

DEVELOPMENT OF HEPATIC LIPIDOSIS

Under most conditions, camelids are extremely hardy and are able to survive extreme conditions. They digest their food efficiently and appear to seek out the most nutritious feeds on a pasture. They are also particularly adapted to intermittent starvation. In one trial we performed at Oregon State University, llama geldings were fed approximately one-sixth of their calculated requirement for three weeks.[3] They showed no outward signs of illness or liver fat accumulation and lost on average less than 5 percent of their body weight, which they regained within a few days of restoring normal amounts of feed. When a similar protocol was used on pregnant or lactating females, which presumably had even higher dietary demands, only half of them developed hepatic lipidosis.[5]

Potentially linked with their survival in harsh environments, camelids have developed certain "diabetic" traits.[1,4] They make little of the hormone insulin and are prone to get high blood sugars when stressed or excited. These traits are of little consequence in healthy camelids, because their digestive system and diet effectively prevent them from overloading themselves with sugar, although diabetic traits may relate to the occurrence of obesity in camelids exposed to a constant rich diet.

In addition to lowering blood sugar, insulin plays an important role in regulating body fat and utilizing protein. Again, healthy camelids have systems that take care of these issues. Low levels of insulin production may become important under two sets of circumstances: conditions that further lower insulin production and counteractive conditions that overwhelm insulin's capacity to lower blood sugar and regulate body fats and proteins.

Conditions that further lower insulin production are varied and hard to prove. Insulin is made by the pancreas, but primary diseases of the alpaca pancreas are extremely rare. Insulin is a protein hormone, meaning that its production may be impaired in camelids with low blood protein or on protein-deficient diets. Conditions that reduce blood protein include internal and external parasitism, gastrointestinal bleeding (ulcers, tumors, enteritis, and inflammatory bowel disease), liver or kidney disease, tumors, malnutrition, and anorexia, among others. Lack of certain specific amino acids, hormones from the gastrointestinal tract, or activity of the autonomic nervous system may also decrease insulin secretion.

Counteractive conditions that overwhelm insulin's capacity to lower blood sugar and regulate body fats and pro-

teins may also be factors. Here is where camelids' uniqueness plays an important role: many other species make ample insulin to avoid this effect, but the balance between insulin and its antagonists is much more precarious in camelids, and camelids do not have the capacity to increase insulin production on the scale that other animals can. Thus, factors that promote the production of insulin antagonists in camelids may have a far more potent effect than they do in other species.

Our research has identified epinephrine (adrenaline) as an important insulin antagonist.[2] Epinephrine increases blood sugar, increases the mobilization of body fat stores, and potentially impedes the uptake of fat from the blood by various tissues. This may cause fat to accumulate in the liver and cause hepatic lipidosis. Because epinephrine is well recognized as a stress hormone, we believe there is a direct connection between stressful situations and hepatic lipidosis. Examples of stressful situations include pens with overcrowding or excessive dominance behavior, new environments where a camelid must establish its position in the hierarchy, pens with frequent changes of animals for the same reasons, extreme hot or cold temperatures, transport, underfeeding, orphaned crias, contact with predators, breeding competition between males, disease states, excessive handling, and doubtless other unidentified problems. These factors may affect individuals or herds, depending on the specifics, and may be fatal or merely coincidental.

Hepatic lipidosis is frequently a complication of other disorders, but it is one mechanism by which those diseases may lead to the death of the camelid. Not treating the lipidosis will negate the positive effects of other treatments, whereas treating the lipidosis may allow the camelid to recover from both lipidosis and the original disease. Thus it becomes important to recognize which camelids are at risk.

IDENTIFYING HEPATIC LIPIDOSIS

Most owners will become aware of fatty liver disease only after losing a camelid. In a sick individual, identification of the disorder might have allowed for specific treatments to be instituted. In a herd representative, the death of one camelid might herald more cases and support the need for changes in herd management.

Definitive identification involves physical and microscopic examination of a piece of liver. Liver is easy to obtain postmortem, but testing a live camelid involves taking a liver biopsy. Although generally safe, this procedure may have severe or even fatal complications, and may be unnecessary and misleading. Liver fat can accumulate in a matter of days, so a negative biopsy for lipidosis on one day does not rule out its later development.

In sick camelids, we identify the presence of hepatic

lipidosis or camelids at risk for developing it by measuring fat fractions in the blood along with blood indicators of liver dysfunction or damage.[5,6] These tests appear to be far more sensitive than the definitive liver biopsy, and also allow for earlier identification of the disorder. The most important blood fat fractions are NEFA (fat coming from fat cells and going to the liver) and beta-hydroxybutyrate (fat "mishandled" by the liver). These tests are not available at all labs, so owners and veterinarians should investigate where they can be run before a crisis hits. Testing for blood triglycerides is a routine test that may be helpful in some cases, but blood triglycerides were abnormal in only 71 percent of camelids with hepatic lipidosis in one study, and were only alarmingly abnormal in 29 percent of those cases.[5] The highest triglyceride values were often found right before death.

The most important abnormal liver blood tests are for the enzymes GGT and AST, and less reliably for alkaline phosphatase. These tests reveal abnormalities with the liver but not specifically lipidosis. Our experimental studies have revealed that increases in fat fractions occur several days prior to increases in liver enzymes, and still earlier than the actual identification of fat in the liver by biopsy.[5] Therefore, we believe that measuring fat fractions offers the best way to identify at-risk camelids *before* they develop irreversible lipidosis.

Blood sugar is usually high in affected camelids, a sign of stress, unless they are in the group of heavily lactating dams, in which case it might be low.[5,6] This increase in sugar represents a major difference between hepatic lipidosis in camelids and sheep, goats, or cattle. In those ruminants, the disorder is due to inadequate carbohydrate or energy, and hence they have low blood sugars. In camelids the disorder appears to be due to stress; hence they have high blood sugars.

Blood protein fractions also warrant inspection. Decreases in blood protein frequently accompany lipidosis, due to protein malnutrition, parasitism, or some other process, although normal blood protein concentrations do not preclude the possibility of lipidosis.

Dietary analysis may be helpful. Lack of sufficient protein or even specific amino acids appears to be more important than lack of sufficient calories in most cases. Hay should be tested, even if it is from known sources, as quality can vary from year to year. Pastures should be inspected to ensure there is adequate growth. Dry, eaten-down, or out-of-season pasture may not have much protein. I have an unproven bias toward pasture with some degree of leafy browse. In their natural environments, camelids seek out the highest-quality forage, and that may come in the form of broadleaf plants, which typically contain more protein than pasture grasses. Supplements are less important in the development and prevention of hepatic lipidosis, because they usually provide more minerals and carbohydrates than protein.

Blood tests remain the cornerstones of our identification strategy, because the main clinical signs of hepatic lipidosis are vague and nonspecific, and a liver biopsy does not identify onset of the disease in camelids. Clinical signs may include the following: affected camelids may separate themselves from the herd and lie down more than normal. They may appear dull and may not rise when approached. Retching and gurgling are occasionally described, although these signs only appear in the later stages. Affected camelids may go from a normal appearance to being dead within 24 to 48 hours. Once one camelid is affected, the herd manager must pay special attention to others in the herd, particularly in the same pen. We have dealt with outbreaks that have lasted up to 6 weeks with up to 16 camelids lost.

TREATMENT AND PREVENTION

In a herd situation, where no camelid is clinically affected but where the identification of a previous case makes the owner believe the herd might be at risk, the simplest things to do are to increase protein in the diet and to decrease stress. To achieve this, we recommend supplementing high protein forage like tested good-quality (>12% protein) grass or alfalfa hay, or leafy browse like blackberry leaves. (Blackberry leaves are also my favorite treatment for camelids with poor appetites—they will often eat blackberry leaves when they refuse all other feeds.) To decrease stress, I recommend lowering the pen density to minimize hierarchy battles, stopping transport and breeding activity, limiting introductions of new camelids to each pen, spreading feeders out or increasing their number, increasing the supply of forage, and providing facilities to deal with weather extremes. The possibility of parasitic and other diseases also needs to be addressed.

When a camelid is showing clinical signs, more aggressive treatment is warranted. The affected camelid should be removed from competitive stresses and provided with the most palatable forages. Medical treatments, including injections of insulin and solutions containing glucose and amino acids, appear to lower blood sugar and fat fractions, and may help provide energy to the cells that need it.[1,2] Many camelids will respond if these treatments can be instituted in a timely fashion, but the rapidity of death after the initial onset of signs of disease in some camelids makes the window for successful medical intervention very small.

Given the variety of triggers for hepatic lipidosis, it is impossible to make a single recommendation for prevention. Decreasing stress and providing adequate nutrition and parasite control are the cornerstones. Recognizing at-risk camelids for early intervention is another important factor. Sick camelids are often enigmatic. Some will be at risk for developing lipidosis, whereas others will not, and without comprehensive evaluation by experienced individuals with adequate facilities, it may be impossible to tell the difference. It is my belief that earlier, more specific identification of any illness and hence earlier, more specific treatment is more likely to lead to a patient's survival. This is especially true with hepatic lipidosis.

REFERENCES

1. Cebra, C. K., S. A. McKane, and S. J. Tornquist: Effects of Exogenous Insulin on Glucose Tolerance in Alpacas. *American Journal of Veterinary Research* 62: 1544–1547, 2001.
2. Cebra, C. K., and S. J. Tornquist: Effects of Epinephrine and Insulin on Blood Biochemical Constituents in Llamas and Alpacas. *American Journal of Veterinary Research* 65: 1692–1696, 2004.
3. Cebra, C. K., and S. J. Tornquist, et al.: The Effects of Feed Restriction and Amino Acid Supplementation on Glucose Tolerance in Llamas. *American Journal of Veterinary Research* 65: 996–1001, 2004.
4. Cebra, C. K., and S. J. Tornquist, et al: Glucose Tolerance Testing in Llamas and Alpacas. *American Journal of Veterinary Research* 62: 682–686, 2001.
5. Tornquist, S. J., and C. K. Cebra, et al.: Metabolic Changes and Induction of Hepatic Lipidosis during Feed Restriction in Llamas. *American Journal of Veterinary Research* 62: 1081–1087, 2001.
6. Tornquist, S. J., and R. J. Van Saun, et al.: Histologically-confirmed Hepatic Lipidosis in Llamas and Alpacas: 31 Cases (1991–1997). *Journal of the American Veterinary Medical Association* 214: 1368–1372, 1999.
7. Ueda, J., C. K. Cebra, and S. J. Tornquist: Effects of Exogenous Long-acting Insulin on Glucose Tolerance in Alpacas. *American Journal of Veterinary Research* 65: 1688–1691, 2004.

THE CAMELID EYE IN HEALTH AND DISEASE
Juliet Gionfriddo, DVM, MS

THE NORMAL CAMELID EYE

Camelid eyes are very prominent, and these large eyes are often what attracts people to keeping camelids as pets. In fact, camelid eyes are about the same size as those of cows or horses, although alpacas and llamas have much smaller heads.[4] The camelid cornea (the clear portion of the eye) is also relatively large, covering almost the entire eyelid opening so that almost no "white" (sclera) is visible. This causes the eyes to seem even more prominent.[4] Alpacas often have very long eyelashes and have three sets of tactile hairs (called vibrissae) on the upper and lower eyelids.

Camelids lack eyelid margin glands (meibomian glands).[4,5] In most other domestic mammalian species these glands produce the outer, oily layer of the tear film. Instead, camelids have a large, sebaceous (oil-producing) gland at the middle corner of the eye that makes this tear layer.[4]

The third eyelid (nictitating membrane) of the alpaca is large and functions to spread tears over the eye and wipe off debris from the surface of the cornea, like a small windshield wiper. Only the leading edge of the third eyelid may be seen in most alpacas, and this edge can be pink in color or it may be dark brown. This eyelid may protrude across the cornea in sick alpacas or in alpacas with eye disease.

The normal iris in the alpaca eye may be dark brown or golden, or nonpigmented (which makes it look blue), or it

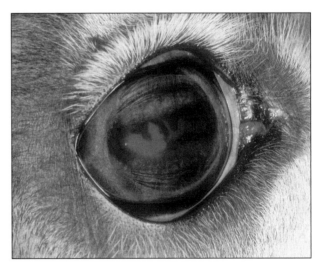

The normal eye of a camelid. The eyelashes are long, the margin of the third eyelid is unpigmented, and the iris is a two-toned brown.

may be a combination of blue and some shade of brown. The color of the iris makes no difference in the ability of the animal to see. One of the most striking features of the camelid eye is the presence of a large pupillary ruff. This structure is actually layers of folds of the tissue lining the back of the iris (the posterior iridial pigment epithelium). It is similar to, but more extensive than, the globular masses (corpora nigra) that protrude from the horse iris. The function of the pupillary ruff is to shade the pupil and thereby decrease the amount of light entering into the eye and reaching the retina, similar to a sun visor. Such shading is very important because these animals evolved in the high mountains of South America where there are few trees and little natural shade. The pupil is horizontally elliptical in shape. This shape allows for extensive pupillary closure to decrease the amount of light entering the eye in bright, sunny conditions.

The back of the camelid's eye (the fundus) lacks a tapetum.[4,5] The tapetum is the shiny, reflective area (present in many other species) that is often seen when a light is directed into the eyes. The absence of the tapetum does not affect the ability of camelids to see. Three sets of large blood vessels emerge from the optic disc (optic nerve head) of the alpaca. One large pair goes dorsally and the vessels wind around each other, and two pairs go horizontally.

DISEASES OF THE CAMELID EYE

Unfortunately, there has been little research into diseases of the camelid eye. A few papers have been published on acquired and hereditary diseases, but little is known about many of the ocular diseases to which camelids are susceptible.[5,6] Investigation into camelid eye diseases and the ability of the camelid eye to fight off disease are currently underway.

As in most other animal species that have been tested, numerous bacteria are present in the conjunctival sac (semiclear membrane lining the eye and eyelids) of most camelids.[4,5] Investigators have found both nonpathogenic (non-disease-causing) and pathogenic (disease-causing) bacteria from normal camelid eyes.[4,5] This means that even camelids with normal, noninfected eyes frequently have bacteria present that can cause disease under the proper conditions. These conditions include low immunity (such as with failure of passive transfer), high stress, or corneal trauma such as a scratch or ulcer. All eye scratches or red eyes should be checked by a veterinarian as soon as possible so that proper antibiotic therapy can be initiated and severe infection prevented.

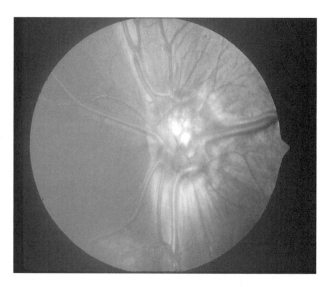

The fundus of a normal camelid. The optic disc is pinkish white and numerous large blood vessels are emanating from it. There is no tapetum in a camelid fundus.

Eyelid and Nasolacrimal Diseases

Congenital (present at birth), infectious (caused by a bacteria, virus, or parasite), and traumatic eyelid diseases occur in camelids.[4,5,6] Eyelid lacerations are not common but can be serious because of possible damage to the eye itself. Most eyelid lacerations should be sutured by a veterinarian. Congenital eyelid problems include entropion (rolling inward of the eyelids), ectropion (rolling outward of the eyelids), eyelid cysts, and ingrown hairs on the eyelids (trichiasis).[4,5,6] These eyelid problems may cause pain, tearing, squinting, and corneal ulcers due to rubbing of the eyelid hairs and lashes on the cornea. Therefore, most congenital eyelid problems should be evaluated by a veterinarian (preferably an ophthalmologist) to determine if surgical correction is needed. Since some of these problems may be genetically based, breeding of animals with congenital eyelid problems is discouraged. Infection of the eyelids may be present at the same time as bacterial skin infections.[5,6]

Nasolacrimal system (the tear drainage system of the eye) problems are common in camelids. Malformations of the holes in the eyelids that drain tears away from the eye (puncta) are the most common nasolacrimal problem.[6,14] The main problem resulting from this malformation is chronic tearing or wet face. Malformed puncta may be surgically opened or enlarged. The puncta or the duct leading from the eyelid to the nose may also be occluded by debris. This also causes excess tearing and may lead to infection of the ocular drainage system. If this occurs, the tear ducts can be opened and flushed and treated with antibiotics.

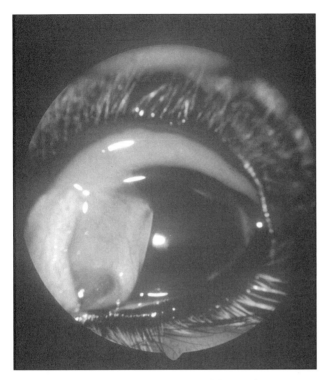

This eye of an alpaca cria is affected with bacterial conjunctivitis. The puffy conjunctiva is also red. The third eyelid is protruding, showing its motion across the globe in a horizontal plane.

Conjunctival Diseases

The conjunctiva is the semiclear, pink membrane that lines the eyelids and covers the surface of the eye, up to the cornea. Infections of the conjunctiva are common in camelids and are often caused by bacteria. Bacterial conjunctivitis (inflammation of the conjunctiva) may be secondary to infections elsewhere in the body. One cria had a bacterial infection in both nose and eye. He probably transferred this bacteria to his eye by rubbing his nose with his foreleg and then rubbing his eye. Most bacterial infections of the conjunctiva can be cleared up with appropriate antibiotic therapy. A culture of the eye should be taken to identify the bacteria causing the problem and determine the most effective antibiotic treatment.

Conjunctivitis caused by chlamydial organisms and parasites have also been reported in camelids. *Thelazia californiensis* is a tiny worm found underneath the eyelids of many animals, including camelids. This parasite is transmitted from animal to animal by flies. Its presence in the eye usually causes a mild conjunctivitis, but can lead to severe inflammation of the cornea and conjunctiva and to corneal ulcers.[2,5]

A camelid cria with a conjuntival cyst. Although rare, this condition has been reported in several crias.

Conjunctival diseases may also be caused by trauma (such as running into bushes or kicks to the eye by other animals) or foreign bodies. Congenital cysts have also been reported. Wounds of the conjunctiva generally heal very well without suturing. If the eyelid is also damaged, however, suturing is often required.

Corneal Diseases

A recent study showed that corneal ulcers (breaks in the outer layers of the cornea) are the most common problems for which llamas are presented to veterinary teaching hospitals.[6] Alpacas are also prone to corneal trauma.[7] Foreign bodies, lacerations, and infections have been reported in camelids.[4,5,6] No infectious agents are known to invade the intact cornea.[3,4,5,6] Ulcers can, however, become infected by bacteria that are normally present in the eye or by bacteria that are present on the foreign object that initiated the ulcer. Corneal trauma may also be seen in alpacas that are recumbent because of tick paralysis, meningeal worms, or prolonged illness, and particularly in newborns who are ill and unable to stand. These animals' corneas often dry out and become excoriated because of a decreased ability to blink to protect the eye and spread tears over the cornea. They may get straw, dirt, or other foreign objects in their eyes.

Treatment of corneal disease usually involves using antibiotics in the eye. The selection of the proper antibiotic is based on the type of bacteria present. Large or deep corneal lacerations or ulcers are considered emergencies, and a veterinarian or veterinary ophthalmologist should be contacted immediately after these problems are noticed. Some corneal wounds may be sutured directly. In other cases, eye-saving procedures such as corneal or conjunctival grafts may be performed.[5]

Lens Diseases

Cataracts (opacities of the lens) are the most common abnormalities of the camelid lens.[6] Many llamas have very small focal cataracts that do not cause severe visual deficits. Whether small cataracts progress to involve the whole lens and lead to complete blindness is unknown. Large cataracts in camelids, involving the entire lens, do impair vision and may cause blindness. In the past, cataract surgery was considered difficult to impossible due to the large numbers of complications associated with cataract surgery in camelids.[9] Fortunately, the success rate of cataract surgery has increased dramatically due to recent research that has led to changes in cataract surgical procedures in camelids.[1,8,12]

Although the inheritance pattern of cataracts in camelids has not been established, it is very likely that cataracts are hereditary. Because of this, no animal with cataracts should be bred. Routine eye examinations of all potential breeding camelids should be done by a veterinarian or veterinary ophthalmologist to avoid inadvertently breeding affected animals.

Diseases of the Vitreous, Retina, and Optic Nerve (Posterior Segment)

Congenital and infectious diseases of the retina, vitreous (the gel filling the back of the eye), and optic nerve of camelids have been reported.[4,5,6,10,11,13] Multiple congenital abnormalities often occur in the same eye. Documented congenital malformations of the posterior segment include colobomas (holes) in the sclera and optic nerve head, retinal maldevelopment, and retinal detachment.[4,5,6] Many of these congenital defects cause complete or partial blindness. Although many posterior segment defects are known to be hereditary in cattle and sheep, their heritability has not been established in camelids. Because of the possibility that these ocular problems are hereditary, animals with posterior segment defects should not be used in breeding programs.

There are numerous reports of chorioretinitis (inflammation of the retina and its underlying blood supply) and panuveitis (inflammation of the entire eye) in camelids, but the cause of these diseases has been established in very few cases. Dr. Murray Fowler described several camelids with ocular inflammation whose ocular problems were preceded by either respiratory or gastrointestinal disease.* The cause of the secondary eye problems was not established.

Two infectious systemic diseases have been shown to cause severe diseases of the posterior segment of the cam-

*Murray E. Fowler, DVM, personal communication, 1994.

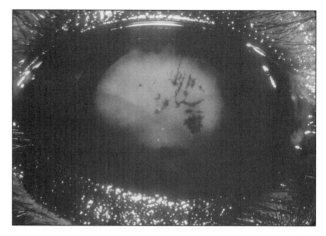

A dense cataract in a camelid. This was causing blindness and was removed successfully with surgery.

elid eye. The most well known is equine herpes virus 1 (EHV-1).[10,13] Llamas and alpacas contract this disease through contact with infected members of the horse family (including horses and zebras). EHV-1 usually produces only a mild disease in horses, but in camelids it may cause severe neurologic signs such as head tilt and paralysis. Ocular signs include rapid sideways movement of the eyes (nystagmus) and blindness due to chorioretinitis and inflammation of the optic nerve. Numerous treatments have been tried, but none has been effective and most animals become permanently blind.

Systemic fungal infections also may cause chorioretinitis in camelids.[11] A young female alpaca had signs of blindness, head tilt, and walking in circles. The alpaca stopped eating, and despite intensive treatment, her condi-

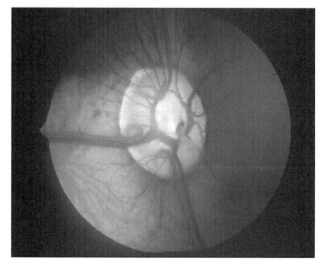

An optic-nerve coloboma in an alpaca.

tion worsened and she died. The common fungus (bread mold) *Aspergillus* was found all over the alpaca's body, including the eye.

Miscellaneous Eye Diseases

Congenital visual deficits are being diagnosed with increasing frequency in camelids. Numerous cases of blind neonatal crias were seen at Colorado State University.[5] On examination, these animals' eyes appeared normal. In each case, vision returned gradually and no cause was found.

Glaucoma (increased pressure in the eye) is rare in camelids and has been reported in only two animals.[5,6] Both of the glaucoma cases were secondary to inflammation inside the eye.

Tumors of the eye are also very rare in camelids, and only two ocular tumors have been reported at veterinary teaching hospitals in the United States and Canada.[5,6] Neither of these was squamous cell carcinoma (a common tumor found on the eyelids, cornea, and conjunctiva of humans and other animals). The rarity of ocular tumors is a very interesting aspect of llama eyes. Squamous cell carcinoma is thought to be caused by exposure to ultraviolet light. Since camelids do not seem to be susceptible to this tumor, it is possible that they developed a protective mechanism of some kind during their evolution in the high mountains of South America where there is high-intensity ultraviolet radiation and little shade. The investigation into this possible protective mechanism is underway.

DETECTING SIGNS OF OCULAR DISEASE IN ALPACAS

Most diseases of the camelid eye require diagnosis and treatment by a veterinarian or veterinary ophthalmologist, and many conditions are considered emergencies that require prompt attention. A veterinarian should be called immediately if an alpaca shows signs of rapid onset of blindness, severe squinting of the eyelid(s), severe swelling of the eyelid(s), ocular discharge that is milky or yellowish (puslike), bleeding from the eye, or whitening of the cornea (the clear windshield over the eye). Acute onset of signs such as intermittent squinting, excessive tearing (clear discharge), or slight swelling of the eyelids can sometimes be treated by the owner. However, if signs persist more than one or two days, a veterinarian should be consulted.

If the animal is tractable, the owner can examine the eye. The eyelids can be opened gently and the globe inspected for evidence of foreign bodies such as grass, twigs, parasites, and dust. If a foreign body is seen, it can be flushed from the eye using human eyewash (purchased

A prurlent (puslike) ocular discharge in an alpaca with an infected ocular system. This type of discharge should be reported to a veterinarian as soon as it is noticed.

over the counter). In no circumstances should an owner place an instrument or finger in the eye of an alpaca to remove debris, as this could damage the cornea.

No medications should be used on the eye without consulting a veterinarian. Many ophthalmic preparations contain corticosteroids. These decrease healing of corneal ulcers and could cause them to worsen to the point of ocular rupture. Antibiotic ointments are contraindicated in instances where there is a corneal perforation, and therefore should not be used arbitrarily in a red eye. The petroleum base of these ointments could enter the eye and lead to intraocular inflammation and loss of sight.

The majority of ocular diseases in alpacas can be cured if treated early and properly. Owners should quickly examine their animals' eyes daily and call a veterinarian promptly if there are any questions about the condition of the eyes.

REFERENCES

1. Andrew, S. E., D. E. Anderson, and A. M. Willis: Corneal Endothelial Cell Density, Corneal Thickness and Corneal Diameters in Normal Alpacas. *Proceedings of the 31st Annual Meeting of the American College of Veterinary Ophthalmolgists,* Montreal, Quebec, Canada, 2000.
2. Fowler, M. E.: *Medicine and Surgery of South American Camelids,* p. 391. Ames: Iowa State University Press, 1989.
3. Gelatt, K. N., G. B. Otzen Martinic, and J. L. Flaneig et al.: Results of Ophthalmic Examinations on 29 Alpacas. *Journal of the American Veterinary Medical Association* 206: 1,204–1,207, 1995.
4. Gionfriddo, J. R., and D. S. Friedman: Ophthalmology of South American Camelids: Llamas, Alpacas, Guanacos and Vicuñas. In *Current Veterinary Therapy 3: Food Animal Practice* (J. L. Howard, ed.), p. 842. Philadelphia: Saunders, 1993.

5. Gionfriddo, J. R.: Ophthalmology. In *Veterinary Clinics of North America: Food Animal Practice* 10(2) (J. L. Howard, ed.). Philadelphia: Saunders, 1994.

6. Gionfriddo, J. R., J. P. Gionfriddo, and S. G. Krohne: Ocular Diseases of Llamas: 194 Cases (1980–1993). *Journal of the American Veterinary Medical Association,* in press.

7. Gionfriddo, J. R.: Unpublished data. 1996.

8. Gionfriddo, J. R., and M. Blair: Congenital Cataracts and Persistent Hyaloid Vasculature in a Llama (*Lama glama*). *Veterinary Ophthalmology* 5: 65–70, 2002.

9. Ingram, K. A., and R. L. Sigler: Cataract Removal in a Young Llama. *Proceedings of the 1983 Annual Meeting of the American Association of Zoo Veterinarians,* Tampa, Florida, 1983.

10. Paulsen. M. E., S. Young, and J. A. Smith et al.: Bilateral Chorioretinitis, Centripetal Optic Neuritis, and Encephalitis in a Llama. *Journal of the American Veterinary Medical Association* 194: 1,305–1,308, 1989.

11. Pickett, J. P., C. P. Moore, B. A. Beehler et al.: Bilateral Chorioretinitis Secondary to Disseminated Aspergillosis in an Alpaca. *Journal of the American Veterinary Medical Association* 187: 1,241–1,243, 1985.

12. Powell, C. C., T. M. Nuhsbaum, and J. R. Gionfriddo: Aqueous Misdirection and Ciliary Block (Malignant) Glaucoma After Cataract Removal in a Llama. *Veterinary Ophthalmology* 5: 99–101, 2002.

13. Rebhun, W. C., D. H. Jenkins. R. C. Riis et al: An Epizootic of Blindness and Encephalitis Associated with a Herpesvirus Indistinguishable from Equine Herpesvirus 1 in a Herd of Alpacas and Llamas. *Journal of the American Veterinary Medical Association* 192: 953–956, 1988.

14. Sapienza, J. S., R. Isaza, D. E. Brooks et al.: Atresia of the Nasolacrimal Duct in a Llama. *Veterinary and Comparative Ophthalmology* 6: 6–8, 1996.

15. Schuh, J. C. L., J. G. Ferguson, and M. A. Fisher: Congenital Coloboma in a Llama. *Canadian Veterinary Journal* 32: 432–433, 1991.

BONE SEQUESTRATION IN GROWING ALPACAS

Denis Ryan, MVB, MRCVS

A *bone sequestrum* is a fragment of dead bone separated from adjoining sound bone. I have written the only previous report regarding bone sequestration in the long bones of young growing alpacas.[1] Between 1996 and 2002, I dealt with eight such cases and have had personal communications about many more. There have also been several cases of mandibular bone sequestration. The long-bone cases that I dealt with were either partial or full thickness. Partial-thickness sequestration involved only part of the cortex of the affected bone, whereas a full-thickness sequestrum affected the full circumference of the cortex.

There could be many reasons why bone sequestration comes about. At this point none are proven. Radiographs have been sent to me of two crias that had to have developed this condition in utero, judging by the amount of periosteal reaction around their sequestra at seven days of age. I have personally seen a case in a seven-day-old cria, which is likely to be too young for the whole process of sequestration and subsequent periosteal reaction to have occurred postnatally.

Although the periosteal reaction does occur incredibly quickly once it starts, I do not believe that the ischemic process that brings about the sequestration necessarily happens in a hurry. (*Ischemia* is localized tissue anemia due to obstruction of the inflow of arterial blood.) Yet my experience is that this problem is more often diagnosed in the neonatal period. I do not think failure of passive transfer

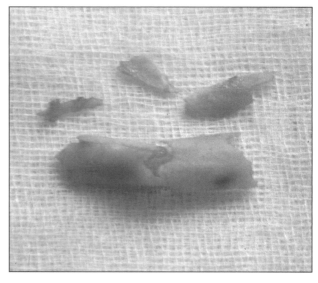

Sequestrum bone fragments are surgically removed.

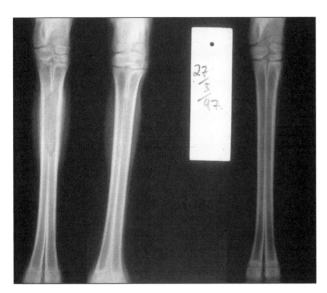

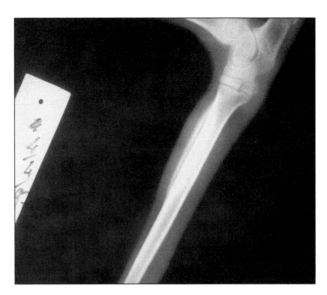

Right Day 1 (03/21/97): little change.
Center Day 6 (03/27/97): periosteal reaction and evidence of new bone.
Left Day 14 (04/04/97): marked periosteal reaction and new bone with obvious sequestrum.

The sequestrum is at the proximo-dorsal aspect of the metatarsus.

has a major role in the etiology or susceptibility, as all of the affected crias I have checked have had adequate IgG levels. I do believe that the site and perhaps the extent of sequestration either may be random in the long bones or indeed could be due to alterations in blood supply to part of that particular bone at a particular stage of the cria's or fetus's development, resulting in increased risk of blood-borne bacteria lodging at these sites.

Cases of mandibular bone sequestration have been diagnosed and treated in a similar way to the leg bone sequestra previously described. The difference is that the alpacas were two year olds. The mechanism of development of sequestration at this location in older alpacas may be due to the changes in blood flow that normally occur as a result of dental growth. Attempts to yield positive cultures from these cases have been negative. Most of these alpacas were kept in unnatural climatic conditions at a tropical location for 12 months, where the temperature and relative humidity were consistently high. Alpacas also get osteomyelitis of the mandible due to bacterial infection—these two conditions may need to be differentiated radiographically, as surgery is the preferred treatment for a sequestrum.

My personal hypothesis for the cause is that an embolism of neutrophils and bacteria lodges in the slow-moving circulation to a section of the cortical bone, resulting in a proliferative neutrophilic reaction that produces a local vascular occlusion and resultant avascular necrosis. Alpacas have proven difficult to obtain microbiological cultures

from, despite the presence of frank pus in many cases. However, in this particular disease process, the causative bacterial agent may be killed off by the cria's immune response, but the embolism results in an overreaction of the inflammatory response, damaging the blood vessel supplying the area of bone that now becomes sequestrated. Symptoms develop only later when the periosteal proliferation around the sequestrum starts to cause pain and swelling, which could be quite some time after the original bacterial insult has come and gone.

It is interesting to note that the incidence of reported umbilical infections or joint illness in the alpaca cria is relatively low. In neonates of other livestock species these are common occurrences. The preferred site for bacteremias to settle out may well be the cortical bone circulation rather than joints in this species. This condition does not occur in the South American camelid as frequently as joint illnesses in other species. I am aware of at least one case where two sites of sequestration occurred in one animal, further supporting the bacteremia theory.

I am not advocating that one should neglect to take radiographs of an acutely lame cria on day 1. Fractures from flash kicks are common, and necessary treatment would be delayed if radiographs were not performed at this point. The major point in the diagnosis of this condition is that if initial radiographs are unrewarding, repeating the procedure even as early as one week later is well worthwhile. Few clinicians would have found any describable abnormalities of the affected area in initial radiographs, but six days later there was a very different picture. So far I have personally seen sequestrations in three femurs, two metatarsals, one radius, one tibia, and one metacarpal, as well as several mandibles. It is my belief that they could occur at most long-bone locations.

When left for a period of time prior to surgical intervention, there can be much periosteal reaction. Currettage needs to be extensive over the sequestrated area and is tedious. At least two views should be taken close to the time of surgery to assist the surgeon in determining the position and depth of curretting required to expose the sequestrum. If left even longer, a discharging tract is likely to ensue.

Lastly, a word about postoperative care of wounds in crias where it has not been possible to attain primary closure or there has been wound breakdown because often very little tissue is left to work with. I have managed these cases with regular wound dressings using solosite, melolin, a gauze bandage, and one of the vet wraps. Wounds are cleaned with .01 percent iodine solutions, and due to the presence of an open medullary cavity, I give antibiotics.

Thus, bone sequestration can be successfully resolved through careful attention to radiology and surgery. Getting second radiographs may be critical to getting the diagnosis. Knowledge of up-to-date processes for maintaining anesthesia in South American camelids is advisable for the successful outcome of the prolonged surgical procedure required.[1]

REFERENCE

1. Ryan, D.: Sequestrations in the Bones of Young Alpacas. *The Alpaca Registry Journal* 2 (2): 24–29, Summer-Fall 1997.

Chapter 22

Geriatric Alpacas

Eric Hoffman

An 18-year-old alpaca
on a cold day.

Geriatrics has to do with disease and care issues associated with old age. The concept of "geriatric alpacas" is a subject that does not appear in South American literature. In South America most alpacas have been consumed as food or have succumbed to any number of ailments by the time they reach 12 years of age.

In South America alpacas are all-purpose livestock. They provide fiber, meat, and skins to those who raise them. If an animal is no longer productive, it is usually slaughtered. Harsh natural conditions, with near-total dependence on natural forage subject to periodic droughts, cull animals who are weak or unable to garner enough body fat to make it through a lean period when nutritional forage is scarce. Nature has a habit of culling the very young and the aged during a drought or other kinds of climatic extremes.*

In North America, Australia, the United Kingdom, Europe, and other "new alpaca regions," owners and veterinarians find themselves faced with a new management challenge—how to care for aged alpacas. In North America some animals are living well past 17 or even 20 years and producing offspring throughout their lifetime. The availability of good-quality forage throughout the year, consistent parasite control, and the desire of many owners

to prolong an alpaca's life past its natural productive years combine to create a subgroup of alpacas that can be categorized as either aged or geriatric.

Numerous issues are related to caring for older alpacas. Considerations include coping with conformation-related problems, breeding decisions, special nutritional and care needs, awareness of an alpaca's place in the herd hierarchy, assessing quality of life, understanding the aging process, and knowing when euthanasia is appropriate.

It's no secret that all living things age and eventually die. How to slow the aging process has obsessed people for centuries. The Spanish conquistador Ponce de Leon wandered around Florida during the sixteenth century looking for the "fountain of youth," which he believed would reverse the aging process. For his efforts, he died a premature death. In more recent times, humans have pursued different anti-aging approaches ranging from cosmetic surgery to special diets and spiritual pursuits. Still, aging happens. Rest assured, you will deal with aging and dying alpacas if you breed alpacas.

The goal of any alpaca owner should be to prolong the lives of his or her alpacas and do so in a way that maximizes an animal's period of productivity and quality of life. Indeed, an important measurement of a breeding and management program could be the number of animals that remain productive and healthy late in life. How can this be achieved?

---

*Dr. Rufino Quilla, long-time alpaca veterinarian and alpaca owner, personal communication, Juliaca, Peru, June 25, 2002.

BEST HEDGE AGAINST AGING: CAREFUL ANIMAL SELECTION

Careful selection of initial stock is the first and probably most important hedge on aging. Most alpaca owners purchase animals that become the nucleus of their breeding program. Even after the original stock has passed from the scene, the progeny and the genes they inherited from the initial herd are still there.

Expect Conformational Defects to Worsen with Age

Unfortunately, neophyte alpaca owners sometimes select animals without adequate knowledge of alpaca conformation. Alpacas with serious inherited conformational problems are likely to impact the development of a herd for many years through their offspring. Therefore, learning about alpaca conformation and avoiding animals with serious conformational flaws are important.

Alpacas with serious conformational flaws often do not survive as long as animals with good to excellent conformation. With time the weak fetlock becomes the collapsed fetlock; the severe sickle-hock becomes the swollen and crippling joint, and in general the badly aligned and stressed joint can become arthritic, resulting in pain and suffering. Breeding females with conformational flaws often experience problems due to extra body weight and the general stress of pregnancy.

Animals with good conformation are less apt to develop joint-related problems that adversely affect both quality of life and productivity. But even animals with no apparent conformational flaws may develop quality-of-life conformational weaknesses with the passage of time.[4]

Expect Fewer Crias from Females Emaciated During Lactation

Animal selection should include an assessment of the alpaca's general health and ability to maintain a healthy body condition (judged by a body score of 3). Maintaining a reasonable body condition is especially important in evaluating females. In ideal conditions a young or middle-aged alpaca should be able to produce a healthy offspring annually.

Both the chronically overweight (5 body score) and the chronically underweight alpaca (1 or barely 2 body scores) may have difficulties with aging earlier in their lives than an animal that is more capable of maintaining a healthy body condition. The chronically thin alpaca may require management that includes a longer recovery period between births and premature cessation of breeding activities. Particular females (and often their entire lineage) have difficulty maintaining a healthy body score (2 to 4),

Structural failures appear in older animals. Note the collapsing pasterns on this 17 year old.

especially while lactating. Weight loss in mothers is normal during lactation, but some females become so emaciated that they take many months after the cria is weaned to return to a healthy body condition. Poor-quality or not enough forage can cause emaciation. But if good-quality nutritional intake is sufficient and parasites are not the cause of weight loss, chances are the lactating female who becomes emaciated is a health risk over the long haul, despite the best husbandry practices.

Breeding an excessively thin animal is not a sound practice. The responsible breeder may find it necessary to lengthen the time between pregnancies to allow an emaciated female sufficient recuperation time. The female that undergoes continual radical fluctuations in body condition is operating on a thin margin and is a likely candidate for a plethora of health problems.

This female shows signs of aging as she copes with her cria. She is underweight at the beginning of lactation (note ridge along spine) and fiber regeneration in a year's time is only about 1 inch (2.54 cm). These symptoms indicate that she may not survive raising her cria.

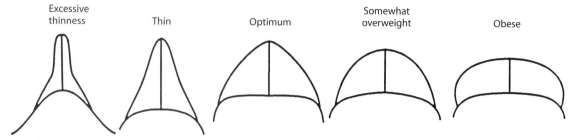

Figure 22.1 Body scoring is an important tool to assess how well an alpaca is aging. Many older alpacas have difficulty maintaining an optimum body condition. Alpacas whose body scores are below optimum may need special management considerations (see Chapter Chapter 4: Husbandry, Chapter 9: Feeding the Alpaca, and Chapter 15: On-Farm Assessment and Diagnosis).

Source: Figure first published in *The Alpaca Registry Screening Manual* by Murray Fowler, DVM, and Eric Hoffman.

EH/CAB

Assess the Condition of the Teeth

Healthy teeth are essential for processing food. The incisors act to procure the food by pressing vegetation against the upper palate and tearing it free in a subtle head-twisting motion (grazing). The grasses are then chewed by the molars at the back of the mouth, which grind the food before it is swallowed.

Alpacas with misaligned incisors that either protrude past the dental pad (overshot) or fall short (parrot mouth) are usually surprisingly capable of procuring food, despite these defects. Worn or missing teeth are a different matter. If the incisors are missing or the molars are worn, procuring food and chewing it properly may be much more difficult.

IDENTIFYING THE SIGNS OF AGING

When is an alpaca old? Aging occurs at a different rate in each animal. In general, alpacas more than 12 years of age can be considered old. Nutrition, care, climatic conditions, inheritance, number of pregnancies, and other factors all affect the rate of aging. However, some old alpacas remain healthy and can reproduce until they are 16 to 19 years of age. Individual alpacas have produced live offspring at 23 years of age.

What are the signs of aging? What changes signal significant milestones in aging? The observant alpaca owner realizes aging is usually a slow process, but eventually change is very evident. Often aging occurs in concert with other signs. Common signs of aging are listed in Table 22.1.

COPING WITH AGING

None of the aging signs in Table 22.1 means death is imminent, but indicate that an alpaca's care needs have most likely changed. If your goal is to prolong an animal's life,

you may have to formulate an individual management plan or adjust the care for that particular animal.

For example, an alpaca that suddenly or gradually finds itself at the bottom of the herd pecking order will experience more stress. Loss of status invariably means being forced from prime feeding spots and probably loss of body condition. It may also mean the animal has to spend energy defending itself and avoiding "bullies." These changes, along with difficulties in chewing food efficiently, may all coalesce into a downward spiral in general health. In social design alpacas have inherited a fairly uncompromising hierarchical herd structure from their vicuña progenitors. In this system old animals who can no longer enforce their will on others and stand their ground are pushed to the side. In times of harsh conditions they are often the first to perish.[2] Alertness to an older animal's general health can add many years to an alpaca's life.

Table 22.1 Aging alpaca checklist.

Age greater than 12 years
Inability to gain weight and maintain a bodyscore of 2, 3, or 4, or a permanent, marked drop in the normal body score
Loss of status in the herd hierarchy, often coupled with the inability to act assertively with aggressive alpacas
Worn molars or missing incisors
Difficulty (including increased slowness) in chewing food efficiently
Disorientation when forced to move rapidly
Sore or swollen joints, including intermittent lameness
Difficulty in achieving a sternal position after lying laterally
Meager regeneration of fleece after shearing
Development of cataracts
Disorientation when moved to a new enclosure
Marked drop in activity level and reluctance to stand
Difficulty or slowness in standing

The body score reveals an aged alpaca in poor condition. Peruvian Ale Revilla grasps the spine of an emaciated older alpaca, which has a body score of 1.

Providing a Supportive Environment

Once signs of aging appear, adjustments to daily care may allow the alpaca to maintain a healthy existence. First, keep track of the body score and the animal's interactions with its paddock mates. Alpacas who have lost status in the herd hierarchy and are hard-pressed to maintain an acceptable body score often do better in an enclosure with just a few mild-mannered animals. In such a setting the eating process can go on uninterrupted, at whatever pace the aged alpaca prefers. In some cases (especially in dry lot feeding), isolating an alpaca and feeding it alone is the best way to ensure proper nutrition.

The Cruel Side of Herd Hierarchies

The herd hierarchy can be cruel. Loss of status can be especially stressful if a female has a cria by her side, or in male herd groups in which the slightest weakness is often exploited by paddock mates who constantly intimidate a weaker animal.

In nature the social mechanisms that separate the old from the main group are most noticeable in times of hardship when the old are forced from a feeding area, giving the strong (and most viable reproductive group) more food and better chances for survival.[2] With alpacas the human manager can manipulate the physical and social environment in

ways that are conducive to the best possible life for an older animal.

Off-loading Unproductive Animals

As their herds age, owners must decide what to do with males who are no longer contributing to the gene pool and females who have quit producing crias or who have been taken out of a breeding program due to health considerations. The aged alpaca's coat is probably poor quality and may be mostly medullated hairs once the finer hairs have dropped away. The aged alpaca usually has little market value.

Many livestock businesses send animals such as these to slaughter. In North America and other "new alpaca countries," old animals are often sold cheaply or even given to people wanting to own an alpaca but not pay for one. This *off-loading* of unproductive animals needs to be approached with humane treatment in mind. Just finding someone who will take an unproductive animal is not enough. It is often a cruel fate that awaits the casually discarded alpaca. I am aware of off-loaded alpacas dying of starvation due to inadequate diet, dying after being fed poisonous plants, dying of thirst, being attacked and killed by dogs due to inadequate fencing, developing serious skin problems because of going unshorn, and becoming lame because their toenails were not trimmed.

Off-loading needs to include a careful assessment of the conditions the alpaca will face. In some cases providing a novice owner with an information kit about basic needs will result in adequate care. If there are serious doubts that an animal will receive adequate care, not releasing the animal is the correct course, and finding a responsible new owner is the ethical thing to do. If the animal receives inadequate care and suffers, the original owner is at least partially responsible.

Many owners simply allow old animals to live out their years without relocating them. They believe that raising alpacas includes the responsibility of caring for their animals from the moment they are born until their last breath.

Moving Old Animals

Aged animals often become very fixed in their routines. Moving them to a new enclosure (or ranch) may result in disorientation. Moving an animal on an especially hot day or during unusually cold and wet weather may be fatal. The geriatric alpaca may not find a water source or the shelter for protection from harsh weather. If an aged animal is moved into a new herd, it may have difficulties in establishing a sufficient rank in the herd pecking order. When moving an older animal, observe how it reacts and how it relates to other alpacas.

Alpacas can usually handle dry cold weather, but wet cold weather that soaks to the skin can result in hypothermia and threaten their lives. Suris are more vulnerable to this condition than huacayas.

Often sudden cold rain or wet snow falling on an unprotected older animal may end its life. Older animals require extra attention and there are ethical considerations about quality of life in their last years.

Moving an old animal sometimes brings to light aspects of aging that weren't noticed previously. For example, when an 18-year-old alpaca was moved to a pen adjacent to its usual pen, it made no attempt to locate the water source and continually stood next to the fence that separated it from its original pen. The animal held its head to one side and its ears toward the ground when it walked—which is the head position employed by blind alpacas. The alpaca's eyes were examined and cataracts were found in both eyes. The alpaca was practically blind. With eyesight failing, the animal had learned to move around its original paddock so adroitly that its deteriorating sight had gone unnoticed. In the new setting the animal could no longer function well enough to meet its most basic needs. Moving old animals requires more attention than opening a gate, releasing the animal, and walking away.

Sensitivity to Harsh Weather

Old animals of any kind are more vulnerable than young and middle-aged animals to harsh weather conditions. If the alpaca's body score is low and it was recently shorn, it will be especially vulnerable if cold and wet weather arrive unexpectedly. Older alpacas should be sheared with the animal's well-being in mind. An alpaca past 12 years of age probably has fleece of marginal value, so shearing becomes primarily a health issue. Too much or too little fleece can be harmful. After 10 to 12 years, fleece regeneration usually falls off precipitously. Many old animals are capable of regenerating only an inch (2.5 cm) or less a year. If an alpaca is being kept in a cold climate with brief summers, not shearing at all may be advisable, or shearing but leaving an inch (2.5 cm) of fleece on the animal may offer it protection for the ensuing winter. Under cold conditions it is advisable to outfit an aged animal in a lined jacket that holds in body heat and eliminates the wind-chill factor. Shelter is especially important for older animals.

Older animals can also be more susceptible to overheating during high temperatures and high humidity. Monitor the respiration rate of older animals on hot days. If an animal is stressed, cool it off with water or another cooling method. When assigning animals to various enclosures, take into consideration shade, prevailing breezes, and other environmental factors that would benefit an older animal. In especially hot weather, fairly subtle differences, such as shade and a slight breeze, can make a difference in how well an alpaca can cope with the heat.

Breeding Decisions for Old Females

Pregnancy and lactation are stressful to females; they can contribute to a female's death if she is not in good health or is excessively thin. Such deadly diseases as fatty liver disease (hepatic lipidosis) are directly related to body condition and the ability of an alpaca to sustain itself properly. Old females that are bred throughout their lives often die when they have given birth and are coping with the demands of lactation, which become more than their body can cope with.[1,3]

When is it time to quit breeding a female? Or when should the intervals between pregnancies be lengthened to allow a female sufficient time to restore her health? The alpaca breeder may find that an older female with a decent body condition plummets so rapidly in her weight loss with the commencement of lactation that the cria must be weaned early or supplemented for the health of the mother. These decisions can be difficult to make.

Some alpaca owners breed their alpacas nonstop until they literally drop dead. Other approaches are more humane and may result in longer productivity. As a general rule, if a female can no longer gain weight after a pregnancy or if lactation results in emaciation, excuse the female from her next pregnancy until she has demonstrated the ability to rejuvenate herself. In some cases an alpaca may take two years to reach a good body condition. In other cases the female may remain too thin to breed and may develop other age-related problems. Such problems as structurally compromised joints and the impact of the weight and stress of another pregnancy need to be considered. If prolonging life and humane management are goals, it may be time to retire a female from a breeding program.

Nutritional and Dental Management

Old alpacas often eat slowly and will literally have the best food eaten from around their mouths by voracious younger animals in crowded feeding areas. Low stocking levels, numerous feeding areas, and isolation from other animals during feeding are all worth considering with aged animals. In general, older animals do better on a higher protein diet. Supplements of varying kinds have also been cited by experienced breeders as helpful. See Chapter 9: Feeding the Alpaca for suggestions on the nutritional needs of geriatric alpacas.

An aging alpaca has problems masticating food because its molars are worn and no longer work efficiently. Properly functioning molars are essential for survival. After the food is swallowed it is regurgitated into the mouth, forming a cud that is chewed vigorously and returned for digestion. Depending on the condition of the molars, the degree of inefficiency in processing food may be minor or so severe that an alpaca can slowly starve due to its inability to masticate food properly.

Molars can be expected to flatten and wear with time, causing less efficient chewing. However, if molars wear unevenly and fail to mesh correctly, corrective measures, utilizing the services of a veterinarian, may be necessary to maximize the alpaca's ability to maintain sufficient food intake. Also, the pain of an abscessed molar (often first noticed by swelling or a drain at the bottom of the jaw) can adversely affect the chewing process.[4]

For the especially dedicated alpaca owner, special diets have been concocted for camelids that can no longer chew efficiently enough to consume a sufficient amount of food. Llama breeders Sally and Paul Taylor of Bozeman, Montana kept a very old stud alive whose molars were worn to the gum line by feeding the animal a gruel that it could swallow. This extended the animal's life several years.

Reluctance to Get Up

An old alpaca's reluctance to get up may be a serious symptom that something is wrong. Diagnosis should include a veterinarian, unless the breeder is very experienced. For an instant cursory field assessment the owner can do the following: Check the respiration to see if it is depressed or elevated, check the body score to see if the animal is emaciated, and take a rectal temperature to see if it is either too low or too high. When an old animal doesn't get up, there are some common scenarios.

The animal may be dying. Declining (below normal) body temperature; obvious discomfort; depressed, shallow, elevated, or labored breathing; and obvious abdominal pain may be indicators (see Chapter 16: Routine Herd Health).

Other reasons an alpaca doesn't get up are not so dire. It's common for an old alpaca to sprawl on its side to sun itself or take a dust bath, but have a great deal of trouble righting itself. Often the owner will find the animal in a sprawled position with its head and back pointing downhill, which is a much more difficult position for righting itself than an animal sprawled with its back and head facing uphill. An animal stuck in a downhill position is often a weakened, emaciated animal that simply no longer has the strength to right itself. An assessment of the animal's body score and muscle development on its upper legs will indicate how weak it may be.

For the alpaca owner finding an animal in this position, thinking the animal is near death is a common response. Most likely the animal's poor condition had existed for some time. It may be too weak to stand and its inability to right itself is the first time the owner realizes the problem. Panicking or deciding to euthanize the animal is not warranted at this point. The first thing to do is to right the animal by tucking its legs under it and rolling the animal into a sternal position. Often the animal will get up on wobbly legs, walk off, and begin eating.

If the alpaca is unable to stand, it is advisable to keep it in a sternal position until a veterinarian arrives. Place the animal against a wall or fence, placing a bale snugly against its other side to hold it in this position. Many an emaciated animal (that was neglected) has been nursed back to health to live many more years. The animal may have been in this position for quite some time, so offer it food and water. Under most circumstances, a veterinarian's guidance is warranted to successfully rehabilitate an animal in this condition.

DECIDING WHEN TO EUTHANIZE

In the 1970s I knew a veterinarian who euthanized all the guanacos in a llama herd because he believed they carried "wild blood." When I asked if he intended to euthanize all the guanacos in Argentina because they also carried wild blood, the veterinarian laughed and explained his rationale. The guanacos were running with llamas and breeding with them, which wasn't a desirable outcome for the herd's development. He explained that separating the two species with a fence wasn't a solution because, to his way of looking at things, the guanacos had no value and weren't worth feeding.

Another veterinarian suggested that a 16-year-old ema-ciated alpaca should be euthanized, reasoning it was doing poorly and was past its productive years. The alpaca in question had been in a large herd situation and was not strong enough to assert itself during feeding. The animal had trouble standing for long and was clearly weak. It also had a heavy parasite load. The owner blamed himself for the animal's condition (explaining he hadn't been monitoring his animals carefully enough) and decided to try to save the animal by feeding it in a less competitive setting and treating the parasites. Two years later the alpaca gave birth to a gorgeous female cria and went on to birth two more babies before being retired from breeding forever. At age 21 the alpaca was still enjoying life.

A third veterinarian euthanized an alpaca who was 15 years of age when he determined that the alpaca had a defective immune system—it had suffered pneumonia four times and a host of other infectious diseases in a four-year period. The alpaca was ill for more than half its life and despite numerous plasma transfers could not maintain its immune system. The animal was ill again in what appeared to be the final decline. It was emaciated, had difficulty breathing, became disoriented on a few occasions, and no longer cared to socialize with its herd.

In a fourth case, a Peruvian friend and I came upon two Quechua women dressed in elaborate festival clothes near Santa Rosa in the Peruvian higlands. The women were carefully finishing the sectioning of an alpaca's carcass that

Alpacas crowd the hay cart on a winter morning.

had been killed (cutting the throat is the usual method) and skinned within the hour. My friend had the following exchange with the two women.

"Why did you choose this alpaca?"

They smiled and looked a little puzzled. One woman answered with a laugh, "Because this one came close to our house and we needed meat."

"How old was this animal?"

"Two or three years, maybe more,"

"How long will this meat feed your family?"

"Many days, if we dry it correctly."

As the preceding scenarios illustrate, there are numerous rationales for "putting down" camelids. In one case, concern for species purity was the justification. The animals that were "put to sleep" were a species of little value to the attending veterinarian. In part, the rationale was based on ignorance and a one-dimensional value system.

In the second case, not knowing all the facts almost resulted in the termination of an animal's life before it was warranted. The veterinarian made an on-the-spot judgment based on what he saw, the age of the animal, and what he believed was a good time to end the animal's life. It turned out that the owner's sense of obligation to his animal's well-being, knowledge of the alpaca's medical history, and willingness to put forth the effort to care for the animal in an intensive manner resulted in prolonging the alpaca's life many more years.

In the third case, an alpaca was euthanized because it had suffered most of its life. Because of its chronic ailments and declining condition it would suffer the remainder of its life. Its life was ended to stop the suffering.

In the last instance, as it has been done for thousands of years in South America, an alpaca was slaughtered to feed a highland family. This animal was chosen because it was the easiest to catch.

There are a range of views on when it is appropriate to euthanize an alpaca. The first three cases illustrate three approaches: euthanizing animals that don't fit a breeding program (in South America culling means sending animals to slaughter for meat), euthanizing animals who appear to be in decline but are not terminally ill, and euthanizing alpacas who are terminally ill and suffering.

The appropriate time to end an alpaca's life is the owner's decision. Before a life is ended, it is incumbent on the owner to fully assess the reasons an animal is being considered for euthanasia. If a veterinarian is involved, he or she acts as an advisor and should be able to determine if the animal is terminally ill and suffering. The owner needs to ask if the reason the alpaca is doing poorly is a result of inattentiveness, and if the alpaca's condition can be improved by better care. Lastly, death is a natural consequence of living and its eventuality needs to be faced soberly with the animal's needs in mind. If the alpaca is terminally ill, suffering, and can no longer have a reasonable quality of life, your last decision on its behalf should be the humane one.

REFERENCES

1. Anderson, D.: Fatty Liver Disease in Alpacas. *The Alpaca Registry Journal* 3(1): 23-26, Winter-Spring 1998.
2. Hoffman, E.: The Many Ways Guanacos Talk. *The Alpaca Registry Journal* 5(1): 55-63, Spring 2000.
3. Smith, B., S. Tornquist, and R. Van Saun: Hepatic Lipidosis in the Camelid: A Different Perspective. *The Alpaca Registry Journal* 3(1): 26-29, Winter-Spring 1998.
4. Timm, K., B. Smith: Preparing for the Aged Alpaca. *The Alpaca Registry Journal* 6(1): 22-27, Spring 2001.
5. Van Saun, R.: Feeding the Pregnant Alpaca. *The Alpaca Registry Journal* 5(1): 3-11, Spring 2000.

Chapter 23

Poisons

Eric Hoffman

The rattlesnake (*Crotalus* sp.) is found throughout the United States.

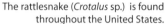

Poisons cause significant numbers of deaths in livestock every year. In the state of California, 3 to 5 percent of the livestock die annually from ingesting poisonous plants of one kind or another.[1] As alpaca populations grow, we can assume alpacas will be among the unfortunate animals who meet their demise by eating the wrong thing. Conversely, many breeds of livestock forage in pastures with some poisonous plants but do not ingest them. For the alpaca manager, avoiding poisons of all kinds is a matter of minimizing exposure through knowledge of plants and other agents in areas occupied by alpacas.

IMPORTANCE OF GOOD FORAGE

In general most kinds of livestock will not eat poisonous plants when ample good-quality forage is available. Therefore, the first rule in avoiding problems from poisonous plants is to provide enough good-quality food, so alpacas don't opt for a plant they would usually ignore.[1,3,5,8]

South America has no reported cases of poisoning, which probably means that large-scale die-offs due to ingesting toxin have not occurred. Although camelids evolved in the plant community of South America, their ability to distinguish between harmful and nonharmful plants is not a certainty. In many instances there is no knowledge of how alpacas will react when exposed to plants never before encountered. We do know that the "new alpaca countries" have had numerous incidents of alpacas eating poisonous plants and manufactured poisons.

Five Concepts for Minimizing Poisoning

Here are five concepts to keep in mind in providing healthy forage, free of poisons. The first will seem obvious: Eliminate poisons. Know the types of plants in your pastures and know the toxic plants in your area. Inspect the hay you purchase and be able to identify the plants in it. Hays containing a variety of plant types sometimes include poisonous plants.

Second, alpacas have an inclination not to eat most poisonous plants. It is common to enter paddocks that are picked bare, except for a few toxic plants such as lupine (*Lupinus* sp.) or tansy ragwort (*Senecio jacobaea*). The owner is often surprised to learn the only thing standing between a dead alpaca and a live one is an animal's innate sense that a plant is undesirable and thus refrains from eating it.

Third, never rely on an alpaca's discretionary powers to avoid poisonous plants. This is not a contradiction to concept two, but rather an acknowledgment that exceptions can be tragic and irreversible. If hunger becomes acute enough, most animals will resort to eating whatever is available. In North American rangeland environments, as much as 40 percent of the plant life can contain varieties of toxic plants. There are plenty examples of alpacas who failed to identify a poisonous plant and died as a consequence.

Fourth, make sure supplemental pellets and grains are manufactured by a reputable processor, whose products are tested and proven with camelids.

Fifth, nutritious hays will help maintain the proper level of microrganisms in the digestive tract, which strengthens the animal to cope more effectively with toxins, should they be ingested.[5] The digestive tract, with the rumen and multiple stomachs, works to degrade many poisons.

Good food is the best hedge against bad food!

Four Stories of Poisoning

An event in the High Sierra with llamas illustrates how quickly a poison can strike. Several friends and I hiked with seven llamas to a High Sierra lake. The two-day trek to the lake covered more than 25 miles and went smoothly. Upon arrival the llamas were unloaded and tied out to graze in a rich, green meadow area adjacent to a crystal-clear lake, with a backdrop of lofty, snow-patched peaks. A more pristine sight would be hard to imagine. Other than a small crudely made sign on a broken board nailed to a tree at the side of the lake, there were few traces of people. The sign carried an interesting message: "Trudge, our faithful mule, died here—1989. May Trudge's spirit bless this place."

As campsites were being staked out and tents pitched, someone noticed that one llama was foaming at the mouth and breathing rapidly. Then two other animals displayed the same symptoms. Something was wrong, but what? The animals had all arrived in good shape and immediately began grazing voraciously. The llamas were gathered up and walked to an area with no forage, so no more food could be ingested. In all, four animals were stricken. They had all been tethered in close proximity to one another, about 10 meters from the inscription about Trudge's demise.

Things didn't look good for the llamas. Rapid breathing, foam around the mouth, drooling, and a visibly weakened condition followed. Rectal temperatures were below normal. Two animals vomited. The other two animals were very still and clearly depressed. We examined the plants where they had grazed and found what looked like a small wild onion among the meadow grasses. We would later learn that the plant was death camas (*Zigadenus* sp.), which occurs throughout the mountains of the western United States, though less commonly in high meadows (*Z. venenosus*) than the foothills (*Z. paniculatus*).

Nobody knew what kind of poisoning had occurred, though all agreed the animals had ingested "something." The party had a stomach tube in the emergency kit. At the

A llama in the High Sierra recovers from eating death camas (*Zigadenus* sp.). After it began shaking and vomiting, it was "tubed" with crushed charcoal, which may have saved its life. The animal had been tethered in the "lush" pasture directly behind where it is standing. Death camas grows among common grasses, which makes it particularly dangerous.

rate the health of these previously robust animals was deteriorating, we decided to act. We ground up charcoal from the firepit, mixed it with water, and "tubed" the two sickest animals, hoping the charcoal would absorb the toxins. Two animals began shivering. The llamas were covered with blankets, and a pound of alfalfa pellets was distributed in front of each animal, should they want something to eat. Normally the pellets would have been inhaled, but the stricken animals were too sick to eat and showed signs of abdominal cramping. Mike Larrabee, owner of two of the stricken animals, and I decided to go for help (18 miles away). After walking in the dark with headlamps for 10 miles, we made contact with veterinarian Robert Pollard from a backcountry ranger's phone. Then we continued hiking and at two in the morning we met the veterinarian in a parking lot. Mike, a former Olympic gold medalist in the 400 meters, took on the task of packing in 80 pounds of alfalfa. Should the animals live, they would need high-protein food. I traveled lighter and left first, carrying what might be lifesaving medications.

After hiking all night, we staggered into camp to find that all four llamas were somewhat better off. Two were eating. One was looking as if he might start eating soon. The fourth was still visibly depressed and was reluctant to rise. This animal was visibly wobbly when it walked. The worst had passed, and only one animal appeared to still be in danger. The next morning all stricken animals were eating again, but clearly they were in a weakened state. The party stayed near the lake for two more days, allowing the llamas to eat mixtures of alfalfa and carefully selected meadow grasses. The journey back to the trailhead was a slow one. No load was put on the sickest animal. The party stopped often to let the sickest animal rest and graze. All animals recovered. Death camas poison works quickly. Luckily the llamas were stopped from eating before they had ingested a fatal dose, and the charcoal may have absorbed some of the toxins. The all-night hike to save the animals was probably unnecessary. It didn't make our sore feet feel any better to know they would have recovered without our all-night walking marathon.

Two other incidents further illustrate that poisons can pop up in unsuspected places. At a large national auction more than a dozen alpacas became ill, one or two gravely ill. It turned out that the sod used in the display stalls had been sprayed with a toxic chemical.

In a horrifying incident, a neighbor dumped garden trimmings into a pen of alpacas, and five animals lay dead two hours later. Leaves from oleander (*Nerium oleander*), the popular nonnative ornamental shrub in the western United States, were in the offerings to the animals. Unfortunately, the neighbor didn't know that an alpaca who ingests four or five oleander leaves will die of acute cardiac failure. Death due to oleander poisoning is fairly common in California.

Lastly, a large group of alpacas shipped by seagoing freighter were off-loaded and put in a warehouse that had held phosphate fertilizers. As government bureaucrats haggled over import regulations, the animals began dying.

Table 23.1 Five pointers about stock poisoning.

1. Know the possible poisonous plants in areas where your animals will be housed. Be especially vigilant when releasing alpacas into an area no alpaca has lived in before, or when alpacas are moved to a new setting. Remove questionable plants prior to alpaca occupation, NOT afterward!
2. If your paddock is along a public road or property with oleander, post warnings not to feed the alpacas garden trimmings.
3. Expect llamas/alpacas to be less discriminatory in their dietary selection when they are hungry or thirsty. Animals that are thirsty will eat plants they would otherwise avoid. This is also true with animals under stress in tight quarters without space or easy access to food.
4. Know the symptoms of poisoning and have a plan on how to cope with it. The best plan is in prevention rather than treatment, which in many cases will be futile.
5. If you are unsure about a plant, collect it (or its leaves, flower, and seed) and take it to a local arboretum, farm extension service, or other appropriate authority for identification. When in doubt, pull it out!
6. If you are transporting animals, inspect the actual conveyance (truck, trailer, etc.) and transit-holding areas (quarantine facility, warehouse, etc.) for poisons prior to occupancy.

Driven by hunger because food had not been laid out for them, many animals had ingested the fertilizer.

We should learn from the past. These examples illustrate some general guidelines on how to avoid poisoning, as listed in Table 23.1.

TYPES OF POISONS

Poisons come in many forms: insecticides, heavy metals, fungi, plants, and insect and snake venoms.

Insecticides

All forms of livestock are susceptible to some level of insecticide ingestion. Along fences and corrals, beware of sprayed insecticides of all kinds, but especially organic phosphates. Symptoms include depression, salivation, foaming at the mouth, diarrhea, and muscle spasms.

Heavy Metals

Lead, mercury, arsenic, molybdenum, and copper are elements found in long-lasting synthetic pollutants, such as paint, lubricants, and agricultural effluents. Heavy metal poisoning has been reported in humans, cattle, sheep, and horses. It is probable that camelids are also susceptible. Organs or the reproductive and birthing process are affected. Unfortunately, poisoning is not detected until a cumulative buildup affects health. Runoff and upstream sources distribute heavy metals into areas where they were not previously present.

Mycotoxins

Mycosis studies the growth of fungus and also refers to diseases from fungus growth. Mycotoxins are toxic substances produced by certain fungi, especially molds. Mycotoxins can occur in grasses eaten by alpacas. Table 23.2 lists the more common mycotoxins and their host plants.

Moldy Hays Alpaca owners will encounter moldy hays from time to time. Moldy hays should not be fed to alpacas. Some molds are harmless, others are deadly. Mold occurs in hays due to a combination of variables that include humidity, storage conditions, wetness on the hay at time of baling, plant types, and growing region. Heavy losses have occurred in cattle and sheep due to moldy hays. The sweet clovers (*Melilotus alba* and *M. officinalis*) are often associated with toxic molds affecting cattle.

Toxic Grains Contaminated grains and improperly formulated pellets, fed as supplements, have accounted for significant losses in cattle. Wheat, oat, corn, and barley grains can become infected with dangerous fungi (mycotoxins), usually due to storage conditions. *Claviceps* is one of the more common fungi associated with deaths in cattle,

Table 23.2 Mycotoxins in grasses, their host plants, and symptoms of poisoning.

Poisoning	Host Plant	Fungus	Conditions	Symptoms
Ryegrass staggers	Ryegrass (Lolium sp.)	Endophyte	Mycotoxin in plant stem	Shaking, staggering, odd head positions, wide stance; not usually fatal, but very long-lasting
Ergotism	Ryegrass and other grasses	Claviceps sp.	Wet spring, ergots replace seeds	Gangrene on extremities
Fescue poisoning	Tall fescue (Festuca arundincea)	Endophyte	Seed contaminated before planting, problem mostly in Southeast USA, not Southwest	Lameness, reproductive problems: abortion, dystocia, inhibition of milk production, prolonged gestation
Phalaris staggers	Hardinggrass (Phalaris aquatica); Reed canarygrass (Phalaris arundinacea)	Endophyte	Seasonal availability, usually early spring	Like ryegrass staggers, but often fatal

sheep, and alpacas. For more on the toxic aspects of grains (and pellet supplements), read "Eating Too Much Grain, Tainted Grain, or Pellets" at the end of the chapter.[8]

Poisonous Snakes and Insects

Venomous snakes are not a worry in the South American highlands, but poisonous snakes have killed llamas and alpacas in "new alpaca countries," such as the United States and Australia. The surest way to minimize the snake threat, even in areas they frequently occur, is to take away hiding places and food sources. This means removing any nonessential materials in or around paddocks where snakes might hide. It also means minimizing rodent populations by storing grains in rodent-proof containers and creating a "rodent-hostile" environment.

In North America In North America the rattlesnake (Crotalus sp.) is the most widespread poisonous snake, with numerous species and subspecies. Quality of habitat and availability of food determine density. The largest is the eastern diamondback (C. adamanteus). The alpaca's curiosity makes it especially vulnerable to rattlesnake bites. A rattlesnake strikes a defensive posture when it coils and warns an approaching animal by shaking its rattle. This is just the kind of thing that piques the curiosity of a young alpaca, who investigates by lowering its head to sniff and study the rattling reptile. If a bite on the nose is the outcome, the alpaca is in grave danger of dying if intervention isn't swift. Nose bites have proven to be fatal in some cases because the nostrils and windpipe swell shut and the alpaca suffocates.

North America has three other poisonous snakes, all occurring in the Southeast. The copperhead (Agkistrodon mokasen) has been responsible for killing llamas on a few occasions, even though its poison isn't as toxic as North America's other poisonous snakes. The other two are the cottonmouth (Agkistrodon piscivorus) and the coral snake (Micuroides sp.) The former lives in swamps where alpacas don't live, and the latter is so secretive that snake collectors are hard-pressed to find them. The coral snake is the most

colorful, with a black nose and yellow band around its neck followed by wide black bands, narrow yellow bands, and red bands in a repeating sequence. Neither is much of a threat to alpacas.

Two poisonous spiders reside in North America: the black widow (Latrodectus mactans, L. hesperus) and the brown recluse (Loxoceles reclusa). No poisonings have been reported, and the likelihood of serious poisoning is remote.

A host of other insects deserve mention. Wasps, bees, ants, biting flies, and mosquitoes can all be annoying or even life threatening depending on the species, its numbers, and level of aggression. The worst scenario occurs when an animal is in a small enclosure or tethered near an infestation of these insects and can't flee. In this situation a swarm attack can be lethal, due either to the suffering inflicted by the insects or to the alpaca's reaction in attempting to avoid them. Fire ants, residents of the southeastern United States, have killed livestock that can't flee and are in close proximity to an ant colony. Mosquitoes are also vectors for dangerous diseases, primarily in warmer regions.[2]

In Australia Australia is in a class by itself when it comes to poisonous anything, including snakes. Most of the poisonous snakes belong to the Elapidae family. The best known on Australia's formidable list are the tiger, brown, king brown, yellow-bellied black, red-bellied black, taipan, copperhead, and death adder. All of these snakes carry very potent venom. The taipan wins top honors for deadliest because it strikes three or four times in the blink of an eye, assuring that one of the bites will most likely deliver venom. Fortunately, it is found in tropical Queensland where few alpacas live.

In Australia's prime alpaca states of New South Wales and Victoria, the tiger (Notechis scutatus) and brown (Pseudonaja textilis) snakes are significant concerns. Mature tiger snakes are about 1 meter long and range in color from pitch black to grey with markings of broad bands of darker and lighter color. The brown snake is responsible for the greatest number of human and animal bites. It is a bold snake, brown and sleek in color, and measures up to 2

Australia has many species of poisonous snakes. The tiger snake (*Notechis scutatus*) is found throughout the primary alpaca-growing regions, along with the brown snake (*Psuedonaja textilis*). Most tiger snakes have alternating grey and black bands, although the one in the picture is entirely black.

The bracken fern (*Pteridium aquilinum*) is found in North America, Europe, and Australia. New growth is the most toxic—it is carcinogenic and can lead to convulsions and death in ruminants if they consume enough.

meters in length. Seeing a full-grown brown snake slithering quickly through grass makes most people recoil and flee. A brown snake is sometimes discovered under front porches or near watering places for livestock—it often seems undeterred by human activity.

Luckily many of Australia's poisonous snakes have small fangs and often do not discharge venom successfully when they strike. However, if they are successful, the venom attacks the nervous system and is very deadly. Paralysis starts in the rear legs and works forward. Total inability to move, swallow, or make noise precedes failure of the brain's central nervous system, resulting in death.

Australia also has the funnel web spider (*Atrax robusta*), the world's deadliest spider, whose poison rivals a tiger snake. Luckily the funnel web is a reclusive spider who spends its days hiding between rocks and tree debris. The likelihood of a bite to an alpaca is remote.[4]

Snake Poison Treatments If a rattlesnake has bitten an alpaca (usually on the face), inject antivenin and establish airflow (by use of tube or tracheotomy). The animal should be kept calm and not stimulated into fleeing and increasing its heartbeat.

With Australian snakes the correct antivenin must be administered soon after the bite to be effective, and a specific antivenin is required for the specific snake. For example, the brown, tiger, and king brown all have different antivenins. When it is not known what snake did the bit-

ing, the best chance is choosing the antivenin of the most common snake in the area.

COMMON TOXIC PLANTS

Poisonous plants have both regional and broad distributions—you will see the overlap in species around the world. Potency in poisons varies from one poisonous species to another and varies greatly in the same species at different times of the year. More detailed information and color images of poisonous plants can be located on the internet. Just enter the common plant name. Alpacas sample a wide range of plants in the plant communities they occupy. This smorgasbord approach to eating may result in sampling a toxic plant but not ingesting enough to do serious damage. Table 23.3 lists the possible symptoms of toxic poisoning from suspect plants and fungi.

In North America

Table 23.4 lists some of North America's deadliest plants, their habitats, and symptoms in animals. Some of the most common ones are discussed in more detail below.

Arrowgrass (*Triglochin maritima* and *T. palustris*) This grasslike plant has long, narrow, fleshy, rounded leaves from 6 to 18 inches (15−45 cm) tall. Arrowgrass is found

Table 23.3 Possible symptoms of toxic poisoning and suspect plants and fungi.[1,2,3,5,7,8,9]

Black locust

Gastrointestinal Symptoms

Diarrhea/Abdominal Pain	Constipation	Vomiting	Excessive Salivation
black locust	fiddleneck	azalea	arrowgrass
cocklebur	larkspur	cocklebur	azalea
death camas	nightshade	death camas	death camas
false hellebore	ragwort	false hellebore	milkweed
fiddleneck	wild tobacco	fiddleneck	nightshade
foxglove		jimsonweed	rhododendron
milkweed		milkweed	star thistle
nightshade		nightshade	St. Johnswort
oleander (bloody)		rhododendron	
ragwort		water hemlock	
water hemlock		wild tobacco	
wild tobacco			
yew			

Nervous System Symptoms

Convulsions	Coma	Loss of coordination	Dilation of pupils	Excitability
cocklebur	death camas	azalea	locoweed	arrowgrass
fitweed	greasewood	bracken fern	milkweed	bracken fern
lupine	lupine	greasewood	nightshade	chokecherrry
milkweed	poison hemlock	horsetail	poison hemlock	larkspur
nightshade	water hemlock	laurel	water hemlock	locoweed
water hemlock	yew	locoweed		lupine
wild tobacco		lupine		poison hemlock
		poison hemlock		yew
		rhododendron		
		ryegrass staggers		

Respiratory Symptoms

Slow and labored breathing	Rapid breathing
bracken fern	arrowgrass
buckeye	chokecherry
chokeberry	St. Johnswort
death camas	wild tobacco
false hellebore	
halogeton	
horsetail	
locoweed	
mushroom	
nightshade	
western chokeberry	
yew	

Reproductive Symptoms

Abortion and/or deformed offspring
death camas
false hellebore
locoweed
lupine
poison hemlock
tall fescue
western yellow pine
wild tobacco

General Symptoms

Possible selenium toxicity	Depression	Rapid heart failure	Great thirst	Fever likely	Photosensitivity
broom snakeweed	buckeye	oleander	black nightshade	bracken fern	beargrass
locoweed	death camas		jimsonweed	horsetail	buckwheat
	houndstongue			oak (new growth)	lantana
	oak				St. Johnswort
	wild tobacco				mustard
					poison oak/ivy

throughout the United States around alkaline water: coastal wetlands, mudflats, and high above the timberline, if conditions are correct. Plants are the most dangerous in the spring and fall, and are sometimes mistakenly harvested with hays. The poison dissipates with time as it dries.

Symptoms The poison in arrowgrass is hydrocyanic (prussic) acid. Death is rapid if enough is consumed. First symptoms are excessive salivation, shallow breathing, and discomfort. Convulsions, muscle tremors, and weakness in the hindquarters precedes respiratory failure and death.

Bracken Fern (*Pteridium aquilinum*) One of the most widely distributed ferns in North America, bracken fern is distinguished from other ferns with triangular-shaped fronds that occur in leaflets along stems attached to a central stem. On the underside of the fronds are brown, rough, pinhead-sized spores. The plant spreads via underground runners.

Unlike most ferns, bracken ferns are often found in recently disturbed open areas following fires or overgrazing. They often occur in large, open forests common in mountainous areas of the western United States.

Symptoms This plant must usually be consumed for a day or more to have a lasting impact. With horses symptoms occur once a horse's diet is made up of 20 percent bracken fern for a day or more. Symptoms often occur in the fall after nutritional forages have been depleted. In sheep symptoms include high temperature, blood in fecal matter, and possibly blood in nostrils. Depression and a ragged coat may be present. Death may occur in two to ten days.

Castorbean (*Ricinus communis*) A popular ornamental plant in the United States, castorbean often occurs in the wild on its own. The large lobed leaves are 3 feet (1 m) across. Small, white flowers appear on a narrow stock. The plant will grow to 15 feet (5 m) in temperate areas where it can live through the winter. The seeds are especially poisonous.

Castorbean grows best in temperate areas anywhere it is planted and thrives with plenty of water. In the wild it is found near water sources.

Symptoms Shock, diarrhea, and possibly elevated temperature.

Cocklebur (*Xanthium spinosum* and *X. strumarium*) Cockleburs are a well-known weed throughout much of the temperate United States. It has large, triangular, heart-shaped leaves, and grows to 3 feet (1 m) supported by a single stem. The plant's name comes from its brown burlike seed pods with rough coverings of hooked barbs that attach themselves to anything that brushes against them. The seed pods always come in twos.

Cockleburs thrive at lower elevations in wet or moist areas. They are sometimes the first plant to appear in an overgrazed pasture and often grow in disturbed soil such as floodplains, around water holes, or tilled soil. Consumption of young plants only a few days or weeks old causes havoc in pig populations. Seeds may germinate in the spring or late in the summer depending on the availability of water.

Symptoms In pigs, vomiting, weakness, and low temperature are preliminary signs. These will likely be followed by convulsions and a bicycle-running motion with the hind legs while the animal lies on its side. Death is often rapid, from 3 to 30 hours after first signs.

Death Camas (*Zigadenus* sp.) Death camas is especially dangerous because it is readily eaten by alpacas, llamas, and other livestock. It is a member of the lily family but looks like flowering wild grass or onion. Death camas has long green leaves with a stock in the center and yellow or white

Figure 23.1 Death camas (*Zigadenus* sp.) is grasslike with a bulbous root similar to an onion. It becomes green earlier than most plants in the spring, making it tempting for livestock of all kinds. Death camas has been implicated in the poisoning of llamas and alpacas in the western United States. Its small flowers are usually white or yellow and occur on a single stock in clusters. The flower stock can be twice as tall as the plant and the plant itself can be 30 percent taller than the drawing.

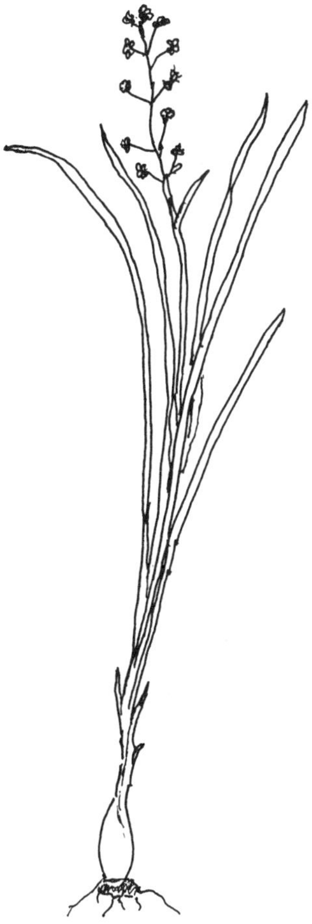

EH/CAB

Table 23.4 Some of North America's deadliest poisonous plants.[1,2,3,5,8]

Plant	Habitat	Known Animals Affected	Symptoms
Arrowgrass (*Triglochin maritima*)	Alkaline soils, marshy areas, coastal and lakesides, most of USA, S. Canada	Ruminants	Acts quickly; shortness of breath, coma
Beargrass (*Nolina texana*)	Southwest	Sheep, cattle, horses	Photosensitization
Black greasewood (*Sarcobatus vermiculatus*)	Colorado, Mojave, and other western deserts	Ruminants	Drowsiness, weakness
Black locust (*Robinia* sp.)	Throughout USA, ornamental, naturally occurring tree that puts out runners into pastures	All livestock	Diarrhea and shock
Black nightshade (*Solanum nigrum*)	Low elevations, shady and open fields, throughout USA	Ruminants, ground-eating birds	Loss of coordination, loss of appetite, great thirst
Black walnut (*Juglans nigra*)	Throughout USA, S. Canada, ornamental and commercial, toxic in fall and winter, bark most toxic	Reported mostly in horses	Loss of appetite, swelling in limbs, increased respiraton and heart rate, recovery likely
Bracken fern (*Pteridium aquilinum*)	Throughout USA, S. Canada, damp and sunny foothills	Horses, ruminants	In horses, clumsy walking, difficulty breathing. In sheep and cattle, nervousness, high temperature, death in 1 to 20 days, possible death depending on amount consumed
Broom snakeweed (*Gutierrezia sarothrae*)	Dry areas in central and western USA	All livestock	Selenium toxicity in selenium-rich soils
Buckeye (*Aesculus* sp.)	Eastern woodlands	All livestock	Breathing problems, depression, loss of appetite, coma
Buckwheat (*Fagopyrum esculentum*)	Throughout USA	Sheep, cattle	Photosensitization
Cocklebur (*Xanthium*)	Low alkaline areas, pastures along streams, throughout USA, S. Canada	Hogs, sheep, cattle	Fast acting; vomiting and muscle tremors in cattle
Death camas (*Zigadenus* sp.)	Throughout USA, but mostly plains and West, mountains to elevation of 10,000 ft, several species	Llamas, alpacas, sheep, cattle, horses	In camelids, fast acting, foaming at mouth, drooling, depression, depressed temperature, weakness, loss of appetite, abortions, death possible
False hellebore (*Veratrum* sp.)	Throughout USA and S. Canada, mountain meadows	Sheep, horses, cattle	In small amounts, depressed heartbeat, salivation, breathing difficulties
Fiddleneck (*Amsinckia* sp.)	Warm areas, can grow in crops and wind up in baled hay for livestock	Primarily affects horses, but also reported in hogs and cattle	Diarrhea, wandering aimlessly, biting self and dirt, rectal prolapse in cattle, bloody feces, liver damage, death possible
Fitweed (*Corydalis caseana*)	High areas in West, along streams	Cattle, sheep	Affects central nervous system, weakness, convulsions; when severe, death likely
Foxglove (*Digitalis purpurea*)	USA, shade, gardens, bitter tasting, eaten as last resort	All livestock	GI tract upset, possible kidney and heart damage, dizziness, abdominal pain and diarrhea
Halogeton (*Halogeton glomeratus*)	West, overgrazed or disturbed soils	Sheep very susceptible	Labored breathing, weakness, coma
Horsetail (*Equisetum* sp.)	Wet stream banks, widespread	Horses, seldom cattle and sheep	Similar symptons to bracken fern
Jimsonweed (thorn apple) (*Datura*)	Woodlands, disturbed soil, widespread in West and Southwest	Cattle, sheep, horses, probably llamas	Great thirst, convulsions, vomiting
Larkspur (*Delphinium* sp.)	Most elevations, well-drained soil, common in plains, Rockies, and California, most toxic in spring	Cattle	Constipation, weakness, trembling, possible bloating
Laurel, azalea, rhododendron (*Leucothoe, Rhododendron, Menziesia* spp.)	Ornamental plants, throughout much of N. America	Sheep, goats, llamas	Frothing, irregular walking, muscle spasms, weakness
Littleleaf horsebrush (*Tetradymia*)	Low, dry hills from Mojave Desert to central Oregon	Sheep	Poison is cumulative, weakness

Table 23.4 continued

Plant	Habitat	Known animals affected	Symptoms
Locoweed (*Astragalus* and *Oxytropis* spp.)	Dry areas throughout West	Goats, sheep, cattle, horses, hogs, and most likely camelids	Unpredictable behavior, selenium toxicity possible with some species, long-term unthriftiness, appetite for more loco weed!
Lupine (*Lupinus* sp.)	Dry areas in mountains of West, to 11,000 ft	Sheep, goats, probably camelids	Depression in sheep, trembling in cattle, with associated birth defects
Milkweed (*Asclepias* sp.)	California and other areas in the West, dry grasslands, washes, and dry ditches	Cattle, sheep, possibly camelids	Broad-leafed species: weakness, depression, diarrhea. Narrow-leafed species: convulsions, loss of coordination, grinding teeth, coma, death possible
Mountain mahogany (*Cercocarpus montanus*)	Rocky Mountains, dry slopes and tablelands	Ruminants, horses	Cyanide poisoning, mostly in fall
Mushroom (*Amanita*)	Intermediate elevations, in and around forests	Sheep, goats	Difficulty breathing, lockjaw, stupor, death
Mustard (*Brassica* sp.)	Throughout USA and S. Canada, roadsides, fields, pastures lower elevations	Ruminants	Must be consumed in large amount to be toxic; GI upset, weight loss, photosensitization, dark urine, blindness, abortion
Oak (*Quercus* sp.)	Many species in USA, new growth causes gallotanin poisoning, possibly acorns in fall	Sheep, cattle, probably camelids	Fever, depression, loss of appetite
Oleander (*Nerium oleander*)	Ornamental, popular highway and screen plant, warm parts of USA	All livestock and people	4 to 5 leaves kills an alpaca; bloody diarrhea, cardiac arrest; fast acting
Poison hemlock (*Conium maculatum*)	Throughout USA, S. Canada	All livestock	Depression, weakness, convulsions, birth defects
Ragwort (*Senecio* sp.)	Throughout USA, daisylike yellow flower, some varieties commonly found in pastures; also can be baled in hays	Horses, cattle	Symptoms almost identical to fiddleneck
Rhododendron and azalea (*Rhododendron* sp.)	USA and S. Canada, popular ornamental	All livestock	Coordination problems, vomiting, foaming at the mouth
St. Johnswort (*Hypericum*)	N. California and Northwest, open grasslands to 5,000 ft	Sheep, goats, cattle	Skin blisters, rapid breathing, salivation
Sorghum (in wild form Johnsongrass) (*Sorghum halepense* [wild]; *Sorghum vulgare* [commercial crop])	Most of USA	All livestock	Cyanide poisoning, even after dried
Stagger grass (*Amianthium muscaetoxicum*)	Eastern USA	Cattle, sheep, possibly camelids	Alkaloid poisoning
Star thistle (*Centaurea solstitialis*)	Throughout USA	Horses (must be consumed in large amounts, probably too thorny for camelids)	Inability to work mouth, death by starvation and dehydration, convulsions
Tobacco (wild) (*Nicotiana attenuata*)	Southwest and dry areas in West	Cattle, sheep, rabbits	Depression, breathing irregularities, abdominal pain
Water hemlock (*Cicuta*)	Western USA, damp areas	Cattle, sheep, probably llamas	Violent convulsions, severe abdominal pain
Western chokecherry (*Prunus*)	Throughout USA in canyons, woodlands, mountains	Cattle and sheep	Fast acting, difficulty breathing, spasms, coma
Western sneezeweed (*Helenium* sp.)	Rockies and Sierras to 11,000 ft, most potent in spring	Sheep, cattle, horses	Cumulative poison, weight loss, low energy
White ragweed (*Ambrosia tomentosa*)	Dry hills, Southwest	Cattle, sheep	Nitrate poisoning
White snakeroot (*Eupatorium rugosum*)	Eastern USA, woods, cleared areas, good soil	Sheep, cattle, horses	Respiratory problems, shaking, death
Western yellow pine (*Pinus ponderosa*)	Western mountain areas	Cattle, buffalo, alpacas, llamas	Probable cause of abortions
Yew (*Taxus* sp.)	Ornamental hedge plant throughout USA	Sheep, cattle, horses, camelids	Diarrhea, collapse, and death

flowers. Anchored in the ground by a bulblike root with a meager root system, it stands from 4 to 20 inches (10–51 cm) tall. Death camas often occurs in meadows along with lush forage grasses. Poisoning due to death camas ingestion has been reported in both llamas and alpacas from the Dakotas to California.

Death camas occurs in hilly areas between 2,100 and 10,000 feet (700–3,333 m). It greens early in the spring (and summer in upper elevations) and is often fully developed before grasses have emerged, causing greater risk to livestock who will settle for what's available. Grazing animals have been known to eat death camas when lush meadow grasses are available and plentiful. Death camas is found in the western United States as far east as Texas, Oklahoma, Nebraska, and the Dakotas, and in all states northward including southern Canada.

Symptoms Foaming at the mouth or drooling, rapid breathing, vomiting, trembling, weak pulse, depression, weak and wobbly legs, depressed temperature, blindness (sometimes), and convulsions. Abortions in camelids have also been reported.

Fiddleneck (*Amsinckia* sp.) Also called tarweed and fireweed. Fiddleneck is a spindly, one-stemmed plant whose stem and leaves are covered in stiff hair. The small yellow flowers occur on one side of the stem in a coiled cluster resembling a fiddle's neck. Small nuts are produced by the flowers.

Fiddleneck is found in sandy, exposed areas throughout the western United States below 6,000 feet (1,800 m). This plant often finds its way into the first cutting of hays harvested in dry environments. Even as it dries it remains toxic, especially the seeds.

Symptoms Fiddleneck is one of a group of "cumulative toxic" plants that must be consumed for a few days or weeks to cause a serious problem. First signs may include loss of appetite, constipation, diarrhea (possibly bloody), and yellowish mucus. Poisoned animals act strangely, rubbing fences, possibly biting themselves. The prognosis for animals showing multiple symptoms is not good. The liver is permanently damaged. Death may occur over weeks or days.

Houndstongue (*Cynoglossum officinale*) This attractive big-leafed plant has a single stem, which rarely reaches 3 feet (1 m) in height. The leaves emanate from the stem and are bluish green and spear shaped. The flowers are small and range in color from red to brown. Seeds are burlike. Most livestock won't eat it when it is green and healthy. However, houndstongue often grows near hay fields and can be harvested and baled with hays. It remains toxic in dry form and is readily eaten by horses, cattle, and sheep.

Relatively small amounts eaten over a period of time can cause sickness.

Houndstongue occurs throughout the United States and is found along roadsides and in pastures, and is often among the first plants to establish itself in disturbed soils.

Symptoms Dullness, aimless wandering, increased respiration rate, diarrhea, possibly constipation, liver failure, and death.

Locoweed (*Astragalus* and *Oxytropis* spp.) Locoweed is one of the few poisonous plants that many people have heard of who aren't involved with livestock. It is associated with Hollywood movies about the settling of the West and cattle drives. The generic term locoweed takes in two families of plants, *Astragalus* and *Oxytropis*; about 100 species are represented. As a group they are small, dry, bushlike plants with leaves opposite each other on thin stems. The pealike flowers vary in color from species to species. The seed pods are also pealike in formation and look oversized for the plant.

Locoweeds are found in dry, open areas in the western United States. Cattle and horses in rangeland situations are the traditional victims. They must eat substantial amounts of the weed for two weeks before its effects are noticed. Some varieties of locoweed found in selenium-rich soils retain toxic levels of selenium.

Symptoms Irritability, erratic and dangerous behavior, and possibly impaired vision. Animals can recover from poisoning but are likely to be unfit for some time.

Lupine (*Lupinus* sp.) This showy flowering plant is familiar to most Americans living in the western United States. There are many species, but generally lupine has a small, palmlike leaf structure with leaves radiating outward from the terminus of each stem. Flowers on most species are purple or blue and appear in flower-studded shafts poking skyward from the leaves. Lupine is usually between 6 inches and 6 feet (15 cm and 2 m) tall. Not all species of lupine are poisonous, so it is incumbent to know one lupine from another when it involves your alpacas.

Lupine usually occurs in low hills and higher mountain areas in poor-quality soils.

Symptoms Loss of coordination, stumbling, wandering aimlessly, and drowsiness. Convulsions and death may follow. Lupine has also been identified with birth defects in sheep and cattle.

Nightshade (*Solanum* sp.) This widespread plant is represented by more than 20 species alone in California. Nightshade is a close relative of the tomato. The flowers on the more common species are usually star shaped like a tomato flower. When the fruit ripens, it looks like a small tomato but may range in color from green to black. However, the tomato comparison doesn't always hold true. Some nightshades have silver and white flowers that are not star shaped.

Nightshades thrive in dry open areas, often from surfaces that have been abused by endless use. Poisoning strengths vary from one plant species to the next and vary with the change in seasons.

Symptoms Often both the nervous and digestive systems are affected. Vomiting, diarrhea with blood, and convulsions are usual symptoms. Nervous system signs include sleepiness, shallow breathing, lying on one side, partial paralysis, and death.

Oak (*Quercus* sp.) Oaks are a plentiful family in the United States with deciduous and evergreen oaks. The family is best characterized by its sculpted leaves (sometimes with sharp points around the leaf's perimeter), acorns (fruit), and dense, irregular trunks. Gambel oak (*Q. gambelii*) and shinnery oak (*Q. havardii*) are two of the most notorious for livestock poisoning. New growth in all oaks is thought to be the most toxic part of the tree, but this varies from one species to the next. New growth occurs in the spring. Old growth and dead leaves are thought to be nontoxic in most species.

Acorns have been associated with the poisoning of some kinds of livestock, but experts disagree on what, if any, effect acorns have on alpacas. Some experts think acorns pose little threat to alpacas and can be readily consumed. Browsers (goats) have high tolerance to oak consumption, while grazers (cattle) seem to be more sensitive. Alpacas are often housed among oak trees with no known negative impact. I have observed alpacas eating acorns with no ill effects.

Oaks are common throughout the United States and vary between smallish bush-sized species to immense trees with trunks 6 feet (2 m) thick. Toxicity levels vary from one species of oak to the next. Species identification and talks with local ranchers and knowledgeable plant specialists are warranted if oaks are prevalent in an area being considered for alpacas for the first time.

Symptoms Dark diarrhea, loss of appetite, rumen stoppage, depression, possibly fever, frequent urination, and increased thirst.

Oleander (*Nerium oleander*) Oleander is arguably the single most dangerous plant to alpacas living in the United States. Oleander is one of the most popular ornamental plants in the United States—hardy, adaptable plants requiring little water while producing white, pink, or red flowers in their upper branches. Oleander's narrow, pointed leaves can be confused with bay leaves (*Umbellularia* sp.), used in cooking. Unfortunately, oleander is a documented

Oleander (*Nerium oleander*) is a popular ornamental shrub and one of the deadliest plants in the world. An alpaca eating four to five leaves will most likely die. It affects the heart and is slower to dissipate than other poisons. Alpacas will readily eat oleander, even with good-quality forage available.

killer of alpacas, usually when someone offers garden trimmings as a treat to a group of alpacas. It takes only about five leaves of an oleander to kill an alpaca.

Oleander is found throughout the United States along highway medians, lining fences and driveways, and too often in areas near livestock. An animal escaping from a pen for a short time and browsing can easily fall victim to oleander poisoning. If you have oleanders on your property, removing them and warning your neighbors about their toxicity may be the wisest solution to avert a tragedy.

Symptoms Depression and reluctance to stand are early symptoms, followed by severe diarrhea and possibly colic. Death can occur within hours of ingestion, without diarrhea, if enough poison has been absorbed rapidly. The poison causes heart failure. Death can take several days.

Poison Hemlock (*Conium maculatum*) Poison hemlock is often mistaken for water hemlock because of the similar name and appearance. Both plants are deadly. Both plants are hollow stemmed and have similar small white flowers configured in umbrella fashion. The differences are subtle. Poison hemlock has purple patches on the lower parts of the plant stem and is a smaller plant than water hemlock. Poison hemlock is usually around 3 feet (1 m) tall, though it can be taller in optimum conditions. Poison hemlock looks similar to parsley and has a peculiar disagreeable odor.

Poison hemlock is sometimes found in hay fields and grows in dry to moist, fertile soils. It is not found in mountains above 5,000 feet (1,500 m). Poison hemlock often greens before other plants, making it a tempting plant in the spring if good forage is not readily available.

Symptoms Weakness in the hind limbs, shaking, depressed pulse, coma, and death are an expected sequence. Symptoms are fast to develop, usually within an hour or two following ingestion.

Ragwort (*Senecio* sp.) Ragwort is a dreaded plant in Europe, North America, Australia, and New Zealand. A member of the sunflower family, with numerous species, most of the more common varieties resemble a tall daisy with yellow flowers that appear in clusters. In the United States, tansy ragwort (*S. jacobaea*) is found along creeks and in pastures, often near water sources. Groundsel (*S. vulgaris*) often appears in hay-growing areas and can be found in harvested hays. Ragwort is bitter tasting and alpacas are reluctant to eat it if there is suitable forage. I have seen large areas of pasture infested with ragwort that alpacas have ignored. Still, there are reports of suspected ragwort poisoning from England to New Zealand. Ragwort has been found in baled hay in England and North America.

Symptoms Loss of interest in food, depression, diarrhea (possibly with blood), constipation, and strange behavior. Behaviors may include unusual gait; pushing against bushes, fences, and other objects; and abnormal chewing behavior. Death may occur rapidly or over a few days.

St. Johnswort (*Hypericum perforatum*) Also known as klamathweed and goatweed, this plant is found throughout the United States. St. Johnswort stands about 3 feet (1 m) tall and is not a remarkable-looking plant. It has a single stem that branches more frequently near the top. The leaves are about quarter sized and oval in shape. If you hold a leaf up to intense light, there are visible thin dots where light shines through. The star-shaped flowers are yellow with black dots and grow in clusters at the top of the plant.

St. Johnswort is more dangerous than plants with greater toxicity because sheep and goats (and presumably llamas and alpacas) will graze on it in a pasture setting with healthy forage plants nearby. St Johnswort is commonly found in areas recently cleared, along roadsides, and in pastures. The seed capsules are the most toxic part of the plant.

Symptoms Victims show photosensitivity. Affected animals will avoid light and develop blisters on their skin. Light-skinned animals are often the most severely affected. Animals may also develop diarrhea and salivate excessively.

Tansy ragwort (*Senecio jacobaea*) is found in pastures, along creeks, and sometimes in bales of hay.

Tall Fescue (*Festuca arundinacea*) A common pasture grass in the Southeast, Midwest, Northwest, and parts of Canada, tall fescue is usually good forage but it can harbor dangerous mycotoxins (ergopeptine alkaloids). Poisoning is commonly reported in cattle and sheep and is likely to affect alpacas and llamas as well. Usually cattle affected by mycotoxins in tall fescue have grazed in an infected area for two weeks or more before signs appear. The plant is a typical-looking grass about 4 inches (10 cm) tall with a central seed stalk about 12 inches (40 cm) or more.

Infected fescue occurs primarily in the Southeast and in turf grasses sold for trade shows and home use. If you are contemplating running alpacas on fescue pasture, it is wise to inquire about mycotoxins and talk with livestock owners in the area.

Symptoms In cattle, extremities develop sores and become infected, sometimes developing into gangrene. In hot summer weather, affected animals show less heat tolerance and coats become "rough." Cattle and sheep grazing in infected areas often develop birthing problems: weak babies, abortions, and dystocias.

Pine needles of the western yellow pine (*Pinus ponderosa*) have been implicated in abortions in camelids. The distinctively large, airy pine with its unique bark pattern is common in the mountains of the western United States. The pine is easy to identify: Its needles are exceptionally long, growing 4 to 12 inches (10–33 cm) in groups of three, and its cones are 2 to 5 inches (5–10 cm) long with prickly spines that point outward. The western yellow pine hybridizes with the Jeffrey pine (*Pinus jefferyi*). It is not known whether the hyrids are poisonous. Most pine needles from other species aren't considered poisonous.

Water Hemlock (*Cicuta* sp.) Water hemlock is probably the single most dangerous naturally occurring plant in North America. It is an errant member of the carrot family, when eaten, it kills people as well as animals. It is characterized by small white umbrella clusters of flowers. Its thick-at-the-base stem is hollow, and it grows to 9 feet (3 m) in height. Its leaves have pronounced veins that extend to the serrated inner edge of the leaves.

Water hemlock is found along water courses and is not commonly eaten by passing animals. It is most dangerous in spring when it greens more quickly than other plants and is more apt to be tempting. Most known poisonings occur when an animal pulls the plant from the ground and eats the root.

Symptoms Poisoning and death occur rapidly, usually within minutes after signs first show themselves. Foaming at the mouth, convulsions, visible pain, and death are the symptoms and the outcome.

Western Yellow Pine (*Pinus ponderosa*) This common pine is also known as ponderosa pine. Mature trees are immense, growing to 120 feet (40 m) or taller. The needles are long, 4 to 7 inches (10–18 cm) and occur in bundles of twos and threes. The cone is oval shaped and has sharp barbs.

Western yellow pine is prevalent in low mountains in the West, particularly the Sierra foothills. Cattle, buffalo, and llamas have been identified as animals being affected. A few mouthfuls of needles will not poison an animal. Usually poisoning occurs when needles or bark are consumed for a week or more in moderate amounts. It is usually a food of last resort.

Symptoms Western yellow pine is proven to cause premature births and stillborns in cattle. Interuterine bleeding, partial cervical dilation, and other negative impacts on reproductive organs have been observed. Poor digestion due to effects on pH and change in microorganisms in the rumen are likely outcomes.

Yew (*Taxus* sp.) Yew is a common ornamental hedge plant found in most of the United States and southern Canada. There are more than 15 species of yews, some of the better known ones originating in England. Yews are usually a dense dark green or blue-green shrub with needlelike leaf clusters that resemble fir trees, only with most yews their form is much more compact and impenetrable looking than the open, long-branched fir. Yews are also instantly distinguished from pine-cone-producing firs by small, cup-shaped individual fruits at the tips of new growth in female yews. Often the yew needle configuration is V shaped or flat.

Yews are often found in shady areas. They thrive in alkaline soils and have been successfully planted throughout North America, except in areas where they will be exposed to direct sunlight in soaring temperatures. They can withstand freezing temperatures. They are found in the wild in northern California and the Pacific Northwest.

Symptoms Depressed temperature, erratic pulse, and hyperactivity, followed by deteriorating coordination and collapse. If ingestion has been substantial, death may be immediate with no symptoms.[1,2,3,5,8]

In Europe

Table 23.5 lists some of the poisonous plants in the United Kingdom and Europe, with habitats, type of toxicity, and symptoms of ingestion.

In Australia

Incredible as it may sound, there are more than 1,000 species of poisonous plants living in Australia. Many of these occur in areas outside of the primary livestock-growing regions.

Table 23.6 lists some of Australia's deadliest plants. It shows the most common plants associated with livestock poisoning in the two most alpaca-populous states, New South Wales and Victoria.

In some cases, the plants on this list have not been specifically associated with poisoning alpacas. However, if a plant affects a ruminant species, there is a high likelihood that it will also affect an alpaca. It is interesting to note that many of the plants associated with livestock poisoning are the same worldwide.

Table 23.5 Partial poisonous plant list for the United Kingdom and Europe.*

Plant Name	Description	Habitat	Type of Toxicity	Symptoms
Black nightshade (*Solanum nigrum*)	Annual, to 60 cm, berries	Found as weed in crops	Alkaloids, nitrates	Abdominal pain, depression, loss of coordination
Box (*Buxus sempervirens*)	Native to UK, evergreen tree, shrub	Common hedge plant	Alkaloids, bad taste	Diarrhea, staggering, convulsions, respiratory failure, resulting in death
Bracken fern (*Pteridium aquilinum*)	Fronds a meter or more, runners	Prefers acid soils	Carcinogenic with enzyme thiaminase resulting in Vitamin B1 deficiency	Loss of coordination, respiratory distress, possible fever, rapid heartbeat, untreated convulsions and death
Cowbane (*Cicuta virosa*)	Perennial grows from tuberous roots, toothed leaves, and small, white, flat-topped clusters of flowers at tips of purple striped or mottled stems	Prefers damp areas, ditches, pastures, wetlands	Roots have alcohol named cicutoxin, a deadly poison	Convulsions, death
Cuckoo pint (*Arum maculatum*)	Perennial with large leaves, flowering organs, resembles male and female genitalia	Thrives in shady areas, widespread	All parts are poisonous	Drooling, swelling around the mouth, total loss of coordination, death
Deadly nightshade (*Atropa belladonna*)	1.5 m shrub, many species; fruits are smallish; tomatolike berry	Likes open, dry, sunny areas	Potent alkaloid poisons	Dilated pupils, excitability, loss of coordination
Foxglove (*Digitalis purpurea*)	150 cm in height, common purple, bell-shaped flower	Hardy in many environments, hedge plant throughout much of Europe	Contains cardiac glycosides	Diarrhea, abdominal pain, tremors, convulsions
Hemlock (*Conium maculatum*)	2 m in height, purple-spotted stem	Widespread over all of Europe	Toxic alkaloids	Paralysis, convulsions, death by respiratory failure
Hemlock water dropwort (*Oenanthe crocata*)	Distinctive tuberlike roots	Found mostly in UK	Very potent poison	Convulsions, death
Horsetail (*Equisetum* sp.)	Fleshy stem to 80 cm	In wet areas throughout Europe	Contains thiaminase	Kidney damage or death (see bracken fern)
Iris (*Iris pseudacorus/ foetidissima*)	Yellow, stinks	Found in UK	Entire plant is poisonous	Fever, diarrhea with blood

The yew (*Taxus* sp.) is a common hedge plant in North America, Europe, New Zealand, and Australia. There are more 15 species, all of them poisonous.

Table 23.6 Partial poisonous plant list for Australia.

Common Name	Botanical Name
Bracken fern	*Pteridium esculentum*
Datura	*Datura* sp.
Deadly nightshade	*Atropa belladonna*
Heliotrope	*Helitropium*
Lantana	*Lantana* sp.
Oleander	*Nerium oleander*
Paterson's curse	*Echium plantagineum*
Phalaria	*Phalaria* sp.
Ragwort	*Senecio* sp.
Rhododendron and azalea	*Rhododendron arboreum*
St. Johnswort	*Hypericum* sp.

Note: There are two common fungal/grass diseases reported in Australia—ryegrass staggers (a mycotoxin) and sporodesmin/facial eczema (liver failure).

Source: Thanks to Denis Ryan, MVB, MRCVS, of Torquay, Victoria, and Joann Rothique, of the Australian Alpaca Association, for their time and assistance in compiling this table.

Table 23.5 continued

Plant Name	Description	Habitat	Type of Toxicity	Symptoms
Laburnum (*Laburnum anagyroides*)	Tree with yellow flowers in peapod configuration	Popular ornamental tree	Alkaloid poison	High fever, abdominal pain, staggering, convulsions, death likely when seeds are ingested
Larkspur (*Consolida ajacis*)	Popular ornamental perennial herb, blue, purple, or white blossom clusters, deeply toothed green leaves	Popular in flower gardens throughout Europe	Alkaloid poison	Excitability, breathing problems, loss of coordination, pain
Lily of the valley (*Convallaria majalis*)	White flowers, small plant	Native to UK	Glycoside poison	Uneven pulse, dilated pupils, excessive salivation
Linseed (*Linum usitatissimum*)	Slender, erect annual herb, pale blue, five-petaled flowers, capsule-shaped fruit	Cultivated in Europe for oil	Glycoside poison, oxygen kept from brain	Staggering, dilated pupils, slobbering, rapid pulse, convulsions; death can be very rapid
Privet (*Ligustrum* sp.)	Another hedge plant; clippings offered to animals accounts for many deaths	Throughout Europe	Poison works on many fronts	Paralysis, dilated pupils, rapid pulse
Ragwort (*Senecio jacobaea*)	Perennial starts flat, grows to 3-foot clusters of small, daisylike, yellow flowers, with dark green, rough-edged leaves	Widespread in Europe, grows with hay and is harvested, more readily eaten by livestock after it dries, ability to grow with hay plants makes it especially dangerous	Alkaloid poison	Loss of coordination, pupils dilate, digestive tract problems including abdominal pain and diarrhea, paralysis; onset can be cumulative or very rapid
Rhododendron (*Rhododendron ponticum*)	Showy flowers	Popular ornamental shrub to small tree throughout Europe	Potent poison	Diarrhea, pain, slobbering, constipation, weak pulse, erratic breathing
Yew (*Taxus baccata*)	Dark to blue green, appearance of small conifer	Widespread as hedge plant throughout Europe	Strong alkaloid poison	Weak pulse, drop in body temperature, excitable, loss of balance, death

*The list does not pretend to represent every toxic plant found in Europe. Nor are there data proving that these poisons, common to most forms of livestock, have actually killed alpacas. See Table 23.3 for more on symptoms.

Source: This table was made possible due to the efforts of Nick Weber in the United Kingdom.

Table 23.7 Partial list of toxic plants of New Zealand.[6,7]

Buttercup (*Ranunculus* sp.) Leaves are the best identifiers because they resemble a bird's foot. Buttercup is sometimes called crow's foot. Flowers are usually yellow and occur on long stalks. Plant is most dangerous when hungry animals are introduced to it. Under most circumstances livestock avoid it.

Foxglove (*Digitalis pupurea*) This weed is found on both North and South Island. Foxglove is deadly in relatively small doses to all kinds of livestock.

Hemlock (*Conium maculatum*) Found on both South and North Islands, this is one of New Zealand's deadliest plants to livestock. It usually occurs in wet areas. The plant looks somewhat like parsley but has a purple stem and unpleasant smell. It is usually a plant of last resort to grazing animals who have no good forage to eat.

Inkweed (*Phytolacca octandra*) Found primarily on the northern extremes of South Island, this is a dangerous plant. Its black berries are especially tempting and poisonous.

Jerusalem cherry (*Solanum diflorum* and *pseudocapsicum*) Found in two closely related species on both South and North Islands, this shrub with attractive orange fruit is very poisonous.

Lily (*Convallaria* sp. and *Pieris* sp.) *Convallaria* is known as the Lily of the Nile in New Zealand. All of the plant is poisonous, especially the orange berries. *Pieris* enjoys the common name of "lily" when it is actually a member of the heather family and not a true lily.

Ngaio (*Myoporum* sp.) These plants are usually easy to identify. They grow wild along the coast , but they are also grown domestically. When held to light their leaves display pronounced leaf spots. Native species occur in both Australia and New Zealand. The purple berries are very poisonous.

Nightshade (*Solanum* sp.) This is a well-represented family in New Zealand. The leafy parts are especially poisonous. Some of the more common varieties are: poroporo, potato, bittersweet, and black nightshade. Nightshade is prevalent on both islands.

Oleander (*Nerium oleander*) This attractive import is among the most poisonous and dangerous plants for livestock in the world. Three to five leaves will result in death for an alpaca.

Ragwort (*Senecio jacobaea*) This plant occurs on both islands and sometimes grows with hays. The poison exists in the dry leaves. The plant must be ingested over a period of time, but it is deadly and causes the liver to fail.

Rhododendron and Azalea (*Rhododendron* sp.) Huge family with more than 800 species, most of which are poisonous. Common ornamental shrub in New Zealand. The treelike *Rhododendron arboreum* on the South Island is common. Its pink flower is especially poisonous.

Tutu (*Coriaria* sp.) This is one of New Zealand's most deadly plants. There are two species: *arborea*, which grows in low areas and tends to appear in areas disturbed by human activities, and *sarmentosa*, which is smaller and grows in high areas. Both have black inviting berries with poisonous seeds.

Yew (*Taxus baccata*) All parts of the plant are extremely poisonous. Yew is a popular hedge plant on both islands.

Sources: Information contained here was graciously shared by Landcare Research New Zealand Ltd., 1999 (W.R. Sykes). Thanks is also in order to Dr. George Davis, who helped procure this information.

In New Zealand

New Zealand has its share of poisonous plants. There are more than 150 poisonous species, many of them introduced from other continents. Table 23.7 lists some of the more common ones that are dangerous to livestock.

For more information in New Zealand, contact the National Poisons Information Centre, urgent line: 03 474 7000, nonurgent line: 03 479 1200. Or contact Manaaki Whenua Press by e-mail: mwpress@landcare.cri.nz.

In South America

The literature on camelids in South America does not mention poisonous plants as a problem in alpaca raising. Yet, when individual breeders are asked about toxic plants on the altiplano, invariably two plants are mentioned, which are described in Table 23.8.

Table 23.8 Poisonous plants on the puna of South America.

Pinco pinco (*Ephedra americana*)	Grows in rainy season, affects bone growth and strength, resulting in increase in fractures
Garbancillo or sannca layo (*Astragalus* sp.)	Grows in dry season; causes blindness and lack of coordination; addicting.

Source: Dr. Rufino Quilla, Juliaca, Peru, 2002.

Plant Poison Treatments

The best treatment is to avoid poisonous plants altogether by being careful and eliminating them. In many instances there is no known treatment or antidote, especially if more than an hour has passed since ingestion. Treatments exist for some poisons, but most treatments were developed for cattle, sheep, pigs, and horses. Just how camelids will react is not always known.

Numerous nonspecific therapies can be worthwhile. IV fluids to combat dehydration and blood transfusions are two of them. Introducing activated charcoal into the digestive tract as an absorbent has worked well to blunt the impact of many poisons. Purgatives are also used. If you suspect poisoning, attempt to get a sample of the suspect plant and call a veterinarian immediately.

Since the passage of time is critical in poisonings, the smart alpaca breeder has developed a strategy for poisons that can be applied quickly. Being able to "tube" an animal to introduce absorbents may mean the difference between life and death. Having activated charcoal on hand and other medicines recommended by your veterinarian may make a difference. Plan ahead for poisons.[1,2,3,5,8]

POTENTIAL HARM FROM NONPOISONOUS SUBSTANCES

Eating Harmful Nonpoisons

Identifying toxins and learning how to avoid them has been the focus of this chapter. However, a wide range of "eating opportunities" that don't involve toxic plants or substances can lead to situations that kill or sicken an alpaca. Alpacas have been known to eat both plastic foam and fiberglass insulation from around pipes and in walls of barns. There have been incidences of choking on middle-sized fruits, such as crab apples, banana peels, and acorns. If your alpacas have opportunities to eat nonstandard foods, assess the potential dangers.

Diet Change

Many kinds of livestock can become ill when their diet is suddenly changed. Often a "richer" diet (heavy in legumes, following a diet of grass hay) will result in diarrhea in alpacas. Alpacas are not as sensitive to dietary change as some other forms of livestock, but slow transitions to a new feed type are usually better than a rapid change. Transitions to new foods are often very abrupt when animals are transported.

Eating Too Much Grain, Tainted Grain, or Pellets

Grains (crushed oats and barley) are often fed as supplements and treats to alpacas in the "new alpaca growing countries." Beware of grains, especially too much grain. Alpacas have been known to gorge on grains and pellets, causing severe discomfort and on rare occasions death. Overeating grain has occurred both through ignorance on the part of owners, who deliberately allow free access to grains, and by accident when an alpaca has gained access to grain storage due to a gate left ajar or a lid left off a container. Grains should be stored out of reach from alpacas and rationed in very small amounts.

Usually symptoms of "grain gorging" are two-fold: evidence an alpaca has had access to a large helping of grain coupled with acute abdominal stress. Ty McConnell, DVM, a seasoned camelid veterinarian, remembers being called to a ranch to help with a slow birth. When he arrived, a large group of people had gathered with a video camera to watch and help in the "impending" birth. The animal was lying on one side and groaning loudly. After performing his examination, he explained that the impending birth was really abdominal discomfort from eating too much grain.

Alpacas near Puno, in southern Peru, graze on their natural food, rich *bofadales*, a plant community with very few toxic plants.

After gorging of this kind, two or three days of diarrhea will likely follow. Alpacas don't normally die from gorging on grain, but have done so in rare instances. The other common domestic ruminants—cattle, sheep, and goats—are more sensitive to overeating grain and are more likely to become bloated and die from excessive grain consumption.

Tainted grains or pellets are a different story. Most of a group of alpacas that ate grains or pellets tainted with organophosphates died, as did an animal that ate a formulated pellet mixture that was so rich in selenium that acute toxicity occurred. Improperly formulated pellet supplements have resulted in numerous deaths in the United States. Alpacas will almost always gorge on grains offered them, so knowing whether a grain is contaminated and its content are important! Supplements are not risk-free!

When an alpaca overconsumes grain, the rumen's microbes and pH can be affected radically. This may result in cramping, intestinal inflammation, difficulties in digesting food, and diarrhea. It may take several days for the rumen to return to normal.*

---

*Ty, McConnell, DVM, longtime camelid veterinarian, personal communication, Scotts Valley, CA, August 2002.

REFERENCES

1. Fowler, M., A. L. Craigmill, B. Norman, and P. Michelsen: *Livestock-Poisoning Plants of California.* Davis: Division of Agricultural Sciences, University of California, pp. 4–23, 1982.
2. Foster, S., and Roger Caras: *Field Guide to Venomous Animals and Poisonous Plants: North America North of Mexico*, p. 121. Boston: Houghton Mifflin,1994.
3. Hoffman, E., and M. Fowler: *The Alpaca Book*, pp. 239–243. Herald, CA: Clay Press, 1995.
4. Hoffman, E. *Adventuring in Australia*, 2nd ed. p. 505. San Francisco: Sierra Club Books/Random House, 1999.
5. Sampson A. W., and H. E. Malmsten: *Stock-Poisoning Plants of California*, pp. 1–83. Berkeley: University of California Experiment Station, 1949.
6. Sykes, W. R.: *Plants in the North Island Poisonous to Children*, pp. 1-8. Lincoln, New Zealand: Manaaki Wheuna Press, 1999.
7. Sykes W. R.: *Plants in the South Island Poisonous to Children*. pp. 1-8. Lincoln, New Zealand: Manaaki Wheuna Press, 1999.
8. Weathers, S.: *Field Guide to Plants Poisonous to Livestock: Western U.S.*, p. 227. Fruitland, Utah: Rosebud Press, 1998.
9. Weber, N.: *Guide to Poisonous Plants*, unpublished material, pp. 1–3, 2002.

Author's Note: Perhaps the best sourcebook on livestock poisoning is *A Guide to Plant Poisoning of Animals in North America* by Anthony P. Knight, BVSC, MS, and Richard G. Walter, MA, Botany. This 366-page book contains color photographs of poisonous plants and maps of their distribution, and discusses poisoning agents and possible strategies and medical interventions. For a copy, contact Teton New Media, P.O. Box 4833, 125 South King Street, Jackson, Wyoming 83001; phone, 888-770-3165.

Section Six

Genetics

Overleaf This young suri is a rarity. It was born of huacaya parents in one of the first importations to the United States.

Chapter 24

Basic Genetic Principles and Implications for Breeding

D. Phillip Sponenberg, DVM, PhD

Alpacas have been selectively bred for 6,500 years.

WHAT IS GENETICS?
WHAT CAN IT DO FOR BREEDERS?

Genetics is the study of how traits pass down generation to generation. It began as a science in the early 1900s,[4] and interest and knowledge in genetics have exploded in the last few decades. This knowledge explosion has resulted in a peculiar situation in which genetics has lost some of its mystery, yet at the same time breeders often expect it to accomplish things that it cannot. Clearheaded thinking about how genetics can work for breeders is key to making dramatic progress in alpaca breeding programs. Excellent breeding programs are greatly aided by an appreciation of genetics, but also depend on the somewhat intuitive aspects of the art of breeding—the "eye of the breeder." Science and art go hand in hand in the best breeding programs.

Many people think that genetics is a predictive science—accurately predicting the color, conformation, or other genetic details of the next cria to hit the ground. Alas, genetics does not work in an absolutely, finely detailed, predictive way. Instead, genetics can be more accurately viewed as a science of possibilities. Viewing genetics as a science of possibilities instead of a science of certainties can greatly help the breeder, because the choices for possibilities can be narrowed to those desired by the breeder in the next generation of alpacas. Knowing genetics can take some of the surprises out of breeding programs but never completely eliminates them.

Genetics can be immensely helpful in predicting the overall range of expected types within the offspring of certain pairs of alpacas. Genetics is pretty good at predicting what will happen over the next 100 crias, but not very good (in most instances) at predicting the fine details of the next individual one. Knowledge of genetics is an extremely powerful tool for animal breeders, although its strengths and weaknesses both need to be appreciated to gain its greatest benefits.

HOW GENES WORK

At a very basic and molecular level, genes control just about everything that happens in an animal. Genes are sequences of DNA (deoxyribonucleic acid), and they directly control the production of proteins, which in turn governs most aspects of both the structure and the metabolism of an animal. Genes are essential, but the impact of the environment is also crucial in determining the final outcome of genetic instructions. The finest genetic instructions in the worst of environments are unlikely to lead to excellence, and likewise the best of environments can make a substandard set of instructions actually work out pretty well. Understanding these limitations to genetics will help breeders get the most out of genetics. As a first step it is important to understand some key concepts of how genes function in individuals as well as in populations.

521

Genes Are Paired

Genes, with few exceptions, work in pairs. Each individual alpaca gets one member of the pair from its sire, one from its dam. Each individual alpaca, in its own turn, donates one of each pair to its offspring. This concept of pairs is absolutely essential because genetics "works" on the basis of these pairs—the interaction of the members of each pair, as well as the interactions of the different pairs with each other. Breeders who understand the concept of pairing, halving, and then pairing again at each generational step will be able to use genetics very effectively in their breeding programs.

Genes Are Discrete Pieces of Information

A mental picture to help understand the fundamental character of an animal's genetic component is imagining the animal as a big bowl and the genes as mixed dried beans. Beans of different colors, shapes, and sizes represent different forms and sizes of genes. At each generational step the bean mixture is split in half, and combined with a half from another bowl (the mate in the pairing). The result is that the mixtures change each time, although the individual identity of each gene (bean) remains intact and could indeed be teased out if the technology, time, and money were all available to do so.

The concept of a "bowl of beans" is an accurate one, and contrasts with the somewhat intuitive, although inaccurate, view held by many people that genes are like a "bowl of water"; hot water from one parent mixes with cold water from the other parent to yield a "just right" lukewarm offspring. In this view it would be impossible to tease out the individual genetic components (and their temperature) for the next generation. One of the key concepts to understanding genetics is that individual components retain their identity and characteristics throughout the generations.

Each individual alpaca is the result of genes and environment, and the genetic component is the sum total of all those pairs of genes. If the genes are the units of interest, then the population can be imagined as a "jiggling" of the genes down through the generations as they are mixed up and recombined into new combinations at each generational step (mixing up those beans). The animal breeder's task is to use the favorable combinations more heavily than the unfavorable ones, so that the jiggling goes in a positive direction.

Genetic Definitions

A few definitions must be mastered to understand and use genetics most effectively.[4] Some of these definitions are somewhat technical and tricky, but they all help in under-

standing the elegant and intricate beauty of genetics and how it is useful to the breeder.

Phenotype *Phenotype* refers to the appearance of an animal, or more broadly to any trait (internal or external) that can be measured or documented. It is reasonably accurate to think of a phenotype as "what is seen" or "what is manifested" by an animal. This could be color, size, or even some metabolic and therefore internal working. A phenotype is a result of the interaction of genes and environment, and for most traits it is impossible to separate genetic and environmental components. Also, for most traits documenting phenotype is much more possible than figuring out the genetic or environmental components.

Genotype *Genotype,* in contrast, refers to the genetic makeup of an individual. The genotype refers to the specific genetic variants that are present, regardless of the way they are expressed as a result of environmental-genetic interactions. The main importance of the definitions is to understand this relationship:

$$genotype + environment = phenotype$$

For many traits (coat color, eye color) the genotype is much more important than the environment. For others, such as the ability to do some tasks, the environment (training) is more important than the genotype, although individuals do vary in their level of trainability, and certainly some of those differences are genetic.

Locus Genes reside in a very specific and orderly array that can be imagined somewhat like a string of beads. The strings are chromosomes, which are microscopic structures in the nucleus of each cell. Each chromosome has a unique and consistent array of genes, all arranged in the same specific order throughout all alpacas. Thus, each gene has a specific site, which occurs on both members of a specific pair of chromosomes. This site is called a *locus* (plural is loci), which can be thought of as the address or specific location for that gene. Locus describes the specific site on both chromosomes that codes for a specific gene.

Allele One key to how genetics works for animal breeders is that animals vary in their genotype—some are better for what the breeder wants, some are worse. This variability resides at the various loci, so that genes vary. The different variants of a gene (at a specific locus) are called *alleles* of the gene. Many people use gene and allele interchangeably, but this does not need to become confusing. The key concept is that variation does occur in the specific genetic instructions, so that one member of a gene pair might be different from the other member. Variation in genetic material is essential if animals are to vary in genetic worth and therefore

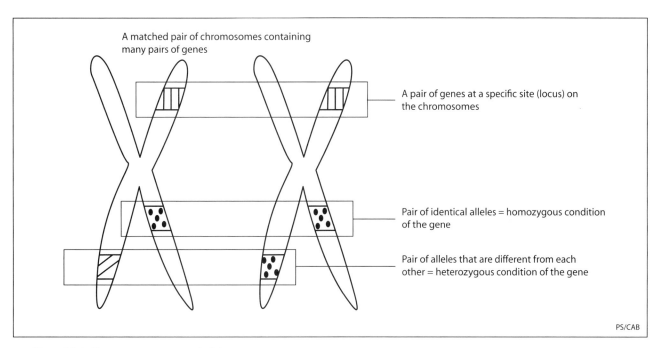

Figure 24.1 Chromosomes, genes, and alleles.

Gene Interactions

Pairs of genes can interact in different ways, and each of these ways has a term to describe it so that people can communicate accurately and concisely exactly what is happening. Members of a pair can either be identical or they can be different one from the other. When the members of a pair are identical, this is called the *homozygous* condition. This term basically means that such animals have only a single genetic contribution to make to the next generation because they have no variation at that locus. If the members of the pairs are different, then the condition is called *heterozygous*, and such animals can obviously contribute either one or the other of the alleles (forms) of the gene to the next generation, which provides for variation in the offspring's genotypes (see Figure 24.1).

Dominant and Recessive Alleles If a pair is made up of identical members (homozygous), then obviously whatever that specific allele codes for is the character (phenotype) that is expressed. If a pair is made up of different members (heterozygous), then a few different things can happen. One possibility is that only one (a specific one) of the pair is expressed, and the other is hidden—the one that is expressed is called *dominant* and the one not expressed is called *recessive*. This is a key issue: Dominant alleles (genes) essentially cover up recessive alleles (genes). The important result is that recessive alleles can trail along for many generations without being expressed, until they are paired up with another identical recessive allele and are therefore able to be expressed. As a result, recessive phenotypes (what is expressed) tend to show up as surprises, and they tend not to reproduce themselves very well unless mated to the same recessive phenotype or to a dominant phenotype that carries the recessive as an unexpressed variant.

Incomplete Dominant and Codominant Alleles In some situations where members of the gene pair are different, each member can be detected in the phenotype so that, even though the members are different, nothing is hidden. These situations are called *incompletely dominant* or *codominant*. The differences between these two are subtle, but can be important. Blood types are a great example of a codominant system—everything is expressed, nothing is hidden. Codominance implies that the individual alleles are producing a product that can be measured directly, so each allelic product is its own character and is either expressed (if present) or not (if absent).

Good examples of incomplete dominance are not documented in alpacas, but are common in other species. Palomino horses are a good example—if both genes are "normal" or dark, the horse is chestnut (reddish). If one "dark" and one "light" gene are present, the horse is palomino (yellowish). If two doses of the light gene are present, then the horse is cream with blue eyes. Incomplete dominance implies a single trait (color, in this example) with different levels of expression in each homozygote and heterozygote. Incomplete dominance involves one character with three phenotypes—the two homozygous phenotypes and a heterozygous phenotype somewhere in between the homozygous ones—one for each genotype.

An example of the subtlety of genetic definitions is a specific sort of pituitary dwarfism in German shepherd dogs. If the growth rate of puppies is the trait of interest, then the abnormal gene behaves as a complete recessive because only homozygotes (those puppies with two of the dwarf alleles) are dwarf. Investigation led to a test for a product of growth hormone called somatomedin. Normal homozygotes (two of the nondwarf alleles) have high levels of somatomedin, and dwarf homozygotes (two of the dwarf alleles) have very low levels. Heterozygotes (one each of the alleles) have an intermediate level that is still sufficient to provide for a normal growth rate but is detectable as lower than normal by the specific test for it. Thus, if somatomedin levels are the trait of interest instead of the growth rate, the level is effectively an incompletely dominant trait because the substance has three different levels relating to the three different genetic conditions possible in the dogs. Further investigation has led to identification of the two forms of the gene, which can now be documented as "normal" or "dwarf," and all three combinations of these (heterozygous or homozygous) can be directly detected—that is, each allele (normal or dwarf) is expressed. Thus, the alleles themselves are codominant, but technology is required to detect the alleles themselves rather than their products or consequences.

A Punnett Square Example Introductory genetics courses use *Punnett squares* to demonstrate a few key concepts of genetics. In Punnett squares, one parent's genotype is across the top of a grid and the other parent's genotype is along the left side of the grid. A single locus has a 2×2 grid, because the genes are paired in the parents but each provides only one to the offspring.

In this example the parents are tan, but each carries a recessive for black. (This is explained further in Chapter 25: Genetics of Fiber Type and Coat Color.) The locus is designated by a capital letter, and the variants possible at that locus are represented by superscripts. Thus, the shorthand for tan is A^T and for black is A^a. The parents are each therefore $A^T A^a$ and have one copy of each of the two alleles.

Parental genotype	A^T (tan)	A^a (black)
A^T (tan)	$A^T A^T$	$A^T A^a$
A^a (black)	$A^T A^a$	$A^a A^a$

The first important concept in the square is that each parent has two alleles, and in this case they are different from each other. The second concept is that each parent can donate only one allele to its offspring. The third concept is that these donations are matched with the donation from the other parent to yield the final pair in the offspring.

The top left offspring has received two tan alleles, and so is tan. In addition, this animal in its own turn can donate only tan alleles, because it is homozygous. The important concept here is that, even though the parents both carried a recessive black allele, it is now gone, and this specific animal cannot donate this allele to its offspring because it is not present. Remember that genes are discrete pieces of information—once the information is gone, it is gone for good unless reintroduced from some other source. The top right offspring has received a black allele from one parent and a tan one from the other. The bottom left offspring is similar, although the parental sources for the alleles are the reverse of the top right one. The bottom right offspring has received two black alleles, and is therefore homozygous for this allele. It is black, even though it had two tan parents. It has also lost the tan information of the parents and cannot donate this to its own offspring.

Epistasis A subtle and important genetic concept is that certain allelic combinations at some loci can mask the expression of other loci. This is somewhat like dominance and recessiveness but involves multiple loci instead of a single locus. In this situation the masked locus is referred to as *hypostatic* (or "standing below"), and the genotype doing the masking is called *epistatic* (or "standing above"). Epistasis introduces a level of complexity to genetics that can seem daunting, but it also reflects the intricacy of the interactions of genes and loci to produce the alpacas that breeders and owners value and enjoy.

The critical concept for the way alleles and loci interact is that various mechanisms exist for hiding portions of the genome. The hidden parts may be good or may be bad, and breeding strategies can use them to advantage if carefully constructed. The hidden portion can provide surprises, some pleasant and others unpleasant, to the breeder. Understanding the mechanisms that provide for hiding a portion of the genome can greatly aid breeders in either bringing these to light or assuring that they stay hidden.

Gene Frequency Versus Dominance

A widespread misconception is that common phenotypes are dominant and uncommon ones are recessive. The relative frequency of a trait is simply a matter of allele frequency, or how many copies of a specific allele are present in a population. The relative frequency has absolutely nothing to do with the dominance or recessiveness that are inherent characteristics of the alleles.

Good examples come from color in horses. White in horses is dominant, and yet this color is very, very rare because the allele causing this color has a very low frequency among horse populations. Alternatively, chestnut in horses is recessive, and yet some entire breeds (such as the Suffolk) are chestnut because selection has fixed the gene frequency at 100 percent. These frequencies in no way change the fundamental character of the alleles as either dominant or recessive. In crosses of Suffolks to black Percheron horses, few if any of the foals are going to be chestnut, because nearly all of them will pick up the dominant allele from the Percheron parent and will be bay or black. The 100 percent gene frequency of chestnut in Suffolk horses has in no way changed the inherent characteristics of the chestnut allele as a recessive one.

Additive/Quantitative Inheritance

The genetic control for many traits is called *additive, quantitative,* or *polygenic.*[4] This is especially so for traits that are "how much," such as speed, size, trainability, fiber density, and fiber fineness. These traits are in contrast to those that are "either/or," such as black versus brown, spotted or unspotted. The either/or traits are generally controlled by single pairs (or a few pairs) of genes.

Quantitative traits are also controlled by single genes, just by so many of them that they each make only a small contribution to the final phenotype. The action of so many genes begins to resemble the "bowl of water" concept of genetics instead of the "bowl of beans" concept, but the individual pieces of genetic information are still present. For quantitative traits the individual genes are numerous, and the small contribution of each makes it nearly impossible to determine the contribution of any single gene.

HERITABILITY

Most quantitative traits (and most fiber traits are included in this group) have significant contributions of both genetic and environmental influences. Each of these traits is controlled to a differing extent by the genetic contribution as well as the environmental contribution to the overall phenotype. These genetic and environmental components can be teased out by complicated procedures that yield a statistic called *heritability*. Heritability is a numerical indication of the relative contribution that additive genes make to the final phenotype of a specific trait.

The final equation for any trait controlled by additive genes is:

phenotype = heritability plus environmental influence: $P = H^2 + E^2$

The H^2 component is the heritability, which is the square of the additive genetic component (for statisticians this is a variance, although breeders can use the concept without resorting to the fine details of all that this means). Heritability varies from zero to one, with higher numbers reflecting a greater importance of additive genetic variation than lower numbers. Lower numbers for heritability indicate that environment is relatively more important than are genes.

Heritability estimates are few and far between for alpaca traits but are well documented for many traits of other species. Certain sorts of traits show a consistent trend in degree of heritability across several species so that some reasonable extrapolations are possible. Traits such as fiber density, fiber length, fiber fineness, and growth rate of animals all have relatively high heritabilities. Traits involving reproduction and disease resistance tend to have very low heretibilities. Traits such as milk production fall into the middle range.

Degree of Heritability and Selection Methods

The degree of heritability can help guide the tactics used in a breeding program. Traits of high heritability usually respond well to direct selection based on the production of the individual animal because such traits have little environmental influence, so that the phenotype of the animal is a reasonable guide to its genotype, and therefore to its value as a breeding animal. In contrast, the phenotype of traits of low heritability does not so accurately betray the genotype, and so for such traits it is more helpful to select on the basis of family performance (ancestors and progeny) than on the performance of the individual animal alone. Elaborate progeny testing programs can greatly improve traits of low and moderate heritability, but these programs generally involve such large numbers of progeny that they are unrealistic for North American alpaca breeders.

Performance of large families for traits of moderate heritability can be used to predict the likely genetic value of an individual breeding animal. These predictions are estimations and come from complicated and intricate calculations. These result in a value usually called Estimated Progeny Difference (EPD), Estimated Breeding Value (EBV), or something with a similar name. The specific name given this figure varies somewhat among breeds that use this tactic. Whatever the label, the figure is an estimate of the relative change (positive or negative) that a breeding animal can be expected to pass on to its offspring. This figure is usually expressed in whatever unit of measure is appropriate (such as microns for fiber diameter or pounds for fleece weight). These figures also come with a "repeatability" figure, which is an expression of the relative accuracy of the prediction. Animals on which many progeny have been measured are likely to have a more highly repeatable (and therefore more accurate) EPD than are animals with lower numbers of offspring. Both the EPD and the repeatability are important if the goal is to select sires that can improve the herd. Older animals, by virtue of having had many offspring, are likely to have more accurate (repeatable) EPDs than are younger animals that have produced fewer. EPDs can be useful, but should not guide every breeding decision.

Fortunately for alpaca breeders, several of the traits of most interest (fiber, conformation) have reasonably high heritabilities and so selection based on the individual's performance (or phenotype) is accurate enough for good progress to be possible in breeding programs without needing to resort to elaborate progeny testing programs.

Production of Phenotypic Extremes for Quantitative Traits

The phenotype, or performance, of quantitative traits varies in any population. The range is usually "low to high" or "poor to excellent" with relatively few animals at either of the extremes and the bulk of animals in the middle range. Selection generally favors those at the top end of the range. When considering animals at the top end, though, remember that their superiority is based not only on genetics but also on environment. In practical terms this means that the phenotype of a superior animal is likely to be the result of a decent set of genes, but also a superior environment.

Reverse logic can be used for the poorest animals: These tend to have poor genotypes but also very poor environments. Either extreme is likely to be somewhat surprising in the production of offspring, because the offspring will tend to converge back toward the population average instead of clustering around the extreme performance of the extreme parent. This convergence occurs because it is not possible to consistently recreate the specific environment leading to the exceptional extreme performance of the parent.

SELECTION

Selection is critically important in breeding programs, and it simply means that some animals get to reproduce more than do other animals.[4,5] Selection occurs in any population as soon as some individuals, male or female, produce more offspring than do other animals. The breeder's job is to assure that selection is taking the population in a desired direction, so that selection favors desirable animals and penalizes those not as desirable.

Selection Differential

Selection differential indicates the relative genetic superiority of animals that do reproduce. In alpacas the selection differential for females is pretty low. That is, nearly every female is used for reproduction and therefore gets a chance to pass along her genes for good or ill. In essence this means that little selection is occurring on the female side of the equation.

For male alpacas the selection differential is higher than that for females, but how much higher varies with individual breeding programs. Some males are used on only a few females, and some are used on many. Likewise, in some herds nearly every male that is born is used for reproduction, for others only a small percentage (likely never fewer than 5%) are used. The overall result is that the selection differential for male alpacas is indeed higher than for females, but still only moderate when compared to many other species. This result can be for good or bad, depending on how the selection is used.

An example that illustrates the degree to which selection can proceed comes from dairy cattle. The selection differential for dairy bulls is probably the highest of the common domesticated species, because only one bull in thousands is used for artificial insemination. Some evidence is developing in dairy cattle that the very high selection differential has resulted in a somewhat narrow genetic base, which might have long-term consequences for the overall genetic health of some populations. However, the relatively low selection differential for many alpaca herds indicates that more genetic progress is easily possible than is currently being realized.

Selection Goals

The point of selection is to dictate the form of the succeeding generations. Selection determines which traits tend to get passed along and which do not. The results of contrasting selection goals are easy to demonstrate for Peruvian versus North American alpacas. While certainly individual breeder's goals differ in both locations, the general trend is that Peruvians favor white alpacas and favor huacaya fiber. In North America the opposite is generally true (with exceptions, of course). The result of the selection exerted in the two areas is that the gene frequencies, and therefore the phenotypic frequencies, of the two alpaca populations are going to increasingly differ because the selection pressures are different. That is, in each setting somewhat different animals are selected for increased rates of reproduction. Each country, region, and breeder have slightly different selection goals, and these goals greatly influence which alleles, and the variants they cause, to become either common or rare.

Selection works because it changes allele frequencies. In essence, selection limits (or at least alters) the component genes in the population that can jiggle down to the next generation. The desirability of selection is hardly debatable for disease traits (get rid of the genes, get rid of the disease), but is more subjective for other traits such as color and fleece variants. Selection is value neutral as a concept, so that by itself it is neither good nor bad. Selection has powerful and profound consequences for populations, depending on how it is used.

BREEDING PHILOSOPHY

A crucial first step for breeding programs, and one that is not intuitive to many people, is to decide upon a breeding philosophy.[5] Philosophies include conservation, improvement, and a host of others. A conservation philosophy is going to dictate different goals and actions than a strict animal improvement philosophy, which is also going to be different than a companion animal philosophy.

Philosophy drives goals. Why are animals being bred, and what is the mental picture of the ideal animal? Is the goal show wins? Conformation? Certain fiber characteristics? Certain colors? A specific temperament? Maintaining a specific bloodline? Without answering these questions honestly very little progress is possible in a breeding program. Progress is difficult enough as it is—and is definitely enhanced by acknowledging a philosophy and the goals that go along with it.

A unifying philosophy is essential to achieve any goals. Assigning priorities to these goals is also very important. Is color more important than limb conformation? Is stature more important than temperament? Each breeder will have a slightly different list of priorities, and this is perfectly acceptable. What is very important, though, is for each breeder to be consistent in breeding decisions. A specific philosophy driving specific goals will ensure a consistent breeding program so that progress and success are more assured than if decisions are made haphazardly.

No single philosophy is wrong; each is just different. Many discussions, and even some heated arguments, can stem from different breeders having different philosophies. Breeders representing a variety of philosophies are probably good for the overall health of the genetic resource, because each breeder is doing something slightly different. Thus the population maintains sufficient genetic diversity so that future generations of breeders can select alpacas for their programs from among the available variations.

Diversity of approaches must be channeled in a positive direction, though, as some philosophies are fundamentally different from others and can be expected to produce ani-

mals that are of little use to some other breeding programs while of immense use to others. Remember that the breeding of alpacas, as is true of breeds within all domestic species, occurs within a political framework of a breeders' organization. Keeping the different philosophies and variables in one relatively peaceful framework is important in managing the diversity necessary for maintaining the genetic resource. An example from another species is the split of many sheep flockbooks into two sections, one for white and one for colored sheep, with little communication among the breeders of the two types. For some breeds this split only further endangers an imperiled resource, and more inclusive organizational and political frameworks may better serve the fostering of the breed as a genetic resource.

BREEDING STRATEGIES

Breeding strategies include inbreeding and outbreeding, with varying levels of each. Each strategy has an appropriate place in a healthy population structure,[5] because each does something different. They are value neutral, and each is appropriate in different situations and for different goals.

Inbreeding

Inbreeding includes any mating in which the mated animals have ancestors in common. That is, the mating "doubles up" on certain ancestors. Inbreeding can happen to varying degrees. When first-degree relatives (parent to offspring, sibling to sibling) are mated, the result is generally regarded as *inbreeding*. When more distant matings are accomplished (grandparent to grandoffspring, aunt to nephew), the matings are more likely to be considered *linebreeding*. There is no magic point at which the boundary between inbreeding and linebreeding is drawn, and the idea that "it is linebreeding if it works, and inbreeding if it does not" pretty much sums up the idea that these two are arbitrary points along a continuum.

Inbreeding tends to make animals more genetically uniform. That is, the pairs of genes become more and more likely to be similar than they are likely to be different. Gene uniformity has a variety of consequences, which can be good or bad depending on what goes into the mix. That is, good things can become consistent or bad things can become consistent. Therefore, inbreeding must be accompanied by selection. Very, very good and consistent populations of animals in a variety of species have been accomplished by inbreeding to varying degrees. The key strength of an inbred or linebred animal is that the gene pairs are generally alike, so the animal produces very uniform offspring. This is one of the main strengths of a linebred animal—predictability.

Consistency in size, color, and yield.

The "bowl of beans" concept of genetics might help to illustrate this point. Inbreeding basically goes back repeatedly to the same bowl of beans (the common ancestor). The result is that the same beans are more likely to get put into the next generation than if a completely different bowl of beans were used. The beans, therefore, tend to aggregate in a more consistent array than in a population where a different mix is constantly introduced at each generational step, as would be the case in a strictly outbreeding situation.

Some breeders characterize moderate linebreeding as a strategy for "locking in a trait." This phrase reflects a strategic goal of providing genetic uniformity in an animal so that it can then be used widely and predictably in a breeding program. This is the positive aspect of inbreeding —it can and does produce some excellent animals of great value for consolidating genetic progress in a population.

A very important aspect of inbreeding is that as it proceeds and the gene pool gets narrower and narrower, traits of general fitness tend to suffer in a population. This phenomenon is called *inbreeding depression*. Affected traits usually include reproductive traits, milk production, growth rates, and size traits. Disease resistance traits may also suffer, although this varies. The point here is that inbreeding, especially if not associated with selection, has consequences that may be disastrous. Inbreeding de-

pression is also more likely to occur following repeated, multigenerational inbreeding than it is to occur following a single inbred mating. So while inbreeding can be a powerful tool in some situations, it is a somewhat risky strategy. Breeders who undertake an inbreeding program must be fully prepared to cull offspring in the event that the desired outcome is not achieved.

Outbreeding

Outbreeding tends to do the opposite of inbreeding. It tends to make populations more variable by matching up unlike members in the gene pairs. Outbred animals, because they have unlike gene pairs, tend to produce variable offspring so that predictability is decreased.

Outbred matings are those that do not have ancestors in common. Outbreeding or outcrossing can vary in extent, just like inbreeding. The widest outbreeding is to mate an alpaca to a llama, guanaco, or vicuña. Many people would class this as crossbreeding, much as they do in other species when different breeds are mated together. The trick to outbreeding is that the products of the initial cross are likely to be very uniform. If 100 crias were produced, they may actually end up looking like near copies of one another to the extent possible in any animal-related endeavor. So where is the variability? It is locked up in the heterozygous condition of each of these outbred animals. When these uniform animals are used for reproduction, they in turn produce extreme variability because they can transmit only half of each variable pair to the next generation.

To go back to the bowl of beans, in an outbred animal the bean mixture is more likely to be diverse than in an inbred animal. All the different types of beans are still there, but they are generally paired up with unlike beans in the heterozygous condition. In an inbred animal the beans are more likely to "double up" in a homozygous condition, while in the outbred situation they are more likely to occur in a heterozygous condition. So while the allele frequencies may well be identical in outbred and inbred populations, those alleles are found in markedly different situations: homozygous in inbred populations, heterozygous in outbred populations.

Which Is Best?

Outbred animals can be very, very productive animals. The initial outbred products can be uniform, and they also excel in those very traits that suffer under inbreeding: vitality, reproduction, and growth. The peculiar qualities of inbreeding and outbreeding are used to great advantage in some animal industries. Egg-laying chickens, for example, are the result of crossing two distinct inbred parental or grandparental lines. The resulting hens are phenotypically uniform heterozygotes as a consequence of the linebreeding behind the parents, which constrains each gene pair to be two identical alleles of specific genes. They are also vigorous because the gene pairs are unlike. And they are useless for anyone else to breed from, because they will produce uneven offspring. This tactic protects the investment of the breeder companies, because it does not matter into whose hands the actual laying hens fall. They simply cannot produce predictable offspring.

So which is best—inbreeding or outbreeding? The answer depends entirely on the breeder's goals. Inbreeding tends to bring recessive genes to the light of day by forcing them into pairing with one another. That can be good or bad, depending on the trait and the selection imposed on it. Alternatively, outbreeding tends to hide recessive genes. However, these genes remain in the population, and in a form against which selection cannot occur because they are not expressed. Some deleterious genes could therefore become very widespread in a population before even being discovered. A good example is the combined immunodeficiency of Arabian foals. About 20 percent of Arabian horses carry this allele, resulting in about 4 percent of all foals born being affected. The allele was allowed to get to this high frequency by lack of selection on the part of breeders. Recent development of a test for this allele will allow breeders to avoid mating carriers and thereby the

production of defective foals. But the high frequency of carriers will dictate caution in pairing members of this breed for many generations to come, so it is always prudent to try to decrease the frequency of such an allele.

For most breeds of livestock, and by extension for alpacas, breeding programs using a variety of strategies are healthiest for the genetic resource. Some inbreeding in certain situations is advisable, as long as it is accompanied by selection and as long as breeders are fully aware that the result is likely to be either very good or very bad. An example is a female with some truly rare and exceptionally good trait. Mating her back to a son could consolidate this trait quickly and effectively. The goal of such a mating would be a son that exemplifies her excellence. Inbreeding, in this situation, has managed to take the genetic material that was only nominally available in a female form and make it much more widely usable in a male form.

A similar example is an animal (male or female) of extremely good phenotype. Half son to half daughter matings would produce some animals that locked in this level of performance, so that superior breeding animals could be more widely used than the original single animal. It is an undeniable fact that excellent inbred animals are incredibly useful in breeding programs, even though the mating strategy that produces them also runs the risk of producing some disasters. A strategy of alternating inbreeding and outbreeding generation to generation makes it possible to consolidate phenotypic excellence without losing vigor. As always, though, selection is the key to using inbreeding to good advantage while avoiding the risks of inbreeding depression.

Most alpaca breeders will opt for the immediately safer outbreeding strategy, and this is recommended in most situations. Remember, though, that outbreeding does not reduce the frequency of alleles, but only assures that they are usually heterozygous. So to use outbreeding as a strategy for reducing the incidence of defective phenotypes is valid, but this strategy does not reduce the frequency of genes causing them.

IMPORTANCE AND USE OF A DNA-BASED REGISTRY

The importance of the DNA typing of alpacas is largely to assure that pedigrees are accurate. DNA typing allows the genetic material in the chromosomes (which is DNA) to be catalogued to a level of detail that is reasonably unique to each individual and can therefore become an accurate form of identification. The unique DNA fragments can be tracked through the generations, which explains their usefulness in parentage validation. DNA typing is currently mostly concerned with the establishment of pedigree accuracy. It does not presently concentrate on trying to relate specific DNA variants with specific genes. Studies may one day allow specific alleles (such as color, defects, fiber traits) to be identified as specific DNA fragments. At that point DNA typing will be directly helpful to breeders as they make breeding decisions.

An example from horses is that the frame overo pattern has been identified as a specific DNA fragment. This allele causes attractive spotting in heterozygotes, but white foals that die soon after birth in homozygotes. The significance of the DNA test is that it is now possible to assure the mating of horses such that the desired spotted heterozygotes can be produced with no risk of a lethal homozygote.

For parentage validation to be entirely accurate, both males and females need to be DNA typed. Where only males are typed, it is possible to validate only the male side of each pedigree. Male pedigree is generally accurate enough, but does leave a door open for either deliberate or accidental misidentification of dams. If accurate pedigrees are essential, then DNA validation of both sires and dams is likewise essential.

DEFECTS

A variety of physical defects occurs in alpacas, and these are important to alpaca breeders because the production of defective crias has two negative aspects.[1,2,3,6,7] One negative is the loss or suffering of the baby. The second loss is the tarnished image of the parents producing the defective baby and their subsequent diminished value as breeding animals. Few (if any) defects in alpacas have yet to be proven genetic in origin, but certainly some are good candidates: choanal atresia and severe angular limb deformities. In the lengthy list of defects in alpacas in Table 24.1, none is yet proven genetic. No one sets out to produce defective animals in a breeding program, yet defective young are occasionally produced. Defects can be considered in a few broad categories: congenital defects, genetic defects, and environmental defects.

Congenital Defects

A *congenital defect* simply means a defect that is present at birth. Congenital, by itself, does not imply a genetic cause for the defect, although many of them are indeed genetic in origin. A good example of a nongenetic, yet congenital, defect is the limb abnormality associated with the use of thalidomide in pregnant women.

Genetic Defects

Genetic defects are those defects that are caused directly by genes and not by environmental influences. Most genetic defects are congenital (present at birth), but some are not evident until later. Those present at birth are very much easier to manage and document than are those that show up later. Late-onset genetic defects include some degenerations that can occur in certain animals, such as progressive retinal atrophy in some breeds of dogs. This atrophy is not evident at birth, develops at a few years of age, and is genetic in its cause in most breeds.

Defects, if genetic, can usually be traced to one of several candidate genetic mechanisms or modes of inheritance. Each separate defect is usually controlled by a single, or at most a few, distinct modes of inheritance. Very few defects are caused by dominant alleles, as they would be quickly eliminated from the population because dominant alleles are rarely if ever hidden. Exceptions include some defects with a late onset, because these can escape detection until after animals have reproduced.

Those defects caused by single recessive alleles are more problematic, and most single-gene defects do indeed have a recessive mode of inheritance. This phenomenon is somewhat intuitively obvious because this type of inheritance allows the allele to persist unexpressed in carriers, which allows it to escape negative selection. The genes can thereby persist in the population because selection is ineffective at identifying and removing all of them. A third common type of inheritance pattern for defects is polygenic. This pattern is relatively common and involves a whole host of challenges for breeders.

Single-Gene Defects In the event that a certain defect is shown to be due to simple single genes, then selection becomes relatively easy.[4] The affected animals can be culled, and modern genetic techniques offer the promise that blood or DNA tests can be developed to spot carriers. Carriers can then be used wisely in reproduction. If a carrier is only average, the best idea is to cull. If a carrier has some other excellent traits, then the carrier could be used on a limited basis, hoping to replace the carrier with a noncarrier offspring that is excellent but that does not carry the defective allele. The key to the single gene traits is that on average half of the offspring will be carriers, but the other half will not. A single gene can therefore be tracked and eliminated with careful breeding practices. While this is occurring, defective offspring can be avoided by the simple strategy of never mating carrier to carrier.

Polygenic Defects Other defects are due to polygenes.[4] These traits include some, such as most cardiac defects, in which animals have no defect until the number of genes

Table 24.1 Defects of alpacas, categorized by organ or system. Comments comparing to other species may be helpful in pointing more to a genetic cause or an environmental cause.[1,2,3,6,7]

Defect	Comment
Skeletal System	
arthrogrypposis	Fusion of joints, usually knee or hock. Frequently associated with head or spinal abnormalities, many of which are viral in other species.
angular limb defects	Forelimbs or hindlimbs can have both genetic and environmental contributions.
hemivertebra	Small and misshapen vertebrae, which can lead to paralytic problems. A differing incidence among breeds of other species (notably dogs) suggests that some of these are genetic in origin.
patellar luxation	Kneecap failing to remain in its usual groove. The result is gait abnormality and degeneration of the joint. Likely to have both genetic and environmental causes.
polydactyly	Extra toes. This varies among species from genetic in some to the occasional odd nongenetic variant in others.
syndactyly	Fusion of toes. In most species this is genetic.
scoliosis	Crooked spine.
agenesis of tail	Missing tail.
crooked tail (tail scoliosis)	Twisted or crooked tail. Genetic in some breeds of dogs.
crooked toenails	Toenails curve inward or outward. Some of these are congenital and potentially genetic, others are more likely to be environmental from chronic poor foot care.
contracted tendons	Flexible joints but without full range of motion due to tendons being short. Frequently environmental, and usually transitory if treated early.
Head and Face	
cerebellar hypoplasia	Small posterior segment of brain resulting in uncoordinated motion or inability to rise. In various species this is either an environmental condition (usually viral) or can be genetic.
choanal atresia	Imperforate opening between nasal and oral cavities. Cria cannot both eat and breathe simultaneously and does poorly. Evidence on genetic control is mixed, so if genetic it is not a simple single-gene trait.
cyclopia	Single eye. Usually due to toxins or certain viruses in the fetus.
meningocele	Malformed brain and cranium. Some examples in some species are genetic, others are environmental.
wry face	Crooked, nonsymmetric face. Not genetic in most species.
hydrocephalus	Excess internal fluid in brain replacing brain tissue. Can be either genetic or environmental in many species.
inferior brachygnathism	Shortened lower jaw. Causes in many species include genetic and environmental influences.
superior brachygnathism	Shortened upper jaw. Causes in many species include genetic and environmental influences.
inferior prognathism	Lengthened lower jaw. Causes in many species include genetic and environmental influences.
superior prognathism	Lengthened upper jaw. Causes in many species include genetic and environmental influences.
retained deciduous incisors	Failure of milk teeth to shed, resulting in multiple teeth as permanent teeth grow in.
nares agenesis	Nostrils fail to develop. Cause unknown.
narrow face, stenotic nasal cavity	Abnormally thin face, with diminished nasal cavity and inability to move sufficient air.
cleft palate	Incomplete roof of mouth, allowing communication between mouth and nose. In several species this is either genetic or environmental with similar apppearance of both types.
Eye	
cataract	Opaque lens. Many causes in several species, some are environmental but many are genetic.
blindness	Many causes, including both genetic and environmental in several species.
entropion	In-turned eyelid. Usually a fairly complicated trait that involves some genetic component as well as an environmental one.
ectropion	Out-turned eyelid. More rare than entropion, and can be confused with some stressed animals everting eyelids slightly as a display.
hypoplasia of eyelid	Eyelids insufficient to completely cover eyes, resulting in irritated eyes.
blue eyes	Lack of complete pigmentation of eye. Many different genetic causes, some with other associated defects (deafness) but many without such association. Not always a defect.
Ears	
curled margins	Margins of ear curl inward.
long ears	Ears of correct shape but too long. Likely polygenic.
gopher ears	Small residual ears. Genetic in both sheep and goats, and so may well be in alpacas.

Table 24.1 continued

Defect	Comment
Reproductive System	
cervical agenesis	No cervix present. May be related to segmental aplasia.
double cervix	Two cervixes. Usually a minimal problem. Likely some genetic influence in cattle.
segmental aplasia	Failure of lumen to develop along some region of uterus. Genetic in cattle.
uterus unicornis	Extreme segmental aplasia, with only one uterine horn.
hermaphrodite	Wide variety of intersex conditions. Some have genetic causes.
ovarian hypoplasia	Small ovaries, usually due to too few germ cells. Genetic in most species in which this has been studied. Leads to shortened reproductive life.
ovarian aplasia	Extreme ovarian hypoplasia, and if unilateral is probably a specific defect that also involves the kidney on the affected side.
twinning	Dominant trait that tends to pass from mother to offspring.
freemartin	Rare intersex condition in twins.
crooked penis	This is frequently acquired rather than congenital.
short penis	Penis too short, impedes mating.
cryptorchidism	Failure of descent of testis into scrotum. Unilateral or bilateral. In nearly every species studied it is genetic, and likely polygenic.
monorchidism	Only a single testis develops. Commonly associated with only one kidney, and likely a genetic trait.
testicular hypoplasia	Small testes from too few germ cells. In most species this is a genetic trait.
Digestive System	
atresia ani	No anus present.
atresia coli	Portion of the colon absent. Most likely environmental in cattle.
megaesophagus	Dilated esophagus resulting in regurgitation.
Cardiovascular System	
patent ductus arteriosus	Failure of fetal communication between arteries to shut down. Polygenic threshold trait in most species.
ventricular septal defect	Abnormal communication between main chambers of the heart. Polygenic threshold trait in most species.
other heart defects	Include atrial septal defects, persistent right aortic arch, tetralogy of Fallot, transposition of great vessels. Each is separate, and each is most likely genetic in origin, with most being polygenic threshold traits.
Miscellaneous	
single kidney	Usually related to monorchidism or ovarian aplasia. Likely a genetic trait.
extra teats	More than four teats. Frequently these are vestigial and nonfunctional. In most species this is a polygenic trait.
lack of a teat	One or more teats missing.
hypoplastic teats	Teats too short for easy nursing by cria.
hernia	Includes umbilical, inguinal, and diaphragmatic, with each a separate defect. Some are genetically conditioned in some species.

passes some threshold. Above the threshold the defect is expressed, and with increasing numbers of genes the severity of the defect is increased. Because the defect is associated with many genes, it is impossible to use simple breeding strategies to eliminate these. Any animal with the defect and any animal that is a first-degree relative (parent, sibling) is more likely to have lots of these genes than is a random member of the population. That means that, with few exceptions, selection should be sure and firm against bearers of such defects as well as their first-degree relatives. Philosophy will come into play here; does the breeder put priority on eliminating the defect compared to the desir-

ability of using the breeding animal for its possible positive traits?

Environmental Defects

Environmental causes for defects include drugs, other chemicals that are either administered or otherwise in the environment, and other agents such as viruses. All of these agents are called *teratogens*, or are teratogenic, and they result in defects that arise during fetal development. These defects are better documented in other species than in alpacas. Defects caused by chemicals generally cluster on specific properties but across family groups or other genetic lineages (breeds, for example). They also tend to cluster over a defined time period that relates to the exposure period during the previous gestation.

A similar pattern occurs in sheep and goats following exposure to certain viruses. In such herds it is usual to have normal offspring, then a rash of defective offspring, then a return to normal offspring, all within a few days of the same lambing/kidding season. The defective offspring are tightly clustered in a short period that relates to the specific exposure to the virus during gestation. A "herd outbreak" of defects is more likely environmental than it is genetic.

Deciding Whether Defects Are Genetic or Environmental

Not all defects are caused by genetic influences, and it can be important to decide accurately if a specific defect that is encountered is genetic or not. A few general guidelines will help to establish that a defect is more likely genetic or more likely environmental in origin.

Genetic defects usually vary in incidence among breed or family lines, so any difference in incidence among different genetically isolated groups points more to a genetic origin than an environmental one. Most genetic defects also occur as somewhat sporadic events rather than an explosive increase in the incidence of the defect. Genetic defects usually occur following the mating of carriers, and then only a portion of the offspring is affected with many more unaffected.

Tracking down the fine details of the cause of some specific defects can be frustrating and time-consuming. In addition, some individual defects can have multiple causes. Cleft palate in dogs, for example, can have multiple causes that result in an identical defect. Causes include at least two different genetic mechanisms as well as a host of teratogenic chemicals. Figuring out which mechanism is behind a specific cleft palate puppy can be extremely difficult.

Some defects defy any attempt to easily catalog them as either genetic or environmental. Some of these are relatively severe, such as extra toes. Others are more cosmetic, such as very tiny or missing ears. Some cases of these defects are likely to be sporadic background "noise" of occasional defects that are present in all species. To be safe, though, none of these should be used for reproduction.

When Is It a Defect?

Defects nearly all vary in the extent to which they are expressed. An example is rear limb angularity, or "cow-hocks," in which the hocks are closer together than the feet. Very few animals stand truly square behind (in any species), and in some very highly selected breeds an ex-

treme squareness and "correctness" actually contribute to some difficulty in mobility, especially as the animals age.

Many animals, of all species, have a very slight to moderate degree of cow-hocks, and some breeders of more primitive and adapted breeds insist that a mild degree of this helps with mobility in rough country. However, it is also undeniable that a moderate to extreme degree of cow-hocks can lead to impaired movement as well as to early degeneration of joints and limbs.

The point here is that most conformational details vary on a continuum from a perceived ideal (straight, well-formed limbs) through an intermediate "grey zone" where the animals are not conformationally perfect but neither are they functionally compromised, into a region where the animals are obviously defective. Drawing the boundary between "ideal" and "substandard" and "defective" is very difficult for these traits.

Defect or Aesthetic Preference?

For some characteristics, especially those traits that do not affect soundness, the issue of defectiveness is very relative. Exactly where a trait becomes aesthetic preference or defect varies from breeder to breeder as well as from trait to trait. A suri newborn in an elite huacaya herd is likely to be considered defective, while the same animal in a suri herd would be most welcome. Similarly, for many years colored newborns in white herds were considered defective.

Fleece type and color may seem to be trivial examples of this phenomenon, but other traits are also involved. Examples include blue eyes, which are tolerated in some breeding programs but anathema to others. Ear length is another example.

Assortative Mating (Mating of Extremes)

The subject of *assortative mating* can help in understanding some defects. Assortative mating simply means the deliberate mating of animals that are similar (positive assortative mating) or very different (negative assortative mating). This strategy is distinct from either inbreeding or outbreeding, and it can be accomplished with either of those strategies.

Positive assortative mating, when accomplished with conformational traits, translates into the mating of similarly extreme animals. In many species this can include the mating of very large to very large, very small to very small, or any other peculiarity of conformation (cute, short heads, really short ears, very long or very short legs, and on and on). In many species, dogs being the best example, positive assortative mating results in extreme breeds such as dachshund, Boston terrier, Irish wolfhound, Saint Bernard, and a host of others that fall outside the norm for the original species. Positive assortative mating can be bad or good, but frequently brings along associated defects. Some of the defects depend on exactly what goes into the original mix, as a sort of founder effect. Other defects may be direct spin-offs of the specific extreme that is the target of selection.

An important example comes from cats. Shortheadedness is desired in the Persian, and these animals have very few problems, although some at the extreme end have minor trouble breathing through their noses. Selection for a similar head shape in the Burmese has inadvertently centered on a single gene that results in the desired short head in heterozygotes but in a brain abnormality in homozygotes. These die shortly after birth. One of the lessons from this example: Single extreme phenotypes can have multiple and distinct genetic causes (polygenic in Persians, single gene in Burmese). Another lesson: Extremes can cause animals to trespass over the limit of soundness, especially if some single gene providing for the desired conformation is also capable of producing defects. This lesson applies especially to conformational extremes and only very rarely to extremes of fiber quality.

Overall soundness and conformational quality need to be the bottom-line minimum when selecting breeding stock. Slow progress with soundness is better than fast, extreme progress that might well leave overall soundness behind. Finally, very extreme animals may be that way from an extreme genetic mechanism, and not all of these are good. Breeders interested in these should proceed with caution.

Blue Eyes

Blue eyes are controversial in many livestock species, and alpacas are no exception. Many blue-eyed animals appear to be perfectly normal. Blue eyes are sometimes just the odd variant in an otherwise unremarkable animal. That is, the animal is fully pigmented and normal, just that it has blue eyes. Blue-eyed humans are a good example of this point.

In several species many instances of blue eyes are related to white spotting patterns. In some of these species, certain of these patterns are associated with blindness, nightblindness, or deafness. This statement is a long way from saying that all blue eyes are defective, but indicates only that in certain instances blue eyes can be associated with specific defects.

The main issue surrounding blue eyes is to decide whether they are associated with any defects, and if so, what to do about it. If blue eyes are not associated with defects (and this is most likely the case with dark-coated animals that have blue eyes), then the best thing is to ignore them.

A few white-coated blue-eyed alpacas appear to be deaf. A very, very important question for these animals is whether or not this matters. If the deaf animals are able to receive and give enough social signals to live relatively normal lives in a herd situation, then they do not experience any decline in quality of life stemming from their blue eyes or from their deafness. The question is: Does this condition matter to the animal?" If the answer is no, then don't worry about it. If the trait does adversely affect the animal in its intended use in its intended environment, then steps should be taken to eliminate the trait.

Most people with deaf alpacas relate that the animals appear to be fully competitive with their peers, and so this trait probably does not matter to alpacas in most situations. Indeed, most owners indicate that documenting the deafness is reasonably difficult because the animals are so astute at picking up visual cues that their deafness is well hidden. Obviously, such animals should not be subjected to clicker training or put into other situations where hearing is essential.

The impact of blue eyes in breeding decisions is somewhat different. Different philosophies are possible on this one. An extreme philosophy would be to cull all of them from breeding. The opposite extreme is to ignore them and mate alpacas while ignoring their eye color. A middle route would be to avoid the mating of blue-eyed animals to one another. This middle-of-the-road approach is likely to mitigate any suboptimal baggage that the trait might have, simply because the breeder is avoiding the mating together of extreme animals.

TRACKING DEFECTS

It is critically important to react to defects appropriately—worry about them when it is worthwhile, and ignore them if they are very rare. The incidence rate of defects is therefore important, but is usually unknown. If a defect occurs in only 1 of 200 births or fewer, it is probably not worth worrying about very much. If 1 in 100 or 1 in 50, then it is worth worrying about. Some sort of anonymous, accurate tracking system is needed to track the incidence of these defects, so that an increasing incidence can be met with appropriate action, while rare ones can largely be ignored.

Few breed organizations have ever adequately addressed the documentation and tracking of defects, which can be extremely important as an early warning mechanism for important genetic defects. Some of the best tracking systems are provided by the artificial insemination companies with dairy cattle breeds. The companies provide opportunities for farmers to file reports of the parentage and defects of all defective calves. Most of these are sporadic "background noise" defects, but a few do turn out to be truly heritable defects. Such a tracking system works in the dairy industry because the males are nearly all owned by the companies or cooperatives that provide the sires. They eagerly seek out information, and individual farmers have an inherent incentive to report defects because they do not own the bull but merely use his frozen semen.

The alpaca situation is vastly different from the dairy cattle situation. One important distinction is that males are usually individually owned and are used on fewer mates than is the case in dairy cattle. It is in a breeder's immediate interest not to document defects in crias, for the suspicion that a sire is producing these could easily and quickly erode his economic value. For a tracking system to function well, it needs to be as inclusive as possible, which means the tracking may need to be anonymous, although unlinking the cria information from the pedigree of necessity limits its usefulness in assessing a defect as genetic in origin.

Anonymous tracking has few incentives other than the intangible "good for the genetic resource," which requires breeders to sacrifice some self-interest for that of the community. Anonymous tracking, while not as powerful as more fully documented tracking, would provide enough information for any change in incidence, or a surge in occurrence, to be detected early enough to provide some sort of alert for breeders that further and more direct investigations may be necessary.

A step above anonymous tracking would be a confidential tracking system in which the identity of the affected animal is known only to the registry organization or designated agents such as research personnel. The identity would never be made public. This strategy could assure early detection and documentation of genetic defects, but would work only if breeders are confident that the system is truly and completely confidential.

CULLING

Culling is essentially negative selection in that culling removes certain phenotypes (and thereby genotypes) from the breeding population. Any animal that is not allowed to reproduce is in essence culled from the breeding population, although this means vastly different things in South America where alpaca meat is consumed and in North America where culled animals are generally used for fiber or pets.

Some traits will be culled from nearly all populations, such as any life-threatening defect. For other defects it is possible to achieve nearly universal agreement as to the advisability to cull. Included are severe angular limb deformities or other structural abnormalities that impede soundness and function.

The most sure genetic progress can be made by linking culling with selection, so that defects are decreasing in frequency at the same time excellent traits are increasing. This implies some turnover in the population as the bottom end is removed to make room for newly recruited youngsters that have better phenotypes.

Rates of culling are going to vary from situation to situation. In South America rates of culling up to 30 percent are possible. Such high rates are rare in North America, but could go far in assuring the increasing excellence of North American alpacas.

GENERAL APPROACHES FOR GENETIC IMPROVEMENT

Genetic improvement theory eventually boils down to choosing the specific matings that will provide the next generation of offspring. Several different factors affect such choices, not the least of which is the practical availability of certain sires and dams. A general rule is that all matings should be undertaken to provide some improvement over the parental phenotypes. That sounds harmless enough, yet can be very difficult in real situations.

One important aspect to planning matings is to balance any weaknesses that may be present in the parents. A cow-hocked or knock-kneed animal should rarely be mated to a similar one. The goal should be to correct these faults, realizing that nutrition as well as breeding factor into these defects. The most successful tactic is to balance a fault in one animal with a strength in the mate. That is, mate a cow-hocked animal to a straight-limbed one. It is rarely successful to play defects off one against the other, such as mating cow-hocks to bowlegs. Such a strategy usually only compounds problems instead of solving them.

Generally breeders expect the males to make up for weaknesses in females, because males are used on more mates than are females. In practice this means that male selection must be very careful indeed.

Selecting Animals for Reproduction

Selecting animals that are destined for reproduction is as much art as science. All breeders should constantly be evaluating the performance of their animals and should mentally delegate the superior ones as the parents of the next reproducing generation. This obviously means something different for male and female alpacas in North America, but the underlying logic remains true

Breeding extremes can take many forms. All four South American camelid species can interbreed and produce fertile offspring.

Breed Maintenance

Maintaining a breed, or in the case of alpacas, two variants of one species, is a tricky and complicated business. Several factors are important for success, and these factors can tend to pull against each other in some circumstances.

Two important issues are *predictability*, so that mating of two similar animals reproduces the same type (implying genetic consistency), and *genetic variability*, because it contributes to overall vigor as well as providing variation useful for future selection. Predictability and variability can be seen as two end points of a single line, with one extreme being so variable as to be nearly totally unpredictable. At the other extreme is absolute uniformity and predictability such that variability (and vigor) is diminished. Breeding populations must stake out a region between these two extremes where variability is sufficient for vigor without sacrificing predictability.

The mechanics of breed maintenance are going to involve decisions by many breeders, and the breed organization needs to assure open dialogue so that philosophic differences are channeled in a positive direction that helps the genetic resource.

Documenting Extremes of Performance

The positive side of tracking within a population involves the documentation of extremes of performance. If an alpaca is in the top few percent of the population of any parameter, recognition is very important because it can assure that truly exceptional animals do not languish underused in small breeding programs, but are more able to be used widely to improve the general population of alpacas.

Such documentation could take several different forms, but a possible strategy is to decide upon certain levels of performance of a variety of individual traits that would allow the animal to be identified as having a premium phenotype for that trait. Such traits might include fiber fineness, fiber uniformity, fleece weight, and the like. Traits such as conformational excellence can also be quantified, although this generally needs to involve trained observers so that such measures are repeatable and unbiased. While at first blush it would seem that showring wins might accomplish some measure of overall conformational and fiber excellence, the reality is that these traits are much better assessed by means that are completely unbiased and quantifiable, and that are ideally undertaken by completely disinterested parties.

Specific details of categories for documenting performance are somewhat arbitrary, but a split of fiber diameter could usefully include animals whose average diameter is below 20 microns, below 17 microns, and below 15 mi-

and is the important point. It is always safer to select animals with great performing ancestors than to select the odd superior phenotype that springs from marginal or poor parents.

Specifically, some animals establish track records of years and years of phenotypic excellence. These include males and females that produce consistent and superior fleeces year after year. Also included are females that reproduce consistently on time and produce high-quality offspring. Such animals should be designated as the parents of potential future sires. They should also have harmonious conformation, which leads to a specific and somewhat subjective "look." Experienced stockbreeders can detect these animals as likely to produce superior offspring and to produce them repeatedly. These animals are the most useful to a breeding program, especially as the parents of future sires. Such a strategy assures that sires have a long pedigree of phenotypic, and therefore likely genotypic, excellence behind them.

crons. Fiber uniformity needs to include those with very low coefficients of variability, such as below 25 percent, below 23 percent, and below 20 percent. Fleece weights should be on an unskirted basis, and might include figures of 10 pounds (4.5 kg) or over, 12 pounds (5.5 kg) or over, and 15 pounds (6.8 kg) or over for annual production. The principle here is to set a very restrictive top standard, but also to include animals in other categories that are approaching that standard, as set apart from the general population of more average performance.

The risk of not having a system of documenting phenotypic excellence is that the alpaca breeding community is very likely to miss the truly exceptional animal that is born into a small breeding herd that does not show or advertise. All breeders, large and small, should be able to participate in breed improvement. Documenting phenotypic excellence by some mechanism that is equally available to all breeders is therefore ideal.

SHOWING

The showring can be a very important factor for determining the relative economic value of breeding animals, but breeders should keep the showring, and showring success, in perspective. Remember that the showring is selecting for whatever balance of traits appeals to the specific judges involved. It is indeed possible to select for showring success as a sort of genetic trait, and this will be very important to many breeders because it does have economic value. Translating that into biologic value can sometimes be tricky.

In some species, and also in the rare-breed conservation world, an alternative to strictly competitive showing has been developing over the last several decades. This alternative is *card grading*, originally developed in the United Kingdom as a strategy for quickly narrowing down huge classes of individual birds that were presented at large poultry shows.

The principle of card grading is that the animals are each evaluated only against a specific breed standard, not against one another. The result is that each animal is then given a card, with blue cards for Excellent, red for Good, yellow for Acceptable, and white for Unacceptable or does not conform to standard.

Card grading is very different from a strictly ordered placement of animals in a showring, for it results in groups of animals that are rated as being similar with regard to the standard. The end result is a useful signal that no single animal is best for everything. Indeed, within the blue and red categories will be individual animals that are much more

A Peruvian quarantine worker named Lucas holds a male alpaca being screened for export to Australia.

useful for specific breeding programs than are others in the same group. In the same categories, other individuals will be more logical choices for other breeding programs. Each breeding program is likely to need something different, so that all blue card animals may indeed be "best" for some specific situation.

A somewhat useful addition to card grading at some gatherings is to card grade first, and follow with a more traditional show of the blue cardholders. This sequence effectively accomplishes both ends—a general assessment of phenotypic worth and a more specific rank ordering of the superior individuals.

SUMMARY

Genetics is useful in individual breeding programs, but also for maintaining and improving the overall population of alpacas. Many breeders, each pursuing their own individual goals and directions, can all synergize with one another, especially if all are reasonably knowledgeable about basic genetic principles as they apply to individual performance as well as populations. Consolidating the current desirable traits in alpacas, while striving to recapture some of the exquisite extremes displayed by pre-Conquest mummified alpacas, should be possible with clearheaded thinking and resolute action on the part of breeders.

REFERENCES

1. Calle, R. E.: *Animal Breeding and Production of American Camelids*. Lima: Ron Henning-Patience, 1984.
2. Fowler, M. E.: *Medicine and Surgery of South American Camelids*. Ames: Iowa State University Press, 1989.
3. Hoffman, E., and M. E. Fowler: *The Alpaca Book: Management, Medicine, Biology, and Fiber*. Herald, CA: Clay Press, 1995.
4. Nicholas, F. W.: *Veterinary Genetics*. Clarendon Press, Oxford. 1987.
5. Sponenberg, D. P., and C. J. Christman: *A Conservation Breeding Handbook*. Pittsboro, NC: American Livestock Breeds Conservancy, 1995.
6. Sumar, J.: Maxilare deprimidos en auquenidos o prognatismo mandibular. Peru, IVITA, *Boletin, Extraordinario* 3: 50–53, 1968.
7. Sumar. J.: Defectos congénitos y hereditarios en alpacas. In *Convencion Internacional Sobre Camelidos Sudamericanos V. Libro de Resumenes*. IVITA-Unversidad Nacional Mayor de San Marcos. Estacion de Altura, La Raya, Cusco, June 6–21, 1985.

Chapter 25

Genetics of Fiber Type and Coat Color

D. Phillip Sponenberg, DVM, PhD

Black phenotypes.

INHERITANCE OF SURI FLEECE TYPE IN ALPACAS

The two fleece types of alpacas, suri and haucaya, are fascinating because few other fiber-producing species have such discrete and extreme variations in fiber type. The inheritance of suri versus huacaya fleece type is an interesting biological phenomenon and is also of importance to alpaca breeders. Unraveling the genetic mechanism behind these fleece types can help to direct breeding programs aimed at either one of these very distinctive and important fibers. Some South American literature tends to support the contention that careful breeding programs can consolidate the two fleece types into relatively pure breeding types with fewer than 1 percent off-type offspring produced.[2,3,14,15]

An Australian group, including highly respected geneticists, has proposed that the suri fleece type is inherited as a single dominant allele.[6] That is, alpacas having this allele in either the homozygous or heterozygous state will be suri, while alpacas homozygous for the alternate form of the gene will be huacaya. While this hypothesis appears to explain their data very well, the data generated by the American registry provide some evidence that the single-gene theory may not be adequate to explain all cases. Both theories assume, of course, that all alpacas are accurately registered as either suri or huacaya, with no animals misregistered.

Data from the Alpaca Registry Inc. are presented in Table 25.1, and are the basis of the following discussion and conclusions. Some of this discussion is necessarily technical. The conclusions are useful even without an intricate understanding of the logic for arriving at them.

Table 25.1 includes data only for alpacas with parentage verified by DNA testing; animals imported either in pregnant females or as adults are not included. This assures that these data are as accurate as possible and free of parentage errors. This accuracy is important because some rare phenomena appear to shed light on the inheritance of suri fleece type, and these rare phenomena must be carefully substantiated as true by parentage validation.

On occasion the mating of two huacayas can produce suri offspring. This happened only 4 times in 19,637 such matings, but remains an important finding. The production of any suris from huacaya × huacaya matings indicates that a single dominant allele is not the whole story. For the single dominant allele hypothesis to be true, the suris from these matings must be new mutations to the suri allele. Four such events in nearly 20,000 matings would indicate a very high mutation rate and thus is an unlikely explanation.

The data indicate other problems with the hypothesis of a single dominant allele. If a single dominant allele were the entire mechanism for producing suris, then some suris would be expected to be homozygous and some would be

Male Parent	Female Parent	Offspring by Fleece Type		Total Offspring	X² If a Single Dominant Allele	Probability Level
		Huacaya	Suri			
suri	suri	278	1,702	1,980		
huacaya	huacaya	19,633	4	19,637		
huacaya	suri	19	7	26	5.5	<0.025
suri	huacaya	70	49	119	3.7	>0.05
total suri × huacaya		89	56	145	0.12	<0.05

Unusual markings for a suri.

heterozygous. This expectation matches the South American experience of some highly selected suri populations producing fewer than 1 percent huacaya offspring. The frequency of the huacaya allele in the suri population can be deduced by the results of suri by suri matings, and by the data would be $\sqrt{278/1980}$. This indicates that the overall frequency of the suri allele in the suri population is 0.6, and the overall frequency of the huacaya allele is 0.4.

The frequency of these two alleles can be used to validate the data of the suri to huacaya matings. The expected value, using the huacaya frequency of 0.4, for the suri male to huacaya female matings is 48 huacaya and 70 suri offspring, which is nearly the reverse of what actually happened. The X^2 value is 16.83, $p<0.01$. This result departs significantly from what is expected and indicates that the single-gene hypothesis is unlikely to be the explanation of suri inheritance in this population. Basically, too many huacayas are consistently produced.

Likewise, the expectation for the huacaya male to suri female matings is 10 huacaya and 16 suri offspring, which deviates from the observed 19 and 7. The X^2 value for these data is 10.1, $p<0.01$, which is a highly significant difference from the expected situation of the single-gene hypothesis.

A relatively simple genetic mechanism is still likely for the difference between suri and huacaya fleece type, although the most simple single-gene hypothesis is not adequate to explain these data. Most alpacas are clearly suri or huacaya, with few intermediates, which indicates that the underlying genetic mechanism is unlikely to be very complicated. That is, the difference is more likely a few genes than a polygenic system involving several genes. In a polygenic system these two variants would likely be extremes along a continuum, with many intermediate types in between. The general lack of intermediates in alpaca fleece types argues strongly that the genetic control of these two types is based on only a few genes.

However, while the vast majority of alpacas are clearly suri or huacaya, importation screeners in South America, as well as some North American breeders, have noted alpacas that are phenotypically intermediate. These animals tended to look like huacayas at a distance, but close examination of the fleeces revealed relatively little crimp as well as high luster. Such fleece types were generally limited to a few source herds, and whether these are truly intermediate between suri and huacaya or are yet another fleece variant of alpacas is undetermined at this time. Extensive breeding tests would have to be accomplished to tease out the details. The presence of these intermediates should be noted, though, as they may indicate that the suri story is complicated rather than simple.

Deducing the mechanism for the genetic determination of the suri fleece type from these data is not entirely possible, although hypotheses consistent with the data are possible. A final answer would depend on planned experimental matings, which are unlikely to occur in the present North American alpaca breeding community.

A possible, and indeed likely, theory is that some independent genetic mechanism suppresses the suri phenotype in the presence of a dominant suri allele. That is, genes at another locus or loci suppress the genotype that should have been produced, overriding the genotype at a single major locus.

If this suppressor is the result of a simple genetic mechanism, then two mutually exclusive choices are that the suppressor is due to either a dominant or a recessive allele. If the suppressor were dominant, then the huacayas coming from suris are indeed huacaya and have failed to get the suri allele in any form. In contrast, the huacayas resulting from suri to huacaya matings might include some huacayas that are suppressed suris, and these huacayas would be capable of producing suri offspring on occasion. This is consistent with the data as far as they go. The frequency of the suri suppressor would be around .34, and roughly half of the genetic suris from suri × huacaya crosses would be suppressed and would look like huacayas.

If the suppressor is recessive, then the huacayas from the suri to suri matings include some (probably many) repressed suris, and the suppression would be common in suris as well as in huacayas. The data do not contradict this hypothesis, and from the data it is impossible to tell the frequency of the suppressor in the population. This hypothesis does complicate the situation more than the previous one, and while the proof is not available, it is probably less likely to be true than the hypothesis of a single dominant suppressor.

The relative rarity of suri offspring from huacaya to huacaya matings indicates that the presence of the suri allele in the huacaya population is rare, and of course the suri allele is always suppressed in phenotypic huacayas. The suri to huacaya results suggest that the mechanism for suppression of the suri phenotype is reasonably common, so that an excess of huacaya offspring in that mating strategy can be expected. This conjecture fits more with a dominant mode for suri suppression than with a recessive mode, although certainly the proof is yet to be accomplished.

These phenomena have some practical implications. The rarity of the suri allele in huacayas indicates that suri will only rarely pop up as a surprise in huacaya to huacaya matings, so this mating strategy is a long shot for suri production. The high incidence of suri suppression in the huacaya population, as demonstrated by the results of the suri to huacaya matings, suggests that the huacayas produced by this strategy include both genetic huacayas lacking the suri allele, and suppressed suris that have the allele but are unable to express it. These animals could have a potential role in suri breeding efforts but cannot be detected visually, and so their potential contributions will continue to go unrealized. The suris, from whatever mating strategy, are indeed suri and will reproduce as such in a mating program.

The likelihood of suri suppression suggests that the most predictable suri mating system is to mate suri to suri, for this eliminates the chance that the suri suppressor can

Two coat types: huacaya, left, and suri.

enter the population and decrease the efficiency of suri production. That is, in suri to suri matings all of the suri offspring are just that—suri, while all of the huacaya offspring are just that—huacaya. The mating of suri to huacaya results in suri offspring that are suri and nothing else, but also results in huacayas that are of two types—genetic huacayas and suppressed suris. These will be easily confused, and will defeat predictability for at least a few generations. If the eventual goal is predictably pure-breeding suris, then the only sound strategy to assure this is to mate suris exclusively to suris. If, on the other hand, the goal is quick expansion of suri numbers, then the mating of suri to huacaya certainly helps to accomplish this goal.

The biology of these two fleece types suggests that the wisest general course is to mate within the types (suri to suri, huacaya to huacaya) and that exceptions to this should be for very specific goals and for improvement of specific characteristics. Complete exclusion of such matings is far too drastic, because suri to huacaya crosses can introduce rare colors into the suri, or other characteristics that might be valuable. Likewise, such crosses can also benefit huacayas by introducing certain fleece characteristics. Strategies that absolutely prevent the crossing of the two types may result in slower or stopped progress in certain characteristics.

Suri type does involve more than just the fiber, because other phenotypic traits distinguish suris from huacayas. For fleece as well as nonfleece traits to be consolidated, probably the wisest breeding strategy is to ensure that suris resulting from suri to huacaya matings are then mated back to suris. Such a mating strategy should probably continue for a few generations to adequately establish a truly suri phenotype on the results of the initial cross. This strategy complicates breeding programs, but provides a specific and targeted strategy for maintaining and consolidating the huacaya and suri types as distinct from one another, without insisting on an absolute barrier between the two types.

INTRODUCTION TO COLOR GENETICS

Color in alpacas is fascinating, and much fact as well as mythology surround the subject. Although alpaca fiber is frequently touted as coming in 22 distinct colors, a close look at show rules indicates that this is simplistic, because the rules state that alpacas at the boundary of two color classes are arbitrarily placed into the darker category. This rule reflects the reality that color varies continuously from black to white and includes everything in between.

Alpacas do come in many different colors, and these generally relate to specific genotypes. The genetic control of color is somewhat sloppy, though, so a single major genotype can lead to a handful of visually distinct but related colors. At the same time, a single color designation (especially for fleece colors) can actually include a few distinct genotypes. The lack of an absolute one-to-one correspondence of genotype and color phenotype compounds the complexity of the color genetics subject, but diligent study can unravel many of the mysteries.

Only a very few studies have been published on alpaca color, and those were generally undertaken before some of the critical concepts had been worked out in sheep, horses, mice, and other species.[3,13,16] This may sound like a trivial detail, but color genetics within any species works best when viewed through the consistencies that are present across species. Comparative data are not present for alpacas, so the following thoughts are largely my own, and come from work with color genetics in horses, dogs, sheep, and goats.[4,5,7,8,9,10,12] Alpaca data have been included and analyzed whenever possible. Those data have been few, but have supported the outline presented here. In short, this is an educated guess, but all the hard evidence does support this guess as valid.

Basic Aspects of Pigment Biology

One of the difficulties of color genetics in a fleece-bearing species such as alpacas is that most investigators focus only on fleece color. This approach overlooks details of color in nonfleeced portions of the animals and can result in some crucial details being overlooked. A prerequisite for any good investigation of alpaca color genetics includes a very accurate and detailed classification of the color of the animals involved.

The main problem with the simpler classing of animals by fleece color alone is that multiple genotypes (genetic combinations in an individual animal) can lead to the same final color phenotype (external appearance). Likewise, single genotypes can lead to multiple final color phenotypes, depending on all the modifiers present. Color genetics is inherently complicated, and unless viewed in detail, it is not going to provide many answers that can help breeders.

A consistent and basic approach in dealing with color genetics will greatly aid in standardizing communication. The first step is to separate color from white. White is the absence of color. White results when color is taken from animals, even though these animals still have an underlying directive for color production. By separating white and color, you can begin to understand the cause of each. Understanding color is an important first step, and then understanding white and patterns of white patches and white hairs can be better achieved. Overall whiteness can be problematic, and the Michell charts list multiple types of white. Lumping these whites together is not going to impede this discussion and is a valid first step in trying to sort out the big picture of color genetics.

Basic Color Considerations

Given the basic aspects above, a first principle is to consider color on the whole animal. Details of face and leg color can be vital in understanding the genetic control of color, even though these areas have little direct importance for the fleece and its color.

Pigments in alpacas are produced by *melanocytes,* which form the pigments, package them, and then deposit them in the cells of the skin or hair (fiber) to result in colored skin and hair. White areas arise from two mechanisms— either a lack of pigment cells in certain regions or the presence of relatively inactive or weakly active cells that are either incapable of forming pigments or of putting them into skin and hair cells.

Pigments in alpacas include two main classes.[11] One is *eumelanin* (YOO-mel-a-nin), which is generally black or some derivative of black such as blue grey or very rarely chocolate brown. Eumelanin is generally consistent wherever it appears throughout the coat. That is, it is either black, or blue grey, or chocolate brown, but never two of these on the same animal. Thus, when assessing browns, any black in the coat indicates that the brown that is present is not eumelanin.

The other pigment is *pheomelanin* (FEE-o-mel-a-nin), which is basically a tan color and includes any brown with a red shade to it. Pheomelanin in alpacas varies from very light fawn, through all the fawn shades, to red brown, and even to a very dark mahogany or chocolate brown. In contrast to eumelanin, pheomelanin can and frequently does vary in intensity on different regions of a single animal. At the very darkest end of the variation of pheomelanin, it is easily possible to confuse it with chocolate brown eumelanin. This distinction may be trivial in alpacas, where nearly all of the browns, tans, and fawns are caused by pheomelanin and not by eumelanin.

The coat of the vicuña, from which alpacas descend, illustrates these points. Vicuñas have minor black trim on the head and legs (especially the nail beds). These regions are eumelanic. Remaining areas of the body are pheomelanic, and range from darker shades over the top of the animal to very pale shades ventrally. This specific color pattern aids in disrupting the outline of the animal, especially at dawn and dusk, and makes them less obvious to predators.

CONTROL OF COLOR

In this section I list the various genetic loci that are likely to control alpaca color and discuss what each is doing. The action of these loci are additive in yielding a final color. After discussing color, I focus on white or patterns of white superimposed over the color. This approach focuses first on genes before moving to color classification. Specific details that are more hypothetical are noted as they are discussed. The system proposed here has been validated by the experiences of several breeders, but is still only a proposal

Determination of color class is difficult at certain ages because color can change. The age at which to determine color class can therefore be important. The initial coat of crias can be lighter than the subsequent coat, so classification is most accurate at first shearing.

Agouti Locus

The *Agouti* locus is a major determinant of color in several species, and it appears to be so in alpacas.[1, 4,5,8,9,10,12] The *Agouti* locus controls the distribution of black versus tan pigment throughout the coat. The result is usually a symmetrical distribution of pigment, so that the animal is the

same side to side. Alpacas appear to have relatively few variants at this locus, but still have enough so that the *Agouti* locus appears to be a major determinant of color variation in alpacas. It is therefore the most important locus to understand.

Dominance relationships among *Agouti* locus alleles are consistent in that all tan areas are expressed. The result is that patterns that are more tan are dominant to patterns that are less tan. Several of the *Agouti* locus patterns have both black and tan areas. These patterns with an obvious interplay of tan and black areas are the easiest patterns to ascribe to the *Agouti* locus, because the symmetrical interplay of black and tan is very typical of patterns controlled by this locus in all species of animals.

Colors that are almost certainly determined by *Agouti* locus alleles follow. These alleles, their symbols, and their range of colors are summarized in Table 25.2.

Tan These animals vary from fawn to a bright clear red. They have minor black trim at the nail beds, around the eyes, and around the mouth. The result is a nearly uniform color based on tan. Only close inspection reveals the residual black areas. Usually animals with this allele are medium to pale tan, and are classed as fawn or beige. This, or a similar allele, also appears capable of making a stark white animal. These would be white with dark eyes.[4]

Tan with Minor Black Trim These animals are close to the tan animals, but have minimal black areas on the nose, around the eyes, on the ear tips, and on the feet that can extend up the fronts of the legs for a short distance.

Red with Black Trim This pattern has larger and more obvious black areas than do tan or tan with minor black trim. These areas include the face and lower leg, with very distinctive black stripes down the fronts of the lower legs.

Table 25.2 Alleles at the *Agouti* and *Extension* loci.

Locus	Allele	Symbol	Range of Fleece Colors
Agouti	tan	A^T	beige, light fawn, medium fawn
	tan with minor trim	A^+	beige, light fawn, medium fawn, dark fawn
	red with black trim	A^r	medium fawn, dark fawn, red, light brown
	bay	A^b	red, light brown, medium brown, dark brown
	black with light belly	A^T	black
	mahogany	A^m	mahogany, off-black
	black	A^a	black
Extension	dominant black	E^D	black, bay black
	wild type (neutral)	E^+	as determined by *Agouti* locus
	red or tan	E^e	medium fawn

Fleeced areas are generally a medium to dark reddish brown, although color varies from a dark fawn through a dark coffee brown color.

Bay This pattern has a red or brown body with a black head and solid black lower legs and feet.

Black with Light Belly This is a rare variant. Animals are black with a very distinctly cream belly. This is expected, from homology with other species, to be an *Agouti* locus allele. Aside from the cream belly the pattern is not shaded, and by fleece category would be black.

Mahogany This pattern is extensively black but retains some red or black regions, usually with a dark intermixture of red or brown fibers in with black ones. The blackest regions are usually the head, legs, and back. Shading from light to dark is minimal.

Black As the name suggests, these animals are solid black with no tan or red areas. Some black animals fade, others do not, and the control for that is probably not at the *Agouti* locus. The result is black fleeces on those that do not fade, and somewhat off-black dark brown fleeces on those that do fade.

Summary For the *Agouti* locus, if nothing else controls color, the paler shades can on occasion produce darker shades because the paler shades are dominant. Each pattern should be able to reproduce only itself or one of the darker members of the series, as these darker members can be masked as recessives. The patterns should be able to produce only a paler member of the series following mating to an animal with a pale variant. That is, black to black should only yield black. Pale fawn mated to pale fawn should (across a population) produce mainly pale fawns, but also should produce just about everything else at least rarely, and very much depends on the genotype of the specific animals that are mated.

Remember that each animal can have only two of these variants, and generally only expresses the paler of the two. So an animal with a tan allele and a red with black trim allele will appear fawn visually but could produce red-brown with black trim crias if mated appropriately. This animal could not produce blacks, no matter how mated, because it simply does not have the genetic machinery to allow for that.

At the *Agouti* locus, black is the best "test cross" to see what recessives are lurking in the other colors. Black is recessive to all other colors, and so whatever alleles animals are carrying will eventually come to light following mating to a black mate. This strategy could be overdone throughout a population, though, and would so drastically increase the frequency of black that other interesting and useful colors could become rarer within the population. A small amount of evidence in other species suggests that those animals that carry black as a recessive *Agouti* allele may be darker, on average, than those that do not. For example, bay homozygotes are likely to be lighter reds than are bays that carry black, which are more likely to be darker and browner. This tendency, however, is not absolute, and great variation in final color occurs between the two types.

Extension Locus

The *Extension* locus has an intricate, predictable, and complicated interaction with the *Agouti* locus. Some small amount of evidence indicates that this locus accounts for some color results, and so it is important to include some discussion of it. In most cases in alpacas the *Agouti* locus appears to be the main determiner of color. Where the *Extension* locus does come into play, color predictions are more confusing and difficult because some *Agouti* and some *Extension* colors are visually identical but genetically distinct. However, variation at the *Extension* locus appears to be very rare, so the *Agouti* locus is the important locus to understand.

Extension acts somewhat opposite to *Agouti* in that black is dominant and red/tan is recessive. The black and the red variants at the *Extension* locus are also epistatic to *Agouti*. This is complicated, but is essential to understand if color genetics is to make any sense. The most likely alleles at *Extension* include the following three.

Dominant Black As the name suggests, this allele is dominant. It is dominant to other members of this locus and also masks any of the *Agouti* patterns behind the black color. Strangely, dominant black in most species is somewhat "weaker" than the *Agouti* recessive black, and is frequently off-black or very dark brown instead of true black.[7] This subtle distinction can help to detect these animals in some cases. The main significance of a dominant black allele is that black to black could indeed result in some segregation of other *Agouti* patterns. This allele is therefore responsible for some very confusing results in an otherwise orderly system, because it is impossible to distinguish all recessive blacks from dominant blacks on visual inspection alone. Each type of black behaves very differently in a breeding program, which can be a source of breeder headaches. Fortunately, this dominant black allele appears to be rare, if it exists at all, so that blacks can generally be assumed to be an *Agouti* locus phenomenon, and therefore be easy to understand. The vast majority of black to black matings produce only black or occasionally off-black animals, and so dominant black, if it exists, is very rare.

Wild Type or Neutral This allele can be considered neutral because it allows the expression of the *Agouti* locus. This sounds confusing, but is simple to remember because every animal with an *Agouti* pattern must be expressing this allele. The "wild type" name is a convention because guanacos and vicuñas have this allele, although it results in guanaco/vicuña colors only when the appropriate *Agouti* locus allele is also present.

Red or Tan This allele is recessive and results in a completely and uniformly tan coat with no black hairs anywhere, although skin can be black. Most alpacas of this color are a uniform tan or fawn. This color, though recessive, also masks the *Agouti* locus, so that surprises are easily possible with these animals. As an example, a uniform fawn could have red with trim and red-brown with black trim at the *Agouti* locus. Mating this animal to a black animal that is wild type at *Extension* and black at *Agouti* will result in red with trim or red-brown with black trim crias. Most fawn or beige animals are caused by the *Agouti* locus, and not by this allele. Very close examination may be necessary to adequately distinguish the two types visually.

Summary The *Agouti* and *Extension* loci probably account for most of the color variation in alpacas, with the *Agouti* locus the main determiner of color in colored alpacas. *Extension* appears to be important in only a very few blacks and in a very few uniform fawns. These two cases can make color breeding predictions difficult but are important only in those rare cases.

A few breeders do have well-documented instances of black to black matings resulting in fawn crias. This occurs more frequently in suri matings than in huacaya matings. These matings indicate that *Extension* is likely to be segregating various alleles. It is impossible to tell, though, whether this is *dominant black* masking an *Agouti*-type fawn, or whether it is the *tan* segregating from the *Agouti* locus black. Further matings will be necessary to be certain about the identity of the alleles involved.

Other Genes That Might Affect Color

A few other rare phenomena can also affect color, at least theoretically. Whether these are important, or even occur, in alpacas is debatable. However, as more and more alpacas are produced, a few "new" colors will likely emerge, and discussing the mechanisms for these will help breeders to identify and use them when that time comes.

Shaded Colors—the *Pangaré* Locus Several alpaca color patterns are shaded so that the ventral part of the animal is paler than the dorsal part. These could be included in the *Agouti* locus, which would be consistent with similar patterns in sheep and goats.[1,8,9,10,12] If this were the case, then the shaded patterns would each have a separate *Agouti* locus allele. In contrast, in horses and donkeys the shaded patterns are superimposed over base colors by a locus other than *Agouti*, and it remains to be determined with certainty one way or the other in alpacas.[7]

One powerful argument for the hypothesis that the shaded patterns are "overlay" patterns at a locus other than *Agouti* is that each nonshaded color has a shaded counterpart (see Table 25.3). Thus, if they were an *Agouti* phenomenon, then each nonshaded allele in alpacas would have a counterpart shaded allele. Since this is unusual in animals, it is more likely that shading is superimposed over *Agouti* patterns, with each pattern thereby having a shaded counterpart by means of this modification by another locus. Limited color production data also suggest that the pale areas are an overlay phenomenon rather than an *Agouti* phenomenon.

The light superimposed pattern is similar to the situation in horses and donkeys in which the *Pangaré* locus has such an action. For alpacas the overlay changes uniform tans to shaded fawns. Tan with minor trim is transformed into the color pattern of vicuñas. Red with black trim is transformed to the pattern of guanacos, with a darker top color than vicuñas, and also a distinctive striping pattern on the lower legs. Bay changes to shaded red, and mahogany or black is changed to shaded mahogany. All of these patterns have the distinctive pale areas on lower neck and belly, and creeping up the flanks onto the body.

A powerful argument in favor of shading being an overlay phenomenon independent of *Agouti* is that each major solid color (fawn, red, brown, black) has a shaded counterpart. This is unusual if the *Agouti* locus is the entire story. The significance of this to breeders is that the entire range of colors is available in both a shaded and a nonshaded version. If uniform color throughout fleeces is desired, then obviously the nonshaded colors are more desirable. If, alternatively, the subtle shading is desired, then the shaded variants are more valuable.

Table 25.3 Nonshaded variants and their shaded counterparts in alpacas.

Nonshaded Variant	Shaded Variant
tan	shaded fawn
tan with minor trim	vicuña
red with black trim	shaded red (guanaco)
bay	shaded red or shaded brown
black with light belly	light-bellied shaded mahogany (rare)
mahogany	shaded mahogany
black	shaded mahogany

Dilution An important mechanism in many species is dilution. This general phenomenon can cause light colors. Dilution factors in many species include several different loci with a number of different alleles.[5,7] This means that the overall topic of dilution is complicated, although if taken apart component by component, some potentially useful trends can be discerned. Dilution factors appear to be reasonably rare in alpacas.

Dilution genes in other species have a variety of actions, with each pattern of action yielding clues for the genetic cause of the dilution. Some dilution loci affect only eumelanin, the result generally being chocolate brown with some genes, and uniform slate blue/grey with others. These colors are very distinctive in species in which they occur. The biggest clue that one of these diluters is present is that *all* the eumelanin in an animal is affected—face, body, short hair, fleece. Diluters with action only on eumelanin leave pheomelanin untouched, and so it is fully and intensely expressed.

Some other dilution factors, in other species, affect only pheomelanin. These diluters usually take the typical tan or red-brown of pheomelanin and lighten it to gold, "yellow," cream, or even to ivory or white. These diluters fail to act on eumelanin, which remains fully black. It is very unlikely that any diluters of these classes exist in alpacas. The evidence for this is a general lack of gold fleece types that have black points. This combination would be expected from a diluted bay, and it occurs only very rarely. Selection in favor of such combinations could potentially increase their frequency among alpacas.

Other dilution factors affect both pigment types. These would result in an overall lightening of both eumelanin and pheomelanin. These animals, regardless of underlying base pattern, are lightened to more pale colors.

These distinctions in the action of any potential diluters are helpful in ascertaining whether multiple dilution mechanisms are at work, because each pattern of action is usually consistent with a specific dilution gene. In species where multiple dilution factors exist, they can sometimes combine in individual animals to yield some unusual results. Such combinations also act in unusual ways in a breeding program, if the breeder is unaware that multiple dilution factors are present.

A few colors in alpacas are candidates for dilution. Certainly dilution of pheomelanin might be present in some of the fawn types, because these are basically light pheomelanic colors. A powerful argument against this, though, is the fact that a real black-pointed bay with gold or light fleece is very rare, if it occurs at all. This combination should occur if dilution of pheomelanin is the mechanism for fawn color. It is therefore more likely that the fawns are simply *Agouti* locus alleles, and most breeding results point in that direction. Gold tones are rare among alpacas, unlike their presence in sheep's wool.

Occasional crias are born with a tantalizingly gold fleece and distinctive black trim. Most, if not all, of these then subsequently mature into a more usual bay or red color by the first shearing. The distinctive gold color is therefore shorn off with the first fleece, never to recur on the same animal. Whether or not a permanent gold fleece is possible is a problem that has not yet been solved. This color would be a welcome addition to the wide array of alpaca fleece colors.

One rare color that might indeed be due to dilution is dark charcoal grey with no intermixture of white or other colors. That is, these animals have a uniformly dark grey color throughout the fleece, with some slight dilution of the short face and leg hair as well. The overall result is a dark charcoal color that is distinctly bluer than black, and yet is very dark. This color is likely to be due to the action of a dilution gene. An educated guess is that it is a dominant gene, so that charcoal to black matings should produce about 50 percent black and 50 percent charcoal crias. The action on pheomelanin is not determined, but it is doubtful that it does act much on pheomelanin.

Brown Locus Another dilution locus sometimes postulated in alpacas is the *Brown* locus. In other species this locus has alleles that change all black to a flat, chocolate brown (the brown of chocolate Labrador retrievers). The key to this locus is that the appropriate alleles change all the black to brown, leaving no black. The few alpacas that could be classified as chocolate brown all have black trim, so that the *Brown* locus could not have been responsible for these colors. Variation at this locus may not occur in alpacas, although breeders should always be alert to it popping up, because it could lead to a new and interesting array of fleece colors.

Because dilution effects in alpacas are very rare, making breeding recommendations on them is difficult. If breeders have animals that are candidates for dilution, then certainly they can be mated to maximize the potential for reproducing the dilute colors. The safest recommendation is to mate to a fully intense animal with the same *Agouti* phenotype as the diluted animal. So, for example, mate charcoal grey to black. This provides for expression of the potential dilution gene without much extraneous color variation, so that breeders can more likely determine the genetic mechanisms at work.

Another phenomenon that may be related to dilution is the tendency of some animal's fleeces to weather and fade. In sheep these tendencies have been shown to have some genetic control. Some blacks, for example, fade to brown or off-black, while others retain a good true black color. This fading is complicated, and some animals are basically born faded, with the darker color growing in after the birthcoat has emerged. These subtle changes may be revealing something about the underlying color genes present in the animal, but no data have yet helped to unravel their mystery. Mating nonfading to nonfading is probably a very good way to increase nonfading animals, while mating fading to fading animals is probably warranted if fading is desirable. In a mature fiber market both types would be useful, and so there is no inherent advantage or disadvantage with either type.

Harlequin A rare color in alpacas is what is termed appaloosa in llamas. Harlequin is a better name for this pattern, because the pattern has important differences from the patterns of the Appaloosa horse.[7] Harlequin alpacas have dark, generally round, spots scattered over the body. The background to the dark spots is usually a lighter color, but not white. The subtle interplay of dark and light areas usually results in a very distinctive color that is particularly apparent on the face and legs, where the short hair provides a crisper contrast between the light and dark areas than do the fleeced areas. The harlequin effect on black results in nearly black, round, dark spots on a grey background on the body. The face is marked with smaller round, dark spots on a nearly white background. On other background colors it probably results in a somewhat similar appearance, only with red or brown spots on a beige background.

White Spotting White spotting has a specific connotation for color geneticists and basically includes any regions or individual hairs of the coat that have failed to obtain pigment.[5,7,9,12] The result is white hairs or patches. Some of the patterns are distinctively and obviously spotted; others are more subtle patterns where white hairs are mixed

Table 25.4 Genes causing patterns of white spotting.

Pattern of White/Locus	Allele	Symbol
Grey	grey	G^G
	nongrey	G^+
Piebald spotting	spotted	S^s
	nonspotted	S^+
Tuxedo spotting	tuxedo	Tu^{tu}
	nonspotted	Tu
Roan	roan	Rn^R
	nonroan	Rn^+
Speckled	speckled	Sp^s
	nonspeckled	Sp^+

into the base coat, resulting in roan patterns. Multiple patterns of white spotting occur in most species, and alpacas appear to be no exception. Each is under distinct genetic control (see Table 25.4), so that these patterns can be added in any combination onto any single background color. This is consistent with the situation in other species. For example, horses have ten genetically distinct spotting patterns.

White spotting patterns have a consistent peculiarity in that each pattern can vary from very minimal to very extensive. In the middle range of expression the different patterns can usually be distinguished one from another. At the extensive ends of the ranges they can be confused with one another or with white alpacas. At the minimal ends of the ranges they can be confused with solid-colored alpacas that lack white spotting.

Piebald Spotting Piebald spotting is one pattern of white spotting in alpacas. Piebald animals generally have color remaining around the eyes as eye patches, and usually white encircles the neck at some point. White is usually expressed ventrally and on the legs. The inheritance of piebald spotting is somewhat confusing. Many llama breeders insist that it is recessive, and it may well also be so in alpacas. In some herds, though, it has dominant characteristics.

At the dark end of the range piebald animals could easily be confused with nonspotted animals, and at the pale end with white animals. Piebald spotting can be superimposed over any background color, but is more obvious on the darker colors because the contrast is greater. This pattern is more common in llamas than in alpacas, but occurs in both, and by itself is no indication of past crossbreeding of the two species.

Tuxedo or Caped Spotting The tuxedo (or "caped" as a translation from Spanish "capirote") pattern can be confused with piebald spotting but is a different pattern under separate genetic control. This pattern generally has white on the underline from the head to the rear. Most tuxedo animals have color remaining on the back of the neck, barrel, and back, and are white on the face, lower neck, legs, and belly. This pattern can be superimposed over any background color and is probably inherited as a dominant gene. Although superficially similar to the pallor of the head and neck on grey animals, this pattern is distinct and can be combined with any base color. It should not be confused with grey, as the two patterns are distinct genetically.

White with Dark Head Some animals are distinctly white with dark heads and feet. This pattern is almost certainly not one of the other spotting patterns, such as piebald or tuxedo. The logic for this conclusion is that the piebald and tuxedo patterns nearly always involve the head and legs, and so an extensively marked animal (as a white one would certainly be) is expected to have obvious white areas on the face and legs, instead of preserving these as colored remnants in an otherwise white coat. These extensively spotted animals retain pigment on the head and lower legs, which is not expected of the other two patterns. The details of the inheritance of this pattern are not documented, for such animals are frequently classed as white due to their fleece color.

Minimal White Marks Minimal white marks are reasonably common on the heads and legs of alpacas. Because these marks do not usually affect the fleeced portions of the animals, they are usually overlooked as being important to color genetics. Frequently these marks are small enough to be inconsequential, and their genetics are probably complicated.

Large patches of white on the head are especially likely to be showing the presence of a minimally expressed spotting pattern (piebald or tuxedo). This can be critically important if certain colors or patterns are either favored or not favored in the progeny. A similar line of thinking holds true for most large, white patches involving the feet and lower legs.

Odd, small, white patches along the belly or sides are probably not related to major spotting genes. Animals with these spots can probably be used in a breeding program much as would any truly solid colored animal.

Grey Grey alpacas generally have white or nearly white heads, and the coat over the ears and top of the head is usually dark. They frequently have white legs, and the body coat is a combination of dilute (grey), dark, and intermixed hairs. The result is usually a reasonably uniform grey fleece, although the animals betray their peculiar mixture of colored areas when freshly shorn. Dark grey animals can be confused with nongreys, and light grey animals can be confused with white animals. Grey is likely a dominant allele. However, the darkest ones do not behave genetically the same as the medium and light ones, and they tend to reproduce their grey color more rarely than do the other classes. Some of this tendency may be due to very dark greys being misclassed as nongreys.

Greys appear never to be homozygous. The proof for this would be a grey producing only grey and no nongrey offspring following mating to nongrey mates. In every instance where greys have been mated to nongreys in sufficient numbers, some nongreys have been produced. This demonstrates that the greys do not have two doses of the grey gene. In addition, grey to grey matings consistently produce about two greys to every nongrey. This also points to a lack of homozygous greys.

The nomenclature of greys is important to alpaca breeders. Grey on a black background yields silver greys (dark, medium, or light). Grey on a mahogany background or a dark bay background yields the browner sort of rose grey. Grey on a light bay or red with black trim background yields the redder version of rose grey. On a fawn background grey can be difficult to appreciate, and is likely to be missed as contributing to the final color. The tip-off to the presence of grey on these pale colors can be the pale head and legs, although not all white-faced fawns have grey as the cause for this color.

The dark spots on greys are usually the background color, so that on silver greys these are black, on brown rose greys they are brown, and on red rose greys they are red. On several alpacas, though, the dark spots vary considerably, so that silver greys sometimes have both black and brown or red dark spots in addition to the expected black ones.

Roan Roan is currently a rare pattern in alpacas in North America. Roan bodies vary from red roan to black or grey roan, depending on the base color. These animals have dark heads and legs, with the color of these regions depending on the base color of the animal. The roan pattern appears to behave as a dominant allele, much as similar patterns in other species. These animals are very distinctive, although fleeces are similar to the more usual greys with white heads. The dark-headed roan pattern can be superimposed over any background color, and it is especially stunning on a red or black background. Roans are rare and do not have the distinctive dark spots of the greys.

Some roans do not have uniform roaning, but instead have a heavier introgression of white hairs into the lower neck and lower sides than they do up over the back. This variant could be missed but appears in the same families as dark-headed roans and is probably due to the same gene. These shaded roans occur most commonly in suris but have also been seen in huacayas. These shaded animals are less extensively roan, with minor roan areas that are usually on the sides. Either extreme of the pattern, shaded or dark-headed, is very distinct from grey.

Speckled Speckled alpacas are very distinctive. The dark manifestations of this pattern are colored but have distinctive small white speckles along the belly and lower neck, which extend somewhat up onto the sides. More extensively marked animals can be nearly white, with colored heads and small to medium-sized colored spots scattered throughout the coat. In the minimal and medium ranges of expression, this variant would result in a very interesting fleece that might superficially resemble grey or harlequin as a shorn product. While details of the inheritance are un-

certain, the consistent occurrence of this rare pattern in a few outbred families suggests that it is due to a dominant allele.

Other Spotting Patterns Other spotting patterns are almost certainly possible. Suris, especially darker fawn suris, frequently have white areas in a distribution not expected of the other patterns. The contrast with the fawn is somewhat confusing, and so characterizing exactly what is going on is difficult.

White

White is a difficult fleece color (or lack of color) to understand completely because it is an end point that can be achieved through different means. White animals could be very dilute, could be very white spotted, or could be both. The important concept is that multiple mechanisms for whiteness probably exist in alpacas. Each of these is likely to be caused by a different genetic mechanism, yet all end up being superficially similar as to color classification. The result is that not all whites are equal in a breeding program.

Many white alpacas produce white or pale offspring following mating to any other color, indicating that dominant mechanisms for whiteness are relatively common among alpacas. This dominance is also alluded to in some South American research. A few white alpacas consistently produce the color of their mates, indicating that such animals are recessive to all other variants. The problem is to distinguish these types of white visually, and of course that cannot be done. Only breeding results could distinguish these types one from another.

Blue Eyes

Blue-eyed White Blue-eyed white is a specific type of white that is controversial. Some of these animals are deaf. Since most owners indicate that they function normally in alpaca society, this condition appears not to be very debilitating. From the alpaca's viewpoint it may not matter much whether it can hear or not, although owners tend to impute serious consequences to it from a humane point of view. Obviously, if clicker training were a strategy, then the deafness would be a problem for both the alpaca and the owner.

A small amount of evidence points to at least one genetic mechanism for producing blue-eyed white animals. At least some are the result of combining spotting (probably either the piebald or the tuxedo types) with grey. Whether this accounts for very many blue-eyed whites is uncertain, but it does account for some. This information can be useful, because blue-eyed whites mated to dark, nonspotted mates will produce (in about equal proportions) solid colored, spotted, grey, and blue-eyed white.

Obviously, mating the blue-eyed whites to each other will produce mostly blue-eyed whites, but also other colors such as darks, greys, and spotted as occasional options.

The occurrence of blue-eyed whites from a combination of spotted and grey patterns implies that greys and spotted animals should not be mated together if the goal is to avoid blue-eyed whites. Following the mating of a spotted and a grey animal, the expectation is equal numbers of grey, spotted, solid, and blue-eyed white offspring. Many white-faced dark animals are minimally spotted, and so these must not be mated to greys if blue-eyed whites are not desired. White or pale-faced fawns probably also fit in here, and can have a risk of blue-eyed white crias if mated to grey or spotted animals.

Blue Eyes in Colors Other Than White The issue of eye color is very complicated, and most blue-eyed animals see and hear fairly normally. Completely avoiding all blue-eyed animals is probably not possible. Multiple genetic mechanisms probably account for the different types of eye colors, and some eye colors are more common with some fleece colors than others. A generally safe strategy in most instances is to mate blue-eyed animals to dark animals with dark eyes. Animals with dark grey, dark blue, or eyes that are a mixture of colors are probably not the same genetically as the blue-eyed whites and pose little threat to a breeding program aimed at avoiding them. Some light eyes seem to be connected with certain colors (especially grey) and may pop up whenever such animals are bred. Most of these appear to hear fine.

COLOR IDENTIFICATION

A uniform system of color identification could greatly aid understanding, communication, and color genetics studies. Such a system is not entirely straightforward or intuitive, but here is a proposal. The first step is the identification of the basic color scheme. This is usually the pattern of tan versus black areas and generally reveals the basic *Agouti* pattern present. A second important detail is the presence or absence of pale shading on the body. A third detail is to recognize the final fleece color, because this is likely to detect any dilution factors present. Most current identification systems are concerned only with final fleece color and therefore leave out the other important factors. The goal of putting the first three details together is to appreciate the range of fleece colors available from each *Agouti* allele. Finally, a fourth detail is the addition of any white areas or hairs. Such a detailed system can be daunting, but is the only way to fully achieve a thorough understanding of color genetics for alpacas.

1. Basic *Agouti* pattern
2. Presence or absence of pale ventral shading
3. Final fleece color
4. Any white areas or hairs

BREEDING FOR COLOR

Strategies for breeding for specific colors are speculative at this point, but a few principles are probably safe. First, and hardly surprising, is that the best way to reproduce a color is to mate two of the desired color together. That is not always possible, though, and reproducing rare colors can be intriguing and frustrating.

Mating any color to a solid black animal is probably the quickest way to ascertain what is lurking behind lighter-colored animals. This strategy is also probably sound for reproducing rarities like the dark and shaded mahogany animals, at least a portion of the time. This strategy is also useful for rare patterns such as the harlequin/appaloosa and uniform charcoal greys. Eventually it will be interesting to see what these modifications do to other base colors, but numbers will have to increase first before sufficient breeding animals are available to do the test matings required to tease out these fine points. Mating black animals to lighter animals also has a tendency, across large numbers, to deepen reds and fawns to darker and more somber colors. This tendency is not uniform across all animals, but is enough of a trend to have implications across large numbers of animals.

White animals are the greatest unknowns because it is certain that many of them are hiding some genetic machinery for color production under their whiteness. If white is desired, then clearly white to white matings are the best way to proceed. If colored offspring are desired, then white to dark (and probably bay, mahogany, or black) are the matings most likely to disrupt the whiteness and reveal what is underneath.

The inheritance of color is complicated. The results produced by alleles at each of the different loci act together, and the final combination of their actions yields the one result that we appreciate as the color of an alpaca. By taking the different components and analyzing them individually, we can appreciate the intricacies of how the final colors are produced. Understanding the significance of the components is also the basis for being able to manipulate them in breeding programs to produce the colors that are desired.

Remember that while color is important and fascinating in all of its intricacy, it is only one among many critical factors to consider in a well-thought-out breeding program to produce sound, colorful alpacas with great fleece characteristics.

GOING FROM COLOR TO GENOTYPE

Getting to the color genotype from the color phenotype can be difficult in some situations, although this is an important step because the genotype is the only issue that has relevance to producing the next generation. A few overriding concepts are important

It is impossible to tell what white and very pale animals are hiding by visual inspection alone, although a close inspection of animals can reveal some important information. White animals come in a few distinct types. One of these is stark white with no pigment. These animals reveal nothing, and therefore depending on them to produce other colors is a risky tactic. Some of them can indeed produce other colors by strategically mating them, but deciding which can and which cannot is not possible by looking only at the external color.

White animals with blue eyes generally reveal that they have the genetic machinery to produce grey as well as spotted animals. This information can be used to great advantage by breeders interested in greys, generally by mating the blue-eyed white animals to dark, solid colors. Due to the combination of grey plus spots yielding blue-eyed whites on occasion, it is safest to mate these to very dark animals with no white on them. Unless, of course, the stark white fleece of a blue-eyed white is desired, in which case they should be mated together to maximize the production of crias with this color and fleece type. Realize, though, that even mating them to one another is likely to produce a proportion of crias that will be grey, solid, or spotted rather than white. Blue-eyed whites also reveal nothing about their base color. Those based on black, mahogany, or bay may well produce dark-colored crias. Those based on pale tan backgrounds may never be able to produce a really dark-colored cria.

Some white animals have dark pigment, usually restricted to the skin, and usually around the nose, eyes, and feet. Conventional wisdom holds that these might be more likely to produce color when mated to dark mates, although complete data on this point are lacking. If producing color from white is a goal, though, then these whites with pigment are more likely to do so than the whites with no pigment, with the blue-eyed whites as a special class that counters this general rule.

A few white animals have distinct small spots of pigment, either on the face and legs or also on the body. These animals most likely represent a few different genetic types. Some of these are likely to be very heavily spotted animals, meaning that their white spots are so large that they end up being essentially white. These animals can be mated to dark animals to try to tease the background color away from the spots, although some of these matings will produce a proportion of spotted offspring. Others of these are likely to be truly white, but have somehow picked up the odd pigmented spot by an accident of development. This happens rarely, although when discussing a specific class of animals (in this case, white with pigmented spots), such accidents are overrepresented, and might lead owners to be wrongly optimistic about the chances for dark colors from at least some such animals.

Fawn phenotypes are also variable and can be quite confusing. Fawns come in a few distinct shades. Several different genotypes likely lead to similar fawn phenotypes. A few subdivisions of fawn are reasonably obvious. Some fawn animals have fawn heads and legs. These animals are probably truly colored, and some of them (not all, but some) are likely to be hiding darker and more recessive *Agouti* alleles. They are genetically pale, but are nonspotted and nongrey.

White-faced fawns are a very confusing color class. Most of these are reasonably pale, and the white face indicates that more is occurring than simply pale color. Some of these are likely to be fawn greys with both a fawn and a grey pattern overlapping. Others are likely to be spotted fawns, only the pale background color results in a relative lack of definition of the spotting. In either case, mating these to solid-colored dark animals is the most likely strategy to reveal which components are present. Mating them to one another may result in some white offspring as well as fawn, along with occasional dark crias, depending on the specific fawn individuals involved. Mating them to solid fawns (with fawn faces and legs) is likely to result in solid fawn as well as white-faced fawn offspring. To maximize the possibility of dark offspring, these will need to be mated to a dark mate. If avoiding blue-eyed whites is important, then they should not be mated to greys or to spotted animals.

Dark colors include red, brown, bay, mahogany, and black. In each case these can be hiding very little. The reds that have minimal black trim can vary in fleece color from fawn through a rich dark red, and could potentially mask several of the darker colors. Only testmating will tell, and this must be to a dark color (ideally black for the best test) to be an adequate test. Not all reds will carry darker colors, but some will.

Bays vary from some that are more red to others that are more brown. These can hide very little information and could produce only black or mahogany as a surprise. Black, of course, cannot hide surprises at all.

A few other details of color phenotype can help to unravel some mysteries. Dark colors with white faces (or white legs) are frequently minimally spotted rather than truly solid. This is important only in the choice of mates, as mating them to greys could occasionally produce blue-eyed whites. Mating them to spotted animals or to one another increases the chances of spotted offspring. Mating them to solid-colored dark animals limits the offspring to dark, white-faced dark, and perhaps a few spotted offspring.

Dark animals with a few stray white patches are perplexing. Some of these may be minimally spotted. Their significance is that they could indeed reproduce as if spotted. Many of these, though, are probably not spotted at all, especially if the white is not on the face (blaze, star, or white muzzle) or feet and lower legs. The odd small white spot on the side or belly is probably just an accident on a colored animal, analogous to a birthmark on people. These animals should reproduce as if solid colored.

Looking at color phenotype can give important insights into the color genotype. This information can help the breeder make some informed choices that aid in achieving goals. In addition, the more that is known about the background of an animal, the more is known about the genotype. For example, a white or fawn animal with a black parent must be carrying black, so that the correct mating could tease black or another dark color (depending on mate) out of that animal. So if black was an essential goal and only fawn animals were available, then the selection could be limited to those that have a black parent.

Remember that while the lighter colors can mask the darker ones, this is far from saying that each light animal is masking darker colors. Some fawns, for example, will only produce fawn regardless of the mate because the fawn is homozygous. What this means is that across a population of fawns the breeder could expect all darker colors to pop out as surprises, but for each individual fawn this might not be true. The only way to know which light colors carry which dark ones is either through pedigree (color of parents) or production (color of offspring). Such information can be very helpful to some breeders who have specific color goals.

It is also critical to remember that dominant alleles are nearly always expressed. So if the goal is grey, then it only makes sense to breed to greys. The black offspring from a grey to grey mating have lost the piece of information to make grey, and so they themselves cannot provide it to their offspring. It is inaccurate to look at a consistently grey pedigree background on a black animal and expect it to produce greys if mated to nongreys. This is simply not the way genetics works. If a dominant allele is desired (grey, spots), then it must be present in at least one of the parents. Otherwise it simply is not there, even if it was present in all parents and grandparents.

ACKNOWLEDGMENTS

Cleve and Bev Fredericksen were kind enough to share data from their herd, and this helped immensely to target some interesting facts as reasonably well established or as needing further work. Conversations and observations with Doug and Denise Caldwell were also very instructive. Andy Tillman has tantalized me with a few results, which have also shaped my thinking. Nance Sturm, Ingrid Wood, Gail Campbell, Eric Hoffman, Kenneth Hart, and Elizabeth Paul have all provided useful and interesting observations, as well as thought-provoking discussion.

REFERENCES

1. Adalsteinsson, S., D. P. Sponenberg, S. Alexieva, and A. J. F. Russel: Inheritance of Goat Colors. *Journal of Heredity* 85: 267–272. 1994.
2. Bustinza Choque, V.: *Razas de Alpacas de Altiplano: Suri y Wacaya.* Centro de Publicaciones IIDSA-UNA. Puno, undated.
3. Cordonea, N., C. Novoa, J. Sumar, and E. Franco.: Herencia de Color y Tipo. *Anales de Coversatorio Nacional sobre Dessarollo de Camelidos Sudamericanos,* II. Lima, Peru, pp. 123–125, August 23–27, 1982.
4. Hart, Kenneth: The Dominant White in Alpacas Is the Most Dominant Gene in the Agouti Series. Honors Thesis, University of Western Australia, November 2001.
5. Lauvergne, J. J., C. H. S. Dolling, A. L. Rae, C. Renieri, D. P. Sponenberg, and B. Denis: Coat Colour Loci. *Mendelian Inheritance in Cattle 2000.* European Association of Animal Production Publication no. 101. Wageningen, The Netherlands: Wageningen Pers, 2000.
6. Ponzoni, R. W., D. J. Hubbard, R. V. Kenyon, C. D. Tuckwell, B. A. McGregor, A. Howse, I. Carmichael, and G. J. Hudson: Phenotypes Resulting from Huacaya by Huacaya, Suri by Huacaya, and Suri by Suri Alpaca Crossings. *Proceedings of the Association for the Advancement of Animal Breeding and Genetics* 12: 136–139.
7. Sponenberg, D. P. *Equine Color Genetics.* Iowa State Unversity Press, Ames, Iowa, 1996.
8. Sponenberg, D. P., C. H. S. Dolling, A. L. Rae, R. S. Lundie, C. Renieri, and J. J. Lauvergne: Coat Colour Loci (Category 1). In *Mendelian Inheritance in Sheep 1996 (MIS 96)* (J. J. Lauvergne, C. H. S. Dolling, and C. Renieri, eds.), pp. 13–57. COGOVICA/COGNOSAG, Clamart, France, and University of Camerino, Camerino, Italy.
9. Sponenberg, D. P.: Genetics of Colour and Hair Texture. In *The Genetics of Sheep* (L. Piper and A. Ruvinsky, eds.). Wallingford, England: CAB International, 1997.
10. Sponenberg, D. P.: Breeding for Colored Angora Goats. In *The Angora Goat: Its History, Management, and Diseases,* 2nd ed. (S. Mitcham, and A. Mitcham eds.), pp. 212–227. Sumner, Iowa: Crane Creek Publications, 1999.
11. Sponenberg, D. P., S. Ito, K. Wakamatsu, L. A. Eng.: Pigment Types in Sheep, Goats, and Llamas. *Pigment Cell Research* 1: 414–418. 1988.
12. Sponenberg, D. P., S. Alexieva, and S. Adalsteinsson: Inheritance of Color in Angora Goats. *Genetics, Selection, Evolution.* 30: 385–395, 1998.
13. Tillman, J.: Coat Color Inheritance in Llamas and Alpacas. Part 1. *Llama World* 1(3): 4–9, 1983.
14. Velasco. J., N. N. Condonrena, D. D. Kres, P. J. Bufrening, and R. Blackwell: Breed Characteristics, Color, and Weight Inheritance in Alpacas 53: 156, 1981.
15. Villarroel, J.: Las Fibras. In *Avances y Perspectivas del Conocimiento de los Camélidos Sud Americanos.* Santiago, Chile: FAO, Oficina Regional de La FAO Para America Latina y el Caribe, 1991.
16. Wall, B., and R. Cole: Predicting Coat Colour in Alpacas. *Town and Country Farmer* 30, pp. 28, Autumn 1996.

Chapter 26

Breeding to Improve Fleece Quality

George Davis, MAgrSc, DSc

A promising six month old.

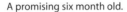

Because the main product from alpacas is their versatile fiber, most serious breeders have a keen interest in improving fleece quality through the application of genetic principles. A feature of the early development of the alpaca industry outside of South America is that there seems to be no shortage of breeders claiming to have "top genetics." Unfortunately, the term *genetics* is frequently abused in the alpaca industry. We often hear about "superior genetics," but what are they? What was objectively measured? At what age? In what environment? In what country? How many animals were running together in one herd?

To help clarify the discourse, this chapter will cover trait selection, heritability, and selection methodologies that can be used to improve both a herd and the breed. The prerequisites for genetic progress are three:

1. The breeding objective must be carefully defined.

2. The trait must be measurable.

3. There must be variation between individuals that is in part heritable.

An alpaca's pedigree tells you what it could be, its phenotype tells you what it should be, and its progeny tells you what it is. Just because an alpaca happens to have a pedigree is no reason to believe it has "top" or even "good" genetics. All it means is that its parents are known. Whether its genetics are good, bad, or indifferent depends both on how the breeder has selected the parents in the first place and on the subsequent chance assortment of genes that it has inherited from each of its parents.

The old saying "breed off a donkey and you get an ass" also holds true for alpaca breeding. To make genetic gain, breeders need to ensure that animals selected as parents for the next generation are genetically superior to those that are not kept for breeding. There are no guarantees in livestock breeding, but breeding from genetically superior individuals always greatly improves the odds. Genetic improvement is not an aimless pursuit, and therefore it is essential to define the traits of interest.

DEFINING THE TRAITS OF INTEREST

The breeder must understand what qualities the fiber processor most wants in order to achieve the maximum value from alpaca fiber production. These qualities must also be those that the processor is prepared to pay for. There are a number of examples in other fiber-producing livestock where processors identify particular traits they want, but they are not prepared to pay any significant premium for fleeces with these attributes. The extra returns from selecting for a specific trait should determine whether it makes good business sense to include it in a genetic improvement program.

The different fiber and pet markets in the alpaca industry pose particular problems for the breeder in deciding

A collection of studs from Peruvian breeder Don Julio Barreda, who for several decades has bred to create greater fleece weights on his animals.

which traits to select for. On the one hand is a manufacturer who requires fiber of uniform color and low micron to manufacture elite garments, and on the other is a customer who wants nothing but piebalds because they are just the cutest darned things.

Defining the traits of interest should not be confused with breed specifications, which should be broad and are primarily designed to eliminate llama- and guanaco-type animals from the alpaca gene pool. Breed specifications ensure that "off-types" are not retained for breeding. However, it is quite possible to have a herd that consistently meets the requirements of the breed specifications but never makes any true genetic progress.

Traits of interest are the measurable characteristics that the breeder considers important in setting breeding objectives. When alpacas are bred for fiber production, selection is likely to focus on fleece weight, fiber diameter, staple length, and medullation. The emphasis on color depends on whether the commodity or craft market is targeted; the genetic aspects of color were discussed in Chapter 25: Genetics of Fiber Type and Coat Color.

Traits of interest vary between breeders, and it is vital that breeders make their own choices as long as their animals meet broad breed specifications. Some will put the main emphasis on fiber diameter, others on fleece weight or color. Many may wish to select for all three traits together. In the broad context of genetic improvement the list could be further extended by including reproductive traits and growth traits. To select for multiple traits requires an index, discussed later in this chapter.

Standardized Measurement for Each Trait

Many breeders succumb to the temptation to quote fiber diameter from the first fleece as an indication of the merit of a particular individual. This is always the finest fleece, so the micron figure looks great in an advertisement. Breeders of another fiber-producing livestock animal, the sheep, have known for years that environmental and maternal influences make measurement of the first fleece meaningless. One of the environmental influences is date of birth, which for sheep spans about two months. For alpacas it spans 12 months! The cria that shows poor growth to weaning because its mother has not been a good milk producer will quite likely have a finer fleece, but that is due to the effects of environment and not genetics.

Fleece measurements should start with the second fleece, which equates to the hogget fleece in sheep. Leaving an alpaca unshorn until it is 18 months old does not count

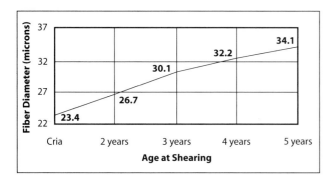

Figure 26.1 Effect of age on fiber diameter.[4]

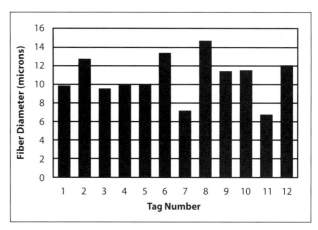

Figure 26.2 Increase in fiber diameter from one to five years of age.[4]

as a second fleece because the fiber grown as a cria is still part of the sample. Furthermore, the rate of growth of the fleece from 12 to 18 months in an unshorn alpaca is likely to be less than in an alpaca growing its second fleece over this period, and this discrepancy will affect the fleece characteristics and thus distort the results. Alpacas shorn at 8 months and again at 20 months of age produced 23 percent more fiber over this total period than those unshorn as crias and first shorn at 20 months of age.[5]

Traits should be compared between contemporaries—that is, alpacas of similar age and subjected to the same management. The period of fiber growth should also be the same, which is another reason why the first fleece should be ignored. Measuring fiber weight requires a set interpretation of what constitutes a year's growth. A year is made up of 365 days, not 18 months! Seldom will alpacas be shorn at exactly 365-day intervals, but as long as it is close to that period it is possible to adjust the value to 365 days. For example, an alpaca clipping 2.15 kg following a shearing interval of 390 days has grown 2.15/390 = 0.0055 kg per day. Multiplying this figure by 365 equals 2.01 kg, which is the adjusted 365-day weight.

Alpaca fleeces become coarser with age. The important measures for genetic improvement are whether or not their rankings stay the same as the animal grows older and whether certain individuals retain a very low micron throughout their life. At Tara Hills High Country Research Station in New Zealand, the fiber diameter of 12 male alpacas was measured each year in their first 5 years (see Figure 26.1).

As expected, all became coarser with age. However, the extent to which individuals became coarser showed considerable variation (see Figure 26.2).

Table 26.1 shows that ranking these individuals on their first fleece as a predictor of ranking at 5 years of age was only 67 percent accurate. In other words, it is highly likely that the individual that had the finest fleece in the

group as a cria would not have the finest fleece in the group at five years of age. In contrast, the second fleece as a predictor of ranking at 5 years of age was 92 percent accurate. Therefore, the individual with the finest fleece at two years of age will very likely be the same animal that has the finest fleece at five years of age. If the breeding goal is low fiber diameter at five years of age, it is not realistic to wait until an animal is five years old before selecting breeding stock. Data in Table 26.1 suggest that measurement at two years of age will give a good estimate, but measurement as crias will probably be misleading. The message is clear: Breeders committed to real genetic progress should be patient and resist the urge to make any measurements on the first fleece.

There is a very strong tendency in alpacas for fiber diameter to increase with age and also with level of nutrition. Nevertheless, some individual alpacas ignore the textbooks and maintain very low fiber diameters throughout life. The histogram showing an 11-year-old female with a 20.6 micron fleece (see Figure 26.3) is an example of this phenomenon. If this characteristic can be shown to be inherited, it should be included in the traits of interest, as it would significantly improve the value of fleeces from older animals.

The best sample site for estimating fiber diameter of a fleece is the midside.[1,7] Typically a single midside sample is collected, but it has been suggested that consideration should be given to taking duplicate samples.[1]

Table 26.1 Ranking alpacas for fiber diameter at five years of age.

Age at Measurement	Accuracy of Prediction (%)
Cria	67
2 year old	92
3 year old	96
4 year old	95
5 year old	100

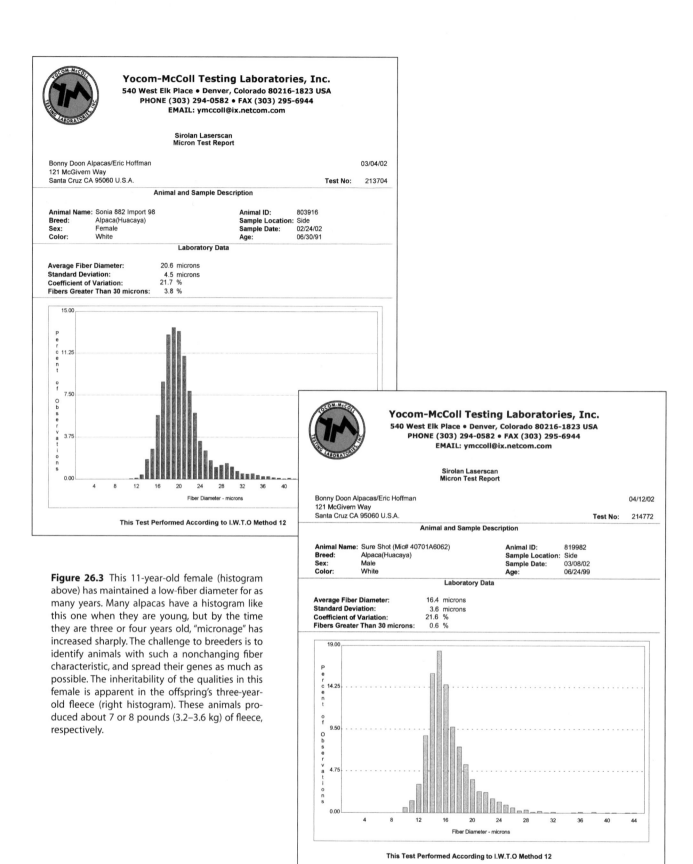

Figure 26.3 This 11-year-old female (histogram above) has maintained a low-fiber diameter for as many years. Many alpacas have a histogram like this one when they are young, but by the time they are three or four years old, "micronage" has increased sharply. The challenge to breeders is to identify animals with such a nonchanging fiber characteristic, and spread their genes as much as possible. The inheritability of the qualities in this female is apparent in the offspring's three-year-old fleece (right histogram). These animals produced about 7 or 8 pounds (3.2–3.6 kg) of fleece, respectively.

Objective or Subjective Measurement?

The foregoing discussion on the trait of interest implies objective measurement. A few alpaca breeders are advocating subjective measurements of characteristics such as handle and crimp to estimate fiber diameter, fiber length, and weight of fiber. This concept of using subjectively measured traits (e.g., skin and staple characteristics) to improve correlated traits (e.g., fiber diameter and fleece weight) that can themselves be directly objectively measured seems somewhat counterintuitive.

Fortunately, modern technology is readily available that alpaca breeders use to accurately and objectively measure fiber diameter and variation (CV), and ancient technology is also available to measure length (ruler) and weight (scales). Objective measurement of fiber diameter also allows the percentage of guard hairs to be measured, which can then be used as a further criterion for selecting replacement breeding stock. Given the ready access to quite inexpensive objective measurement for the actual trait, the subjective measurement of what are only claimed to be correlated traits would seem likely to slow rather than accelerate genetic improvement.

A comparison between these two approaches was carried out in Merino sheep in Australia and showed that genetic improvement was achieved by both methods.[3] However, although these data showed that both methods resulted in genetic gain, the index-based selection including fiber diameter and fleece weight, assuming a 10 percent micron premium, resulted in *greater* improvements in both fiber diameter and fleece weight than was achieved by indirect measurement based on the subjectively measured traits.

HERITABILITY

Fortunately, the heritabilities are high for the two most important fiber traits in alpacas—fleece weight and fiber diameter. Records from the Tara Hills herd estimate the heritabilities of fleece weight and fiber diameter at 0.63 and 0.73, respectively (see Table 26.2). These high heritabilities mean that an individual's own value (its phenotype) for either of these traits, relative to its contemporaries, is a good predictor of its genetic merit. Having progeny records will certainly improve the accuracy of prediction, but often the breeder needs to make selection decisions on stud males before progeny have been generated.

Further studies of alpaca herds are needed to get more reliable estimates of the heritabilities. For example, the high heritability for greasy fleece weight in Table 26.2 is in contrast to other estimates of 0.35 and 0.22 to 0.35.[2,6]

Table 26.2 Heritability of fleece traits in alpacas.[7]

Trait	Heritability
Greasy fleece weight	0.63
Clean fleece weight	0.68
Fiber diameter	0.73
Yield	0.67
Staple length	0.57
Staple strength	0.16
Resistance to compression	0.69

High heritabilities would allow useful comparisons to be made between sires if they were run in a common environment, because they imply that when run together in the same herd most of the differences between individuals is of genetic rather than environmental origin. Because male alpacas are not used for breeding for at least their first two years, breeders could take the opportunity to run shorn yearling alpacas from different herds together on a central property for their second year and take measurements at the end of that time. Of course, such a central herd evaluation will identify winners and losers, and it is important that benefits be there for all participants.

To encourage participation, an agreement could be made at the outset that contributors would be entitled to a specified number of services from the top sires at a discounted rate. While there are obvious benefits to owners of the top sires, access to these genetics would also benefit owners of lower-ranked animals by enabling them to improve the quality of their stock. This approach requires a high level of cooperation among breeders who are truly committed to genetic improvement. This method has been successful in other livestock industries and could be the way forward for the alpaca industry as herd sizes increase.

SELECTION DIFFERENTIAL

After meeting the three prerequisites of defining a breeding objective, selecting a measurable trait, and selecting a heritable trait, to make genetic progress there must be *selection pressure*—that is, superior animals are chosen as parents for the next generation. Selection pressure is greatest in males because fewer are needed for breeding and therefore they have the greatest impact on genetic gain. Selection in females cannot be ignored, but unfortunately at this early stage of the alpaca industry outside of South America, there is practically no selection pressure on females because almost all females born from registered parents are themselves registered and used to breed the next generation of registered progeny.

The term *selection differential* is used as a measure of the amount of selection that has been done. It is defined as the difference between the average of those selected to enter the herd and the average of the original unculled herd. For example, if in a group of 2 year olds that averaged 2.0 kg for fleece weight, those chosen as breeders averaged 2.5 kg, the selection differential would be $2.5 - 2.0 = 0.5$ kg.

Generation Interval

Generation interval is the average age of parents when their offspring are born in the herd. The generation interval is likely to be longer in alpacas than sheep because they live about three times as long. Genetic gain per year is calculated from the following formula:

$$\text{Genetic gain per year} = \frac{\text{Heritability} \times \text{Selection differential}}{\text{Generation interval}}$$

A low generation interval requires greater use of young sires and less dependence on old sires. Nevertheless, the above formula is only a guideline, and a breeding program should always have a place for an old sire that has proved himself over the years to have truly outstanding genetics. Continuing to use an old sire for sentimental reasons is quite another matter, and won't speed up genetic gain.

Estimated Breeding Value

EBV describes an individual's genes for a specific trait. Put simply, the EBV is the value of an animal as a parent. The EBV is a prediction and not an absolute value measured on the animal itself. The EBV is expressed in measured units, which for alpacas could be microns of fiber diameter or kilograms of fleece weight. EBVs cannot be compared across different herds unless reference sires have been used. For example, a sire with an EBV for fleece weight of +0.2 kg in a herd where the average fleece weight is 2.5 kg should be a much better sire than one with the same EBV in a herd where the average fleece weight is only 1.5 kg, assuming the environmental influences are similar in both herds.

To determine the EBV for fiber diameter of an alpaca sire, his fiber diameter must first be adjusted for date of birth, sex, liveweight, herd, etc., and then expressed as the difference from the average adjusted fiber diameter (or other trait) of all contemporary males in the herd. The EBV is then derived by using a weighting factor, which includes the heritability, and can include correlations between traits and the number of records on the sire's relatives. The EBV is calculated by multiplying the adjusted fiber diameter deviation by the weighting factor.

A male alpaca with an EBV for fleece weight of +0.2 kg mated with average females in the herd would be ex-

pected to leave progeny averaging +0.1 kg above the herd average, because the male provides only half the genes of the progeny. Only where he was mated to a female that also had an EBV of +0.2 kg would the offspring be expected to average +0.2 kg.

SELECTION METHODOLOGIES

To exert selection pressure, breeders must use a selection system to maximize genetic gain. Common systems are index selection, independent culling level, and sire referencing.

Index Selection

Where more than one trait is being selected for at the same time, the breeder needs an index that weights the different traits. The phenotypic correlation between fleece weight and fiber diameter in the Tara Hills herd was 0.32 for 2 year olds and 0.40 for adults.[7] This means that as fleece weight increases, so does fiber diameter (see Table 26.3). Because breeders generally wish to increase fleece weight and decrease fiber diameter, this is known as an unfavorable correlation. On the other hand, favorable correlations are a bonus because selecting for one will improve both. In alpacas there is a very high favorable correlation (0.99) between greasy fleece weight and clean fleece weight (see Table 26.4). Hence, there is negligible benefit in measuring clean fleece weight because selection for greasy fleece weight will attain the same objective.

An index needs to be weighted for the different traits, and this is done in other livestock by placing an economic

Table 26.3 Single trait selection for improved fiber.

	Herd Mean	Fleece Weight (Top 10%)	Fleece Diameter (Top 10%)
Fleece weight (kg)	1.9	2.9	1.4
Fiber diameter (micron)	31	33	24

Table 26.4 Correlations among the main fleece characteristics in two-year-old alpacas.[7]

	Clean Fleece Weight	Yield	Fiber Diameter	Staple Length	Resistance to Compression
Greasy fleece weight	0.99	0.01	0.32	0.39	0.08
Clean fleece weight		0.17	0.37	0.40	0.07
Yield			0.25	0.07	0.20
Fiber diameter				−0.03	−0.01
Staple length					0.16

value on each trait while taking account of heritability. The trait with the highest value makes up the highest proportion of the index. For alpaca traits such as fiber diameter and fleece weight, breeders will differ in the weightings they wish to use, and at this stage of the industry it is a difficult task to put an accurate economic value on these traits. Furthermore, these traits have a negative correlation, so the top animal for fleece weight is almost certain to be ranked lower for fineness.

When records from 38 two-year-old males were analyzed in the Tara Hills herd, the animal ranked first on fleece weight was twenty-fifth for fineness, whereas the male ranked first for fineness was thirty-sixth for fleece weight. The best overall male for both traits ranked sixth for fleece weight and sixth for fineness, which illustrates that the strength of the correlation differs between animals allowing genetic progress to be made, even where traits are negatively correlated, provided that there are large numbers to select from. The more traits that are selected simultaneously, the slower the progress in any one trait.

Independent Culling Level

An alternative to index selection is a system called independent culling level. Whereas an index weights each trait according to its heritability and economic value, the independent culling level establishes a threshold level for each trait; if an individual is outside that level for any one trait, it is culled. For example, a breeder could decide that no animal coarser than 30 microns or with a fleece weight below 1.5 kg will be kept for breeding. In this herd an animal clipping 5 kg but with a fiber diameter of 31 microns would be culled, whereas in an index-based selection program the extra fleece weight from this animal might be found to offset the higher fiber diameter.

Index and independent culling levels can be combined if independent culling levels are established to eliminate extreme animals and index selection is applied to the remainder. A breeder may decide that if a fleece is 35 microns, no breeding from the animal should take place, even if its fleece weight is 10 kg! On the other hand, if a fleece is 32 microns, the animal may be retained if it has a very high fleece weight resulting in a suitably high index value.

Sire Referencing

Using BLUP (best linear unbiased predictor) methodology, it is possible to link animals across herds to separate genetic effects from environmental effects. If there is effective linkage (at least two link sires per herd), the herd is enlarged because animals in separate herds and born in different years can be directly and accurately compared. The

The huacaya and suri shown here possess impressive fleeces of nearly 15 pounds (6.8 kg). If they are carrying one-year fleeces, these animals would be truly exceptional. If they are carrying two-year fleeces, they are neglected animals with slightly above average fleece weights.

link sires provide the benchmark with which progeny of all other sires in the participating herds can be ranked. In selecting for highly inherited traits in alpacas, such as fiber diameter, useful sire referencing would involve two link sires in addition to the other herd sires being used, and at least ten progeny per sire.

As an example of how sire referencing works, a reference sire may leave offspring in one herd averaging 23 microns, but in another herd where the feeding is at a higher level his offspring may average 28 microns. A sire used in the first herd with progeny averaging 25 microns would be inferior to the reference sire (2 microns coarser), whereas a sire used in the second herd, also with progeny averaging 25 microns, would be superior to the reference sire (3 microns finer). This illustrates the pitfalls in selecting breeding animals on fiber diameter alone without any comparative information. Unfortunately, sire referencing is limited to larger herds where sufficient progeny of each male can be generated.

There are only a small number of large breeding herds in which good genetic progress can be made by selecting within the herd. Most stud breeders have fewer than 100 breeding females, and in the absence of sire referencing, they are essentially multipliers. They are multiplying the number of animals with improved genetics derived from the large herds, but within their own small herds they are able to exert little effective selection pressure. Sire referencing interconnects herds of different sizes, and by creating one large herd through the sire linkages, enables all the contributing herds to make genetic gain.

CHOOSING A STUD BREEDER

As the alpaca industry in countries outside South America matures, it will increasingly become two-tiered. Genetic gain will be driven by those in the stud industry (top tier) who will be in business to provide high-quality studs to the commercial industry (second tier). The discussion in this chapter has been largely directed to those in the stud industry, but improving fleece quality will also be a goal for many in the commercial industry.

The key to genetic improvement in the commercial industry is the choice of stud breeder, since the flow of genetics is from the stud herd down to the commercial herds. The chosen stud breeder should preferably either have a large herd or be linked to a larger population through sire referencing. The stud breeder needs to share your genetic goals. If your aim is to breed alpacas with low fiber diameter, you get no benefit by going to a breeder where the main emphasis is on fleece weight.

The stud breeder should be using objective measurements that validate claims made about the merit of any animal, and the records should be available to the client. The stud animals need to be affordable, so it is wise for commercial breeders on a factory outlet budget to avoid breeders operating at boutique store prices. The aim should be to buy the best that you can afford. It is generally true that an average animal from a top herd is likely to be genetically superior to the top animal from an average herd.

REFERENCES

1. Aylan-Parker, J., and B. A. McGregor: Optimising Sampling Techniques and Estimating Sampling Variance of Fleece Quality Attributes in Alpacas. *Small Ruminant Research* 44: 53–64, 2002.
2. Blackwell, R. L.: Evaluation and Genetic Improvement of Sheep and Goats in Extensive Management Systems. *Partners in Research: A Five-Year Report of the Small Ruminant Collaborative Research Program,* pp. 139–144, Davis, CA: University of California, 1983.
3. Daily, H. G., R. W. Ponzoni, P. I. Hynd, R. J. Grimson, K. S. Jaensch, and W. S. Pitchford: An Evaluation of 'Soft Rolling Skin' as a Selection Criterion for the Genetic Improvement of South Australian Merino Sheep. *Proceedings of the Association for the Advancement of Animal Breeding and Genetics* 12: 516–519, 1997.
4. Davis, G. H.: Some Factors Affecting Fibre Production in Alpacas. *Proceedings AAA(NZ) Conference*, 1–2 September 2001, Christchurch, New Zealand, pp. 1–20.
5. Davis, G. H., T. Wuliji, and G. H. Moore: Growth and Fibre Production of Alpacas Farmed in New Zealand. *Proceedings Alpaca Industry Seminar,* Roseworthy, South Australia, pp. 15–17, 1993.
6. Velasco, J.: Mejoramiento Genético de Alpacas. *Anales III Reunion Cientifica Anual. Soc. Peruana de Prod. Animal.* Lima, 1980.
7. Wuliji, T., G. H. Davis, K. G. Dodds, P. R. Turner, R. N. Andrews, and G. D. Bruce: Production Performance, Repeatability and Heritability Estimates for Live Weight, Fleece Weight and Fibre Characteristics of Alpacas in New Zealand. *Small Ruminant Research* 37: 189–201, 2000.

Chapter 27

Maintaining a DNA Registry for the Good of the Breed

Eric Hoffman

Alpacas in Switzerland.

The alpaca in its purest form is a remarkable fiber-producing animal. The alpaca did not occur in the wild, but was created from selective breeding practices that spanned thousands of years. DNA testing wasn't available to the Incas and the other ancient cultures who created and managed millions of alpacas. Nonetheless, their methods of selection and husbandry created a fiber-producing animal superior to many alpacas living today. We will never know the details of this great story of animal husbandry. Perhaps the answers lie in the ancient *quipus*, whose rope messages are still often a mystery.[5]

It is ironic that ancient cultures created a fiber animal that has deteriorated in fiber quality with the coming of Europeans. The irony continues when we consider that to restore alpacas to their full potential in fiber quality, we incorporate sophisticated DNA science to safeguard and improve the alpaca gene pool.

WHAT IS A REGISTRY?

In its simplest historical form, a registry was an official written record of births, naming sire and dam, so that breeders could improve their herds through selective breeding. In a contemporary context, with the advantages that technology offers, registries can now be far more than fill-in-the-blanks registries.

Fill-in-the-Blanks Registries

A "fill-in-the-blanks registry" is the type in which the owner registers an animal by merely filling in a form that states the suspected sire and dam of an offspring. Such registries have high rates of error due to inaccurate information, sloppy record keeping, and dishonesty.

Often when fill-in-the-blanks registries are verified by DNA testing, the inaccuracy rate is so pervasive that "recorded" lineages are not what they seem. I was once hired to work with a European equine registry that was kept by a national government wanting to preserve a rare breed. The registry was a fill-in-the-blanks type and did not rely on scientific verification of any kind. In one day of looking through the registry's documentation, it became clear that the registry was basically inaccurate. A much desired stud was listed as having bred mares in different countries on the same date! The use of the stud book information for selective breeding decisions was questionable at best.

Authentic Registries

Authentic registries are selective about which animals are included. Offspring are accepted only after a DNA test verifies that they belong to two registered parents.

An authentic alpaca registry is a system of recording pedigrees using the most accurate scientific methods

569

available. In the context of modern science and in ideal economic conditions, all lineages should be scientifically verifiable, using either blood typing or DNA micro-satellite methods to ensure 99 percent accuracy in parent identification.

A registry that does not incorporate scientific verification usually lacks the essential features of certainty and thus the integrity to allow accurate tracking of lineage, scientific genetic studies, or identification of animals belonging to the registry's gene pool.

Before looking at how an authentic registry should work, let's look at some of the pros and cons.

PROS AND CONS OF DNA REGISTRIES

Alpaca registries should preserve and improve the species. Written in 1988, the first alpaca registry was actually created because alpacas can be bred successfully with three other species (technically five species when including Bactrian and dromedary camels), and there was fear that cross-species breeding with the large llama population already in North America would destroy the newly imported alpaca species there. Because of the introduction of DNA testing, the goal of excluding crossbreeding with llamas has been realized. North America boasts the world's largest population of alpacas that cannot be bred to llamas.

The Value of a Pedigree

A pedigree is "a list of ancestors; record of the family tree." The term carries a lot of weight in dog and horse breeding circles; all it means is there is a record of a lineage. If the record does not involve DNA verification, there will likely be no proof to authenticate the written record. A pedigree involving DNA-tested lineage verifies with certainty a particular lineage and thus is helpful in making breeding decisions.

But neither a pedigree that is solely a written record nor one in which DNA positively verifies a lineage guarantees the qualities of a particular animal or means the animal is free of genetic disease. A pedigree merely means the animal in question is part of recorded ancestry—if this includes DNA testing then accuracy is assured.

The true value in a pedigree is in the qualities a pedigree should represent. If a pedigree alpaca has qualities that aren't desirable, it may be an animal you don't want in your program. If the pedigree alpaca has traits you think are desirable, it may be of use to your program and its ancestry may assist you in making breeding decisions. For example, if a tui alpaca produces 3 pounds (1.3 kg) of fleece during its first shearing and another animal at the same micron level and age produces 13 pounds (5.9 kg) of fleece, and they are both structurally sound, clearly the second's pedigree is the more desirable.

The difference in having verifiable pedigrees and not having them is that when a positive trait appears the animal's ancestry will be known, allowing the breeder to make the most of the entire ancestry. Conversely, when there is no pedigree, all breeding decisions are based solely on phenotypic information. Pedigrees are not a seal of approval, but rather a record that can be used as a tool to improve a herd by emphasizing certain bloodlines and discontinuing others.

Benefits to Alpaca Owners

An authentic alpaca registry can thus provide these benefits to alpaca owners:

1. Create healthy, productive animals with accurate records.

2. Work toward goals in fiber quality that guarantee excellence.

3. Identify each alpaca with a 99 percent accuracy based on scientific testing.

4. Provide a certificate verifying each animal's identity and lineage.

5. Preserve the phenotypic characteristics of alpacas as a unique species. Lineages can be carefully monitored to create a "pure" alpaca gene pool by excluding animals from llama, huarizo, guanaco, paco/vicuña or vicuña lineages.

6. Create a genetically controlled and closed population whose identities are known and whose gene pool can be supplemented through a screening process agreed upon by registry members (a feature in many registries, but not all).

7. Accurately monitor genetics and incorporate programs of genetic improvement.

8. Eliminate or identify genetic diseases by identifying carrier animals and excluding them from the gene pool.

9. Improve the species through the adoption of well-researched, precise, objectively measured breeding practices.

10. Create a closed market (controversial).

Possible Detriments

Registries can have their downside as well:

1. Registry population can become a closed gene pool, retarding the improvement of the species and channeling selection to a narrow range of bloodlines.

2. Depending on the local economy, the costs of running a DNA registry may be prohibitive, exclusionary, and unaffordable to many breeders.

3. Aggressive entities within the registry may consolidate or monopolize a market (registry population) and define the pedigree with self-serving criteria.

4. Pervasive influence of well-promoted bloodlines may occur, creating a rigid hierarchical structure that is discouraging to entry-level breeders wishing to develop their own bloodlines.

5. Registry rules may forbid pursuing or obtaining desirable genetic material.

6. Registry rules can inhibit initiative, innovation, and the application of new knowledge in the selection of animals and the breeding process.

Table 27.1 Example of subgroup deprivation in a closed registry.

Grey Animals
Spectrum of colors: light grey, silver grey, medium grey, etc.
Nine shades of grey.
If all categories are combined, the total number of registered animals is 1,238, or 7.8 percent of the population.

Source: Data collected from ARI, Brad Smith, DVM, PhD, presentation, Denver, Colorado, 1998.

HOW AN AUTHENTIC REGISTRY SHOULD WORK

The Alpaca Registry Inc., headquartered in Kalispell, Montana, now houses about 45,000 alpacas (circa 2003). It is the first DNA-based alpaca registry in the world. The following essential aspects of an alpaca registry are based on my experience as the registry's author and board member for seven years.

The first rule is to keep a registry as simple as possible and clearly focused on its goal and mission statement.

Creating a Registry Goal

A registry will be well served by creating an overall generalized goal for participating breeders. An effective registry goal articulates an alpaca vision that unites and empowers alpaca breeders in their mission of alpaca raising. Here, for example, is a possible goal:

> Through selective breeding practices, maintain an alpaca population that is free of significant genetic disease and capable of producing a consistently high-quality fiber that is directly competitive in price and reputation with cashmere.

A goal such as this addresses the general genetic health of the animals, provides the vision of what needs to occur to improve fiber quality, and unites breeders wherever they are in the world.

In the alpaca business, especially in countries where animals (not fiber) are the primary market, too much time and energy have been spent on controlling markets and excluding one another from the marketplace by manipulating registry rules. Large and small breeders must work to achieve the mutually beneficial recognition of alpaca as the world's preeminent luxury fiber. Instead of promoting unification to enhance the industry, too many registries focus on building small, restrictive markets controlled (genetically and economically) by a few large entities operating within the registry population. The alleged goal is to enhance the value of each animal in such a registry by controlling the population within the registry. Meanwhile the world hardly knows alpacas exist. Today cashmere has the greatest name recognition of all the luxury fibers, and there are few registries associated with cashmere production.

Developing a Mission Statement

Often animal registries are formed with the general intent of preserving or improving a breed (or species), but without clear operating principles to articulate *how* this will be done. Adherence to a guiding mission statement ensures that the focus and essential mission of a registry is not lost. Here is an example of a mission statement: "To ensure the accuracy and integrity of all pedigree information in the registry database for the use of the registry and its members." The purpose of registering alpacas might be to:

1. Verify pedigree through scientific means for all new alpacas being registered and permanently record and maintain this information.

2. Compile information to be used by veterinarians and researchers.

3. Facilitate compliance among alpaca owners by providing a simple, economically feasible registration process.

4. Make essential information in the database available to registry members.

5. Maintain a nondiscriminatory species registry that defines the characteristics of "the alpaca" (*Vicugna pacos*) as a species, but does not discriminate against alpacas based on artificial criteria.

6. Provide information to facilitate the purchase and sale of registered alpacas.

7. Support, through whatever means are available, scientific research of genetic and health issues particular to alpacas.

8. Ensure that a registry is economically solvent and operates with long-range survival in mind.

9. Avoid entanglements with other organizations whose association with the registry would destabilize it, increase liability, increase expenditures, and result in unequal treatment of all registry members.

DNA Systems and Collection Technologies

All DNA tests are not the same. Blood markers emphasizing a wide assortment of characteristics can be utilized. The lack of standardized DNA testing is a worldwide problem for a range of domestic animal breeds. For the most part there has been little attempt to coordinate or standardize DNA analysis between registries, which means that sharing lineage data from one registry to the next may be time-consuming or even impossible.

For an alpaca registry in the beginning stages of development, employing a DNA testing system that is compatible with other registries makes good sense, even if the registry is closed to importation. A registry that does not have the capability to become compatible with other registries may find itself in a weak position to exchange genetic material should the will of the membership demand it.

The most tested and refined DNA testing system for alpaca and llama parentage verification is the Ten Marker Test from the University of California at Davis. This system was created and improved upon by Dr. Cecilia Penedo. The system boasts 98 percent accuracy in parentage identifications. A private Heidelberg-based German firm, Generatio, has replicated the UC Davis system, added eight markers of its own, and boasts 99 percent accuracy on parent verification. Dr. Eberhard Manz and his colleagues created the system and, at the time of this writing, were hoping to procure the testing contract for the registries forming in Europe. One of their selling points is that their system is both compatible with the UC Davis system and slightly more accurate. There are also DNA-testing laboratories specializing in camelids in Australia, Canada, Chile, and England.

The UC Davis system has operated since 1987, and has accurately identified the parents of thousands of alpacas and llamas. The UC Davis system, like many testing systems, is in the public domain and is not controlled by a copyright or patent.

DNA collection techniques include blood sample analysis, hair root follicle analysis, and buccal swab cell samples.

Blood Sample Analysis There are two methods for blood collection: dry collection and wet collection. Dry collection occurs when a small drop of blood is placed on absorbent paper, sealed in a plastic bag, and shipped to the testing facility. Blood is usually collected by pricking an ear. This

Pat Long, DVM, checks the mammary region for abnormalities.

system does not require refrigeration and is the easiest method for collecting a blood sample.

Wet collection is more problematic, especially if it must be shipped from one country to another. There may be prohibitive protocols. However, experts who have worked with all forms of DNA collection point out that wet blood is the best collection method for testing procedures. Collection requires syringe extraction from a vein, transfer to a vial, refrigeration, rapid and expensive courier delivery from the site to the testing facility, careful storage, and highly trained technicians to analyze the blood.

Hair Follicle Analysis Many horse registries prefer DNA sampling by hair follicle analysis. Hair follicle analysis has resulted in DNA identification of alpacas, but was declared inconsistent and is being abandoned by UC Davis and other laboratories involved in the DNA testing of camelids.

Buccal Swab Test Samples The buccal swab test has undergone trials at UC Davis and has also proved to be inconsistent as a method of DNA collection. Identification is made from cells collected from the inside of the animal's cheek, using a small stiff brush. If this method can be made more reliable, it offers several advantages. No refrigeration is required, there is only a brief period of air drying, and it is easy to handle. This method, or a similar one, may prove to be more economical and time-efficient than the time-tested serology methods currently employed. An inexpensive DNA test such as this is what is needed to help registries develop in South America.[1,2,3,4]

SCREENING: THE CREATION OF AN INTERNATIONAL STANDARD FOR EVALUATING INBOUND ALPACAS

The idea of screening inbound alpacas came about for several reasons. In the mid-1990s there appeared to be a wide range in the quality of alpacas entering North America. Importers could select from thousands of animals living in South America. Not all importers possessed the same degree of knowledge about alpacas or the same standards of animal care and ethics.

Political pressure to slow the rate of importation into North America was growing within the industry. Screening evolved as a way to force importers to select the best animals based on general health, phenotypic and fiber characteristics, and the absence of serious conformational defects.

After a series of meetings held at the University of California at Davis and Oregon State University in Corvallis, two screening forms were developed that resulted in all inbound animals into North America being screened in a two-tiered system: phenotype and veterinary screening plus a fiber requirement. In practice, the two-tiered screening process evolved into four screeners for the typically large shipments of between 200 and 500 alpacas that were occurring at that time. Two veterinarian and two phenotype screeners were sent to the exporting country to evaluate animals for importation to North America. The two-tiered system separated responsibilities into different areas of expertise, but both systems worked in support of each other and provided a comprehensive evaluation of each animal with a thoroughness rarely applied to livestock. Many registries around the world have adopted these forms for their own screening purposes; one example is the British Llama and Alpaca Association (see the screening forms that follow).

Screening also provided revenue. A surcharge of US $500 per animal was collected by the Alpaca Registry Inc. These funds were primarily used to run the registry and to finance marketing and research efforts. In all, more than US $2.5 million in revenue was generated through the screening process for the registry until screening ended in 1998. Other registries adopted the same standards and collected a surcharge after this date.

Screening Tasks and Scoring an Animal

In this system, the veterinary screener's primary task was to look for defects that are universally recognized as unacceptable in an alpaca. For example, an alpaca with only one testicle, cataracts, heart murmur, crooked spine (scoliosis), or leg defects that compromised its mobility or longevity

Brad Smith, DVM, checks the angle on the front legs against a template.

was eliminated on the spot. The phenotype screener was responsible for recording each animal's eartag and microchip number, weight, and withers height, and for deducting points for subpar body condition, average to below average fleece densities, and a gradient of structural defects not severe enough for outright disqualification by the veterinary screeners. Deductions (sometimes resulting in outright disqualification) were also made for phenotype characteristics that showed influences of nonalpaca camelids (llamas, vicuñas, guanacos, huarizos).

Animals not measuring up to minimal requirements for adult size were disqualified, as were animals in poor physical condition. The phenotype screener also procured a fiber sample from each animal for analysis. Fiber was extracted from a midpoint on the flank and analyzed in four areas: average fiber diameter in microns (AFD), standard deviation (SD), coefficient of variation (CV), and microns over 30. Each one of these areas was assigned 15 points.

Each animal began with a score of 100 points (45 possible from fiber results, 55 possible from conformation/phenotype evaluation). An alpaca had to score 80 points or more to be accepted. An animal who failed two of the fiber requirements (15 points each, adding up to a 30-point deduction) was automatically disqualified. An animal also

Physical Examination Screening Checklist

British **Camelids**
The British Llama and Alpaca Association

Name of import _____ ○ male ○ 1 - 2 years

Lot Number _____ Microchip number _____ ○ female ○ 2 - 3 years

Ear Tag Number _____ Date of Inspection _____ ○ 3+ years

Head
disqualifying trait present ☐ yes ○ no

Face ○ normal
wry face
◇ slight <2°
☐ moderate 2°- 5°
☐ severe >5°
air movement in both nostrils
◇ yes
☐ no

Ears ○ normal
◇ long
◇ short
◇ frostbitten
☐ gopher
☐ curled (fused)

Eyes ○ normal
◇ ectropion
◇ lacerated
◇ corneal opacity
◇ dilated pupil
◇ constricted pupil

☐ entropion
☐ cataract
☐ evidence of blindness
☐ persistent pupillary membrane
◇ tearing
evidence of blocked tear ducts

Teeth ○ normal
◇ retained deciduous insisors
◇ canine teeth erupted
☐ superior brachygnathism
undershot jaw with central incisors protruding more than 5 mm
☐ inferior brachygnathism
parrot mouth, overshot jaw with dental pad protruding more than 5 mm beyond the lower incisors

Comments _____

Neck and Body
disqualifying trait present ☐ yes ○ no

Throat latch
○ normal
◇ swelling

Cervical Spine
○ normal
◇ symetrical
☐ scoliosis

Movement of neck
○ normal

Thoracic and lumbar spine
○ normal
◇ lordosis
◇ kyphosis
☐ scoliosis

Tail
○ normal
straight no bends or kinks
☐ twisted

Comments _____

Front Limbs
disqualifying trait present ☐ yes ○ no

Front View ○ normal
◇ base wide
◇ base narrow

Carpal valgus
◇ slight <5°
◇ moderate <10°
☐ severe >15°

◇ bowed out at carpus
◇ splay footed

◇ pigeon toed
☐ polydactyly
☐ syndactyly

Side View ○ normal
◇ camped forward
◇ camped behind
◇ buck kneed

Calf kneed
◇ slight <175°
◇ moderate 170° - 175°
☐ severe <165°

Angulation
◇ okay
◇ too straight
◇ too flexed

Pastern angles
☐ cocked ankle >90°
☐ down in fetlock <30°

Comments _____

Cardiovascular
disqualifying trait present ☐ yes ○ no

Heart ○ normal
☐ heart murmur

Comments _____

The British Llama and Alpaca Association, like many other emerging registries, uses standardized screening forms to evaluate imported alpacas as a way to improve the overall quality of imported stock. The British and numerous other registries have used the original Alpaca Registry Inc. (North America) forms to set standards for their animals and in the process have contributed to creating a de facto universal standard. Between 1996 and 2002, more than 12,000 alpacas worldwide were evaluated with various versions of these forms. The form shown here is for veterinary screening.

Reproductive

disqualifying trait present ☐ yes ○ no

Male ○ normal

Testicles	Consistency
☐ both testicles not in scrotum	☐ hard
☐ cryptorchid - one testical	☐ too soft
☐ size - length <30 mm	☐ scrotal edema

Female ○ normal

☐ abnormal position of vulva

☐ clitoris enlarged - evidence of intersex

Comments _____

Rear Limbs

disqualifying trait present ☐ yes ○ no

Rear View ○ normal

	Cow-hocked	
◇ base wide	◇ slight <5°	◇ bowed out at hock
◇ base narrow	◇ moderate <10°	◇ splay footed
	☐ severe >10°	◇ pigeon toed

Side View ○ normal

	Angulation	Sickle hocked	
◇ camped forward	◇ post legged	◇ slight - hock angle <135°	☐ cocked ankle - pastern angle >90°
◇ camped rearward	◇ too much flexion	◇ moderate -hock angle <130°	☐ down in fetlock - pastern angle <30°
		☐ severe - hock angle <125°	☐ luxating patellas

Comments _____

Miscellaneous Defects

disqualifying trait present ☐ yes ○ no

Teats ○ normal

☐ does not have normal anatomical placement of 4 normal teats

Hernias ○ no

☐ umbilical >10 mm

☐ Scrotal

Toenails ○ normal

◇ elongated

◇ curled

◇ abnormal horn

Other defects ○ normal

☐ Other defect(s) present

Screening panel members are obliged to report any other serious defects that are present and that should, in the veterinarian's professional opinion, result in disqualification.

Comments _____

Examination Outcome

Having conducted an examination of this alpaca, the undersigned verifies that the animal is;

○ found to be free of listed defects within the limit of this field examination done without any laboratory assistance. This verification does not constitute a guarantee that the animal is free from all contenital or genetic defects.

signed: _____   date: _____

☐ Disqualified for the above noted defect(s)

A second signature is required for disqualification

signed: _____   date: _____   signed: _____   date: _____

○ indicates there are no defects   ◇ indicates traits which are abnormal but not disqualifying   ☐ indicates disqualifying traits

Phenotype Characteristics Evaluation

British **Camelids**
The British Llama and Alpaca Association

Name of import		○ male
Lot Number	Microchip number	○ female
Ear Tag Number	Date of Inspection	
Height	Weight	

minimum at withers 810 mm (32")   minimum 47 kg (103 lbs)

A total of 55 points are available on this portion of the evaluation, plus an additional 5 points if the fleece density is very dense. An alpaca receiving a combined phenotype and fibre score of 80 points will be accepted for registration if it otherwise qualifies

Total Points [   ]

Instructions:
⊘ tick here for normal characteristics   ☑ tick here for fault characteristics   ring all deductions   enter the score for each section (maximum score less any deductions)

Shape of Head, Muzzle and Ears
deductions   score = [   ]

Head and Muzzle	○ normal	☐ Llama like	-10
		☐ moderately large	-2
		☐ fragile face or roman nose (score on degree of fault)	-2
Ear	○ normal spear shaped	☐ asymetric spear	-2
		☐ rounded	-2
		☐ banana shaped	-15
		☐ pancake ear or other anomalies	-15

maximum score +10 [   ]

Body Score
deductions   score = [   ]

○ thin	△	☐ excessive thinness (emaciated)	-20
○ optimum		☐ obese	-15
○ somewhat overweight			

maximum score +15 [   ]

Fleece Density (Huacaya)
deductions   score = [   ]

| ○ dense | ☐ average | -3 |
| | ☐ light fleece | -10 |

maximum score +15 [   ]

| ◇ very dense | | +5 |

maximum score increase to 20

Luster and Curl (Suri)
deductions   score = [   ]

| ☐ absence of luster | -7 |
| ☐ absence of curl | -8 |

maximum score +15 [   ]

This British Llama and Alpaca Association form is for phenotype screening.

Conformation and Balance

deductions   score = ☐

Leg conformation	⭕ correct			
buck kneed or knee sprung	⭕ normal	☐ moderate	-5	per front leg
calf kneed or sheep kneed	⭕ normal	☐ moderate	-7	per front leg
sickle hocked		☐ mild	-3	
		☐ moderate	-10	
cocked ankle	⭕ normal	☐ present	-20	
down on pasterns	⭕ normal	☐ present	-5	per pastern, possible -20
post legged in rear or straight legged in front	⭕ normal	☐ present front	-2	
		☐ present back	-5	
front view	⭕ normal	☐ knock kneed mild	-3	
		☐ knock kneed moderate	-10	
		☐ pigeon toed	-5	
		☐ base narrow	-3	
		☐ base wide	-3	
		☐ bow legged	-3	
rear view	⭕ normal	☐ cow hocked mild	-3	
		☐ cow hocked moderate	-10	
		☐ pigeon toed	-5	
		☐ bow legged	-3	
		☐ base narrow	-3	

Balance or correct proportion of legs body and neck

long legged	⭕ no	☐ yes	-5	
short legged	⭕ no	☐ yes	-5	
short neck	⭕ no	☐ out of proportion	-5	
long neck	⭕ no	☐ out of proportion	-5	
tail set	⭕ normal	☐ high (Llama like)	-5	
sway backed or hump back	⭕ normal	☐ abnormal	-5	
locomotion	⭕ normal	☐ excessive winging	-7	
		☐ crossing mid-line	-7	

maximum score   +15 ☐

Phenotype Screener   Phenotype Screener

signed: date: signed: date:

⭕ normal characteristic no points deduction   ☐ fault characteristic with points deducted   ◇ characteristic with additional points

Fibre Characteristics Evaluation Form

British Camelids
The British Llama and Alpaca Association

Huacaya Fibre Characteristics	Deductions	SCORE =

Micron Count (maximum 26 micron)

Per micron (or fraction thereof) > 26 micron	-10	maximum score	+15

Standard Deviation (SD)

Micron
17 or less   max SD = 3.5
17.1 - 19   max SD = 4.0
19.1 - 21   max SD = 4.5
21.1 - 23   max SD = 5.0
23.1 or more   max SD = 5.5

Per 0.5 micron (or fraction thereof) > maximum	-5	maximum score	+15

Percent Fibre > 30 microns

For each percentage point > 5% of fleece	-5	maximum score	+15

Suri Fibre Characteristics	Deductions	SCORE =

Micron Count (maximum 27 micron)

Per micron (or fraction thereof) > 27 micron	-10	maximum score	+15

Standard Deviation (SD)

Micron
17 or less   max SD = 4.0
17.1 - 19   max SD = 4.5
19.1 - 21   max SD = 5.0
21.1 - 23   max SD = 5.5
23.1 or more   max SD = 6.0

Per 0.5 micron (or fraction thereof) > maximum	-5	maximum score	+15

Percent Fibre > 30 microns

For each percentage point > 5% of fleece	-5	maximum score	+15

TOTAL POINTS:.......................(Max 45)

Signed--

British Camelids Ltd would like to thank Murray Fowler, Eric Hoffman and Brad Smith for their permission to use this system.

The British Llama and Alpaca Association uses this form to evaluate an animal's fiber characteristics.

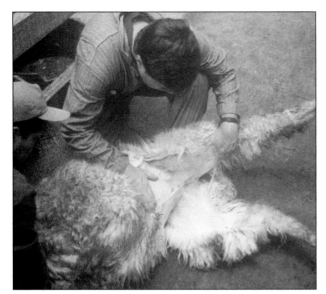

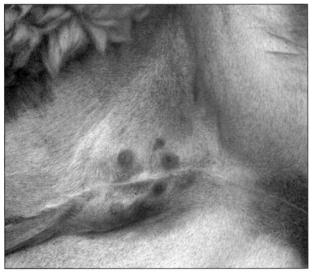

Left An alpaca's underside is checked for extra teats and hernias.

Above Weighing alpacas for a registry.

Left Animals in quarantine.

Below A recording microchip.

Left Extra teats.

received a 6-point deduction for minor phenotype or physical faults), such as banana-shaped ears (a llama characteristic) or being underweight (a poor body condition of 1). Each fault's point deduction was marked on a form, showing the importer specifically why a deduction was taken. The screener had to sign the form, and there was an appeal process. Accountability of all parties involved was integral to the screening process and formalized by a contract specifying roles.

Screening Is Not Judging

Do not confuse a screening evaluation with what goes on in the show ring. Judging has to do with selecting animals compared to one another and prioritizing the group in the ring. This process is largely subjective and usually involves minimal physical contact with the animals. Screening has to do with performing an objective hands-on evaluation of numerous aspects of a particular animal and recording each finding. Screening can be physically demanding, requiring containment and manipulation of uncooperative animals.

The screening process allows owners (importers) to review each animal's evaluation. Even though many hundreds of animals were disqualified from ARI registration through screening between 1995 and 1998, less than 1 percent of screening results were protested by importers, proving that it is possible to establish objective forms of evaluation that all parties can understand and accept. Today the basic elements of this original screening process continue to be used worldwide.

When an alpaca is screened, its mouth is opened, its bite is measured with calipers, its testicles or vulva opening are measured, its height is measured, and its weight is recorded. The alpaca is made to walk and its legs and conformation are assessed (if there is doubt, its legs are wrapped to compress the fiber and better view the legs' true profile). Its eyes are checked for defects and its underside is examined for hernias, extra teats, and other anomalies. Its back and tail are palpated, its body score is felt and recorded, and its heartbeat is checked.

An International Standard

Dr. Brad Smith, Dr. Murray Fowler, and I designed much of the original screening system with input from the international camelid community.* It is a system in which objective measurement is emphasized. It is not necessarily a system that is applicable to all situations, but it does offer the alpaca world a model for further refinement and discussions. Much of the original screening standard was eventually adopted, in part or in full, by the Australian

---

The Alpaca Registry Screening Manual by Eric Hoffman and Murray Fowler, 1996.

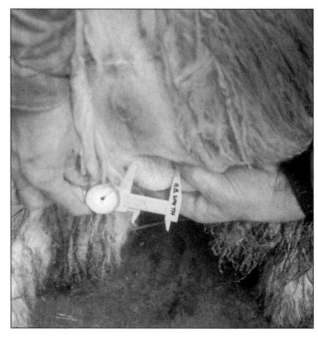

Testicles are measured.

Alpaca Association (both screening standards and stud certification), the British Alpaca Society, the British Llama and Alpaca Association, the Canadian Llama and Alpaca Association, Asociacion de Criadores de Camelidos del Sur, the International Lama Registry, the Peruvian government, and independent importations to Europe. In practice, the screening standard created for North American importation has become the international standard defining an acceptable alpaca.

Evolving Standard and Thoughts for Change The standard originally created for the Alpaca Registry Inc. was dropped in 1998 when the membership voted to cease all importation to the United States, ending the infusion of new genetics in favor of market protectionism and international isolation. But the knowledge gained from screening and its value for developing registries has lived on. These screening standards and the people who developed them have been employed by emerging alpaca registries in other parts of the world, resulting in upgrading the quality of animals selected for their breeding stock.

In the North American system, screening was applied to about 7,000 animals, representing about 18 percent of the stock in the registry (circa 2001). Other later registries have applied screening standards to a greater percentage of their founding stock, theoretically creating a starting point based on consistent phenotype criteria and veterinary screening. For the most part, screening has been reserved for inbound animals, not progeny or registered parents.

Improving the Screening Standard for Greater Efficiency
Screening for physical defects is refined and efficient. This aspect of evaluating alpacas has become fairly well tuned in

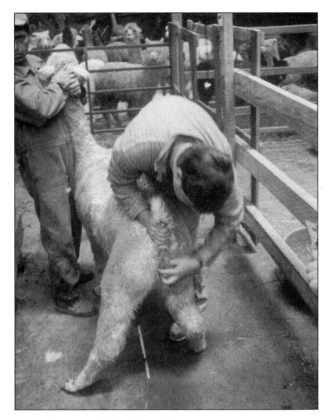
A vulva is checked for abnormalities.

the course of many years of screening thousands of animals for numerous registries.

Fiber assessment is another matter. When the screening standards were written, they deliberately focused on young South American animals whose micron counts were low—20 to 26 microns is the range desired by the mills manufacturing alpaca products. These young animals often arrived in the quarantine stations at the end of the dry season. Because of their age and poor diet, their micron counts were the lowest they would ever be. The fiber screening standards worked well for these animals—young and on lean diets.

The screening standard was not created with older animals in mind, whose micron count naturally coarsens with the passage of time, nor was it devised for animals that are being moved back and forth between countries with unlimited good-quality forage. Since the standards were written, we have learned that an alpaca's average micron count can change more than 3 microns in as little as three months by merely enriching the diet. Average micron on living animals is a transitory measurement.

A diet of rich hay impacts fiber production by creating greater fleece weight but also greater microns. Screening older animals and animals on rich diets under the present standards makes it difficult to successfully export an older alpaca, and thus is sometimes counterproductive to procuring beneficial genetic traits.

Measurement of an animal's pelage (hair follicles) would probably be a more equitable way to judge fiber potential because the follicular patterns do not change much as an animal ages or undergoes dietary changes. An objective, inexpensive assessment could be done with a laboratory assessment of standard deviation or coefficient of variation. This might also include an objective assessment of density or verifiable fleece weight yields, providing the records were unquestionably accurate.

Measuring Results Objectively Two important points must be remembered about assessment involving a registry. Assessment programs should focus on data that are incorruptible and objective, such as an end-product (fiber diameter, fleece weight, or possibly a combination of both). Data such as lineage verification, number of registered offspring, fleece weight, testicle size, and a verifiable histogram are other types of useful information that can be recorded objectively. A registry should not record general or artificial criteria that have no bearing on production or soundness, or that cannot be quantified.

From time to time there is talk about including show results in alpaca registries. Historically, there has been little enforcement of conflict-of-interest rules for show judges anywhere in the world. While steps are being taken to help ensure unbiased show judging, show results still only indicate an animal's rank according to show standards; they include nonessential criteria and do not include a hands-on soundness examination (see Chapter 7: Shows). An alpaca chosen as a show winner in South America was recently disqualified from inclusion in a DNA-based registry through the screening process after extra teats and a crooked tail were discovered. Similar incidences have occurred in other parts of the world.

The size differences in these two year olds demonstrate why height and weight are important measurements.

Common Myths About Screened Alpacas

Once while sitting in the village of Santa Rosa high in the Peruvian highlands, I struck up a conversation with several campesinos who worked for a prominent camelid broker in the region. They began looking at a copy of a North American camelid publication. They thumbed through its pages and then stopped at an advertisement and began laughing and pointing at it. In a short time 15 campesinos were busily discussing the ad. One of them explained that the animals being advertised as a special breeding group from Bolivia with unique characteristics were actually animals that had been born and raised on a nearby coop in Peru. The men claimed to have helped select and transport the animals across the border to another broker.

You will hear many comments and generalizations about imported animals. Some of the generalizations may have validity, but many are incorrect, being advertising creations more than anything else. Is the alpaca a Peruvian, Chilean, Bolivian, Argentinean, Australian? There are people who will buy only Peruvian animals and believe Chilean, Bolivian, and all other alpacas are inferior to all Peruvian alpacas. There are people who believe Accoyo (a farm in Peru) alpacas are superior to all others. When I served on the ARI board of directors, I was phoned by a woman who wanted to know if it was safe to breed a Chilean (alleged origin) to a Peruvian (alleged origin) alpaca. She wanted to know if they were separate breeds!

Generalizations about country of origin can be misleading and counterproductive. More importantly, generalizations have a habit of replacing the essential aspects of evaluating an animal's soundness and fiber qualities, the core areas of assessment on any fiber-bearing animal regardless of its origins.

Very good-quality animals were among those screened in Chile, Bolivia, Peru, Australia, and New Zealand. Animals were also rejected from all of these countries (and all identifiable subgroups and farms) because of serious defects or substandard fiber quality. In some subgroups particular defects were common, such as cow-hock and extra teats. In others these defects were less common. Some groups were uniformly large or uniformly small in stature. Excellent histograms were procured from animals departing Bolivia, Peru, New Zealand, Australia, and Chile and poor histograms were obtained from animals screened in these countries as well. What do the categories Chilean, Bolivian, Peruvian, and Australian really mean? The answer: It may mean that the animal in question may have come from the country it was exported from and not much more.

For many years thousands of animals were screened for export from Chile. Many of these alpacas were born and raised in Chile, but many were not. The Quechuas living in the highlands of northern Chile have no word for "suri" in their vocabulary for the simple reason that that breed type does not occur there. Nonetheless, hundreds of suris found their way to Chilean export stations during the late 1990s. In some cases, importer employees would describe how the suris were smuggled into Chile for export. One importer was caught twice by Chilean authorities while moving alpacas from Peru to Chile for export. Though he was reprimanded, he continued to export. The underlying reason for moving animals to Chile for export was that Chile was free of foot-and-mouth disease (FMD) for most of the 1990s, so the quarantine protocol between Chile and other countries was much more relaxed and less expensive than the U.S. protocols with Peru and Bolivia, since the latter two countries were not free of FMD.

One Chilean exporter would openly joke about the special *bofadales* (large naturally occurring pasture areas in the highlands). "When I go there at night the animals are grazing on the Chilean side. When I go to the same bofadeles during the day they are grazing on the Peruvian side. This is why I prefer to collect animals at night." This man is an exception. Most exporters follow the rules.

DEVELOPING ALPACA REGISTRIES

Outside of the traditional alpaca-raising South American countries of Bolivia, Chile, Ecuador, and primarily Peru, alpacas can be found in the following countries in growing populations: Australia, Belgium, Canada, China, Denmark, France, Germany, Israel, Ireland, Italy, Japan, Luxembourg, Mexico, the Netherlands, New Zealand, Poland, Portugal, Russia, South Africa, Spain, Sweden, Switzerland, the United Kingdom, and the United States. Undoubtedly this list will expand.

In these new populations the following registries, with varying degrees of selective choosing of founder stock and scientific verification (blood typing or DNA), have been formed (figures rounded):

- Alpaca Registry Inc. (45,000, North America)
- British Alpaca Society (2,500 screened)
- British Llama and Alpaca Association (2,500 screened)
- Asociacion de Criadores de Camelidos del Sur (1,150, Chile)
- Canadian Llama and Alpaca Association (12,000)
- Australian Alpaca Association (39,000, Australia; 3,000, New Zealand)

Table 27.2 shows the number of alpacas screened for these registries. Mainland Europe is home to about 10,000

Table 27.2 Alpacas screened for registries.*

Country	Number Screened	Percent of National Herd	Size of National Herd	Suris
Australia/NZ (IAR)	5,500	12%	42,000	258
Britain (BAS & BLAA)	5,000	62%	8,000	na
Canada (CLAA)	3,500	34%	12,000	na
Chile (ACASUR)	1,150	100%	1,150	95
North America (ARI)	7,687	17%	45,000	7,953
Europe			10,000	500

*Data collected in 2002; percentage screened will decrease in registries in which screening no longer occurs.

Sources: The following individuals helped in the collection of this data: Joann Rothique (Australia), Nick Weber (Britain), Joy Whitehead (Britain), the Buhrman family and Lavona Fercho (Canada), Peter Hill (Chile), Hartwig Von Webel (Germany), Murray Bruce (New Zealand), and Dar Wassink (North America).

alpacas. Efforts are underway to organize all of Europe into a single cohesive registry; but at this time there is no DNA-based registry anywhere in Europe.

The Australian Alpaca Association's registry, the International Alpaca Registry (IAR), DNA tests only "certified males" but does not DNA test females, which means offspring are not scientifically verified (see form). All other registries in the above list require DNA testing of both parents. Also, all offspring must be DNA tested and proven to be from registered parents before entry into the registry is granted. All of these registries have used screening for varying portions of their foundation stock.

The Chilean registry (ACASUR) plans to screen offspring and cull animals born of registered parents that do not meet the screening standards developed for North American stock. This is the only registry seriously talking about screening and excluding offspring of registered parents. How this rule will fare when Chilean breeders realize that they have produced offspring who cannot be registered is unknown at this time. However, if this is instituted successfully, the Chileans will change the makeup of the animals in their registry rapidly. To date, other registries have not sought to eliminate substandard animals produced by registered parents.

INTERNATIONAL TRANSFER OF ALPACAS AND INTERNATIONAL REGISTRIES

In South America there is keen interest in selling animals to markets that will pay premium prices, but some of these markets have closed their doors by ceasing screening activities. Alpacas imported into the United States and Canada will not be registered by the Alpaca Registry Inc. or the Canadian Llama and Alpaca Association, the two registries on the North American continent. In these instances, the strategy of using the registry as a trade barrier has worked,

at least for awhile. In truth, registry rules banning new imports cannot stop importation, but they can stop the registering of inbound animals into their registry. Importation of animals is regulated by protocols between countries. Buyers are reluctant to buy an unregistered alpaca. There are at least three approaches to overcoming trade barriers: a legal challenge, creating an international registry, and making reciprocal agreements between existing registries.

Legal Challenge

Breeders may decide to lodge a legal challenge against the registry on grounds that fair trade has been impeded—that closing a registry is an artificial manipulation of the market that is detrimental to some while others benefit. This has not been attempted to date. Such a legal challenge would be costly and could fail. If the challenge succeeded, the impact could be unhindered importation with none of the quality-control, filtering advantages that screening offers.

An International Registry

A group of breeders might opt to create an inclusive international registry allowing membership to anyone with an animal registered in any national registry. Funding and governance would be an interesting challenge. Petty jealousies and perceived privilege and manipulations have created disharmony in several registries. Creating an international governing board that avoids the perception of currying favor to a particular region may be difficult, but there are international cattle registeries that function well.

Reciprocal Agreements Between Registries

Reciprocal agreements between registries can facilitate orderly international trade in alpacas. Many horse and cattle registries have reciprocal agreements with same-breed registries in other parts of the world.

In practice, the Australian Alpaca Association's registry, the International Alpaca Registry (IAR), has a policy of reciprocal agreements, without declaring it as such. Even though it has sometimes closed its registry to unregistered inbound alpacas from South America, it has accepted registration certificates (and animals) from other parts of the world purchased by Australians wanting to procure new bloodlines abroad.

The Australian approach of recognizing pedigreed animals from other registries but not dictating all aspects of what qualities animals should have at least allows Australian breeders to make selections that they believe are best.

Another approach would be to identify the needs of the registry's population. This may take many forms once more is learned about specific chromosomes through such projects as the Alpaca Research Foundation-initiated genome

AUSTRALIAN ALPACA ASSOCIATION INC.
APPLICATION AND VETERINARY REPORT FOR MALE CERTIFICATION

APPLICATION

I, _____ of _____
       (Block Letters)   (Block Letters)

the owner of the male alpaca described below, apply to have it certified as free from visible genetic faults.

IAR : _____   Ident No: _____

I enclose the **registration certificate** for the animal and the **fee of $200** for certification and **fee of $110** for DNA recording. I declare that to the best of my knowledge, the information in this application is correct.

(Owner's Signature) _____ (Date) _____

VETERINARY REPORT (Inspecting veterinarian to place an X in appropriate box on each line)
Disqualifying Defects : The presence of any one of the following defects will exclude any male alpaca from Certification.

		NO	YES
DNA:	Sample Taken		

HEAD

		NO	YES
Face	wry (twisted) face		
	roman nose		
Ears:	abnormal long		
	obvious short		
	gopher		
	curled (fused)		
	banana		
	pancake		
Eyes:	entropion		
	ectropion		
	tearing (evidence of blocked tear ducts)		
	cataract		
	evidence of blindness		
	persistent pupillary membrane		
Teeth:	superior brachygnathism (with central incisors protruding more than 0.3 cm beyond the dental pad measured from the outside of the teeth)		
	inferior brachygnathism (with front edge of dental pad protruding > 0.5 cm beyond the lower incisors, measured from the outside of the teeth.)		

LIMBS-FRONT

		NO	YES
Front View:	severe carpal valgus (>15°)		
	bowed legged		
	severe splay footed		
	severe pigeon toed		
	polydactyly		
	syndactyly		
Side View:	buck kneed		
	severely calf kneed (<165°)		
	pastern angles: cocked ankle (>90°)		
	down on fetlock (<30°)		

LIMBS-REAR

		NO	YES
Rear View:	severe cow hocked (>10°)		
	bowed legged		
	severe splay footed		
	severe pigeon toed		

LIMBS-REAR Continued

		NO	YES
	polydactyly		
	syndactyly		
Side View:	severe sickle hocked (hock angle < 25°)		
	cocked ankle (pastern angle >90°)		
	down on fetlock (pastern angle <30°)		
	patella upward fixation		
	luxating patella		

NECK AND BODY

		NO	YES
Cervical, Thoracic and Lumbar spine:	scoliosis		
	lordosis		
	kyphosis		
	thoracic wall deformities		
Tail:	twisted tail		
	no tail		
	short (must cover scrotum)		
	kinked tail		

REPRODUCTIVE/URINARY

		NO	YES
Testicles:	two testicles not in scrotum		
	length < 3 cms		
	uneven in size and abnormal consistency		

CARDIOVASCULAR/RESPIRATORY

		NO	YES
Heart:	murmur, arrhythmia , abnormal heart rate		
Respiratory:	lack of air movement		

MISCELLANEOUS DEFECTS

		NO	YES
Teats:	less than 4		
Any Hernias:	at greater than 2 years old		
Llama Like:			
Body Condition 1,5	1 - emaciated, 5 - obese / 1 and 5 disqualifies	P	
Other Defects:	The examining Veterinarian is obligated to report any other serious defects that are present and that should, in the Veterinarians' professional opinion, result in disqualification. (See separate cover)		

This report records the results of my inspection of the listed features of the alpaca described in this application.

Veterinarian Name:_____

Veterinarian Address: _____

Veterinarian Signature: _____ Date: _____

OFFICE USE (Initial and date)
Registration Committee decision: Yes/No: _____ I.A.R Processing: _____ Fees Paid: _____
(DISTRIBUTION: Original - AAA Registration Committee   First (Green) Copy - Applicant   Second (Yellow) Copy - Veterinarian)

The Australian Alpaca Association adopted a standard for "certified" stud alpacas as a means of improving the general quality of the national herd. The criteria were adapted directly from the Alpaca Registry Inc. forms that were developed in North America before spreading to other parts of the world.

project, which will identify 1,600 microsatellites in the alpaca.* Often it is mutually advantageous (new genetics, marketing, etc.) to have reciprocal agreements between registries that exchange specific information about their respective populations. For reciprocal agreements to be mutually beneficial, the two registries involved should attempt to identify desirable animals. For example, if one registry keeps careful records of color inheritance patterns and annual fleece weights, and knows its general population needs to reduce its average microns, the registry might look for a population of animals in another registry that has numerous lineages of very fine-fleeced animals. The same registry with a grasp of its color genetics might be reluctant to enter an agreement with a registry whose animals have coarse or unpredictable fleeces and poor records of essential fiber production criteria.

Like trading partners in any form of commerce, both need to benefit for the relationship to flourish and continue. A well-run registry can focus on depleted numbers and fashion an agreement that is mutually beneficial. Reciprocal agreements between registries in the international arena may require compliance with national laws, regulations, and protocol development.

Reciprocal agreements make it possible to control the quality of animals allowed to influence a gene pool. Here are some of the ways.

1. Common practice: Provides the option to acquire desirable genetic material from outside sources (already a feature of many animal registries).

2. Mutually beneficial arrangement: Trading between registries can increase the size of the market and increase the diversity in a gene pool.

3. Quality and flow control: Reciprocity, in concert with research, can ensure that a gene pool's quality is maintained or improved by tailoring screening standards for desired traits.

4. New genetics: Less than 2 percent of the alpacas in the world belong to a registry of any kind. Clearly there are valuable gene pools outside the existing registry populations.

5. Offsets monopolistic practices: Closing a registry entirely allows large entities to reap the benefit of pervasive influence in a fully protected market. Market domination does not necessarily mean quality. Allowing a mechanism to retrieve genes outside a closed system allows for greater economic self-determination of member farms.

*Pat Long DVM, personal communication, Temuco, Chile, May 5, 2003.

ARTIFICIAL INSEMINATION AND EMBRYO TRANSFER

Although these reproduction methods did not exist for alpacas in 1988 when the Alpaca Registry Inc. was written, both artificial insemination (AI) and embryo transfer (ET) were deliberately forbidden for several reasons:

1. Introducing these methods can have a widespread impact on both the genetic makeup and the value of animals in the registry.

2. Unwanted genetic material can be introduced into the gene pool in the form of genetic diseases and unwanted traits.

3. AI and ET present complicated ethical, legal, and genetic ramifications that will be far reaching.

ET in alpacas is now possible and reliable. AI is also possible but more difficult to accomplish (see Chapter 12: Male Reproduction). The emergence of these technologies will undoubtedly appear attractive to some alpaca breeders. From a pragmatic point of view, AI and ET offer a more expedient form of importation and transfer of large amounts of genetic material than the traditional method of live-animal importation involving expensive, complicated quarantines and protocols. With ET and AI, importation can be accomplished by putting test tubes in a suitcase and carrying them to new destinations. Discussions about allowing the use of AI and ET should include questions about how and where genetic material is collected, verified, and introduced to a DNA registry gene pool. After all, the reason the Alpaca Registry Inc. was created was to keep the influences of other species of camelids out of the alpaca gene pool!

AI and ET have caused rapid changes in appearance, genetic make up, and end-product for some breeds of livestock. For cattle breeds that benefited from AI and ET, the objective was usually to increase the amount of weight (meat) on an animal that was sent to slaughter at a relatively young age.

The American Quarter Horse Association (AQHA), with 336,000 members, allowed ET but attempted to limit the number of registered offspring from a particular mare to one a year. However, this did not withstand a legal challenge. An AQHA owner, wanting unlimited use of ET and the ability to register however many offspring as could be produced, filed a US $10 million lawsuit against the AQHA on grounds that it violated antitrust laws in the state of Texas. Though the AQHA had tried to regulate the impact of ET on its industry, in the end the court set the legal precedent for how much control a breed association can expect to maintain. Other horse breeder associations, such as Jockey Club Thoroughbreds, forbid AI and ET, and only offspring from "live coverings" are allowed in their registry. Any registry contemplating the inclusion of ET and AI as acceptable reproductive techniques needs to research legal questions prior to adoption.

There are several reasons AI and ET are valuable techniques. Transportation costs and stress on animals that would have been moved hundreds of miles for breeding are not necessary. ET has proven useful in horses that are not capable of carrying a foal to term but have desirable traits. Preserving a desired blood line has been accomplished by flushing an embryo from a female for implantation in another female. Transfers have even been done successfully after a mare has died.

Probably the most often heard reason for using both ET and AI is the rapid spreading of "superior genetics." However, this proposition is not as simple as it may seem. Who decides what are superior genetics? What if one or two characteristics that are desired and spread throughout a gene pool also carry genetic diseases? With so little known about the genetic blueprint of alpacas, the criteria for selection need to be carefully examined.

An incident, not involving AI or ET, comes to mind as an example of what can happen. A highly promoted alpaca stud in North America produced superior fleeces. However, he was severely knock-kneed and would have failed screening into the Alpaca Registry Inc. using importation screening standards. Nevertheless, the animal's offspring (many with knock-knees) were sold far and wide. Eventually, the animal was found to be the source of offspring with choanal artresia, a lethal genetic condition. Promotion provided the means for this animal to have pervasive genetic influence.

If the use of ET and AI is driven by promotion, with little or no regard to comprehensive genetic considerations, it will likely benefit those who advertise best, at the expense of those who have comparable or better males but meager advertising budgets. Neither technology should be considered without comprehensive genetic-testing standards in place to ensure the safety of any chosen genetic material.

Without a doubt the introduction of AI and ET into any gene pool will have an economic impact. Questions about who controls AI and ET need to be considered. Use of these technologies will change the stud service market. Will their introduction work to benefit the species at a reasonable price? Or will they become a get-rich scheme benefiting a handful of people who control the technology?

Special-Interest (Separate Breed) Registries

Special-interest registries are a possibility to achieve specific goals. This concept could take several forms. The most obvious would be a separation of suris and huacayas into separate registries. As all alpaca owners know, alpacas exist in two breedtypes: huacayas and suris. There is no way to distinguish one from the other in current DNA parentage verification. The problem of breed-type verification has been painfully evident in recent decisions by the Alpaca Registry Inc. (ARI). Photographs (that show the fleece type) accompanying registration papers were used to verify the breed type of an animal being registered from the time suris first entered the registry until 2002. However, the photograph requirement was eliminated by vote of the ARI membership on the ARI board's initiative. The board argued that photographs were inconvenient and could be fraudulent, so they were irrelevant. The photograph has been replaced by a box to check on a form that designates a registered animal as either a huacaya or suri. Reducing breed-type verification to checking a box is hardly a step forward in attempting to discourage fraud and to record breed type. The Australian registry has a similar breed designator: Simply mark an S or H in the box for breed with no other verifier. This may seem like a small point, but a much larger issue is involved here.

Viewpoints differ on how best to maintain suris as a separate breed. No DNA test distinguishes between the two breeds. Suris are relatively rare, with an estimated 40,000 suris in the world today. If they were a wild species instead of a domestic one, they would be categorized as a "threatened species" due to their rarity. However, with domestic animals no such designation exists. Management of suris as a breed is arguably at an important crossroads. Primarily within the ranks of the "new alpaca-owning countries" there is a vocal contingent advocating breeding suris to huacayas to create more suris. The view by the authors addressing the topic in this book is that under most circumstances breeding suris to suris is the best way to preserve suris. This is also the view of all but one prominent South American suri breeder I interviewed (see Chapter 10: Fiber and Chapter 25: Genetics of Fiber Type and Coat Color).

Suri owners are far outnumbered by huacaya owners in all registries in which both huacayas and suris are registered. With no scientific way to distinguish between breed types and the elimination of photographs as a type verifier in one of the largest registries, the specter of falsifying lineages (as to coat type) is now painfully clear. This fact, coupled with the open advocacy of breeding huacayas to suris, threatens (in the minds of many knowledgeable suri breeders) the existence of the suri breed itself and defeats the reason for going to the trouble to do DNA testing and scientifically verify a lineage. This issue is felt more acutely by suri breeders (who are not a majority in any registry), who ultimately must decide if the preservation of suri as a breed is better accomplished in a separate registry where attention to coat type is given the highest priority in tracking lineages. Such a registry, with a limited gene pool to begin with, may become international in scope to make the most of the genetic material available in the world.

There is also growing interest in other types of special-interest registries, most having to do with marketing strategies.

CONTENTIOUS ISSUES

Overlapping Jurisdictions

In 1989 there was one DNA-based alpaca registry in the world, the Alpaca Registry Inc. (ARI). Now there are many alpaca registries and others are being created. As these registries define themselves and issue rules for their respective memberships, there will be overlapping jurisdictions and difficult issues to resolve. For example, the Canadian government requires alpaca owners to belong to a national Canadian registry. At the same time Canadians are among the first and the largest subgroups in the Alpaca Registry Inc.

When ARI was formed, it included all of North America, though there are now some advocates in the United States for making ARI a U.S.-only registry. This somewhat xenophobic response to a tightening marketplace would cause severe economic hardship to Canadian owners, a subgroup who has been in good standing since the registry's inception.

In Europe there are similar contending viewpoints on developing a registry that spans all of Europe including Britain, which has two registries for alpacas (the British Alpaca Society and the British Llama and Alpaca Association). The issue of who controls a registry—one or two large entities or the rank-and-file breeder—is in many ways similar to the forces at work in North America.

The Australian Alpaca Association's registry also includes New Zealand, which has more than 3,000 alpacas. Though New Zealanders and Australians are served by the same registry, most of the decision making is done in Australia, which has caused stress between the two groups of owners from time to time. In the years to come, intelligent decisions that serve the entire group's best interests are essential to each registry's survival.

Closing a Registry to Inbound Alpacas

Creating a DNA-based registry allows a population of animals to become a "locked box" or an island, separate from the larger whole. In practice the emerging registries outside of South America have developed a recurring pattern. Importers bring animals from country A in South America to country B in some other part of the world. When breeders in the receiving country decide they have enough of the correct type of animals in their inventory, and before would-be competitors can get the opportunity of selecting from a wide range of sources, the "developing" registry declares itself closed and the importation of animals stops.

In the United States the people leading the move to close the registry were often the ones who had the largest herds or were among the most active marketers. In a matter of days they moved from being aligned with importers as the favored volume customers of imported animals, or working as importer representatives, to attacking and vilifying importers as a threat to alpacas. As they moved to consolidate their closure of the North American market (registry) by attacking anyone who stood in the way, the impact on the Peruvian breeders, whose hard work had finally paid off in exports to lucrative markets, was never part of the debate. Ironically, farm names and lineages such as Accoyo, Alianza, and Macusani from Peru have survived (or been "borrowed"), while Peruvians and other South Americans have been effectively banned from the U.S. market.

In Britain the roles of the key actors took different paths. There were disagreements over control and governance that resulted in a division in alpaca breeders and the emergence of two registries, the British Alpaca Society (BAS) and the British Llama and Alpaca Association (BLAA). Each has developed different types of governance. In Europe a large importer sought to control the market by putting roadblocks in the way of others who wanted to organize a European-wide registry. At the time of this writing breeders from Belgium, France, Germany, Italy, Switzerland, and Scandinavia have met to organize a single registry.

Australia has had its share of heated debates and has intermittently been closed and opened to allow unregistered animals from South America to pass through the registration process and into the Australian Alpaca Association's registry (International Alpaca Registry). However, in Australia imports were never entirely cut off. The Australians have recognized the pedigrees and registration from other registries, such as the Alpaca Registry Inc., headquartered in the United States. So a person living in Australia who wants to import an alpaca from a breeder in the United States is allowed to do so and reregister it in Australia.

The Infusion of Politics into a Registry

In the United States the closure movement was led by a small group of well-organized advocates who deluged alpaca owners with weekly mailers and internet messages, creating an atmosphere of fear and hysteria. Their message was that the market was about to be overrun by imported animals. In fact, less than 800 animals were scheduled for importation in that year (1998).

There were two sides to the issue. The closure referendum was initiated by an ARI board member without formal discussion by the board. The majority of the ARI board (1998) responded to the total closure referendum with an alternative proposal of allowing an annual import of 300 animals (less than 1 percent of the registered population).

The ARI board saw their counterproposal as an answer to genetic concerns (a viable breeding population didn't exist in some colors) and concerns over monopolistic practices that might follow a total closure. They were cast as advocates of an "open registry" and "a special-interest group," when in fact the debate was really about allowing or not allowing less than 1 percent of carefully selected new genetic material to enter the registry annually.

The "none at all, from anywhere" group prevailed and celebrated with cheers and high-fives at the 1998 AOBA conference where the voting results were announced. However, much to the surprise of some closure advocates, the closure initiative had been written in such a way that importers were allowed several months to organize and bring in their "last" imports. The result was a deluge of imported alpacas, far above what had been planned, as importers hurried to get their animals into a closing market. Approximately 3,000 imported alpacas were screened into the registry in the months following closure. It would have taken 10 years to achieve this number if the advocates for 300 imports a year had won instead of lost at the polls.

Hypocrisy seemed to become a virtue. Some of the most outspoken and adamant proponents of the need to close the U.S. registry and market from imports quietly purchased many of the animals arriving after the closure initiative passed. When closure was finally enacted, leading closure advocates were in the strongest market position to sell to the captive market they had just created, all the time claiming to protect the small breeder. The closure-with-no-exceptions position was further solidified in 2002 when the ARI board initiated a vote of the membership making total closure a by-law. Such is the state of the introduction of new genetic material into the United States via the Alpaca Registry Inc.

In 2003 the registered alpacas living in the United States number about 45,000 animals, nearly all of them DNA typed and proven to be the offspring from two registered parents. This is the largest population of alpacas in the world that cannot be bred with llamas because of the requirement of DNA testing both parents. Only the offspring of registered parents are accepted into the registry. Theoretically, this registry can be closed to inbound stock or opened to outside animals depending on the wishes of the people belonging to the registry. But the reality is that once a registry is closed most breeders don't look farther than their own borders for new genetics.

Here is a checklist for a cooperative healthy registry.

1. Leadership fosters an atmosphere of mutual trust and openness.

2. All decisions are aimed at strengthening the registry for the improvement of the breed.

3. All animals and owners are treated equally.

4. Both sides of issues are clearly presented.

5. Responsible dissent is respected and allowed.

6. Leadership accepts the outcome of the elective process.

7. Different views on issues appear in printed material.

PROTECTING OUR ANDEAN-SOURCE HERDS

South American breeders control the largest numbers of alpacas in the world. Current registry practices and expenses exclude them from overseas alpaca markets. For the last 17 years foreigners have purchased alpacas inexpensively in South America and sold them for great profit throughout the world.

South America is home to approximately three million alpacas. Many of these animals are owned by Quechua and Aymara herders living in poverty. Other animals are owned by cooperative farms and large land owners who must run frugal operations to survive. There is frustration and some anger in South American countries about being squeezed out of the markets in North America where registries have been closed.

I had a telling conversation with Dr. Alfonso Martinez, the president of Consejo Nacional de Camelidos Sud America (CONACS), in 1998. CONACS is a ministry post in the national government of Peru. Dr. Martinez expressed anger and dismay about the closing of several registries. He was wrestling with ways to create a

It is ideal for black alpacas to have a uniformly black coat. Some black coats fade in the sun and others do not.

Animals that are distinctly off-black, especially following shearing, are more accurately called mahogany than black. Weathering can achieve a similar look, but is not present in a freshly shorn animal.

This bay-colored animal demonstrates that extensive black trim (shown here on the face) can combine with fairly bright and distinct red shades of fleece.

The light mahogany coat on this alpaca is also called dark bay. The extensive black trim on its face combines with a dark brown-red body.

Some agouti patterns are distinctively striped, as is the one on this llama. This specific pattern, with black fronts to the legs and a dark head, is one component of the wild guanaco pattern. This animal lacks the light overlay that is typical of the guanaco pattern.

Red animals usually have less black trim on the lower legs and face than do bays. The nose and eye rims are characteristically black.

This animal is light red with trim; the black highlights on the nose and around the eyes are obvious.

Fawns come in a number of subvarieties. Noting the details can help to predict the color outcomes of matings. The light-faced fawn of this pair could well produce grey or spotted off-spring; the solid-colored fawn is less likely to do so unless those patterns come from the mate. A light-faced animal must be used carefully with certain colors (grey, spotted) if blue-eyed whites are not desired.

This fawn has a lighter head, but the body is distinctly unshaded.

Shading can be superimposed over any color. This animal is genetically black with a shaded overlay, which usually results in a shaded mahogany.

This llama demonstrates the combination of light overlay and agouti pattern that results in the guanaco pattern. This coat is a fairly dark example.

Distinctive pale areas along with distinctive leg markings distinguish the vicuña pattern. This animal is a very dark example.

At the pale end of the spectrum, a light overlay can be superimposed over a tan animal that has minimal black trim. The coat shown here is lighter than the vicuña pattern but similar to it.

Some animals need close inspection. The components of this animal's coat are: pale with minimal trim, a light overlay, and a white or light head. Appropriately mated, this animal would probably produce a wide range of colors.

When very pale fawn animals have light heads and are also shaded, the result can be very pale, as on this animal.

This female alpaca has a very subtle pattern. She is basically black with a light overlay, resulting in a very dark mahogany. In addition, the black has been lightened to a steely blue grey, and she is a very good candidate for a dilution mechanism.

A harlequin or appaloosa design is more common in llamas than alpacas, but occurs in both. The heads are very distinctive, as on the animal shown here.

The dilution and spotting effects of harlequin can result in interesting fleece colors. Most of these examples would be classified as grey, but are more complicated and subtler than most greys.

White animals are noteworthy for their whiteness and reveal very little about their ability to produce colored offspring. Subtle characteristics such as pigmented toes, skin, and tongue may point to an increased ability to produce colored offspring when compared to those whites that lack such pigment.

White is common among suris. The luster of the fiber shows to great advantage when white.

Grey animals typically have extensive white on legs and head, although a few exceptions occur. Nearly all grey animals also have very dark spots. On some animals the spots can be a different background color than the grey areas. An example would be a silver grey with a few distinctly brown dark spots. These spots show better following shearing.

Roan is a reasonably rare color and is very distinctive. The resulting fleeces are similar to the usual white-faced greys.

Animals with white faces and white legs are frequently expressing minimal extents of spotting patterns. These animals must be mated carefully if spots and blue-eyed whites are not desired as progeny colors. This points to the importance of noticing much more than fleece color, as this animal would shear an entirely black prime fleece.

Some rare patterns nearly defy classification. This suri is a dark brown or mahogany, but also has a distinctive roan pattern along the sides. This is likely a dark manifestation of roan.

Most minimally expressed spotting, such as on this dark red-brown with extensive trim, is dramatically noticeable as a white face.

Some alpacas have multiple and complicated effects that all contribute to the final color. This male is basically red with minor trim, and is also shaded. The base color has been further modified by a roan pattern, which is shaded and not uniform. The result is a complex interplay of red, fawn, and white hairs. This animal is lightly roaned over the entire body, although some becomes lost in the light ventral shading. The neck is more obviously roan than the body, a typical characteristic of shaded roans. The pattern is probably due to the same allele as in a more obviously dark-headed roan.

As spotting becomes more extensive it becomes less possible to miss it in the phenotype of the animal, although deciding which specific pattern is present can be difficult in minimally marked animals.

This piebald animal demonstrates the asymmetry of the pattern, as well as the propensity to go around the neck and to frequently spare portions of the head. The background color of this animal is tan with minor black trim.

Extensively spotted animals can end up with stark white fleeces. This suri only has color on large patches on the head.

Tuxedo spotting results in white ventrally and color on the back and back of the neck. It passes from generation to generation very consistently.

Speckling is quite rare, and both this dam and offspring have it. The dam is minimally marked, the youngster much more dramatically marked.

The speckled pattern tends to be darker up over the back, and tends to leave darkly pigmented regions on the head, even in the extensively marked cria in this photo.

superior pool of animals for export, and talked about using the ARI screening standard but raising the bar for fiber quality as a means of identifying superior animals. The big challenge for Martinez was the cost of starting a registry. Creating a DNA-based registry is not cheap. The current DNA analysis of US $29 per sample is prohibitively expensive in many areas. Says Dr. Martinez, "We can identify the best animals, but how can Peru afford to undertake a competitive registry with the DNA registries around the world?"

The challenge in many alpaca-raising countries is how to create a scientifically verifiable registry at a lower cost than is now possible. These countries want to take their rightful place among regions with registries that realize that genetic improvement through the international exchange of animals (or genetic material) has great potential for population improvement.

Dr. Martinez left his ministry post soon after President Alberto Fujimori fled the country in 2000. When new President Alejandro Toledo took office in 2001, he appointed Enrique Moya to head CONACS. Moya has continued many of the same policy recommendations as Martinez. He too would like to see Peruvian alpaca growers do better in the world market.

There is much talk in Peru these days on how best to remain a player in the world's alpaca animal market. The irony is there is no doubt Peru is the world center of alpaca fiber processing. From both the private and public sector there is talk of creating a "source herd" for exportation. There is little doubt that Peru and other Andean countries have many thousands of animals that can easily pass the strictest screening requirements. The animals selected for this group would need to be inspected, evaluated, and identified for certification. The emphasis would be on superior fiber yields within specific adult micron ranges.

A VISION FOR THE FUTURE

This should be a time of great opportunity for all alpaca breeders. Alpacas are becoming increasingly popular throughout the world. To realize our potential in the world marketplace, working for common goals makes the most sense. Here are some suggestions on how to use registries to advance the cause of *all* alpaca growers, not just a few who have cordoned off lucrative markets.

1. Preserve the species known as the alpaca (*Vicugna pacos*), and improve the best qualities of the alpaca through the use of authentic, science-based registries that pursue genetic plans of improvement and do not become mired in greed and protectionism as the primary motivations for decision making.

2. Aggressively market alpaca as the world's most exciting and enjoyable luxury fiber, while pursuing genetic practices to improve the worldwide quality of alpaca fiber.

3. Agree upon international import/export standards and certification to define an acceptable alpaca. A de facto screening standard has already been used by all registries in operation today. This standard could be improved and formally recognized worldwide. Recognition of a minimal standard would be a large step toward improving the species.

4. Support the creation of a high-quality certified Andean alpaca population that serves as a genetic reservoir, with special emphasis on preserving suris as a breed. This concept could be realized by many different partners.

5. Develop mutually beneficial import/export protocols. Healthy livestock businesses recognize the need for new genetics and commerce with other parts of the world. To declare yourself separate after you've taken what you think you need is shortsighted. An infusion of new blood with genetic improvement in mind would enhance two-way commerce in alpacas and result in faster development of superior animals.

Achieving collective goals would result in "ALPACA" being the most frequently heard response to the question, "What's the best natural fiber in the world?" Since the total luxury fiber market represents only 2.6 percent of the world's natural fiber production, there is much work to be done (see Table 27.3).

The dialogue on the use of registries and their role in the development of alpacas is in its infancy. Differences in opinion need to be explored with a spirit of cooperation, since globally our fates in the alpaca industry are linked. Intelligent management of registries can allow us to move forward together.[1,2]

Table 27.3 Production by species of luxury fibers.*

Luxury Fiber	Annual Production (tons)
Alpaca	5,000
Cashmere	15,000
Mohair	22,000
Angora rabbit	8,500
Sheep in Australia, New Zealand, and South Africa	1,851,000

*Luxury fibers, including alpaca, represent only 2.6 percent of natural fiber production.

GLOSSARY

DNA Deoxyribonucleic acid is the basic hereditary unit in all living things that transfers essential information from one generation to the next. Scientists Francis Crick and James Watson discovered and explained the double-helical redundant structure of DNA nearly 50 years ago. Their discovery has changed the understanding of inheritance forever. The science of these pairings is expressed in a four-letter DNA alphabet in the bases of A, T, C, and G. In the double helix an A may pair to a G on the opposite strand and vice versa. In humans, giraffes, alpacas, and other large organisms, the DNA is usually found in the nucleus of cells. Each nucleus usually has around six billion base pairs spread among their chromosomes.

DNA markers Segments of DNA whose sequences can be compared across individuals of the same species. These areas of comparison are often referred to as "sign posts" by geneticists. Scientists attempt to choose sign posts with low rates of mutation and high rates of polymorphism. This way, distinctions between individuals can easily be made in parentage verifications.

chromosomes Microscopic rod-shaped bodies that separate during mitosis (cell division). The chromosomes carry DNA genes that transfer hereditary characteristics to the next generation. The chromosome number is constant within each species. All six living members of the camel family have the same number of chromosomes!

efficacy A term that is synonymous with "probability of exclusion." The greater the probability of exclusion, the greater the efficacy.

exclusion The scientific proof that a particular individual (or mating) could not have resulted in the genetic material found in another individual. The greater the probability of exclusion, the greater the efficacy and the more ironclad the registry. The DNA-based tests for camelids created at the University of California at Davis have an efficacy rate of 98 percent, whereas the test designed by Generatio in Heidelberg, Germany, has an efficacy rate of 99 percent. These two tests are close to foolproof.

gene An operational segment of DNA that defines a function or characteristic of an organism. Scientists theorize that in humans, horses, and alpacas there are between 50,000 and 100,000 genes. In a particular cell there may be as many as 3,000 genes.

genotype In the most basic terms, *genotype* refers to the genetic material possessed by an individual, as opposed to *phenotype,* which refers to what appears (or shows) in an individual. More specifically, genotype refers to variants in a segment of DNA. The segment is not necessarily a gene. In animals such as humans, horses, and alpacas, two variants are present and are inherited from the parents—one variant from the father and one from the mother.

microsatellite A term used by DNA scientists to describe a segment of DNA in which the bases repeat themselves in tandem sequences, for example: CTGTTAATTGCACA-CACACACACACACACACACA. CA is repeated 12 times and each parent contributed the same number of variants (12) to the offspring's genetic identity.

parentage verification A DNA test to determine whether or not a specific female or male could be the parent of a specific offspring.

sequencing Recording or reading the order of bases (A, T, C, G) that make up a particular DNA segment, such as CTAGGAT.

REFERENCES

1. Feld, E.: High-Tech Breeding: A Look at Our Options. *horsecity.com*, pp. 1–3, March 2002.
2. Hoffman, E.: How Registries Facilitate the Improvement of Alpacas. *The Alpaca Registry Journal* 6(1), Spring 2001.
3. Hoffman, E.: *Creating Registries That Can Operate Internationally* (Lecture and Slide Show). International Alpaca Association Alpaca Festival, Arequipa, Peru, October 27, 2000.
4. Owens, A.: Guarding the Gene Pool. *AQHA Update.* American Quarter Horse Association, pp. 2–3, Fall 1994.
5. Owens, A.: Why'd They Do That? . . . and Answers to Other Questions About AQHA's Change to DNA Testing for Parentage Verification. *The Quarter Horse Journal,* pp. 58–67, December 1994.
6. Thorson, S. J.: Pandora's Box. *Western Horseman* 67: 10, pp. 77–82, October 2002.
7. Wheeler, J. C.: *The Domestic South American Cameliadae: Past, Present, and Future.* Lima, Peru: Universidad Nacional Mayor de San Marcos, Facultad de Medicina Veterinaria, pp. 1–18, 1993.

INDEX

Page numbers in **bold** indicate lengthy discussion of a topic.

A

AAA. *See* Australian Alpaca Association
abdominal pain, 228, 492, 506, 517. *See also* colic
abortion, 373–374
    drug-induced, 373
    due to bovine viral diarrhea virus, 467–468
    due to heat stress, 471
    due to plant toxins, 504, 506
    infectious disease causes, 373, 435, 457, 462
    posttravel abortions, 161, 168
    potential related problems, 380, 390
    storms, 373
abscesses, 390, 391, 419
    lumpy jaw, 419, 422, 458
    of teeth, 421, 422, 474, 492
Accoyo herd, 278, 319, 582
achromotrichia, 193
acid detergent fiber (ADF), 196, 200–201. *See also* fiber, dietary
acidosis, 225
acorns, 511
actinomyces bacteria, 422
activated charcoal, to treat poisoning, 426, 502, 516
additive genetic traits. *See* quantitative genetic traits
adenovirus, 461
ADF. *See* acid detergent fiber
Aesculus sp., 506, 508
aesthetic valuations
    conformation, 67, 76
    fiber qualities, 67
AFD. *See* average fiber diameter
agalactia, 218, 405
age
    aggression and, 49
    estimating, from teeth, 345, 421
    of fetus, estimating, 372
    fiber quality and, 278, 279, 284, 490, 562–564
    See also geriatric alpacas
agression, 51
    behaviors of, 37, 39, 40, 41–42, 45, 51
    feeding and, 107
    herd, 45, 46–47
    as rabies symptom, 460
    territoriality and, 49–50

    toward humans, 39, 49, 125
    See also fighting; male aggression
aging. *See* geriatric alpacas
agistor/agistment, 121–122
Agouti locus color determination, 543–545
    photos of patterns, 550, 551
AgResearch (New Zealand), 279–280
AI. *See* artificial insemination
air conditioning, 111
    in vehicles, modifying, 172–173
air transport, 173–176
alarm calls, 35, 39–40, 42, 46
alert downer cow syndrome, 192
alert stance, 35, 36, 39
alfalfa, 203, 204, 206, 216
alignment. *See* conformation
allele, defined, 522–523
Alpaca and Llama Show Association (ALSA), 143
Alpaca Fiber Coop, 305
alpaca hybrids. *See* huarizos; hybridization; *specific hybrids*
Alpaca Mark labeling, 307, 311
Alpaca Owners and Breeders Association. *See* AOBA
Alpaca Registry Inc. (ARI), 30–31, 153, 571
    ban of AI and ET, 585
    Canadian membership in, 587
    closure of registry to imports, 580, 583, 587, 588
    on crimp, 265
    international adoption of screening standard, 31, 573, 580
    number of animals screened, 582, 583
    phenotype screening requirements, 155
    photo requirement, 586
    screening fees, 573
    screening standards, 30–31, 60, 61, 150–151, 573, 585
    screening standard termination, 580
Alpaca Research Foundation, 283, 583, 585
Alpaca Show Division Handbook (AOBA), 143
ALSA (Alpaca and Llama Show Association), 143
    Show Manual, 263
altiplano climate, 109, 112, 114, 319, 470, 472
altiplano husbandry, 215–216, 236, 319, **447–454**
    diseases, 437–444

hybridization problem, 7, 26, 28–29, 30, 236, 305
modern breeding practices, 29–30
predators, 88, 89, 90
Sarcocystis and, 440
See also Andean pastoralism; South America; *specific countries*
aluascay, 21
Alvarado, Julio Cuba, 29, 278
Amanita mushrooms, 509
Ambrosia tomentosa, 509
American Quarter Horse Association (AQHA), 585–586
American Society for Testing Materials (ASTM), 255, 271, 307
Ammianthium muscaetoxicum, 509
Amsinckia sp., 506, 508, 510
anatomy, **57–82**
    camelids vs. true ruminants, 18
    digestive anatomy, 18, 180–182
    eyes, 485–490
    female reproductive anatomy, 361–365, 397, 398
    gait and, 58–59
    male reproductive anatomy, 335–337
    skeletal, 8, 59
    species comparisons, 8
    See also conformation; dentition
ancestry of alpacas, 4–7, 8, 58
Andean pastoralism, 3–4
    current problems, 29–30
    daily patterns, 4, 141
    feeding systems, 214–215
    influence of Spanish Conquest, 4, 5, 20, 23, 26–27, 235–236
    modern Andean husbandry, 236, 319, 447–454
    photos, 14, 15, 16
    pre-Conquest, 4, 19–21, 26, 235–236
    twentieth-century changes, 27–28
    See also altiplano husbandry; South America; *specific countries*
Anderson, Scott; *photo, 323*
anemia, 192, 193
angora fiber, 298, 300, 309, 589
animal identification and history, 345, 382, 427
anorexia. *See* appetite, lack of
anovulatory follicles, 383–384, 389
antelope, 457
anthelmintics, 432, 434
anthrax, 456
ants, 504

591

breeding management, *continued*
    timing and frequency of breeding, 339–340
    See also breeding for color; breeding for fleece quality; breeding stock selection; culling
breeding soundness examinations (BSE), females, 382–383
breeding soundness examinations (BSE), males, 343–352
    animal identification and history, 345
    mating ability evaluation, 348
    physical examination, 345–348
    sample form, 344
    semen collection and evaluation, 348–352
    See also veterinary examinations
breeding stock selection, 50, 451, 454, 525–527, 535–536
    index selection, 566–567
    sire referencing, 567–568
breed standards, 536
    adoption of, ABOA rule, 156
    breed improvement and shows, 151, 158
    impact of, 150–151
    registries' role in maintaining, 570
    in show judging, 147, 149
    suri breed maintenance, 586–587
Brewster, Margaret, 292
Brester Alpacas; *photo, 292*
brightness (fiber), 26
Brisket disease, 439
britch, 311
British Alpaca Society, 31, 60, 61, 582, 587
British Llama and Alpaca Association, 31, 61, 573, 582, 587
    sample screening checklists, 574–578
broadside displays, 34–35, 36, 49
broken bones. *See* bone fractures
Brooke, Chas, 304
broom snakeweed (*Gutierrezia sarothrae*), 506, 508
brown fleece color, 543, 544, 546, 554, 559
Brown locus color determination, 546–547
brown recluse spider, 504
brown snake, 504–505
browse, 204–205
brucellosis, 373, 456–457
Bruford, Michael, 7
BSE. *See* breeding soundness examinations
buccal swab DNA testing, 572
buckeye (*Aesculus* sp.), 506, 508
buck-knee, 67, 68
buckwheat (*Fagopyrum esculentum*), 506, 508

bulbourethral glands, 336, 337
BUN (blood urea nitrogen), 184–185, 185–186, 223
bundling (fiber), 258–259, 265, 266, 293, 311; *photo, 259*
burns, 426
Burrell, Patty, 175
burrowing animals, 91
    deterrents for fences, 93, 94
bursa. *See* ovarian bursa
business plan, husbandry as foundation of, 85
buttercup (*Ranunculus* sp.), 516
Buxus sempervirens, 514
buying and selling animals
    conflict-of-interest issues, 154–155
    insurance concerns, 160
    prepurchase health exams, 422, 423
    See also stock selection
BVDV (bovine viral diarrhea virus), 461, **467–468**
B vitamins, 193, 194, 195, 198

C

calcium, 192, 201, 224
    deficiency, 192, 226
    in forages, 200, 205, 206–207, 208, 209, 216
    sources and recommended intake, 194
    in supplements, 210, 211
    urolithiasis and, 228
calf-knee, 63, 67, 68
calf sleds, 134
California conflict-of-interest rules, 153
Callen, John, 305, 306
calls, training animals to respond to, 136
calories, 187. *See also* energy
camas (dromedary-guanaco hybrid), 5, 6, 24; *photo, 25*
camelids
    distribution map, 23
    hybrid species, 5, 6
    in North America, 4, 58
    Old World, 5, 6, 17, 24
    New World, 4–5
    species photos, 17
    See also South American camelids; wild camelids
Camel Reproduction Centre, 5
camels, 5, 6, 297, 300, 309, 457; *photo, 17. See also* camas
camped backward (under), 68
camped forward, 63, 68, 75
camped out (rear leg), 75
Canada
    fiber marketing and processing, 302
    imports, 310, 583

national herd size, 583
    registries and screening, 582, 583, 587
    screening standard adoption, 31
    transport documentation requirements, 160
    See also North America
Canadian Llama and Alpaca Association, 31, 61, 582, 583
canchones, 4, 141, 449, 451; *photos, 85, 448*
canine teeth, 428, 474
    trimming, 428–429, 430
    See also fighting teeth; teeth trimming
caped spotting, 547
capturing animals, 124, 125–126, 136. *See also* catch pens; restraint
c'ara llamas, 24
carbohydrates, 188–189
    in feed supplements, 212
    fermentation process, 182–183, 185, 188–189
    forestomach acidosis, 225
    glucose metabolism, 185–186
    in grass forages, 202
    starch content of feed, 201
    See also fiber, dietary
carcass disposal, 88, 120–121
card grading, 158, 537–538
carding (fiber processing), 241, 244, 245, 301, 311
carding lubricants, 244
cardiovascular defects, 532
cargo vans, 172–173
Carpenter, Jim; *photo, 147*
carpus valgus. See knock-knee
carrying animals, 132
carrying capacity (land), 86, 214
carrying capacity (loads)
    alpacas, 137
    llamas, 57, 137
carts, 116
    training with, 137, 140
cashmere fiber, 260, 283, 284, 298, 300, 309–310, 571, 589
castorbean (*Ricinus communis*), 507
castration
    vs. cryptorchidism, testing for, 342
    of orchitic testicles, 343
cataracts, 75, 488, 531
catch pens, 94–95, 98, 123
cats
    alpaca responses to, 35, 39, 47
    breeding for extreme phenotypes, 147, 149, 534
    as disease carriers, 91, 435
    wild, as predators, 48, 58, 88, 89–90
cattle
    digestion, 180, 183, 184, 185

conformation, *continued*
  correct, importance of, 59–60
  defects listed, 67–70, 73, 74, 75, 76
  defined, 57
  dentition, 73–74
  desirable traits, 60–61, 67, 75
  evaluation techniques, 61
  gait and, 58–59, 60
  mating ability and, 345
  phenotype considerations, 75–76
  photos, 62–67, 71–74, 76, 77–81
  proportion and balance, 60–61,
      78–79
  sample screening checklists, 577, 584
  in show judging, 143, 145, 150, 156
  size, 60
  terminology of defects, 75, 533
  in vicuñas, 58–59
  visual health assessment, 416, 420
  See also specific defects
congenital defects, 75, 150, 530
  of eyes and eyelids, 486, 487, 488,
      489
  lists of, 67, 531
  missing teeth, 421, 422
  in neonates, 403, 407–408
  ovarian and uterine disorders, 389,
      390
  possible causes of, 471
  testicular disorders, 340, 341–342
  See also specific defects
Conium maculatum, 506, 509, 511–512,
      514, 516
conjunctival diseases
  cysts, 487
  conjunctivitis, 410, 449, 487
Consejo de Camelidos Sudamericanos
      (CONACS), 28, 278, 454, 588
consistency, 311. *See* uniformity
Consolida ajacis, 515
constipation, 473, 506
contagious diseases. *See* infectious
      diseases; *specific diseases*
contagious ecthyma, 459
contracts, agistment, 122
Convallaria sp., 516
convulsions, 192, 456, 458, 506
Coolaroo Alpacas, 292
cooling. *See* heat, protecting against
cooling-off behaviors, 54, 55, 104, 105
coordination, loss of, 461, 506. *See also*
      ataxia
copper, 193, 194, 201, 224
  deficiency, 193–194, 209
  in forages, 209
  in supplements, 210, 211
  toxicity, 192–193
copperhead, 504

copulation, 338–339, 340, 355, 367,
      385. *See also* mating behaviors
coral snake, 504
Coriaria sp., 516
cornea/corneal diseases, 487
  trauma, 487
  ulcers, 486, 487
corn gluten meal, 212
coronavirus, 461, 477, 478
corpus luteum, 363, 382
  during pregnancy, 372, 386, 388
  in estrus cycle, 368–369, 386
  illustrated, 362
  persistent luteal activity, 389
  postpartum changes, 363, 379
corrals. *See canchones*; pens
Corran, Eric, 247
cortical cells, 250–251, 311
corticosteroids, 373
Corydalis caseana, 506, 508
cottage industry fiber processing,
      247–248
cottonmouth, 504
cotts, 244, 311
Couchman, Bob, 281–282
cougars. *See* mountain lions
coughing, 462
coverage, 311–312
cowbane (*Cicuta virosa*), 514
cow-hock, 64, 67, 69, 75, 533
coyotes, 89, 90, 94
CP. *See* crude protein
cream fleece color, 546
creep feeding, 218, 219
crias
  chewing by, 54
  communicative behaviors, 38, 39, 40,
      41
  defense of, 38, 47
  disease risks, 120, 464–466
  feed and milk supplements for nurs-
      ing crias, 218, 219, 227
  mortality rates of, in South America,
      215
  nutritional needs, 189, 190, 195,
      219–220
  orphaned, 407
  play, 50, 60
  predators, 89
  water hazards, 55
  weaning, 39, 183, 218, 219
  See also neonates; weanlings
crimp (fiber), 261–266, 263
  amplitude and frequency, 262,
      264–265
  defined, 263, 312
  density and, 258–259
  examples, 262, 263, 282
  fineness and, 258–259, 293

  of huacaya, 283, 284, 294
  importance, 264
  importance to processing, 265
  as quality marker, 252, 264, 283, 284
  as show judging criterion, 147, 148
  uniform, 262, 266
  See also crinkle; curvature
crinkle (fiber), 261–266, 293
  amplitude and frequency, 262, 264
  defined, 263, 312
  examples, 262, 263, 282
  of huacaya, 294
  See also crimp; curvature
crossbreeding. *See* hybridization
cross fencing. *See* fencing; internal fenc-
      ing
crossing the midline, 67, 73
crowding, 472
  aggression and, 52
  disease risks, 96, 433, 466
  during travel, 168
  feeding and, 92, 107
crude fiber content of feeds, 200. *See
      also* fiber, dietary
crude protein (CP)
  content of forages, 203, 205,
      206–207, 209, 215
  feed analysis for, 200, 201
  maintenance requirements, 191
  in supplements, 210, 211
cryopreservation of semen, 354–355,
      355–356
cryptorchidism, 340, 342, 346, 532
Cryptosporidia, 410, 477, 480, 481
Cuba Alvarado, Julio, 29, 278
cuckoo pint (*Arum maculatum*), 514
cud chewing, 52–53
culling, 535
  by eye color, 534
  by fleece color, 30, 253
  by fleece weight, 28, 256–257, 278,
      310
  independent culling level selection,
      567
  lack of, in new alpaca countries, 305
  in South America, 30, 253, 257, 305,
      451, 454, 535
cumbi, 21
curiosity, expressions of. *See* alert stance
curl (fiber), 252, 261, 312
  as suri characteristic, 266, 295–296
curvature, 259, 261, 263, 312
  examples, 262, 263
  fineness and, 265, 283, 284
  frequency, 264–265, 266
  histogram measurements of, 265,
      273–275
  testing for, 293
  uniformity, 266

diseases
   European, introduction to the
      Andes, 5
   infectious, **455–468**
   noninfectious, **469–492**
   See also specific diseases
dispersal
   South American herd spacing, 187
   in the wild, 48, 51
displays. *See* body postures
DM. *See* dry matter
DNA
   defined, 590
   evidence, in alpaca classification, 5, 7
   markers, 590
   testing, 7, 28, 31, 529–530, 572
DNA registries, 7, 31, **569–590**
   AI and ET bans, 585–586
   closure of registries to imports, 580,
      583, 587–589
   cost as barrier to development, 589
   DNA systems and collection, 572
   fair trade issues, 583, 585, 587–589
   goals and mission statements,
      571–572, 589
   in new alpaca countries, 582–583
   overlapping jurisdictions, 587
   pros and cons, 570–571
   reciprocal agreements among, 583,
      585
   screening process and standards,
      573–582
   special-interest registries, 586–587
   suggestions for the future, 589
   tips for cooperation among mem-
      bers, 588
   See also screening; *specific registries*
documentation requirements, transport-
      ing animals, 159–161, 456
dogs
   breed standards, 147
   camelid meat consumption by, 440,
      442
   dingoes, 90, 94
   dog-proof fencing, 86, 93, 94, 98,
      100, 101
   domestic, as predators, 88–89, 90,
      91, 94,
   domestic, responses to, 35, 40, 45,
      47, 140
   guard dogs, 90–91, 442, 450, 451
   as *Sarcocystis* hosts, 437, 438, 440,
      442
domestication, 3, 4, 19–20, 48
dominance (genetics), 523–524,
   524–525
dominance (animal). *See* herd hierarchy
dominance displays. *See* standoffs
donkeys, 92

down in the pastern (weak fetlock), 66,
   69
drawing (fiber processing), 312
dromedary camels, 5, 6, 17
dropped pastern, 67
drought, on the *puna*, 451
drugs. *See* medications
drying (fiber processing), 241, 244, 312
dry lot feeding systems, 105, 214
   feeder design and placement,
      105–108
dry matter (DM)
   content of feeds, 199, 200, 222
   intake, 184
Dubovi, Dr. Edward, 468
dung piles
   as communications, 43, 44
   inspecting, 428
dwarfism, 79
dyeing, 243, 245, 250, 253–254
   huacaya fiber, 294
   suri fiber, 301
dysentery, 461
dystocia, 399–402
   possible causes, 504
   potential effects, 380, 381, 390, 391,
      403, 405

E

eagles, 90
ear and neck hold (earing), 128–129,
   326
ear problems, 416
   frostbite, 472–473
   mites, 416, 436
ear/ears
   defects, 30, 67, 69–70, 75, 76, 81,
      531
   length, 67, 75, 531, 533
   set, 67
   signals, 39, 41
   visual health assessment, 416
eastern diamondback, 504
EBV (estimated breeding value),
   525–526, 566
Echium plantagineum, 515
E. coli, 477
   vaccination, 411
economic
   incentives for fleece quality, 306–307
   influences on fiber quality, 29, 238,
      276–277
   interest disclosures by show judges,
      151–152, 153, 155
ectopic testis, 340
ectropion, 486, 531
Ecuador, vicuñas in, 18
Edensmith, Sherry, 136, 166–167

EE (electroejaculation), 348, 350
EE (ether extract) feed analysis, 200
EHV-1. *See* equine herpes 1 (one)
"80-80" rule, 109–110, 470–471
ejaculation, 337, 339
   ovulation induction and, 367
elasticity (fiber), 250, 267, 296, 312
electric blowers, for fleece/fiber cleaning, 321, 325
electric fencing, 92, 93, 94, 101–102
electroejaculation, for semen collection,
   348, 350
electronic identification, 345
elk, 91, 456
Elkins, Joy, 156
Elser, George; *photo, 27*
El Yaral mummies, 18, 21, 22, 26
   crinkle example, 262
   fiber photos, 10
embryo/embryonic
   death, 218, 370, 372–373, 380, 384
   development, 370, 371–372
   transfer (ET), 585–586
   vesicle, 371–372, 373
endocrinology
   female reproduction, 361, 371, 372,
      385–389. *See also* estrus cycle
   hormonal diagnosis of pregnancy,
      371, 384–385
   male sexual function, 352
   See also specific hormones
endometritis, 384, 390
endoparasitism, 480–481
endophyte fungi, 218, 504
enemas
   for cooling, 110, 471
   for neonates, 409
energy, as essential nutrient, 187–191
   blood metabolite analysis, 223
   deficiency, 224–225
   feed energy content, 187–188, 200,
      201, 204
   maintenance requirements, 189, 216,
      217
   requirements for different physiolog-
      ic states, 217–220
   See also metabolizable energy
energy concentrates, 197
England
   exports, 308
   foot-and-mouth disease outbreak in,
      95
   imports, 30, 310
   national herd size, 583
   registries and screening, 582, 583,
      587
   screening standard adoption, 31, 573
   fiber marketing and processing, 247,
      302

Peruvian alpaca industry involvement in, 27
See also United Kingdom
enteritis
    clostridial, 464–467
    neonates, 410
    parasitic, 477–478
enterotoxin, clostridial, 465–466
entropion, 486, 531
environmental conditions
    disease hazards and, 427, 455
    energy requirements and, 196, 224
    fiber quality factors, 250, 278–279, 562
    forage quality factors, 208
    meningeal worm and, 445
    in natural habitat, 109, 112, 114, 214, 319, 470, 472
    Sarcocystis and, 441–442
    See also climate; cold weather; diet; heat; weather
environmental defects, 532–533
EPD (estimated progeny difference). *See* estimated breeding value
epidermal membrane, neonates, 403
epididymis
    disorders of, 343, 347
    examination of, 345–348
episiotomy, 400
epistasis, 524
equine herpes 1 (one), 432, 461, 488
equipment and supply recommendations, 116–118
Equisetum sp., 506, 508, 514
ergotism, 504
essential nutrients, 186–196, 199
    feed analysis, 198–201
    See also nutrition; *specific nutrients*
estimated breeding value (EBV), 525–526, 566
estimated progeny difference (EPD). *See* estimated breeding value
estrogen, 385, 386, 387–388
estrus
    cycle, 366–367, 383, 385–387
    cycle, postpartum reestablishment of, 380
    signs of, 364, 365, 367
ET (embryo transfer), 585–586
ether extract feed analysis, 200
ethics, conflicts of interest (show judging), 151–155
ethoxyquin, 198
eumelanin, 542–543, 546
Eupatorium rugosum, 509
Europe/European
    alpaca population in, 582–583
    early alpaca imports, 30
    exports, 308, 309

fiber marketing and processing, 247
imports, 310
livestock, in South America, 5, 27
registry development, 583, 587
toxic plants of, 514–515
transport documentation requirements, 160
See also specific countries
euthanization, 499–500
Evans, Rick, 154, 155
evolution
    of behaviors, 47–48
    gait evolution, 58–59
    of South American camelids, 4–7, 8, 58
excitability, as poisoning symptom, 506
exportation
    of animals, from South America, 236, 582, 587–589. *See also* importation of animals; international transport
    of fiber from South America, 310
Extension locus color determination, 543, 544–545
eye anatomy, 485, 486
eye/eyes, **485–490**
    blue, 531, 533, 534, 557, 558, 559
    color, 67, 485–486
    diseases/problems, 410, 449, 486–489, 531, 534
    examinations, 489
    normal, 485–486
    set, 67
    See also specific diseases
eyelid diseases/problems, 486, 489, 531
eyesight, 35, 40, 59
    blindness, 488, 489, 531, 534
    defects, 75, 534

F

fabric. *See* textile manufacturing; textiles
face defects. *See* head and face defects
FADs (foreign animal diseases), 456
Fagopyrum esculentum, 506, 508
Faiks, Jan, 113–114
Faiks, Jim, 113–114, 137, 176
fair trade, registry rules and, 583, 585, 587–589
false hellebore (*Veratrum* sp.), 506, 508
family group
    interaction, 50
    organization, evolution of, 48
fans, for cooling, 111
farm layout. *See* layout
farm management, husbandry as foundation of, 85
fascioliasis. *See* liver flukes

fats, dietary, 188
fatty liver disease (hepatic lipidosis), 223, 224, 225–226, **482–485**
    age at onset, 482–483
    in crias, 468
    development, 483
    identifying, 483–484
    in old females, 482
    treatment and prevention, 484–485
fawn fleece color, 543, 545, 546, 557, 559
    fiber characteristics
    photos, 550, 551, 552
    price premiums for, 28, 237, 306–307
    of suris, 300–301
FDA (Fibre Fineness Distribution Analyser), 270
fear, expressions of, 35, 39–40, 41, 61
fecal testing, for parasites, 432, 433, 434
feeders, 52, 105–108
feeding, **179–232**
    before and during travel, 161–162, 164, 177
    behaviors, 41, 107, 214
    cleanliness concerns, 106–107
    in cold weather, 112
    competition for food, 96
    dietary changes, 216, 218, 220, 517
    diet formulation, 216, 217–220
    digestive anatomy and physiology, 180–186, 187–188
    disputes, 38
    equipment for, 116
    establishing a routine, 428
    feeder design and location, 52, 105–108
    food preferences, llamas vs. alpacas, 21, 214
    groups, 216–217
    injury hazards, 177
    intravenous, 431
    management, 109, 213–220
    nutritional status assessment, 220–224
    old animals, 490, 492
    orphaned crias, 407
    overview, 179–180, 228
    social hierarchy and, 52
    supplemental feeds, 209–213
    systems, 214–216
    See also diet; feeds; grazing; nutrition *entries*; water *entries*
feed intake
    capacity, 184
    supplements and, 210
    overload, 479–480
    undigested, 478

feeds
    additives to, 198
    energy content of, 187–188, 200, 201
    moisture content of, 184, 186, 197, 199
    nutrient composition analysis, 198–201
    sample collection, 222
    supplemental, 209–213
    types and components of, 196–198
    See also forage *entries*; grains; hay; pellet supplements
feed tag information, evaluating, 212–213
feet, blisters on, 460. *See also* foot and toe conformation; toenails
feline predators, 48, 58, 88, 89–90
felt/felting, 267, 302, 312
female infertility, 382–385, 390
female reproduction, **361–396**
    diagnosing reproductive disorders, 382–385
    embryo transfer, 585, 586
    endocrinology, 361, 371, 372, 385–389
    estrus cycle and ovulation induction, 366–369, 385–387
    fertilization, 363
    glossary, 392–393
    infertility, 382–385, 390
    parturition signs and stages, 376–379
    postpartum disorders, 380–381, 390–391
    postpartum period, 379–380, 381, 388–389
    pregnancy, 363, 370–372, 381
    pregnancy diagnosis, 371–372, 382
    pregnancy disorders, 372–376
    pregnancy length, 371, 372, 375
    puberty, 365–366
    reproductive anatomy, 361–365, 397, 398
    reproductive system diseases, 389–391
    seasonality, 366, 372, 447
    sexual receptivity, 367, 369, 387
    See also breeding management; breeding soundness examinations, females; mating behaviors; obstetrics and neonatology; parturition
fence-post restraint, 126–127
fencing, 86–102
    basic design requirements, 92–94
    dog-proofing, 86, 93, 94, 98, 100, 101
    excluding disease carriers, 91–92
    excluding predators, 88–90, 92
    fences as territorial boundaries, 49

gates, 87, 93, 99
importance of, 86
injury hazards, 86–87, 95, 98, 100–101, 101–102
layout, 85–86
material types, 97–102
pen purposes and design, 86, 94–96
perimeter vs. internal fencing, 92–94
portable fence panels, 96–97
posts and installation, 97–98
segregating species, 92
separating territorial males, 49
fertility rates, 339, 340, 370, 380
    after artificial insemination, 355, 356
    in South America, 215
fertilization, 363, 369–370
fescue, tall (*Festuca arundinacea*), 504, 512–513
fescue poisoning, 218, 504
Festuca arundinacea, 504, 512–513
fetal/fetus
    abnormalities, delivery complications and, 401
    age determination, 372
    death, 401
    heart rate, 373
    sex determination, 371
fetal development, 370–372
    effect of bovine viral diarrhea virus (BVDV), 467–468
    environmental defects and, 532–533
fetal position, posture, and presentation, 397
    abnormal, 400, 401–402
fetlock
    collapsed, 66, 67, 69, 75, 488
    conformation, 66, 67, 69
    defined, 69
fever, 424
    as disease symptom, 419, 456, 457, 458
    from heat stress, 470
    as poisoning symptom, 506
    postpartum, 380
    potential effects, 345
fiber, **235–318**
    blends, uses of, 246, 312
    characteristics. *See* fiber evaluation criteria; fleece characteristics
    chemistry, 250
    coverage, 67
    hair, 313, 315
    handling tables, 322, 332
    marketing, 254
    microscopic structure of, 249–252, 295, 297–300, 304
    photos of products, 289, 290. See also textile manufacturing; textiles

records, 28, 119, 259, 321–322
regrowth, 256–257, 314
samples, collecting, 270, 282–283, 563
specialty, 313, 315
strength, 250, 266–267, 305, 565
structure and composition, 249–252, 294–296, 304
trade, pre-Conquest, 4, 19, 20–21, 22, 26
yield. *See* yield
See also other fiber *entries*
fiber classes/classifications, 311
    broadening, 305–306
    in color, Peruvian mills, 18, 256; *photos, 290, 291*
    in fineness, Peruvian mills, 254–255, 296, 300, 303
    in new alpaca countries, 303, 305–306
    See also fleece sorting and grading
fiber diameter
    age and, 278, 279, 563–564
    diet and, 190, 278, 279, 581
    measurement methods, 270
    medullation and, 251
    species comparisons, 8, 18
    use parameters based on, 245
    See also fineness (fiber); histograms
fiber, dietary, 182, 184, 195–196
    in feed supplements, 210, 211, 212
    in forages, 200–201, 203, 205, 206–207, 209
    supplements for old animals, 220
fiber evaluation criteria, 252–276
    AAA scoring system, 268
    aesthetic criteria, 67
    correlations among, 257–259, 261, 267, 566–567
    glossary, 311–316
    histogram study, 283–284
    objective criteria, 255–267
    objective vs. subjective measurements, 565
    rankings of, 245, 247, 252, 253, 258, 296, 300
    in registry screening process, 573, 578, 581
    in show judging, 148–149
    subjective criteria, 267
    See also specific criteria
fiber evaluation techniques, 268–276
    fleece scoring, 268
    grid sampling, 259, 261, 268
    mill buyers, 237
    sample collection, 270, 282–283, 563
    tactile assessment, 238, 267, 271
    visual inspection, 268–269, 278
    See also histograms

fleece characteristics, *continued*
    vicuña-type, 293
    See also fiber *entries*; guanaco fiber; suri fiber; vicuña fiber
fleece color, 18, 253–254
    color chart photos, 290, 291
    color classes, 256, 296
    color diversity as processing challenge, 254, 303
    consistency and matching, 21, 243, 244, 254, 255
    demand for natural colors, 254
    diversification, 235, 254
    photos, 549–556
    price premiums for light colors, 28, 237, 307
    production statistics by color, 307
    recording, 321–322
    show color classes, 144
    sorting for, 238, 256
    suri fleeces, 301
    visual assessment for, 268
    weathering/fading, 546–547
    See also breeding for color; color genetics
fleece growth
    energy requirements, 190
    poor, as deficiency symptom, 192
    rates, 256–257, 303, 491, 563
fleece judging, at shows, 143, 144, 145, 158, 320
    criteria for, 147–148, 148–149
    See also fiber evaluation criteria; fiber evaluation techniques
fleece preparation
    before shearing, 320–321
    See also fiber processing
fleece sorting and grading, 238, 240, 244
    classing challenges in new alpaca countries, 302–303, 305–306
    color classes, 144, 256
    crimp and, 263
    fineness classes, 255, 296, 300, 303
    in Peru, 238, 296
    at shearing, 331–332
    suri fleeces, 296, 300
fleece weight, 259, 303
    defined, 312
    density and, 252, 257–259, 260
    diet and, 190
    dishonest additions to, 237
    excellence standards, 537
    heritability, 565
    as mill-buying criterion, 29, 236, 237–238, 305, 310
    optimizing fineness and, 277–278
    record fleeces, 278
    record keeping, 28, 259
    in show judging, 148, 149

staple length and, 256–257
    total vs. clean, 259
    vicuña, 248, 249
    weighing, 259, 321
flehmen behavior, 36, 43, 44, 339
flies, 431, 504
    controlling, 120
flight, 35
flooring materials
    shearing floor, 322
    stalls and barns, 115
    trailers, 171
FMD (foot-and-mouth disease), 95, 459–460, 461, 582
foaming at the mouth, 503
folk cures, 449
follicles (hair). *See* density; hair follicles
follicles/follicular (ovaries/ovarian), 361, 362, 363, 380, 382
    abnormalities, 383–384
    cysts, 367
    luteinization, 367, 368
    -stimulating hormone. *See* FSH
    waves, 366–367, 380, 385–387
food storage, 108–109, 208
foot-and-mouth disease (FMD), 95, 459–460, 461, 582
foot and toe conformation, 58, 71
    extra toes, 30, 67, 69, 71, 410, 531
    fused foot, 67, 69, 71, 531
    pigeon-toes, 67, 70, 73, 75
forage plants, 197, 201–207
    forbs and browse, 204–205
    grasses, 201–203, 216
    legumes, 202, 204, 206, 207–208
    nutrient composition of, 203, 205, 206, 207, 209
    nutritional quality factors of, 207–208
    sample collection for testing, 222
    sedges and rushes, 205, 207
    in South America, 183, 185, 205, 207, 214–215, 448
    urolithiasis and, 228
    See also hay
forage quality
    assessing need for supplements, 209–213
    assessment of, 208, 222–223
    cria stomach development and, 183
    factors in, 207–208
    North vs. South America, 215–216
    poisoning risk and, 501
    seasonal variability, 215
    vitamin content, 194–195
forages
    blending, 216
    defined, 197
    dry. *See* hay

forage management practices, 197, 200, 208
    moisture content, 186, 197, 199
    nutrient content, 197, 200, 209
    nutrient content variability, 209
    sample collection, 222
    silages, 197, 199
    testing of, 208, 222–223
forbs, 204–205
foreskin. *See* prepuce
forestomach
    acidosis, 225
    system, 180–182
Fowler, Murray, 31, 60, 61, 70, 143, 488, 580; *photo, 145*
foxes
    as disease carriers, 91, 94, 437, 460
    as predators, 48, 89, 455; *photo, 450*
foxglove (*Digitalis purpurea*), 506, 508, 514, 516
fractures. *See* bone fractures
Franco, Enrique; *photo, 27*
Frank, Lona; *photo, 431*
freemartin, 532
freestanding restraint, for shearing, 326–327
freezing of semen, 354–355, 355–356
frostbite, 112, 472–473
FSH (follicle-stimulating hormone), 366, 385, 386, 387, 388–389
fungal diseases, 461–462, 488–489. *See also specific diseases*
fungal toxins. *See* mycotoxins
funnel web spider, 505
fur, 312
fused ear, 69
fused foot (toes), 67, 69, 71, 531

G

gaits, evolution of, 58–59. *See also* locomotion
galloping, 59, 60
gambel oak (*Quercus gambelii*), 506, 511
gami, 21
Garaycochea, Ignacio, 238
gastritis, 434
gastric ulcers, 479
gastrointestine/gastrointestinal anatomy and processes. *See* digestive anatomy and physiology
    nematodes, 433–434
gastropods, as meningeal worm hosts, 445
gatekeeping, by males, 49, 50
gates, 87, 93, 99
GE (gross energy), 188
gene frequency, 525
Generation, 572

H

handle (fiber), *continued*
  defined, 313
  dyeing and, 250, 254
handpieces. *See* shears and attachments
hardinggrass (*Phalaris aquatica*), 504
Harker, Rick, 167
Harker, Sandra Revilla; *photo, 455*
harlequin color, 547, 553
Harry S. Truman Animal Import
    Center, 109
hay, 197, 502
  core sample collection, 222
  delivery, 108, 116
  fiber content, 200
  heating during storage, 208
  moisture content, 197, 199
  moldy, 208, 462, 503
  nutrient content by maturity stage,
    203
  nutrient content compared to
    nutrient requirements, 209
  nutrient content, North American
    hays, 206
  nutrient content variability, 209
  vs. pasture, nutrient content, 200
  protein content, 201
  storage, 108, 208
  vitamin content, 195
  See also forage *entries*
hcG injections, 367, 369
head
  and neck deviations, fetal posture,
    401
  injury signs, 425
  signals, 39
  tilt, 425, 488, 504
  visual health assessment, 415–416
head and face defects, 531
  wry face, 67, 70, 75, 408, 531; *photo,*
    70
head and muzzle shape, 67, 76; *photos,*
    80
health assessment and diagnosis,
    415–426
  behavioral problem indicators, 53,
    415. *See also* locomotion problems
  blood tests, 223, 431, 475
  clinical tests, 424
  comprehensive veterinary exams,
    422, 424
  emergencies, 424–426. *See also* med-
    ical emergencies
  eye examinations, 488, 489
  hands-on assessment techniques,
    419–422
  for old animals, 492–499
  overall quality assessment, 422, 423
  quick visual assessment, 415–419

routine body condition assessment,
    222, 225
  See also breeding soundness examina-
    tions; veterinary examinations;
    specific disorders
health care, routine, 118, **427–432**
  agistment and, 121
  parasite controls, 432, 433
  questions to ask the vet, 427
  recommended routines, 415, 428,
    433, 446
  record keeping, 427
  weighing, 419
  See also teeth trimming; toenail trim-
    ming; vaccinations
health certification, transporting ani-
    mals, 159–160, 456, 459
health problems. *See* female reproduc-
    tion; infectious diseases; male
    reproduction; noninfectious dis-
    eases; parasites; poisons and poi-
    soning; *specific conditions*
health records, 119, 345, 382, 427
heart defects, 532
  in neonates, 407–408
heart failure, 425, 503
heat, protecting against, 55, 109–112,
    470–472, 491
  air transport, 173–174
  ground transport, 163–164,
    165–166, 172–173
heating stalls, 113
heat stress, 109–110, 470–472
  emergency responses, 166, 471–472
  signs of, 419, 471
  testicular degeneration from, 342
  treating acute, 471–472
heat stroke, 419, 424, 427
heavy metal poisoning, 503
Hebditch, Rachel, 304
height. *See* size
Helenium sp., 509
heliotrope (*Heliotropium* sp.), 515
Hemiauchenia, 4, 58
hemlock. *See* poison hemlock; water
    hemlock
hemlock water dropwort (*Oenanthe cro-
    cata*), 514
hemoglobinuria, 192
hemorrhagic follicles, 383–384, 389
hepatic lipidosis (fatty liver disease),
    223, 224, 225–226, **482–485**
  age at onset, 482–483
  from bovine viral diarrhea virus, 468
  development, 483
  identifying, 483–484
  in old females, 482
  treatment and prevention, 484–485
herd behavior, 46–47

banding instinct, 46, 123, 138, 139
  herd aggression, 45, 46–47
  predator responses, 40, 41, 45,
    46–47, 48, 59
herd hierarchy
  in aging animals, 489, 490
  family groups, 48, 50
  feeding and, 216
  stress and, 48, 51–52, 489
  testosterone levels in dominant
    males, 338
heritability (genetics), 525–526
hermaphroditism. *See* intersexuality
hernia, 532
heterozygosity, 523, 524, 529
Hicks, Janie, 257, 264
hierarchy. *See* herd hierarchy
high-tensile fencing. *See* New Zealand
    fencing
histograms, 150, 249, 270–276, 313
  average fiber diameter (AFD), 261,
    272, 280
  coefficient of variation (CV), 261,
    272, 537
  common errors, 282–283
  of curvature measurements, 265,
    273–274
  for desirable characteristics, 276,
    280, 293
  effects of environmental factors,
    278–279
  effects of diet on, 280, 282
  examples, 273–275, 285–288, 564
  interpreting, 282–283, 285–288
  laser-scanning methods, 270–271,
    276
  of medullation measurements,
    273–274
  of micron measurements, 270–272,
    276
  microns >30, 272
  relative importance of, 270, 272, 276,
    283
  sample collection, 267–268, 270,
    282–283
  standard deviation (SD), 271–272,
    280
  study of fiber characteristics,
    283–284
  testing services, 272
  See also histograms; Sirolan
    LaserScan
history of alpacas, **3–32**
  ancestry and classification, 4–7, 8, 58
  domestication process, 19–20
  export outside the Andes, 30–31
  fiber processing and trade, 4, 19,
    20–21, 235–236

phosphorus , *continued*
in supplements, 210, 211
urolithiasis and, 228
photosensitivity, as poisoning symptom, 506
physical examinations. *See* breeding soundness examinations; health assessment and diagnosis; veterinary examinations
Phytolacca octandra, 516
pica, as deficiency symptom, 192
picket lines, 165
piebald spotting, 547, 555
Pieris sp., 516
pigeon-toes, 67, 70, 73, 75
pigments, 542–543. *See also* color genetics
pigs, 91, 457, 460, 461
Pinus ponderosa, 506, 509, 513
pituitary hormones. *See* FSH; LH
Pizarro, Francisco, 4, 20, 23
placenta, 379
retention of, 193, 380, 390, 391, 400
placentation, 370–371
placentitis, 373, 380
plants, toxic, 228, 501, 506–516. *See also* specific plants
plasma
fibrinogen levels, 403
transfusions, for neonates, 406
plastic rail fencing, 98, 100
play, 50, 60
pneumatic knot, 245, 314
pneumonia, 419, 425, 455
from bovine viral diarrhea virus, 468
fungal (aspergillosis), 461–462
poison hemlock (*Conium maculatum*), 506, 509, 511–512, 514, 516
poisons/poisoning, 228, **501–518**
Australian toxic plants, 515
dealing with poisoning, 426, 516
European toxic plants, 514–515
examples of, 502–503
harmful ingestion of nontoxic substances, 517–518
importance of good forage, 501
minimizing risk of, 228, 501–502, 503
mycotoxins, 218, 503–504
New Zealand toxic plants, 516
North American toxic plants, 501, 505, 507–514
plant poisoning, 506, 516. *See also* specific plants
poison types, 503–505
of predators, 90, 451
snakes and insects, 90, 91, 504–505
South American toxic plants, 516
Pollard, Robert, 502

polydactyly/polydactylism, 30, 67, 69, 410, 531; *photos, 71, 410*
polydipsia, 192
polyuria, 192
ponderosa pine (*Pinus ponderosa*), 506, 509, 513
ponds, 55, 105, 112
population. *See* specific animals; specific countries
portable fences, 96–97
possums, 100
post-leg (rear), 65, 67, 70
postpartum
disorders, 380–381, 390–391
metritis, 380
period, 379–380, 381, 388–389
posturing. *See* body postures
potassium, 192, 194, 201, 224
in forages, 206–207, 209
in supplements, 210, 211
precipitation
cold tolerance and, 112, 113, 472
dietary energy requirements and, 196, 224
disease hazards, 455
in natural habitat, 114, 214
predator response behaviors, 40, 41, 45, 46–47, 48, 59
predators
agistment and, 121
dealing with attacks, 88–89, 91, 425
domestic dogs, 88–89
guard dogs for defense, 90–91, 442, 450, 451
sarcocystosis and, 437
traditional ways of dealing with, 449, 451
wild, 48, 58, 89–90
pregnancy, 363
behaviors during, 39, 41–42, 46
body condition during, 217, 218, 221
calorie needs, 189
diagnosis of, 371–372, 382
due date projection, 372, 376
early embryo development, 370, 371–372
endocrinology of, 386, 387–388
environmental defect causes, 532–533
fatty liver disease and, 225
fertilization, 363, 369–370
heat stress and, 471
late-pregnancy care, 376
length of, 371, 372, 375
maternal risk factors, 96, 161, 168, 418, 471
monitoring, 372–373, 381
nutritional management during, 217–218, 223

placentation and fetal growth, 370–371
prenatal care, 402
signs of imminent parturition, 376
See also obstetrics and neonatology; parturition disorders, 372–376
embryonic death, 218, 370, 372–373, 380, 384
fetal death, 401
overdue pregnancies, 375–376, 504
stillbirth, 193, 373, 380
toxoplasmosis, 373, 435
uterine torsion, 374–375, 377, 400
vaginal prolapse, 375
See also abortion; dystocia
prehistory of alpacas. *See* history of alpacas
premature birth, signs of, 404
prepuce, 336, 337, 338
examination of, 345, 346; *photo, 346*
swelling or prolapse, 340–341
prepurchase examinations, 422, 423
pressurization, air transport, 173–174
prickle/prickle factor, 267, 272, 314
privet (*Ligustrum* sp.), 515
probiotics, 198
production levels (fiber), 303, 305, 306, 308
laser scanning and, 276
luxury fibers compared, 309
productivity, 256, 257. *See also* density; staple length
profile; *photos, 77*
progesterone, 385, 386, 387, 388
levels, pregnancy diagnosis and, 371, 384–385
supplementation, 373
prognathism, 531
prolapse
preputial, 340–341
uterine, 380, 391, 400
vaginal, 375
pronking. *See* stotting
proportion and balance, 60–61; *photos, 78–79. See also* conformation
prostaglandin F2 alpha, 368, 373
during pregnancy, 388
in estrus cycle, 368, 385, 386, 387
injections of, 375–376, 388
prostate gland, 336, 337, 343
Prosur. *See* Grupo Prosur
protective behaviors, 47, 49
protein, dietary, 191, 492
assessing, 184
blood metabolite analysis, 223
deficiencies, 224–225
excess, 185
feed content analysis for, 200–201
fiber quality and, 191, 281

maintenance requirements, 191, 216
supplements, 197–198, 212, 220
requirements for different physiologic states, 217–220
See also crude protein
protein, in fiber structure, 250
protein-energy malnutrition (PEM),
224–225
protein production, by digestive bacteria, 182–183, 184
protozoan parasites, 435
Prunus sp., 506, 509
Pteridium aquilinum, 505, 506, 507, 508,
514, 515
puberty
female, 365–366
male, 337–338
Pucara culture and textiles, 20
Pugh, David, 109, 110, 470–471
puna
environment on, 114, 319, 447
vegetation and forage, 447–448
See also altiplano *entries*
Punnett square example, 524
pyometra, 382, 383, 384, 390–391
pyosalpinx, 384, 389

Q

Quality Llama Products, 247
quantitative genetic traits, 525, 526
quarantine
pens, 95–96
policies, 96
Quechua people, 3, 26, 27; *photos, 14,
15, 16, 278, 449, 450*
Quercus sp., 506, 509, 511
Quicaño, Isabel, 29, 278
quipus, 21, 22; *photos, 10, 22*

R

rabbits, 91. *See also* angora
rabies, 91–92, 456, 460
vaccination, 432
raccoons, 91, 92, 100, 460
ragwort (*Senecio* sp.), 501, 506, 509, 512,
515, 516
rail fencing, 95, 98, 99, 100
rain. *See* precipitation
Ramirez, Antonio, 464–465
Ranunculus sp., 516
rats, 91
rattlesnakes, 501, 504
ravens, 90
recessiveness (genetics), 523, 524–525,
529, 530
reciprocal agreements, between registries, 583, 585

record keeping, 119
bloodlines, 29–30
fleece weights and characteristics, 28,
119, 259, 260, 293, 321–322
health/breeding histories, 119, 345,
382, 427
software for, 119
of visual assessments, 269
Redden, Hilary, 272
red fleece color, 543, 544, 546, 559;
photos, 550, 555
reed canarygrass (*Phalaris arundinacea*),
504
registries
closure of registries to imports, 580,
583, 587–589
fill-in-the-blanks vs. authentic,
569–570
goals and mission statements,
571–572, 589
histogram use, 272
international registry development,
583
market manipulation by, 55, 571,
583, 585
in new alpaca countries, 582–583
reciprocal agreements between, 583,
585
See also DNA registries; screening;
specific registries
regurgitation, night, 476
relaxed posture, 36
relaxin, 388
religious beliefs, Inca husbandry and,
19, 21, 26
rental vehicles, for transporting animals,
172–173
reproduction
records, 119, 345, 382
small size and, 60
system defects, 532
See also female reproduction; male
reproduction
reproductive anatomy
female, 361–365, 397, 398
male, 335–337
reproductive behavior. *See* mating
behavior
reproductive disorders
female, 389–391
male, 340–343
See also infertility; *specific disorders*
reproductive traits
heritability, 525
inbreeding depression and, 528
respiration. *See* breathing
resting (fiber processing), 244, 245, 250,
304, 314
restraint, 116, **123–134**

approaching and capturing animals,
124, 125–126, 136
assessing individual behavior,
123–124
basic advice, 125
carrying adult animals, 132
catch pens, 94–95, 98, 123
chukkering, 132–133, 177
control points for, 326
dangerous males, 125
during travel, 132, 165, 170, 171,
176
equipment for, 116–117, 130–131
halter and lead-rope restraint,
116–117, 126
handler injury risks, 124–125, 134
herd behavior and, 123
hold types, 127–129
lead-rope to fence-post, 126–127
neonates and weanlings, 129, 130
restraining chutes, 117, 130–131
for shearing, 322, 325–330
shearing tables, 117, 131–132, 330
sick or disabled animals, 134
take-down, 133–134
retina diseaess, 488
Revilla, Ale; *photos, 418, 490*
Revilla Harker, Sandra; *photo, 455*
rheas, 294
rhododendron (*Rhododendron* ssp.), 506,
508, 509, 515, 516
Rich-Nes Alpacas; *photo, 289*
Ricinus communis, 507
rickets, 192, 195, 226–227, 427
ringworm, 462
Riverina Fleece Testing Services, 272
roan fleece color, 548; *photos, 554, 555*
Robbins, John, 247
Robinia sp., 506, 508
rodents, 91, 100
rolling, 53–54
to correct uterine torsion, 374, 375
during labor, 377, 400
into sternal position, 492–499
roman nose, 67
rope walking, 73
Rosadio, Raul, 7
rose gray fleece color, 548
rotavirus, 461
roughages, defined, 197
rovings, 241, 245, 314; *photo, 290*
royal alpaca (fineness grade), 255
ruminant vs. camelid digestion, 7, 18,
180–183, 184
running. *See* locomotion
Rural Alianza, 28, 29, 262, 278, 307,
319
rushes, 205, 207
ryegrass (*Lolium* sp.), 504

S

St. Johnswort (*Hypericum perforatum*), 506, 509, 512, 515
sales agents, conflict-of-interest issues, 154–155
saline water, 187, 192
salivation
    excessive, 460, 461
    losing, out of mouth, 475–476
    as poisoning symptom, 503, 506
salt, 194, 198
    salt-based mineral supplements, 210
    in supplements, 210, 211
    See also sodium
Salt, Sir Titus, 27
sampling/sample collection
    for DNA, 572
    for feed, 222
    for fiber, 270, 282–283, 563
    grid, 259, 261, 268
sand, for bedding, 171
sanitation, 120–121, 428, 455
    carcass disposal, 88, 120
    during travel, 165
    manure removal, 116, 120, 164, 165, 428, 435
    potential food/water contamination, 105, 107
    preshearing paddock cleanliness, 321
    waterers, 103
Sarcobatus vermiculatus, 508
sarcocystosis, **437–444**
Sarfaty, Gilberto, 265
sawdust, for bedding, 171
scabby mouth, 459
scale/scale structure (fiber), 249
    defined, 314
    as handle, 267
    of suri and huacaya, 266, 295–296, 297
scales (weighing), 117–118, 321
scent communication, 43–44
Schnelle, Florette, 173
Schulz, Jurgen, 30
Schurek, Ken, 173
scoliosis, 67, 70, 531
scouring (fiber processing), 240, 244, 245, 301, 314
scratching, 54
screaming, 41
screeching, 41, 49, 50
screening, 31, 573–582
    bite standard, 74
    conflict-of-interest issues in, 154–155
    effectiveness of screening standards, 580–581
    evaluation process, 573, 580

    fees, 573
    fiber assessment, 573, 578, 581
    forms, 75–76, 150, 151, 573
    inclusion of show judging results, 581
    international adoption of ARI standard, 31, 573, 580
    number of animals screened by individual registries, 582, 583
    objective measurement, 581
    phenotype screening, 75–76, 573, 576
    proportion standard, 61
    sample checklists, 574–578, 584
    vs. show judging, 580
    size standard, 60
    standards origins and impact, 31, 150–151, 573, 580
scrotum, 335, 336
    examination of, 345–348
    heat stress signs, 471
    trauma of, 342
SD. *See* standard deviation
seasonality
    altiplano husbandry, 215, 447
    forage quality variability, 215
    reproduction, 366, 372, 447
    rickets syndrome, 226–227
sedges, 205, 207
segmental aplasia, 384, 390, 391, 532
selection
    differential, 526, 565–566
    goals, 526
selection (genetics), 526–527. *See also* breeding management; culling; stock selection
selenium, 193, 194, 219
    calculating intake amount, 212–213
    deficiencies, 193, 209, 427
    in forages, 209
    supplementation, 192, 212–213, 411
    in supplements, 210, 211
selenium toxicity, 193
    of pellet supplements, 518
    of plants, 506, 510
selling animals. *See* buying and selling animals
semen
    analysis, 349, 350–352, 353
    collection, 348–349
    ovulation induction and, 367–368
    preservation, 354–355
    substandard, 342, 343
seminomas, 343
Senecio sp., 501, 506, 509, 512, 515, 516
sentinel friends, 47
septicemia, 410
sex glands, male, 336, 337, 343

sexual maturation
    female, 365–366
    male, 337–338
SGS Wool Testing Service, 272
shaded fleece colors, 545, 548; *photos, 551, 552, 555*
shaking, 54
    as poisoning symptom, 504
shatush fiber, 298
shearing, 109, 113, 314, **319–332**
    above skin level, 324
    coat preparation, 320–321
    fleece regrowth after. *See* fleece growth
    fleece sorting and storage, 331–332
    handler injury risks, 327
    injury and stress hazards, 323–324, 325, 327, 472
    old animals, 491
    paddock preparation, 321
    record keeping, 257, 321–322
    restraint methods, 322, 325–327, 330; *photos, 328–329*
    shearers' notes, 330–332
    shearing pattern by fleece section, 331–332
    timing of, 257, 319–320
    tools and equipment for, 321–325
    traditional, 236, 319, 450, 451
    weather concerns, 321, 322–323
shearing tables, 117, 131–132, 330
shears and attachments, 305, 323–325
sheen. *See* luster
sheep, 91, 92, 457
    digestion, 180, 184
    as disease carriers, 433, 434
    fleece quality improvement, 257–258, 260
    See also wool
sheep fence. *See* field fencing
shelter, 95, 112, 113, 114–115, 491. *See also* housing
shinnery oak (*Quercus havardii*), 511
shipping animals
    air transport, 173–176
    commercial ground shippers, 169–170
    See also transportation
short fiber, 244. *See also* staple length
shows, **143–158**, 536
    AOBA show rules litigation, 155–156, 157
    breed and species standards, 149–151
    card grading as alternative to, 158, 537–538
    committees for, 145–146
    conflicts of interest, 151–155, 581
    history, 143

staple/staple length, *continued*
  visual assessment of, 268
    for worsted vs. woolen processing, 245
Stapleton, Ian, 251
starches, dietary. *See* carbohydrates
stareoffs. *See* standoffs
star thistle (*Centaurea solstitialis*), 506, 509
starvation, 224–225
Statement of Economic Interests, 151, 153
static electricity reduction, fiber processing, 241, 244, 301
sterility, male, 342. *See also* infertility
stillbirth, 193, 373, 380
Stobart, Robert, 251, 261, 263, 265, 266, 283
stocking
  density, 86, 214
  rates, 86, 442
stock selection
  for aging characteristics, 488–489
  for breeding, 50, 451, 454, 525–527, 535–536, 566–568
  fiber-related, 271, 276
  selection methodologies for fiber improvement, 566–568
  See also culling
stomach, 180–182
  size changes with age, 183
stotting, 44–45, 60
straddling (restraint method), 129
straight-legs (front), 70
straw, for bedding, 171
streams, 105
stress/stressors, 469–470
  herd hierarchy and, 48, 51–52, 489
  and homeostasis, 469–470
  major, 470–475
  shearing-related, 325
  signs of, 425
  travel-related, 161, 168, 178
stress-related diseases, 51–52, **469–475**
  blood tests for, 475
  cold stress, 472–473
  dental problems, 474
  digestive tract problems, 473–474
  fatty liver disease. *See* fatty liver disease
  fractures, 474–475
  heat stress, 470–471
striping, 550
strongylus worm, 434
studs
  breeding, 568
  certification forms for, 150
  housing, 49
  introduction of, 29, 141
  territorial behaviors of, 49

stud selection, 50, 343, 568
  on altiplano, 451, 454
  differential, 526, 565
  sire referencing, 567–568
stud service
  disease risk considerations, 96
  market, 586
submissive behaviors, 37, 38–39, 46
  as danger sign, 39, 140
  at mating, 38, 339, 369
  by pregnant females, 371
sugars, dietary. *See* carbohydrates; glucose
sulfur, 192, 193, 194, 201
  in forages, 206–207
  in supplements, 210, 211
sun bleaching (fiber), 257, 315
sunburn risk, close shearing, 324, 331
sun exposure, vitamin D synthesis and, 226
sunning, 53, 54
superfine alpaca fiber, 255, 277
supplemental feeds, 209–213
  nutritional evaluation, 212–213
  See also mineral supplements; pellet supplements; vitamin supplements; *specific nutrients*
supplies and equipment, 116–118
suris/suri alpacas, 7, 10, 582
  breeding management, 541–542
  breed-type maintenance challenges, 586–587
  defined, 315
  color genetics, 300–301, 545, 548, 557
  environmental adaptation, 302
  origins and current range, 8, 23, 294, 301, 302
  photos, 9, 152, 233, 294 , 327, 391, 540, 541, 567
  population, 294, 583, 586
  separate registries for, 586–587
  weather susceptibility, 112, 302, 472
suri fiber, 266, 294–302
  colored, 300–301
  curl in, 252, 266, 295; *photo, 266*
  defined, 315
  disposition, 296
  elasticity, 296
  fineness, 18, 255, 296, 300, 303
  growth rates, 302
  handle, 267
  histogram examples, 285
  and. huacaya fiber compared, 294–296, 302
  inheritance of, 539–542
  lock structure, 295
  luster, 294, 295, 296, 302
  microscopic structure of, 297–298, 299, 300

processing and uses, 301, 302
  rarity, 294
  show judging criteria, 148–149
  scale structure, 249, 266, 267, 294, 295–296, 302
  smoothness and softness, 296, 301, 302
  sorting classes, 296, 300–301
  spinning and weaving, 301
  yield, 248, 301
suri fleece
  color photos, 148, 553, 554, 556
  and huacaya compared, 294, 302
  inheritance, 539–542
suri-huacayas, 302, 541–542
suri llamas, 26; *photo, 25*
swayback (lordosis), 67, 70, 75, 77
swayback (neonatal ataxia), 193
sweet clover (*Melilotus* sp.), 503
swelling
  of jaw or throat, 476
  rapid, 425
swimming, 55, 105
Switzer, Chris, 247
Switzerland
  early alpaca imports, 30
  screening standards, 61
syndactyly. *See* fused foot (toes)

T

tactile fiber assessment, 238, 267, 276
tail
  photos of characteristics, 76
  defects, 67, 531
  length, 67
  set, 67, 76
  signals, 38, 39
  visual assessment of, 269
  wagging, 409
  wraps, before parturition, 376
take-down, 133–134
taming and training, **135–142**
  animals' responses to, 138, 139
  enticing animals into catch pens, 95
  group behavior, 141
  herd imprinting and, 50
  methods and equipment, 137–141
  to minimize male aggression, 140, 141–142
  reference books, 138, 142
  safety issues, 140
  training objectives, 135–137
tan fleece color, 545, 552, 555
tansy ragwort (*Senecio jacobaea*), 501, 512, 515, 516
tapeworms, 434, 446
Tara Hills fiber trait studies, 563, 565
tarweed. *See* fiddleneck

Tasmanian devils, 90
Taxus sp., 506, 509, 513–514, 515, 516
Taylor, Paul and Sally, 492
TB. *See* tuberculosis
TDN. *See* total digestible nutrients
tear duct problems, 486
Teasdale, D. C., 263, 266
teats
    abnormalities, 365, 532
    blisters or sores on, 459, 460
    See also udders
teeth
    estimating age from, 345, 421
    examining, 420–422
    extractions, 474
    grinding, 228, 416
    misaligned, 476–477
    in old animals, 474, 489, 492
    See also dental problems; dentition;
        fighting teeth; incisor teeth
teeth trimming, 74, 428–430
    restraint for, 330, 428–429, 430
Telarmachay (archaeological site), 19
temperament, 126, 135, 141. *See also*
    aggression
temperature (body). *See* body tempera-
    ture
temperature (weather)
    dietary energy requirements and, 196
    in natural alpaca habitat. *See* climate
temperature extremes, protecting
    against, 109–114
    in air transport, 173–174
    for old animals, 490, 491
    for suris, 112, 302, 472
    in travel vehicles, 162–163, 172–173
    See also cold weather; heat; ther-
        moregulation
tenderness/tender breaks (fiber), 250,
    315
tendons, contracted, 531
Ten Marker Test, 572
tensile strength (fiber), 250, 266–267,
    396, 315, 565
teratomas, 389
territoriality, 48–50
    behaviors of, 33, 34, 43, 45, 49
    male aggression and, 49–50,
        141–142
terrorism, in Peru, 28, 30
testicles/testicular
    biopsy, 342, 352, 354
    disorders, 340–343, 346, 347, 532;
        photos, 331, 346
    examination, 345–348; *photos, 346,*
        347, 354, 422, 580
    heat stress signs in, 471; *photo, 471*
testicle size and development, 335, 336,
    337, 338

cryptorchidism, 340, 342, 346, 532
    degeneration, 342, 346
    hypoplasia, 340, 341–342, 532
    measuring size, 347
testing services (fleece), 272
testosterone levels, 337–338
    aggression and, 340, 343
    to differentiate cryptorchidism and
        castration, 342
tetanus, 410, 456, 458–459
    vaccination, 431–432, 459
Tetradymia sp., 508
textile manufacturing
    modern process of, 243
    suitability of alpaca for particular
        uses, 245, 246, 247
    worldwide, alpaca's niche in, 309
    See also fiber processing
textiles
    fiber, 315
    photos, 289–292
    pre-Conquest, 20–21, 235–236;
        photos, 10, 11, 12, 13
    woven, suri fiber for, 301
texture, 315
Thelazia californiensis, 487
thermometers, 163, 419
thermoregulation, 186, 196, 220, 470
    in cold conditions, 224
    in old animals, 220
    See also cooling-off behavior; heat
        stress
thirst
    as poisoning symptom, 506
    See also dehydration
thorn apple. *See* jimsonweed
throat swelling, 476
ticks, 342, 436
    paralysis from, 436, 487
tiger snake, 504, 505
Tillman, Andy, 42–43
Timm, Karen, 60, 61
toe/toes
    conformation; *photos, 71*
    extra, 30, 67, 69, 410, 531; *photos, 71,*
        410
    toenail/toenails
    color, 67
    crooked, 531
    trimming, 130, 428, 429; *photos, 130,*
        134
    trimming restraints, 129–130, 133,
        134, 330
togavirus, 461
tongue blisters or sores, 459, 460
tops, 242, 244, 315
total digestible nutrients (TDN), 188,
    201, 216

TDN content of forages, 203,
    206–207, 209
toxic
    shock, 380
    substances. *See* poisons
toxoplasmosis, 373, 435
trade barriers, registry rules as, 583, 585,
    587–589
trailers. *See* vehicles and trailers
training. *See* taming and training
transparent templates, to evaluate con-
    formation, 61
transportation, **159–178**
    air transport, 173–176
    documentation requirements,
        159–160, 456
    feeding and watering, 164–165, 175,
        177
    insurance, 160
    international transport, 132, 159,
        173, 176, 455, 456, 459
    loading and unloading animals, 132,
        136, 166–167, 168, 171, 177
    moving old animals, 490–491
    potential medical problems, 177–178
    preparing animals for travel,
        161–162
    restraint during, 132, 165, 170, 171,
        176
    rules for successful transport,
        162–169
    sick and injured animals, 134,
        176–177
    using commercial shippers, 169–170
    vehicles and trailers, 160–161,
        170–172
    See also moving animals
trauma
    corneal, 487
    to female reproductive organs, 381,
        390, 391
    scrotal, 342
travel. *See* transportation
trichiasis, 486
Triglochin maritima, T. palustris, 505,
    506, 507, 508
trussed-prone restraint, for shearing,
    327–329
tuberculosis, 456, 459
tui fleece, 562
    handle of, 267
    quality and, 280, 563
    recording state of, 259, 270
    weight, 278, 280
tumors
    ocular, 489
    ovarian, 389
    testicular, 343

white-tailed deer, 91, 434, 445
wild animals
    as disease carriers, 91–92
    as predators, 48, 58, 89–90
wild camelids
    bachelor herds, 50, 52, 141
    behavior evolution, 48
    body posturing, 33–34, 38
    cooling-off behaviors, 55
    distribution map, 23
    dung marking, 43
    family group interaction, 50
    hierarchy and stress, 48, 51
    locomotion displays, 45
    male aggression, 125
    population, 8, 18, 248, 255, 294
    predator responses, 47
    rolling behavior, 54
    sarcocystosis in, 437, 439
    territoriality, 33, 43, 50
    use of fiber from, 235
    vocalizations, 39, 40
    See also guanacos; vicuñas
wild predators, 48, 58, 89–90
Wildt, Agnes and Richard, 289
wild tobacco (*Nicotiana attenuata*), 506,
    509
wind
    cold stress and, 112, 472
    dietary energy requirements and,
        196, 224
winding (fiber), 244–245
windswept legs, 63
winging, 67, 73
wire mesh fencing, 95, 98, 100. *See also*
    no-climb fencing
WNV (West Nile virus), 456, 461
wolves/wolverines, 89
wooden fence posts, 97–98

wooden rail fencing, 98
wood rats, 100
wood shavings, for bedding, 171
Wool Handbook, The (Teasdale), 263, 266
wool (sheep's), 315
    amplitude and frequency, 264
    compression resistance, 263
    crimp/crinkle, 260, 263, 284, 294
    curvature, 261, 263, 284
    density, 257–258, 260
    elasticity, 296
    fiber characteristics, 283–284
    fiber processing, 242, 245, 316
    fineness, 277
    improving characteristics of, 258,
        260
    nutrition and, 190
    production statistics, 308
    scale structure, 266, 267, 296, 298,
        300
    softness, 296
    weights, 260, 277
    See also sheep
wool (fleece)
    cap, 269, 316
    loss, 105, 418–419, 435
worming, 432, 433, 446
    restraint for, 330
worms, types of, 433–434, 435. *See also*
    meningeal worm
Worrell, Charlene, 146
worsted fiber processing, 238, 242,
    244–245, 316
wry face, 67, 70, 75, 408, 531; *photo, 70*
Wuliji, Tumen, 252, 253, 257, 258, 259,
    260